# Encyclopedia of Microbiology

Second Edition

*Volume 1  A–C*

# Encyclopedia of MICROBIOLOGY

## Second Edition

### *Volume 1  A–C*

Editor-in-Chief

## Joshua Lederberg

The Rockefeller University
New York, NY

## ACADEMIC PRESS

A Harcourt Science and Technology Company

San Diego    San Francisco    New York    Boston    London    Sydney    Tokyo

This book is printed on acid-free paper. ∞

Copyright © 2000, 1992 by ACADEMIC PRESS

All Rights Reserved.
No part of this publication may be reproduced or transmitted in any form or by any means, electronic or mechanical, including photocopy, recording, or any information storage and retrieval system, without permission in writing from the publisher.

Requests for permission to make copies of any part of the work should be mailed to:
Permissions Department, Harcourt Inc., 6277 Sea Harbor Drive,
Orlando, Florida 32887-677

Academic Press
*A Harcourt Science and Technology Company*
525 B Street, Suite 1900, San Diego, California 92101-4495, USA
http://www.apnet.com

Academic Press
24-28 Oval Road, London NW1 7DX, UK
http://www.hbuk.co.uk/ap/

Library of Congress Catalog Card Number: 99-65283

International Standard Book Number: 0-12-226800-8 (set)
International Standard Book Number: 0-12-226801-6 Volume 1
International Standard Book Number: 0-12-226802-4 Volume 2
International Standard Book Number: 0-12-226803-2 Volume 3
International Standard Book Number: 0-12-226804-0 Volume 4

PRINTED IN THE UNITED STATES OF AMERICA
00  01  02  03  04  05  MM  9  8  7  6  5  4  3  2  1

# Contents

C

# Contents of Other Volumes

---
F
---

---
G
---

VOLUME 3

## VOLUME 4

### Q

### R

V

W

X

# Contents by Subject Area

## STRUCTURE AND MORPHOGENESIS

Cell Membrane: Structure and Function
Cell Walls, Bacterial
Crystalline Bacterial Cell Surface Layers
Developmental Processes in Bacteria
Fimbriae, Pili
Flagella
Outer Membrane, Gram-Negative Bacteria

## SYSTEMATICS AND PHYLOGENY

Acetogenesis and Acetogenic Bacteria
Actinomycetes
*Archaea*
Azotobacter
Bacteriophages
Cyanobacteria
Dinoflagellates
Enteroviruses
*Escherichia coli*, General Biology

Extremophiles
Fungi, Filamentous
Heterotrophic Microorganisms
Retroviruses
Rhinoviruses
Spirochetes
Viruses, Overview
Yeasts

## TECHNIQUES

Detection of Bacteria in Blood: Centrifugation and
    Filtration
Germfree Animal Techniques
Identification of Bacteria, Computerized
Microscopy, Confocal
Microscopy, Electron
Microscopy, Optical
Polymerase Chain Reaction (PCR)
Temperature Control
Transgenic Animal Technology

# *Preface*

The scientific literature at large is believed to double about every 12 years. Though less than a decade has elapsed since the initiation of the first edition of this encyclopedia, it is a fair bet that the microbiology literature has more than doubled in the interval, though one might also say it has fissioned in the interval, with parasitology, virology, infectious disease, and immunology assuming more and more independent stature as disciplines.

According to the *Encyclopaedia Britannica,* the encyclopedias of classic and medieval times could be expected to contain "a compendium of all available knowledge." There is still an expectation of the "essence of all that is known." With the exponential growth and accumulation of scientific knowledge, this has become an elusive goal, hardly one that could be embraced in a mere two or three thousand pages of text. The encyclopedia's function has moved to becoming the first word, the initial introduction to knowledge of a comprehensive range of subjects, with pointers on where to find more as may be needed. One can hardly think of the last word, as this is an ever-moving target at the cutting edge of novel discovery, changing literally day by day.

For the renovation of an encyclopedia, these issues have then entailed a number of pragmatic compromises, designed to maximize its utility to an audience of initial look-uppers over a range of coherently linked interests. The core remains the biology of that group of organisms we think of as microbes. Though this constitutes a rather disparate set, crossing several taxonomic kingdoms, the more important principle is the unifying role of DNA and the genetic code and the shared ensemble of primary pathways of gene expression. Also shared is access to a "world wide web" of genetic information through the traffic of plasmids and other genetic elements right across the taxa. It is pathognomonic that the American Society for Microbiology has altered the name of *Microbiological Reviews* to *Microbiology and Molecular Biology Reviews.* At academic institutions, microbiology will be practiced in any or all of a dozen different departments, and these may be located at schools of arts and sciences, medicine, agriculture, engineering, marine sciences, and others.

Much of human physiology, pathology, or genetics is now practiced with cell culture, which involves a methodology indistinguishable from microbiology: it is hard to define a boundary that would demarcate microbiology from cell biology. Nor do we spend much energy on these niceties except when we have the burden of deciding the scope of an enterprise such as this one.

Probably more important has been the explosion of the Internet and the online availability of many sources of information. Whereas we spoke last decade of CDs, now the focus is the Web, and the anticipation is that we are not many years from the general availability of the entire scientific literature via this medium. The utility of the encyclopedia is no longer so much "how do I begin to get information on Topic X" as how to filter a surfeit of claimed information with some degree of dependability. The intervention of editors and of a peer-review process (in selection of authors even more important than in overseeing their papers) is the only foreseeable solution. We have then sought in each article to provide a digest of information with perspective and provided by responsible authors who can be proud of, and will then strive to maintain, reputations for knowledge and fairmindedness.

The further reach of more detailed information is endless. When available, many specific topics are elaborated in greater depth in the ASM (American Society of Microbiology) reviews and in *Annual Review of Microbiology*. These are indexed online. Medline, Biosis, and the Science Citation Index are further online bibliographic resources, which can be focused for the recovery of review articles.

The reputation of the authors and of the particular journals can further aid readers' assessments. Citation searches can be of further assistance in locating critical discussions, the dialectic which is far more important than "authority" in establishing authenticity in science.

Then there are the open-ended resources of the Web itself. It is not a fair test for recovery on a specialized topic, but my favorite browser, google.com, returned 15,000 hits for "microbiology"; netscape.com gave 46,000; excite.com a few score structured headings. These might be most useful in identifying other Web sites with specialized resources. Google's 641 hits for "luminescent bacteria" offer a more proximate indicator of the difficulty of coping with the massive returns of unfiltered ver-

biage that this wonderful new medium affords: how to extract the nuggets from the slag.

A great many academic libraries and departments of microbiology have posted extensive considered listings of secondary sources. One of my favorites is maintained at San Diego State University:

http://libweb.sdsu.edu/scidiv/
microbiologyblr.html

I am sure I have not begun to tap all that would be available.

The best strategy is a parallel attack: to use the encyclopedia and the major review journals as a secure starting point and then to try to filter Web-worked material for the most up-to-date or disparate detail. In many cases, direct enquiry to the experts, until they saturate, may be the best (or last) recourse. E-mail is best, and society or academic institutional directories can be found online. Some listservers will entertain questions from outsiders, if the questions are particularly difficult or challenging.

All publishers, Academic Press included, are updating their policies and practices by the week as to how they will integrate their traditional book offerings with new media. Updated information on electronic editions of this and cognate encyclopedias can be found by consulting www.academicpress.com/.

*Joshua Lederberg*

# *From the Preface to the First Edition*

*(Excerpted from the 1992 Edition)*

For the purposes of this encyclopedia, microbiology has been understood to embrace the study of "microorganisms," including the basic science and the roles of these organisms in practical arts (agriculture and technology) and in disease (public health and medicine). Microorganisms do not constitute a well-defined taxonomic group; they include the two kingdoms of Archaebacteria and Eubacteria, as well as protozoa and those fungi and algae that are predominantly unicellular in their habit. Viruses are also an important constituent, albeit they are not quite "organisms." Whether to include the mitochondria and chloroplasts of higher eukaryotes is a matter of choice, since these organelles are believed to be descended from free-living bacteria. Cell biology is practiced extensively with tissue cells in culture, where the cells are manipulated very much as though they were autonomous microbes; however, we shall exclude this branch of research. Microbiology also is enmeshed thoroughly with biotechnology, biochemistry, and genetics, since microbes are the canonical substrates for many investigations of genes, enzymes, and metabolic pathways, as well as the technical vehicles for discovery and manufacture of new biological products, for example, recombinant human insulin. . . .

The *Encyclopedia of Microbiology* is intended to survey the entire field coherently, complementing material that would be included in an advanced undergraduate and graduate major course of university study. Particular topics should be accessible to talented high school and college students, as well as to graduates involved in teaching, research, and technical practice of microbiology.

Even these hefty volumes cannot embrace all current knowledge in the field. Each article does provide key references to the literature available at the time of writing. Acquisition of more detailed and up-to-date knowledge depends on (1) exploiting the review and monographic literature and (2) bibliographic retrieval of the preceding and current research literature. . . .

To access bibliographic materials in microbiology, the main retrieval resources are MEDLINE, sponsored by the U.S. National Library of Medicine, and the Science Citation Index of the ISI. With governmental subsidy, MEDLINE is widely available at modest cost: terminals are available at every medical school and at many other academic centers. MEDLINE provides searches of the recent literature by author, title, and key word and offers online displays of the relevant bibliographies and abstracts. Medical aspects of microbiology are covered exhaustively; general microbiology is covered in reasonable depth. The Science Citation Index must recover its costs from user fees, but is widely available at major research centers. It offers additional search capabilities, especially by citation linkage. Therefore, starting with the bibliography of a given encyclopedia article, one can quickly find (1) all articles more recently published that have cited those bibliographic reference starting points and (2) all other recent articles that share bibliographic information with the others. With luck, one of these articles may be identified as another comprehensive review that has digested more recent or broader primary material.

On a weekly basis, services such as Current Contents on Diskette (ISI) and Reference Update offer still more timely access to current literature as well as to abstracts with a variety of useful features. Under the impetus of intense competition, these services are evolving rapidly, to the great benefit of a user community desperate for electronic assistance in coping with the rapidly growing and intertwined networks of discovery. The bibliographic services of Chemical Abstracts and Biological Abstracts would also be potentially invaluable; however, their coverage of microbiology is rather limited.

In addition, major monographs have appeared from time to time—*The Bacteria, The Prokaryotes,* and many others. Your local reference library should be consulted for these volumes.

Valuable collections of reviews also include *Critical Reviews for Microbiology, Symposia of the Society for General Microbiology, Monographs of the American Society for Microbiology,* and *Proceedings of the International Congresses of Microbiology.*

The articles in this encyclopedia are intended to be accessible to a broader audience, not to take the place of review articles with comprehensive bibliographies. Citations should be sufficient to give the reader access to the latter, as may be required. We do apologize to many individuals whose contributions to the growth of microbiology could not be adequately embraced by the secondary bibliographies included here.

The organization of encyclopedic knowledge is a daunting task in any discipline; it is all the more complex in such a diversified and rapidly moving domain as microbiology. The best way to anticipate the rapid further growth that we can expect in the near future is unclear. Perhaps more specialized series in subfields of microbiology would be more appropriate. The publishers and editors would welcome readers' comments on these points, as well as on any deficiencies that may be perceived in the current effort.

My personal thanks are extended to my coeditors, Martin Alexander, David Hopwood, Barbara Iglewski, and Allen Laskin; and above all, to the many very busy scientists who took time to draft and review each of these articles.

*Joshua Lederberg*

# Guide to the Encyclopedia

The *Encyclopedia of Microbiology, Second Edition* is a scholarly source of information on microorganisms, those life forms that are observable with a microscope rather than by the naked eye. The work consists of four volumes and includes 298 separate articles. Of these 298 articles, 171 are completely new topics commissioned for this edition, and 63 others are newly written articles on topics appearing in the first edition. In other words, approximately 80% of the content of the encyclopedia is entirely new to this edition. (The remaining 20% of the content has been carefully reviewed and revised to ensure currency.)

Each article in the encyclopedia provides a comprehensive overview of the selected topic to inform a broad spectrum of readers, from research professionals to students to the interested general public. In order that you, the reader, will derive the greatest possible benefit from your use of the *Encyclopedia of Microbiology*, we have provided this Guide. It explains how the encyclopedia is organized and how the information within it can be located.

## ORGANIZATION

The *Encyclopedia of Microbiology* is organized to provide maximum ease of use. All of the articles are arranged in a single alphabetical sequence by title. Articles whose titles begin with the letters A to C are in Volume 1, articles with titles from D through K are in Volume 2, then L through P in Volume 3, and finally Q to Z in Volume 4. This last volume also includes a complete subject index for the entire

work, an alphabetical list of the contributors to the encyclopedia, and a glossary of key terms used in the articles.

Article titles generally begin with the key noun or noun phrase indicating the topic, with any descriptive terms following. For example, the article title is "Bioluminescence, Microbial" rather than "Microbial Bioluminescence," and "Foods, Quality Control" is the title rather than "Quality Control of Foods."

## TABLE OF CONTENTS

A complete table of contents for the *Encyclopedia of Microbiology* appears at the front of each volume. This list of article titles represents topics that have been carefully selected by the Editor-in-Chief, Dr. Joshua Lederberg, and the nine Associate Editors. The Encyclopedia provides coverage of 20 different subject areas within the overall field of microbiology. Please see p. v for the alphabetical table of contents, and p. xix for a list of topics arranged by subject area.

## INDEX

The Subject Index in Volume 4 indicates the volume and page number where information on a given topic can be found. In addition, the Table of Contents by Subject Area also functions as an index, since it lists all the topics within a given area; e.g., the encyclopedia includes eight different articles dealing with historic aspects of microbiology and nine dealing with techniques of microbiology.

## ARTICLE FORMAT

In order to make information easy to locate, all of the articles in the *Encyclopedia of Microbiology* are arranged in a standard format, as follows:
- Title of Article
- Author's Name and Affiliation
- Outline
- Glossary
- Defining Statement
- Body of the Article
- Cross-References
- Bibliography

## OUTLINE

Each entry in the Encyclopedia begins with a topical outline that indicates the general content of the article. This outline serves two functions. First, it provides a brief preview of the article, so that the reader can get a sense of what is contained there without having to leaf through the pages. Second, it serves to highlight important subtopics that will be discussed within the article. For example, the article "Biopesticides" includes subtopics such as "Selection of Biopesticides," "Production of Biopesticides," "Biopesticide Stabilization," and "Commercialization of Biopesticides."

The outline is intended as an overview and thus it lists only the major headings of the article. In addition, extensive second-level and third-level headings will be found within the article.

## GLOSSARY

The Glossary contains terms that are important to an understanding of the article and that may be unfamiliar to the reader. Each term is defined in the context of the article in which it is used. Thus the same term may appear as a glossary entry in two or more articles, with the details of the definition varying slightly from one article to another. The encyclopedia has approximately 2500 glossary entries.

In addition, Volume 4 provides a comprehensive glossary that collects all the core vocabulary of microbiology in one A–Z list. This section can be consulted for definitions of terms not found in the individual glossary for a given article.

## DEFINING STATEMENT

The text of each article in the encyclopedia begins with a single introductory paragraph that defines the topic under discussion and summarizes the content of the article. For example, the article "Eyespot" begins with the following statement:

> **EYESPOT** is a damaging stem base disease of cereal crops and other grasses caused by fungi of the genus *Tapsia*. It occurs in temperate regions world-wide including Europe, the USSR, Japan, South Africa, North America, and Australasia. In many of these countries eyespot can be found on the majority of autumn-sown barley and wheat crops and may cause an average of 5–10% loss in yield, although low rates of infection do not generally have a significant effect. . . .

## CROSS-REFERENCES

Almost all of the articles in the Encyclopedia have cross-references to other articles. These cross-references appear at the conclusion of the article text. They indicate articles that can be consulted for further information on the same topic or for information on a related topic. For example, the article "Smallpox" has references to "Biological Warfare," "Polio," "Surveillance of Infectious Diseases," and "Vaccines, Viral."

## BIBLIOGRAPHY

The Bibliography is the last element in an article. The reference sources listed there are the author's recommendations of the most appropriate materials for further research on the given topic. The bibliography entries are for the benefit of the reader and do not represent a complete listing of all materials consulted by the author in preparing the article.

## COMPANION WORKS

The *Encyclopedia of Microbiology* is one of a series of multivolume reference works in the life sciences published by Academic Press. Other such titles include the *Encyclopedia of Human Biology, Encyclopedia of Reproduction, Encyclopedia of Toxicology, Encyclopedia of Immunology, Encyclopedia of Virology, Encyclopedia of Cancer,* and *Encyclopedia of Stress.*

# *Acknowledgments*

The Editors and the Publisher wish to thank the following people who have generously provided their time, often at short notice, to review various articles in the *Encyclopedia of Microbiology* and in other ways to assist the Editors in their efforts to make this work as scientifically accurate and complete as possible. We gratefully acknowledge their assistance:

**George A. M. Cross**
Laboratory of Molecular Parasitology
The Rockefeller University
New York, NY, USA

**Miklós Müller**
Laboratory of Biochemical Parasitology
The Rockefeller University
New York, NY, USA

**A. I. Scott**
Department of Chemistry
Texas A&M University
College Station, Texas, USA

**Robert W. Simons**
Department of Microbiology and
    Molecular Genetics
University of California, Los Angeles
Los Angeles, California, USA

**Peter H. A. Sneath**
Department of Microbiology and Immunology
University of Leicester
Leicester, England, UK

**John L. Spudich**
Department of Microbiology and
    Molecular Genetics
University of Texas Medical School
Houston, Texas, USA

**Pravod K. Srivastava**
Center for Immunotherapy
University of Connecticut
Farmington, Connecticut, USA

**Peter Staeheli**
Department of Virology
University of Freiburg
Freiburg, Germany

**Ralph M. Steinman**
Laboratory of Cellular Physiology
    and Immunology
The Rockefeller University
New York, NY, USA

**Sherri O. Stuver**
Department of Epidemiology
Harvard School of Public Health
Boston, Massachusetts, USA

**Alice Telesnitsky**
Department of Microbiology and Immunology
University of Michigan Medical School
Ann Arbor, Michigan, USA

**Robert G. Webster**
Chairman and Professor
Rose Marie Thomas Chair
St. Jude Children's Research Hospital
Memphis, Tennessee, USA

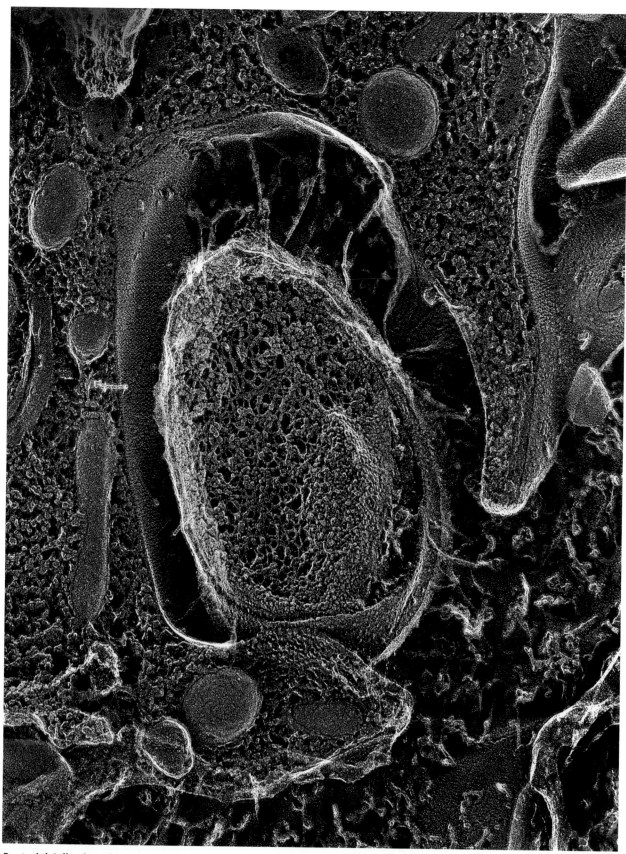

**_Bacterial Adhesion._** The attachment of uropathogenic _Escherichia coli_ to the luminal surface of the bladder epithelium by type 1 pili as visualized by high-resolution freeze-fracture, deep-etch electron microscopy. See article ADHESION, BACTERIAL (Vol. 1).

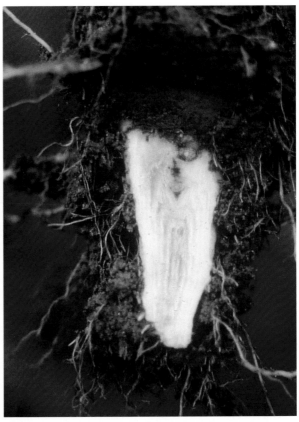

**Beet Necrotic Yellow Vein Virus (BNYVV).** Top left: Sugar beet leaf systemically infected with BNYVV. Top right: Cross section through a BNYVV-infected sugar beet with pronounced beardedness. The tap root is very small and shows a pronounced discoloration of the vascular system. Bottom: Influence of BNYVV with various RNA compositions on the yield of mechanically inoculated sugar beets. K represents the noninoculated control; the numbers refer to combinations of RNA species. See article BEET NECROTIC YELLOW VEIN VIRUS (Vol. 1).

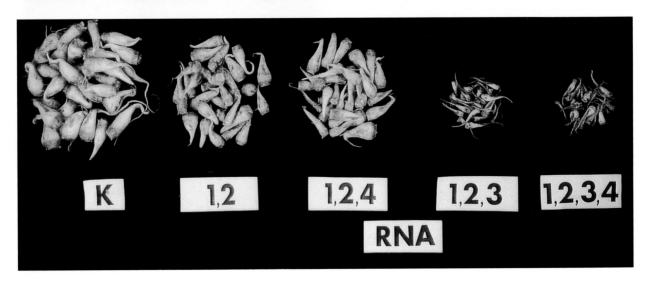

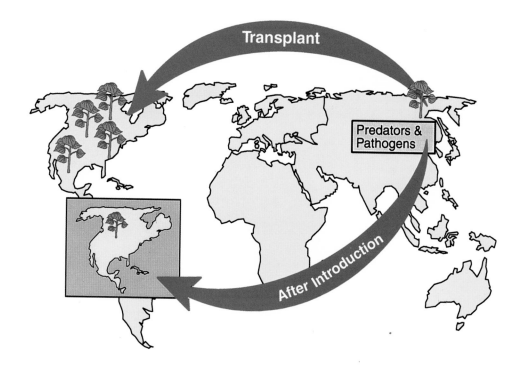

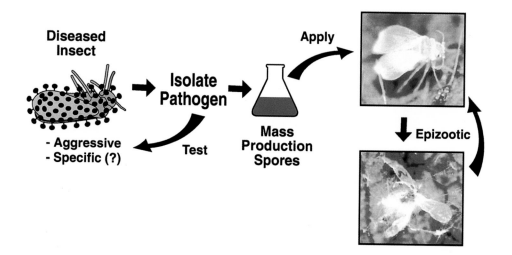

***Biological Controls.*** Top: The classical approach; native predators and pathogens of an introduced weed or insect pest are introduced into the new ecosystem. Control occurs when the native enemies of the pest reduce the pest population to manageable levels. Bottom: The inundative (biopesticide) approach; this commercially attractive control measure uses aggressive, specific pathogens of the weed, insect, or plant disease to control pests. The living microbial pathogen is mass produced and applied in an inundative fashion when pest control is required. After contact, the biopesticidal propagules infect and kill the pest host. See article Biopesticides, Microbial (Vol. 1).

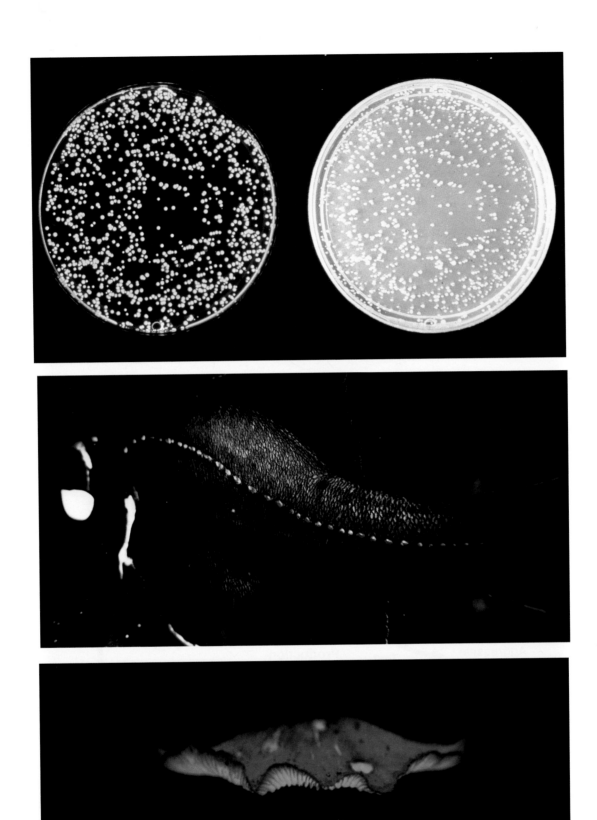

***Bioluminescence.*** Top: Colonies of luminous bacteria photographed by their own light (left) and in room light (right). Light is emitted continuously but is controlled by a quorum sensing mechanism (autoinducer) and is thus not proportional to growth or cell density. Middle: The flashlight fish (Photoblepharon) showing the exposed light organ, which harbors luminous bacteria and is located just below the eye. A special lid allows the fish to turn the light on and off. Photograph by Dr. James Morin. Bottom: Bioluminescent mushroom photographed by its own light. Photograph by Dr. Dan Perlman. See article BIOLUMINESCENCE, MICROBIAL (Vol. 1).

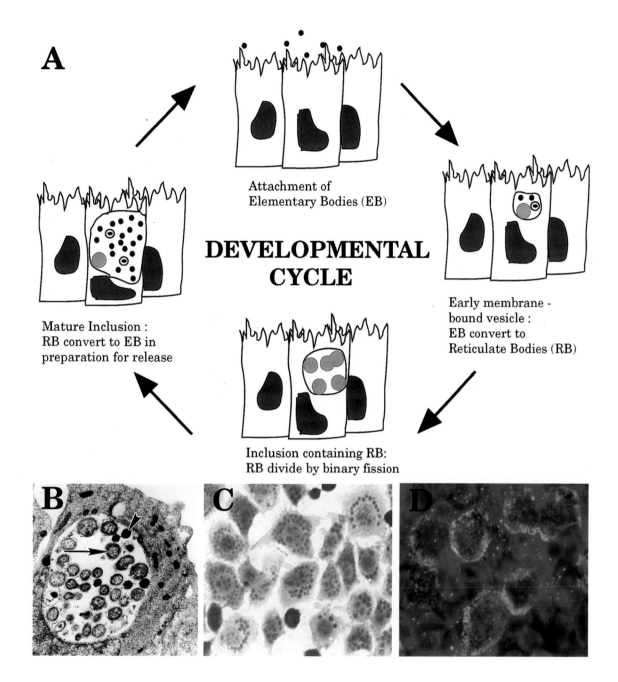

**A**

Attachment of
Elementary Bodies (EB)

**DEVELOPMENTAL CYCLE**

Early membrane -
bound vesicle :
EB convert to
Reticulate Bodies (RB)

Mature Inclusion :
RB convert to EB in
preparation for release

Inclusion containing RB:
RB divide by binary fission

**B**   **C**   **D**

*Chlamydial Developmental Cycle.* The cycle (A) begins with the attachment of elementary bodies (EB) to susceptible host cells. After entry, EB convert to reticulate bodies (RB) that grow and divide within the membrane-bound intracellular inclusion. RB eventually convert back to infectious EB in preparation for release and infection of neighboring host cells. (B) Electron microscopic view of an intracellular inclusion of *C. trachomatis* containing both EB (arrowhead) and RB (arrow). (C) Visualization of multiple *C. psittaci* inclusions per host cell using the Giemsa staining procedure; inclusions appear as "grape-like" clusters surrounding the nucleus. (D) Visualization of single *C. trachomatis* inclusions per host cell by fluorescence microscopy using a chlamydia-specific antibody. Inclusions are bright green. See article CHLAMYDIA (Vol. 1).

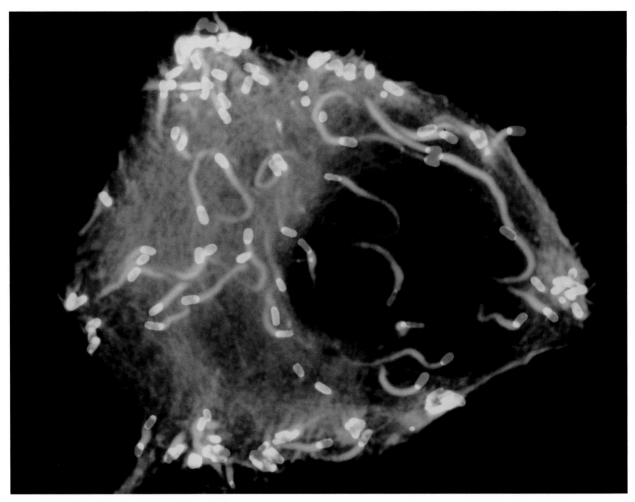

**Enteropathogenic Bacteria.** Pathogens such as *Shigella* are a common cause of inflammatory infections in the colon and small intestine. Above, actin tail formation by *S. flexneri.* Actin microfilaments are polymerized at one end of the bacterium and help it to move within the host cell cytoplasm. Bacteria are stained in red and actin in green. The areas where bacteria and actin colocalize appear in yellow (courtesy of Coumarin Egile and Philippe J. Sansonetti). See article Enteropathogenic Bacteria (Vol. 2).

**Eyespot.** A damaging stem base disease of cereal crops and other grasses, eyespot is caused by fungi of the genus *Tapesia.* Shown here are colonies of *T. yallundae* and *T. acuformis* with smooth and feathery margins, respectively. See article Eyespot (Vol. 2).

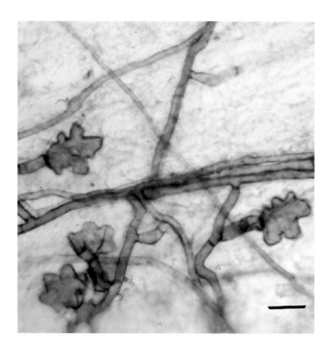 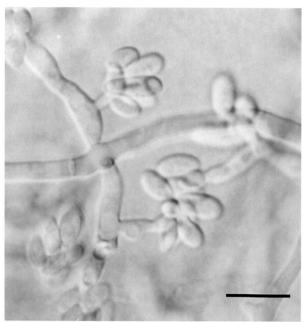

**Gaeumannomyces graminis.** *Gaeumannomyces graminis* is a widely distributed species of fungus that colonizes the root and crown tissue of many members of the grass family. Top left: Hyphopodia of *G. graminis* var. *graminis* on centipede grass. Magnification = 400X. Top right: Phialospores and phialides of *P. graminicola* in culture. Magnification = 400X. Bottom: A golf course with evidence of Bermudagrass spring dead spot caused by *G. graminis* var. *graminis*. Root rot causes plant necrosis with consequent yellowing. See article GAEUMANNOMYCES GRAMINIS (Vol. 2).

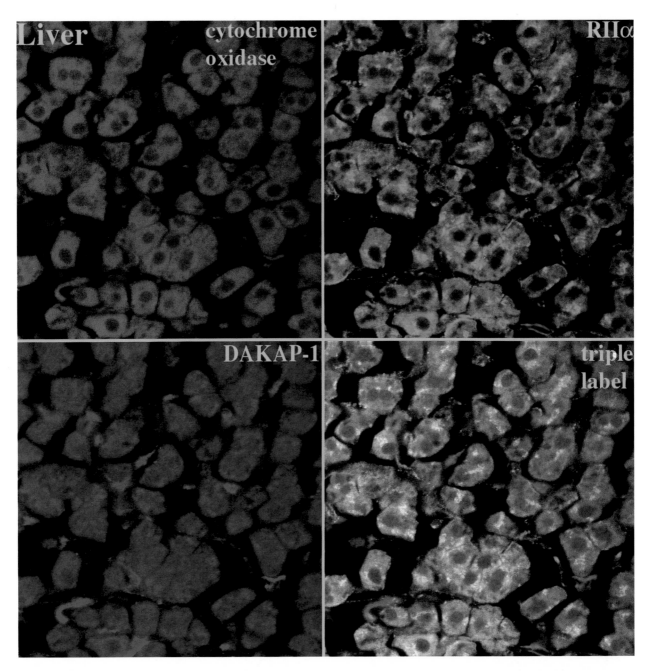

***Confocal Microscopy.*** The field of optical microscopy has been revolutionized in recent years by the widespread use of confocal microscopes. Shown here, immunohistochemistry performed by triple-antibody labeling of a 70-μm slice of liver tissue. LSCM (laser scanning confocal microscopy) was used to record images of a 3-μm optical section near the surface of the slice. The red label (rhodamine) shows the distribution of cytochrome c antibodies, which specifically label mitochondria, and hence are not in the nucleus (the circular regions inside each cell). The green label (fluorescein) shows the distribution of RIIα, which produces a typical Golgi labeling pattern inside the hepatocytes. The blue label (cy-5) shows DAKAP-1 labeling. DAKAP-1 is a unique anchoring protein for regulatory subunits of protein kinase A (PKA), which are involved in cAMP-mediated cell signaling pathways. It is unique in its anchoring of both RIα and RIIβ regulatory subunits of PKA. Triple labeling shows the superposition of the three antibody labeling patterns. Colocalization of the different antibodies produces the different colors; e.g., overlap of blue and red labels produces a violet color. See article MICROSCOPY, CONFOCAL (Vol. 3).

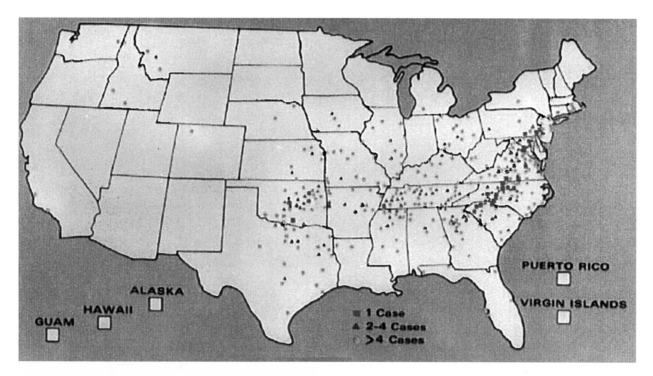

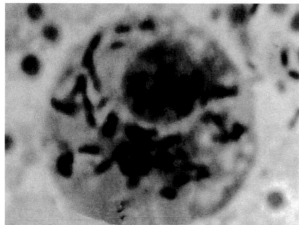

**Rickettsial Diseases.** Top: Distribution of cases of Rocky Mountain Spotted Fever in the United States, about 1980. Left: Cell with intracellular Rickettsiae. See article TYPHUS FEVERS AND OTHER RICKETTSIAL DISEASES (Vol. 4).

**Trypanosomes.** Bottom left: Giemsa-stained endothelial cells infected with *T. cruzi*. Note the numerous amastigotes. Bottom right: Endomyocardial biopsy from a patient with Chagas' disease. Note the inflammation and fibrosis (courtesy of Dr. Alain C. Borczuk, North Shore University Hospital, Manhasset, NY). See article TRYPANOSOMES (Vol. 4).

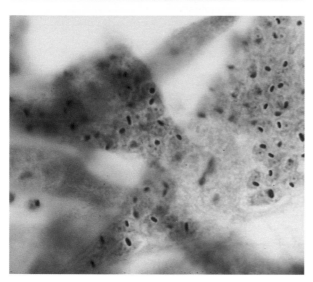

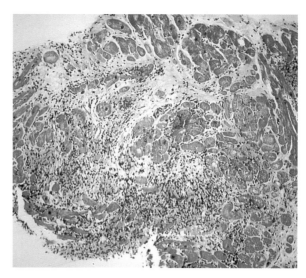

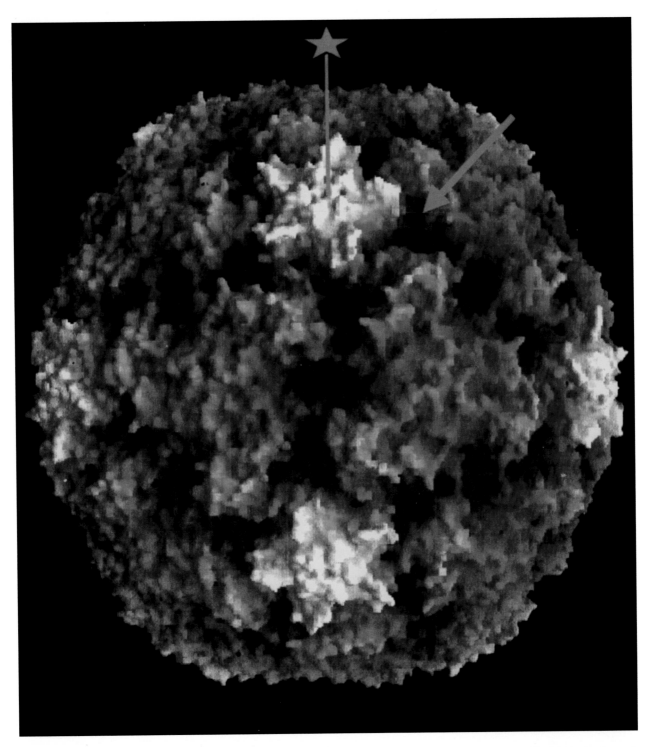

***Rhinovirus.*** Human rhinovirus (HRV) is the single most frequent causative agent of the common cold. HRV is the largest genus of viruses of the family *Piconarviridae.* Seen above, a molecular graphics image of human rhinovirus 14. The star-shaped region corresponds to the pentamers formed by the convergence of five adjacent VP1 units (star symbol). ICAM-1, the receptor for the majority of HRV serotypes, binds within the the canyon, off each tip of the star (arrow). [Courtesy of Jean-Yves Sgro, University of Wisconsin, Madison, who made the image based on X-ray data, as published by Rossmann *et al.* (1985). *Nature* **317**, 145–153.] See article RHINOVIRUSES (Vol. 4).

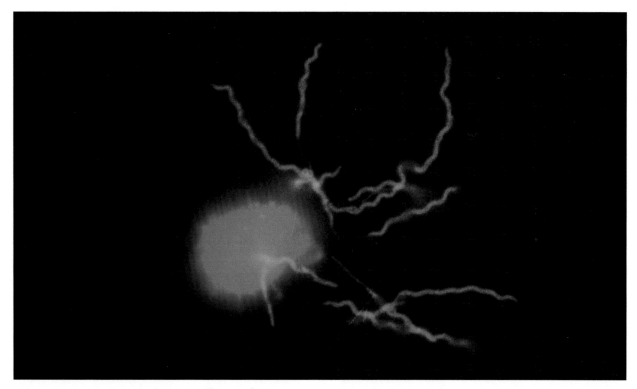

***Lyme Disease.*** The causative agent of Lyme disease, the spirochete *Borrelia burgdorferi*, shown attached to human platelets. The spirochetes were illuminated by a green-fluorescent anti-Lyme spirochete antibody, the platelets with a red-fluorescent anti-integrin antibody. See article LYME DISEASE (Vol. 3).

## H&E          GFAP          PrP

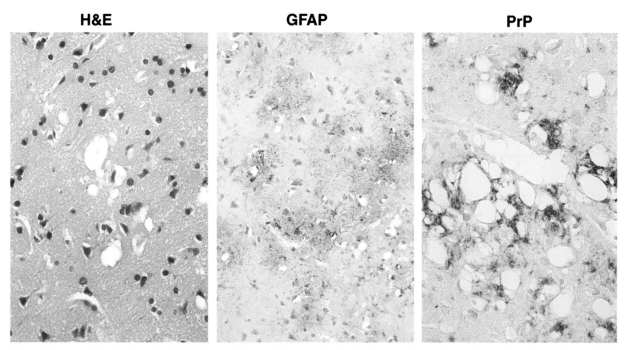

***Prions.*** Hematoxylin-Eosin stain (left) shows the typical vacuoles in the brain of a patient affected with CJD (Creutzfeld-Jakob disease) which leads to the spongiform appearance. Proliferation of reactive astrocytes is visualized by staining with antibodies against glial fibrillary acidic protein (GFAP, middle). PrP protein deposits are shown with anti-PrP immuno-staining. See article PRIONS (Vol. 3).

**Rust Fungi.** The rust fungi are a cosmopolitan group of fungi noted as parasites on a wide range of plants, including important cereal food crops. Top left: Leaf or brown rust of wheat caused by *Puccinia recondita* f. sp. *tritici*. Top right: Stem or black rust of wheat caused by *P. graminis* f. sp. *tritici*. Bottom: Mint rust caused by *P. menthae*. Distortion of stems occurs due to vascular infection during the aecial stage. [Courtesy of Ms. J. Edwards, University of Melbourne, Australia.] See article RUST FUNGI (Vol. 4).

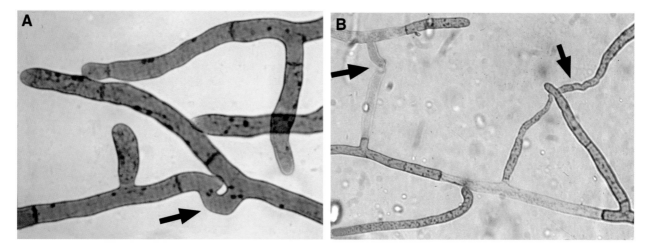

**Rhizoctonia.** The genus *Rhizoctonia* represents a very large and diverse group of fungi, many of which are significant plant pathogens. Top: Interaction of *R. solani* hyphae on a glass slide. Left (A): Compatible interaction (indicated by arrow). [Photograph provided by Donald Carling.] Right (B): Incompatible interactions (indicated by arrows). Bottom: Symptoms of Rhizoctonia disease caused by basidiospore infection on leaves of different plant species. Upper left: Target spot of tobacco. [Photograph provided by David Shew.] Upper right: Foliar blight of soybean. Lower left: Foliage blight of sugar beet. [Photographs provided by Shigeo Naito.] Lower right: Web blight of snapbean. [Photograph provided by Graciela Godoy-Lutz.] See article RHIZOCTONIA (Vol. 4).

***Smut of Barley and Wheat.*** Top left (A): Covered smut of barley caused by *Ustilago hordei*. Note compact spore masses that are liberated and spread to healthy seeds during harvesting. Top right (B): Loose smut of wheat caused by *U. tritici.* The spores become wind-borne during heading and infect healthy flowering wheat spikes.

***Disease Cycle of Wheat Bunt.*** Bottom: (A) Mature wheat spike infected with common bunt. (B) Healthy seeds (left), partially bunted seeds (center), and bunt balls (right) originating from a single infected wheat head. (C) Broken bunt ball showing mass of teliospores. These become attached to healthy seeds during harvesting or spread over the soil surface. (D) Teliospores of *Tilletia controversa,* the dwarf bunt fungus, showing spore ornamentation. (E) Wheat field infected with common bunt. See article SMUTS, BUNTS, AND ERGOT (Vol. 4).

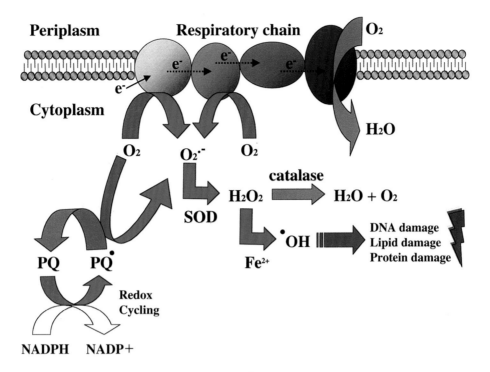

***Oxidative Stress.*** Top: The majority of the oxygen that enters the cell is reduced to water by the respiratory chain, a reaction that consumes four electrons. However, a small proportion of the oxygen molecules can be reduced in a series of one-electron reactions. Molecular oxygen forms superoxide ($O_2^{\cdot-}$) by reaction with reduced components of the respiratory chain. Superoxide can also be formed by reaction with redox-cycling drugs such as paraquat (PQ), which is enzymatically re-reduced at the expense of NADPH. Superoxide is eliminated by superoxide dismutase (SOD) to form hydrogen peroxide ($H_2O_2$). Hydrogen peroxide can either be detoxified by conversion into water and oxygen by catalase, or react with reduced transition metals such as iron and copper to form hydroxyl radical ($^{\cdot}OH$). Hydroxyl radical is a highly reactive molecule than can damage virtually all the fundamental cellular components. Red arrows indicate reactions that yield oxidants. Green arrows indicate reactions that yield innocuous products. See article Oxidative Stress (Vol. 3).

***RecA.*** Bottom: Structure of RecA protein determined by X-ray crystallography. Three-dimensional structure of the RecA protein with functional domains assigned on the basis of biochemical, genetic, and structural data. (Reprinted with permission from Kowalczykowski *et al.*, 1994. *Microbiol. Rev.* **58:** 401–465.) See article RecA (Vol. 4).

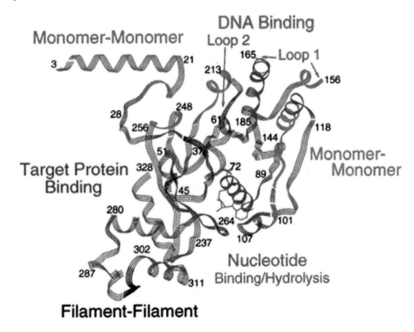

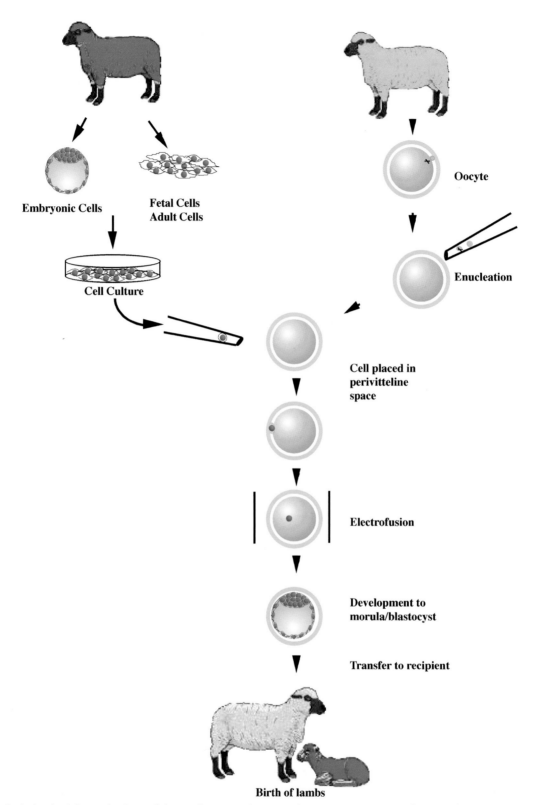

**Embryonic Cells**

**Fetal Cells Adult Cells**

**Cell Culture**

**Oocyte**

**Enucleation**

**Cell placed in perivitteline space**

**Electrofusion**

**Development to morula/blastocyst**

**Transfer to recipient**

**Birth of lambs**

***Transgenic Animals.*** Schematic view of the nuclear transfer procedure. Oocytes derived from Scottish Blackface (symbolized as a yellow sheep) are enucleated. The donor cell derived from a different sheep breed (symbolized as a red sheep) is placed under the zona pellucida into the perivitelline space. The cell nucleus is introduced into the cytoplast by electrofusion, which also activates the oocyte. The reconstructed embryo is then either cultured *in vitro* up to blastocyst stage or is transferred into a pseudopregnant intermediate recipient ewe. At day 7, embryos are assessed for development. Late morulae and blastocysts are transferred into final recipients. Pregnancies resulting from nuclear transfer are determined by ultrasound scan at about 60 days after estrus, and development is subsequently monitored at regular intervals. See article TRANSGENIC ANIMAL TECHNOLOGY (Vol. 4).

# ABC Transport

**Elie Dassa**

*Institut Pasteur*

## GLOSSARY

**binding protein** Extracytoplasmic part of an ABC importer. It binds the substrate with high affinity and presents it to the transmembrane domains.

**gene fusion** Genetic manipulation allowing the fusion of two genes. Transcriptional fusions are done in such a way that expression of the first gene could be monitored by the phenotype of the second. Translational fusions lead to the in-frame fusion of two coding sequences. The latter were used to establish the topological disposition of integral membrane proteins.

**nucleotide-binding domain** Part of the ABC transporter involved in energy coupling. This part is hydrophilic, highly conserved, and involved in ATP binding and hydrolysis.

**orthologs** Genes that evolved within a single organism by gene duplication followed by divergence. Their products (isoforms) in general have the same function in different organisms.

**paralogs** Genes that evolved either by speciation or by divergence. Their products in general have similar functions in different organisms.

**proteoliposomes** Membrane vesicles made *in vitro* by incorporating detergent-solubilized membrane proteins into artificial bilayer lipid vesicles or liposomes.

**transmembrane domain** Intramembranous part of an ABC transporter. It is formed of several hydrophobic helices that cross the lipid bilayer of the membrane. It contains the substrate-recognition sites.

**Walker motifs** Short sequence motifs found by J. E. Walker in ATPases, myosin, kinases, and other ATP-requiring enzymes. These motifs are involved in the recognition of nucleotides. They are also found in the nucleotide-binding domains of ABC ATPases.

**TRANSPORT SYSTEMS** are of critical importance for living organisms, and selective permeability to nutrients and metabolites was probably the first distinctive property of primitive cells. Functionally and structurally different transporters have been identified in living organisms and they were involved in the uptake (import) of nutrients or in the excretion (export) of toxic or waste molecules. It is customary to distinguish primary transporters, which couple transport directly to the hydrolysis of ATP (P-, H-, or V-type ATPases), from secondary transporters, in which the energy used derives indirectly from ATP hydrolysis, such as phosphotransferase systems and ion gradient-dependent transporters.

Among primary transporters, the ATP-binding cassette (ABC) superfamily is comprised of systems that are widespread in all living organisms (Ames *et al.*, 1992). These systems form the largest family of paralogs ever found, and they are involved in many living processes including not only transport but also transcriptional and translational regulation, DNA repair, drug resistance, pathogenicity, and immune response. In humans, the functional importance of ABC transporters is highlighted by the fact that several severe genetic diseases such as cystic fibrosis are the consequence of their dysfunction. These systems are characterized by the same overall organization of four structural domains: two very hydrophobic membrane spanning or transmembrane domains (TMDs) and two hydrophilic cytoplasmic domains peripherally associated to the cytosolic side of the cytoplasmic membrane (Fig. 1). The four domains may be independent or fused in several ways (Higgins, 1992). The primary sequence of the hydrophilic cytoplasmic domains is highly conserved, displaying conserved Walker motifs A and B common to ATPases and another motif characteristic of the ABC transporter, the LSGGQ or signature motif. In well-characterized systems, these hydrophilic domains were found to bind and to hydrolyze ATP, thereby coupling transport to ATP hydrolysis (Schneider and Hunke, 1998). At this point, they are called nucleotide-binding domains (NBDs). ABC transporters are involved in the export or import of a wide variety of substrates ranging from small ions to macromolecules. This article will focus on import ABC systems, which are found only in prokaryotes and where the four constitutive domains are carried in general by independent polypeptides. By contrast, export systems are found in all living organisms and generally have the TMDs fused to the NBDs. In eukaryotes, the four domains are very often fused on a single polypeptide, with alternating TMDs and NBDs.

## I. OVERVIEW

ABC import systems are also called binding protein-dependent (BPD) transport systems (Boos and Lucht, 1996). They are unidirectional transporters, and the substrate is not modified during transport. In addition to the basal core structure of ABC transporters, for proper function they require an extracytoplasmic substrate-binding protein (Fig. 1). These components are located in the periplasmic space of gram-negative bacteria. They are released from bacteria by a cold osmotic shock procedure, and the corresponding transport systems are transiently inactivated due to the loss of the binding protein. In all cases studied, the released proteins were shown to bind substrates with a high affinity. If such proteins are introduced back into the periplasm of cells lacking these components, either because they were osmotically shocked or because of a mutation, transport could be restored. In gram-positive bacteria, which do not have a periplasmic space, the substrate-binding protein is an extracellular lipoprotein bound to the external face of the cytoplasmic membrane by

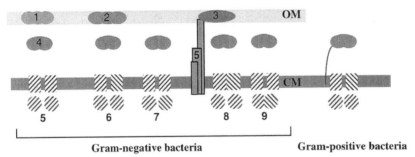

**Fig. 1.** Organization of extracellular binding protein-dependent transport systems. The membranes of bacteria are represented schematically. OM, outer membrane; CM, cytoplasm membrane. All systems share the same organization. First, they all have an outer membrane channel that may be a nonspecific trimeric porin (1), a specific trimeric porin (2), or a high-affinity outer membrane receptor (3). The energy needed by the latter to translocate substrates into the periplasmic space is transduced from the cytoplasmic to the outer membrane by the TonB, ExbB, and ExbD complex (5). Second, they have a periplasmic (gram-negative bacteria) or an extracellular (gram-positive bacteria) solute binding protein (4). Third, they have a cytoplasmic membrane complex composed of two integral membrane proteins (TMD; squares) and two ATP-binding subunits (NBD; circles). A system could be composed of a homodimer of TMD and a homodimer of NBD (5), a heterodimer of TMD and a homodimer of NBD (6), and two heterodimers of TMD and NBD (7). The two TMD's (8) or the two NBD's (9) could be fused on the same polypeptide.

an N-terminal acyl glyceryl cysteine. This anchor is responsible for maintaining the substrate-binding protein in close vicinity to the membrane components. BDP transporters are extremely diverse in their substrate specificities. Each transport system is specific for a single substrate or for a family of structurally related substrates, such as maltose and maltodextrins. The nature of the substrates that are transported is very diverse and includes mono- and oligosaccharides, organic and inorganic ions, amino acids and short peptides, ironsiderophores, metals, polyamine cations, opines, and vitamins (Higgins, 1992). These systems are very efficient since they are able to concentrate nutrients up to $10^4$-fold even when the concentration of the nutrient in the external medium is below the micromolar range. As a consequence, BDP transporters are scavenging systems able to extract trace elements from the environment.

## II. PROPERTIES OF THE COMPONENTS OF BPD TRANSPORTERS

### A. Outer Membrane Components of Gram-Negative Bacteria

To be efficiently transported into the cytoplasm, a nutrient must cross the three layers of the gram-negative bacterium envelope. Substrates must first pass through the outer membrane and can use three pathways (Fig. 1). First, most small substrates, with a molecular mass <650 Da, cross the outer membrane through the non-specific or generalized porins such as OmpF and OmpC (Nikaido, 1996). The importance of such porins in transport processes is highlighted by the fact that mutants lacking these proteins are pleiotropically affected in the utilization of several substrates. Second, when the size of the substrate exceeds the size handled by generalized porins, a specific or specialized porin is used. The best example known is maltoporin, the *lamB* gene product which is essential for the transport of maltodextrins of more than three glucose residues. In contrast with general porins, the genes coding for such specialized porins are often genetically linked to the regions encoding the rest of the transporter and their expres-

sion is tightly coregulated. Finally, the systems for uptake of iron siderophores and vitamin $B_{12}$ must deal with the complication that the substrates are in exceedingly low amounts in the environment. The molecular mass of the transported molecules is approximately 700–1000 Da, which is above the limit size of porins. For these reasons, iron siderophore compounds are first bound by high-affinity outer membrane receptors (Braun *et al.*, 1998). These receptors are also channels through which the substrates are translocated into the periplasm. Substrates are released from the high-affinity substrate-binding site by virtue of an energy expense. Studies with the *Escherichia coli* ferrichrome *fhu* transport system indicate that the translocation of the substrate is dependent on the cytoplasmic membrane electrochemical gradient. Moreover, since there is no evidence for energy sources in the periplasmic space or in the outer membrane, energy from the cytoplasmic membrane should be transduced to outer membrane receptors. This step is achieved by three cytoplasmic membrane proteins, ExbB, ExbD, and TonB, and there is evidence that these proteins form a complex in the envelope. TonB and ExbD have a single transmembrane segment and a large hydrophilic periplasmic domain. It is postulated that these domains interact with a conserved region of the outer membrane receptors, the TonB box, allowing the release of the substrate and its diffusion through the channel. It is remarkable that outer membrane receptors have the highest specific recognition site for iron siderophores and vitamin $B_{12}$. For instance, siderophores such as coprogen, ferrichrome, and aerobactin are recognized by specific receptors (FhuE, FhuA, and IutA, respectively) but are transported into the cytoplasm by the same BPD transporter (FhuBDC). Moreover, the affinity of the periplasmic-binding protein FhuD for ferrichrome is lower than that of FhuA.

### B. The Periplasmic or Extracytoplasmic Substrate-Binding Components

With the exception of iron siderophore transport systems discussed previously, the substrate recognition site with the highest specificity is on the substrate-binding proteins in other BDP transporters. For instance, two different substrate-binding proteins use with the same cytoplasmic components, as shown for the histidine and the lysine–arginine–ornithine-binding proteins (BPs) which use the same HisMPQ cytoplasmic membrane transporter. Only a few substrate-binding lipoproteins have been characterized biochemically and structurally from gram-positive organisms. Most of the knowledge on substrate BPs is from the study of proteins from gram-negative bacteria. The molar ratio of the BPs over the cytoplasmic membrane components is usually high. For instance, the periplasmic concentration of maltose BP could be as high as 1 m$M$. One of the roles of BPs is to maintain a high concentration of bound substrate in the close vicinity of the outer face of the cytoplasmic membrane. Due to their abundance and to the ease of purification, they were the first components of BPD transporters to be analyzed thoroughly and even used as biotechnology tools. The *E. coli* maltose BP is very popular due to its capacity to be fused to foreign peptides or polypeptides without losing its functional properties. Then hybrid proteins can be purified in a single step by affinity chromatography.

BPs are monomeric and bind substrates with affinities ranging from 0.1 to 1 $\mu M$. Studies on the kinetics of binding revealed that there was one substrate binding site per molecule of protein. The three-dimensional structure of several BPs was determined, most notably in the laboratory of F. A. Quiocho (Quiocho and Ledvina, 1996). From these structural studies, it appeared that all BPs adopt a similar folding pattern composed of two globular domains or lobes, called the N- and the C-lobe since they contain the N- and the C-terminal ends of the protein. Each lobe is composed of a so-called $\alpha\beta$ fold that includes plated $\beta$-sheets and is surrounded by $\alpha$-helices and connected by loops. The two lobes are connected by two or three connecting strands (the hinge region). This structure determines a cleft where the substrate inserts. BPs undergo a large conformational change on binding of substrates. This conformational change has been established using a variety of methods, including limited proteolysis, variation of intrinsic fluorescence, and resolution of three-dimensional structure in the presence and absence of substrate. It consists of the rotation of the two globular domains around the hinge, putting the two lobes in close contact and trapping the substrate deeply within the cleft. In the maltose BP, such conformational change includes a twist of the two domains relative to each other. It has been speculated that this conformational change allows the substrate-loaded BP to interact with its cytoplasmic membrane partners and therefore to initiate transport, but its mechanism is not known in detail. Does the substrate trigger the closing of the structure or does the protein exist in two different conformations, with the closed form being stabilized by the substrate? The fact that some closed forms of BPs may be purified and even crystallized in the absence of ligand does not support the trigger model. Some BPs are also chemoreceptors involved in chemotaxis by signaling the presence of substrates to chemotactic transducers. This is the case for maltose, galactose, and ribose BPs. They interact with the Tar (maltose BP) and the Trg (galactose and ribose BPs) chemotransducers, respectively.

## C. The Hydrophobic Cytoplasmic Membrane Proteins

One or two hydrophobic cytoplasmic membrane proteins are components of BPD transport systems (Fig. 1). They are proposed to constitute a pore or a channel through which substrates cross the cytoplasmic membrane. The two proteins form a heterodimeric complex as demonstrated in the maltose and the histidine transport systems. For systems with only one protein, as in the glutamine transport system of *E. coli*, it has been postulated but not yet demonstrated that the TMD forms a homodimer. These proteins are integral membrane proteins, and computer-assisted predictions of secondary structure and topology indicate that they span the cytoplasmic membrane. In well-characterized systems, they have been shown to be accessible to proteolytic digestion from the cytoplasmic and the periplasmic sides of the membrane. In the vast majority of cases, they contain six transmembrane segments folded in an $\alpha$-helical conformation and joined by loops of variable size. The N and C termini of the proteins point toward the cytoplasm. There are several exceptions to this general scheme, such as the FhuB protein of the ferrichrome transport system that is made of 20

(2 × 10) transmembrane segments and the ProW protein from the glycine–betaine transport system in which the N terminus is in the periplasmic space. Considerable efforts have been made to establish experimentally the topological disposition of such proteins. Gene fusion approaches using periplasmic enzymes that are active only in the periplasm (alkaline phosphatase or β-lactamase) as reporters were instrumental in these studies. In general, the results of such experimental analyses were consistent with the prediction of transmembrane segments and topology as inferred from the primary structure. However, there is no easy way to identify accurately the residues that are at the boundaries of the membrane.

## D. The Nucleotide-Binding Component

This is the most conserved component in the BPD systems. Oligopeptide and branched chain amino acid transporters usually have two different but strongly similar NBDs, whereas ribose and arabinose (monosaccharide) transporters have a single NBD made of two duplicated and fused subunits (Fig. 1). All other transporters have a single NBD and experimental evidence suggests that two such subunits are present in the complete transporter. It is clear that ATP hydrolysis by the NBD is the energy source for BPD transport. This has been demonstrated *in vitro* on membrane vesicles and on solubilized transporters reconstituted in proteoliposomes. Also, some purified NBDs display a constitutive ATPase activity that is generally unaffected by the transported substrates, suggesting that NBDs do not have a substrate recognition site. The ATPase activity is inhibited by ADP and non-hydrolyzable ATP analogs. Some transporters are inhibited by N-ethyl maleimide; this inhibition was determined to be due to the covalent modification of a single cysteine residue in the Walker A ATP-binding motif.

## III. FEATURES OF THE SEQUENCE OF SUBUNITS AND IMPLICATIONS FOR EVOLUTION

The sequences of BPs display very little overall sequence similarity, in contrast to their closely related tertiary structures. A careful sequence analysis of 52 BPs revealed that they can be grouped into eight families of more strongly related proteins (Table I). Remarkably, clustering of sequences was in agreement with the chemical nature of the substrate. The degree of sequence divergence was too high to establish rigorously that all BPs are homologous (i.e., that they are of common origin), but this idea is supported by their common structural organization. Interestingly, a class of BPs involved in the uptake of polar amino acids, such as histidine, arginine, and glutamic acid, were strongly related in terms of primary sequence to the extracellular domain of eukaryote metabotropic or ionotropic glutamate receptors. It was recently shown that conserved residues play similar roles in eukaryote receptors and in bacterial BPs, suggesting a common mechanism for ligand binding.

In general, TMDs are more conserved than BPs, but it is nevertheless difficult to demonstrate that they are homologous. It is possible to group the proteins into clusters of strongly related sequences, and clustering reflects the substrate specificity of the system. The clusters defined in such analyses are very similar to those defined for substrate BPs (Table I). In transport systems with two different TMDs, the TMDs are generally more closely related to each other than to TMDs of other systems. This strongly suggests that they have arisen by duplication from an ancestor system with a single TMD. In good agreement with this idea, proteins from systems with a single TMD are found near the root of the phylogenetic tree computed for the cluster. All TMDs of BPD transporters display a short conserved motif, the EAA motif (Fig. 2), located approximately 100 residues from the C terminus. The motif is hydrophilic and it was found to reside in a cytoplasmic loop located between the penultimate and the antepenultimate transmembrane segment in all proteins with a known topology. The conservation of this motif indicates an important functional role, and it was suggested that it could constitute a site of interaction with the conserved cytoplasmic NBDs. This was recently found to be true.

NBDs display a region of homology that extend more than 200 residues. A phylogenetic analysis of the sequence of BPD transporter NBDs revealed that

**TABLE I**
**Clustering Patterns of ABC Binding Protein-Dependent Transport System Subunits**[a]

| Extracellular solute binding proteins | Integral cytoplasmic membrane proteins | ATP binding proteins |
| --- | --- | --- |
| Oligosaccharides and multiple sugars (cluster 1) | Oligosaccharides (subclusters 1b and 1c) | Oligosaccharides |
| Ions (cluster 6) | Ions (subcluster 1a) | Ions |
| Hexoses and pentoses (cluster 2) | Monosaccharides (cluster 7) | Monosaccharides |
| Polar amino acids and opines (cluster 3) | Polar amino acids and derivatives (cluster 2) | Polar amino acids and derivatives |
| Aliphatic amino acids (cluster 4) | Hydrophobic amino acids (clusters 5 and 6) | Hydrophobic amino acids |
| Peptides and nickel (cluster 5) | Oligopeptides and nickel (clusters 3 and 4) | Oligopeptides and nickel |
| Iron complexes (cluster 8) | Iron siderophores (cluster 8) | Iron siderophores |
| Metals (cluster 9) | Metals (cluster 9) | Metals |

[a] Systems involved in the transport of similar substrates are grouped in clusters of similar sequences. The clustering patterns of the different subunits of these systems are strongly related.

these proteins descend from an ancestor protein. Moreover, the proteins segregate into clusters strongly related to those found for TMDs and for the BPs (Table I). This finding suggests that the partners of BPD transporters evolved as a whole unit by gene duplication. This notion is supported by the fact that the genes encoding BPD transporters are organized into operons. Since similar BPD transporters are found in archaea and eubacteria, the putative common ancestor of such systems probably appeared before the separation of the two phyla, approximately 4 billions years ago. Recently, we analyzed 200 NBDs from eukaryotes and prokaryotes. ABC importers and exporters segregated into two groups of sequences independently of the organisms in which they were found. This remarkable disposition suggests that the divergence between these two functionally different types of ABC systems occurred once in the history of these systems and probably before the differentiation of prokaryotes and eukaryotes (Saurin *et al.*, 1998). The putative ancestral organism probably harbored complex and functionally well-differentiated ABC import and export systems. This conclusion supports the notion that ABC proteins or domains are ancient and efficient devices for coupling translocation of substrates to primary energy sources. Prokaryotes maintained the two families of systems, whereas eukaryotes probably acquired export systems through the symbiotic bacteria that are the putative ancestors of organelles.

## IV. FUNCTIONAL MECHANISM

The role of BPs in transport was investigated by analyzing the effects of mutations or by analyzing mutants lacking such proteins. Since it was found that such mutants were not able to carry out transport, like osmotically shocked bacteria, it was concluded that free substrate has no access to the other components of the system (Shuman and Panagiotidis, 1993). Therefore, the BP should interact with the membrane components to deliver substrates. The interaction of BPs with their cognate TMDs was studied biochemically by a variety of methods, including chemical cross-linking and limited proteolysis. However, it was not possible to characterize in detail the regions involved in such interactions, even on purified reconstituted transporters. This interaction was studied by genetic approaches in the maltose transport system of *E. coli* and in the histidine transport system of *Salmonella typhimurium*. Revertants able to transport substrates in the absence of BP were successfully isolated from transport-negative BPs mutants but the global affinity of the system was dramatically lowered, although the selectivity of the transporter was not greatly affected. These properties suggested that a latent recognition site for substrates was unmasked in such mutants. In the maltose transport system, mutations were found to reside in the genes determining the TMDs MalF and MalG. By contrast, in the histidine transport system, these mu-

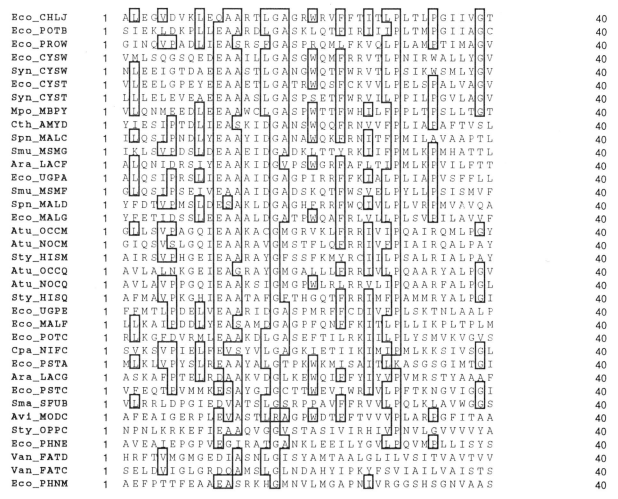

**Fig. 2.** Alignment of selected sequences of integral membrane proteins in the conserved EAA region. This region is located approximately 100 residues from the C terminus. Proteins are identified with the abbreviated name of the bacterium followed by the name of the protein. Ara, *Agrobacterium radiobacter;* Atu, *Agrobacterium tumefaciens;* Avi, *Azotobacter vinelandii;* Cpa, *Clostridium pasteurianum;* Cth, *Clostridium thermosulfurogenes;* Eco, *Escherichia coli;* Mpo, *Marchantia polymorpha chloroplast;* Sma, *Serratia marcescens;* Smu, *Streptococcus mutans;* Spn, *Streptococcus pneumoniae;* Sty, *Salmonella typhimurium;* Syn, *Synechococcus sp.;* Van, *Vibrio anguillarum*. Identical residues in at least 45% of the sequences are shown in boxes.

tations were found to be located in the gene of the NBD HisP. The reasons for such discrepancy between the two systems are not clear. However, it was found that in both cases the BP-independent mutants displayed a constitutive ATPase activity when the membrane complexes were reconstituted into proteoliposomes. By contrast, in wild-type complexes the ATPase activity was only detected in the presence of substrate-loaded BP. This suggests that the mutations in TMDs and in NBDs have the same consequence which results in continuous cycling of ATPase activity, thereby unmasking a substrate recognition site. Then, it was observed that maltose BP-independent mutants were unable to function in the presence of the wild-type maltose-binding protein MalE, and it was concluded that the protein engaged faulty interactions with the mutated MalF and MalG proteins. This observation led to the isolation of suppressor mutations of this phenotype in the *malE* gene. In addition, dominant-negative mutations in *malE* were

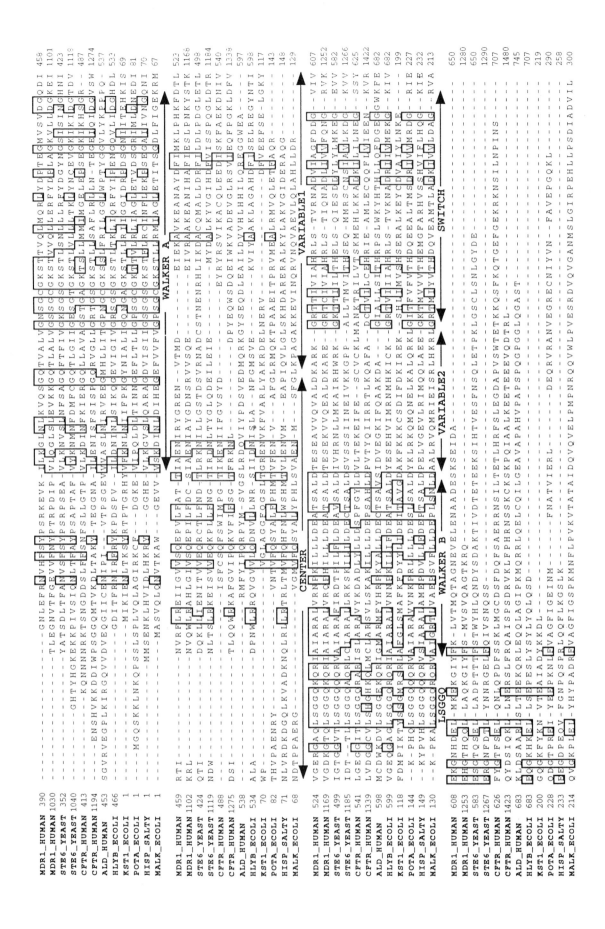

characterized. The location of the mutations on the three-dimensional structure of MalE led to the conclusion that the N-lobe of MalE interacts with MalG and the C-lobe with MalF (Shuman and Panagiotidis, 1993).

The TMDs of BPD systems are synthesized in very low amounts and when overproduced, they are very often toxic for the cell. Because of these limitations, biochemical study very difficult. To identify the proteins, gene fusions to $\beta$-galactosidase and the generation of defined peptide antibodies were used successfully. Genetic approaches were developed to characterize TMDs. Linker insertion, point mutations, and suppressor analysis in genes encoding the TMDs of the maltose transporter led to the emergence of two ideas: The TMDs contained at least one substrate binding site and interaction with the BP was a key step of transport. A model of the arrangement of transmembrane segments of the MalF and MalG heterodimer was proposed based on topological studies and genetic data (Ehrmann *et al.*, 1998). Transmembrane segments create a large pore through which substrates can cross the cytoplasmic membrane. The role of the conserved EAA motif was investigated in detail in the maltose and in the ferric hydroxamate transport systems. This motif was found to be important for interactions between TMDs and NBDs.

Several attempts have been made to model the NBDs of ABC transporters on structurally characterized ATPases to understand the mechanism of coupling ATP hydrolysis to transport. These models suggest that the NBDs comprise a nucleotide-binding pocket involved in ATP binding and hydrolysis made of the Walker motifs A and B and a large helical domain with no counterparts in other ATPases located between the two Walker motifs (Fig. 3). These analyses led to the suggestion that the conserved K

residue in Walker motif A is crucial for binding the $\beta$ and the $\gamma$ phosphates of ATP, whereas the conserved D residue in Walker motif B is involved in interacting with the $Mg^{2+}$ ion that is linked to ATP. Mutations in these residues generally affected ATP hydrolysis and binding. The conserved LSGGQ or linker motif has been proposed to mediate conformational changes induced by ATP hydrolysis between the ATPase and the TMDs of ABC transporters, a notion which is not entirely consistent with the altered ATPase activity due to mutations in LSGGQ reported in many export and import systems from different organisms (Schneider and Hunke, 1998). The helical domain was proposed to mediate the interactions between TMDs and NBDs. Indeed, mutations in the helical domain in general alter transport without affecting ATP binding.

Careful examination of the predicted secondary structure (Fig. 3) indicates two regions in the helical domain. The center region encompasses a short predicted $\beta$ sheet that contains a highly conserved Q residue. Although mutations of this residue do not affect ATP hydrolysis, it was proposed that the region could be involved in ATP binding. A region named variable 1 with no obvious sequence conservation extends from the center region to the LSGGQ motif and is predicted to be constituted by $\alpha$ helices. In ABC export systems, mutations in this region have been suggested to alter the interaction between TMDs and NBDs. In addition to the LSGGQ motif, other loosely conserved regions have been identified. A region named variable 2 is predicted to adopt an $\alpha$ helical conformation and mutations in this regions have similar effects as those in the variable 1 region. A switch region comprises the more distal part of ABC subunits that carry a highly conserved H residue. In ATPases with a known structure, this region is involved in the transmission of conformational

---

**Fig. 3.** Alignment of NBD of ABC transporters. Boxes represent 50% amino acid identity. The different regions discussed in the text are indicated in bold characters under the corresponding sequences. The following ABC transporters are considered: MDR1_HUMAN, multidrug-resistance P-glycoprotein (human); STE6_YEAST, mating $\alpha$ factor secretion protein (*Saccharomyces cerevisiae*); CFTR_HUMAN, cystic fibrosis transmembrane regulator (human); ALD_HUMAN, adrenoleukodystrophy-linked peroxisomal protein (human); HLYB_ECOLI, hemolysin A secretion protein (*Escherichia coli*); KST1_ECOLI, capsular polysialic acid secretion protein (*Escherichia coli*); POTA_ECOLI, polyamine uptake ATPase (*Escherichia coli*); HISP_SALTY, histidine uptake ATPase (*Salmonella typhimurium*).

changes induced by ATP binding or hydrolysis. Consistent with this hypothesis, a mutation in the conserved H residue of MalK inactivated the transporter, but the ATPase activity of the protein is unaffected. From these secondary structure–function analyses, a model has been built for the functional domains of NBDs (Fig. 4). It is predicted that the NBDs comprise three domains: (i) an ATP-binding pocket composed of Walker A and B motifs that bind ATP and of the center and LSGGQ regions that participate in ATP hydrolysis; (ii) a TMD interaction interface composed of the variable 1 and variable 2 regions (this seems correct since there is little overall sequence similarity between in TMDs); and (iii) switching regions such as the switch or the LSGGQ motifs that link the two first domains and allow the propagation of conformational changes between the ATP-binding pocket and the TMD interface (M. Mourez, 1998, PhD thesis).

The sites of interactions between NBDs and TMDs were characterized *in vivo* and *in vitro* in the maltose transport system. Mutations in the conserved EAA region led to a transport-negative phenotype. Transport-negative mutations were found to belong to two classes. In the first class, the MalK NBD, normally located in the cytoplasmic membrane, was found mostly in the cytosol. In the second class, the cellular location of MalK was not affected. The different phenotypes of mutations further suggested that EAA regions were involved in two kind of interactions—binding of NBDs to the membrane and transmission of functional signals to NBDs. From the two classes of transport-negative mutants, suppressor mutations restoring transport were found in the *malK* gene. They mapped mainly into the variable 1 and variable 2 regions of MalK. MalK was shown to bind *in vitro* to everted membrane vesicles containing MalF and MalG and to reconstitute a functional transport (Mourez *et al.*, 1998). ATP binding and hydrolysis were shown to increase the binding of MalK, suggesting that its interaction with MalF and MalG was increased in the presence of nucleotides. When incu-

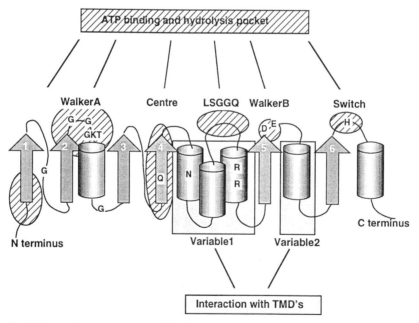

**Fig. 4.** Secondary structure model of the ATP-binding domain. This model is based on secondary structure predictions on an alignment of 225 ATP-binding domains and on the analysis of the effects of mutations described in ABC systems. The model shows three postulated regions: the ATP-binding pocket, the surface of interaction with hydrophobic proteins, and the switching regions that transmit conformational changes between the two first domains.

bated with nucleotides, MalK underwent a large conformational change that rendered the helical domain accessible to proteases. We have shown that a single proteolytic site, unveiled by ATP binding in purified MalK, was not accessible when MalK was reconstituted with MalF and MalG. This suggests that the MalK helical domain inserts into the MalFG complex in the presence of ATP, a notion which is consistent with the higher efficiency of binding and with the observation that HisP and MalK were accessible to proteases from the exterior of spheroplasts when the cognate TMDs were present (Schneider and Hunke, 1998). These results indicate that the EAA regions of TMDs are in close contact with the helical domains of NBDs. This notion is consistent with other genetic analyses of NBDs that have suggested a role of the helical domain in the interactions with TMDs (Schneider and Hunke, 1998). Thus, the EAA region–helical domain interface would couple the energy of ATP hydrolysis to transport.

The purification of the whole transporter and its reconstitution into proteoliposomes was achieved in the maltose and in the histidine transport systems (Nikaido, 1994). Molecular weight measurements were consistent with a stoichiometry of two TMDs and two NBDs. The ATPase activity of reconstituted whole transporters was sensitive to *ortho*-vanadate, an inhibitor specific to the P-type ATPases, although there was no evidence for a phosphorylated state. Remarkably, purified NBDs were not affected by this inhibitor. ATP is hydrolyzed cooperatively in the whole reconstituted maltose and histidine transport complexes but not in the purified NBDs (Boos and Shuman, 1998). Moreover, it was found that a mutation blocking ATP hydrolysis in only one of the two MalK subunits in the maltose transporter resulted in a complete absence of ATP hydrolysis and transport. These data are consistent with the idea that the two NBDs cooperate in transport and that a functional interaction between NBDs and TMDs is needed for such cooperation.

## A. Functional Models

From the previously discussed genetic and biochemical studies, several functional models have been proposed and all are based on the same assumptions; however, only two will be considered here. The first is based on the study of binding protein-independent mutants (Fig. 5A). The BP should interact with the TMDs initiating a signal which would trigger ATP hydrolysis-dependent conformational changes, which in turn would result in the unidirec-

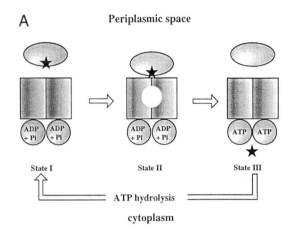

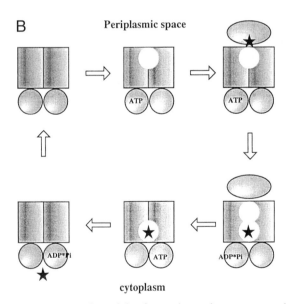

**Fig. 5.** Functional models of ATP-dependent transport in ABC transporters. TMD's are represented by rectangles and NBD's by solid circles, the solute binding protein is represented by ellipses, the substrate is represented by black stars, and substrate binding sites on the TMD's are shown as white circles. (A) Model based on the behavior of binding protein-independent mutants. (B) Model based on the properties of ATP hydrolysis in ABC transporters (see text for details).

tional transport of the substrate. This model postulates that the transporter cycles through three states. The interaction of the BP state I complex results in a conformational change leading to state II, but there are no clear data indicating at which state ATP is hydrolyzed (Boos and Shuman, 1998). The second model (Fig. 5B) accounts for the results obtained from the analysis of eukaryote ABC transporters, such as the multidrug-resistance protein P-glycoprotein and the cystic fibrosis transmembrane regulator protein (Senior and Gadsby, 1997). This model assumes that two molecules of ATP are required for the translocation of one molecule of substrate and that binding and hydrolysis into the two NBD are not equivalent. Binding of the first ATP will allow the interaction of the BP with the TMDs and the delivery of substrate to a periplasmic substrate binding site on the TMDs. Hydrolysis of ATP would allow the movement of the substrate from the periplasmic to the cytoplasmic substrate binding site. The binding and hydrolysis of a second molecule of ATP would be required to release the substrate into the cytoplasm. This model proposes a unified scheme for the mechanism of ABC transporters, but a precise determination of the stoichiometry of ATP, substrate, and substrate binding sites has to be made.

## V. PERSPECTIVES

At least three crystal structures of ABC (NBD) proteins will be available by the time this encyclopedia is published. This will open the way for understanding the interactions between NBDs and TMDs. The next goal is to achieve the crystallization of the whole transporter. More genetic and biochemical data will be needed to understand the nature of the interactions and the conformational changes that occur during translocation of substrates.

### See Also the Following Articles

CELL MEMBRANE: STRUCTURE AND FUNCTION • CHEMOTAXIS • PROTEIN SECRETION

### Bibliography

Ames, G. F., Mimura, C. S., Holbrook, S. R., and Shyamala, V. (1992). Traffic ATPases: A superfamily of transport proteins operating from *Escherichia coli* to humans. *Adv. Enzymol. Related Areas Mol. Biol.* **65**, 1–47.

Boos, W., and Lucht, J. M. (1996). Periplasmic binding protein-dependent ABC transporters. *In* "*Escherichia coli* and *Salmonella* Cellular and Molecular Biology" (F. C. Neidhardt, Ed.), 2nd ed., pp. 1175–1209. ASM Press, Washington, DC.

Boos, W., and Shuman, H. (1998). Maltose/maltodextrin system of *Escherichia coli*—Transport, metabolism, and regulation. *Microbiol. Mol. Biol. Rev.* **62**, 204–229.

Braun, V., Hantke, K., and Köster, W. (1998). Bacterial iron transport: Mechanisms, genetics and regulation. *In* "Iron Transport and Storage in Microorganisms, Plants and Animals" (A. Sigel and H. Sigel, Eds.), pp. 67–145. Dekker, New York.

Ehrmann, M., Ehrle, R., Hofmann, E., Boos, W., and Schlosser, A. (1998). The ABC maltose transporter. *Mol. Microbiol.* **29**, 685–694.

Higgins, C. F. (1992). ABC transporters: From microorganisms to man. *Annu. Rev. Cell Biol.* **8**, 67–113.

Mourez, M., Jehanno, M., Schneider, E., and Dassa, E. (1998). *In vitro* interaction between components of the inner membrane complex of the maltose ABC transporter of *Escherichia coli*: Modulation by ATP. *Mol. Microbiol.* **30**, 353–363.

Nikaido, H. (1994). Maltose transport system of *Escherichia coli*: An ABC-type transporter. *FEBS Lett.* **346**, 55–58.

Nikaido, H. (1996). Outer membrane. *In* "*Escherichia coli* and *Salmonella* Cellular and Molecular Biology" (F. C. Neidhardt, Ed.), 2nd ed., pp. 29–47. ASM Press, Washington, DC.

Quiocho, F. A., and Ledvina, P. S. (1996). Atomic structure and specificity of bacterial periplasmic receptors for active transport and chemotaxis: Variation of common themes. *Mol. Microbiol.* **20**, 17–25.

Saurin, W., Hofnung, M., and Dassa, E. (1998). Getting in or out. Early segregation between importers and exporters in the evolution of ABC transporters. *J. Mol. Evol.* **48**, 22–41.

Schneider, E., and Hunke, S. (1998). ATP-binding-cassette (ABC) transport systems: Functional and structural aspects of the ATP-hydrolyzing subunits/domains. *FEMS Microbiol. Rev.* **22**, 1–20.

Senior, A. E., and Gadsby, D. C. (1997). ATP hydrolysis cycles and mechanism in *p*-glycoprotein and CFTR. *Sem. Cancer Biol.* **8**, 143–150.

Shuman, H. A., and Panagiotidis, C. H. (1993). Tinkering with transporters. Periplasmic binding protein-dependent maltose transport in *E. coli*. *J. Bioenerg. Biomembr.* **25**, 613–620.

# Acetic Acid Production

## Munir Cheryan

*University of Illinois*

### GLOSSARY

**aerobic process**   A process that requires the presence of oxygen to proceed.

**anaerobic process**   A fermentation that requires the complete absence of oxygen.

**downstream processing**   A series of unit operations or processes to recover, isolate, and purify the desired component from a fermentation mixture.

**fermenter**   The vessel in which fermentation is conducted.

**productivity**   The amount of the product produced per unit volume per unit time.

**ACETIC ACID**   ($CH_3COOH$) is the principal constituent of vinegar. The first vinegar was probably a result of spoiled wine, considering that the Latin word *acetum* means sour or sharp wine. Thus, it has been produced as long as wine making has been practiced and therefore dates back to at least 10,000 BC.

## I. HISTORICAL BACKGROUND

Acetic acid was used as a medicinal agent and was probably the first known antibiotic. For most of human history, acetic acid was produced by fermentation of sugar to ethyl alcohol and its subsequent oxidation to acetic acid by microorganisms.

This process was supplemented in the nineteenth century by wood distillation. In 1916, the first dedicated plant for the production of acetic acid by chemical rather than biological means became commercial. This method was based on acetylene-derived acetaldehyde, and it marked the advent of inexpensive, industrial-grade acetic acid and the birth of a viable industry based on its use. The advantages of chemical synthetic routes include high acetate concentrations (35–45% by weight), high production rates, and acetic acid generated in the free acid form. The major disadvantages are the need for high temperatures, high pressures, and good agitation, the threat of explosion, the high cost of catalysts, and the dependence on nonrenewable, uncertain sources of raw materials (crude oil). In 1995, annual production of acetic acid by the petrochemical route in the United States was 4.68 billion pounds, ranking 35th among all chemicals produced (Anonymous, 1996). Production increased at an annual rate of 18% from 1993 to 1995. Vinyl acetate ranked 41st, averaging 3 billion pounds in 1993–1995.

Fermentation production routes have traditionally been aimed at the food market. Vinegar production usually requires lower capital investment, has shorter start-up times, and can generate different types and flavors of vinegar when different carbohydrate sources are used. Furthermore, the raw material (e.g., corn, sugarcane, and sugar beet) is a renewable resource. The cost of acetic acid from chemical synthesis ranges from 15 to 35¢/lb on a 100% basis, whereas it is 35–45¢/lb from aerobic fermentation.

Acetic acid has a wide variety of uses, as shown in Fig. 1. There is a large market for vinyl acetate due to the demand for synthetic fibers. Calcium mag-

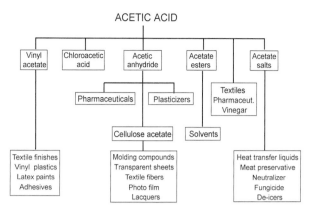

**Fig. 1.** Uses of acetic acid (reproduced with permission from Cheryan *et al.*, 1997).

nesium acetate and potassium acetate are relatively new applications used primarily as noncorrosive, environmental friendly alternatives to chloride salts for deicing roads and for airport runways and as heat exchange fluids.

## II. ACETIC ACID PRODUCTION

Acetic acid as an industrial chemical is currently produced from fossil fuels and chemicals by three processes: acetaldehyde oxidation, hydrocarbon oxidation, and methanol carbonylation. It can also be produced by biological routes using either an aerobic or an anaerobic route.

### A. Aerobic Process

Food-grade acetic acid is produced by the two-step vinegar process. The first step is the production of ethanol from a carbohydrate source such as glucose. This is carried out at 30–32°C using the anaerobic yeast *Saccharomyces cerevisiae*:

$$C_6H_{12}O_6 \rightarrow 2\ CO_2 + 2\ CH_3CH_2OH$$

The second step is the oxidation of ethanol to acetic acid. Although a variety of bacteria can produce acetic acid, only members of *Acetobacter* are used commercially, typically the aerobic bacterium *Acetobacter aceti* at 27–37°C. This fermentation is an

incomplete oxidation because the reducing equivalents generated are transferred to oxygen and not to carbon dioxide:

$$2\ CH_3CH_2OH + O_2 \rightarrow 2\ CH_3COOH + 2\ H_2O$$

The overall theoretical yield is 0.67 g acetic acid per gram glucose. At the more realistic yield of 76% (of 0.67 g; i.e., 0.51 g per gram glucose), this process requires 2.0 pounds of sugar or 0.9 pounds of ethyl alcohol per pound of acetic acid produced. Complete aeration and strict control of the oxygen concentration during fermentation are important to maximize yields and keep the bacteria viable. Submerged fermentation has almost completely replaced surface fermentation methods. The draw-and-fill mode of operation can produce acetic acid at concentrations up to 10% w/w in continuous culture at pH 4.5 in approximately 35 hr.

### B. Anaerobic Process

In the 1980s, another process for production of acetic acid emerged based on anaerobic fermentation using *Clostridia*. These organisms can convert glucose, xylose, and some other hexoses and pentoses almost quantitatively to acetate according to the following reaction:

$$C_6H_{12}O_6 \rightarrow 3\ CH_3COOH$$

*Clostridium thermoaceticum* is also able to utilize five-carbon sugars:

$$2\ C_5H_{10}O_5 \rightarrow 5\ CH_3COOH$$

A variety of substrates, including fructose, xylose, lactate, formate, and pyruvate, have been used as carbon sources in an effort to lower substrate costs. This factor is also important if cellulosic renewable resources are to be used as raw materials.

Typical acidogenic bacteria are *Clostridium aceticum, C. thermoaceticum, C. formicoaceticum,* and *Acetobacterium woodii.* Many can also reduce carbon dioxide and other one-carbon compounds to acetate.

Most research has been done with *C. thermoaceticum.* It was isolated from horse manure. It is an obligate anaerobe, gram-positive, spore-forming, rod-shaped, thermophilic organism with an optimum growth temperature of 55–60°C and optimum pH of 6.6–6.8. The anaerobic route should have a lower fermentation cost than the aerobic process. The theoretical yields are higher: 3 mol of acetic acid is produced per mol of glucose consumed (i.e., 1 g acetic acid/g glucose). Actual yields with *C. thermoaceticum* have ranged from 0.85 to 0.90 g/g. However, downstream processing costs are higher with the anaerobic process since only 13–20 g/l acetic acid is produced by the wild strain in batch fermentation and 50–60 g/l with mutant strains.

The fermentation of sugars to acetate is a complex process. As shown in Fig. 2, 1 mol of hexose is metabolized by the Embden–Meyerhof pathway to yield 2 mol of pyruvate, which is further metabolized to 2 mol of acetate (formed from carbons 2 and 3 of the pyruvate) and to 2 mol of $CO_2$ (formed from the carboxyl groups). The 2 mol of $CO_2$ serves as an electron acceptor, where 1 mol $CO_2$ is finally reduced to methyltetrahydrofolate ($CH_3THF$). The $CH_3THF$ then combines with the second $CO_2$ and coenzyme A (CoA) forming acetyl-CoA and finally the formation of the third mol of acetate. The overall reaction can be written as follows:

$$C_6H_{12}O_6 + 2 H_2O \rightarrow 2 CH_3COOH + 2 CO_2 + 8 H^+$$
$$+ 8e^- \ 2 CO_2 + 8 H^+ + 8 e^- \rightarrow CH_3COOH + 2 H_2O$$

The formation of the third mol of acetate involves tetrahydrofolate enzymes, carbon monoxide dehy-drogenase (CODH), NADP-dependent formate dehy-drogenase (FDH), and a corrinoid enzyme. These enzymes are metalloproteins; e.g., CODH contains nickel, iron, and sulfur; FDH contains iron, selenium, tungsten, and a small quantity of molybdenum; and the corrinoid enzyme (vitamin $B_{12}$ compound) con-tains cobalt. *Clostridium thermoaceticum* does not have any specific amino acid requirement; nicotinic acid is the sole essential vitamin.

In most typical batch fermentations, cell concen-tration initially increases exponentially and then de-creases toward the end of the fermentation. Acetate concentration also increases and then levels off (Cheryan *et al.*, 1997). High glucose concentration inhibits the initial growth of *C. thermoaceticum*. How-ever, after adaptation, the fermentation proceeds rap-idly. There appears to be a minimum ratio of nutrient concentration to glucose concentration to produce acetic acid. If glucose is still available but the nutrient is not, the microorganism will produce by-products such as fructose.

Acetate production from glucose by *C. thermoace-ticum* generates 5 mol of ATP per mol of glucose consumed (Fuchs, 1986). This results in high levels of cell mass per mol of glucose consumed. To main-tain productivity, the cells must balance their ATP supply and demand. Since growth consumes more ATP than maintenance, most of the acetic acid pro-duced by *C. thermoaceticum* occurs during the growth phase. When cells use yeast extract as a source of amino acids, nucleotides, and fatty acids, they will need less ATP than if they have to synthesize these compounds using ammonium ions as the starting material. Thus, assimilation of ammonium ions is important if cells are to recycle the ATP generated during production of acetic acid. Therefore, ammo-nium sulfate (a cheaper nutrient) could partially re-place yeast extract without resulting in formation of by-products such as fructose. Medium cost could be lowered further by substituting corn steep liquor for yeast extract.

## III. FERMENTER DESIGNS

Industrial fermentation processes have evolved from the simple "let-alone" method involving a par-

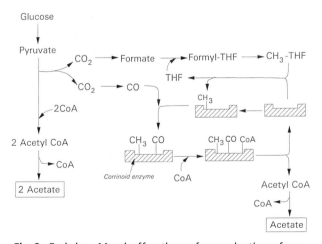

***Fig. 2.*** Embden–Myerhoff pathway for production of ace-tic acid (reproduced with permission from Cheryan *et al.*, 1997).

tially filled open container of wine exposed to air to the "field" fermentation in which a series of casks are filled with wine and inoculated in series by the vinegar produced in the previous casks. In the "Orleans" method, holes are bored into the casks and a glass tube is inserted to allow the addition and removal of vinegar. The "trickling" or "German" process is a surface fermentation in which the microbial population is attached to an appropriate support (usually beechwood shavings) and the wine is trickled down while a large volume of air is sparged up through the bottom of the tank. This process was the basis for the manufacture of the trickling generator that incorporates forced aeration and temperature control. The partially converted solution collects at the bottom and is cooled, pumped back up to the top, and allowed to trickle down until the reaction is complete. Ethanol conversion to acetic acid is 88–90%; the rest of the substrate is used in biomass production or lost by volatilization. Advantages of this process include low costs, ease of control, high acetic acid concentrations, and lower space requirements. The costs of the wood shavings, long start-up time, loss of ethanol by volatilization, and production of slime-like material by the *Acetobacter* (e.g., *A. xylinum*) are problems. Furthermore, there are often local zones of overoxidation, uneven aeration, and heat development.

The next technological advance occurred in 1949 when Hromatkar and Ebner applied submerged fermentation techniques to oxidation of ethanol to acetic acid. The level of gas-phase oxygen is crucial to this process, and thus, efficiency is based on broth aeration with oxygen. For industrial processes, 10–18% ethanol and five times the nutrients used for surface fermentation are the starting conditions for fermentation. When the concentration of ethanol reaches 0.4–2.4 g/l, 50–60% of the solution is removed and replaced with fresh substrate containing 10–18% ethanol. There is usually approximately 80 mg of dry bacterial solids per liter. The productivity is 1.7–2.1 g acetic acid per liter per hour, and the process is operated in a semi-continuous manner that helps to minimize variation in the product. During refilling, charging is slow with consistent mixing to prevent bacterial damage and/or death. Dead cells cause foaming; hence, mechanical defoaming

techniques are used to eliminate this problem. Compared to surface fermentation, submerged fermentation results in higher productivity, faster oxidation of ethanol, smaller reaction volumes, low personnel costs due to automation, fewer interruptions due to clogging by shavings, and lower capital investment per product amount, even though the ratio of productivity to capital investment is higher.

Much of the work done with this fermentation has been performed with batch fermenters, in which all the carbohydrate and nutrients are added at the start of the fermentation. With fermentations that are substrate inhibited, a better method is to use the fed-batch mode of operation. This significantly improves the performance of the *C. thermoaceticum* fermentation (Cheryan *et al.*, 1997). Continuous fermentation with immobilized whole cells has been used to increase the productivity of homoacetogenic fermentations. However, cell immobilization has been plagued by oxygen-transfer problems.

On the other hand, cell-recycle fermenters using a membrane module as the separation device have been shown to vastly increase the productivity of several anaerobic fermentations, such as ethanol and lactic acid (Cheryan, 1998), and may have some advantages over immobilized cells, such as higher concentration of free cells, no diffusion limitation, excellent mixing in the bioreactor, and a cell-free product stream. The greatest advantage is that cell concentrations far in excess of normal levels can be used with no danger of cell washout. However, high productivity and high product concentration are mutually exclusive in such high-rate fermenters. The yield of acetate was 0.85–0.9 g/g glucose consumed.

A "draw-and-fill" bioreactor in combination with a membrane appears to be the optimum design. In this design, the reaction vessel is operated as a batch fermenter. At the end of the fermentation, a portion of the fermentation broth is withdrawn through the membrane module. The cells are recycled, and the reaction vessel is charged with fresh substrate.

In batch fermentation without cell recycle, acetic acid production is proportional to the amount of yeast extract and trace salts supplied in the medium. For all types of bioreactors studied, increasing dilution rate increases volumetric productivity but decreases specific productivity (grams acetate produced per gram cells). Thus, in cell-recycle bioreactors, the nutrient supply should be increased in proportion to cell concentration to realize the full potential of the microorganism.

## IV. DOWNSTREAM PROCESSING

Downstream processing refers to the series of unit operations used to isolate, purify, and concentrate the product. Downstream processing often determines the economic feasibility of the process. The first operation is cell separation, which can be done by cross-flow microfiltration. When a microfilter or ultrafilter is combined in a semi-closed loop configuration to the bioreactor or fermenter, it becomes a powerful tool to dramatically improve the productivity of the fermentation while simultaneously providing a cell-free broth for subsequent downstream processing. Other membrane technologies, such as nanofiltration and electrodialysis, are useful in subsequent stages of downstream processing to separate and perhaps concentrate the acid (Cheryan *et al.,* 1997). However, other techniques will have to be used if a purified industrial-grade acetic acid is required.

Depending on the physical and chemical nature of the fermentation products, the cell-free broth is subjected to chromatography, electrophoresis, crystallization, precipitation, extraction, distillation, and/or membranes. Solvent extraction with azeotropic distillation is the preferred method for chemically derived acetic acid, whereas freeze concentration is used for vinegar. Both require substantial amounts of energy since a change in phase of the solvent is required. Simple distillation, although technically feasible, may not be economical since the fermentation broth typically consists of 90–95% water. Furthermore, if the acetate is required in the free acid form, there will be additional cost to convert the salt form produced in the anaerobic fermentation to the free acid form.

Liquid–liquid extraction has been used to recover acetic acid from the chemical manufacture of cellulose acetate, vinyl acetate, and other acetate products. Extraction solvents are ethers, ketones, or alcohols. In addition, the relative amounts of dissociated and undissociated acid in the feed solution are important. Extraction efficiency is high when the organic acid is present in the undissociated (acid) form (i.e., at a low pH). This makes it difficult to use with the anaerobic acetate process unless the fermentation broth is acidified or subjected to bipolar electrodialysis.

### See Also the Following Articles
BIOREACTORS • CLOSTRIDIA • FERMENTATION

### Bibliography
Agreda, V. H., and Zoeller, J. R. (1993). "Acetic Acid and Its Derivatives." Dekker, New York.
Anonymous (1996). *Chem. Eng. News* 74(15), 15–19.
Cheryan, M. (1998). "Ultrafiltration and Microfiltration Handbook." Technomic, Lancaster, PA.
Cheryan, M., Parekh, S., Shah, M. M., and Witjitra, K. (1997). *In* "Advances in Applied Microbiology, Volume 3" (S. L. Neidleman and A. I. Laskin, Eds.), pp. 1–33. Academic Press, New York.
Crueger, W., and Crueger, A. (1990). *In* "Biotechnology: A Textbook of Industrial Microbiology," 2nd ed., pp. 143–147. Sinauer, Sunderland, MA.
Ebner, H., and Follmann, H. (1983). *In* "Biotechnology" (H. J. Rehm and G. Reed, Eds.), pp. 387–407. Verlag Chemie, Weinheim.
Fuchs, G. (1986). *FEMS Microbiol. Rev.* **39,** 181–213.
Ghose, T. K., and Bhadra, A. (1985). *In* "Comprehensive Biotechnology" (M. Moo-Young, Ed.), Vol. 3, pp. 701–729. Pergamon, New York.
LeMonnier, E. (1965). *In* "Kirk–Othmer Encyclopedia of Chemical Technology," Vol. 8, pp. 386–404. Wiley-Interscience, New York.
Ljungdahl, L. G. (1983). *In* "Organic Chemicals from Biomass" (D. L. Wise, Ed.), pp. 219–248. Benjamin/Cummings, Menlo Park, CA.
Nickol, G. B. (1979). *In* "Microbial Technology" (H. J. Peppler and D. Perlman, Eds.), Vol. 2, pp. 155–172. Academic Press, New York.

# Acetogenesis and Acetogenic Bacteria

**Amaresh Das and Lars G. Ljungdahl**

*University of Georgia*

## GLOSSARY

**autotrophs**  Organisms that can grow on $CO_2$ as the only source of carbon.

**chemoautotroph**  Microorganisms that can grow at the expense of $CO_2$ and inorganic substrates as sources of carbon and energy, respectively.

**$CO_2$ fixation**  A biological process that reduces or fixes $CO_2$ into a more reduced and complex form of organic compound.

**heterotrophs**  Organisms that can use forms of carbon more complex than $CO_2$.

**methanogens**  Obligate anaerobic organisms that produce methane as the primary metabolic end product.

**obligate anaerobes**  Organisms which can grow without oxygen.

**sulfate-reducing bacteria**  Anaerobic bacteria that use sulfate as a terminal acceptor for growth.

**THE TERM *ACETOGENESIS***  has been and still is ill defined and misused. Many microbiologists refer to acetogenesis as a way of producing acetate by any process, including fermentations of organic substrates and an autotrophic type of synthesis from $CO_2$ and other one-carbon precursors. It seems important to distinguish between a fermentative process of acetate formation and an autotrophic synthesis of acetate. We favor the definition that microorganisms forming acetate by a linear combination of two molecules of $CO_2$ or CO are acetogenic. Microorganisms producing acetate and other acids by fermentation are defined as acid producing or acidogenic.

There are three metabolic processes used by bacteria to produce acetate from $CO_2$: (i) the acetyl-CoA pathway (also referred to as the Wood–Ljungdahl pathway), (ii) the glycine synthase pathway, and (iii) the reductive citric acid cycle. The acetyl-coenzyme A (CoA) pathway is distinguished from the other two pathways in that acetyl-CoA is the first two-carbon compound formed from two C1 precursors. In this article, we will limit our discussion to different aspects of the acetyl-CoA pathway and to those acetogenic bacteria which use this pathway for growth and conservation of energy.

## I. INTRODUCTION

The first observation of acetogenesis from $CO_2$ was reported in 1932 in cultures obtained from sewage sludge. Four years later, a mesophilic gram-positive anaerobic bacterium *Clostridium aceticum* was isolated which could metabolize glucose into acetate and produce acetate when exposed to $CO_2$ and $H_2$. However, the metabolic potential of *C. aceticum* could not be exploited further because the organism was considered lost. The organism was revived in 1981. Much of the work on acetogenesis has been carried out using *Clostridium thermoaceticum* as a type strain, which was isolated in 1942. This bacterium remained the only acetogen available until 1967, when an isolate thought to be *C. aceticum*, was isolated. However, it did not fit the original description of *C. aceticum* and was renamed *Clostridium formicoaceticum*. Acetogens were not investigated much before 1967 because there was a lack of understanding of the importance of these bacteria and because appropriate techniques to grow and cultivate strictly anaerobic bacteria were not generally available. In 1969, Hungate described a basic technique to isolate and cultivate anaerobic bacteria. This technique or its modifications are now routinely used by researchers for isolation and cultivation of bacteria from anaerobic environments.

## II. GENERAL PROPERTIES OF ACETOGENIC BACTERIA

Acetogens are obligate anaerobes found in virtually all anoxic environments, including digestive tracts of animals and humans, sediments of estuaries, fresh water, salt lagoons, and soils. As a group they grow in temperatures ranging from 6 to 65°C. *Clostridium thermoaceticum* was for a long time considered an heterotroph, which used $CO_2$ as the terminal acceptor of electrons generated from fermentation of glucose, fructose, or xylose. The first acetogen found to grow autotrophically with $CO_2$ and $H_2$ as the sole carbon and energy source was *Acetobacterium woodii*. The discovery that *C. thermoaceticum* grows autotrophically was made later. Most acetogens are considered facultative autotrophs, which are capable of growing in a wide range of organic substrates, including sugars, alcohols, carboxylic acids, aromatic compounds, halogenated carbon compounds, and $CO_2$ and CO. Recently, new properties of acetogens were uncovered. In addition to $CO_2$, they are able to use several other compounds as electron acceptors, such as dimethyl sulfoxide (DMSO), sulfite, thiosulfate, and nitrate. Some of the acetogens carry out mixed acid fermentations in which butyrate is produced as one of the final products. Examples include *Clostridium mayombei*, *Clostridium pfennigii*, *Acetonema longum*, *Eubacterium limosum*, and *Butyribacterium rettgeri*. Thus, the acetogens have a very complex

physiology and they are genetically, phenotypically, and phylogenetically very different. Their physiological diversities include gram type, temperature optima, mol % GC content, and cell shapes as listed in Table I. To date, no acetogenic representative has been found belonging to *Archea*. A total of 64 bacterial species have been isolated, of which most can grow autotrophically on $CO_2$ plus $H_2$. Among these species, 43 have been classified and they belong to 13 different genera (Table I). The remaining 21 are not classified. It should be noted that the most studied acetogens, *C. thermoaceticum* and *C. thermoautotrophicum*, have been renamed *Moorella thermoacetica* and *Moorella thermoautotrophica*, respectively. Since most literature citations still refer to these acetogens as clostridial species, we will use the old names throughout the article.

## III. THE AUTOTROPHIC ACETYL-COENZYME A PATHWAY OF ACETOGENESIS AND ITS UNIVERSAL ROLE IN ONE-CARBON METABOLISM

### A. Historical Aspects and Features of the Acetyl-Coenzyme A Pathway

In 1936, the following reaction was proposed for acetate biosynthesis from $CO_2$ and $H_2$ in *C. aceticum*:

$$4H_2 + 2CO_2 \rightarrow CH_3COOH + 2H_2O \qquad (1)$$

The significance of this reaction was not realized until 1942 when it was shown that *C. thermoaceticum* could produce 3 mol of acetate from 1 mol of glucose using the following reaction:

$$C_6H_{12}O_6 \text{ (glucose)} \rightarrow 3CH_3COOH \qquad (2)$$

Although simple in chemical balance, there was no process known at that time to explain the formation of more than 2 mol of acetate from 1 mol of glucose. The only metabolic process known to cleave glucose was glycolytic 3-3 cleavage that generates pyruvate from which 2 mol of acetate could be formed. It was suggested that the fermentation of glucose by *C. thermoaceticum* could involve refixation of $CO_2$ with reductive synthesis of acetate using electrons generated during glucose fermentation

***TABLE I***
**Physiological Properties of Described Genera of Homoacetogenic Bacteria**[a]

| Genus | No. of species | Morphology | Gram type | Growth temperature (°C) | mol % GC |
|---|---|---|---|---|---|
| *Acetoanaerobium* | 3 | Rod | + or − | 37 | 34–40 |
| *Acetobacterium* | 11 | Rod | + | 27–30 | 38–48 |
| *Acetitomaculum* | 1 | Rod | + | 38 | 34 |
| *Acetogenium* | 1 | Rod | − | 66 | 38 |
| *Acetohalobium* | 1 | Rod | − | 40 | 34 |
| *Acetonema* | 1 | Rod | − | 30 | 52 |
| *Clostridium* | 11 | Rod | + or − | 30–60 | 22–42 |
| *Moorella* | 2 | Rod | + | 58 | 54 |
| *Eubacterium* | 1 | Rod | + | 37 | 48 |
| *Peptostreptococcus* | 1 | Coccus | + | 37 | 45 |
| *Ruminococcus* | 2 | Coccus | + | 37 | 45 |
| *Sporomusa* | 7 | Rod | + | 30 | 42–48 |
| *Syntrophococcus* | 1 | Coccus | − | 37 | 52 |

[a] From Drake (1994).

(Fig. 1). In 1945, from tracer experiments using $^{14}CO_2$ it was demonstrated that acetate was labeled in both carbons. Later, by using $^{13}CO_2$ and mass analysis, it was confirmed that one molecule of acetate was synthesized from two molecules of $CO_2$. These results led to the foundation of the acetyl-coenzyme A (CoA) pathway.

Figure 2 shows the total synthesis of acetate from $CO_2$ by the acetyl-CoA pathway which was elucidated in studies of *C. thermoaceticum*. Carbon dioxide is

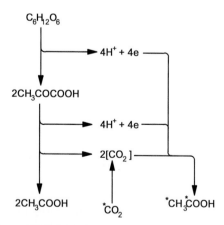

***Fig. 1.*** Fermentation of glucose to 3 mol acetate showing $CO_2$ as the electron acceptor and the synthesis of one-third of the acetate from $CO_2$.

fixed in two reactions catalyzed by formate dehydrogenase (FDH) and carbon monoxide dehydrogenase/acetyl-CoA synthase (CODH/ACS). The latter enzyme catalyzes both the reduction of $CO_2$ to CO and the synthesis of acetyl-CoA. Formate formed in the FDH reaction is the precursor of the methyl group of acetyl-CoA. It is reduced as a one-carbon intermediate of tetrahydrofolate ($H_4F$) to methyl-$H_4F$. Enzymes involved are formyl-$H_4F$ synthetase, methenyl-$H_4F$ cyclohydrolase, methylene-$H_4F$ dehydrogenase, and methylene-$H_4F$ reductase (Fig. 2). The methyl group of methyl-$H_4F$ is transferred to the cobalt of a protein-bound corrinoid. This protein is designated the corrinoid/Fe-S protein (C/Fe-SP), reflecting its content of 5-methoxybenzimidazolylcobamide and a $[Fe_4S_4]$ cluster. The transfer is mediated by a methyl transferase.

The most unique and crucial enzyme of the acetyl-CoA pathway is CODH/ACS. This enzyme from *C. thermoaceticum* has an $\alpha_2\beta_2$ tetrameric quaternary structure. The $\alpha$ and $\beta$ subunits have masses of 81 and 72 kDa, respectively, which were calculated from the deduced protein sequences of their corresponding genes. Each $\alpha\beta$ dimer contains 2 Ni, 12 Fe, and approximately 12 $S^{2-}$ ions. The metal ions are arranged into three clusters, A–C (Fig. 3). The magnetic and electronic properties of these metal clusters

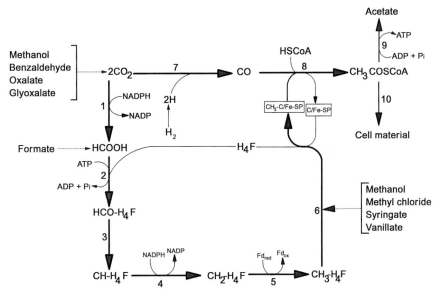

***Fig. 2.*** The autotrophic acetyl-CoA pathway. The reactions are as follows: 1, Formate dehydrogenase (FDH); 2, formyl-$H_4F$ synthetase; 3, methenyl-$H_4F$ cyclohydrolase; 4, methylene-$H_4F$ dehydrogenase; 5, methylene-$H_4F$ reductase; 6, methyl transferase, corrinoid/iron–sulfur protein (C/Fe-SP); 7, CO dehydrogenase (CODH); 8, CO dehydrogenase/acetyl-CoA synthase (CODH/ACS); 9, acetate kinase; 10, anabolism.

have been extensively investigated by Ragsdale, Lindahl, and their groups. Their contributions highlight the architecture of the metal centers in CODH/ACS and their properties. The A cluster is the active site for acetyl-CoA synthesis and it is located in the $\alpha$ subunit. The C cluster is the active site for CO oxidation and $CO_2$ reduction and it is located in the $\beta$ subunit. The B cluster is a ferredoxin-type $[Fe_4S_4]$ cluster. It is also located in the $\beta$ subunit and its proposed function is to transfer electrons from cluster C to an external redox mediator, e.g., ferredoxin. Clusters A and C have similar and very unusual structures, each containing a Ni bridged to one of the irons of a $[Fe_4S_4]$ cluster (Fig. 3). Cluster C appears to have two different states, $C_{red1}$ and $C_{red2}$, depending on its electronic and magnetic properties. The relative conversion between $C_{red1}$ and $C_{red2}$ and their functions have been investigated. It has been proposed that CO binds to and is oxidized by $C_{red1}$ and $CO_2$ binds to and is reduced by $C_{red2}$, and that $C_{red2}$ is two electrons more reduced than $C_{red1}$. The active metal species in cluster A is Ni. The enzyme catalyzes the transfer of a methyl group from the

methylated C/Fe-SP to form a methyl-Ni adduct. The mechanism of this process, including the formation of C–C and C–S bonds between the methyl carbon and carbonyl carbon and between the carbonyl carbon of the sulfur of the CoA, is being investigated.

The NADP-dependent FDH of *C. thermoaceticum* is also a unique enzyme. It consists of two heterodimers. The tetrameric enzyme contains per mol two tungsten, two selenium, 36 iron, and approximately 50 inorganic sulfide molecules. The enzyme is extremely sensitive to $O_2$, with an apparent $K_i$ for $O_2$ of 7.6 $\mu$ mol. It was the first enzyme shown to contain tungsten. The enzyme has been sequenced (GenBank accession No. U-73807). The gene coding for the $\beta$ subunit, *fdh*B, precedes that of the $\alpha$ subunit, *fdh*A, and they are clustered in an operon. The predicted translation product of *fdh*A, the $\alpha$ subunit, has 893 amino acids with a mass of 98 kDa, and that of the $\beta$ subunit consists of 708 amino acids with a mass of 76 kDa. Analysis of the sequence data indicates that the $\alpha$ subunit contains potential binding sites for four $[Fe_4S_4]$ clusters and two $[Fe_2S_2]$ clusters,

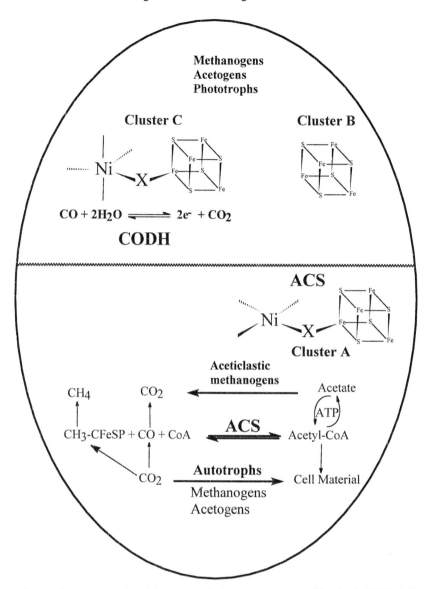

***Fig. 3.*** The proposed architectures of the metal centers (A–C) of CODH/ACS and their functions in CO oxidation and acetyl-CoA synthesis and in reverse reactions in acetogens and other bacteria (reproduced with permission from Ragsdale and Kumar, 1996. Copyright 1996 American Chemical Society).

whereas the $\beta$ subunit may have one [Fe$_4$S$_4$] and one [Fe$_2$S$_2$] cluster. Thus, the enzyme has the potential of binding 48 Fe, which agrees quiet well with chemical analyses. It is possible that the reduction of CO$_2$ to formate is mediated through an internal electron transport chain involving the many iron–sulfur clusters. In addition to the iron centers, the $\beta$ subunit has a binding motif for NADP(H). The $\alpha$ subunit contains a selenocysteine (residue 358), which is encoded by an in-frame UGA codon. It also has a molybdopterine guanine dinucleotide binding motif which presumably is the binding site for the tungstopterine cofactor. The exact structure of this cofactor has not been determined.

## B. The Ecology and Metabolic Diversity of Acetogens and the Global Impact of the Acetyl-CoA Pathway

Acetate is a key intermediate in bacterial metabolism in the anaerobic environment. An example is the degradation of cellulose to methane and $CO_2$. In the anaerobic environment, it has been calculated that approximately $10^{10}$ metric tons of acetate is metabolized per year. Supporting this are results demonstrating substantial production of acetate in forest soil. Approximately 10% or more of the acetate produced is generated from the reduction of $CO_2$ with hydrogen. Production of acetate from $H_2$ and $CO_2$ has been estimated to be approximately $2.3 \times 10^6$ and $1.3 \times 10^4$ metric tons per day in the hindgut of termites and in the large bowel of humans, respectively.

Although the acetyl-CoA pathway appears to be well established, several questions remain regarding the carbon flow. This is specially true for pyruvate. It has been observed with cell-free extracts of *C. thermoaceticum* grown on glucose that in the presence of $CO_2$ or bicarbonate the carbonyl group of pyruvate is a better precursor of the carbonyl group of acetate than $CO_2$. Furthermore, it has been shown that pyruvate is needed for the synthesis of acetate using methyl-$H_4F$ and methyl-$B_{12}$ as precursors of the methyl group of acetate. Pyruvate was not replaced by $CO_2$, NADPH, or ATP. The role of pyruvate in acetate synthesis from $CO_2$ remains obscure and needs further investigation.

The primary use of the acetyl-CoA pathway by acetogens is for the fixation of $CO_2$ and CO, but they also use this pathway for the metabolism of C1 compounds, including formate, formaldehyde, methanol, and methyl chloride, and also for more complex C1 donors such as methoxylated aromatic compounds, including syringate and vanillate, and other compounds, including oxalate, glyoxylate, aromatic aldehydes, and various alcohols. The suggested entrances of the C1 moieties of these compounds into the acetyl-CoA pathway are shown in Fig. 2. Of considerable interest is the discovery that methoxy groups of methoxylated aromatic compounds are used as methyl group precursors of acetate by aceto-

genic bacteria. These compounds are degradation products of lignin and the possibility exists that acetogens are involved in the degradation of lignin in nature. Support for this is provided by the observation that a syringate/$H_2$-consuming acetogenic consortium is present in forest soil. The involvement of the acetyl-CoA pathway in the metabolism of the methoxylated aromatic compounds has been established for *A. woodii* and *C. thermoaceticum*. Methanol is oxidized in *C. thermoautotrophicum* by a PQQ-dependent methanol dehydrogenase and it may enter the acetyl-CoA pathway at several levels (Fig. 2).

Parts of the acetyl-CoA pathway or variations of it are present in other major groups of bacteria, including methanogens and sulfate-reducing bacteria. The reaction sequence of the acetyl-CoA pathway which is common in both acetogens and methanogens is the conversion of a carrier-bound formyl group to a methyl group. The major difference is that the methanogens use tetrahydromethanopterin ($H_4MPT$) as a C1 carrier instead of $H_4F$. Another difference is that in acetogens $CO_2$ is first reduced to formate by formate dehydrogenase. Formate then reacts with $H_4F$ and is converted to formyl-$H_4F$, a reaction catalyzed by formyl-$H_4F$ synthetase (Fig. 2). In methanogens, however, $CO_2$ is first bound to the coenzyme methanofuran (MF) and subsequently reduced to formyl-MF catalyzed by formyl-MF dehydrogenase. No free formate occurs as an intermediate. The formyl group is then transferred from formyl-MF to $H_4MPT$, giving rise to formyl-$H_4MPT$. Subsequent reduction of the formyl group to a methyl is similar in methanogens and acetogens. The methyl group is located at the branching point of different routes leading to methane and acetate. In the case of acetogenesis, the methyl group is first transferred to C/Fe-SP via a methyl transferase and then to CODH/ACS, in which it is condensed with a bound CO, derived from a second molecule of $CO_2$, and CoA to give rise to acetyl-CoA. In methanogens, the methyl group of methyl-$H_4MPT$ is reduced to methane in reactions involving coenzyme M, 7-mercaptoheptonylthreonine phosphate, and a nickel tetrapyrrole, $F_{430}$. Methanogens sustain autotrophic growth on $CO_2$/$H_2$ utilizing a modified acetyl-CoA pathway in which acetyl-CoA is produced as an end product and subsequently used as a precursor for cell material. This involves a corrinoid protein and CODH/ACS. Thus, acetyl-CoA synthesis in methanogens is similar to that of acetogens with the exception that the methyl donor is a methyl-$H_4$MPT instead of methyl-$H_4$F. The sulfate reducers also use the acetyl-CoA pathway for their autotrophic growth on $CO_2$ and $H_2$ in the presence of sulfate as a terminal acceptor. Some methanogens and sulfate reducers use the reversal of the acetyl-CoA pathway to oxidize acetyl-CoA to produce $CO_2$ plus $CH_4$ (in methanogens) or $CO_2$ plus $H_2S$ (in sulfate-reducing bacteria). The cleavage of the C–C bond of acetyl-CoA and the formation of $CO_2$ are catalyzed by CODH/ACS. The widespread use of the acetyl-CoA pathway by distinctly different groups of microorganisms suggests the global importance of this pathway in the metabolism of anaerobic bacteria. Recently, the prebiotic significance of the acetyl-CoA pathway in the chemoautotrophic origin of life was suggested.

## IV. THE CONSERVATION OF ENERGY BY ACETOGENS

### A. Conservation of Energy Coupled to Acetogenesis via the Acetyl-CoA Pathway

Reduction of $CO_2$ to acetate via the acetyl-CoA pathway does not yield energy via substrate-level phosphorylation. Although one ATP is produced in the conversion of acetyl-CoA to acetate with acetyl-phosphate as an intermediate and catalyzed by acetyl-CoA transferase and acetate kinase, one ATP is consumed in the formyl-$H_4$F synthetase reaction (Fig. 2). From classic growth studies using glucose as a carbon and energy source, it was calculated that the acetogens *C. thermoaceticum, C. formicoaceticum,* and *A. woodii* yield 50–70 g of dry cell weight per mole of glucose consumed, which is equivalent to the generation of 5–7 mol of ATP (consumption of 1 mol of ATP yields approximately 10 g of dry cell weight). From glycolytic fermentation of glucose to pyruvate and subsequent oxidation of pyruvate to acetate, 4 mol of ATP is generated at the substrate level, and it was suggested that ATP had to be generated by coupling to an electron transport mechanism. With the discovery that acetogens grow autotrophically and use the acetyl-CoA pathway for production of acetyl-CoA as a precursor for cell material, it was realized that ATP must be generated by a chemiosmotic mechanism. Calculations of free energy changes of reactions of the acetyl-CoA pathway yielded an overall free energy of approximately −90 kJ in the synthesis of acetate from $CO_2$ and $H_2$ (Table II).

The two most exothermic reactions of the acetyl-CoA pathway are the reduction of methylene-$H_4$F to methyl-$H_4$F catalyzed by methylene-$H_4$F reductase (MTHFR) and the formation of acetyl-CoA from methyl-$H_4$F, CO, and CoA. The latter reaction in-

**TABLE II**
**Free Energy Changes under Standard Conditions of Reactions of the Acetyl-CoA Pathway**[a]

| No. | Reaction | $\Delta G_0'$ (kJ/mol) |
|-----|----------|------------------------|
| 1 | $CO_2$ + 2[H] → $HCOO^-$ (formate) + $H^+$ | 3.4 |
| 2 | Formate + $FH_4$ + ATP → formyl-$FH_4$ + ADP + $P_i$ | −8.4 |
| 3 | Formyl-$FH_4$ + $H^+$ → methenyl-$FH_4^+$ + $H_2O$ | −4.0 |
| 4 | Methenyl-$FH_4^+$ + 2[H] → methylene-$FH_4$ + $H^+$ | −23.0 |
| 5 | Methylene-$FH_4$ + 2[H] → methyl-$FH_4$ | −42.0 |
| 6 | Methyl-$FH_4$ + CO + CoA → acetyl-CoA + $FH_4$ | −38.0 |
| 7 | Acetyl-CoA + $P_i$ → acetyl phosphate + CoA | 9.0 |
| 8 | Acetyl phosphate + ADP → acetate + ATP | −13.0 |
| 9 | $CO2$ + 2[H] → CO + $H_2O$ | 21.0 |

[a] From Diekert and Wohlfarth (1994).

volves two separate reactions, the transfer of a methyl group from methyl-$H_4F$ to C/Fe-SP, catalyzed by a methyl transferase, and the condensation of the methyl group with CO and CoA, catalyzed by CODH/ACS (Fig. 2). The thermodynamics of the two half-reactions are still not clear, but it has been proposed that the major part of the free energy is released in the methyl transferase reaction. Both methylene-$H_4F$ reductase and methyl transferase reactions are thermodynamically favorable for the gen-

eration of ATP. The reduction of methylene-$H_4F$ has been proposed for the generation of energy by *C. thermoaceticum* and *C. thermoautotrophicum*. This is supported by the following observations: (i) MTHFR has been shown to be associated with membranes in *C. thermoautotrophicum*; (ii) the redox potential for the methylene-$H_4F$/methyl-$H_4F$ couple is favorable for the reduction of methylene-$H_4F$ to methyl-$H_4F$ with reduced ferredoxin, flavoprotein, or cytochrome $b_{559}$ as electron donor; and (iii) ferredoxin,

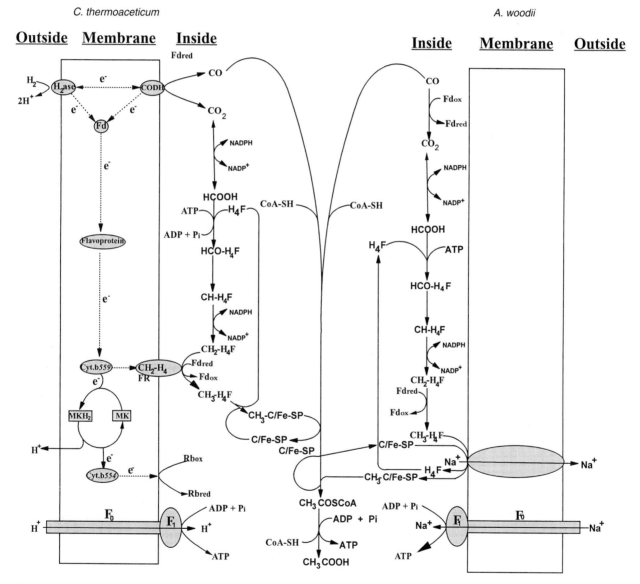

**Fig. 4.** The proposed mechanisms for conservation of energy (ATP) through chemiosmosis and its link to the acetyl-CoA pathway in *C. thermoaceticum* and *A. woodii*.

rubredoxin, cytochromes, a flavoprotein, and a menaquinone are components of the electron transport chain in membranes of the acetogenic clostridia (Fig. 4). Apparently, chemiosmotic energy generated via electron transport is coupled to ATP synthesis catalyzed by a membrane-bound proton-translocating ATP synthase. In *A. woodii*, the methyl transferase reaction has been proposed to be energy conserving based on the analogy that the methyl transferase reaction in methanogens generates energy and is coupled to a primary sodium ion extrusion. Sodium ion has been shown to be required for acetogenesis in *A. woodii*. Furthermore, the methyl transferase in methanogens is found almost exclusively in membranes. Figure 4 shows a comparison of the proposed mechanisms for the generation of chemiosmotic energy in acetogenic clostridia and *A. woodii*.

The use of different ion gradients for the generation of chemiosmotic energy by acetogenic clostridia and *A. woodii* is reflected in the properties of their $F_1F_0$ ATP synthases. Thus, the $F_1F_0$ ATP synthase of acetogenic clostridia is a proton pump, whereas that of *A. woodii* is a sodium pump.

The $F_1F_0$ ATP synthases have been purified and characterized from *C. thermoaceticum*, *C. thermoautotrophicum*, and *A. woodii*. The purified ATP synthases from these bacteria were functionally active in reconstituted proteoliposomes. The enzymes from these bacteria have an identical subunit composition. They consist of six subunits instead of the eight found in the ATP synthases of aerobic bacteria. One of the most outstanding properties of these ATP synthases is that they are fully functional without the *a* and *b* subunits commonly found in the $F_0$ moiety of ATP synthases from aerobic bacteria. The ATP synthases in the acetogens need further investigation.

## B. Conservation of Energy from the Utilization of Electron Acceptors Other Than $CO_2$

Earlier we noted that acetogens can use several alternate electron acceptors, such as nitrate, thiosulfate, dimethyl sulfoxide, and fumarate, instead of $CO_2$. When these compounds are used as terminal acceptors, the acetogens do not produce acetate as

a metabolic end product. Instead, reduced forms of terminal acceptors (e.g., nitrite, sulfide, dimethyl sulfide, and succinate) are produced as metabolic end products. It is not known how the acetogens conserve energy by reducing these terminal acceptors.

## V. SUMMARY

The acetogens belong to an extremely heterogeneous group of anaerobic bacteria. They are present in virtually all anoxic environments and produce acetate from a variety of substrates. Since acetate is a key intermediate in the metabolic turnover of many anaerobic microorganisms, the acetogens play an important role in the metabolism and ecology of anaerobic microorganisms. The significant metabolic potential of the acetogens is their ability to fix $CO_2$ through the acetyl-CoA pathway. The most crucial enzyme in this pathway is CODH/ACS, which catalyzes two important reactions, CO oxidation and acetyl-CoA synthesis. These reactions occur on three metal clusters, designated A–C. The architectures and functions of these metal clusters have been extensively studied. The acetyl-CoA pathway is present in other major groups of bacteria, including methanogens and sulfate reducers. These bacteria utilize the acetyl-CoA pathway to grow autotrophically on $CO_2$ and produce acetyl-CoA as a precursor for cell material, and they use the reversal of the pathway to metabolize acetate. During autotrophic or heterotrophic growth on C1 compounds, the acetogens conserve energy via chemiosmosis but the mechanism of this process is not uniform in all acetogens. In *C. thermoaceticum* and *C. thermoautotrophicum*, the chemiosmotic energy is generated by a membrane electron transport mechanism coupled to a proton-dependent ATP synthase, whereas in *A. woodii* the ATP synthase is driven by a sodium gradient. The acetogens also conserve energy by utilizing different compounds other than $CO_2$ as terminal electron acceptors (e.g., nitrate, DMSO, and thiosulfate).

### *See Also the Following Articles*

AUTOTROPHIC $CO_2$ METABOLISM • ENERGY TRANSDUCTION PROCESSES • HETEROTROPHIC MICROORGANISMS

## Bibliography

Das, A., Ivey, D. M., and Ljungdahl, L. G. (1997). *J. Bacteriol.* **179,** 1714–1720.

Diekert, G., and Wohlfarth, G. (1994). *Antonie van Leeuwenhoek* **66,** 209–221.

Drake, H. L. (Ed.) (1994). "Acetogenesis." Chapman & Hall, New York.

Fauque, G., LeGall, J., and Barton, L. L. (1991). *In* "Variations in Autotrophic Life" (J. M. Shively and L. L. Barton, Eds.), pp. 271–337. Academic Press, New York.

Fuchs, G. (1986). *FEMS Microbiol. Lett.* **57,** 181–213.

Huber, C., and Wächtershäuser, G. C. (1997). *Nature* **276,** 245–247.

Ljungdahl, L. G. (1986). *Annu. Rev. Microbiol.* **40,** 415–450.

Ragsdale, S. W., and Kumar, M. (1996). *Chem. Rev.* **96,** 2515–2539.

Redlinger, J., and Müller, V. (1994). *Eur. J. Biochem.* **223,** 275–283.

Wood, H. G., and Ljungdahl, L. G. (1991). *In* "Variations in Autotrophic Life" (J. M. Shively and L. L. Barton, Eds.), pp. 210–250. Academic Press, New York.

# Actinomycetes

**Martin Krsek, Nathan Morris, Sharon Egan, and Elizabeth M. H. Wellington**

*Warwick University*

## GLOSSARY

**actinomycetes** Widespread gram-positive bacteria which range morphologically from cocci-like fragments to mycelium which may form complex spore structures.

**antibiotic** A microbial product which inhibits growth of susceptible microorganisms.

**leprosy** A wasting disease in man caused by lesions in the extremities.

**linear plasmid** A mobile genetic element which exists as a linear molecule, found in many *Streptomyces* species.

**mycelium** A mass formed from vegetative hyphae.

**secondary metabolites** Compounds such as antibiotics and toxins which have no role in growth of the producing bacteria; production occurs during periods of restricted growth.

**spore** A specialized form of an organism which aids in survival or dispersion.

**tuberculosis** A chronic infectious disease which affects the lungs and other organs.

**THE ACTINOMYCETES** are gram-positive bacteria which have a characteristically high G + C content in their DNA (>55%). The name "Actinomycete" derives from the Greek *aktis* (a ray beam) and *mykes* (fungus) and was given to these organisms from initial observations of their morphology. They are phenotypically highly diverse and are found in most natural environments. Many species produce a wide variety of secondary metabolites, including antihelminthic compounds, antitumor agents, and the majority of known antibiotics, which have been exploited by their use in medicine and agriculture.

## I. INTRODUCTION

The actinomycetes were originally considered to be an intermediate group between bacteria and fungi but are now recognized as prokaryotic. The first descriptions of actinomycetes were made at the end of the nineteenth century with the observation of several human pathogens. Hansen saw the leprosy "bacillus" (later called *Mycobacterium leprae*) in 1874 and Cohn described *Streptothrix foesterii* in 1875 and *Actinomyces bovis* causing lumpy jaw in 1877. Koch identified *Mycobacterium tuberculosis* as the causal agent of tuberculosis in 1882. However, the majority of actinomycetes are free-living, saprophytic bacteria found widely distributed in soil, water, and colonizing plants. The discovery of streptomycin, an aminoglycoside antibiotic from *Streptomyces griseus,* by Schatz and Waksman in 1943 led to increased interest in actinomycetes as a potential source of antibacterial and antifungal antibiotics. Members of the genera *Streptomyces, Actinoplanes,* and *Micromonospora* are also a source of enzymes, vitamins, and enzyme inhibitors.

Actinomycetes can be isolated from soil, water, and plant material. In soil they are involved in the decomposition and mineralization cycles with the production of extracellular enzymes, such as cellulases, chitinases, and lignin peroxidases.

## II. MORPHOLOGICAL CHARACTERISTICS

The characteristic mycelium of hyphae is produced by the majority of genera in which differentiation results in the formation of specialized cell types. Considerable morphological diversity exists within the group (Fig. 1) with the formation of an extensive mycelium of substrate and aerial hyphae, the latter bearing specialized spores or sporangia. Certain genera, such as *Mycobacterium* and *Corynebacteria,* have less well-developed or nonexistent mycelial stages, with the formation of only rods and cocci (Fig. 1). The mycelium may be unstable, with hyphae fragmenting into uneven rods and coccoid-shaped fragments, as observed in *Nocardia* species. The hyphae are coenocyctic whether or not septa develop. Septa have been observed in some species.

The spores are desiccation resistant and can survive in soil in a viable state for long periods. This stage of the life cycle imparts resistance to adverse environmental conditions in the soil such as low nutrient and water availability. The spore wall is thicker than that of the mycelium, and spore chains have a hydrophobic sheath facilitating distribution throughout soil via attachment to organic material and exoskeletons of microarthropods.

Spore germination requires the presence of exogenous nutrients, water, and $Ca^{2+}$. Following germination, the germ tube emerges and branches into a mycelium of hyphae which rapidly colonize organic material such as plant root fragments, soil particles, and dead fungal mycelia (Fig. 2). The nutrient status of the germination site in soil limits the extent of hyphal growth, and the depletion of local nutrients influences the differentiation from vegetative substrate mycelium into aerial hyphae and eventually spore chains (Fig. 2). This process is closely regulated by a complex system of genetic signals. The specific influence of nutrient status appears to be on the timing of sporulation following vegetative growth

SUBORDER /(ORDER)

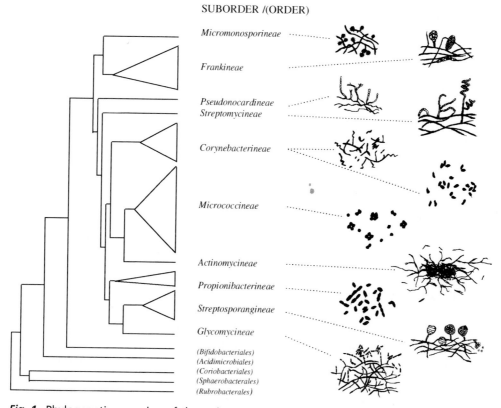

*Micromonosporineae*

*Frankineae*

*Pseudonocardineae*
*Streptomycineae*

*Corynebacterineae*

*Micrococcineae*

*Actinomycineae*

*Propionibacterineae*

*Streptosporangineae*

*Glycomycineae*

*(Bifidobacteriales)*
*(Acidimicrobiales)*
*(Coriobacteriales)*
*(Sphaerobacterales)*
*(Rubrobacterales)*

***Fig. 1.*** Phylogenetic grouping of the actinomycetes based on 16S rRNA sequence comparison.

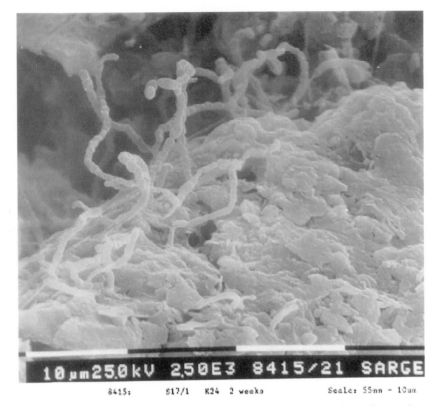

10 μm 25.0kV 2.50E3 8415/21 SARGE

8415:        S17/1     K24    2 weeks              Scale: 55mm – 10um

*Fig. 2.* Streptomycete hyphae colonizing soil matrix after 14 days of growth.

because high nutrient status only delays the onset of sporulation.

*Streptomyces antibioticus* spores contain approximately one-third of the number of ribosomes found in mycelium, and although these spore ribosomes have lower activity compared to those isolated from mycelium, their activity rapidly increases to that of mycelial ribosomes during germination onset. The streptomycete spores are produced mainly for dispersal and they are prepared for germination as soon as conditions are favorable.

## III. TAXONOMY

Actinomycetes were originally classified according to their morphology. Subsequent analysis of chemotaxonomic markers has assisted in the delimitation of genera and differentiation of species in some groups. Cell wall analysis was introduced by Cummins and Harris in 1956 and divided the family into eight types

(Table I). Actinomycetes from the types II–IV can be further distinguished by their whole organism sugar pattern (Table II).

Molecular systematics, based initially on 16S rRNA cataloging ($^{32}$P-labeled 16S rRNA extracted from biomass is digested with ribonuclease T1, and the oligonucleotides obtained are resolved by two-dimensional paper electrophoresis and subsequently sequenced) was introduced by Stackebrandt and resulted in the delineation of actinomycete genera. Sequencing of 16S rRNA genes is now used routinely to group strains within genera and has clarified the position of actinomycetes as a monophyletic group within the high GC clade in the prokaryotic phylogenetic tree (Fig. 1). The anaerobic bifidobacteria form the deepest branch within this high GC group followed by the genus *Propionbacterium*. The remaining actinomycetes have either a well-defined mycelium of hyphae or pleomorphic aerobic rods traditionally classified as coryneform bacteria and cocci in the genus *Micrococcus*. The organization of the class Actinobacteria is depicted in Fig. 1.

### TABLE I
### Cell Wall Chemotypes with Illustrating Families

| Chemotype | I | II | III | IV | V | VI | VII | VIII |
|---|---|---|---|---|---|---|---|---|
| L-Diaminopimelic acid | + | | | | | | | |
| meso-Diamelopimelic acid | | + | + | + | | | | |
| Diaminobutyric acid | | | | | | | + | |
| Aspartic acid | | | | | | v[a] | | |
| Glycine | + | + | | | | | + | |
| Lysine | | | | | + | | v | |
| Ornithine | | | | | + | | | + |
| Arabinose | | | | + | | | | |
| Galactose | | | | + | | v | | |
| | Streptomycetaceae, Nocardioidaceae | Micromonosporaceae | Dermatophilaceae, Brevibacteriaceae, Thermomonosporaceae, Streptosporangiaceae, Frankiaceae | Nocardiaceae, Mycobacteriaceae, Corynebacteriaceae, Pseudonocardiaceae | Actinomycetaceae | Cellulomonadaceae, Micrococcaceae, Microbacteriaceae, Actinomycetaceae | Microbacteriaceae | Cellulomonadaceae, Microbacteriaceae |

[a] v, variable amount.

The suborder Micromonosporineae is characterized by the cell wall chemotype II and sugar pattern D and is composed of the family Micromonosporaceae, which includes the type genus *Micromonospora* and six other genera (Table III). The genus *Micromonospora,* commonly found in soil and aquatic ecosystems, currently has 15 validly described species with several subspecies. The genus can be distinguished by the morphologically characteristic lack of aerial mycelium and the substrate mycelium, which bears single spores. 16S rDNA sequence analysis has shown that these genes have high levels of sequence identity between species, and as a result intrageneric relationships are generally unresolved. Differentiation of species is based on chemotaxonomic markers, pigment production, and physiological characteristics. A probabilistic matrix has been developed for the identification of individual species which allows

### TABLE II
### Whole Organism Sugar Pattern of Actinomycetes from Cell Wall Chemotypes II–IV

| Pattern | Arabinose | Fucose | Galactose | Madurose | Xylose |
|---|---|---|---|---|---|
| A | + | | + | | |
| B | | | | + | |
| C | | | | | |
| D | + | | | | + |
| E | | + | | | |

**TABLE III**
**Taxonomic Classification of the Order *Actinomycetales***

| Suborder | Family | Genus |
|---|---|---|
| Micromonosporineae | Micromonosporaceae | *Micromonospora, Actinoplanes, Catellatospora, Couchioplanes, Catenuloplanes, Pilimelia Dactylosporangium* |
| Frankineae | Frankiaceae | *Frankia* |
| | Sporichthyaceae | *Sporichthya* |
| | Geodermatophilaceae | *Geothermatophilis, Blastococcus* |
| | Microsphaeraceae | *Microsphera* |
| | Acidothermaceae | *Acidothermus* |
| Pseudonocardineae | Pseudonocardiaceae | *Pseudonocardia, Actinopolyspora, Actinosynnema, Amycolatopsis, Kibdelosporangium, Kutzneria, Lentzea, Saccharomonospora, Saccharopolyspora, Saccharothrix, Streptoalloteichus, Thermocrispum* |
| Streptomycineae | Streptomycetaceae | *Streptomyces* |
| Corynebacterium | Nocardiaceae | *Nocardia, Rhodococcus* |
| | Gordoniaceae | *Gordonia* |
| | Mycobacteriaceae | *Mycobacterium* |
| | Dietziaceae | *Dietzia* |
| | Tsukamurellaceae | *Tsukamurella* |
| | Corynebacteriaceae | *Corynebacterium, Turicella* |
| Micrococcineae | Micrococcaceae | *Micrococcus, Arthrobacter, Kocuria, Nesterenkonia, Rothia, Renibacterium, Stomatococcus* |
| | Brevibacteriaceae | *Brevibacterium* |
| | Cellulomonadaceae | *Cellulomonas, Oerskovia, Rarobacter* |
| | Dermabacteraceae | *Dermobacter, Brachybacterium* |
| | Dermatophilaceae | *Dermatophilus, Kytococcus, Dermacoccus* |
| | Intrasporangiaceae | *Intrasporangium, Sanguibacter, Terrabacter* |
| | Jonesiaceae | *Jonesia* |
| | Microbacteriaceae | *Microbacterium, Agrococcus, Agromyces, Aureobacterium, Clavibacter, Curtobacterium, Rathayibacter* |
| | Promicromonosporaceae | *Promicromonospora* |
| Actinomyineae | Actinomycetaceae | *Actinomyces, Mobiluncus, Arcanobacterium* |
| Propionibacterineae | Propionibacteraceae | *Propionibacterium, Luteococcus, Microlunatus, Propioniferax* |
| Streptosporangineae | Streptosporangiaceae | *Streptosporangium, Herbidospora, Microbispora, Microtetraspora, Planobispora, Planomonospora* |
| | Thermomonosporaceae | *Thermomonospora, Actinomadura, Spirillospora* |
| | Nocardiopsaceae | *Nocardiopsis* |
| Glycomycineae | Glycomycetaceae | *Glycomyces* |

the simultaneous evaluation of 20 selected highly diagnostic characters for identification of an unknown *Micromonospora* species.

The genus *Actinoplanes* contains 15 validly described species which have been delimited by 16S rRNA sequence comparisons. Physiological charac-teristics serve to distinguish species, many of which bear sporangia with motile zoospores for dispersal.

The suborder Frankineae comprises five families (Table III). The structure of the biggest group, the symbiotic nitrogen-fixing species within the genus *Frankia*, was initially based on the host range of the species and has not been fully resolved because of difficulties with isolation and cultivation. Many strains currently kept in pure culture were isolated from root nodules of woody dicotyledonous plants from eight families of angiosperms and are the spore-negative type. No spore-positive strains have been isolated from root nodules. Delimitation of species is based on molecular data such as DNA–DNA homology, polymerase chain reaction-restriction fragment length polymorphism, and sequence comparisons of the rRNA and *nif* operons. Based on analysis of 16S rRNA data, four main subdivisions of the genus *Frankia* were recovered: The first group comprised *Frankia alni* and related organisms; the second one comprised unisolated microsymbionts of *Dryas, Coriaria,* and *Datisca;* the third consisted of *Elaeagnus*-infective strains; and the fourth was composed of "atypical" strains.

The suborder Pseudonocardineae comprises one broad family, the Pseudonocardiaceae, with the type genus *Pseudonocardia* and 11 other genera (Table III). This family contains antibiotic-producing groups, and members are still identified on the basis of biochemical characteristics because it is difficult to distinguish them by their morphology. Members of the genera *Actinopolyspora, Amycolatopsis, Kibdelosporangium, Pseudonocardia, Saccharomonospora,* and *Saccharopolyspora* are characterized by the absence of mycolic acids (long-chain α-substituted β-hydroxylated fatty acids in the cell wall having the general formula R′CHOH.CHR″.COOH) and have a cell wall chemotype IV. The genera *Actinosynnema, Kutzneria, Lentzea, Saccharothrix,* and *Thermocrispum* have a wall chemotype III and can be distinguished by other chemical or molecular biological characteristics.

The suborder Streptomycineae consists of the type family Streptomycetaceae containing the genus *Streptomyces* in addition to strains formerly classified as *Actinosporangium, Actinopycnidium, Chainia, Elytrosporangium, Kitasatoa, Kitasatosporia, Microellobosporia,* and *Streptoverticillium.* Members of this genus can be readily isolated from many habitats which together with their production of economically important secondary metabolites, such as antibiotics, has led to overclassification. Of the large number of species (more than 3000), many can be considered as

synonyms. In 1964, the International Streptomyces Project introduced some standard taxonomic criteria for typing of *Streptomyces* species based on morphology and physiology. A numerical taxonomic approach based on phenetic characteristics was completed by Williams and others in 1983 and resulted in a substantial reduction in the number of species. A probability matrix was devised and used to identify 41 species groups by simultaneous analysis of 23 physiological and biochemical tests. This method provides a useful adjunct to 16S rRNA sequence analysis for identification of an unknown strain to a species group. Subgeneric identification can be achieved by analysis of other more variable "housekeeping" genes with roles in cell metabolism.

The suborder Corynebacterineae consists of six families (Table III). The most important and best studied group is the genus *Mycobacterium.* More than 300 species have been published since the discovery of tuberculosis, but the 1977 list of approved species reduced the number to 35 species. Species of the genus can be distinguished by a set of biochemical tests (see the 1994 edition of *Bergey's Manual*) and many diagnostic molecular probes have been reported for identification of *M. tuberculosis* and *M. leprae.*

The suborder Actinomycineae consists of one family Actinomycetaceae with the type genus *Actinomyces,* and the genera *Mobiluncus* recently recognized as causing bacterial vaginosis, and Arcanobacterium. The family is difficult to identify only on the basis of its morphology or biochemical and physiological characteristics, which have to be supplemented by chemotaxonomic and primarily 16S rRNA data.

For the organization of the suborders Micrococcineae, Propionibacterineae, Streptosporangineae, and Glycomycineae, see Table III.

## IV. ECOLOGY

Actinomycetes are widely dispersed in nature and found in most environments. Soil is colonized by actinomycete hyphae which can form aerial mycelia bearing hydrophobic spores dispersed by air, water, and microarthropods (Fig. 2). Some groups such as the actinoplanetes are adapted for water-mediated dispersal and produce motile zoospores within desiccation-resistant sporangia.

Actinomycetes can be isolated using the standard dilution plate procedure but special pretreatments, such as heating of soil, are necessary for recovery of certain groups. Due to their slow growth on isolation media, various methods have been used to reduce the growth of eubacteria such as bacilli and pseudomonads. Actinomycetes produce exoenzymes and can degrade many polymeric substances, such as starch, chitin, cellulose, and lignin. Isolation media have taken advantage of this and soil compounds are often used as the sole carbon and nitrogen source for use in studies which involve selective isolation.

## A. Soil

Soils can contain $10^4$–$10^6$ CFU g$^{-1}$ actinomycete propagules and spores. The soil is therefore a reservoir for large numbers of spores of a wide range of genera. Actinomycetes are also at least partly responsible for the earthy smell of soil due to their production of volatile terpene derivatives such as geosmin. They also play an important role in creating soil structure and cycling of carbon and nitrogen via decomposition and mineralization of plant and animal remains. Actinomycetes are capable of degrading a wide range of substrates, including lignocelluloses, keratin, and chitin. They also play an important role in the bioremediation of hydrocarbon contaminated sites (e.g., members of the genus *Rhodococcus*). The most widespread, and hence most studied, has been the *Streptomyces* genus, but its prevalence may be due to the selectiveness of the isolation techniques used. Streptomycetes exist in soil for extended periods as resting arthrospores that germinate in the occasional presence of exogenous substrates. Nonsporing genera probably exist for long periods as resting hyphal fragments.

Spores of most actinomycetes withstand desiccation and show a slightly higher resistance to dry or wet heat than vegetative bacterial cells. Air-drying soil samples for 2–7 days or heating at high temperatures reduce the ability of gram-negative soil bacteria to outcompete the more slowly growing actinomycetes. If heating at higher temperatures is used, it is essential to air-dry soil before heating in order to

avoid heat damage. Lower temperatures (55–60°C) may be applied to soil suspensions (to isolate, e.g., *Micromonospora* spp. and *Rhodococcus coprophilus*). Isolation can either start directly from a soil suspension or a concentrated soil bacterial fraction can be prepared for isolation.

Many different media and selective inhibitors were used for isolation and enumeration of soil actinomycetes. Some of them have already been mentioned and further details can be found in the ninth edition of *Bergey's Manual of Systematic Bacteriology* (Williams, 1989). Plates are usually inoculated with a sample from an appropriate dilution of a soil suspension. This may be incorporated into molten media to reduce spread of motile bacteria or spread onto the thoroughly dried surface of solidified media. Streptomycetes usually predominate on plates and can outcompete other groups of actinomycetes. Predominance has been discouraged by addition of polyvalent streptomycete phages to the soil suspension immediately before plating.

## B. Rhizosphere

In addition to their ability to colonize bulk soil, many streptomycetes successfully colonize the rhizosphere. The antagonistic ability of streptomycetes by production of antibiotics may allow competition with other faster growing bacteria in the rhizosphere such as pseudomonads and bacilli. Actinomycetes can colonize dry soil due to their filamentous nature, whereas bacteria such as *Pseudomonas fluorescens* require a continuous film of moisture for motility. Streptomycetes can be found in the rhizosphere of many plants and they have been used for biological control of fungal root pathogens, in which their antibiotic production has been implicated in the antagonism.

An important group of rhizosphere actinomycetes is the genus *Frankia*, nitrogen-fixing endosymbionts on roots of various nonleguminous trees and shrubs. Isolation of *Frankia* is usually performed from nodules which are surface sterilized and then crushed or microdissected. Some strains require special isolation media amended by different growth factors such as fatty acids. Small colonies which are sometimes visible only under a microscope can appear after 3–10 days of incubation at 25–33°C, but usually 4–8 weeks are required. Because of the variable germination of spores, *Frankia* in natural environments can be quantified by use of the most probable number method with host plant seedlings.

## C. Composts and Moldy Fodders

The favorable conditions of high organic nutrient content, moist, aerobic, and neutral to alkaline pH conditions in composts and manures, often results in colonization by actinomycetes, mainly thermophiles, which grow well in decomposing organic matter and animal manures. *Rhodococcus coprophilus* has been used as an indicator of fecal pollution from farm animal wastes. Thermophilic fermentation of pig feces and straw by *Thermomonospora* spp. and *Pseudonocardia thermophila* has been used for deodorization. Mesophilic actinomycetes, such as members of the genera *Corynebacterium*, *Microbacterium*, *Rhodococcus*, and *Arthrobacter*, can also occur in sewage sludge.

Many mesophilic and thermophilic actinomycetes play an important role in the deterioration of moist, badly stored fodder and grain. The airborne spores of several actinomycetes developing in these deteriorated materials can cause respiratory allergies and diseases known as farmer's lung, bagassosis, and mushroom worker's lung. Thermophilic, filamentous members of the *Bacillus* group (thermoactinomycetes), however, are often implicated as the causal agent of farmer's lung.

Sampling from composters and fodders can be carried out in a similar way as is done for soil—by shaking or homogenization in a liquid medium, or frequently air dispersal techniques are used. Samples are suspended in a chamber and spores are captured by their rate of sedimentation and size using an Anderson sampler, which is a cylinder containing a series of plates, each with different-sized perforations which then grade the size of particles that are trapped on agar plates beneath each perforated plate.

## D. The Aquatic Environment

Actinomycetes can be isolated from fresh water, seawater, and sediment samples. In marine environments, streptomycetes were found to predominate at shallow depths and actinoplanetes at increasing depths, which suggests that some actinomycetes are indigenous marine microorganisms. Actinomycetes from marine sources have been reported to decompose agar, alginates, laminarin, cellulose, chitin, and oil and other hydrocarbons. They can even grow in jet-fuel storage tanks. They are also suspected to be the main causal agents of earthy tastes and odors that occur in drinking water. The compounds responsible include geosmin and methyl isoborneol and they are produced by streptomycetes in sediments, on plant litter on the banks, or they are washed into water via runoff from surrounding soil.

To obtain water and sediment samples from the sea, many grabs, dredges, and coring devices have been used. Cells can be concentrated from large samples of water by either centrifugation or filtering through membranes which are subsequently incubated on a suitable medium. Recovery of actinomycetes from aquatic habitats may be maximized by sampling surface foam rather than the water because it has been demonstrated that actinomycete species and other bacteria can be concentrated 100- to 1000-fold in river foam. Heat treatment of freshwater samples and sea sediments has been reported to improved actinomycete recovery.

Actinomycetes colonizing leaves and vegetation, which are periodically submerged in water, produce motile spores which can be sampled by plating zoospore-containing supernatant from settled samples of rehydrated organic matter, or various baits (e.g., human hair, pollen, and snakeskin) can be used to attract the motile spores of actinoplanetes.

## E. Other Habitats

Actinomycetes have been recovered from a variety of different environments, such as human mouth and teeth, intestines of arthropods, hindguts of termites, gut contents and excrements of millipedes, surface of millipede legs, rubber rings and seals in water pipes, and decaying wood. Isolation from these environments was achieved using specific selection techniques. It is also possible to detect actinomycetes in environments directly by extraction and analysis of total community DNA. Actinomycetes have been detected in bogs, soils, and termite guts by identification of specific 16S rRNA sequences amplified from DNA extracted from samples.

## V. PATHOGENICITY

Actinomycetes are primarily opportunistic pathogens, and if a physical trauma introduces actinomycetes within a body tissue the organism may slowly proliferate. The most important examples of human pathogenic actinomycetes are species within the group mycobacteria. *Mycobacterium leprae,* the cause of leprosy, was the first pathogenic mycobacterium to be discovered, although it is not cultivated in synthetic media. There are still more than 10 million cases of leprosy worldwide. Other well-known species are *M. tuberculosis,* the cause of tuberculosis in humans and some animals, and *M. bovis,* which causes bovine tuberculosis that may also be transmitted to man. *Mycobacterium africanum* and *M. microti* can also cause human tuberculosis but pathogenicity of the latter is low.

*Mycobacterium tuberculosis* was isolated and studied by Koch in 1882. The disease spreads from person to person by droplets expelled into air by coughing, sneezing, and similar activities and it can persist for a considerable time. Infection occurs through inhalation of such droplets. Vaccination is performed using an attenuated strain of *M. bovis* (BCG). BCG vaccination is effective mainly in northern parts of the world. People in tropical and subtropical areas can show protection as low as 10–20%. This may be due to exposure to mycobacteria growing in the soil. In areas such as Africa, Brazil, and India tuberculosis still causes millions of deaths. Treatment of tuberculosis is based on drug susceptibility. Because of the increasing incidence of antibiotic-resistance strains of the pathogen, chemotherapy involves administration of a mixture of isoniazid, rifampicin, and pyrazinamide antibiotics.

Other mycobacteria can also cause infections of humans and animals (Table IV). In addition, members of other genera, such as *Arcanobacterium, Micrococcus, Nocardiopsis, Oerskovia, Rhodococcus,* and *Rothia,* may be opportunistic pathogens. Spore antigens of *Saccharomonospora* and *Saccharopolyspora* (Faenia) species can also cause allergic alveolitis called farmer's lung.

Some examples of plant pathogenic actinomycetes are given in Table IV. Many phytopathogenic coryneform actinomycetes used to be assigned to the

*TABLE IV*
**Examples of Actinomycete Pathogens**

| Organism | Host | Disease |
|---|---|---|
| *Actinomodura madurae* | Human | Chronic subcutaneous abscesses |
| *Actinomyces bovis* | Animal | Bovine actinomycosis (lumpy jaw) |
| *Arthrobacter ilicis* | Plant | Holly blight |
| *Corynebacterium diphtheria* | Human | Diphtheria |
| *C. cystitidis* | Animal | Bovine cystitis |
| *C. nebraskense* | Plant | Corn blight |
| *Myobacterium avium* | Animal | Avian tuberculosis |
| *M. farcinogenes* | Animal | Bovine farcy, inflammation of the lymphatic system |
| *M. leprae* | Human | Leprosy |
| *M. tuberculosis* | Human | Tuberculosis |
| *M. scrofulaceum* | Human | Chronic cervical lymphadenitis in children |
| *Nocardia asteroides* | Human | Pulmonary nocardiosis |
| *Rhodococcus equi* | Animal | Foal bronchopneumonia |
| *Streptomyces scabies* | Plant | Common potato scab |
| *S. ipomoeae* | Plant | Sweet potato scab |

genus *Corynebacterium,* but accumulation of chemo-taxonomic data, including cell composition, mycolic acid content, and GC content, led to the reclassification of these bacteria in other genera, mainly *Curtobacterium, Clavibacterium,* and *Arthrobacter.* Pathogenicity of coryneform actinomycetes is caused, at least in part, by the production of hormones, polysaccharides, and toxins. They also produce biosurfactants which can help them attach to hosts.

There are few streptomycetes which are capable of infection of plant tissues and cause disease. One of the best characterized is scab disease caused by *Streptomyces scabies,* which occurs in the economically important crops of potatoes and sugar beet. *Streptomyces scabies* seems to be distributed in soil worldwide. It can grow saprophytically in soil or on the roots of various vegetables. Common scab disease causes disfiguration of potato tubers but does not affect the yield or the quality of the flesh.

The pathogen is unable to penetrate the intact skin of the potato tuber but invades young tubers through stomata or newly formed lenticels. The plant tissue reacts by forming a wound barrier; if this is breached, additional barriers may be formed, resulting in increasingly severe forms of disease. Disease severity is influenced by many factors, such as the time of infection, the growth rate of the potato, the variety of the host, and the virulence of the pathogen. Dry weather during the month after tuber induction is critical for infection; irrigation during the period significantly reduces the incidence of the disease. Also, increasing soil acidity (by sulfur amendment) or green manuring can control potato scab. The incidence of common scab is greatest in sandy, well-drained, dry, neutral to alkaline soils. In acidic soils (pH < 5) another streptomycete causes the same disease, for which the new species *S. acidiscabies* was proposed.

## VI. GENETICS

Actinomycetes, in common with other prokaryotes, have a haploid genome. The *Streptomyces* genome is 8 Mb with a characteristically high G + C (mol %) content of between 69 and 73%, and the chromosome is linear in comparison with the circular one commonly found in the majority of other bacteria. Most of the genetic analysis of actinomycetes has been focused on members of the *Streptomyces* genus, in particular *Streptomyces coelicolor* A3(2), and was pioneered by Hopwood and others. Selected members of other genera have been the subject of genetic analysis due to their medical and commercial importance and include species of the genera *Nocardia, Micromonospora, Mycobacterium,* and *Rhodococcus.* It has been shown in *S. coelicolor* that DNA is present in cells in multiple copies per hyphal cell but usually as a single copy in spores. *Streptomyces* genes have a different codon usage when compared to that of other bacteria and need specialized transcriptional factors that recognize promoter sequences different from those typically used by other bacteria.

Genetic exchange between streptomycetes was first revealed by the isolation of prototrophic recombinants from mixed cultures of auxotrophs. Plasmids were first implicated in marker exchange in *S. coelicolor* A3(2) for isolates differing in their "fertility" properties. The first conjugative plasmids, SCP1 and SCP2, were identified, although it took many years to isolate SCP1 due to its large size and linear structure. In addition, plasmids can integrate into the chromosome via specific sites. Plasmids have also been identified in other strains, including *S. rimosus, S. lividans,* and *S. venezuelae.* It has been suggested that covalently closed, circular (CCC) DNA plasmids occur in approximately 30% of all wild-type *Streptomyces* spp. and these can be characterized according to features such as copy number, fertility, host range, and mobility. These plasmids range in size from <4 kb to more than 100 kb. Studies of *S. lividans* strains lacking conjugative plasmids failed to reveal any genuine recombinants; colonies that appeared arose from reverse mutation and it is assumed that all conjugative DNA transfer in *Streptomyces* spp. depends on the activity of plasmids. This process of plasmid-mediated conjugation is very different compared to that in gram-negative bacteria. No mating pair formation occurs and DNA is thought to transfer by some process of hyphal fusion. Minimal replicons of 2 kb can still transfer, so genes encoded by the host chromosome could be involved in transfer. Pock formation is a phenomenon unique to conjugative plasmids of actinomycetes. It is seen when a plasmid-containing spore germinates on a lawn lacking the same plasmid. Under these conditions, transfer of the plasmid leads to a circular zone or "pock" where growth or development of the newly infected recipient culture is retarded. Many plasmids were found to be large, linear molecules as determined by pulsed-field gel electrophoresis (the sample is subjected, alternately, to electric fields which are mutually perpendicular). An example of these linear plasmids is SCP1 from *S. coelicolor,* which confers resistance to methylenomycin and forms highly stable chromosomal integrants. Restriction analysis has shown the presence of two long-terminal repeats of 80 kb each and SCP1 carries a protein covalently bound to each 5′ of the DNA. These elements, termed "invertrons," are believed to be involved in plasmid replication. There are still many uncertainties regarding the conjugal properties of *Streptomyces* plasmids; for example, it is not known whether the plasmid DNA is transferred in double- or single-stranded form, although there is some evidence of the former. Plasmid transfer has been reported between streptomycetes in soil and this may facilitate mobility of traits allowing adaptation to different environments.

Temperate and virulent phages are readily obtained for many streptomycetes and some have been developed for use as vectors. Virulent phages have been described with genome sizes ranging from 40 to 100 kb with a G + C content of 55–73%. Some restriction sites were found to be much rarer than those in chromosomal or plasmid DNA. Most temperate phages isolated resembled coliphage l in possessing DNA with cohesive ends which is packaged into phage particles during lytic infections in a process in which multimeric genomes are cut by endonuclease recognition into single genomic lengths. One of the most developed *Streptomyces* DNA cloning vector was produced from $\phi$C31 and derivatives of this have been used to package small segments of DNA for cloning experiments.

The genetics of differentiation has been studied in detail for *S. coelicolor.* The switch from mycelia to spore development provides a model for studying prokaryotic differentiation. Work by Chater and others has identified a set of genes involved in the differentiation cycle from spores to mycelia to spores

again. Two classes of mutants have been studied: those lacking aerial mycelia (*bld* mutants) and those that fail to develop mature spores (*whi* mutants). The nature of the *bld* and *whi* gene products and their complex interactions are being unraveled and have allowed an understanding of the regulation of differentiation in *Streptomyces* spp. Six genes were defined as responsible for the early stages of sporulation and a smaller number were identified that control the later stages. These genes code for regulators, polyketide spore pigments, sigma factors, and other uncharacterized proteins. Some *bld* mutants were found to affect antibiotic production in addition to morphological differentiation, indicating some degree of coordinate genetic control. These so-called pleiotropic genes play an important role in the global regulation of antibiotic production and differentiation in actinomycetes.

Recent advantages in the understanding of the genetic and biochemical basis of antibiotic production has led to the characterization of gene clusters containing biosynthetic, resistance, and regulatory genes clustered together and all involved in the production of a specific antibiotic or a chemical family of antibiotics. The best characterized clusters involve genes coding for the production of actinorhodin and streptomycin. Approximately 30 genes are involved in the formation of the aminoglycoside antibiotic streptomycin. Regulatory genes such as *strR* have been identified and these respond to a signaling butyralactone, A factor, via a regulatory cascade sensing changes in the external environment. The entire cluster of genes (*act*) responsible for biosynthesis of the pigmented benzoisochromanequinone polyketide, actinorhodin, was cloned on a 35-kb fragment of chromosomal DNA from *S. coelicolor.* This fragment was expressed in the actinorhodin-sensitive and nonproducing strain, *S. parvulus,* which was then found to produce actinorhodin without killing itself. Actinorhodin is a polyketide molecule synthesized by a polyketide synthase which catalyzes repeated condensation cycles between acyl thioesters to form a growing carbon chain. Genetic techniques have been used to determine the programming of polyketide synthases which determine the formation of many structurally diverse natural products. This has allowed many rational design techniques to be used for the production of polyketides by combinatorial biosynthesis.

## VII. BIOTECHNOLOGY

### A. Antibiotics

Actinomycetes, in common with other bacteria, have many uses in the field of biotechnology. Of particular importance is the production of many chemically and functionally diverse antibiotics which are used in both human and veterinary medicine (Table V). These compounds can be defined as having the capacity to inhibit growth or destroy other microorganisms. Antibiotics are usually produced in low concentrations as secondary metabolites at specific stages during the growth cycle. They are not essential for growth of the producing organism but can give a selective advantage in the natural environment. Approximately 11,900 antibiotics had been

described by 1994, and it is estimated that approximately 60–70% can be attributed to actinomycetes and that of these, more than 50% are produced by *Streptomyces* spp. Of all the antibiotics discovered, approximately 160 are in clinical use.

Antibiotic resistance is an ever-increasing problem in both human and veterinary medicine. Many bacterial diseases that were previously controllable are becoming more prevalent. An example of this is the reemergence of tuberculosis, caused by *M. tuberculosis*, especially in immunocompromised patients. Common methods of antibiotic resistance include modification of the antibiotic target and changes in a either the uptake or the efflux of the antibiotic from the bacterial cell. The transfer of resistant determinants between bacteria coupled with selective pressure caused by the overuse of some antibiotics has allowed many groups of bacteria to develop multiple resistances to most antibiotics in clinical use.

Actinomycete-derived antibiotics have been used in agriculture for the past 40 years as feed additives

***TABLE V***
**Examples of Medically Important Compounds Produced by Actinomycetes**

| Organism | Compound | Activity |
|----------|----------|----------|
| *Actinomadura carminata* | Carminomycin | Antitumor |
| *Saccharopolyspora erythraea* | Erythromycin | Broad-spectrum antibiotic |
| *S. albovinaceus* | Rifamycin B | Antiviral |
| *S. albus* | 8-Azaguanine | Antiviral |
| *S. aureofaciens* | Tetracycline | Antibiotic |
| *S. avermitilis* | Avermectin | Veterinary antiparasitic drug |
| *S. clavuligerus* | Clavulanic acid | Inhibits $\beta$-lactamase activity |
| *S. griseus* | Candicidin | Antifungal |
| *S. griseus* | Cycloheximide | Antifungal, used in agriculture |
| *S. griseus* | Streptomycin | Antibiotic |
| *Amycolatopsis mediterranei* | Rifamicins | Antibiotic |
| *S. nodosus* | Amphotericin B | Antifungal |
| *S. noursei* | Nystatin | Antifungal |
| *A. orientalis* | Vancomycin | Antibiotic |
| *S. peucetius* | Daunorubicin HCl | Antitumor |
| *S. rimosus* | Oxytetracycline | Antibiotic |
| *S. venezuelae* | Chloramphenicol | Broad-spectrum antibiotic, antiviral |
| *S. verticillus* | Bleomycin sulfate | Antitumor, used in the treatment of lymphomas |
| *S. fradiae* | Tylosin | Growth promotion |
| *S. hygroscopicus* | Bialaphos | Herbicide |
| *S. hygroscopicus* | Herbimycin | Herbicide |
| *S. cinnamonensis* | Monensin | Growth promotion |

for growth promotion in farm animals. Although the mode of action is not completely understood, these additives cause weight gain mainly by affecting the animal's gut microflora (suppressing wasteful methanogens). Although antibiotics licensed for human use are not used in animal feed, the structural diversity between these natural products is often very low. This suggests a possible route for the transmission of antibiotic resistance into the human health sector. Antibiotics such as streptomycin which are no longer used clinically have been applied for the control of rots in soft fruits in orchards. Actinomycete natural products are also used as control agents against a wide variety of agricultural pathogens. Cyclohexamide is used as an antifungal agent to control mildew in roses and onions, turf diseases and a variety of tree blights and rusts. The agricultural applications of antibiotics are many and varied, including insecticide and herbicide activity (Table V).

## B. Enzymes

Enzymes are of great importance in biotechnology, with uses in the food and detergent industry (Table VI). The diversity of actinomycete secondary metabolites means that screening for enzymatic activity is of commercial value. The best known example is D-xylose isomerase produced by *S. rimosus* and *Actinoplanes* spp. The enzyme is released by cell lysis and then immobilized for use as a solid in granules or powder. Other important enzymes include chitinases from *Streptomyces* spp. and cellulases from *Thermonospora stutzeri*.

Actinomycetes, and streptomycetes in particular, have been used for bioconversion or biotransformation reactions. Xenobiotics or drugs such as hormones can be converted to a more useful product using specific enzymatic conversion. Biotransformation has been particularly valuable in the alteration of hormones and steroids for the pharmaceutical industry.

## C. Biodegradation

Because of the considerable metabolic diversity of actinomycetes, they are able to degrade many diverse natural products, including cellulose, chitin and lignin. Many actinomycetes have the ability to degrade recalcitrant xenobiotics. *Rhodococcus* spp. can degrade many compounds, including substituted benzenes, phenols, halogenated phenols, and alkanes. These bacteria have been used to bioremediate chlorinated phenolics in soil, chlorophenol-containing groundwater, and soil contaminated with pentachlorophenol. It is also possible to use these bacteria in conjunction with other species to ameliorate sites. A mixture of *Rhodococcus*, *Pseudomonas*, and *Flavobacterium* can degrade alicyclic hydrocarbons using unsubstituted phenols as the only source of carbon.

## See Also the Following Articles

RHIZOSPHERE • SECONDARY METABOLITES • VACCINES, BACTERIAL

### TABLE VI
**Examples of Commercially Important Enzymes Produced by Actinomycetes**

| Organism | Enzyme | Use |
|---|---|---|
| *Corynebacterium* spp. | L-Phenylalanine dehydrogenase | Production of L-phenylalanine for artificial sweeteners |
| *Nocardia* spp. | Cholesterol oxidase | Blood cholesterol determination |
| *Streptomyces* spp. | Restriction endonucleases | Various uses in molecular biology laboratories |
| *Streptomyces* spp. | Chitinases | Degradation of fungal cell walls |
| *Streptomyces* spp. | Proteases | Additives to household detergents |
| *Streptomyces* spp. | Amylase | Preparation of high-maltose syrups |
| *Thermomonospora* spp. | Cellulase | Detergent and clothes manufacture |
| *Streptomyces* spp. | D-Xylose isomerase | Production of D-fructose from syrups |
| *Streptomyces* spp. | Chitinases | Processing of chitin wastes |
| *S. cyanogenus* | Urate oxidase | Determination of uric acid in biological fluids |

## Bibliography

Balows, A., Truper, H. G., Dworkin, M., Harder, W., and Schleifer, K.-H. (Eds.) (1992). "The Prokaryotes," Vol. 2. Springer-Verlag, New York.

Berdy, J. (1995). Are actinomycetes exhausted as a source of secondary metabolites? *In* "Proceedings of the 9th International Symposium on the Biology of the Actinomycetes" (V. G. Debabov, Y. V. Dudnik, and V. N. Danilenko, Eds.), pp. 13–34. All-Russia Scientific Research Institute for Genetics and Selection of Industrial Microorganisms, Moscow.

Goodfellow, M., and Williams, S. T. (1983). Ecology of actinomycetes. *Annu. Rev. Microbiol.* 37, 189–216.

Jensen, P. R., Dwight, R., and Fenical, W. (1991). Distribution of actinomycetes in near-shore tropical marine sediments. *Appl. Environ. Microbiol.* 57, 1102–1108.

Lacey, J. (1988). Actinomycetes as biodeteriogens and pollutants of the environment. *In* "Actinomycetes in Biotechnology" (M. Goodfellow, S. T. Williams, and M. Mordarski, Eds.), pp. 359–432. Academic Press, New York.

Lechevalier, M. P. (1988). Actinomycetes in agriculture and forestry. *In* "Actinomycetes in Biotechnology" (M. Goodfellow, S. T. Williams, and M. Mordarski, Eds.), pp. 327–358. Academic Press, New York.

Logan, N. A. (1994). "Bacterial Systematics." Blackwell Science, Inc., Boston, MA.

Waksman, S. A., and Curtis, R. E. (1918). The occurrence of actinomycetes in the soil. *Soil Sci.* 4(4), 309–319.

Wheelis, M. L., Kandler, O., and Woese, C. R. (1992). On the nature of global classification. *Proc. Natl. Acad Sci. USA* 89, 2930–2934.

Williams, S. T. (Ed.) (1989). "Bergey's Manual of Systematic Bacteriology," Vol. 4. Williams & Wilkins, Baltimore, MD.

# Adhesion, Bacterial

## Matthew A. Mulvey and Scott J. Hultgren

*Washington University School of Medicine*

## GLOSSARY

*adhesin*  A molecule, typically a protein, that mediates bacterial attachment by interacting with specific receptors.

*extracellular matrix*  A complex network of proteins and polysaccharides secreted by eukaryotic cells. Functions as a structural element in tissues, in addition to modulating tissue development and physiology.

*invasin*  An adhesin that can mediate bacterial invasion into host eukaryotic cells.

*isoreceptors*  Eukaryotic cell membrane components which contain identical receptor determinants recognized by a bacterial adhesin.

*lectins*  Proteins that bind carbohydrate motifs.

**ADHESION**  is a principal step in the colonization of inanimate surfaces and living tissues by bacteria. It is estimated that the majority of bacterial populations in nature live and multiply attached to a substratum. Bacteria have evolved numerous, and often redundant, mechanisms to facilitate their adherence to other organisms and surfaces within their environment. A vast number of structurally and functionally diverse bacterial adhesive molecules, called adhesins, have been identified. The adhesins expressed by different bacterial species can directly influence bacterial tropism and mediate molecular crosstalk among organisms.

# I. MECHANISMS OF BACTERIAL ADHESION

Bacterial adhesion to living cells and to inanimate surfaces is governed by nonspecific electrostatic and hydrophobic interactions and by more specific adhesin–receptor binding events. Studies of bacterial adherence indicate that initial bacterial interactions with a surface are governed by long-range forces, primarily van der Waals and electrostatic interactions. The surface of most gram-negative and many gram-positive bacteria is negatively charged. Thus, bacteria will often readily adhere nonspecifically to positively charged surfaces. In some cases, bacterial proteins possessing hydrophobic surfaces, including many adhesins, can also mediate nonspecific bacterial interactions with exposed host cell membrane lipids and with other hydrophobic surfaces encountered in nature. If the approach of bacteria to a surface, such as a negatively charged host cell membrane, is unfavorable, bacteria must overcome an energy barrier to establish contact. Protein-ligand binding events mediated by bacterial adhesins can often overcome or bypass repulsive forces and promote specific and intimate microbial interactions with host tissues and other surfaces.

Bacteria can produce a multitude of different adhesins, usually proteins, with varying specificities for a wide range of receptor molecules. Adhesins are presented on bacterial surfaces as components of filamentous, nonflagellar structures, known as pili or fimbriae, or as afimbrial (or nonfimbrial) monomeric or multimeric proteins anchored within the bacterial membrane. Other nonprotein components of bacterial membranes, including lipopolysaccharides (LPS) synthesized by gram-negative bacteria, and lipoteichoic acid in some gram-positive bacteria, can also function as adhesive molecules. Adhesins are often only minor subunits intercalated within pilus rods or located at the distal tips of pili, but they can also constitute the major structural subunits of adhesive pili. The molecular machinery required for the synthesis of many different adhesive pili and afimbrial adhesins is conserved, although the receptor specificities of the different adhesins can vary widely. Many bacterial adhesins function as lectins, mediating bacterial interactions with carbohydrate moieties on glycoproteins or glycolipids. Other adhesins mediate direct contact with specific amino acid motifs present in receptor proteins. Plant and animal cell surfaces present a large array of membrane proteins, glycoproteins, glycolipids, and other components that can potentially serve as receptors for bacterial adhesins. Protein constituents of the extracellular matrix (ECM) are also often used as bacterial receptors. In some cases, ECM proteins can function as bridges, linking bacterial and host eukaryotic cells. In addition, organic and inorganic material that coats inanimate surfaces, such as medical implants, pipes, and rocks, can act as receptors for bacterial adhesins, allowing for the establishment of microbial communities or biofilms. Adhesins also mediate interbacterial associations, facilitating the transfer of genetic material between bacteria and promoting the coaggregation of bacterial species in sites such as the oral cavity.

A single bacterium can often express multiple adhesins with varying receptor specificities. These adhesins can function synergistically and, thus, enhance bacterial adherence. Alternately, adhesins may be regulated and expressed differentially, allowing bacteria to alter their adhesive repertoire as they enter different environmental situations. To date, a large number of bacterial adhesins have been described, but relatively few receptors have been conclusively identified. Bacterial adhesins can show exquisite specificity and are able to distinguish between very closely related receptor structures. The ability of bacterial adhesins to recognize specific receptor molecules is dependent upon the three-dimensional architecture of the receptor in addition to its accessibility and spatial orientation. Most studies to date of bacterial adhesion have focused on host–pathogen interactions. Numerous investigations have indicated that bacterial adhesion is an essential step in the successful colonization of host tissues and the production of disease by bacterial pathogens. Examples of adhesins expressed by bacterial pathogens and their known receptors are presented in Table I. To illustrate some of the key concepts of bacterial adhesion, the modes of adhesion of a few well-characterized pathogens are discussed in the following sections.

## A. Adhesins of Uropathogenic *Escherichia coli*

Uropathogenic strains of *E. coli* are the primary causative agents of urinary tract infections among humans. These bacteria can express two of the best characterized adhesive structures, P and type 1 pili. These pili are composite organelles, consisting of a thin fibrillar tip structure joined end-to-end to a right-handed helical rod. Chromosomally located gene clusters, that are organizationally as well as functionally homologous, encode P and type 1 pili. The P pilus tip fibrillum contains a distally located adhesin, PapG, in association with three other tip subunits, PapE, PapF, and PapK. The adhesive tip fibrillum is attached to the distal end of a thicker pilus rod composed of repeating PapA subunits. An additional subunit, PapH, anchors the PapA rod to the outer membrane.

The P pilus PapG adhesin binds to the $\alpha$-D-galactopyranosyl-(1-4)-B-D-galactopyranoside (Gal$\alpha$(1–4)Gal) moiety present in the globoseries of glycolipids, which are expressed by erythrocytes and host cells present in the kidney. Consistent with this binding specificity, P pili have been shown to be major virulence factors associated with pyelonephritis caused by uropathogenic *E. coli*. Three distinct variants of the PapG adhesin (G-I, G-II, and G-III) have been identified that recognize three different Gal$\alpha$(1–4)Gal-containing isoreceptors: globotriaosylceramide, globotetraosylceramide (globoside), and globopentaosylceramide (the Forssman antigen). The different PapG adhesins significantly affect the tropism of pyelonephritic *E. coli*. For example, urinary tract *E. coli* isolates from dogs often encode the G-III adhesin that recognizes the Forssman antigen, the

*Adhesion, Bacterial*

**TABLE I**
**Selected Examples of Bacterial Adhesins and Their Receptors**

| Organism | Adhesin | Receptor | Form of receptor[a] | Associated disease(s) |
|---|---|---|---|---|
| *Escherichia coli* | P pili (PapG) | Galα(1–4)Gal | GL | Pyelonephritis/cystitis |
| | Type 1 pili (FimH) | D-mannose (uroplakin 1a & 1b, CD11, CD18, uromodulin) | GP | Cystitis |
| | Curli (CsgA) | Fibronectin/laminin/ plasminogen | ECM | Sepsis |
| | Prs pili | Galα(1–4)Gal | GL | Cystitis |
| | S pili | α-sialyl-2,3-β-galactose | GP | UTI, newborn meningitis |
| | K88 pili (K88ad) | IGLad (nLc₄Cer) | GL | Diarrhea in piglets |
| | K99 pili (FanC) | NeuGc(α2-3)Galβ4Glc | GL | Neonatal diarrhea in piglets, calves, & lambs |
| | *DR family* | | | |
| | DR | | | UTI |
| | DR-II | Decay Accelerating | P | UTI |
| | AFA-I | Factor (SCR-3 domain) | | UTI |
| | AFA-III | | | UTI, diarrhea |
| | F1845 | | | diarrhea |
| | Nonfimbrial adhesins 1–6 | Glycophorin A | GP | UTI, newborn meningitis |
| | M hemagglutinin | Aᴹ determinant of glycophorin A | GP | Pyelonephritis |
| | Intimin | Tir (EPEC encoded phosphoprotein) | P | Diarrhea |
| *Neisseria* | Type-4a pili | CD46 | GP | |
| | Opa proteins | CD66 receptor family/ HSPG | P / GL | |
| | Opa₅₀ | Vitonectin/fibronectin | ECM | Gonorrhea/meningitis |
| | Opc | HSPG/Vitronectin | GL / ECM | |
| | LOS | ASGP-R | GP | |
| | Inducible adhesin | Lutropin receptor | GP | |
| *Listeria monocytogenes* | Internalin | E-cadherin | GP | Listeriosis (meningitis, septicemia, abortions, gastroenteritis) |
| *Haemophilus influenzae* | Hemagglutinating pili | AnWj antigen/lactosylceramide | GP / GL | Respiratory tract infections |
| | Hsp-70-related proteins | Sulfoglycolipids | GL | |
| | HMW1, HMW2 | Negatively charged glycoconjugates | GP | |
| *Campylobacter jejuni* | CadF | Fibronectin | ECM | Gastroenteritis |

*continues*

*Continued*

| Organism | Adhesin | Receptor | Form of receptor[a] | Associated disease(s) |
|---|---|---|---|---|
| *Yersinia* | Invasin | $\beta_1$ integrins | P | Plague, Enterocolitis |
| | YadA | Cellular fibronectin/ collagen/laminin | ECM | |
| *Bordetella per-tussis* | FHA | CR3 integrin | P | Whooping cough |
| | Pertactin, BrkA | Integrins | P | |
| | Pertussis toxin | Lactosylceramides/ gangliosides | GP/GL | |
| *Mycobacterium* | BCG85 complex, FAP pro-teins | Fibronectin | ECM | Tuberculosis, leprosy |
| *Streptococcus* | Protein F family | Fibronectin | ECM | Pharyngitis, scarlet fe-ver, erysipelas, im-petigo, rheumatic fever, UTI, dental caries, neonatal sepsis, glomerulo-nephritis, endocar-ditis, pneumonia, meningitis |
| | Polysaccharide capsule | CD44 | GP | |
| | ZOP, FBP4, GAPDH | Fibronectin | ECM | |
| | Lipoteichoic acid (LTA) | Fibronectin/macrophage scavenger receptor | ECM/GP | |
| | M protein | CD46/fucosylated glycoconjugates/fibro-nectin | GP/ECM | |
| *Staphylococcus* | FnbA, FnbB | Fibronectin | ECM | Skin lesions, pharyngi-tis, pneumonia, en-docarditis, toxic shock syndrome, food poisoning |
| | Can | Collagen | ECM | |
| | Protein A (Spa) | von Willebrand factor | GP | |
| | ClfA | Fibrinogen | ECM | |
| | EbpS | Elastin | ECM | |

[a] P, protein–protein interactions; GP, interaction with glycoproteins; GL, glycolipids; ECM, extracellular matrix proteins.

dominant Gal$\alpha$(1–4)Gal-containing isoreceptor in the dog kidney. In contrast, the majority of urinary tract isolates from humans express the G-II adhesin that preferentially recognizes globoside, the primary Gal$\alpha$(1–4)Gal-containing isoreceptor in the human kidney.

In comparison with P pili, type 1 pili are more widely distributed and are encoded by more than 95% of all *E. coli* isolates, including uropathogenic and commensal intestinal strains. The type 1 pilus tip fibrillum is comprised of two subunits, FimF and FimG, in addition to the adhesin, FimH. The adhesive tip is connected to the distal end of a thicker pilus rod composed of repeating FimA sub-units. In addition to its localization within the pilus tip, the FimH adhesin also appears to be occasion-ally intercalated along the length of the type 1 pilus rod. FimH binds to mannose containing host re-ceptors expressed by a wide variety of host cell types and has been shown to be a significant viru-lence determinant for the development of bladder infections. Natural phenotypic variants of the FimH adhesin have been identified by Sokurenko *et al.* (1998), which differentially bind to mono-mannose structures. Interestingly, most uropathogenic isolates express FimH variants that bind well to mono-mannose residues, whereas most isolates from the large intestine of healthy humans ex-press FimH variants that interact poorly with mono-mannose structures. Mono-mannose residues are abundant in the oligosaccharide moieties of host pro-teins, known as uroplakins, that coat the luminal surface of the bladder epithelium. *In vitro* binding assays by Wu *et al.* (1996) have demonstrated that type 1-piliated *E. coli* can specifically bind two of the uroplakins, UP1a and UP1b. Scanning and high-resolution electron microscopy have shown that type 1 pili can mediate direct and intimate bacterial contact with the uroplakin-coated bladder epithelium (Fig. 1).

The assembly of P pili and type 1 pili requires two specialized assembly proteins: a periplasmic chaperone and an outer membrane usher. Periplasmic chaperones facilitate the import of pilus subunits across the inner membrane and mediate their delivery to outer membrane usher complexes, where subunits are assembled into pili. Homologous chaperone/usher pathways modulate the assembly of over 30 different adhesive organelles, expressed by uropathogenic *E. coli* and many other gram-negative pathogens. Among the adhesive structures assembled via a chaperone/usher pathway by uropathogenic *E. coli* are S pili, nonfimbrial adhesin I, and members of the Dr adhesin family. This family includes the uropathogenic-associated afimbrial adhesins AFA-I and AFA-III and the fimbrial adhesin Dr, in addition to the diarrhea-associated fimbrial adhesin F1845. These adhesins recognize the Dr$^a$ blood group antigen present on decay accelerating factor (DAF), a complement regulatory factor expressed on erythrocytes and other tissues, including the uroepithelium. These four members of the Dr adhesin family appear to recognize different epitopes of the Dr$^a$ antigen. The Dr adhesin, but not the other three, also recognizes type IV collagen. Members of the Dr adhesin family are proposed to facilitate ascending colonization and chronic interstitial infection of the urinary tract. It is unclear why the Dr and F1845 adhesins assemble into fimbria while AFA-I and AFA-III are assembled as nonfimbrial adhesins on the bacterial surface. It has been suggested that afimbrial adhesins, such as AFA-I and AFA-III, are derived from related fimbrial adhesins, but have been altered such that the structural attributes required for polymerization into a pilus are missing while the adhesin domain remains functional and anchored on the bacterial surface.

## B. Neisserial Adhesins

*Neisseria gonorrhoeae* and *N. meningitidis* are exclusively human pathogens that have developed several adhesive mechanisms to colonize mucosal surfaces. Initial contact with mucosal epithelia by *Neisseria* species is mediated by type-4a pili. These adhesive organelles are related to a group of multifunctional structures expressed by a wide diversity of bacterial species, including *Pseudomonas aeruginosa, Moraxella* species, *Dichelobacter nodus,* and others. Type-4a pili are assembled by a type II secretion system that is distinct from the chaperone/usher pathway. They are comprised primarily of a small subunit, pilin, that is packaged into a helical arrangement within pili. The type-4a pilin can mediate bacterial adherence, but in *Neisseria* species, a separate, minor tip protein, PilC, has also been implicated as an adhesin. A eukaryotic membrane protein, CD46, is proposed to be a host receptor for type-4a pili expressed by *N. gonorrhoeae,* although it is currently unclear which pilus component binds this host molecule.

Following primary attachment mediated by type-4a pili, more intimate contact with mucosal surfaces is apparently established by the colony opacity-associated (Opa) proteins of *Neisseria* species. These proteins constitute a family of closely related but size-variable outer membrane proteins that are expressed in a phase variable fashion. Opa proteins mediate not only adherence, but they also modulate bacterial invasion into host cells. A single neisserial strain can encode from 3 to 11 distinct Opa variants, with each Opa protein being expressed alternately of the others. The differential expression of Opa variants can alter bacterial antigenicity and possibly modify bacterial tropism for different receptors and host cell types. Some Opa variants recognize carbohydrate moieties of cell surface-associated heparin sulphate proteoglycans (HSPGs), which are common constituents of mammalian cell membranes. The majority of Opa variants, however, bind via protein–protein interactions to CD66 transmembrane glycoproteins, which comprise a subset of the carcinoembryonic antigen (CEA) receptor family of the immunoglobulin superfamily. Individual Opa variants specifically recognize distinct CD66 receptors and this likely influences both the tissue tropism of *Neisseria* and the host cell responses to neisserial attachment. In addition to pili and Opa proteins, the lipopolysaccharide (lipooligosaccharide, LOS) and a distinct outer membrane protein, Opc, expressed by *Neisseria* can also influence bacterial adhesion and invasion. Deconvoluting the various roles of the different adhesive components

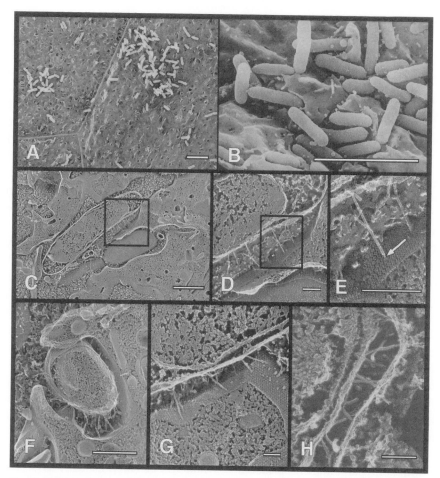

***Fig. 1.*** Type 1 pilus-mediated bacterial adherence to the mouse bladder epithelium was visualized by (A and B) scanning and (C–H) high-resolution freeze-fracture, deep-etch electron microscopy. Mice were infected via transurethral inoculation with type 1-piliated uropathogenic *E. coli*. Bladders were collected and processed for microscopy at 2 hrs. after infection. Bacteria adhered randomly across the bladder lumenal surface, both singly and in large, biofilmlike microcolonies, some of which contained several hundred bacteria (A and B). The type 1 pili-mediating bacterial adherence were resolved by high-resolution electron microscopy techniques. The adhesive tips of type 1 pili make direct contact with the uroplakin-coated surface of the bladder epithelium (D through G). Hexagonal arrays of uroplakin complexes are visible. The boxed areas in (C) and (D) are shown magnified, respectively, in (D) and (E). In (H), type 1 pili span from the host cell membrane on the right to the bacterium on the left. These images demonstrate that type 1 pili can mediate intimate bacterial attachment to host bladder epithelial cells. Scale bars indicate 5 $\mu$m (A and B), 0.5 $\mu$m (C and F), and 0.1 $\mu$m(D, E, G, H). Also see color insert. (Reprinted with permission from Mulvey, M. A., *et al.* (1998). Induction and evasion of host defenses by type 1-piliated uropathogenic *Escherichia coli. Science* **282,** 1494–1497. Copyright 1998 American Association for the Advancement of Science.)

of *Neisseria* during the infection process remains a major challenge.

## C. Adhesins of *Haemophilus influenzae*

*H. influenzae* is a common pathogen of the human respiratory tract. Isolates of *H. influenzae* can be divided into encapsulated and nonencapsulated, or nontypable, forms. Prior to the use of *H. influenzae* conjugate vaccines, capsulated strains of *H. influenzae* were the primary cause of childhood bacterial meningitis and a major cause of other bacteremic diseases in children. Vaccines effective against nontypable strains have not yet been developed and these strains remain important human pathogens, causing pneumonia, otitis media, sinusitis, and bronchitis. Several adhesins have been identified which facilitate the colonization of the respiratory epithelium by both encapsulated and nontypable *H. influenzae.*

During the initial stages of the infection process, nontypable *H. influenzae* associates with respiratory mucus, apparently through interactions between bacterial outer membrane proteins (OMPs P2 and P5) and sialic acid-containing oligosaccharides within the mucus. Both nontypable and encapsulated strains of *H. influenzae* can initiate direct contact with the respiratory epithelium via adhesive pili. Over 14 serological types of adhesive pili have been indentified in *H. influenzae*. These pili are composite structures assembled by chaperone/usher pathways similar to those used by uropathogenic *E. coli* to assemble P and type 1 pili. Piliated strains of *H. influenzae* preferentially bind to nonciliated cells or damaged epithelium. The pili of *H. influenzae* can recognize the AnWj antigen, in addition to gangliosides and other compounds containing siallyllactoceramide. Following initial attachment mediated by pili, the polysaccharide capsule of encapsulated strains is reduced, enabling a second adhesin, Hsf, to establish more intimate bacterial contact with host epithelial cells. Hsf assembles into short, thin fibrils on the bacterial surface. While Hsf expression is restricted to encapsulated strains of *H. influenzae*, a subpopulation of nontypable strains expresses a Hsf homolog called Hia. Both Hsf and Hia share homology with other bacterial adhesins including AIDA-1, an adherence factor produced by diarrheagenic *E. coli.*

Instead of adhesive pili and Hia, the majority of nontypable *H. influenzae* isolates produce two alternate adhesins: high molecular weight surface-exposed proteins called HMW1 and HMW2. These two adhesins share significant sequence identity with each other and are similar to filamentous hemaglglutinin (FHA), an adhesin and colonization factor expressed by *Bordetella pertussis*. HMW1 and HMW2 have distinct adhesive specificities and may function at different steps in the infection process. The receptors for the HMW adhesins appear to be negatively charged glycoconjugates that have not yet been completely defined. Nontypable *H. influenzae* encodes several other adhesive factors, including two Hsp-70-related proteins, which can mediate bacterial binding to sulfoglycolipids. Interestingly, other heat shock proteins have been implicated in the adherence of other microbial pathogens including *Helicobacter pylori*, *Mycoplasma*, and *Chlamydia trachomatis*.

Work by St. Geme and coworkers (1998) has highlighted an additional adhesin, Hap, which is expressed by virtually all nontypable *H. influenzae* isolates. Hap mediates low-level adherence to epithelial cells, complementing the binding activities of pili and Hia or HMW1 and HMW2. Hap also promotes interbacterial associations leading to bacterial aggregation and microcolony formation on the epithelial surface. The mature Hap adhesin consists of a C-terminal outer membrane protein domain, designated $Hap_\beta$, and a larger extracellular domain designated $Hap_s$. The $Hap_s$ domain, which is responsible for mediating adherence, has serine protease activity and can be autoproteolytically cleaved, releasing itself from the bacterial surface. Interestingly, secretory leukocyte protease inhibitor (SLPI), a natural host component of respiratory-tract secretions, which possibly protects the respiratory epithelium from proteolytic damage during acute inflammation, has been shown to inhibit Hap autoproteolysis and enhance bacterial adherence. Despite the presence of SLPI, $Hap_s$-mediated adherence *in vivo* is likely transient. Over time, the eventual autoproteolysis and release of the $Hap_s$ adhesin domain from the bacterial surface may allow bacterial spread from microcolonies on the respiratory epithelium and aid the bacteria in evading the host immune response. Identification of the receptor molecules recognized by Hap awaits further studies.

## D. Adherence to Components of the Extracellular Matrix

One of the principal functions of the ECM is to serve as substrate for the adherence of eukaryotic cells within animal tissues. The ECM is composed of polysaccharides and numerous proteins including fibronectin, vitronectin, laminin. elastin, collagen, fibrinogen, tenascin, entactin, and others. Thin flexible mats of specialized ECM, known as basal laminae or basement membranes, underlie all epithelial cells and surround individual fat cells, muscle cells, and Schwann cells. Binding of ECM proteins is one of the primary mechanisms used by many pathogenic bacteria to adhere to host tissues. Bacterial adhesins have been identified which recognize specific components of the ECM and a few adhesins, such as the $Opa_{50}$ protein of *Neisseria* and the YadA adhesin of *Yersinia enterolitica,* are able to recognize multiple ECM components. Some bacterial adhesins preferentially recognize immobilized, cell-bound ECM components over soluble forms. The YadA adhesin expressed by *Y. enterolitica,* for example, mediates adherence to cell-bound fibronectin, but not to soluble fibronectin within plasma. This may allow *Y. enterolitica* to more efficiently bind tissue rather than circulating molecules.

The tissue distribution of ECM components can directly influence the tropism of a bacterial pathogen. For example, *Mycobacterium leprae,* the causative agent of leprosy, binds LN-2, an isoform of the ECM component laminin. This ECM component recognizes a host cell-surface receptor, $\alpha$-dystroglycan, and serves as a bridge linking host and bacterial cells. *M. leprae* targets the Schwann cells of the peripheral nervous system and can also invade the placenta and striated muscle of leprosy patients. The tissue distribution of LN-2, which is restricted to the basal laminae of Schwann cells, striated muscles, and trophoblasts of the placenta, directly correlates with sites of natural infection by *M. leprae.*

In contrast to the restricted tissue distribution of LN-2, most components of the ECM are more widely apportioned and can interact with receptor molecules expressed by a broad range of cell types present within a variety of different tissues. By interacting with widely distributed components of the ECM, bacteria greatly enhance their adhesive potential. Numerous bacteria are able to bind fibronectin, an ECM component present in most tissues and body fluids and a prominent constituent of wounds. The bacterial adhesins that bind fibronectin are diverse. For example, *E. coli* and *Salmonella* species express thin, irregular, and highly aggregated surface fibers, known as curli, that bind fibronectin in addition to other receptor molecules. *Mycobacterium* species produce at least five fibronectin-binding molecules, three of which are related and collectively known as the BCG85 complex. *Streptococcus* expresses an even larger number of different fibronectin-binding adhesins, including ZOP, lipoteichoic acid, GAPDH, FBP54, M protein, and several related molecules represented by Protein F. Binding of Protein F and related adhesins to fibronectin is specific and essentially irreversible. Members of the Protein F family of adhesins have similar domain architectures, although they appear to interact with fibronectin differently. Protein F possesses two distinct domains, composed of repeated sequence motifs, which bind independently of each other to different sites at the N-terminus of fibronectin. Additional fibronectin-binding proteins related to the Protein F family of adhesins have also been identified in *Staphylococcus.* These gram-positive bacteria, in addition to producing fibronectin-binding proteins, can also express an array of other adhesive molecules, which bind other widely distributed ECM components, including collagen, fibrinogen, and elastin. By encoding a large repertoire of adhesins able to recognize ECM components, *Streptococcus, Staphylococcus,* and other pathogens, presumably, increase their capacity to effectively bind and colonize sites within host tissues.

## II. CONSEQUENCES OF BACTERIAL ADHESION

Research in recent years has demonstrated that interactions between bacterial adhesins and receptor molecules can act as trigger mechanisms, activating signal transduction cascades and altering gene expression in both bacterial and host cells. Zhang and Normark showed in 1996 that the binding of host cell receptors by P pili activated the transcription of a sensor–regulator protein, AirS, which regulates the bacterial iron acquisition system of uropathogenic *E. coli*. This response may enable uropathogens to more efficiently obtain iron and survive in the iron-poor environment of the urinary tract. Around the same time, Wolf-Watz and colleagues showed, using *Y. pseudotuberculosis*, that bacterial contact with host cells could increase the rate of transcription of virulence determinants called Yop effector proteins. More recently, Taha and coworkers (1998) demonstrated that transcription of the PilC1 adhesin of *N. meningitidis* was transiently induced by bacterial contact with host epithelial cells. The PilC1 adhesin can be incorporated into the tips of type-4a pili, but it can also remain associated with the bacterial outer membrane, where it can, presumably, facilitate pilus assembly. The up-regulation of the PilC1 adhesin may enhance bacterial adherence to host cells by promoting the localization of PilC1 into the tips of type-4a pili.

Signal transduction pathways are activated within host eukaryotic cells in response to attachment mediated by many different bacterial adhesins. For example, the binding of type-4a pili expressed by *Neisseria* to host cell receptors (presumably, CD46) can stimulate the release of $Ca^{++}$ stores within target epithelial cells. Fluxes in intracellular $Ca^{++}$ concentrations are known to modulate a multitude of eukaryotic cellular responses. Similarly, the binding of P pili to Gal$\alpha$(1–4)Gal-containing host receptors on uroepithelial cells can induce the release of ceramides, important second messenger molecules that can influence a number of signal transduction processes. Signals induced within urepithelial cells upon binding P-piliated bacteria result in the up-regulation and eventual secretion of several immunoregulatory cytokines. The binding of type 1-piliated and other adherent bacteria to a variety of host epithelial and immune cells has also been shown to induce the release of cytokines, although the signaling pathways involved have not yet been well defined. In some cases, bacteria may co-opt host signal transduction pathways to enhance their own attachment. For example, binding

of the FHA adhesin of *B. pertussis* to a monocyte integrin receptor complex activates host signal pathways that lead to the up-regulation of another integrin, complement receptor 3 (CR3). FHA can bind CR3 through a separate domain and, thus, enhance the adhesion of *B. pertussis*.

The activation of host signal pathways following bacterial attachment can result in dramatic rearrangements of the eukaryotic cytoskeleton, which can lead to the internalization of adherent bacteria. Many pathogenic bacteria invade host eukaryotic cells to evade immune responses or to pass through cellular barriers, such as the intestinal epithelium. In some cases, bacteria introduce effector molecules into their target host cells to trigger cytoskeletal rearrangements and intense ruffling of the host cell membrane that results in bacterial uptake. In other situations, bacterial adhesins (which are sometimes referred to as invasins) more directly mediate bacterial invasion by interacting with host cell membrane receptors that sequentially encircle and envelope the attached bacterium. This type of invasion is referred to as the "zipper" mechanism and requires the stimulation of host signaling cascades, including the activation of protein tyrosine kinases. The invasin protein of *Yersinia* and internalin expressed by *Listeria* can both mediate bacterial internalization into host cells by such a zipper mechanism by interacting with $\beta_1$-integrin and E-cadherin, respectively. The Opa proteins of *Neisseria* can also mediate bacterial internalization into host cells by a zipperlike mechanism. Recent work by several labs has indicated that fimbrial adhesins, such as FimH within type 1 pili, can also function as invasins.

## III. TARGETING ADHESINS FOR ANTIMICROBIAL THERAPY

Bacterial adhesin–receptor binding events are critical in the pathogenesis of virtually every bacterial disease. In some cases, the knockout of a specific adhesin can greatly attenuate bacterial virulence. Uropathogenic *E. coli* strains, for example, which have been engineered to express type 1 pili lacking the FimH adhesin, are unable to effectively colonize the bladder. Similarly, a P-piliated pyelonephritic strain of *E. coli* lacking a functional PapG adhesin is unable to infect the kidney. For many other bacteria, attachment is a multifaceted process involving several adhesins that may have complementing and overlapping functions and receptor specificities. In these cases, it has been more difficult to discern the roles of individual adhesins in disease processes. The construction of mutants with knockouts in more than one adhesin is beginning to shed light on the interrelationships between multiple bacterial adhesins.

The central role of bacterial adhesins at the host–pathogen interface during the infection process has made them attractive targets for the development of new antimicrobial therapies. Vaccines directed against individual adhesins and adhesive pili have had some success in the past. However, antigenic variation of the major immunodominant domains of some adhesive organelles and the immunorecessive nature of others have frustrated progress in this area. Fortunately, by unraveling the molecular details of adhesin structure and biogenesis, substantial progress is being made. For example, the identification of FimH as the adhesive subunit of type 1 pili and the elucidation of the chaperone/usher pathway used to assemble these adhesive organelles has made it possible to purify large quantities of native FimH and to test its efficacy as a vaccine. Unlike the major type 1 pilus subunit, FimA, there is relatively little heterogeneity among the FimH adhesins expressed by diverse *E. coli* strains. The use of purified FimH as a vaccine, rather than whole type 1 pili in which FimH is present only in low numbers, has proven to significantly enhance the host immune response against the FimH adhesin. In early trials, FimH-vaccinated animals showed substantial resistance to infection by a wide variety type 1-piliated uropathogenic *E. coli* strains.

In addition to the prophylactic approach of generating vaccines to inhibit bacterial adhesion, other anti-adhesin strategies are being explored. With increased knowledge of the mechanisms used to assemble adhesins on the bacterial surface, it may be possible to design specific inhibitors of adhesin biogenesis. For example, synthetic compounds that specifically bind and inactivate periplasmic chaperones could potentially inhibit the biogenesis of a wide range of bacterial adhesive organelles. The use of soluble synthetic receptor analogs that bind bacterial adhesins substantially better than the natural monomeric ligands represents an additional strategy for inhibiting bacterial attachment and colonization. Recent advances in the synthesis of multimeric carbohydrate polymers have highlighted the possibility of creating high affinity receptor analogs that could potentially work at pharmacological concentrations within patients. Such compounds could also be used to competitively remove adherent bacteria from medical implants, industrial pipes, and other surfaces. Furthermore, it may be possible to inhibit multiple bacterial adhesins with a single compound by incorporating several receptor analogs within a single carbohydrate polymer. Continued research into the structure, function, and biogenesis of bacterial adhesins promises not only to enhance our knowledge of pathogenic processes, but may also help augment our current arsenal of antimicrobial agents.

## See Also the Following Articles

FIMBRIAE, PILI • *HAEMOPHILUS INFLUENZAE*, GENETICS • PROTEIN SECRETION

## Bibliography

Dalton, H. M., and March, P. E. (1998). Molecular genetics of bacterial attachment and biofouling. *Curr. Op. Biotech.* 9, 252–255.

Dehio, C., Gray-Owen, S. D., and Meyer, T. F. (1998). The role of neisserial Opa proteins in interactions with host cells. *Trends Microbiol.* 6, 489–495.

Finlay, B. B., and Falkow, S. (1997). Common themes in microbial pathogenicity revisited. *Microbiol. Mol. Biol. Rev.* 61, 136–169.

Foster, T. J., and Höök, M. (1998). Surface adhesins of *Staphylococcus aureus*. *Trends Microbiol.* 6, 484–488.

Goldhar, J. (1996). Nonfimbrial adhesins of *Escherichia coli*. In "Toward Anti-Adhesion Therapy for Microbial Diseases" (Kahane and Ofek, eds.), pp. 63–72. Plenum Press, New York.

Hultgren, S. J., Jones, C. H., and Normark, S. (1996). Bacterial adhesins and their assembly. In "*Escherichia coli* and *Salmonella*," Vol. 2 (F. C. Neidhardt, ed.), pp. 2730–2756. ASM Press, Washington, DC.

Jacques, M., and Paradis, S-E. (1998). Adhesin–receptor interactions in *Pasteurellaceae*. *FEMS Microbiol. Rev.* 22, 45–59.

Jenkinson, H. F., and Lamont, R. J. (1997). Streprococcal adhesion and colonization. *Crit. Rev. Oral Biol. Med.* **8**, 175–200.

Lingwood, C. A. (1998). Oligosaccharide receptors for bacteria: A view to a kill. *Curr. Op. Chem. Biol.* **2**, 695–700.

Sharon, N. (1996). Carbohydrate–lectin interactions in infectious disease. *In* "Toward Anti-Adhesion Therapy for Microbial Diseases" (Kahane and Ofek, eds.), pp. 1–8. Plenum Press, New York.

Soto, G. E., and Hultgren, S. J. (1999). Bacterial adhesins: Common themes and variations in architecture and assembly. *J. Bacteriol.* **181**, 1059–1071.

Whittaker, C. J., Klier, C. M., and Kolenbrander, P. E. (1996). Mechanisms of adhesion by oral bacteria. *Annu. Rev. Microbiol.* **50**, 513–552.

# Aerobic Respiration:
# Oxidases and Globins

### Robert K. Poole
*The University of Sheffield*

I. Oxygen as Biological Electron Acceptor:
   Friend and Foe
II. Architecture and Synthesis of Aerobic
   Respiratory Chains
III. Oxygen-Reactive Proteins: Oxidases
IV. Microbial Globins

## GLOSSARY

**aerobic respiration** Energetically downhill electron transfer from a donor molecule or ion to oxygen, which is reduced to water with concomitant coupled ion translocation and thus generation of an electrochemical gradient.

**anaerobic respiration** Energetically downhill electron transfer from a donor molecule or ion to a molecule other than oxygen or to an ionic species, with concomitant coupled ion translocation and thus generation of an electrochemical gradient.

**chemiosmotic mechanism** Transduction of energy between two forms via an ion electrochemical gradient (usually of protons but sometimes of sodium) across a membrane. Examples of such membranes are the cytoplasmic membrane of bacteria and the inner mitochondrial membrane of a microbial eukaryote.

**cytochrome** Hemoprotein in which one or more hemes is alternately oxidized and reduced in electron transfer processes.

**electrochemical gradient** The sum of the electrical gradient, or membrane potential ($\Delta\psi$), and ion concentration across a membrane (the latter is often defined as $\Delta$pH for protons).

**electron acceptor** Low-molecular-weight inorganic or organic species that is reduced in the final step of an electron transport process.

**electron donor** Low-molecular-weight inorganic or organic species that is oxidized in the first step of an electron transport process.

**electron transport** The transfer of electrons from a donor molecule (or ion) to an acceptor molecule (or ion) via a series of components (i.e., a respiratory chain), each capable of undergoing alternate oxidation and reduction. The electron transfer can either be energetically downhill, in which case it is often called respiration, or energetically uphill, which is called reversed electron transfer.

**globin** Hemoprotein which reacts with dioxygen, generally reversibly and without reduction of the released oxygen.

**oxidase** Hemoprotein that binds and reduces oxygen, generally to water. The term "oxygen reductase" better describes the function. Terminal oxidases are classified according to whether their reducing substrate is a cytochrome or quinol. Thus, the archetypal mitochondrial oxidase (EC 1.9.3.1) is also called cytochrome $c$ oxidase, since the immediate donor of electrons for the oxidase is cytochrome $c$. In contrast, both major oxidases in *Escherichia coli* are ubiquinol oxidases in which a fully reduced ubiquinone donates two electrons to the enzyme. That oxidases are classified according to their reductant is often forgotten, and confusing oxymorons result. Thus, strictly, "cytochrome $bd$ oxidase" (*E. coli*) is meaningless: this enzyme does not oxidize cytochrome $bd$—it is cytochrome $bd$. More appropriate names are "cytochrome $bd$-type oxidase," "cytochrome $bd$ quinol oxidase," or just "cytochrome $bd$."

**oxidative phosphorylation** Adenosine triphosphate (ATP) synthesis coupled to a proton or sodium electrochemical gradient, generated by electron transport, across an energy-transducing membrane.

**oxidative stress** The sum of the deleterious intracellular events elicited by partial reduction products of dioxygen, especially superoxide radical, peroxide, and hydroxyl ion.

***protonmotive force*** The proton electrochemical gradient across an energy-transducing membrane in units of volts or millivolts.

***quinone*** Lipid-soluble hydrogen (i.e., proton plus electron) carrier that mediates electron transfer between respiratory chain components.

***redox potential*** Measure of the thermodynamic tendency of an ion or molecule to accept or donate one or more electrons. By convention, the more negative the redox potential, the greater the propensity for donating electrons and vice versa.

***respiration*** The sum of electron transfer reactions resulting in reduction of oxygen (aerobically) or another electron acceptor (anaerobically) and generation of protonmotive force.

***respiratory chain*** Set of electron transfer components, which may be arranged in a linear or branched fashion, that mediates electron transfer from a donor to an acceptor in aerobic or anaerobic respiration.

**AEROBIC RESPIRATION** is a series of coupled oxidation and reduction reactions that result in the transfer of electrons from an appropriate electron donor (such as a reduced coenzyme) to oxygen. It provides the ability to conserve energy in the form of adenosine triphosphate (ATP) or to perform energy-demanding processes (such as solute transport and motility) through generation of a protonmotive force.

The definition of aerobic respiration may also be taken to include (as it does in multicellular organisms) the transport and storage of oxygen, the ultimate electron acceptor in these organisms (or even, in animals, the movements of the thorax required for inhalation and exhalation of air). The sequential redox reactions are catalyzed by respiratory chains, generally branched, which comprise substrate dehydrogenases, quinones, cytochromes, and one or more terminal oxidases assembled in the bacterial cytoplasmic or eukaryotic mitochondrial membrane. Electron transfer between components is made possible by the presence in these component parts of hemes, flavins, iron-sulfur ([Fe-S]) clusters, and metal ions such as copper, all of which can exist in oxidized or reduced forms.

In terms of energy conservation, respiration-coupled oxidative phosphorylation via the trans-

membrane protonmotive force is substantially more efficient than fermentation, allowing faster growth and attainment of higher yields of biomass per mole of energy substrate used. Aerobic respiration is identical in principle to anaerobic respiration, except that, in the latter, an electron acceptor other than oxygen is used.

Microorganisms that can use only oxygen as the terminal electron acceptor are called obligate aerobes; those that cannot use oxygen and whose growth may even be inhibited by oxygen are called obligate anaerobes. A third class of microorganisms, exemplified by *Escherichia coli,* can grow aerobically or anaerobically and are termed facultative. The respiratory chain of *E. coli* (Fig. 1) is a very well-documented example of a complex branched arrangement of components which together result in the oxidation of a wide variety of substrates (e.g., NADH, succinate, malate, lactate, and hydrogen; not shown in Fig. 1). Electrons are donated to quinones, small lipid-soluble hydrogen (i.e., electron and proton) carriers that mediate electron transfer between dehydrogenase and reductase components of respiratory chains. Bacteria contain two main types of respiratory quinones: benzoquinones, such as ubiquinone, and naphthoquinones, such as menaquinone and demethylmenaquinone (Søballe and Poole, 1999). Quinone reduction to quinol results from substrate oxidation by respiratory dehydrogenases, and quinol re-oxidation to quinone is coupled to reduction of downstream oxidase components. Thus, quinones/quinols act as shuttles of reducing power between upstream and downstream redox proteins. Although quinones are often considered to be highly mobile in the lipid bilayer of the membrane, several protein components of the respiratory chain have specific quinone-docking or -binding sites. In *E. coli,* to a first approximation, electrons destined for transfer to oxygen as terminal oxidant are transferred to ubiquinone and then to one or both major oxidases, cytochromes *bo'* and *bd* (discussed later). Electrons destined for transfer to terminal oxidants other than oxygen are transferred to menaquinone and then to one or more major terminal reductases, only three of which are shown in Fig. 1. Note that nitrate reductase can accept electrons from either ubiquinone or menaquinone. As a result of these electron transfer

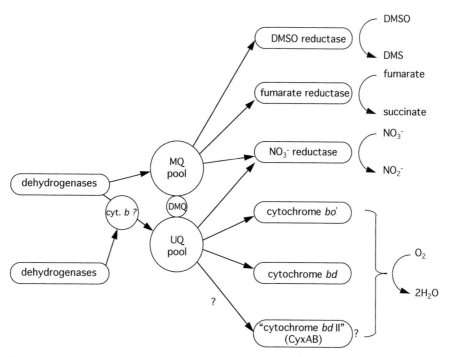

**Fig. 1.** The respiratory chains of *E. coli:* paradigm for the branched electron transport systems of facultatively aerobic bacteria. Dehydrogenases transfer electrons from numerous electron donors to a pool of quinones. There is evidence for the intermediary role of cytochrome(s) *b.* Generally, electrons from ubiquinone (UQ) are passed to terminal oxidases that use oxygen or nitrate as terminal electron acceptors, whereas electrons from menaquinone (MQ) are taken to reductases that use anaerobic electron acceptors. Demethylmenaquinone (DMQ) is not important as a mediator of electron flux but is a biosynthetic intermediate with low activity in respiration. Oxygen is reduced to water via two major oxidase complexes: cytochromes *bo'* and *bd.* A third oxidase ("*bd*II") resembling cytochrome *bd* has been identified but it has no known function. Only three of the many anaerobic reductases that reduce, respectively, dimethylsulfoxide (DMSO) to dimethylsulfide (DMS), fumarate to succinate, and nitrate to nitrite are shown.

reactions, protons are pumped or otherwise translocated from the cytoplasm outwards, thus generating a protonmotive force.

This model system exemplifies many of the most important characteristics of bacterial respiratory chains, namely (i) their branched nature at both "dehydrogenase" and "reductant" ends, (ii) the use of oxygen or alternative electron acceptors, (iii) the presence of numerous types of cytochromes and quinones, (iv) "cross-talk" between pathways optimizing the possibility of each reductant being paired with a wide choice of oxidants, and (v) concomitant proton translocation and energy transduction. This article

is concerned only with the use of oxygen as electron acceptor.

## I. OXYGEN AS BIOLOGICAL ELECTRON ACCEPTOR: FRIEND AND FOE

### A. Thermodynamic Considerations

In aerobic respiration, an electron donor is oxidized, and electrons derived from this oxidation are transferred sequentially through the electron carriers noted previously and used to reduce oxygen. For the complete reduction of oxygen to water, which requires four electrons, the standard redox potential ($E^{o\prime}$) of the couple is $+820$ mV. Thus, use of oxygen as an electron acceptor is more likely to result in higher ATP yields by oxidative phosphorylation than is use of $NO_3^-/NO_2^-$ ($E^{o\prime}$ + 430 mV) or fumarate/succinate ($E^{o\prime}$ + 33 mV) (both of which may be used in bacterial anaerobic respiration) and pyruvate/lactate ($E^{o\prime}$ − 190 mV) (the last being an important reaction in fermentative energy conservation).

## B. Properties of Oxygen That Constrain Its Biological Usefulness

Oxygen, more correctly the dioxygen molecule, is an odorless and colorless gas that is thought to have appeared in the atmosphere of the earth approximately $2 \times 10^9$ years ago as a result of photosynthetic activity. The use of oxygen in aerobic respiration is not without its difficulties. Its kinetic inertness requires activation by a metal center which, in aerobic respiratory chains, generally comprises two transition metals, either a heme–heme couple or a heme–copper couple (see Section III). Oxygen is also only moderately soluble—an aqueous air-saturated solution containing about 200 $\mu M$ oxygen at 37°C. It is generally assumed that dioxygen, being a small uncharged molecule, will diffuse readily across biological membranes and that no significant oxygen concentration gradient exists across respiring bacterial membranes or between cytoplasm and mitochondrial matrix in eukaryotes. Recent work suggests, however, that a metabolic advantage results from expression of microbial globins (see Section IV), which may act, as in higher organisms, to facilitate transport or storage of oxygen for aerobic respiration. However, oxygen-reducing oxidases have high affinities for the ligand, with $K_m$ values typically in the submicromolar range.

Only the four-electron reduction of oxygen to water is "safe" since intermediate reduction products are toxic and reactive:

$$O_2 \rightarrow O_2^- \rightarrow O_2^{2-} \rightarrow H_2O$$

The complete four-electron reduction of oxygen (Wood, 1988) has a redox potential ($E^{o\prime}$) of $+0.815$ V and constitutes the terminal reaction of

aerobic respiratory chains, which is catalyzed by respiratory oxidases.

Transfer of a single electron to oxygen generates the superoxide radical anion ($O_2^-$), a highly reactive species that attacks many key biomolecules. The reactivity of oxygen with metal ions, flavins, and quinone-like molecules (autoxidation) will result *in vivo* in the liberation of superoxide anion. Superoxide is generated, for example, in the process called redox cycling in which an electron donor reacts with oxygen, with the donor becoming oxidized. If this form of the donor can be re-reduced, perhaps enzymically by a diaphorase, it can again donate an electron generating more superoxide. Paraquat (methyl viologen) is an example of a molecule that behaves this way. Superoxide production by neutrophils is a deliberate act of "biological warfare" since the radical is used to attack engulfed bacteria. Superoxide production is also an unusual, apparently purposeful feature of flavohemoglobins (see Section IV) and is probably important in nitric oxide detoxification. *In vivo*, superoxide is scavenged by superoxide dismutase (actually a family of metalloproteins with similar functions) that converts (dismutates) two molecules of superoxide to peroxide and water. Superoxide can be assayed by its ability to reduce biomolecules, most commonly cytochrome *c*.

Transfer of a second electron to oxygen or a single electron to superoxide gives peroxide ($O_2^{2-}$), another reactive species that is scavenged *in vivo* by catalases and hydroperoxidases (a collective term for peroxide-consuming catalases and peroxidases). The two-electron reduction from oxygen to peroxide ($E^{o\prime}$ = 0.281 V) is less energetically favorable than the complete reduction to water but requires fewer electrons. Some oxidases such as glucose oxidase form peroxide as the major/sole product of oxygen reduction, but this is generally not the case when oxygen is reduced in aerobic respiration. The high redox potential for $H_2O_2$ reduction to water ($+1.349$ V) is used by peroxidases (e.g., cytochrome *c* peroxidase).

An additional one-electron transfer to peroxide gives the hydroxyl radical (OH·) and the fourth electron yields water, by far the major product of aerobic respiratory oxygen reduction.

In terminal oxidases, the complement of redox-active sites and the concerted reduction chemistry generally ensure total and rapid reduction of oxygen to water without substantial release of superoxide and peroxide. Nevertheless, the overall reduction process can be dissected into individual electron transfer steps (see Section III.C), the details of which are beyond the scope of this article. The inducible and tightly regulated synthesis of superoxide dismutase and hydroperoxidases effectively counters the "escape" of partially reduced oxygen species from oxidase activity or other oxygen reduction processes.

## II. ARCHITECTURE AND SYNTHESIS OF AEROBIC RESPIRATORY CHAINS

### A. General Features

In general, respiration achieves not only oxygen consumption but also energy conservation by the generation of a protonmotive force. This requires the presence of an intact cytoplasmic or inner mitochondrial membrane in which proton and electrical gradients can be established. Note that some oxygen-consuming processes are not involved in energy transduction and therefore do not require a membrane for function (see Section IV). Respiratory chain components are usually associated with the membrane and are asymmetrically arranged across it. Such asymmetry allows electron transfer events to achieve net consumption of protons from the cytoplasmic compartment (or mitochondrial matrix) and net release of protons into the extracytoplasmic compartment (periplasm in gram-negative bacteria) or mitochondrial intermembrane space. In the cytochrome *bd*-type quinol oxidase of *E. coli*, for example, the substrate (ubiquinol) is oxidized at the outer face of the membrane, where protons are released. Electrons then traverse the membrane via hemes to a pocket opening to the inside of the bacterium. The electrons are used to reduce oxygen to water, a step that requires protons taken from the inside, so that the net result is equivalent to proton translocation, although no protons have been "pumped."

### B. The Mitochondrial Paradigm

The best known and historically most important example of a respiratory chain is that found in the inner mitochondrial membrane of eukaryotes, i.e., all animals, plants, and the vast majority of microbial eukaryotes such as yeast. Here (Fig. 2), the respira-

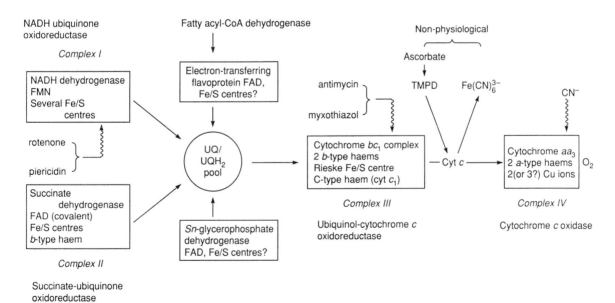

**Fig. 2.** The mitochondrial respiratory chain showing the redox carriers and their relation to the four respiratory chain complexes. Arrows show direction of electron flow; wavy arrows are sites of action of inhibitors (from Nicholls and Ferguson, 1992).

tory chain transfers electrons through a redox potential span of 1.1 V from $NAD^+/NADH$ to the $O_2/H_2O$ couple. Most electrons are transferred from soluble dehydrogenases of the Krebs (tricarboxylic acid) cycle by the $NADH/NAD^+$ couple, but some dehydrogenations cannot reduce $NAD^+$. These, including the succinate dehydrogenase reaction, feed electrons directly into the respiratory chain at a more positive potential. The redox carriers in the chain include flavoproteins, cytochromes, iron-sulfur (non-heme iron) proteins, ubiquinone, and protein-bound Cu. Figure 2 illustrates the sequential electron flow between these components, which are organized into "complexes" and labeled I–IV for historical reasons. Figure 2 also shows the sites of action of some familiar (cyanide and rotenone) and less familiar (antimycin and myxothiazol) respiratory poisons, and it also indicates which experimentally useful oxidants (ferricyanide) and reductants (ascorbate/TMPD) accept electrons from, or donate electrons to, the respiratory chain. Details of the electron transfer components and mechanisms are well beyond the scope of this article (but see Nicholls and Ferguson, 1992).

The general picture of a respiratory chain applies to the mitochondria of most animals and plants and also to mitochondria in eukaryotic micro-organisms, such as protozoa, yeasts, and other fungi. Microbial mitochondria display greater metabolic flexibility and diversity than mitochondria in most higher eukaryotes but not as dramatically as do bacterial respiratory systems.

## C. Special Features of Bacterial Respiratory Chains

The most distinctive feature of bacterial respiratory chains is their branched, flexible, and adaptive nature. Simple, linear pathways involving a small number of dehydrogenases, a quinone, and a terminal oxidase or reductase are uncommon; usually the respiratory pathway is branched at both ends and up to four or more terminal oxidases may be present. Figure 3 shows examples of the composition and organization of these pathways. Constructing such schemes requires integration of many experimental approaches, including determining the range of substrates that can be oxidized, determining the number

and identity of cytochromes using spectroscopic analysis, chemical analysis of quinone types, functional dissection using mutants lacking one or more components, and deducing structural information by sequence analysis of genes. In very few notable cases, crystallographic information has been obtained on protein structures. Recently, the availability of the entire sequences of bacterial genomes has allowed respiratory chain composition (but not function) to be predicted (but not determined) from observing which genes are present (and absent) and therefore which gene products may constitute the respiratory pathways.

In the bacterium *Helicobacter pylori,* a pathogen that is the etiologic agent of chronic gastric ulcers, genome analysis (Kelly, 1998) suggests a surprisingly simple organization (Fig. 3A) in which dehydrogenases (usually including NADPH-linked enzymes) pass reducing equivalents to menaquinone only and then through a cytochrome $bc_1$ complex and a soluble cytochrome $c$ to a single oxidase. This conclusion appears contrary to some spectroscopic information on the cytochrome complement; reconciling and integrating results from several approaches will be an important target for future work. A slightly more complex situation exists in the free-living diazotrophic bacterium *Azotobacter vinelandii* (Fig. 3B) in which electrons from a single quinone pool, in this case ubiquinone, are transferred to at least two (and perhaps three) oxidases, each with distinct structural, kinetic, and functional properties (Poole and Hill, 1997; see Section III.H).

An extreme example is afforded by *Paracoccus denitrificans,* in which three well-characterized oxidases exist that receive electrons from a complex network of upstream components (Baker *et al.*, 1998) which collectively allow oxidation of a wide range of substrates, including methanol and methylamine (Fig. 3C). Note that in *P. denitrificans* and *H. pylori* there is also a peroxidase that transfers electrons from cytochrome $c$ to peroxide, not oxygen, as the terminal electron acceptor.

The presence of multiple oxidases is generally explained by the distinctive properties of each oxidase which may differ in their affinity for oxygen, turnover number, or the stoichiometry of proton translocation. Together with the ability of the respiratory

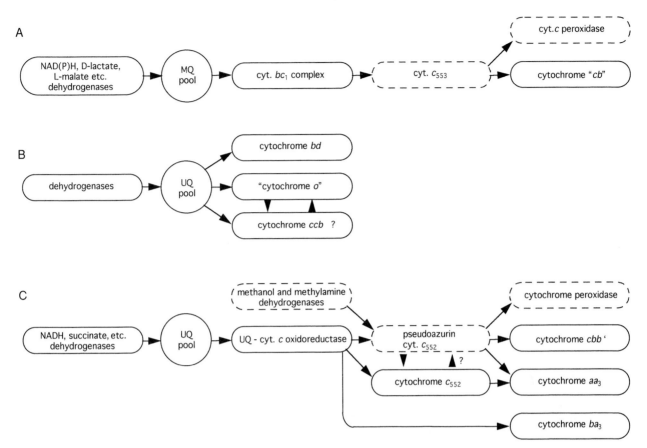

**Fig. 3.** Respiratory electron transfer chains of *Helicobacter pylori* (A), *Azotobacter vinelandii* (B), and *Paracoccus denitrificans* (C). For details, see text. Broken lines indicate soluble components.

chain to oxidize diverse respiratory substrates (e.g., NADH, succinate, and D-lactate), this allows a bacterium to "mix and match" different combinations of dehydrogenases and oxidases to achieve optimal substrate oxidation and energy conservation in a variety of environmental conditions. Not surprisingly, the synthesis of these components is tightly regulated (see Section III.G).

## III. OXYGEN-REACTIVE PROTEINS: OXIDASES

### A. Classes of Oxygen-Reactive Proteins

A characteristic feature of aerobic respiratory chains is the presence of one or (often) several terminal oxidases each having heme(s) as a redox-active prosthetic group. These oxidases are distinct from other cytochromes and other heme proteins that react with oxygen (Table I). The term "cytochrome" implies that the heme group is obligately and alternately oxidized and reduced during protein function, as in cytochromes $b$ and $c$. Terminal oxidases have the additional property that the proximal axial coordination position of the heme iron is vacant, allowing oxygen to be bound and reduced. Oxygen binding is also characteristic of the globins, but the pre-eminent physiological function is not oxygen reduction but reversible oxygen binding and release. However, it should be noted that side-reactions of globin function are known in which, for example, NO bound at the heme may be reduced to nitrate ($NO_3^-$). Microbial globins and putative or actual oxygen sensors are discussed in Section IV. The oxygenases are distinguished by reactions in which

***TABLE I***
**Oxygen-Reactive Proteins Classified by Function**

| Class | Example |
|---|---|
| Oxygen carriers | Myoglobins |
| Terminal respiratory oxidases | Cytochromes $aa_3$, $bo'$, $bd$ |
| Hydroperoxidases | Catalases, peroxidases |
| Oxygenases | Monooxygenases, dioxygenases, cytochrome P450 |
| Other cytochromes | Cytochromes $b$ and $c$ |
| NO-detoxifying proteins | Flavohemoglobin (NO oxygenase and reductase) |
| Oxygen sensors | FixL |

either one (for monooxygenases) or both (for dioxygenases) oxygen atoms are incorporated into the substrate.

## B. General Features and Nomenclature of Oxidases

Oxidases in respiratory chains reduce oxygen to water at the expense of an electron donor such as cytochrome $c$ or a quinone. It should be noted that other heme proteins with oxygen-reducing activity are generally not regarded as terminal oxidases. For example, the oxygen-binding globin of *E. coli* (Hmp) also reduces oxygen (to superoxide anion), but this activity is not linked to energy transduction and appears to have no direct link with the membrane-bound respiratory chain.

Terminal oxidases use the free energy available from oxygen reduction to translocate protons across the membrane. In this respect, they do not differ in principle from other membrane-bound components of the respiratory chain. Thus, anaerobic reductases such as nitrate reductase also translocate protons (Fig. 4A) by consuming two protons from the periplasm and releasing two protons from the complete oxidation of ubiquinol. In certain terminal oxidases (e.g., cytochrome $c$ oxidase), but not in others (e.g., cytochrome $bd$), pumped protons cross the membrane bilayer from interior to exterior by a channel in the oxidase (Fig. 4B).

A variety of heme types are found in respiratory oxidases and other cytochrome components of the respiratory chain. The various heme prosthetic groups differ in substituents on the pyrrole rings that co-ordinate the heme iron. These structures are designated by upper-case letters A, B, C, D, and O, and the corresponding protein-bound cytochromes are described by lowercase letters (e.g., cytochromes $a$, $b$, $c$, $d$, and $o$). According to IUB recommendations, oxygen-binding cytochromes are distinguished by a prime ($'$). Thus, cytochrome $c'$, for example, is a CO- and NO-binding bacterial cytochrome. By this convention, mitochondrial cytochrome $c$ oxidase might be described as cytochrome $aa'$, indicating the presence of two hemes A in the protein, one of which binds oxygen and other ligands. However, since Keilin's time, this oxidase has been known as cytochrome $aa_3$, with the subscript 3 indicating (i) the ligand-binding heme and (ii) the fact that this cytochrome $a$ was the third to be described. The subscript 3 is now, perhaps unwisely, also being used to describe the ligand-binding heme in other oxidases, as in $bo_3$ ($bo'$) and $bb_3$ ($bb'$). Only in the case of cytochrome $c$ is the heme covalently bound to the protein.

## C. Cytochrome $c$ Oxidase

This is a protein complex found in the inner membrane of mitochondria and of certain bacteria and is the terminal oxidase of these respiratory chains, catalyzing the final electron transfer steps from cytochrome $c$ to dioxygen. These oxidases use the free energy available from this redox reaction to pump protons across the membrane via a conducting transmembrane channel.

Cytochrome $c$ oxidases are part of a larger family of oxidases which share (i) a high degree of amino acid sequence similarity within the largest subunit and (ii) a unique catalytic site comprising a heme

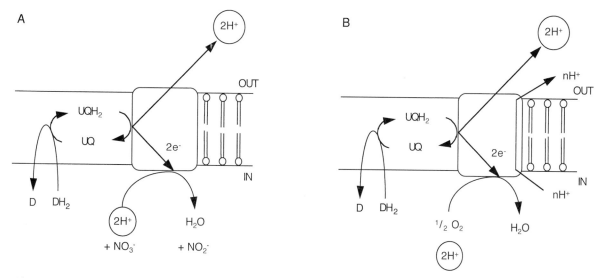

**Fig. 4.** Organization and mechanism of bacterial proton-translocating reductases and oxidases. In these examples, ubiquinol is oxidized to ubiquinone, releasing two protons into the periplasm. Two electrons are transferred through redox centers in the enzyme to the terminal oxidant, e.g., nitrate (A) or oxygen (B). Reduction to nitrite or water, respectively, consumes two protons from the cytoplasm for each pair of electrons. Ubiquinone is re-reduced to ubiquinol by an appropriate electron donor, D. Thus, the reaction in A results in net transfer of two protons from the cytoplasm to the periplasm for each pair of electrons transferred. In B, in addition to these "chemical protons," used in oxygen reduction, protons are pumped from cytoplasm to periplasm by crossing the membrane bilayer via a channel in the membrane.

and a closely associated copper atom. It is at this binuclear site that dioxygen is reduced to water.

Mitochondrial cytochrome *c* oxidases contain three subunits that are encoded by the mitochondrial genome (subunits I–III) and up to 10 proteins encoded by the nuclear genome. Despite this immense complexity, the three-dimensional crystal structures of both the bovine heart mitochondrial cytochrome *c* oxidase and its bacterial (*Paracoccus denitrificans*) counterpart have been solved. The structures of the two oxidases are surprisingly similar: the core subunits (I–III) are almost identical at the atomic level and look like a trapezoid (from the side) or an oval (from the periplasm). These core subunits found in the cytochrome *c* oxidases of *P. denitrificans* and *Rhodobacter sphaeroides* are all that is required for effective electron transfer and proton pumping activities; the function of the other subunits is uncertain.

Figure 5A shows the main features of cytochrome *c* oxidase that are immediately relevant to function. Subunit I binds three metal prosthetic groups (hemes *a* and $a_3$ and $Cu_B$) and most, if not all, of the proton conducting channel(s). Heme *a* plays merely an elec-

tron transfer role, passing electrons to the binuclear heme $a_3$–$Cu_B$ center in which oxygen is bound and then reduced. Heme $a_3$ and $Cu_B$ are only 3–5 Å apart. Heme $a_3$ has an open co-ordination site where not only $O_2$ but also carbon monoxide (CO), cyanide ($CN^-$), azide ($N_3^-$), and nitric oxide (NO) bind.

The binding and reduction of $O_2$ by cytochrome *c* oxidase takes only about 2 ms to complete at room temperature. Consequently, rapid reaction techniques, such as stopped-flow spectrophotometry, time-resolved vibrational spectroscopy, and photolysis experiments at both ambient and very low temperatures, have been essential for delineating the discrete steps that comprise the reaction sequence. Basically, the reaction comprises the following steps:

1. $O_2$ binds to the fully reduced heme $a_3$ to give an oxygenated (globin-like) form. In this complex, $O_2$ has substantial superoxide-like character ($Fe^{3+}$–$O_2^-$).

2. An additional electron is transferred to oxygen from $Cu_B$, oxidizing it and forming the peroxy ($Fe^{3+}$–$O_2^{2-}$) species.

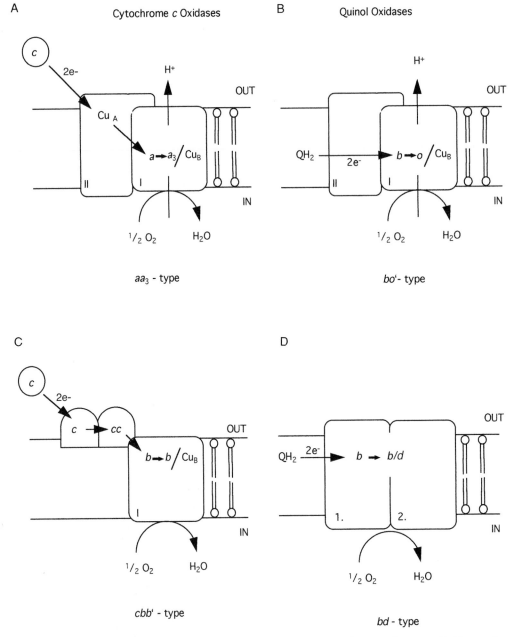

**Fig. 5.** Terminal oxidases classified according to whether they oxidize cytochrome c (A, C) or quinol (B, D). Not all subunits are shown. For details, see text.

3. A third electron donation results in dioxygen bond cleavage, liberating water and forming the oxo-ferryl species ($Fe^{4+}=O_2^-$).

4. A fourth electron regenerates the Fe(III) form of heme $a_3$ and liberates a second water.

The formation of water during these redox steps necessitates proton uptake at the active site of the oxidase on the cytoplasmic (or mitochondrial matrix) side. In addition to these "chemical" protons, changes in protein conformation somehow drive or pump additional protons across the membrane and thus contribute to the magnitude of the protonmotive force. Proton pumping appears to be associated particularly with the uptake of the third and fourth protons.

Site-directed mutagenesis has defined amino acid residues likely to facilitate proton transfer and the ligands that bind the redox-active metal centers. Proton-conducting channels leading to and from the binuclear site are likely to comprise polar amino acid side chains and bound water molecules. Helix VIII is a particularly attractive candidate for providing such a route.

## D. Cytochrome *bo'* and Other Members of the Heme–Copper Oxidase Superfamily

Cytochrome *bo'* is a proton-pumping ubiquinol oxidase. It has been most extensively studied in *E. coli* (see Fig. 1 for its function), but similar oxidases are found in a wide range and large number of bacterial species. The oxidase was discovered more than 40 years ago and named cytochrome *o* (for oxidase) when it was thought to contain heme B. Recent work has revealed a unique type of heme at the oxygen-binding site named heme O; the designation of an *o*-type cytochrome should now be reserved for those oxidases that contain this prosthetic group. Heme O is modified from heme B (protoheme, the type found in globins) by addition of a farnesyl group.

The *E. coli* cytochrome *bo'* complex contains homologs of subunits I–III (Fig. 5B); remarkably, subunit I is more than 40% identical to that of bovine cytochrome *c* oxidase. The main structural distinction between quinol and cytochrome *c* oxidases is in subunit II; in the latter, residues for binding the missing $Cu_A$ center are absent (Fig. 5B).

The structural genes for cytochrome *bo'* in *E. coli* are organized in a single operon, *cyoABCDE,* in which the first four genes encode the oxidase subunits and *cyoE* encodes the farnesyl transferase required for heme O biosynthesis. Regulation of *cyo* operon expression is described in Section III.G.

Although cytochromes $a_3$ and *bo'* are the best studied oxidases in the heme–copper super-family, others do exist. These include cytochrome *c* oxidases

in which heme *c* is covalently linked to subunit II (not shown) and cytochrome *c* oxidases that lack both $Cu_A$ and subunit II but have two membrane-bound cytochrome *c* molecules (Fig. 5C).

## E. Cytochrome *bd*

In terms of subunit composition and sequence and the complement of redox centers, cytochrome *bd* appears to be completely unrelated to oxidases in the heme–copper super-family. The best studied examples are in *E. coli* and *A. vinelandii,* but similar oxidases occur in many gram-negative and gram-positive bacteria and have striking sequence homologies.

The *E. coli* cytochrome *bd* comprises two subunits (Fig. 5D) of molecular mass 58 and 42 kDa. The larger subunit (CydA) binds heme $b_{558}$ and shares two high-spin hemes, *d* and $b_{595}$, with the other subunit (the subscripts indicate the absorption maximum of the reduced form in nanometers). As in the case of *E. coli* cytochrome *bo'*, this oxidase utilizes ubiquinol as the electron donor which binds to the smaller subunit (Fig. 5D). The probable route of electron transfer is ubiquinol–cytochrome $b_{558}$ and cytochrome $b_{595}$–cytochrome *d,* although both cytochromes $b_{595}$ and *d* bind ligands and may act in concert as the site of oxygen reduction. Cytochrome *bd* is not a proton pump, but protons are translocated during respiration as a result of proton release from ubiquinol oxidation at the periplasmic side of the membrane and proton consumption during water formation.

The structural genes for cytochrome *bd* in *E. coli* are organized in a single operon *cydAB*. However, the gene products from an additional, unlinked operon *cydDC* are needed for cytochrome *bd* assembly. The CydD and CydC proteins constitute a membrane transporter of the ABC (ATP-binding cassette) type. The transporter probably comprises these two integral membrane proteins with their ATP-binding sites on the cytoplasmic side. Although the function of this system is unclear, it is probable that ATP is hydrolyzed at the ABC sites on both CydD and CydC, thereby driving the export of a substrate into the periplasm, where it is required for oxidase assembly.

*Escherichia coli* possesses an additional operon which encodes a second oxidase of the cytochrome *bd* type that is called cytochrome *bd*II or CyxAB. The protein subunits are clearly homologs of the CydAB proteins, but the function(s), if any, of this alternative system is not known (see Fig. 1).

## F. Other Classes of Oxidases

Cytochrome $cd_1$ is a soluble oxidase complex that has both oxygen reductase and nitrate reductase activities. However, its main physiological function in, for example, *Pseudomonas aeruginosa,* is nitrite reduction and therefore is not considered further.

"Cytochrome $a_1$" is a term that was introduced in the pioneering days of oxidase research to denote a hemoprotein with spectral properties similar to, but not identical with, those of cytochrome *c* oxidase. In reduced minus oxidized difference optical spectra, the absorption maximum is approximately 590 or 591 nm and not 600–605 nm as anticipated for heme A-containing cytochrome *c* oxidases. Because of the availability of more information on their composition and function, most oxidases previously described as "$a_1$" have been reclassified as (i) soluble hydroperoxidases [i.e., heme B-containing proteins with catalase/peroxidase activities (e.g., *E. coli* hemoprotein *b*-590)] or (ii) the high-spin cytochrome *b* component of *bd*-type oxidases (e.g., cytochrome $b_{595}$ in *E. coli* and *A. vinelandii*).

## G. Regulation of Oxidase Synthesis in *E. coli*

Respiratory oxidases are synthesized only during aerobic or microaerobic growth since they serve no function when oxygen is unavailable. Regulation is achieved by oxygen or some signal characteristic of aerobic metabolism. In *E. coli* (described here because of its intensive study as a model system), the mechanisms of regulation are complex, but two global regulatory systems are of special importance: the transcriptional activator/repressor protein FNR (fumarate and nitrate reductase) and the ArcA/ArcB two-component sensor-regulator apparatus (Guest *et al.,* 1996).

FNR derives its name from its discovery as a key regulator of anaerobic respiratory enzymes. FNR is a 30-kDa protein similar to CRP (cyclic adenosine monophosphate receptor protein) required for expression of carbon catabolic operons. Unlike CRP, it has four cysteine residues which are required for co-ordinating a [4Fe-4S] cluster whose redox status or assembly is dictated by the presence of $O_2$. This in turn determines whether FNR is active (as either a repressor or an activator of operon transcription) or inactive. In its active form, FNR binds to DNA at unique binding sites with the consensus sequence TTGAT-$N_{4-}$-ATCAA (where $N$ is any nucleotide). The result of this binding with its effects on RNA polymerase interactions and local DNA binding is, for example, to inhibit transcription of *cyoA–E*; thus, expression of this operon is shut down anaerobically. In the case of the *cydAB* operon, the effects of FNR are more complex since FNR regulation overlaps with that exerted by Arc to achieve maximal *cydAB* transcription at low, but not zero, $O_2$ concentrations. This is consistent with the known ability of cytochrome *bd* to consume $O_2$ at trace levels.

Homologs of FNR are widely distributed among bacterial genera. Recent work with *A. vinelandii* has revealed a homolog of FNR, termed CydR, which is required for repression of the operon encoding cytochrome *bd*. The consequence of this regulation is that cytochrome *bd* levels in this strict aerobe are highest at high $O_2$ tensions; this is consistent with the much lower affinity for $O_2$ of this oxidase (see Section III.H) compared to that in *E. coli* and also the special need for cytochrome *bd* in nitrogen fixation (see Section III.H).

## H. Multiplicity of Oxidases and Their Functions in Bacterial Respiratory Chains

One of the most distinctive features of bacterial respiratory chains is their branched nature. Commonly, a variety of substrate dehydrogenases feed electrons into a common pool of quinones, which in turn donate electrons to two or more terminal oxidases (e.g., two or three oxidases in *E. coli* and five or more in rhizobia; Delgado *et al.,* 1998). Examples of branched respiratory chains were given in Figs. 1 and 3.

Recent research on the patterns of gene regulation determining oxidase expression and the properties of the individual oxidases has shed light on why so many oxidases may be required. For example, in *E. coli,* cytochrome *bo'* has a moderately high affinity for oxygen ($K_m$ in the micromolar range), is a proton pump, and is synthesized maximally in cells exposed to "high" oxygen tensions (in the micromolar range). Its properties suggest that in such conditions it will effectively terminate respiration with "efficient" generation of protonmotive force, i.e. with a high $H^+/e^-$ ratio.

The alternative major oxidase, cytochrome *bd,* has an exceptionally high affinity for oxygen ($K_m$ in the nanomolar range) and is synthesized maximally under $O_2$-limited or microaerobic conditions. These properties suggest that cytochrome *bd* functions as an $O_2$ scavenger, which allows aerobic respiration to continue at very low $O_2$ availability, albeit with a lowered $H^+/e^-$ ratio. The NADH dehydrogenases of *E. coli* also differ in their contributions to the protonmotive force. Thus, different permutations of dehydrogenase and oxidase allow $H^+/O$ ratios for the oxidation of NADH by $O_2$ to be varied over a wide range (Gennis and Stewart, 1996).

In *A. vinelandii,* cytochrome *bd* serves a special function. This soil bacterium is an obligate aerobe but can fix atmospheric nitrogen as a sole source of nitrogen for metabolism (i.e., it is a diazotroph). The paradox is that the enzyme responsible for nitrogen fixation, nitrogenase, is notoriously sensitive to destruction and inactivation by oxygen. Genetic and physiological studies have proved that cytochrome *bd* is essential for aerobic diazotrophy, presumably by very rapid consumption of $O_2$, so that the cytoplasmic concentration, even in air-saturated growth media, is maintained at too low a level to inactivate nitrogenase. This mechanism, termed respiratory protection (Poole and Hill, 1997), is probably supplemented by conformational changes in the nitrogenase protein complex that resist damage by $O_2$. The up-regulation of cytochrome *bd* when $O_2$ tension in the medium increases is consistent with this special role.

## I. Nonrespiratory Functions for Oxidases?

Recent research has revealed several interesting cases in which specific terminal oxidases appear to be required for adaptation to environmental stress. For example, in *E. coli,* both cytochromes *bo'* and *bd* can function in aerobic respiration; indeed, mutants defective in synthesis in one or the other grow normally under most laboratory conditions. However, mutants defective in cytochrome *bd* but not cytochrome *bo'* do not grow under iron-limited conditions or in the presence of cyanide, and they show reduced viability in the late stationary phase of growth. Similarly, mutants of *Staphylococcus aureus* defective in cytochrome $aa_3$ show reduced survival when starved of certain nutrients. More research is required to explain specific functions for certain oxidases which at first appear functionally redundant.

## J. Oxidases as Taxonomic Tools and in Genomics

Some use has been made of the patterns of cytochromes synthesized by various bacteria in distinguishing between genera and larger groupings of bacteria. The familiar "oxidase" test, for example, distinguishes between bacteria that either can or cannot utilize the redox dyes TMPD (*N,-N,-N',-N'*-tetramethyl-*p*-phenylenediamine) and DMPD (*N,-N*-dimethyl-*p*-phenylenediamine). Generally, a positive result in the oxidase test is taken to suggest the presence of a cytochrome *c* oxidase.

Genomic research is now capable of informing microbiologists about the number and nature of genes that probably encode oxidases in selected bacteria and has provided some surprising results. For example, despite claims based on biochemical research to the contrary, the entire genomic sequence of *H. pylori* reveals genes for only a single oxidase of the cytochrome *cb* type and thus a surprisingly simple unbranched respiratory chain (Fig. 3A). Also, inspection of many bacterial genome sequences shows the presence of genes homologous to genes in *E. coli* that encode enzymes for the first two steps of ubiquinone biosynthesis. However, there is good biochemical evidence that some of these bacteria do not possess ubiquinone (Søballe and Poole, 1999).

## IV. MICROBIAL GLOBINS

The presence in protozoa and fungi of hemoproteins spectrally resembling the hemoglobins of animals and capable of binding oxygen was first recognized by Keilin half a century ago. Despite detailed biochemical investigations of the hemoglobin of the yeast *Candida* in the 1970s by Chance and others, our knowledge of microbial globins has been slow to develop and information on their probable physiological functions is only now emerging.

Many globin genes from microbes, especially from bacteria, have been sequenced, revealing two quite distinct classes of globins distinguished by protein size and the presence in one class of an additional reductase domain (Table II; Poole, 1994).

### A. Single-Domain Myoglobin-like Globins

The smaller single-domain globins constitute a heterogeneous group (Table II); the only member of this group to have been much studied is the globin (Vgb or VtHb) from the gram-negative gliding bacterium *Vitreoscilla*. Although once described as a "soluble cytochrome *o*" on the basis of its $O_2$-reducing ability and the presence of heme B (but see Section III.D), sequencing of the *vgb* gene shows it to be a true globin homolog of 153 amino acids, having the persistent "globin fold" of the polypeptide and the conservation of key amino acid residues in and around the heme pocket. The crystal structure of Vgb has recently been solved, revealing an unusual heme distal site for ligand binding. Although this globin does not possess an FAD-containing reductase domain, as in flavohemoglobins, a potential site for interaction with a discrete reductase partner, previously identified, can be recognized. This interaction is thought to maintain the globin heme in the reduced state necessary for ligand binding.

This soluble protein oxidizes NADH, reduces $O_2$ (predominantly to peroxide), and, in the presence of both NADH and $O_2$, forms an oxygenated species that is soluble for minutes or hours under physiological conditions. Considerable interest has been directed at this protein even though its physiological function is not known. However, the elevated levels observed in *Vitreoscilla* grown in hypoxic conditions, and the finding that multicopy expression of the cloned *vgb* gene in *E. coli* both "rescues" aerobic growth of mutants impaired in activity of the cytochrome *bo'* and *bd*-type oxidases and improves aerobic growth efficiency of various heterologous hosts in which it is expressed, suggest that Vgb is important in delivering or perhaps storing oxygen. The globin may permit respiration by loose association with the membrane, catalyzing electron transfer from upstream membrane-bound respiratory carriers to oxygen. The ability of Vgb to facilitate respiration and enhance growth, particularly under microaerobic conditions, has been exploited biotechnologically by expressing it in a variety of heterologous host cells (*E. coli*, *Streptomyces* sp., *Pseudomonas* sp., and cultured higher cells) with consequent improvements in cell yield and product formation. The small hemoglobins of protozoa consist of 116–121 amino acid residues but have no obvious similarity with other proteins even in the globin family (Takagi, 1993).

What is the normal physiological function(s) of single-domain microbial globins *in vivo*? It is generally assumed that the small sizes of bacterial and even yeast cells preclude the need for any specific mechanisms for $O_2$ transport into and within these cells. Thus, microbial globins, with the possible exception of Vgb described previously, are probably

### TABLE II
**Examples of Microorganisms in Which the Two Major Classes of Microbial Globins Are Found**

| Single-domain globins | Flavohemoglobins |
| --- | --- |
| Bacteria | Bacteria |
| *Campylobacter jejuni* | *Escherichia coli* |
| *Vitreoscilla* | *Alcaligenes eutrophus* |
| Cyanobacteria | *Bacillus subtilis* |
| *Nostoc commune* | *Erwinia chrysthemi* |
| Protozoa | *Salmonella typhimurium* |
| *Paramecium caudatum* | Yeasts |
| *Tetrahymena pyriformis* | *Candida norvegensis* |
| *T. thermophila* | *Saccharomyces cerevisiae* |

not involved in classical hemoglobin-like functions. The cyanobacterial globin GlnN of *Nostoc commune* is thought to be involved in nitrogen fixation in an undefined way. One globin for which a clear function is known is leghemoglobin, a plant protein, for which rhizobia synthesize the heme moiety. Leghemoglobin is found in the peribacteriod space that surrounds nitrogen-fixing bacteroids in the nodules that develop on roots of nitrogen-fixing plants such as legumes. The protein delivers oxygen to the bacteroids poised at very low $O_2$ concentrations compatible with nitrogen fixation and respiration catalyzed by the bacteroid oxidases, which have very high $O_2$ affinity (Delgado *et al.*, 1998).

Another example is FixL, studied in *Rhizobium meliloti*. FixL and its cognate protein partner FixJ constitute a two-component sensor-regulator pair which jointly controls nitrogen assimilation according to oxygen tension. FixL does not possess the "globin fold" or heme pocket amino acid residues characteristic of higher organism globins or most of the globins listed in Table II. However, its mechanism of action as a sensor of $O_2$ and other heme ligands is very globin-like. On binding $O_2$ or other heme ligands, the spin state of the heme iron changes (high spin to low spin) triggering a conformational change that inhibits the kinase activity of the protein.

## B. Flavohemoglobins

The discovery of a hemoglobin in *E. coli* was quite unexpected but has led to the further identification and study of similar two-domain proteins in many organisms (Membrillo-Hernández and Poole, 1997). The *E. coli* globin (Hmp), a product of the *hmp* gene, is composed of 396 amino acids and its amino-terminal 144 residues have 45% sequence identity with Vgb. The carboxy-terminal domain possesses a FAD- and NAD(P)H-binding domain and the sequence is clearly similar to those of other reductases.

Possible functions for the flavohemoglobins are particularly intriguing in view of the diverse biochemical activities they exhibit in the purified form and the complex regulation of their expression in different environmental conditions. For example, the *E. coli* flavohemoglobin is active as a reductase for Fe(III) and cytochrome *c*, and it not only binds $O_2$

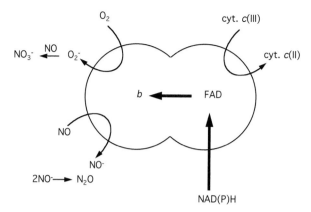

**Fig. 6.** Electron flux in, and redox reactions catalyzed by, the *E. coli* flavohemoglobin, Hmp. The protein comprises two domains: a heme domain (left) and a reductase domain (right). Electrons donated by NAD(P)H are passed by FAD to heme *b* or direct to other electron donors, such as cytochrome *c*. The heme in turn transfers electrons to oxygen, generating predominantly superoxide anion. This superoxy form of the heme is thought to react with NO to generate nitrate ion. Under anoxic conditions the heme can transfer electrons to NO to generate nitrous oxide.

but also reduces it to superoxide anion ($O_2^-$), a powerful reductant that is responsible for oxidative stress (Fig. 6). The response of the redox centers in Hmp to the presence or absence of $O_2$ suggests that it could also act as an $O_2$ sensor. Expression of *hmp* is up-regulated by oxidative stress, stationary phase of growth (involving the alternative sigma factor $\sigma^s$), anaerobiosis (partly as a result of FNR regulation), and the presence of nitric oxide (NO) and agents that exert nitrosative stress, such as sodium nitroprusside and S-nitrosoglutathione (Poole *et al.*, 1996).

At least two mechanisms appear to allow Hmp to play important roles in resisting the effects of NO. Aerobically, Hmp catalyzes an oxygenation reaction in which superoxide generated at the heme of Hmp on binding $O_2$ is attacked by NO to give the innocuous $NO_3^-$ ion. Anaerobically, Hmp reduces NO to $N_2O$ by a poorly understood mechanism. In both activities the ability of the FAD moiety of Hmp to transfer electrons to heme B for ligand binding and reduction is probably crucial.

## See Also the Following Articles

ANAEROBIC RESPIRATION • ENERGY TRANSDUCTION PROCESSES • OXIDATIVE STRESS

## Bibliography

Baker, S. C., Ferguson, S. J., Ludwig, B., Page, M. D., Richter, O.-M. H., and van Spanning, R. J. M. (1998). Molecular genetics of the genus *Paracoccus*: Metabolically versatile bacteria with bioenergetic flexibility. *Microbiol. Mol. Biol. Rev.* **62**, 1046–1078.

Delgado, M. J., Bedmar, E. J., and Downie, J. A. (1998). Genes involved in the formation and assembly of rhizobial cytochromes and their role in symbiotic nitrogen fixation. *In* "Advances in Microbial Physiology, Vol. 40" (R. K. Poole, Ed.), pp. 191–231. Academic Press, San Diego.

Gennis, R. B., and Stewart, V. (1996). Respiration. *In* "*Escherichia coli* and Salmonella. Cellular and Molecular Biology" (F. C. Niedhardt, R. Curtiss, III, J. L. Ingraham, E. C. C. Lin, K. B. Low, B. Magasanik, W. S. Reznikoff, M. Riley, M. Schaechter, and H. E. Umbarger, Eds.), 2nd ed., pp. 217–261. ASM Press, Washington, DC.

Guest, J. R., Green, J., Irvine, A. S., and Spiro, S. (1996). The FNR modulon and FNR-regulated gene expression. *In* "Regulation of Gene Expression in *Escherichia coli*" (E. C. C. Lin and A. S. Lynch, Eds.), pp. 317–342. R G Landes, Georgetown, TX.

Kelly, D. J. (1998). The physiology and metabolism of the human gastric pathogen *Helicobacter pylori*. *In* "Advances in Microbial Physiology, Vol. 40" (R. K. Poole, Ed.), pp. 137–189. Academic Press, San Diego.

Membrillo-Hernández, J., and Poole, R. K. (1997). Bacterial flavohaemoglobins: A consensus sequence and identification of a discrete enterobacterial group and of further bacterial globins. *FEMS Microbiol. Lett.* **155**, 179–184.

Nicholls, D. G., and Ferguson, S. J. (1992). "Bioenergetics 2." Academic Press, London.

Poole, R. K. (1994). Oxygen reactions with bacterial oxidases and globins: Binding, reduction and regulation. *Antonie van Leeuwenhoek* **65**, 289–310.

Poole, R. K., Anjum, M. F., Membrillo-Hernández, J., Kim, S. O., Hughes, M. N., and Stewart, V. (1996). Nitric oxide, nitrite and Fnr regulation of *hmp* (flavohemoglobin) gene expression in *Escherichia coli* K12. *J. Bacteriol.* **178**, 5487–5492.

Poole, R. K., and Hill, S. (1997). Respiratory protection of nitrogenase activity in *Azotobacter vinelandii*—Roles of the terminal oxidases. *Biosci. Rep.* **17**, 303–317.

Søballe, B., and Poole, R. K. (1999). Microbial ubiquinones: Multiple roles in respiration, gene regulation and oxidative stress management. *Microbiology* **145**, 1817–1830.

Takagi, T. (1993). Hemoglobins from single-celled organisms. *Curr. Opin. Struct. Biol.* **3**, 413–418.

Wood, P. M. (1988). The potential diagram for oxygen at pH 7. *Biochem. J.* **253**, 287–289.

# Aerosol Infections

## Edward Anthony Nardell

*Harvard Medical School*

I. Aerosol and Droplet-Borne Infections
II. Historical Background
III. Tuberculosis as a Model Aerosol Infection
IV. Take-Off: Aerosolization and Source Strength
V. Airborne Transport and Air Disinfection
VI. Landing: Infectious Dose

## GLOSSARY

**aerosols**   Gaseous suspensions of fine solid or liquid particles. In this article, aerosols are considered true airborne particles: that is, particles with a negligible settling tendency under average room conditions.

**aerosol infections**   Infections spread by airborne particles, as distinct from droplet-borne respiratory infections which refer to larger respiratory droplets.

**alveolar macrophage**   Scavenging host-defense cells that reside in the alveoli, engulfing inhaled particles, including microorganisms. Alveolar macrophages destroy some engulfed organisms directly, whereas others replicate within them, triggering the release of mediators of cellular immunity.

**droplet nuclei**   Dried residua of larger respiratory droplets which may carry infectious microorganisms. Droplet nuclei of clinical importance are in the 1- to 5-$\mu$m diameter range.

**high-efficiency particle air (HEPA) filters**   A designation for air filters that removes 99.97% of particles 0.3 $\mu$m or larger in diameter. HEPA filters are commonly used in industry to remove airborne particulates and in laboratories and health care facilities to sterilize air.

**personal respiratory protection**   Commonly referred to as masks, respirators are used to protect workers and others from airborne hazards when other control measures provide incomplete protection. For the purpose of preventing respiratory infection, respirators must exclude airborne particles of the size of droplet nuclei, that is, in the 1- to 5-$\mu$m diameter range. "N-95" respirators that exclude 95%

of particulates $\geqq 1$ $\mu$m in diameter have been designated for this purpose. The protection afforded to the wearer by a respirator, however, depends as much on the propensity for face seal leak as it does on the efficiency of the filtration material. For optimal function, respirators should be fit tested. A wide variety of respirators are available for various applications, from simple disposable mouth and nose coverings with substantial face seal leak to sophisticated positive-pressure, HEPA-filtered respirators designed for high-risk procedures.

**respiratory droplets**   Droplets produced by high-velocity airflow over the wet respiratory mucosa, generated by cough, sneezes, and other forced expiratory maneuvers. Some droplets containing microorganisms land on surfaces, extending direct contact transmission. Some droplets evaporate into droplet nuclei, becoming buoyant and vehicles for the transmission of infections spread by the airborne route.

**tuberculosis**   An airborne disease caused by *Mycobacterium tuberculosis*. There are two phases to its pathogenesis: infection with or without clinically apparent primary disease, which usually resolves spontaneously; and post-primary or reactivation disease, occurring in a minority of those infected, often years after infection. Reactivation of latent infection most commonly affects the lungs in which caseating necrosis leads to cavitation, permitting organisms to multiply in large numbers and gain access to the environment as droplet nuclei.

**ultraviolet germicidal irradiation (UVGI)**   A method of air disinfection using ultraviolet irradiation predominantly at the 254-nm wavelength (UV-C). UVGI has been used in ventilation ducts and in free-standing room air handling units and, more efficiently, in the upper room to disinfect room air of airborne pathogens such as measles, influenza, and tuberculosis.

**ventilation**   As used by engineers, the introduction of outside air into buildings for the purpose of diluting and removing air contaminants. Recirculating indoor air may increase comfort levels but does not remove contaminants and often distributes them within buildings. Whereas most homes and small buildings rely on passive ventilation (air infiltrating around windows and doors), larger buildings generally have mechanical heating, ventilation, and air-conditioning (HVAC) systems for comfort and to control the level of common room air contaminants. Although current ventilation standards are not designed to control airborne infections, poor ventilation can increase the rate of transmission.

**AEROSOL INFECTIONS** are those spread by droplet nuclei, airborne particles that remain suspended indefinitely and can transport infectious organisms from human, animal, or environmental sources. Treatment or isolation of the source is usually the most effective control strategy. Air disinfection by ventilation, filtration, or ultraviolet radiation is generally less effective. For high risk exposure settings, personal respiratory protection may be indicated.

## I. AEROSOL AND DROPLET-BORNE INFECTIONS

Although a broader discussion of aerosol infections might include infections associated with large particles, such as dust or large respiratory droplets, which remain suspended in air only briefly before resettling on surfaces, this article will focus on particles fine enough to remain suspended in air indefinitely under ordinary room conditions. Larger respiratory droplets are important in the transmission of numerous infections spread by direct contact with a source and should be considered an extension of direct transmission. Many hospital-acquired infections, for example, are spread from patient to patient on the hands of workers, contaminated by direct contact, or by contact with large droplet aerosols that settle on surfaces. Good hand washing between patients is critical to interrupting such transmission. Operating room procedures are also designed to prevent both direct and droplet-borne infection from surgical staff and from environmental sources. Both direct transmission and droplet-borne transmission require that the source and victim share the same physical space. In contrast, when particles remain suspended in air indefinitely, contact need not be in the same physical space as long as air is shared. For example, transmission of tuberculosis and viral respiratory infections occurs through mechanical ventilating systems between people who have never been in the same room. Table I lists some human infections by their predominant mode of transmission: droplet-borne, airborne (aerosol), or mixed or uncertain transmission.

## II. HISTORICAL BACKGROUND

Air as a source of disease has been the subject of speculation and debate for generations. In response to earlier theories that most diseases were conveyed by unhealthy air, Chapin, in the early twentieth century, proposed that most infections require direct contact, including direct contact with intermediary sources (i.e., insect vectors and contaminated food or water). Although Koch had already demonstrated a bacterial cause of tuberculosis in the late nineteenth

*TABLE I*
**Human Infections by Predominant Mode of Transmission**

| *Droplet-borne transmission* | *Mixed or uncertain transmission* | *Airborne (aerosol) transmission* |
|---|---|---|
| Pneumococcus | Influenza | Tuberculosis |
| Staphlococcus | Rhinovirus | Measles |
| Pertussus | Adenovirus | Rubella |
| Smallpox | Legionella | Brucella |
| Respiratory syncytial virus | Pneumocystis | Anthrax |
| | | Coccidomycosis (other fungal spores) |

century, its potential for airborne spread was not fully appreciated for decades and not scientifically proven until only 40 years ago (Riley and O'Grady, 1961). The debate continues regarding some infections. There is evidence, for example, that rhinovirus, a cause of common colds, is spread predominantly by direct contact, and there is also evidence that airborne spread is a much more efficient mode of transmission. Likewise, legionella pneumonia was initially attributed exclusively to aerosol spread (contaminated water cooling towers and vegetable misters), but there is also strong evidence that ingestion of contaminated potable water, with aspiration in elderly victims, plays an important role (Yu, 1993). Some infections, such as influenza and adenovirus, appear to be transmitted either by large droplet contact or by inhalation of infectious airborne droplets.

The definitive experiments in understanding airborne infections began in the 1930s with observations by a Harvard sanitary engineer, William Firth Wells, who had been engaged by the Massachusetts Department of Public Health to investigate the potential for respiratory infection resulting from the aerosolization of contaminated water, used to keep down dust in New England textile mills. By sampling air using an air centrifuge he had developed, Wells recovered bacteria that were truly airborne. Together with Richard Riley, a medical student working on the project, Wells made two brilliant intellectual discoveries: (i) Airborne particles carrying microorganisms were the dried residua of larger respiratory droplets, evaporating almost instantaneously into "droplet nuclei," and (ii) droplet nuclei might also be the mechanism of person to person transmission of certain respiratory infections, such as measles and tuberculosis (TB). These observations were followed by years of laboratory and field experiments providing a firm scientific foundation for what are now the disciplines of aerobiology and air disinfection (Wells, 1955; Riley and O'Grady, 1961).

One historic experiment, envisioned by Wells and later executed by Riley, warrants further discussion. In order to prove that TB is airborne, and to study its characteristics, Riley established an experimental six-bed ward at the Veterans Administration Hospital in Baltimore during a 4-year period approximately 40 years ago (Riley and Nardell, 1989). Newly diagnosed patients with TB were admitted to the ward, where they remained until treatment took effect. All air from the sealed ward was vented to a penthouse exposure chamber in which hundreds of guinea pigs were housed. Earlier work had shown guinea pigs to be so exquisitely susceptible to airborne tuberculosis that inhalation of a single colony-forming unit (i.e., one droplet nucleus) resulted in infection as determined by tuberculin skin testing. At autopsy, infected animals had solitary sites of infection, usually in the periphery of the lung. Organisms isolated from guinea pigs and humans on the ward were compared by drug susceptibility patterns, often permitting estimates of infectiousness of individual patients. Knowing the breathing rate of guinea pigs, it was possible to use them as quantitative air samplers for infectious droplet nuclei. It is not possible to culture naturally generated tubercle bacilli from the air using mechanical air sampling. More numerous, rapidly growing, and hardier environmental bacteria and fungi tend to overgrow the culture, even when highly selective media are used.

The TB ward experiment demonstrated several important characteristics of airborne transmission: (i) As expected, airborne transmission of TB (without direct contact) was demonstrated; (ii) patients varied greatly in their ability to infect guinea pigs, depending on the extent of their disease, response to treatment, and other ill-defined factors; (iii) concentrations of infectious droplet nuclei (assuming one droplet nucleus caused each infection) in ward air was low, averaging less than 1 in 10,000 ft$^2$; and (iv) in a separate experiment, ultraviolet irradiation of half the exhaust air (in one of two ducts) completely protected exposed guinea pigs during a 2-year period, whereas another colony breathing untreated ward air became infected at the same rate.

In the 1960s, epidemiologic methods correlated the infectiousness of TB cases to cough frequency, quantitative sputum smears, and treatment. Under experimental conditions, the half-life in air of a laboratory strain of TB was found to average approximately 6 hr. There have been important advances during the past several decades in the basic aerobiology of other test microbial species (e.g., *Escherichia coli, Serratia, and Klebsiella*), primarily in the laboratories of Cox (1987). Unfortunately, there has been relatively little recent research on the airborne behavior and control of those species known to be clinically important airborne pathogens (e.g., TB, measles, rhinovirus, legionella, and pneumocystis). Because of the extensive early research on TB, and because it remains the single most important infectious cause of adult deaths globally, TB will be discussed here in greater detail as a model of airborne infection.

## III. TUBERCULOSIS AS A MODEL AEROSOL INFECTION

Figure 1 depicts the propagation cycle of TB in a population of susceptible hosts. Shown are some of the biomedical factors that influence propagation. Not shown are the equally important biosocial determinants of propagation, such as poverty, malnutrition, and poor access to health care. Note that both pathogenesis of disease in the host and airborne transmission are essential to complete the cycle. In recent years, basic TB research has focused on pathogenesis, with little or no attention to the details of transmission. Airborne transmission and its control can be conveniently divided into three components: take-off, aerial transport, and landing. Although the discussion will focus on TB, many of the principles also apply to other airborne infections.

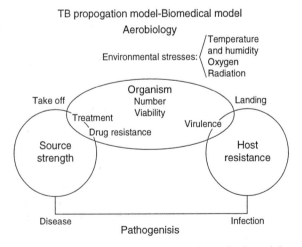

**Fig. 1.** Tuberculosis propagation: Biomedical model.

## IV. TAKE-OFF: AEROSOLIZATION AND SOURCE STRENGTH

### A. Human Sources

Secretions in the lower respiratory tract are normally sterile. However, in persons with respiratory infections, mucociliary secretions carry organisms up to the trachea and pharynx where they are expectorated or swallowed. Coughs, sneezes, and other expiratory maneuvers generate high-velocity airflow over the wet mucosal layer, sheering off droplets that may contain infectious organisms. Factors that influence the generation rate of infectious aerosols are not well defined, but the numbers of organisms present, the force of coughs and sneezes, and the physical properties of secretions are believed to be important. Particle size of aerosols is related to air velocity. In sneezing and coughing, peak airflow in the bronchi approaches 300 m per second, resulting in particles averaging approximately 10 $\mu$m in diameter. Infectious particles consist of respiratory fluid of variable consistency, one or more organisms, and possibly mucus and other debris present in the respiratory tract. Once ejected into the air, large particles settle rapidly onto surfaces, on which they dry and become part of household dust. Although some organisms remain viable in dust, and dust can be resuspended in air, the large average size of dust particles ensures that they will again settle quickly. If inhaled, dust impacts on the upper respiratory tract, which may or may not be vulnerable to any infectious organisms it contains. In the case of TB, infectious particles must reach the vulnerable alveolar region of the lung to initiate infection. Therefore, dust has not been associated with TB transmission. Smaller particles containing viable organisms settle more slowly and evaporate quickly, depending on the solute composition of the droplet and ambient temperature and humidity. As they evaporate and lose mass, they settle more slowly, ultimately settling so slowly (average 0.04 ft/s) that ordinary room air currents are sufficient to keep them airborne indefinitely. Wells called these dried residua of respiratory droplets "droplet nuclei." Airborne or aerosol transmission is also known as droplet nucleus transmission (Wells, 1955; Riley and O'Grady, 1961).

The most important factor reducing the generation rate of infectious aerosols is effective treatment for infections for which treatment is possible. For TB, treatment reduces both the number and the viability of aerosolized organisms. It also reduces coughing. It follows that TB resistant to the antibiotics used remains infectious longer than drug-susceptible TB, adding to the potential for spread of this serious threat. Physical barriers covering the mouth and nose, such as a hand, tissue, or mask, reduce the discharge of large droplets that would otherwise evaporate into droplet nuclei. Prompt identification and isolation of infectious patients is another component of source control, reducing the number of infectious droplet nuclei released into the hospital environment or community, even before treatment becomes effective. Treatment in reducing contagion is so effective, however, that newly diagnosed TB patients, who have already exposed their household contacts before diagnosis, are often not admitted to hospitals for isolation alone but are instructed to limit new contacts while receiving treatment at home.

Based on the numbers of persons (or guinea pigs on the experimental TB ward) infected by an infectious source over a known time period under defined conditions, it has been possible to estimate the average number of infectious droplet nuclei released for several cases of measles and TB. A mass balance equation, similar to those used in epidemiology and in engineering, has been adapted to the study of airborne infection (Riley and Nardell, 1989). This probabilistic model depends on several assumptions that are unlikely to be strictly true under the actual conditions of transmission, but it has been useful in estimating, for example, the effect of changing ventilation when other parameters remain constant. The model assumes steady-state conditions, uniform host susceptibility to infection, uniform virulence of pathogens, and complete air mixing. Details on the derivation and use of this model are found in the review by Riley and Nardell (1989). The equation is as follows:

$$C = S(1 - e^{-Iqpt/Q}),$$

where

$C$ is the number of new cases,
$S$ is the number of susceptibles exposed,
$e$ is the natural logarithm,
$I$ is the number of infectious sources,
$q$ is the number of quanta (infectious doses) generated per unit minute,
$p$ is the human ventilation rate (l/min),
$t$ is the exposure duration, and
$Q$ is the infection-free ventilation (l/min).

Using this equation, the index case of a measles outbreak in an elementary school initially generated an estimated 5000 infectious doses per hour, on average, whereas outbreaks of TB infection have produced estimates that range from approximately 1 to 250 infectious doses per hour (Nardell *et al.*, 1991). The large numbers of organisms generated and lack of host resistance (in the absence of immunization) may explain why measles and chicken pox appear much more contagious than TB. Whereas large numbers of contacts are often infected after only brief exposure to these and other childhood respiratory viruses, infection with TB usually requires prolonged contact, such as living or working with the source case. In a published TB outbreak in which 27 of 67 workers were infected after a month-long exposure to a co-worker with unsuspected TB, the model estimated that the index case produced approximately 13 infectious doses per hour, about 10 times the source strength of the average case on Riley's experimental ward. Unusual infectiousness plus prolonged exposure in a building with recirculated ventilation accounted for the high attack rate of 40%.

The effects of aerosolization on the viability and infectivity of infectious organisms are not well understood for human airborne infections, although experimental work on other organisms may be applicable. As few as 10% of tubercle bacilli remain culturable after being artificially aerosolized. Vulnerability to aerosolization may account for the apparent low generation rate of TB compared to respiratory viruses. It is likely, but unproven, that strains of tubercle bacilli differ in their tolerance to aerosolization or airborne transport under various conditions. Strains that appear especially virulent based on outbreaks are usually considered resistant to killing by alveolar macrophages and other host defenses, but increased tolerance to aerosolization and aerial transport could result in similar increased morbidity.

## B. Environmental Sources

Brucella, anthrax, coccidiomycosis, and legionella are examples of airborne infections with sources in the environment. For brucella and anthrax, the source may be animal carcasses. Mycobacterial infections have also been transmitted to humans by aerosols generated from cadavers (autopsy) and animals (abattoirs), and morticians have a disproportionately high risk of occupational TB. Environmental sources of airborne pathogens are influenced by many factors. After a prolonged drought in southern California, coccidiomycosis spores have been washed from underground burrows by rain and aerosolized by the wind, causing widespread "valley fever." In Pittsburgh and elsewhere, legionella has colonized the hot water supply of hospitals, resulting in frequent nosocomial infections. By periodically turning up the temperature of the hot water and tuning on spigots throughout the building, water colony counts have been reduced, lessening the chance of aerosol spread. Additional means of environmental control of legionella have been recommended.

## V. AIRBORNE TRANSPORT AND AIR DISINFECTION

Environmental conditions such as temperature, humidity, oxidants, and ultraviolet irradiation are believed to influence the viability and infectivity of infectious organisms, but this is based on artificial aerosols under laboratory conditions using a limited range of microorganisms. It is sometimes difficult to predict the net effect on transmission due to complex effects of environmental factors. High humidity, for example, could reduce the number of droplet nuclei generated by slowing dehydration of large droplets, but there is also evidence that high humidity protects airborne organisms from deadly ultraviolet irradiation. The relevance of temperature and humidity on

TB transmission throughout the world is unknown. High TB rates in tropical climates are common, but this is confounded by socioeconomic factors, and high rates also occur in cold climates, for example, among aboriginal people in Alaska and Canada. Humid conditions exist in crowded indoor environments—even in cold, dry climates.

As previously noted, tubercle bacilli (H37Rv) aerosolized under laboratory conditions have been shown to have a half-life of approximately 6 hr. However, ventilation of at least two room air changes per hour is required for the comfort of room occupants. If air mixing within rooms is good, after two air changes only 14% of the original air remains. Therefore, in most circumstances, infectious organisms are cleared by ventilation long before they would die off naturally. This emphasizes the importance of adequate ventilation (or equivalent air disinfection) in reducing the chance of airborne infection in buildings.

## A. Building Ventilation and Air Disinfection

In large buildings, mechanical ventilation systems can either reduce or increase transmission of aerosol infections. Although poor ventilation greatly increases the risk of any airborne infection, even good ventilation can recirculate infectious particles throughout buildings, increasing the number of people exposed beyond those sharing contiguous breathing space. By diluting and removing infectious droplet nuclei, ventilation reduces the probability of infection from known and unknown sources. However, the benefits of ventilation are inherently limited. As a rule, under steady-state conditions, each doubling of well-mixed ventilation is expected to approximately halve the concentration of infectious droplet nuclei, reducing the risk of infection proportionately. However, depending on baseline ventilation, doubling or quadrupling ventilation may not be possible, and risk reductions of one-half to three-fourths may be inadequate protection. In addition to engineering limitations on the capacity of existing ventilation systems, and the high cost of heating and cooling large volumes of outdoor air, high flow rates of ventilation often result in noisy and uncomfortably drafty conditions (Nardell *et al.*, 1991). High rates of ventilation are feasible in operating rooms and small procedure rooms and tolerable for brief periods (e.g., during bronchoscopies or autopsies). Alternative and supplementary methods of air disinfection, such as air filtration and UV air disinfection, may be desirable in high-risk areas.

## B. Filtration and UV Air Disinfection

Filtration media has long been used to remove particulates from air recirculating in heating, air-conditioning, and ventilation systems. To remove respirable particles including infectious aerosols, high- efficiency particulate air filters (HEPAs) have been used in ventilation ducts and in free-standing room air filtration devices. HEPA filters retain 99.97% of particles of the most penetrating 0.3 $\mu$m diameter, well below the 1- to 5-$\mu$m diameter range of infectious droplet nuclei. Although less efficient filters can be as effective and offer less airflow resistance, HEPA filters are manufactured and tested to meet higher standards than are ordinary air filters, making leakage around or through the filter less likely. The disadvantages of higher filtration efficiency are greater cost, airflow resistance, blower size and speed, energy cost, and noise. Filtration is most efficient when it is applied close to the source, where the concentrations of airborne contaminants is high and where relatively less infection-free air must be filtered. Thus, air filtration is the technology of choice for disinfecting the air in small booths used for sputum induction procedures and for administering potentially dangerous aerosols. When used in large rooms, most free-standing filtration units have a limited capacity to add greatly to the number of equivalent air changes without unacceptable noise and drafts. Like ventilation, doubling the number of room air changes through a HEPA filter, if well mixed within the room, will reduce risk by approximately half. Unfortunately, there is a tendency to recapture just-filtered air in the immediate vicinity of free-standing units, thus only slowly capturing contaminated air from more remote corners of the room.

Ultraviolet germicidal irradiation (UVGI) has long been used to sterilize air, especially in indoor spaces in which TB transmission is considered likely (Riley and Nardell, 1989). Short-wavelength (254-nm UV

and UV-C) UV irradiation kills cells by damaging nucleic acids. Fortunately, this UV wavelength, although highly active biologically, has extremely limited penetrating capacity in matter. Although it cannot penetrate the stratum corneum to cause skin cancer, and cannot reach the lens to cause cataracts, it effectively kills the nearly naked infectious airborne pathogens of droplet nuclei. Like HEPA filters, UVGI can be used in ducts and in free-standing, air-disinfecting room units, and it has the advantage of producing less airflow resistance (i.e., less noise) than filters. It this application, UVGI shares many of the disadvantages of air filtration (short-circuiting and a limited number of air changes). For many applications, upper-room UVGI has distinct advantages over UVGI or HEPA filters in ducts or room units. Upper-room UVGI utilizes natural and augmented room air movement in occupied rooms to slowly move air from the breathing space into the upper room, where infectious droplet nuclei are irradiated. Sterile upper-room air returns to the lower room, diluting and displacing infectious air. Without drafts and the noise of blowers, properly installed upper-room UVGI has been shown to produce the equivalent of an additional 10–20 room air changes.

Like all air-disinfecting technologies, upper-room UVGI has limitations. Although vertical room air mixing is generally good in occupied rooms, air can stagnate, for example, if heated air enters from the ceiling, discouraging mixing and reducing the potential benefit of upper-room UVGI air disinfection. Fans ensure air mixing but add noise and drafts and may not be desirable for certain applications. Although UVGI is extremely safe, the perception of occupant risk from unnecessary UV exposure requires continuous education. Current fixture designs direct a narrow beam of intense UV across the upper room, while occupants in the lower room experience minimal exposure. However, education is needed to remind workers not to climb up into the upper room to paint, clean, or perform maintenance without first turning off the fixtures. Even brief direct eye exposure to intensive UV in the upper room can result in painful irritation of the cornea, with symptoms beginning about 12 hr after the exposure. There are no long-term effects of acute exposures and no known effects of chronic low-intensity exposure.

Finding expertise to assist in the design and installation of upper-room UVGI that is both safe and effective is another limitation, although engineering guidelines have recently been published (First *et al.*, 1999).

## VI. LANDING: INFECTIOUS DOSE

Tuberculosis is a true airborne infection not only because particles are generated which become small enough to remain airborne but also because such low-mass particles evade impacting on the upper airways, which are highly resistant to infection, reaching the vulnerable alveoli where they infect alveolar macrophages. Infections caused by large droplets usually invade the upper respiratory tract. Because droplet nuclei are by definition in the 1- to 5-$\mu$m diameter range, the number of infectious organisms each airborne particle can accommodate is limited—no more than two or three in the case of TB. Air sampling data from Riley's experimental TB ward indicated very low concentrations of droplet nuclei in air, suggesting that it is statistically unlikely to become infected by more than a single droplet nucleus at any one time. Riley also estimated that the published rates of infection of student nurses, working on open hospital wards in the era before chemotherapy, were explainable, approximately, by the low average concentrations of droplet nuclei he had measured on the experimental ward. This has been taken to mean that previously uninfected humans, like guinea pigs, appear to be vulnerable to a TB dose as small as a single droplet nucleus. Because droplet nuclei carry so few infectious organisms, and dilution makes inhalation of large numbers unlikely, it should be apparent that the airborne route requires vulnerability of the host to very few organisms, in contrast to some other bacterial infections in which larger infectious doses are required. For example, bacteria are routinely aspirated from the nasopharynx in small numbers without causing infection, whereas larger aspirations of the same organisms during states of decreased consciousness can result in pneumonia. However, it is unlikely that TB infection results from every virulent organism that reaches the alveoli. Acquired and inherited resistance to TB infection are

well-established phenomena. This must mean that for many individuals and populations, some (perhaps most) droplet nuclei that reach the alveoli do not establish infection. In each encounter with TB, whether or not infection occurs depends on the virulence of the microorganism relative to the microbicidal capacity of local alveolar macrophages. It is likely that immunocompromised persons are more vulnerable to new infection as well as to progression or reactivation of latent infection. Microbial virulence and host resistance to infection are discussed in detail elsewhere in this encyclopedia.

### A. Respiratory Protection

Because source strength cannot be reliably reduced by the identification, isolation, and treatment of infectious cases, and air disinfection is imperfect, personal respiratory protection has been recommended as a final barrier against airborne infection. Although respirators with filtration media fine enough to exclude droplet nuclei are readily available, there are two major limitations in the use of personal respiratory protection. First, and most important, the greatest risk of infection is from persons with unsuspected disease, whereas respirators cannot be worn continuously and may not be in use when the risk is at hand. Second, most disposable respirators have a 10% or greater face seal leak, despite appropriate training and fit testing. Like ventilation and filtration, personal respiratory protection is imperfect, but even 90% efficiency when combined with good ventilation can be highly protective in all but the most extreme exposures. For high-risk situations such as frequent exposures, increased vulnerability, or more dangerous organisms such as multidrug-resistant (MDR) TB, higher levels of respiratory protection with much lower chances of face seal leak are recommended.

Respiratory protection is a highly evolved technology that cannot be discussed in detail in this article. In the United States, the National Institute of Occupational Safety and Health (NIOSH) classifies and certifies the performance of personal respirators for use in industry and, recently, for use in health care. For protection against TB, NIOSH has determined that, at a minimum, respirators' filtration media should exclude 95% of particulates larger than 1 $\mu$m in diameter. These so-called "N95" respirators are available in many disposable and non-disposable models from several different manufactures. For high-risk exposures, such as bronchoscopy or autopsies in populations in which MDR TB may be encountered, positive pressure has been recommended. Detailed information on respirator selection, fit testing, and usage is available through the NIOSH web site on the Internet.

In conclusion, aerosols are important ways through which pathogens travel from one host to another or from environmental reservoirs to hosts. Tuberculosis and measles are prototype airborne infections that are spread from person to person by droplet nuclei rather than by larger respiratory droplets. The following characteristics distinguish aerosol infections from droplet-borne infections:

1. Aerosol infections can spread beyond the immediate environment of the source.

2. Transmission is more efficient than direct contact or droplet transmission in that many more people can be exposed at once.

3. Depending on source strength and ventilation, the probability of inhaling an infectious dose varies.

4. Droplet nuclei are small enough to reach the alveoli. For some infections, the upper respiratory tract is resistant.

5. Source control (through treatment or immunization) is usually the best control strategy for airborne infections.

6. Transmission from unsuspected sources limits the efficacy of control through respiratory isolation and treatment.

7. Ventilation dilutes and removes infectious droplet nuclei, but its efficacy is inherently limited.

8. Air filtration and germicidal UV irradiation can supplement ventilation as methods of infection control.

9. Because other control methods are imperfect, personal respiratory protection is generally recommended as additional protection against airborne infections, especially in high-risk situations.

## See Also the Following Articles

AIRBORNE MICROORGANISMS AND INDOOR AIR QUALITY • LEGIONELLA • MYCOBACTERIA • SURVEILLANCE OF INFECTIOUS DISEASES

## Bibliography

American College of Chest Physicians/American Thoracic Society (ACCP/ATS) (1995). Institutional control measures for tuberculosis in the era of multiple drug resistance. ACCP/ATS Consensus Conference. *Chest* **108**(6), 1690–1710.

Centers for Disease Control (1994). Guidelines for preventing the transmission of Mycobacterium tuberculosis in healthcare facilities, 1994. *MMWR Morb. Mortal. Weekly Rep.* **43**(RR-13), 1–132.

Centers for Disease Control (CDC) (1996). "NIOSH Guide to the Selection and Use of Particulate Respirators Certified under 42 CFR 84." National Institute for Occupational Safety and Health, HHS, CDC, Cincinnati, OH.

Cox, C. (1987). "The Aerobiological Pathway of Microorganisms." Wiley, Chichester, UK.

First, M., Nardell, E., Chaission, W., and Riley, R. (1999). Guidelines for the application of upper-room ultraviolet germicidal irradiation for preventing transmission of airborne contagion—Part I: Basic principles. Part II: Design and operations guidance. *ASRAE Transactions* **105**, 869–887.

Nardell, E., Keegan, J., Cheney, S., and Etkind, S. (1991). Airborne infection: Theoretical limits of protection achievable by building ventilation. *Am. Rev. Respir. Dis.* **144**, 302–306.

Riley, R., and Nardell, E. (1989). Clearing the air: The theory and application of ultraviolet air disinfection. *Am. Rev. Respir. Dis.* **139**, 286–294.

Riley, R., and O'Grady, F. (1961). "Airborne Infection." Macmillan, New York.

Wells, W. (1955). "Airborne Contagion and Air Hygiene." Harvard Univ. Press, Cambridge, MA.

Yu, V. (1993). Could aspiration be the major mode of transmission for legionella? *Am. J. Med.* **1**, 13–15.

# *Agrobacterium*

**Paul J. J. Hooykaas**
*Leiden University*

I. The Genus *Agrobacterium*
II. Ti Plasmid
III. T-DNA
IV. Virulence Genes
V. T-DNA Processing
VI. Genetic Modification of Plants

## GLOSSARY

***binary vector*** Cloning vector part of which (the T region) is delivered by *Agrobacterium* into plant cells.

***border repeat*** A 24-bp sequence which is present at both ends of the T region. Both are oriented as a direct repeat.

***crown gall*** The tumorous plant disease induced by *Agrobacterium tumefaciens*.

***hairy root*** The tumorous plant disease provoked by *Agrobacterium rhizogenes*.

***Ri plasmid*** A 200-kbp plasmid present in virulent *A. rhizogenes* strains and which confers virulence on the bacterium. Hence, it is a root-inducing plasmid.

***Ti plasmid*** A 200-kbp plasmid present in virulent *A. tumefaciens* strains and which confers virulence on the bacterium. Hence, it is a tumor-inducing plasmid.

***T region*** Part of the Ti plasmid which is bracketed by a 24-bp direct repeat and which is transferred by *Agrobacterium* to plant cells. Similarly, it is the region in a binary cloning vector which is surrounded by this repeat and which is to be delivered into plant cells.

***vir-gene*** Gene located in the virulence region of the Ti plasmid and which participates in the system with which the T region is transferred to plants.

**THE GRAM-NEGATIVE BACTERIUM *AGROBACTERIUM TUMEFACIENS*** is well-known as a phytopathogen capable of inducing crown gall tumors (Fig. 1) on dicotyledonous plants causing serious losses in horticulture. In nature, infection often occurs at the root crown, hence the name crown gall disease, but aerial infection is also common.

## I. THE GENUS *AGROBACTERIUM*

### A. Crown Gall and Hairy Root Disease

A. C. Braun was first to observe that crown gall cells can proliferate in *in vitro* culture in the absence of the phytohormones that are needed for growth of normal tissue. Apparently, during infection normal plant cells are converted into tumorous crown gall cells. Biochemical analysis of crown gall tumors by G. Morel revealed that crown gall cells also differ from normal cells by the presence of specific compounds which are now called opines and which are condensation products of amino acids and sugars or keto acids (Fig. 2). Different strains of *A. tumefaciens* induce crown galls with a set of opines characteristic for the inducing strain. In this way, octopine, nopaline, etc. strains can be distinguished. The opines produced by the plant tumors can be catabolized by the infecting agrobacteria and used as a source of carbon, nitrogen, and energy. However, nopaline strains catabolize nopaline and not octopine, and octopine strains consume octopine but not nopaline. By inducing opine-producing overgrowths on plants, agrobacteria apparently create an ecological niche for themselves.

### B. Taxonomy

The genus *Agrobacterium* belongs to the Rhizobiaceae family together with *Rhizobium* and *Phyllo-*

**Fig. 1.** Hairy root (left) and crown gall (right) induced by *Agrobacterium rhizogenes* and *A. tumefaciens,* respectively.

*bacterium.* Whereas agrobacteria are phytopathogenic, rhizobia and phyllobacteria are known as plant symbionts provoking root nodules and leaf nodules, respectively. Analysis of 16S rRNA sequences has confirmed the close relatedness of these genera and that the genus *Brucella,* which comprises animal pathogens, is slightly more distantly related. Within

the genus *Agrobacterium* many different species have been recognized, mainly on the basis of their phytopathogenic properties. In addition to *A. tumefaciens,* the crown gall inducer, *A. radiobacter,* which is avirulent, and *A. rhizogenes* have been described. The bacterium *A. rhizogenes* induces the hairy root disease on plants, which is characterized by the abundant proliferation of roots from infection sites (Fig. 1). Hairy roots can grow in *in vitro* culture in the absence of phytohormones and, like crown galls, produce opines. Since the phytopathogenic properties of *Agrobacterium* are determined by plasmids, this taxonomical classification is inaccurate. On the basis of many metabolic properties and on DNA homology, however, agrobacterial strains can be classified into at least three biotypes or species. Biotype 1 strains can grow on minimal sugar–salts medium, have a maximum growth temperature of 37°C, and can be quickly identified by their ability to produce 3-keto-lactose on lactose-containing medium. Biotype 2 and 3 strains need the addition of certain vitamins to their growth medium. They can be distinguished from each other by a difference in their maximum growth temperature (29 vs 35°C), the ability to utilize erythritol as a carbon source, and their sensitivity to salt. Strains belonging to biotype 3, which are infectious specifically on *Vitis vinifera,* have been given the species name *A. vitis.* Biotype 1 strains comprise many of the classical *A. tumefaciens* strains, such as A6, B6, C58, Ach5, and ATCC15955, whereas biotype 2 strains include most of the *A. rhizogenes* strains, including A4, ATCC15834, NCIB8196, and NCPPB1855.

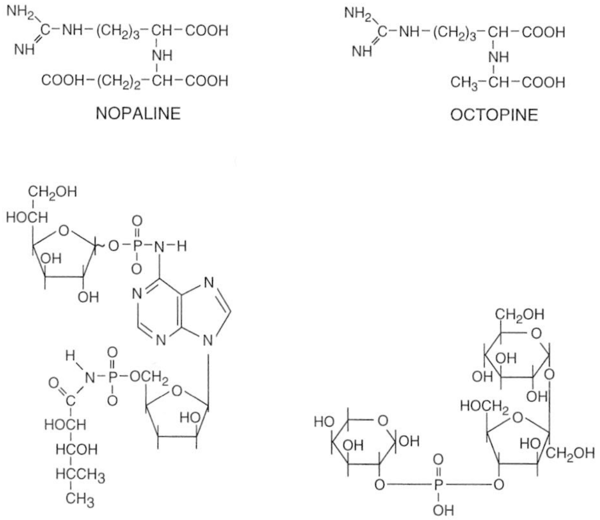

## II. Ti PLASMID

Unlike those of many other bacteria, the genome of *Agrobacterium* consists of two chromosomes, one circular and one linear, and often multiple large plasmids. Approximately 20 years ago research in Gent, Leiden, and Seattle showed that the phytopathogenic properties of *A. tumefaciens* and *A. rhizogenes* are determined by genes located on one of these large (about 200 kbp) plasmids. This plasmid is now known as the Ti (tumor-inducing) plasmid in the case of *A. tumefaciens* and as the Ri (root-inducing)

NOPALINE

OCTOPINE

AGROCIN 84

AGROCINOPINE A

**Fig. 2.** Structures of some opines and agrocin 84, which has some structural resemblance to the agrocinopines.

plasmid in the case of *A. rhizogenes*. Transfer of these plasmids to avirulent strains confers virulence on these bacteria. The host range of the Ti plasmid is not confined to the genus *Agrobacterium*, but transfer to and stable maintenance in *Rhizobium* and *Phyllobacterium* is possible. Introduction of the Ti plasmid in species such as *Rhizobium leguminosarum* and *Phyllobacterium myrsinacearum* makes these tumorigenic on plants. However, virulence is less strong than that seen in the original *Agrobacterium* host. This is suggestive of a co-evolution of the Ti plasmid and the rest of the *Agrobacterium* genome. Some chromosomal virulence (*chv*) genes have been described. Some of these play a role in the bacterial attachment to plant cells, an essential early step in tumorigenesis. Although the factors which are directly involved in attachment have not been precisely defined, it is known that adhesion is a two-step process in which a weak initial interaction is stabilized by bacterial formation of cellulose fibrils leading to firm adhesion. Mutants with chromosomal mutations affecting attachment have been used for cloning genes involved in attachment. Two of these, *chvA* and *chvB*, mediate the production and secretion of periplasmic ß-1,2 glucan. Mutants in *chvA* or *chvB* are avirulent on most plant species due to a lack of attachment. However, there is probably no direct involvement of ß-1,2 glucan in attachment, but the absence of this molecule causes multiple changes in the outer parts of the cell, which also leads to a defect in motility.

In addition to the many genes involved in virulence, the Ti and Ri plasmids, which are built similarly, contain the genes allowing their host to catabolize opines as well as genes for the conjugative spread of these plasmids (Fig. 3). Interestingly, both the catabolic genes and the genes for conjugative transfer are inducible by opines. Indeed, the first evidence for the transfer of a virulence factor (later recognized as being the Ti plasmid) from a virulent to an avirulent strain was observed by A. Kerr during coinfections of plants and is due to the accumulation of opines in the tumors that are formed. Transfer could not be obtained *in vitro* until it was realized that an opine might be needed to induce conjugation and was added to the bacterial mix. Recently, it was found that cell density also plays an important role in the induction of Ti plasmid conjugation. Agrobacteria

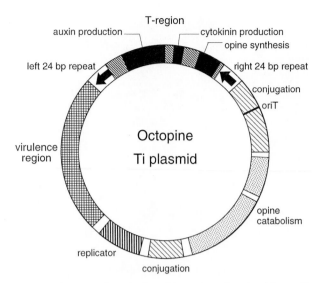

**Fig. 3.** The octopine Ti plasmid. Regions involved in replication, conjugation, and opine catabolism are indicated, as are the Vir region and the T region.

produce N-acyl-homoserine lactones (Fig. 4) via the *traI* gene of the Ti plasmid. When this lipophilic signal molecule, which can easily move into and out of cells, accumulates to a high enough amount in the cell (at high cell density), an opine can bring about the expression of the conjugative transfer genes of the Ti plasmid.

The nopaline Ti plasmids have a locus that makes their hosts sensitive to a bacteriocin called agrocin84, which is produced by a particular *Agrobacterium* strain, K84. This strain was isolated in Australia and found practical use in the suppression of the incidence of crown gall. The locus conferring sensitivity to agrocin84 was identified and determined to encode a system necessary for the uptake of particular opines, agrocinopines, by the bacterium. The chemical structure of agrocin84 (Fig. 2) shows some resemblance to that of the agrocinopines (Fig. 2) in that

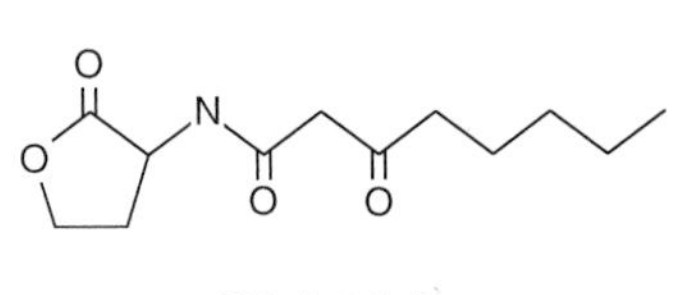

HSL Autoinducer

**Fig. 4.** Structure of the *N*-acyl-homoserine lactone autoinducer of the *A. tumefaciens* conjugation system.

both comprise phosphorylated sugar groups. Therefore, this compound, which seems to be the molecular equivalent of a Trojan horse, is internalized specifically by *Agrobacterium* strains capable of catabolizing the agrocinopines. In this way, strain K84, which is avirulent but nevertheless has a large plasmid with genes for the catabolism of nopaline, gains a competitive advantage over other nopaline strains of *Agrobacterium*.

## III. T-DNA

The finding that crown gall cells are autotrophic (grow in the absence of phytohormones) and produce opines suggested that the contact with *Agrobacterium* had altered their genetic constitution. The development of the blot methodology by Southern paved the way for the detection of the presence of a segment of *Agrobacterium* Ti plasmid DNA in the genome of crown gall cells. The same Ti segment was found in different tumors and therefore this part of the Ti plasmid was called the T (transferred) region or T-DNA when present in the tumor cells. The T-regions of Ti plasmids were found to be bracketed by direct repeats of 24 bp (the border repeat or border sequence), which form the *cis*-acting signal for the transfer apparatus. After integration, parts of these repeats often form the ends of the T-DNA. However, since T-DNA integration occurs via a process of illegitimate recombination, which is mediated predominantly by enzymes of the host plant, there is much variation in the exact ends of the T-DNA. The left end especially may suffer from smaller or larger deletions. Also, during integration small parts of the plant genome are deleted. The T-DNA seems to integrate at a random position in the plant nuclear genome, and it may land in the middle of genes, in between genes, or in areas of repeated DNA. Crown gall cells may contain one copy of the T-DNA or multiple copies at one or multiple loci.

Sequence and mutational analysis has shown that the T-DNA contains several genes (Fig. 3), which are expressed in the transformed plant cells due to the presence of eukaryotic (plant) expression signals at their 3' and 5' ends. The T-DNAs of different Ti plasmids may differ, but the core of the T-DNA is conserved in most of them. This conserved part contains genes coding for enzymes which mediate the production of the phytohormones indole acetic acid (an auxin) and isopentenyl-adenosine phosphate (a cytokinin), thus explaining why crown gall cells grow in the absence of these phytohormones. The T-DNA delivered into plant cells from the Ri plasmid is different from that of the Ti plasmid. However, like the Ti T-DNA, it contains genes which induce an alteration in phytohormone levels and/or phytohormone signaling and hence bring about the differentiation of the transformed cells into autotrophic hairy roots. Both the Ti T-DNA and the Ri T-DNA contain genes which code for enzymes that mediate the biosynthesis of opines (opine synthases) accounting for the production of opines by the transformed cells. The evolutionary origin of the T-DNA genes is unknown, but it is striking that a bacterium possesses genes which are only expressed on transfer to an eukaryotic host. A plant origin, therefore, seems most likely, and indeed one of the Ri T-DNA genes has a eukaryotic intron within the untranslated leader sequence. However, no homologs of the Ti or Ri T-DNA genes have been detected in plants; the natural presence of part of the Ri T-DNA in some *Nicotiana* species is probably due to an ancient transfer event. Homologs of the Ti T-DNA genes involved in auxin and cytokinin production have been detected in other phytopathogenic bacteria which allow these to secrete phytohormones and thus induce gall formation on plants. The evolutionary origin of the T-DNA genes therefore remains unknown.

## IV. VIRULENCE GENES

In addition to the T region, the Ti plasmid has a second region composed of genes that are essential for virulence which is called the virulence (Vir) region and is adjacent to the left end of the T region. Sequence and mutational analysis has revealed that there are more than 20 *vir* genes located in this area (Fig. 5), some of which are essential for virulence on all plant species, whereas others affect the efficiency of transformation and host range. Some of the *vir* genes are grouped together in operons: For example, the *virB* operon contains 11 genes, *virB1*–

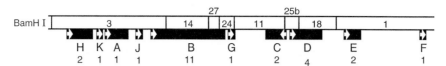

**Fig. 5.** Map of the virulence region of the octopine Ti plasmid. The different *vir* operons A–K are indicated, as are the number of genes they contain and the direction of transcription.

*virB11.* Expression of the *vir* genes is inducible by phenolic compounds (Fig. 6), which are particularly abundant at plant wound sites, whereas certain sugars, such as arabinose, glucuronic acid, and glucose, enhance the rate of induction by the phenolic compounds. In the presence of the proper phenolic inducers the *vir* genes are only induced if the bacteria are present in an environment of low pH (5 or 6), which is reminiscent of the plant exudate in which induction naturally occurs and with a temperature below 30°C.

Control of *vir* gene expression is mediated by a two-component regulatory system consisting of the proteins encoded by the *virA* and *virG* genes (Fig. 7). The VirA protein is an inner membrane chemoreceptor which acquires histidine kinase activity in the presence of the proper inducers and then phosphorylates the other component, VirG, on a specific aspartate residue (Fig. 7). The VirG protein, thus activated, is capable of stimulating the expression of the *vir* genes by binding to a specific sequence, the *vir* box, located in front of the *vir* operons. Phenolic compounds probably bind directly to the VirA protein, but the stimulating sugars first bind to a periplasmic protein encoded by the chromosomal *chvE* gene. The ChvE–sugar complex then exerts its stimulating effect by binding to the periplasmic domain of VirA. Mutations are known in *virA* which make the system hypersensitive for the phenolic compounds and independent of the presence of signaling sugars. The presence of these *virA* alleles or similar constitutive or hypersensitive mutant alleles of *virG*

often leads to increased virulence of the host *Agrobacterium* strain.

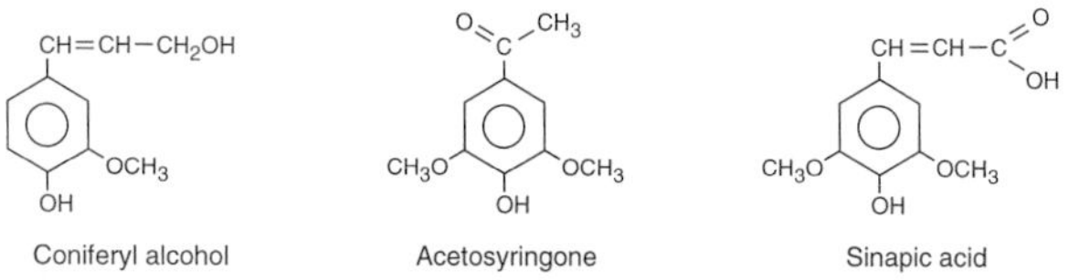

## V. T-DNA PROCESSING

Induction of the *vir* genes leads to the presence of single-stranded copies of the bottom strand of the T region in the cell, which can be detected by Southern blot analysis, after cell lysis. The proteins encoded by the *virD1* and *virD2* genes are essential for their formation. The VirD2 protein belongs to the family of relaxases/DNA strand transferases including the enzymes causing nicking of the *oriT* sequence in *incN, incP,* and *incW* broad host range plasmids. In-

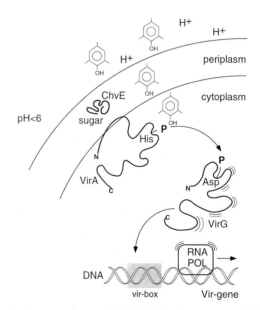

**Fig. 7.** The two-component VirA–VirG system modulating the expression of the *vir* genes. Phenolic compounds and certain sugars (via the ChvE protein) activate the chemoreceptor VirA histidine kinase, which in turn activates the transcriptional activator VirG by phosphorylation of an aspartate residue.

**Fig. 6.** Vir inducers.

Coniferyl alcohol

Acetosyringone

Sinapic acid

deed, the VirD2 protein can break the single-stranded (ss) form of the border repeat *in vitro*. For producing a ss break (nick) at the bottom strand of the double-stranded border repeat *in vitro,* VirD2 needs the assistance of the VirD1 protein. The endonuclease step leads concommittantly to the covalent binding of the VirD2 protein to the 5′ end of the break site (Fig. 8), a reaction which resembles that of type 1 topoisomerases (Top1) and, like that mediated by Top1, is reversible. The border nick in the right border sequence is thought to form the start site for DNA synthesis from the free 3′OH end using the top strand as a template, which is similar to what occurs in rolling circle replication in conjugative plasmids (Fig. 9). The nick site in the left border sequence is thought to be the site at which DNA synthesis stops, leading to the release of the T-strand and subsequent delivery of the T-strand in the recipient plant cell. Near the right repeat a sequence called enhancer or overdrive is present which significantly stimulates

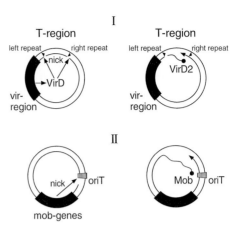

**Fig. 9.** Comparison between T-strand formation and rolling circle replication in conjugative plasmids. Induction of ss breaks at the border repeats (in the Ti plasmid) seems to be equivalent to ss break formation at the origin of transfer of conjugative plasmids, in both cases triggering the production of ss copies of the original DNA molecules which are transferred to recipient cells.

nicking at this repeat and T-strand production; such a sequence is not present near the left repeat. Evidence for the presence of T-strands in transformed plant cells soon after their cocultivation with *Agrobacterium* has been obtained.

Transfer of the T-strand to plants requires the protein complex determined by the *virB* operon and the *virD4* gene. These genes are necessary for the production of a pilus on the surface of *Agrobacterium* which resembles the conjugative pilus of certain classes of plasmids. The *virB* and *virD4* genes indeed share homology with the *tra* genes of such conjugative plasmids and can mediate transfer of an *incQ* mobilizable plasmid from one *Agrobacterium* strain to another. T-DNA transfer thus resembles conjugative plasmid transfer in many respects. Nevertheless, the related systems determined by conjugative plasmids cannot bring about DNA transfer to plants. The secret of *Agrobacterium* must therefore be the presence of accessory functions which are absent from these plasmids. The most obvious of these can be found in the VirD2 protein. In addition to its N-terminal relaxase/strand transferase domain, this protein has a C-terminal domain essential for T-DNA transfer to plants. Within this domain, a nuclear localization sequence (NLS) has been found which helps to direct the T-DNA, to which VirD2 is bound,

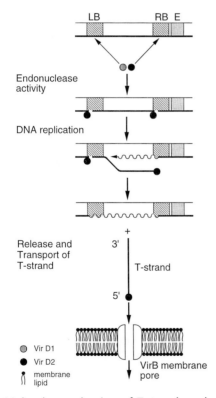

**Fig. 8.** Molecular mechanism of T-strand production. Induction of ss breaks at the border repeats triggers the formation of ss copies of the T region (T-strands) which are delivered into plant cells via the VirB membrane complex.

efficiently to the nucleus. Another protein which assists in the efficient delivery of T-DNA to the plant cell nucleus is the VirE2 protein, a ssDNA binding protein containing an NLS. In the absence of VirE2 T-DNA transfer occurs only with low efficiency and transformed lines contain severely truncated T-DNAs. Cooperative binding of VirE2 to the T-strand apparently protects this against nucleases and helps to direct it to the nucleus. The VirF protein, like VirE2, is introduced into plant cells by the VirB–VirD4 system. This protein affects the efficiency of transformation and is necessary for transformation of particular host plants. It may trigger the targeted proteolysis of certain host proteins to increase transformation. The functions of other genes of the *vir* regulon, including the two *virC* genes, the *virH* genes, *virJ*, and *virK*, are unclear.

## VI. GENETIC MODIFICATION OF PLANTS

The process whereby *Agrobacterium* parasitizes on plant hosts has been named genetic colonization since the bacterium creates a favorable niche for itself by genetically engineering plant cells (Fig. 10). The system used by *Agrobacterium* to mediate T-DNA transfer to plants has been disarmed and optimized for the introduction of genes of interest into plants.

Although *Agrobacterium* only forms tumors on dicotyledonous plants, T-DNA transfer does occur to monocots, including the cereals, but does not lead to tumorigenesis.

The most frequently used methods for the construction of transgenic plants involve the *Agrobacterium* binary vector system, in which a binary vector is introduced into a disarmed *Agrobacterium* strain with a Ti plasmid lacking the T region (helper plasmid). The binary vector has a plant-selectable marker (usually an antibiotic- or herbicide-resistance gene driven by plant expression signals) and a multiple cloning site between a left and right border repeat into which genes can be cloned in *Escherichia coli*. The loaded binary vector is then transferred to an *Agrobacterium* helper strain by conjugation or electroporation from which the T-DNA can be introduced into plants. The system has been applied to produce a myriad of transgenic plants with novel phenotypes, such as resistance to herbicides and various pests, altered flower color, male sterility, potatoes with changed starch content, oil seed crops with modified fatty acid composition, and plants producing edible vaccines. Also, plant research has benefited enormously from this tool. For instance, the creation of transgenic plants with translational fusions of plant genes and versatile reporters, such as *E. coli* ß-glucuronidase and the jellyfish green fluorescent protein, has significantly advanced the analysis of

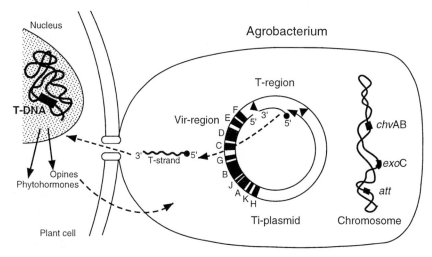

**Fig. 10.** T-DNA transfer from *Agrobacterium* to plants: an overview of the factors involved. See the text for further explanation.

plant expression signals and plant protein subcellular localization and function. Regarding *Agrobacterium,* the analysis of the functioning of some of the Vir proteins in plant cells was only possible after development of the *Agrobacterium*-based plant vector system. The potential use of *Agrobacterium* was increased by the finding that T-DNA transfer occurs efficiently to yeasts and fungi, offering these organisms all the benefits of this versatile and sophisticated genetic engineer.

### See Also the Following Articles

CONJUGATION, BACTERIAL • *ERWINIA* • PLANT PATHOGENS

### Bibliography

Binns, A., and Thomashow, M. F. (1988). Cell biology of *Agrobacterium* infection and transformation of plants. *Annu. Rev. Microbiol.* **42,** 575–606.

Christie, P. J. (1997). *Agrobacterium tumefaciens* T-complex transport apparatus: A paradigm for a new family of multifunctional transporters in eubacteria. *J. Bacteriol.* **179,** 3085–3094.

De Block, M. (1993). The cell biology of plant transformation: Current state, problems, prospects, and the implications for plant breeding. *Euphytica* **71,** 1–14.

Dessaux, Y., Petit, A., and Tempé, J. (1993). Chemistry and biochemistry of opines, chemical mediators of parasitism. *Phytochemistry* **34,** 31–38.

Hooykaas, P. J. J., and Beijersbergen, A. G. M. (1994). The virulence system of *Agrobacterium tumefaciens. Annu. Rev. Phytopathol.* **32,** 157–179.

Kado, C. I. (1991). Molecular mechanisms of crown gall tumorigenesis. *Crit. Rev. Plant Sci.* **10,** 1–32.

Morris, R. O. (1986). Genes specifying auxin and cytokinin biosynthesis in phytopathogens. *Annu. Rev. Plant Physiol.* **37,** 509–538.

Sheng, J., and Citovsky, V. (1996). *Agrobacterium*–plant cell DNA transport: Have virulence proteins, will travel. *Plant Cell* **8,** 1699–1710.

Spaink, H. P., Kondorosi, A., and Hooykaas, P. J. J. (1998). "The *Rhizobiaceae.* Molecular Biology of Model Plant-Associated Bacteria." Kluwer, Dordrecht.

# Agrobacterium and Plant Cell Transformation

### Peter J. Christie

*University of Texas Health Science Center at Houston*

## GLOSSARY

**autoinducer**  An acyl homoserine lactone secreted from bacteria which, under conditions of high cell density, passively diffuses across the bacterial envelope and activates transcription.

**border sequences**  25-bp direct, imperfect repeats that delineate the boundaries of T-DNA.

**conjugal pilus**  An extracellular filament encoded by a conjugative plasmid involved in establishing contact between plasmid-carrying donor cells and recipient cells.

**conjugation**  Transfer of DNA between bacteria by a process requiring cell-to-cell contact.

**mobilizable plasmid**  Conjugal plasmid that carries an origin of transfer (*oriT*) but lacks genes coding for its own transfer across the bacterial envelope.

**T-DNA**  Segment of the *Agrobacterium* genome transferred to plant cells.

**transconjugant**  A cell that has received a plasmid from another cell as a result of conjugation.

**transfer intermediate**  A nucleoprotein particle composed of a single strand of the DNA destined for export and one or more proteins that facilitate DNA delivery to recipient cells.

**type IV transporters**  A conserved family of macromolecular transporters evolved from ancestral conjugation systems for the purpose of exporting DNA or protein virulence factors between prokaryotic cells or to eukaryotic hosts.

**AGROBACTERIUM TUMEFACIENS** is a gram-negative soil bacterium with the unique ability to infect plants through a process that involves delivery of a specific segment of its genome to the nuclei of susceptible plant cells. The transferred DNA (T-DNA) is a discrete region of the bacterial genome defined by directly repeated border sequences. The T-DNA is important for infection because it codes for genes which, when expressed in the plant cell, disrupt plant cell growth and division events.

Approximately 20 years ago, it was discovered that oncogenic DNA could be excised from the T-DNA and in its place virtually any gene of interest could be inserted. *Agrobacterium tumefaciens* could then efficiently deliver the engineered T-DNA to a wide array of plant species and cell types. Transformed plant cells could be selected by co-transfer of an antibiotic resistance marker and regenerated into fertile, transgenic plants. The discovery that *A. tumefaciens* is a natural and efficient DNA delivery vector for transforming plants is largely responsible for the burgeoning industry of plant genetic engineering, which today has many diverse goals ranging from crop improvement to the use of plants as "pharmaceutical factories" for high-level production of biomedically important proteins.

Because of the dual importance of *Agrobacterium* as a plant pathogen and as a DNA delivery system, an extensive literature has emerged describing numerous aspects of the infection process and the myriad of ways this organism has been exploited for plant genetic engineering. The aim of this article is to summarize recent advances in our knowledge of this system, with particular emphasis on chemical signaling events, the T-DNA processing and transport reactions, and exciting novel applications of *Agrobacterium*-mediated gene delivery to eukaryotic cells.

## I. OVERVIEW OF INFECTION PROCESS

*Agrobacterium* species are commonly found in a variety of environments including cultivated and nonagricultural soils, plant roots, and even plant vascular systems. Despite the ubiquity of *Agrobacterium* species in soil and plant environments, only a small percentage of isolates are pathogenic. Two species are known to infect plants by delivering DNA to susceptible plant cells. *Agrobacterium tumefaciens* is the causative agent of crown gall disease, a neoplastic disease characterized by uncontrolled cell proliferation and formation of unorganized tumors. *Agrobacterium rhizogenes* induces formation of hypertrophies with a hairy root appearance referred to as "hairy root" disease. The pathogenic strains of both species possess large plasmids that encode most of the genetic information required for DNA transfer to susceptible plant cells. The basic infection process is similar for both species, although the gene composition of the transferred DNA (T-DNA) differs, and, therefore, so does the outcome of the infection. This article focuses on recent advances in our understanding of the *A. tumefaciens* infection process.

The basic infection cycle can be described as follows (Fig. 1). Pathogenic *A. tumefaciens* strains carry large, ~180-kb tumor-inducing (Ti) plasmids. The Ti plasmid harbors the T-DNA and virulence (*vir*) genes involved in T-DNA delivery to susceptible plant cells. As with many bacterial pathogens of plants and mammals, *A. tumefaciens* infects only at wound sites. As part of the plant wound response, various plant cell wall precursors, including defined classes of phenolic compounds and monosaccharide sugars, are released into the extracellular milieu. These molecules play an important role in the infection process as inducers of the *vir* genes. On *vir* gene

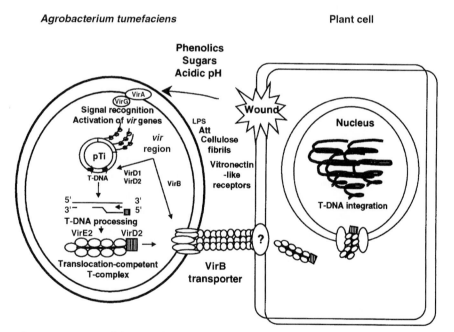

**Fig. 1.** Overview of the *Agrobacterium tumefaciens* infection process. Upon activation of the VirA/VirG two-component signal transduction system by signals released from wounded plant cells, a single strand of T-DNA is processed from the Ti plasmid and delivered as a nucleoprotein complex (T-complex) to plant nuclei. Expression of T-DNA genes in the plant results in loss of cell growth control and tumor formation (see text for details).

activation, T-DNA is processed into a nucleoprotein particle termed the T-complex. The T-complex contains information for (i) export across the *A. tumefaciens* cell envelope via a dedicated transport system, (ii) movement through the plant plasma membrane and cytosol, (iii) delivery to the plant nuclear pore, and (iv) integration into the plant genome. Once integrated into the plant genome, T-DNA genes are expressed and the resulting gene products ultimately disrupt the balance of two endogenous plant hormones that synergistically coordinate plant cell growth and division events. The imbalance of these hormones contributes to loss of cell growth control and, ultimately, the proliferation of crown gall tumors.

## II. TI PLASMID

Genetic and molecular analyses have resulted in the identification of two regions of the Ti plasmid that contribute directly to infection (Fig. 2). The first is the T-DNA, typically a segment of 20–35 kb in size delimited by 25-bp directly repeated border se-

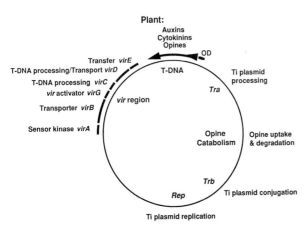

**Fig. 2.** Regions of the Ti plasmid that contribute to infection (*vir* region and T-DNA), cell survival in the tumor environment (opine catabolism), and conjugal transfer of the Ti plasmid to recipient agrobacteria (*tra* and *trb*). The various contributions of the *vir* gene products to T-DNA transfer are listed. T-DNA, delimited by 25-bp border sequences (black arrows), codes for biosynthesis of auxins, cytokinins, and opines in the plant. OD, overdrive sequence that enhances VirD2-dependent processing at the T-DNA border sequences.

quences. The T-DNA harbors genes that are expressed exclusively in the plant cell. Transcription of T-DNA in the plant cell produces 3′ polyadenylated RNA typical of eukaryotic RNA message that is translated in the cytoplasm. The translated proteins ultimately disrupt plant cell growth and division processes resulting in the characteristic tumorous phenotype. The second region of the Ti plasmid involved in infection harbors the genes responsible for processing the T-DNA into a transfer-competent nucleoprotein particle and exporting this particle across the bacterial envelope. Two additional regions of the Ti plasmid code for functions that are not essential for the T-DNA transfer process per se but are nevertheless intimately associated with the overall infection process. One of these regions harbors genes involved in catabolism of novel amino acid derivatives termed opines that *A. tumefaciens* induces plants to synthesize as a result of T-DNA transfer. The second region encodes Ti plasmid transfer functions for distributing copies of the Ti plasmid and its associated virulence factors to other *A. tumefaciens* cells by a process termed conjugation. Intriguing recent work has described a novel regulatory cascade involving chemical signals released both from the transformed plant cells and from the infecting bacterium that activates conjugal transfer of the Ti plasmid among *A. tumefaciens* cells residing in the vicinity of the plant tumor.

## A. T-DNA

The T-DNA is delimited by 25-bp direct, imperfect repeats termed border sequences (Fig. 2). Flanking one border is a sequence termed overdrive that functions to stimulate the T-DNA processing reaction. All DNA between the border sequences can be excised and replaced with genes of interest, and *A. tumefaciens* will still efficiently transfer the engineered T-DNA to plant cells. This shows that the border sequences are the only *cis* elements required for T-DNA transfer to plant cells and that genes encoded on the T-DNA play no role in movement of T-DNA to plant cells. Instead, the T-DNA genes code for synthesis of two main types of enzymes within transformed plant cells. Oncogenes synthesize enzymes involved in the synthesis of two plant growth regulators, auxins and cytokinins. Production of these plant hormones results in a stimulation in cell division and a loss of cell growth control leading to the formation of characteristic crown gall tumors. The second class of enzymes code for the synthesis of novel amino acid derivatives termed opines. For example, the pTiA6 plasmid carries two T-DNAs that code for genes involved in synthesis of octopines, a reductive condensation product of pyruvate and arginine. Other Ti plasmids carry T-DNAs that code for nopalines, derived from α-keto-glutarate and arginine, and still others code for different classes of opines.

Plants cannot metabolize opines. However, as described later, the Ti plasmid carries opine catabolism genes that are responsible for the active transport of opines and their degradation, thus providing a source of carbon and nitrogen for the bacterium. The "opine concept" was developed to rationalize the finding that *A. tumefaciens* evolved as a pathogen by acquiring the ability to transfer DNA to plant cells. According to this concept, *A. tumefaciens* adapted a DNA conjugation system for interkingdom DNA transport to incite opine synthesis in its plant host. The co-transfer of oncogenes ensures that transformed plant cells proliferate, resulting in enhanced opine synthesis. The environment of the tumor, therefore, is a rich chemical environment favorable for growth and propagation of the infecting *A. tumefaciens*. It is also notable that a given *A. tumefaciens* strain catabolizes only those opines that it incites plant cells to synthesize. This ensures a selective advantage of the infecting bacterium over other *A. tumefaciens* strains that are present in the vicinity of the tumor.

## B. Opine Catabolism

The regions of two Ti plasmids coding for opine catabolism have been sequenced and shown to code for three functions related to opine catabolism (Fig. 2). The first is a regulatory function that controls expression of the opine transport and catabolism genes. The regulatory protein is OccR for the octopine catabolism region of plasmid pTiA6. Recent studies have shown that OccR positively regulates expression of the *occ* genes involved in octopine uptake and catabolism by inducing a bend in the DNA at the OccR binding site. Interestingly, octopine

alters both the affinity of OccR for its target site and the angle of the DNA bend, suggesting that octopine modulates OccR regulatory activity. The regulatory protein is AccR for the nopaline catabolism region of plasmid pTiC58. In contrast to OccR, AccR functions as a negative regulator of *acc* genes involved in nopaline catabolism.

The second and third functions, opine transport and catabolism, are encoded by several genes that are transcribed from a single promoter. At the proximal end of the operon is a set of genes that code for one or more transport systems conferring opine-specific binding and uptake. Typically, one or more of these genes encode proteins homologous to energy-coupling proteins found associated with the so-called ATP-binding cassette (ABC) superfamily of transporters. The ABC transporters are ubiquitous among bacterial and eukaryotic cells, and they provide a wide variety of transport functions utilizing the energy of ATP hydrolysis to drive the transport reaction. At the distal end of the operon are genes involved in cleaving the opines to their parent compounds for use as carbon and nitrogen sources for the bacterium.

## C. Ti Plasmid Conjugation

The Ti plasmid transfer (*tra* and *trb*) functions direct the conjugal transmission of the Ti plasmid to bacterial recipient cells. The transfer genes of conjugative plasmids code for DNA processing and transport system that assembles at the bacterial envelope for the purpose of delivering conjugal DNA transfer intermediates to recipient cells. DNA sequence studies have shown that one set of transfer genes codes for many proteins that are related to components of other plasmid and protein toxin transport systems. As described later in more detail, this evolutionarily conserved family of transporters is referred to as a type IV secretion system.

### 1. Autoinduction-Dependent Ti Plasmid Transfer

Recent work has demonstrated that a regulatory cascade exists to activate Ti plasmid transfer under conditions of high cell density (Fig. 3). This regulatory cascade initiates when *A. tumefaciens* imports

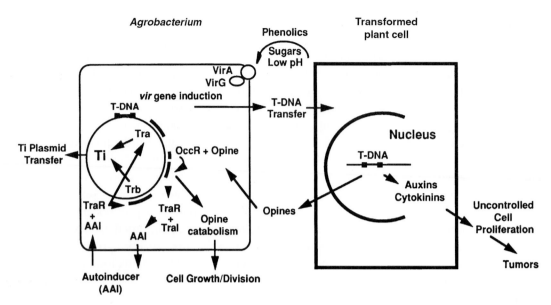

**Fig. 3.** A schematic of chemical signaling events between *Agrobacterium* and the transformed plant cell. Signals released from wounded plant cells initiate the infection process leading to tumor formation. Opines released from wounded plant cells activate opine catabolism functions for growth of infecting bacteria. Opines also activate synthesis of TraR for autoinducer (AAI) synthesis. TraR and AAI at a critical concentration activate the Ti plasmid conjugation functions (see text for details).

opines released from plant cells. For the octopine pTiA6 plasmid, OccR acts in conjunction with octopine to activate transcription of the *occ* operon. Although the majority of the *occ* operon codes for octopine transport and catabolism functions, the distal end of the occR operon encodes a gene for a transcriptional activator termed TraR. TraR is related to LuxR, an activator shown nearly 20 years ago to regulate synthesis of an acyl homoserine lactone termed autoinducer. Cells that synthesize autoinducer molecules secrete these molecules into the environment. At low cell densities, autoinducer is in low concentration, whereas at high cell densities this substance accumulates in the surrounding environment and passively diffuses back into the bacterial cell to activate transcription of a defined set of genes. In the case of *A. tumefaciens*, the autoinducer is an *N*-3-(oxo-octonoyl)-L-homoserine lactone termed *Agrobacterium* autoinducer (AAI). AAI acts in conjunction with TraR to activate transcription of the Ti plasmid *tra* genes and *traI*, whose product mediates synthesis of AAI. Therefore, synthesis of TraR under conditions of high cell density creates a positive-feedback loop whereby a TraR–AAI complex induces transcription of TraI, which in turn results in en-

hanced synthesis of more AAI. It must be noted that this regulatory cascade, involving opine-mediated expression of *traR* and TraR–AAI-mediated expression of Ti plasmid transfer genes under conditions of high cell density, has the net effect of enhancing Ti plasmid transfer in the environment of the plant tumor. Given that the Ti plasmid encodes essential virulence proteins for stimulating T-DNA transfer, *A. tumefaciens* might have evolved this complex regulatory system to maximize the number of bacterial cells in the vicinity of the plant wound site that are competent for delivery of opine-encoding T-DNA to plant cells.

## D. *vir* Genes

The Ti plasmid carries an ~35-kb region that harbors at least six operons involved in T-DNA transfer. Two of these operons have a single open reading frame, whereas the remaining operons code for 2–11 open reading frames. The products of the *vir* region direct events within the bacterium that must precede export of a copy of the T-DNA to plant cells. These events include (i) elaboration of the VirA/VirG sensory transduction system for perception of plant-derived signals and transcriptional activation of the *vir* genes, (ii) T-DNA processing into a nucleoprotein particle for delivery to plant nuclei by the VirC, VirD, and VirE proteins, and (iii) assembly of a transenvelope transporter composed of VirB proteins for exporting the T-DNA transfer intermediate across the bacterial envelope.

### 1. *vir Gene Activation*

Infection is initiated when bacteria sense and respond to an array of signals, including specific classes of plant phenolic compounds, monosaccharides, and an acidic pH that are present at a plant wound site (Fig. 1). Signal perception is mediated by the VirA/VirG signal transduction system together with ChvE, a periplasmic sugar-binding protein, and possibly other phenolic-binding proteins. VirA was one of the first described of what is recognized as a very large family of sensor kinases identified in bacteria and recently in eukaryotic cells. The members of this protein family typically are integral membrane proteins with an N-terminal extracytoplasmic domain. Upon sensory perception, the kinase autophosphorylates at a conserved histidine residue and then transfers the phosphate group to a conserved aspartate residue on the second component of this transduction pathway, the response regulator. The phosphorylated response regulator coordinately activates transcription of several operons, whose products mediate a specific response to the inducing environmental signal. For the *A. tumefaciens vir* system, the response regulator is VirG, and phosphorylated VirG activates transcription of the six essential *vir* operons and many other Ti plasmid-encoded operons that are dispensable for virulence.

VirA senses all three of the plant-derived signals discussed previously. The most important signal molecules are phenols that carry an *ortho*-methoxy group. The type of substitution at the *para* position distinguishes strong inducers such as acetosyringone from weaker inducers such as ferulic acid and acetovanillone. A variety of monosaccharides, including glucose, galactose, arabinose, and the acidic sugars D-galacturonic acid and D-glucuronic acid, strongly enhance *vir* gene induction. The inducing phenolic compounds and the monosaccharides are secreted intermediates of biosynthetic pathways involved in cell wall repair. Therefore, the presence of these compounds is a general feature of most plant wounds and likely contributes to the extremely broad host range of *A. tumefaciens*. VirA functions as a homodimer, and recent genetic studies support a model indicating that VirA interacts directly with inducing molecules that diffuse across the outer membrane into the periplasm. Sugar-mediated inducing activity occurs via an interaction between sugars and the periplasmic sugar-binding protein ChvE. In turn, ChvE–sugar interacts with the periplasmic domain of VirA to induce a conformational change that increases the sensitivity of VirA to phenolic inducer molecules. The periplasmic domain of VirA also senses the third environmental signal, acidic pH, required for maximal induction of the *vir* genes; however, the underlying mechanism responsible for stimulation of VirA activity is unknown.

On the basis of recent crystallographic analysis of CheY, a homolog of VirG, phosphorylation of this family of response regulators is thought to induce a conformational change. Phospho-VirG activates transcription of the *vir* genes by interacting with a *cis*-acting regulatory sequence (TNCAATTGAAAPy) called the *vir* box located upstream of each of the *vir* promoters. Interestingly, both nonphosphorylated and phosphorylated VirG bind to the *vir* box, indicating that a phosphorylation-dependent conformation is necessary for a productive interaction with components of the transcription machinery.

## III. CHROMOSOMALLY ENCODED VIRULENCE GENES

Most studies of the *A. tumefaciens* infection process have focused on the roles of Ti plasmid genes in T-DNA transfer and opine response. Several essential and ancillary chromosomal genes also have been shown to contribute to *A. tumefaciens* pathogenicity. Although mutations in these genes are often pleiotropic, they generally function to regulate *vir* gene expression or mediate attachment to plant cells.

### A. Regulators of *vir* Gene Expression

At least three groups of chromosomal genes have been identified that activate or repress *vir* gene expression. As described previously, the periplasmic sugar-binding protein ChvE complexed with any of a wide variety of monosaccharides induces conformational changes in VirA allowing it to interact with phenolic inducers. Interestingly, *chvE* mutants are not only severely compromised for T-DNA transfer but also show defects in chemotaxis toward sugars, suggesting that ChvE interacts both with VirA and with another membrane protein(s) involved in chemotaxis. ChvE therefore plays a dual role in the physiology of *A. tumefaciens* by promoting chemotaxis toward nutrients and by enhancing the transfer efficiency of opine-encoding T-DNA to plant cells.

A second locus codes for Ros, a transcriptional repressor of certain *vir* operons. As described later, the VirC and VirD operons contribute to the T-DNA processing reaction. Although the promoters for these operons are subject to positive regulation by the VirA/VirG transduction system in response to phenolics and sugars, they are also negatively regulated by the Ros repressor. A mutation in *ros* leads to constitutive expression of *virC* and *virD* in the complete absence of VirG protein. Ros binds to a 9-bp inverted repeat, the *ros* box residing upstream of these promoters. In the absence of plant signals, Ros binding to the *virC* and *virD* promoters prevents the T-DNA processing reaction, whereas in the presence of plant signals Ros repression is counteracted by the VirA/VirG induction system. Interestingly, Ros was recently shown to be a novel prokaryotic zinc finger protein that functions to repress not only the expression of T-DNA processing genes in the absence of a suitable plant host but also the expression of the T-DNA oncogenes in the bacterium.

A second two-component regulatory system has been identified that, like the VirA/VirG transducer pair, senses environmental signals and mounts a behavioral response by modulating gene expression. ChvG is the sensor kinase and ChvI is the response regulator. Null mutations in genes for these proteins result in cells which cannot induce the *vir* genes or grow at an acidic pH of 5.5. The molecular basis underlying the effect of the ChvG and ChvI proteins on *vir* gene expression is unknown.

## B. Attachment to Plant Cells

Binding of *A. tumefaciens* to plant cells is required for T-DNA transfer. Recent evidence indicates there are at least two binding events that may act sequentially or in tandem. The first is encoded by chromosomal loci and occurs even in the absence of the Ti plasmid genes. This binding event directs bacterial binding to many plant cells independently of whether or not the bacterium is competent for exporting T-DNA or the given plant cell is competent for receipt of T-DNA. The second binding event is mediated by a pilus that is elaborated by the *virB* genes (see Section V.B.1).

Binding via the chromosomally encoded attachment loci is a two-step process in which bacteria first attach loosely to the plant cell surface, often in a polar fashion. A series of genes termed *att* are required for this binding reaction. The second step involves a transition resulting in the tight binding of the bacteria to plant cells. The *cel* genes that mediate this form of binding direct the synthesis of cellulose fibrils that emanate from the bacterial cell surface. Recent studies indicate that binding due to these chromosomal functions occurs at specific sites on the plant cell surface. Binding is saturable, suggestive of a limited number of attachment sites on the plant cell, and binding of virulent strains can also be prevented by attachment of avirulent strains. Although the identity of a plant cell receptor(s) has not been definitively established, a good candidate is a vitronectin-like protein found in detergent extracts of plant cell walls. Attachment-proficient *A. tumefaciens* cells bind radioactive vitronection, whereas attachment-deficient cells do not bind this molecule. Intriguingly, human vitronectin and antivitronectin antibodies both inhibit the binding of *A. tumefaciens* to plant cells.

Efficient attachment of bacteria to plant cells also requires the products of three chromosomal loci: *chvA*, *chvB*, and *exoC* (*pscA*). All three loci are involved in the synthesis of transport of a cyclic $\beta$-1,2 glucan molecule. Mutations in these genes are pleiotropic, suggesting that $\beta$-1,2 glucan synthesis is important for the overall physiology of *A. tumefaciens*. Periplasmic $\beta$-1,2 glucan plays a role in equalizing the osmotic pressure between the inside and outside of the cell. It has been proposed that loss of this form of glucan may indirectly disrupt virulence by reducing the activity or function of cell surface proteins. Interestingly, *chv* mutants accumulate low levels of VirB10, one of the proposed components of the T-complex transport system (see Section V), suggesting that $\beta$-1,2 glucan might influence T-DNA export across the bacterial envelope by contributing to transporter assembly.

## IV. T-DNA PROCESSING

One of the early events following attachment to plant cells and activation of *vir* gene expression in response to plant signals involves the processing of T-DNA into a form which is competent for transfer across the bacterial cell envelope and translocation through the plant plasma membrane, cytosol, and nuclear membrane. The prevailing view strongly supported by molecular data is that T-DNA is transferred as a single-stranded molecule that is associated both covalently and noncovalently with Vir proteins. Two proteins identified to date are components of the transfer intermediate: VirD2, an endonuclease that participates in the T-DNA processing reaction, and VirE2, a single-stranded DNA-binding protein which is proposed to associate noncovalently along the length of the single-stranded transfer intermediate (Fig. 1). Intriguingly, recent studies have provided strong evidence that *A. tumefaciens* can export the VirE2 SSB to plant cells independently of T-DNA (see Section IV.B).

### A. Formation of the Transfer Intermediate

More than a decade ago, investigators determined that the T-DNA border repeats are cleaved by a strand-specific endonuclease and that the right T-DNA border sequence is essential for and determines the direction of DNA transfer from *A. tumefaciens* to plant cells. The predominant product of this nicking reaction was shown to be a free single-stranded T-DNA molecule that corresponds to one strand of T-DNA. It was noted that these features of the T-DNA processing reaction are reminiscent of early processing events involved in the conjugative transfer of plasmids between bacterial cells. In the past 10 years, a large body of evidence has accumulated supporting the notion that DNA processing reactions associated with T-DNA transfer and bacterial conjugation are equivalent. Extensive studies have shown

that two systems in particular, the T-DNA transfer system and the conjugation system of the broad host-range plasmid RP4, are highly similar. The substrates for the nicking enzymes of both systems, T-DNA border sequences and the RP4 origin of transfer (*oriT*), exhibit a high degree of sequence similarity. Furthermore, the nicking enzymes VirD2 of pTi and TraI of RP4 possess conserved active-site motifs that are located within the N-terminal halves of these proteins. Purified forms of both proteins cleave at the nick sites within T-DNA borders and the RP4 *oriT*, respectively. In the presence of $Mg^{2+}$, purified VirD2 will catalyze cleavage of oligonucleotides bearing a T-DNA nick site. However, VirD1 is essential for nicking when the nick site is present on a supercoiled, double-stranded plasmid. Both VirD2 and TraI remain covalently bound to the 5' phosphoryl end of the nicked DNA via conserved tyrosine residues Tyr-29 and Tyr-22. Finally, both proteins catalyze a joining activity reminiscent of type I topoisomerases. VirD1 was reported to possess a topoisomerase I activity, but recent work suggests instead that VirD1 supplies a function analogous to TraJ of RP4, which is thought to interact with *oriT* as a prerequisite for TraI binding to an *oriT* DNA–protein complex.

The current model describing the T-DNA and plasmid conjugation processing reactions is that sequence and strand-specific endonucleases initiate processing by cleaving at T-DNA borders and *oriT* sequences, respectively. This reaction is followed by a strand displacement reaction, which generates a free single-stranded transfer intermediate. Concomitantly, the remaining segment of T-DNA or plasmid serves as a template for replacement synthesis of the displaced strand. It is important to note that the single-stranded transfer intermediates of the T-DNA and RP4 transfer systems remain covalently bound to their cognate endonucleases. Considerable evidence suggests that these protein components play essential roles in delivering the respective transfer intermediates across the bacterial envelope.

### B. The Role of VirE2 SSB in T-DNA Transfer

The *virE2* gene codes for a single-stranded DNA-binding protein that binds cooperatively to single-stranded DNA (ssDNA). Early studies supplied evidence that VirE2 binds with high affinity to any ssDNA *in vitro* and that it binds T-DNA in *A. tumefaciens*. By analogy to other SSB proteins that play important roles in DNA replication, VirE2 was proposed to participate in the T-DNA processing reaction by binding to the liberated T-strand and preventing it from reannealing to its complementary strand on the Ti plasmid. The translocation-competent form of DNA therefore has been depicted as a ssDNA molecule covalently bound at the 5′ end by VirD2 and coated along its length with a ssDNA-binding protein (SSB). The single-stranded form of T-DNA delivered to plants is termed the T-strand and the VirD2–VirE2-T-strand nucleoprotein particle is termed the T-complex (Fig. 1).

Considerable evidence indicates that the T-complex represents the biologically active transfer intermediate. The T-complex, composed of a 20-kb T-strand capped at its 5′ end with a 60-kDa endonuclease and approximately 600 VirE2 molecules along its length, is a large nucleoprotein complex of an estimated size of $50 \times 10^6$ Da. This size approaches that of some bacteriophages, and it has been questioned whether such a complex could be exported intact across the *A. tumefaciens* envelope without lysing the bacterial cell. Although this is still unknown, several recent discoveries support an alternative model that assembly of the T-complex initiates within the bacterium but is completed within the plant cell.

Approximately 15 years ago, it was discovered that two avirulent *A. tumefaciens* mutants, one with a deletion of T-DNA and a second with a *virE2* mutation, could induce the formation of tumors when inoculated as a mixture on plant wound sites. To explain this observation, it was postulated that *A. tumefaciens* separately exports VirE2 and VirD2 T-strands to the same plant cell. The *virE2* mutant was proposed to export the VirD2 T-strands (T-DNA donor) and the T-DNA deletion mutant could export the VirE2 protein only (VirE2 donor). Once exported, these molecules could then assemble into a nucleoprotein particle, the T-complex, for transmission to the plant nucleus. In strong support of this model, recent genetic analyses have shown that both the proposed T-DNA donor strain and the VirE2

mutant in the mixed infection experiment must possess an intact transport machinery and intact genes mediating bacterial attachment to the plant cell. Furthermore, current genetic data argue against the possible movement of T-DNA or VirE2 between bacterial cells by conjugation as an alternative explanation for complementation by mixed infection. Finally, a *virE* mutant was shown to incite the formation of wild-type tumors on transgenic plants expressing *virE2*. This finding indicates that VirE2 participates in *A. tumefaciens* pathogenesis by supplying essential functions within the plant.

## C. Role of Cotransported Proteins in T-DNA Transfer and Plasmid Conjugation

As discussed previously, processing of T-DNA and conjugative plasmids results in the formation of a ssDNA transfer intermediate covalently bound at its 5′ end to the nicking enzyme. Recent studies have shown that the protein component(s) of these conjugal transfer intermediates participates in the delivery of the DNA to the recipient cell. In the case of T-DNA, the transferred proteins facilitate movement of the T-DNA transfer intermediate to plant nuclei by (i) piloting the T-DNA transfer intermediate across the bacterial envelope and protecting it from nucleases and/or (ii) directing T-DNA movement and integration in plant cells. In the case of the IncP plasmid RP4, TraI relaxase is thought to promote plasmid recircularization, and a primase activity associated with the TraC SSB is considered to be important for second-strand synthesis in the recipient cell.

### 1. Piloting and Protection

A piloting function for VirD2 is suggested by the fact that VirD2 is covalently associated at the 5′ end of the T-strand and also from the finding that the T-strand is transferred to the plant cell in a 5′–3′ unidirectional manner. A dedicated transporter functions to export substrates to plant cells (see Section V). VirD2 might guide T-DNA export by providing the molecular basis for recognition of the transfer intermediate by the transport machinery. By analogy to other protein substrates exported across the bacterial envelope by dedicated transport machines, VirD2 might have a linear peptide sequence or a protein motif in its tertiary structure that marks this molecule as a substrate for the T-DNA transporter.

Studies of T-DNA integrity in transformed plant cells have shown that the 5′ end of the transferred molecule generally is intact, suffering little or no loss of nucleotides as a result of exonuclease attack during transit. By contrast, the 3′ end of the transferred molecule typically is often extensively deleted. These findings suggest that a second role of the VirD2 endonuclease is to protect the 5′ end of the transfer intermediate from nucleases. Recent molecular studies have also shown that T-DNA transferred to plant cells by an *A. tumefaciens virE2* mutant is even more extensively degraded than T-DNA transferred by wild-type cells, suggesting that VirE2 SSB also functions to protect the DNA transfer intermediate from nucleases during transfer.

### 2. T-DNA Movement and Integration

DNA sequence analyses revealed the presence of a bipartite type of nuclear localization sequence (NLS) near the C terminus of VirD2. The nuclear localizing function of this NLS was confirmed by fusing the *virD2* coding sequence to a reporter gene and demonstrating the nuclear localization of the reporter protein activity in tobacco cells transiently expressing the gene fusion. As predicted, *A. tumefaciens* strains expressing mutant forms of VirD2 with defects in the NLS sequence are very inefficient in delivering T-DNA to plant nuclei. Similar lines of investigation showed that VirE2 also possesses two NLS sequences that both contribute to its delivery to the nuclear pore. Therefore, both VirD2 and VirE2 are proposed to promote T-DNA delivery to and across the plant nuclear membrane. In this context, VirD2 has been shown to interact with a plant NLS receptor localized at the nuclear pore. Of further interest, VirD2 has also been shown to interact with several members of a family of proteins termed cyclophilins. The postulated role for cyclophilins in this interaction is to supply a chaperone function at some stage during T-complex trafficking to the nucleus. *Agrobacterium tumefaciens* has been demonstrated to transport DNA to representatives of prokaryotes, yeasts, and plants. Cyclophilins are ubiquitous proteins found in all

these cell types and therefore may be of general importance for *A. tumefaciens*-mediated DNA transfer.

T-DNA integrates into the plant nuclear genome by a process termed "illegitimate" recombination. According to this model, T-DNA invades at nicks or gaps in the plant genome possibly generated as a consequence of active DNA replication. The invading ends of the single-stranded T-DNA are proposed to anneal via short regions of homology to the unnicked strand of the plant DNA. Once the ends of T-DNA are ligated to the target ends of plant DNA, the second strand of the T-DNA is replicated and annealed to the opposite strand of the plant DNA. Recent mutational analysis of VirD2 showed that a C-terminal sequence termed Ω appears to play a role in promoting T-DNA integration. A recent study also supports a model that VirE2 also participates in the T-DNA integration step, but the precise functions of VirD2, VirE2, and possible host proteins in this reaction have not been defined.

## V. THE T-DNA TRANSPORT SYSTEM

### A. The Essential Components of the T-Complex Transporter

Exciting progress has been made during the past 6 years on defining the structure and function of the transporter at the *A. tumefaciens* cell surface that is dedicated to exporting the T-DNA transfer intermediate to plant cells. Early genetic studies suggested that products of the ~9.5-kb *virB* operon are the most likely candidates for assembling into a cell surface structure for translocation of T-DNA across the *A. tumefaciens* envelope. Sequence analyses of the *virB* operon have supported this prediction by showing that the deduced products have hydropathy patterns characteristic of membrane-associated proteins. Recently, a systematic approach was taken to delete each of the 11 *virB* genes from the *virB* operon without altering expression of the downstream genes. Analyses of this set of nonpolar null mutants showed that *virB2–virB11* are essential for T-DNA transfer, whereas *virB1* is dispensable. As described in more detail later, the VirB proteins, along with the VirD4 protein, are thought to assemble at the cell envelope as a channel dedicated to the export of T-complexes.

## B. The T-Complex Transporter

### 1. Type IV Transporters: DNA Conjugation Systems Adapted for Export of Virulence Factors

DNA sequence studies within the past 4 years have identified extensive similarities between products of the *virB* genes and components of two types of transporters dedicated to movement of macromolecules from or between cells (Fig. 4). The first type, encoded by *tra* operons of conjugative plasmids, functions to deliver conjugative plasmids to bacterial recipient cells. The IncN plasmid, pKM101, and the IncW plasmid, R388, code for Tra protein homologs of each of the VirB proteins. Furthermore, the genes coding for related proteins are often colinear in these respective *virB* and *tra* operons, supporting the view that these DNA transfer systems share a common ancestral origin. Other broad host-range plasmids such as RP4 (IncPα) and the narrow host-range plasmid F (IncF) code for proteins homologous to a subset of the VirB proteins.

DNA sequence studies also identified a related group of transporters in several bacterial pathogens of humans that function not to export DNA but rather to secrete protein toxins (Fig. 4). *Bordetella pertussis,* the causative agent of whooping cough, uses the Ptl transporter to export the six-subunit pertussis toxin across the bacterial envelope. All nine Ptl proteins have been shown to be related to VirB proteins, and the *ptl* genes and the corresponding *virB* genes are colinear in their respective operons. Type I strains of *Helicobacter pylori,* the causative agent of peptic ulcer disease and a risk factor for development of gastric adenocarcinoma, contain a 40-kb cag pathogenicity island (PAI) that codes for several virulence factors, of which several are related to Vir proteins. These Cag proteins are thought to assemble into a transporter for exporting an unidentified protein toxin(s) that induces synthesis of the proinflammatory cytokine IL-8 in gastric epithelial cells. Finally, *Legionella pneumophila,* the causative agent of Legionnaire's disease and Pontiac fever, possesses the *icm/dot* genes, of which *dotG* and *dotB* code for proteins related to VirB10 and VirB11 and others code for homologs of transfer proteins en-

## Type IV Transporters

**DNA Transporters**

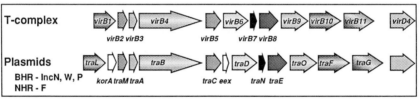

**Toxin Exporters**

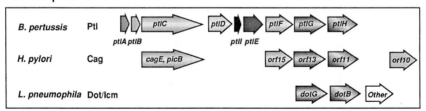

*Fig. 4.* Alignment of genes encoding related components of the type IV transport systems. Of the 11 VirB proteins, those encoded by *virB2–virB11*, as well as *virD4*, are essential for T-complex transport to plant cells. The broad host-range (BHR) plasmid pKM101 encodes a conjugation apparatus composed of the products of the *tra* genes shown. Other BHR plasmids and the narrow host-range (NHR) F plasmid code for Tra proteins related to most or all the VirB genes. A second subfamily of type IV transporters found in bacterial pathogens of humans export toxins or other protein effectors to human cells.

coded by other bacterial conjugation systems. The Icm/Dot proteins are proposed to assemble into a transporter that exports a virulence factor(s) that promotes intracellular survival of *L. pneumophila* and macrophage killing.

The transporters described previously are grouped on the basis of evolutionary relatedness as a distinct transport family. Designated as the type IV secretion family, this classification distinguishes these transporters from other conserved bacterial protein targeting mechanisms that have been identified in bacteria. Although this is a functionally diverse family, the unifying theme of the type IV transporters is that each system has evolved by adapting an ancestral DNA conjugation apparatus or a part of this apparatus for the novel purpose of exporting DNA or proteins that function as virulence factors.

### 2. Functional Similarities among Type IV Transporters

Functional studies have supplied compelling evidence that the type IV transporters are mechanistically related. The non-self-transmissible plasmid RSF1010 of the IncQ incompatibility group possess an *oriT* sequence and mobilization (*mob*) functions for generating a ssDNA transfer intermediate. This transfer intermediate can be delivered to recipient bacteria by the type IV transporters of the IncN, IncW, IncP, and F plasmids. In addition, approximately 10 years ago it was shown using an *A. tumefaciens* strain harboring a disarmed Ti plasmid (with *vir* genes but lacking the T-DNA or its borders) and an RSF1010 derivative that the T-complex transporter could deliver the IncQ transfer intermediate to plant cells. This discovery was followed soon afterwards by the demonstration that the T-complex transporter also functions to conjugally deliver the IncQ plasmid to *A. tumefaciens* recipient cells. Interestingly, *A. tumefaciens* strains carrying both an IncQ plasmid and an intact T-DNA efficiently deliver the IncQ plasmid to plant cells but do not transfer the T-DNA. Preferential transfer of the IncQ plasmid over the T-DNA transfer intermediate could result from the transporter having a higher affinity for the IncQ plasmid or the IncQ plasmid being more abundant than the T-DNA. Of further interest, the coordinate overexpression of *virB9*, *virB10*, and *virB11* re-

lieved the IncQ suppression and restored efficient T-DNA transfer to plant cells. These findings suggest that the T-complex and the IncQ transfer intermediate compete for the same transport apparatus. Furthermore, the data suggest that VirB9–VirB11 stoichiometries determine the number of transporters a given cell can assemble or influence the selection of substrates destined for export.

Although the toxin substrates have not been identified for the *H. pylori* Cag and *L. pneumophila* Dot/Icm transporters, it is intriguing to note that the Dot/Icm system also has been shown to deliver the non-self-transmissible IncQ plasmid RSF1010 to bacterial recipient cells by a process requiring cell-to-cell contact. Also, as observed for T-complex export, the presence of an IncQ plasmid suppresses export of the natural substrate of the Dot/Icm transporter of *L. pneumophila*, resulting in inhibition of intracellular multiplication and human macrophage killing. These parallel findings show that the type IV DNA and protein export systems are highly mechanistically related.

## C. Architecture of the T-Complex Transporter

The T-complex transporter, like other DNA conjugation machines, is proposed to be configured as a transenvelope channel through which the T-DNA transfer intermediate passes and as an extracellular pilus termed the T-pilus for making contact with recipient cells. Most of the VirB proteins fractionate with both membranes, consistent with the view that these proteins assemble as a membrane-spanning protein channel. All the VirB proteins except VirB11 possess periplasmic domains, as shown by protease susceptibility and reporter protein fusion experiments. Although detailed structural information is not available for the T-complex transporter, important progress has been made in the characterization of the VirB proteins, especially in the following areas: (i) characterization of the *virB*-encoded pilus termed the T-pilus, (ii) structure–function studies of the VirB4 and VirB11 ATPases, and (iii) identification of a nucleation activity of a disulfide cross-linked VirB7/VirB9 heterodimer during transporter assembly (Table I).

**TABLE I**
**Properties of the VirB Proteins**

| VirB | Localization | Proposed function |
|------|--------------|-------------------|
| B1 | Periplasm | Transglycosylase |
| B1* | Cell exterior | Cell contact/pilin subunit? |
| B2 | Exported/cell exterior | Cell contact/pilin subunit |
| B3 | Exported | Unknown |
| B4 | Transmembrane | ATPase/transport activation |
| B5 | Exported | Cell contact/pilin subunit? |
| B6 | Transmembrane | Candidate pore former |
| B7 | Outer membrane | Lipoprotein/transporter assembly |
| B8 | Periplasmic face of inner membrane | Unknown |
| B9 | Outer membrane | Lipoprotein/transporter assembly |
| B10 | Transmembrane | Coupler of inner and outer membrane subcomplexes? |
| B11 | Cytoplasm/inner membrane | ATPase/transport activation |
| D4 | Transmembrane | ATPase/coupler of DNA processing and transport systems |

## 1. The T-Pilus

The type IV systems involved in conjugation elaborate pili for establishing contact between plasmid-bearing donor cells and recipient cells. Recent studies have demonstrated that VirB proteins direct the assembly of a pilus which is essential for T-DNA transfer. Electron microscopy studies have demonstrated the presence of long filaments (~10 nm in diameter) on the surfaces of *A. tumefaciens* cells induced for expression of the *virB* genes. These filaments are absent from the surfaces of mutant strains defective in the expression of one or more of the *virB* genes. Furthermore, an interesting observation was made that cells grown at room temperature rarely possess pili, whereas cells grown at ~19°C possess these structures in abundance. This finding correlates well with previous findings that low temperature stimulates the *virB*-dependent transfer of IncQ plasmids to bacterial recipients and T-DNA transfer to plants.

Recently, compelling evidence demonstrated that VirB2 is the major pilin subunit. Early studies showed that VirB2 bears both sequence and structural similarity to the TraA pilin subunit of the F plasmid of *E. coli*. Recent work demonstrated that VirB2, like TraA, is processed from an ~12-kDa propilin to a 7.2-kDa mature protein that accumulates in the inner membrane. During F plasmid conjugation, TraA is mobilized to the surface of the donor cell where it polymerizes to form the pilus. Similarly, the appearance of pili on the surface of *A. tumefaciens* cells induced for expression of the *vir* genes is correlated with the presence of VirB2 on the cell exterior. Finally, VirB2 is a major component of pili that have been sheared from the cell surface and purified.

Many adhesive and conjugative pili possess one or more minor pilin subunits in addition to the major pilin structural protein. Interestingly, VirB1, a periplasmic protein with transglycosylase activity, is processed such that the C-terminal two-thirds of the protein, termed VirB1*, is secreted to the outer surface of the cell. This localization is consistent with a proposed function for VirB1* as a minor pilus subunit. VirB5 might also assemble as a pilus subunit based on its homology to a possible pilin subunit encoded by the IncN plasmid pKM101 transfer system.

## 2. Studies of the VirB ATPases

Two VirB proteins, VirB4 and VirB11, possess conserved mononucleotide binding motifs. Mutational analyses established the importance of these motifs for the function of both proteins. In addition, purified forms of both proteins exhibit weak ATPase activities, suggesting that VirB4 and VirB11 couple the energy of ATP hydrolysis to transport. Both of these putative ATPases appear to contribute functions of general importance for macromolecular transport since homologs have been identified among many DNA and protein transport systems. Of further possible significance, VirB11 and two homologs, TrbB of IncP RP4 and EpsE of *Vibrio cholerae,* have been reported to autophosphorylate. VirB4 and VirB11 might activate substrate transport by using the energy of ATP hydrolysis or a kinase activity to facilitate assembly of the transport apparatus at the cell envelope. Alternatively, by analogy to the SecA ATPase of *E. coli* which uses the energy of ATP hydrolysis to drive translocation of exported proteins, one or both of the VirB ATPases may contribute directly to export of the DNA transfer intermediate. Recent studies have shown that both VirB4 and VirB11 assemble as homodimers. Dimerization is postulated to be critical both for protein stability and for catalytic activity. Accumulation of these ATPases to wild-type levels depends on the presence of other VirB proteins, suggesting that complex formation with other components of the T-complex transporter contributes to protein stability. Specific contacts between these ATPases and other transporter components have not been identified.

### 3. The VirB7 Lipoprotein and Formation of Stabilizing Intermolecular Disulfide Bridges

Detailed studies have shown that VirB7 is critical for assembly of a functional T-complex transport system. VirB7 possesses a characteristic signal sequence that ends with a consensus peptidase II cleavage site characteristic of bacterial lipoproteins. Biochemical studies have confirmed that VirB7 is processed as a lipoprotein. Furthermore, maturation of VirB7 as a lipoprotein is critical for its proposed role in T-complex transporter biogenesis. Recent studies have shown that the VirB7 lipoprotein interacts directly with the outer membrane protein VirB9. The first hint of a possible interaction between these proteins was provided by the demonstration that VirB9 accumulation is strongly dependent on co-synthesis of VirB7, suggesting that VirB7 stabilizes VirB9. Interestingly, this stabilizing effect has been shown to be mediated by formation of a disulfide bridge between these two proteins. VirB7 assembles not only as VirB7/VirB9 heterodimers but also as covalently cross-linked homodimers, and there is

evidence that VirB9 assembles into higher order multimeric complexes. These dimers and higher order multimers might correspond to stable subcomplexes of the larger transport system. In the case of the VirB7/VirB9 heterodimer, considerable evidence indicates that this heterodimer plays a critical role early during transporter biogenesis by recruiting and stabilizing newly synthesized VirB proteins. The heterodimer has been shown to interact with VirB1*. The heterodimer also interacts with VirB10, a cytoplasmic membrane protein with a large C-terminal periplasmic domain. VirB10 has been postulated to join the VirB7/VirB9 heterodimer at the outer membrane with a VirB protein subcomplex located at the inner membrane.

### 4. VirB Protein Stimulation of IncQ Plasmid Uptake by Bacterial Recipient Cells

The T-complex transport system seems designed to function unidirectionally to export substrates to recipient cells. However, a recent discovery indicates that VirB proteins can also assemble as a transenvelope structure that stimulates DNA uptake during conjugation. The fundamental observation is that *A. tumefaciens* cells harboring an IncQ plasmid conjugally transfer the IncQ plasmid to recipient cells expressing the *virB* genes at a frequency of ~1000 times that observed for transfer to recipient cells lacking the *virB* genes. Furthermore, only a subset of *virB* genes, including *virB3, virB4,* and *virB7–virB10,* was required for enhanced DNA uptake by recipient cells. These findings suggest that a subset of the VirB proteins might assemble as a core translocation channel at the bacterial envelope that accommodates the bidirectional transfer of DNA substrates. Such a channel might correspond to an early assembly intermediate that, upon complex formation with additional VirB proteins, is converted to a dedicated T-complex export system.

## VI. *AGROBACTERIUM* HOST RANGE

One of the most appealing features of the *A. tumefaciens* DNA transfer system for genetic engineering is its extremely broad host range. Pathogenic strains of

*Agrobacterium* infect a wide range of gymnosperms and dicotyledonous plant species of agricultural importance. Crown gall disease can cause devastating reductions in yields of woody crops such as apples, peaches, and pears and vine crops such as grapes. Various host range determinants present in different *A. tumefaciens* strains determine whether a given bacterial strain is virulent for a given plant species.

## A. Transformation of Monocots

In the past 5 years, dramatic progress has been made toward the development of protocols for stably transforming agriculturally important monocotyledonous plant species. The first indication of gene transfer involved the introduction of a plant viral genome into a plant host via *A. tumefaciens*-mediated transfer of T-DNA carrying the viral genome. Once inside the plant host, the viral DNA excises from the T-DNA and infects the host, inciting disease symptoms that are characteristic of the virus. This process, termed agroinfection, supplied compelling evidence that *A. tumefaciens* transfers T-DNA to monocot plants such as maize. A notable feature of agroinfection is that the introduced viral DNA incites disease without incorporating into the plant genome. Early efforts to obtain stable transformation of monocot species were unsuccessful. The demonstration of agroinfection and the inability to demonstrate T-DNA integration together led to the suggestion that the T-DNA integration step was somehow blocked in monocots. However, protocols have been developed for the efficient and reproducible stable transformation of rice, corn, wheat, and other monocot species. Key to the success of these protocols was the use of actively dividing cells such as immature embryos. In addition, preinduction of *A. tumefaciens* with phenolic inducers appears to enhance T-DNA transfer efficiencies. Additional factors, such as plant genotype, the type and age of plant tissue, the kinds of vectors and bacterial strains, and the types of selectable genes delivered to plant cells, influence the transformation efficiencies. For rice and corn, most of these parameters have been optimized so that the delivery of foreign DNA to these crop plants is a routine technique.

## B. Gene Transfer to Yeast and Fungi

Intriguing recent work has extended the host range of *A. tumefaciens* beyond the plant kingdom to include budding and fission yeast and many species of filamentous fungi. The successful transfer of DNA to yeast depends on the presence of stabilizing sequences, such as a yeast origin of replication sequence or a telomere, or regions of homology between the transferred DNA and the yeast genome for integration by homologous recombination. When the T-DNA lacks any extensive regions of homology with the *Saccharomyces cerevisiae* genome, it integrates at random positions by illegitimate recombination reminiscent of T-DNA integration in plants (see Section IV.C.2). The transformation of filamentous fungi with *A. tumefaciens* is an exciting advancement. *Agrobacterium tumefaciens* was shown to efficiently deliver DNA to fungal protoplasts and fungal conidia and hyphal tissue. This discovery extends well beyond academic interest because the simplicity and high efficiency make this gene delivery system an extremely useful tool for the genetic manipulation and characterization of fungi. This DNA transfer system is especially valuable for species such as the mushroom *Agaricus bisporus* which are recalcitrant to transformation by other methods. It is also of interest to consider that both *A. tumefaciens* and many fungal species exist in the same soil environment, raising the possibility that *A. tumefaciens*-mediated gene transfer to fungi may not be restricted solely to the laboratory bench.

## VII. GENETIC ENGINEERING OF PLANTS AND OTHER ORGANISMS

The extent to which any biological system is understood is reflected by our ability to manipulate that system to achieve novel ends. For *A. tumefaciens* transformation, the holy grail has been monocot transformation. As described previously, exciting progress has been made toward attaining this objective for several agriculturally important monocot species. Currently, plant genetic engineers are developing the *A. tumefaciens* gene delivery to achieve equally challenging goals such as (i) designing T-

DNA tagging methods for isolating and characterizing novel plant genes, (ii) designing strategies to deliver foreign DNA to specific sites in the plant genome, and (iii) characterizing and genetically engineering other organisms such as agriculturally or medically important fungi.

## A. Overcoming Barriers to Transformation

It is remarkable that all progress in *A. tumefaciens*-mediated monocot transformation has been achieved in the intervening period between the publication of the first and second editions of this encyclopedia. In fact, currently *A. tumefaciens* is the biological DNA delivery system of choice for transformation of most dicot and monocot plant species. The reasons are twofold. First, *A. tumefaciens* is readily manipulated such that plasmids carrying foreign genes of interest are easily introduced into appropriate bacterial strains for delivery to plants. Typically, strains used for gene delivery are "disarmed," that is, deleted of oncogenic T-DNA but still harboring intact Ti plasmid and chromosomal *vir* genes. Foreign genes destined for delivery to plants generally are cloned onto a plasmid that carries a single T-DNA border sequence or two T-DNA border sequences that flank various restriction sites for cloning as well as an antibiotic resistance gene to select for transformed plant cells. If the plasmid carries a single border sequence, the entire plasmid is delivered to plants, and recent work indicates that *A. tumefaciens* can deliver as much as 180 kb of DNA to plants. If the plasmid carries two border sequences, only the DNA bounded by T-DNA borders is delivered to plants. Second, the frequency of stable transformation is often very high, far exceeding frequencies achieved by other gene delivery methods. For example, cocultivation of *A. tumefaciens* with regenerating protoplasts of certain plant species can result in transformation of up to one-half of the protoplasts.

However, with protoplast transformation there is often a significant reduction in the number of transgenic, fertile plants recovered during selective regeneration of transformed protoplasts. For certain species, protoplasts can be transformed but are recalcitrant to regeneration into intact plants. Conse-

quently, other transformation methods have relied on transformation of plant tissues such as excised leaves or root sections. In the case of monocot species such as maize, immature embryos are the preferred starting material for *A. tumefaciens*-mediated DNA transfer. For rice, success has been achieved with callus tissue induced from immature embryos.

In addition to the need to identify transformable and regenerable plant tissues, many varieties of a given species often need to be screened to identify the susceptible varieties. A large variation in transformation efficiencies is often observed depending on which cell line is being tested. This underscores the notion that interkingdom DNA transfer is a complex process dependent on a genetic interplay between *A. tumefaciens* and host cells. Fortunately, many of the agonomically important species are readily transformable, but additional efforts are needed to overcome the current obstacles impeding efficient transformation of other species of interest.

## B. Other Applications

*Agrobacterium tumefaciens* is increasingly used to characterize and isolate novel plant genes by an approach termed T-DNA tagging. Several variations to this methodology exist depending on the desired goals. For example, because insertions are generally randomly distributed throughout the plant genome, T-DNA is widely used as a mutagen for isolating plant genes with novel phenotypes. If the mutagenic T-DNA carries a bacterial origin of replication, the mutated gene of interest can easily be recovered in bacteria by suitable molecular techniques. Furthermore, if the T-DNA is engineered to carry a selectable or scorable gene near one of its ends, insertion downstream of a plant promoter will permit characterization of promoter activity. Conversely, if the T-DNA is engineered to carry an outward reading promoter, insertion can result in a modulation of gene expression with potentially interesting phenotypic consequences. Finally, the discovery that *A. tumefaciens* can transform fungal species of interest means that all approaches developed for plants can be applied to the characterization of fungi.

Although random T-DNA insertion is a boon to investigators interested in characterizing plant or fungal genes, it is an undesired event for plant genetic engineering. In addition to the potential result that T-DNA will insert into an essential gene, insertion often is accompanied by rearrangements of flanking sequences, thus further increasing the chances that the insertion will have undesired consequences. Ideally, T-DNA could be delivered to a restricted number of sites in the plant genome. Recent progress toward this goal has involved the use of the bacteriophage P1 Cre/lox system for site-specific integration in the plant genome. The Cre site-specific recombinase catalyzes strand exchange between two lox sites which, for P1, results in circularization of the P1 genome upon infection of bacterial cells. For directed T-DNA insertion, both the plant and the T-DNA are engineered to carry lox sequences and the plant is also engineered to express the Cre protein. Upon entry of T-DNA into the plant cell, Cre was shown to catalyze the site-specific integration of T-DNA at the plant lox site. The frequency of directed insertion events is low compared to random insertion events, but additional manipulation of this system should enhance its general applicability.

## VIII. CONCLUSIONS

The early discovery that oncogenes can be excised from T-DNA and replaced with genes of interest paved the way for the fast growing industry of plant genetic engineering. Currently, much information has been assembled on the *A. tumefaciens* infection process. This information has been used to successfully manipulate the T-DNA transfer system both to enhance its efficiency and to broaden the range of transformable plants and other organisms. Furthermore, it must be noted that this information has also often established a conceptual framework for initiating or extending the characterization of other pathogenic and symbiotic relationships. The discovery that secreted chemical signals initiate a complex dialogue between *A. tumefaciens* and plant cells as well as other *A. tumefaciens* cells has stimulated a global effort to identify extracellular signals and characterize the cognate signal transduction systems in many bacterial systems. The discovery of T-DNA transport provided a mechanistic explanation for how horizontal gene transfer impacts the evolution of genomes of higher organisms. This discovery also established a precedent for interkingdom transport of virulence factors by bacterial pathogens. Indeed, in only the past 6 years, studies have revealed that numerous pathogens employ interkingdom transport to deliver a wide array of effector proteins to plant and animal hosts. These so-called type III transport systems, like the *A. tumefaciens* T-complex transporter and related type IV transporters, deliver substrates via a process dependent on cell-to-cell contact and, in some cases, elaboration of an extracellular filament or pilus. It is clear that, in the future, studies of all the various aspects of the *A. tumefaciens* infection process will continue to spawn new applications for this novel DNA transfer system and yield new insights about the evolution and function of pathogenic mechanisms that are broadly distributed in nature.

### Acknowledgments

I thank members of my laboratory for helpful and stimulating discussions. Studies in this laboratory are funded by the National Institutes of Health.

### See Also the Following Articles

### Bibliography

Binns, A. N., and Howitz, V. R. (1994). The genetic and chemical basis of recognition in the *Agrobacterium*: plant interaction. *Curr. Topics Microbiol. Immunol.* **192,** 119–138.

Binns, A. N., Joerger, R. D., and Ward, J. E., Jr. (1992). *Agrobacterium* and plant cell transformation. *In* "Encyclopedia of Microbiology" (J. Lederberg, Ed.), pp. 37–51. Academic Press, San Diego, CA.

Christie, P. J. (1997). The *Agrobacterium tumefaciens* T-complex transport apparatus: A paradigm for a new family of multifunctional transporters in eubacteria. *J. Bacteriol.* **179,** 3085–3094.

Christie, P. J., and Covacci, A. (1998). Bacterial type IV secretion systems: Systems utilizing components of DNA conjugation machines for export of virulence factors. *In* "Cellular Microbiology" (P. Cossart, P. Boquet, S. Normark, and R. Rappuoli, Eds.). ASM Press, Washington, DC.

Citovsky, V., and Zambryski, P. (1993). Transport of nucleic acids through membrane channels: Snaking through small holes. *Annu. Rev. Microbiol.* **47,** 167–197.

Das, A. (1998). DNA transfer from *Agrobacterium* to plant cells in crown gall tumor disease. *Subcell. Biochem.* **29**, 343–63.

Fernandez, D., Spudich, G. M., Dang, T. A., Zhou, X.-R., Rashkova, S., and Christie, P. J. (1996). Biogenesis of the *Agrobacterium tumefaciens* T-complex transport apparatus. In "Biology of Plant–Microbe Interactions" (G. Stacey, B. Mullin, and P. Gresshof, Eds.), pp. 121–126. ISMPMI, St. Paul, MN.

Firth, N., Ippen-Ihler, K., and Skurray, R. A. (1996). Structure and function of the F factor and mechanism of conjugation. *In "Escherichia coli* and *Salmonella typhimurium,"* 2nd ed., pp. 2377–2401. American Society for Microbiology, Washington, DC.

Fuqua, W. C., Winans, S. C., and Greenberg, E. P. (1996). Census and consensus in bacterial ecosystems: The LuxR–LuxI family of quorum-sensing transcriptional regulators. *Annu. Rev. Microbiol.* **50**, 727–751.

Nester, E. W., Kemner, J., Deng, W., Lee, Y.-W., Fullner, K., Liang, X., Pan, S., and Heath, J. D. (1996). *Agrobacterium:* A natural genetic engineer exploited for plant biotechnology. *In* "Biology of Plant–Microbe Interactions" (G. Stacey, B. Mullin, and P. Gresshof, Eds.), pp. 111–144. ISMPMI, St. Paul, MN.

Ream, W. (1998). Import of *Agrobacterium tumefaciens* virulence proteins and transferred DNA into plant cell nuclei. *Subcell. Biochem.* **29**, 365–384.

Sheng, J., and Citovsky, V. (1996). *Agrobacterium*–plant cell DNA transport: Have virulence proteins, will travel. *Plant Cell* **8**, 1699–1710.

Spudich, G. M., Dang, T. A. T., Fernandez, D., Zhou, X.-R., and Christie, P. J. (1996). Organization and assembly of the *Agrobacterium tumefaciens* T-complex transport apparatus. *In* "Crown Gall: Advances in Understanding Interkingdom Gene Transfer" (W. Ream and S. Gelvin, Eds.), pp. 75–98. APS Press, St. Paul, MN.

Winans, S. C., Burns, D. L., and Christie, P. J. (1996). Adaptation of a conjugal transfer system for the export of pathogenic macromolecules. *Trends Microbiol.* **4**, 1616–1622.

Zupan, J. R., and Zambryski, P. (1995). Transfer of T-DNA from *Agrobacterium* to the plant cell. *Plant Physiol.* **107**, 1041–1047.

# AIDS, Historical

## David Shumway Jones and Allan M. Brandt

*Harvard Medical School*

## GLOSSARY

**enzyme-linked immunosorbent assay**  An assay used in combination with a Western blot as an effective blood screening test for HIV.

**highly active anti-retroviral therapy**  Combination therapies, typically one protease inhibitor and two reverse transcriptase inhibitors, that have powerful inhibitory effects against HIV reproduction.

**human immunodeficiency virus (HIV)**  An RNA retrovirus identified as the causative agent of AIDS. It is related to a series of Simian immunodeficiency viruses.

**opportunistic infections**  Infections that do not cause significant disease in nonimmunocompromised hosts but that can cause severe disease in victims of AIDS (e.g., Kaposi's sarcoma and *Pneumocystic carinii* pneumonia).

**stigmatization**  The process by which the stigma attached to certain behaviors, notably homosexuality and intravenous drug use, became transferred to AIDS itself, having a substantial impact on theories of, and responses to, the disease.

**ACQUIRED IMMUNE DEFICIENCY SYNDROME (AIDS),**  first identified in 1981, is an infectious disease caused by the human immunodeficiency virus (HIV). The virus attacks the host's immune system, causing its eventual failure. This failure leaves affected individuals vulnerable to many infections and cancers, leading inexorably to severe morbidity and high mortality. Substantial evidence suggests that HIV emerged in the middle of the twentieth century, following the infection of humans with simian immunodeficiency viruses. Spread sexually and through blood, it penetrated populations in Africa, Europe, and the United States in the 1970s. AIDS appeared in the 1980s, caused considerable fear, and provoked dramatic social responses. Despite rapid progress in scientific understanding and medical treatment of the disease, and despite the existence of adequate preventive technologies, HIV spread rapidly throughout the world in the 1980s and 1990s. Disparities in risk of infection and in access to treatment expose critical inequities in the distribution of social and medical resources within developed and developing countries.

## I. PATHOPHYSIOLOGY OF HIV AND AIDS

HIV cripples the body's immune system, making an infected individual vulnerable to other disease-causing agents in the environment. It has an icosahedral structure, with RNA wound around a protein core, enclosed within an envelope formed primarily of two proteins, gp120 and gp41. The retrovirus attacks cells by binding to the CD4 molecule and a coreceptor on the cellular membrane. Once the virion has entered the cytoplasm, a viral enzyme, reverse transcriptase, translates the viral RNA into DNA. Viral DNA, which contains nine genes, is then inserted, by a viral integrase, into the genome of the infected cell. Host machinery transcribes and translates the viral DNA, producing a single long protein. This protein is then cleaved by the HIV protease into reverse transcriptase, the envelope proteins, and the core proteins. New virions are then assembled and bud from the infected host cell.

HIV primarily targets the CD4+ subset of T lymphocytes, known as the helper T cells, which regulate crucial aspects of the normal immune response. However, any cell which expresses CD4 can be infected; infection has been reported in macrophages, epithelial cells in the gastrointestinal and urinary tracts, astrocytes, microglial cells, cardiac myocytes, and a variety of other cell types. Infected individuals can transmit infection through blood, semen, and other genital secretions. Heterosexual transmission is responsible for 70% of infections worldwide. Substantial transmission has also occurred through maternal–fetal infection, homosexual contact, needle sharing by intravenous drug users (IDUs), and contaminated blood products. Transmission has also been reported through organ donation, renal dialysis, artificial insemination, and acupuncture.

Infection initially produces a surge in viral load in the victim's blood (viremia). The viremia triggers a vigorous immune response: Antibodies are generated and the infection is initially contained. This first stage of infection often goes unnoticed, although some individuals experience a flu-like prodromal syndrome characterized by fever, rash, and malaise. After this initial stage, an individual may remain free of symptoms for many years. During this time, the virus continues to attack the immune system and gradually gains the upper hand: The individual's CD4+ count slowly but steadily declines as the immune system becomes increasingly compromised. This latent period, in which hosts are generally healthy, typically lasts 10 years. However, some patients progress to AIDS within a year after infection with HIV, whereas others remain disease-free more than 20 years after infection.

Clinical presentations of AIDS have varied over the course of the epidemic and between different countries. In the United States, the first cases manifested as opportunistic infections with *Pneumocystis carinii* pneumonia (PCP) or as unusual cases of Kaposi's sarcoma (KS). In African countries, a syndrome of chronic diarrhea and severe weight loss ("slim disease") was common; many cases also presented with tuberculosis. The most recent (1993)

criteria for AIDS include CD4+ count below 200 (normally at least 800); a range of opportunistic infections, including tuberculosis; several cancers, notably KS, lymphomas, and invasive cervical cancer; AIDS encephalitis (dementia and severe cognitive and motor deficits); and AIDS wasting syndrome.

HIV is accepted as the causative agent of AIDS by an overwhelming majority of physicians, scientists, and public health experts. However, opposition to this explanation appeared early in the epidemic and has persisted. Noting the existence of cases of AIDS in HIV-negative individuals (idiopathic CD4+ lymphocytopenia), some observers suggested that HIV is an insufficient explanation for AIDS. One theory holds that HIV as well as other factors trigger an autoimmune response which produces the immunodeficiency. Another theory replaces the infection model with a pollution model: A combination of recreational drug use, misuse of antibiotics, multiple sexually transmitted diseases, exposure to impure blood products, and malnutrition all converge to produce AIDS.

## II. ORIGINS OF HIV

HIV was first isolated in January 1983 by Francis Barré-Sinoussi and Luc Montagnier at the Pasteur Institute in Paris. They named it lymphadenopathy virus (LAV) and suspected that it might be the cause of AIDS. In April 1984, Robert Gallo and his team at the National Institutes of Health announced the discovery of another virus which appeared to be the cause of AIDS. Recognizing the virus as a retrovirus related to two retroviruses which Gallo had previously shown to cause lymphoma, they named it human T-lymphotropic virus type 3 (HTLV-III). A third group, led by Jay Levy at the University of California at San Francisco, independently isolated the causative agent of AIDS. After a bitter priority dispute between Montagnier and Gallo, researchers realized that LAV and HTLV-III were the same virus. In 1986 an international commission officially assigned the name HIV. In 1985, a second virus, HIV-2, was identified in some cases of AIDS in West Africa. In 1994, two subgroups of HIV-1 were described—HIV-1 group M (main) and HIV-1 group

O (outlier). In 1998 a third subgroup was described, HIV-1 group N (non-M/non-O), in two individuals in Cameroon. HIV-1 M accounts for 99% of all cases of AIDS. Subsequent work has described 10 subtypes of HIV-1 group M (A–J) which vary in geographic distribution and affinity for modes of transmission.

Careful analysis of viral genetics and host phylogeny has revealed the origins of HIV. The family of retroviruses has two main divisions. The first division, oncoviruses, had been described in animals early in this century. By 1970, the life history of oncogenic retroviruses had been well characterized. Gallo described the first human retroviral pathogen, HTLV-1, in 1980. The second division, the lentiviruses, are cytopathic and not oncogenic. They have been found in a variety of animal species, including horses, goats, humans, and other primates. A group of simian immunodeficiency viruses (SIVs) are the closest relatives of HIV.

The first SIV was identified in 1985 from a rhesus monkey (in captivity) with an AIDS-like illness. Further testing of monkey species has shown that five different strains of SIV can be found in five different species of African primates: sooty mangabeys, African green monkeys, Sykes monkeys, mandrills, and chimpanzees. SIV has never been found in wild primates outside of Africa. Genetic analysis of the different strains suggests a common origin in Africa in the Pleistocene Epoch. Each strain is harmless in its natural host, a fact consistent with the ancient association between the viral strains and their natural hosts. However, when a strain infects an individual from another species, an AIDS-like illness results. For instance, the rhesus monkey from which SIV was first identified was infected with SIVsm (from the sooty mangabey).

HIV seems to reflect a similar phenomena: the infection of humans with different strains of SIV. Links were first made between HIV-2 and SIVsm. Human infections of HIV-2 are found primarily in Sierra Leone, Liberia, and Cote d'Ivoire, countries in which sooty mangabeys are hunted and kept as household pets. Sooty mangabeys in these areas carry strains of SIVsm most closely related to HIV-2. A link between HIV-1 and chimpanzees (SIVcpz) was long suspected but not documented until 1999. Recent analysis has shown that HIV-1 is most closely related to strains of SIVcpz found in a single subspecies of chimpanzee, *Pan troglodytes troglodytes*. The natural range of this subspecies, in Cameroon, Gabon, and equatorial Africa, corresponds with the purported epicenter of HIV infection in humans. The three different groups of HIV-1 (M, N, and O) represent infection of humans with three different strains of SIVcpz.

The AIDS epidemic marks the first time that this organism has spread widely in the human population. Researchers have scrutinized collections of old blood samples searching for early evidence of the presence of HIV. The oldest evidence comes from a 1959 sample from Leopoldville (Kinshasa), Congo. This strain is the common ancestor of three of the current subtypes of HIV-1 group M. The evidence suggests that transmission from primates to humans happened multiple times in the 1940s and 1950s. It is possible that HIV, and AIDS, existed prior to this but was masked by the high prevalence of tuberculosis. Alternatively, HIV might have existed in a non-virulent form until some point in the middle of the twentieth century when it attained a critical combination of virulence and transmissibility. In any case, the apparent rapid evolution of HIV over several decades is a harbinger of changes yet to come.

## III. EMERGENCE AND RECOGNITION OF AIDS

The first cases of AIDS were described in 1981. However, researchers have examined medical records from previous decades to assign retrospective diagnoses of AIDS and reconstruct the prehistory of the epidemic. Although the earliest blood sample of HIV comes from Leopoldville in 1959, the earliest case of AIDS comes from Norway. In 1966, a Norwegian sailor developed lymphadenopathy with recurrent colds. He died in 1976 at age 29 of dementia and pneumonia. His wife and daughter also died of opportunistic infections. Blood samples from all three, taken between 1971 and 1973, tested positive for HIV-1 O. The sailor, who had traveled to Cameroon in 1961 and 1962 and been treated for gonorrhea during the trip, was likely infected then and passed the infection on to his wife and daughter.

The earliest case in the United States has been identified in a teenager from St. Louis. Diagnosed with a severe chlamydial infection in 1968, he died at age 15 in 1969. Autopsy revealed extensive, aggressive KS. Tests on surviving blood samples performed in 1987 confirmed the diagnosis of HIV. Screening of surviving blood samples has revealed the insidious spread of HIV in Africa and the United States. Samples from sub-Saharan Africa show a prevalence of 0.1% in 1959, 0.3% in 1970, and 3% in 1980. Data from clinics for IDUs in New York City show that HIV had entered the city by 1976; 9% of IDUs were infected by 1978, 26% by 1979, 39% by 1980, 50% between 1981 and 1983, and 55–60% by 1984. Other evidence, although not supported with blood tests, is suggestive. Dozens of cases, apparently AIDS, can be found from Africa, Europe, and the United States in the 1970s. These data suggest that HIV existed but was rare in human populations in the 1950s. By the 1970s, parallel epidemics had begun in sub-Saharan Africa, the United States, and Europe. Initially HIV spread invisibly, hidden by its long latency.

In the late 1970s, physicians in New York and California noted the increasing occurrence of KS, PCP, and other rare infections among previously healthy young men. Because of the unusual nature of these diseases, which are typically associated with a failure of the immune system, epidemiologists began to search for characteristics that might link the cases. In the summer of 1981, Michael Gottlieb described an outbreak of PCP among five homosexual men in Los Angeles. By the end of the year, similar cases, as well as unusual cases of KS, had been described among homosexuals and IDUs and female sexual partners of IDUs in Los Angeles, San Francisco, New York City, and Europe. Researchers traced these opportunistic infections to a specific deficit in CD4+ cells. Although several risk groups had been identified, etiological hypotheses focused on particular aspects of "fast-track" gay culture which might explain the outbreak of the disease, including use of amyl nitrite ("poppers") and steroid skin creams, antigen overload, and pathogenic sperm. Some researchers suggested a link to cytomegalovirus.

Other risk groups were identified in 1982. Researchers traced similar cases to contaminated blood products, both blood transfusions and clotting factors used by patients with hemophilia. Tragically, although the risk posed by clotting factor concentrates was soon recognized, many hemophiliacs often had no choice but to continue taking them; eventually, 10,000 individuals were infected in the United States. During the summer of 1982, deaths from opportunistic infections, notably toxoplasmosis, were described among Haitians at detention camps in Florida. The occurrence of cases in diverse risk groups, including gay men, IDUs, heterosexual partners, hemophiliacs, and Haitians, suggested infection with a blood-borne agent. In September 1982, the Centers for Disease Control and Prevention (CDC) replaced the range of early labels [gay plague, gay cancer, and GRID (gay-related immune deficiency)] with a more neutral term: AIDS. By the end of the year, more than 1000 cases had been described.

By early 1983, the CDC had defined AIDS as the result of infection with an unknown transmissible agent, characterized its mode of transmission, and defined four risk groups (the "4H club"): homosexuals, heroin addicts, hemophiliacs, and Haitians. Barré-Sinoussi and Montagnier had isolated LAV. Recognizing that many European cases had links to Africa, researchers speculated that Africa might be the source of the infection. On April 23, 1984, Robert Gallo announced that he had isolated the cause of AIDS—HTLV-III. This allowed the rapid development of a screening test. Identification of HIV allowed intensive scientific scrutiny of the virus. The fortuitous emergence of HIV at exactly the moment when scientists had developed the techniques needed to study it allowed rapid progress in understanding the biology and pathophysiology of the virus. The problems posed by the virus—biologically, clinically, and epidemiologically—quickly moved virology and molecular immunology onto the center stage of scientific research.

In March 1985, the first blood screening tests were licensed. The enzyme-linked immunosorbent assay (ELISA) and Western blot do not detect the virus; instead, they identify the high levels of antibody which are produced in most infected individuals. These tests allowed officials to screen donated blood and protect the blood supply from HIV. They also allowed testing for epidemiological and diagnostic purposes. In 1986, the name of the virus was officially changed to HIV, and HIV-2 was recognized. By 1989, there were 100,000 victims of AIDS in the United States, and by 1991 there were 200,000.

The first cases in Africa were described in Uganda in 1982. Reports from Zaire and Rwanda of patients with slim disease (diarrhea and weight loss), KS, thrush (oral candidiasis), and meningitis began to appear in 1983 and 1984. By 1985, with additional cases in Kenya and Tanzania, the World Health Organization (WHO) began to fear a vast epidemic in Africa. Approximately 90% of the African cases have been heterosexual patients. The first appearance of AIDS in Thailand was described in 1984, but reported rates remained low for several years. Rapid spread began in 1988. Prevalence among IDUs and commercial sex workers quickly approached 50%. By 1991, it had spread into the general population: 10–15% of military conscripts were infected.

In contrast to the rapid spread in these areas, some regions were initially spared. There were few cases of AIDS in Japan in the 1980s, and these were mostly limited to transmission from blood products, which were often imported from the United States. The Soviet Union and Eastern Europe reported few cases before the breakup of the Soviet empire, and most of the acknowledged cases were the result of iatrogenic transmission. For instance, in 1990, Romania reported HIV among 2000 children who had been abandoned by their parents. According to folk practice, many newborns received small blood transfusions to increase their strength; this practice exposed the infants to unsterilized needles and a contaminated blood supply.

As this early history shows, many biological and social factors contributed to the rapid spread of HIV in diverse populations. HIV emerged in Africa during the turbulent social changes which followed decolonialization after World War II. Civil wars produced migrations of refugees. Urbanization disrupted traditional social practices, marginalized women, and promoted prostitution. Improved transportation allowed HIV to spread more rapidly. Increased government spending on military programs sacrificed social services and education. Poorly funded health care programs had to re-use needles; inadequate sterilization facilitated the spread of HIV. Major vaccination campaigns, notably the smallpox eradication program of the 1960s and 1970s, might also have played a role.

Other theories reflect specific cultural biases and concerns. Early commentators blamed specific behaviors that might have spread infection from monkeys to humans, such as the reported use of monkey blood as an aphrodisiac. Some blamed ecological disruption, particularly the destruction of tropical rain forests. In 1985, Soviet and Indian media reported that HIV had been created by biological warfare experts in the United States and tested in Zaire in 1978. This theory received considerable discussion at the Third International Conference on AIDS held in 1987. Investigation has shown that these rumors were actively spread by the KGB beginning in 1983.

The expansion of international commerce and transportation provided increasing opportunities for infected individuals to carry HIV between countries. International aid workers brought the virus from Africa back to their home countries. Tourists who indulged in commercial sex industries became infected. Once HIV gained access to industrialized countries, it had many routes from which to spread. Needle sharing spread HIV among IDUs in New York City in the late 1970s. Also in the 1970s, the flowering of gay identity occurred, particularly in San Francisco; for some gay men, promiscuous, anonymous sex became an important part of their culture. Blood sharing technologies, particularly transfusion and fractionated blood products, had also become more widespread.

## IV. FEAR AND FRUSTRATION IN THE 1980s

As scientists struggled to characterize AIDS and HIV, the epidemic caused considerable suffering and generated a worldwide health crisis. The epidemic began at a moment of relative complacency, especially in the developed world, concerning epidemic infectious disease. Not since the influenza epidemic of 1918–1920 had an epidemic with such devastating potential struck. Developed countries had experienced a health transition from the predominance of infectious to chronic disease and had focused their resources and attention on systemic, non-infectious diseases. In this respect, AIDS appeared at a historical moment in which there was little social or political experience in confronting a public health crisis of its dimension. The epidemic fractured a widely held belief in medical security.

Not surprisingly, early sociopolitical responses were characterized by blame and discrimination. AIDS first appeared among homosexuals and IDUs, two of the most marginalized groups in society. Echoing earlier assessments of other sexually transmitted diseases, observers divided victims of HIV into categories: the "innocent victims," who acquired their infections through transfusions or perinatally, and the "guilty perpetrators," who engaged in high-risk, morally condemnable behaviors. Since the disease was associated with "voluntary" behaviors considered to be immoral, illegal, or both, individuals were typically blamed for their disease (Fig. 1). Some religious groups in the United States, for example, saw the epidemic as an occasion to reiterate particular moral views about sexual behavior, drug use, sin, and disease: AIDS was viewed as "proof" of a certain moral order. Hostile commentators called for a series of regressive, even punitive, measures to control the epidemic, including universal testing and quarantine. Although such measures were never implemented, victims did suffer from discriminatory behavior, including loss of jobs, housing, and insurance. Homophobia became more visible as violence against gays and lesbians increased. The Food and Drug Adminis-

tration (FDA) barred blood donations by members of the risk groups, including all Haitians.

During this early period of the epidemic in the United States, there was also considerable fear of casual transmission, despite reassurances that HIV could only spread through blood or sexual contact. A 1985 poll showed that 47% of Americans believed that infection could be transmitted through shared drinking glasses, and 28% feared infection through toilet seats. The link between AIDS and receiving blood transfusion became transformed into a belief that one could be infected by donating blood. Realtors in California were instructed to warn customers if a house had previously been owned by someone with AIDS. In some communities, parents protested when HIV-infected schoolchildren were permitted to attend school. In one instance, a family with an HIV-infected child—an "innocent victim"—was driven from a Florida town when their home was burned down.

As the disease, deadly and poorly understood, continued to spread, governments and victims' advocacy groups struggled to make difficult decisions. The debates about bath houses are particularly revealing. In the 1970s, an outbreak of hepatitis B revealed that these bath houses, and the sexual behaviors they facilitated, had become dangerous sites of disease transmission. In the early 1980s, they were recognized as a dominant site of transmission of HIV. Many public health officials demanded that they be

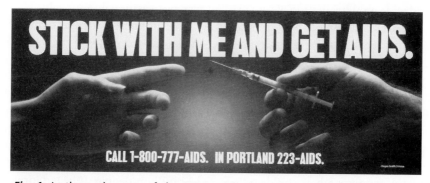

***Fig. 1.*** In the early years of the AIDS epidemic in the United States, AIDS was associated with a series of stigmatized behaviors, as in this poster indicating the risk of shared needles among intravenous drug users. Such stigmatization blamed victims for their disease and hindered early public health efforts to contain the spread of HIV.

closed. The gay community was torn between those who saw bath houses as an essential expression of gay identity and those who feared the growing impact of AIDS. San Francisco shut down its bath houses in 1984, but similar efforts failed in Los Angeles.

Initially, the United States government showed little interest in AIDS. The defined risk groups had little political clout and even less political appeal to the conservative administration of Ronald Reagan. Failing to display leadership crucially needed in the early years of the epidemic, his administration repeatedly denied the need to make special appropriations for HIV and AIDS. However, as the potential ramification of the epidemic became evident, national institutions began to mobilize. Congressional appropriations for research and education increased steeply. The National Academy of Sciences and a presidential commission both issued prominent reports. Meanwhile, international programs proliferated. Medical researchers organized an annual series of international conferences on AIDS beginning in 1985. The WHO established a global program on AIDS in 1986, under the direction of Jonathan Mann, to coordinate international efforts in epidemiologic surveillance, education, prevention, and research. The WHO also tried to guide responses to the epidemic, lobbying against the use of coercive measures such as Cuba's experiment with mandatory isolation of HIV-infected individuals. Instead, it advocated for the use of less restrictive measures to contain the epidemic.

Circumstances changed dramatically in 1985 with the development and wide implementation of screening tests. Just as the CDC definition of four risk groups shaped the early years of the epidemic, the ELISA and Western blot generated a new range of responses to the epidemic. The tests quickly became a crucial method of reassurance: For the first time, people could know whether or not they were infected without the uncertainty of the long latency which preceded the symptoms of AIDS. With the ability to detect HIV, epidemiologists could trace the spread of the epidemic directly, and researchers could study early clinical stages of infection. The tests also allowed public health officials to reestablish the safety of the blood supply. Prior to this, blood banks could only reduce risk by restricting donations from de-

fined risk groups and testing for various surrogates such as hepatitis B, a virus which shares many of the epidemiological characteristics of HIV. Despite these methods, more than 10,000 people were infected by blood products in the United States by 1985. However, with the implementation of universal screening, the safety of the blood supply quickly improved: Since then, there have only been 40 transfusion-related cases of AIDS in the United States.

The advent of screening, however, raised difficult issues about the balance of individual rights and public health. The ability to screen for HIV made it likely that people who were infected but still healthy would suffer the full burden of discrimination faced by people with AIDS. Many questions were debated: Should public health officials require mandatory reporting and case tracing of HIV? Should states demand premarital testing as they did for syphilis? Should employers be able to screen prospective employees? Should health insurers be able to screen prospective customers? Should hospitals be able to test all patients, and should patients be able to demand testing of their doctors? The Department of Defense, citing the risks posed by its vaccination programs and by potential battlefield transfusions, began screening all recruits in 1985; critics of this policy viewed it as a thinly veiled effort to enforce the military's ban on homosexuals. Heated controversy also arose in 1987 when Congress forced the CDC to add HIV to the list of "dangerous contagious diseases" which would be used to ban immigrants from the United States, despite evidence that HIV was not easily communicable.

For the most part, the rights of privacy won out in the United States. Few states required reporting of HIV at a time when reporting of other diseases, from tuberculosis to syphilis, was routine. In other countries the situation was quite different. The Soviet Union, for instance, implemented a massive compulsory testing program. Travelers, homosexuals, soldiers, pregnant women prisoners, and those thought to engage in casual sex were all tested—a total of 142 million people. Infected foreigners were banned from entering the country. The advent of screening also set the stage for a series of tragic scandals. In the United States, public and private blood banks implemented screening relatively quickly. In other countries, notably France and Japan, the tests were not immediately implemented. Thousands of patients, particularly hemophiliacs, were infected. Subsequent investigations have ended in both civil and criminal convictions, with prison sentences for negligent officials and substantial payments to infected victims.

Although the ability to screen for HIV reduced many of the fears associated with the epidemic, many new fears quickly emerged. By 1986, two factors fueled increasing fear in developed countries that heterosexual spread would bring HIV into the general population. First, public health officials began to shift the emphasis from the stigmatized "risk groups" to more precise "risk behaviors," stressing that dangerous behaviors, such as needle sharing and anal intercourse, could be found among people not identified as IDUs or homosexuals (Fig. 2). Second, epidemiologists realized that heterosexual transmission was the dominant mode of spread in Africa and Haiti. Since these epidemics were believed to have begun earlier than those in Europe and the United States,

they were perceived as glimpses into the future of AIDS in Europe and the United States.

The fears were exacerbated by slow progress in developing treatments for HIV and AIDS. Many treatments were hailed initially, including interleukin-2, α interferon, bone marrow transplants, heteropolyanion (HPA-23), and various immune stimulants. However, subsequent work inevitably showed them to be both toxic and of little value. Despite optimistic claims that a vaccine would be available by 1986, researchers had little to show for their efforts by 1988 other than skepticism and pessimism. In the absence of vaccines or treatments, physicians, patients, and public health officials had few options. Health officials advocated prevention through risk elimination, particularly abstinence from sex. Patients with HIV tried diets and alternative medicines to delay the progression to AIDS. Doctors, powerless to stop HIV, could only work to prevent, and then treat, the devastating opportunistic infections of AIDS.

One particular source of frustration for AIDS

*Fig. 2.* During the late 1980s, public health officials increasingly recognized the threat of spread of HIV through heterosexual contact. Campaigns such as this one, moving outside of the traditional risk groups, encouraged women to protect themselves from incurable infection with HIV.

control efforts was the political turmoil which prevented the implementation of many public health programs. Once the two primary modes of transmission had been identified—sexual intercourse and needle sharing by IDUs—two modes of prevention became obvious: free distribution of condoms and sterile needles. In some countries, notably The Netherlands, England, and Canada, such programs were implemented. In the United States, however, the conservative federal government criticized condom and needle distribution programs as condoning morally and legally sanctioned behaviors. In the absence of federal support, grass-roots needle exchange programs were begun in Boston, New Haven, Connecticut, New York, and San Francisco. Some programs received support from local governments, whereas others faced opposition and arrests. Such marginalization seriously impaired efforts to slow the spread of HIV.

Even the excitement over the development of azidothymidine (AZT), the first effective treatment for HIV, was dampened by pessimism and controversy. Once HIV was identified, pharmaceutical companies began screening drug compounds for antiviral activity. In 1985, AZT was shown to block reverse-transcriptase. On the basis of promising results from clinical trials, Burroughs Wellcome received authorization to market AZT in 1987. However, further study showed that HIV could quickly become resistant to AZT, and that AZT conferred little or no long-term survival benefit. Meanwhile, the research process became highly politicized. AIDS activists protested cumbersome FDA regulations which slowed the approval of new drugs. The AIDS Coalition to Unleash Power (ACT UP), founded in 1987 by playwright Larry Kramer, issued scathing critiques, sought increased funding for drug research, and demanded more rapid access to promising treatments. ACT UP also organized drug sharing, buyers clubs, and basement laboratories to provide underground access to potentially valuable treatments. Such advocacy eventually led to major reforms in FDA policy which have facilitated the testing and licensing of new treatments for HIV and AIDS.

By the end of the decade, the panic created by the emergence of AIDS had settled into a new equilibrium. Incidence rates began to level off in Europe and the United States. Public faith in the safety of the blood supply had been restored. Education efforts curtailed the spread of HIV among homosexuals. Fears that HIV would spread into the general population diminished. New cases remained confined to marginalized groups, notably urban minority populations. Even the clinical manifestations of AIDS began to shift: Chronic problems, such as AIDS wasting, became increasingly common as PCP and KS became better controlled. AIDS was no longer seen as a wildfire epidemic that would sweep the globe and threaten civilization. Once compared to the great epidemics of the past—plague, cholera, and influenza—AIDS now evoked comparisons to chronic diseases, particularly cancer. It had become institutionalized with governments, hospitals, and pharmaceutical companies. It had become routinized.

This routinization had adverse consequences. Officials in the United States feared that increased public apathy would lead to decreased vigilance, allowing a resurgence of the epidemic (Fig. 3). Meanwhile, HIV had continued to spread explosively in developing countries. Between 1981 and 1992, the number of cases of HIV in Thailand increased from 0.1 million to 12.1 million—more than a 100-fold increase in just over a decade. However, developed countries, no longer fearing a global pandemic, had become less supportive: International assistance of AIDS decreased for the first time between 1991 and 1992. Much progress had been made, and some fears had abated, but the epidemic continued.

## V. HOPE AND FRUSTRATION IN THE 1990s

As had happened in the past, new discoveries rekindled excitement and hope about HIV and AIDS. By 1991, several new reverse transcriptase inhibitors became available (ddI, ddC, and 3TC); physicians hoped that combination therapy would be more powerful than AZT. In 1994, AZT was shown to reduce maternal–fetal transmission of HIV by more than 50%; this provided a method of preventing a significant burden of new cases of HIV. New techniques allowed physicians to monitor directly the viral load of HIV in the blood of patients. New understanding

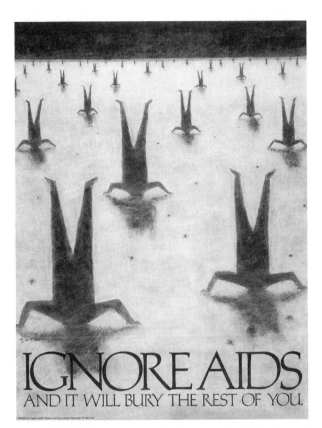

**IGNORE AIDS**
AND IT WILL BURY THE REST OF YOU.

***Fig. 3.*** Belief that HIV would not spread widely beyond traditional risk groups, or beyond marginalized urban populations, generated considerable apathy among many people. Public health officials tried to overcome this apathy by highlighting the general threat that would be posed if HIV were not acknowledged and managed.

of the pathogenesis of HIV suggested new targets for pharmacological intervention: In 1991, researchers hoped that they would soon be able to block the HIV protease, crippling the activity of HIV. The first protease inhibitor, Saquinavir, was approved by the FDA in December 1995 and was soon implemented in conjunction with two reverse transcriptase inhibitors.

This "triple therapy" [highly active anti-retroviral therapy (HAART)] proved to be a powerful weapon against HIV: It could reduce viral load to undetectable levels in some patients. At the 11th Annual International Conference on AIDS in Vancouver in 1996, it was celebrated as a "quantum leap" in HIV treatment. Cautious optimism took root as clinical trials demonstrated the value of HAART.

Combined with continuing preventive programs, HAART radically transformed the epidemiology of HIV in developed countries. Starting in 1995, AIDS deaths decreased in the United States, Europe, Canada, Australia, and New Zealand. The incidence of HIV began to decrease. AIDS, which had been the leading cause of death in young men in 1995, decreased to the fifth leading cause of death. Physicians hoped that it might even be possible to eliminate HIV from patients—curing them of their disease.

However, as had happened previously, initial optimism soon gave way to more realistic expectations. Within 2 years, the limits of HAART had become clear. Outcomes in clinical practice were inferior to those attained in clinical trials. Patients struggled to follow difficult regimens, which required that up to 16 pills be taken each day. Physicians feared that non-adherence to drug regimens would facilitate the emergence of resistant strains. Finally, the regimens were extremely expensive—typically $10,000–20,000 per patient per year. Rapid development of more drugs, including two protease inhibitors and a new class of non-nucleoside reverse transcriptase inhibitors, raised hopes that simpler drug regimens would solve many of these problems. However, researchers increasingly realized that the ability of HIV to insert its genetic material in the genome of host cells made eradication nearly impossible: If treatment were ever stopped, these internal reservoirs of HIV could become seeds of re-infection.

The limits of HAART have re-emphasized the primary importance of prevention. However, as before, preventive efforts remain mired in political debate. For instance, political opposition to needle exchange programs continues, despite evidence that they are the most effective means of preventing HIV among IDUs and that they might actually decrease the prevalence of drug use, presumably because the site of needle exchange becomes a valuable site for educational programs.

The presence of a powerful, if imperfect, treatment regimen and continuing evidence of decreasing AIDS mortality in developed countries facilitated changing attitudes toward the disease. A diagnosis of HIV no longer seemed to be the life-ending event it had been in the 1980s. Patients could hope for therapeutic success, especially if the infection was diagnosed at an early stage. This enabled new policies for HIV testing. In 1996, the FDA licensed home test kits for HIV; although testing services were regulated to ensure that patients who received positive test results by telephone also received adequate counseling, HIV testing became nearly as simple as home-pregnancy tests. Similarly, health officials, physicians, and patient groups became more willing to accept control measures that, during the height of AIDS fear, would have been dismissed as unacceptable infringements of civil liberties. By 1998, 30 states (but representing only 30% of all cases) had established some form of mandatory reporting of HIV. Similar advocacy has begun for mandatory prenatal testing to enable treatment to prevent vertical transmission to the fetus.

This new comfort and optimism toward HIV in developed countries stand in stark contrast to the continuing devastation of developing countries by AIDS. As of the end of 1998, more than 33 million people have been infected with HIV and there have been nearly 14 million deaths from AIDS, 90% of which occurred in developing countries. Most of the victims do not realize they are infected. With a global prevalence of 1% of all people aged 15–49, AIDS will undermine the hopes of developing economies and reverse many of the post-World War II gains in life expectancy.

The explosive spread of HIV began in sub-Saharan Africa, which continues to be the most seriously afflicted area. Estimates suggest that 3% of the African population is infected. Prevalence among risk groups, notably soldiers, truck drivers, migrant farmers, and commercial sex workers, can approach 90%. As many as 30% of women visiting prenatal clinics are infected; high maternal death rates have created a growing burden of AIDS orphans. At the same time, many countries which reported little AIDS in the 1980s now experience growing epidemics. Ukraine, which reported only 44 cases by 1994, had 15,000 cases by 1997. China reported few cases in the early 1990s, but spread among IDUs and commercial sex workers resulted in 200,000 cases by 1996 and 400,000 by 1998. India, which reported only 855 cases by 1990, had 70,000 by 1997, with rates as high as 70% among IDUs. With 3–5 million cases of HIV, India currently has the highest national caseload; by 2000, its burden might exceed that of sub-

Saharan Africa. In developing countries, most transmission (70% of all cases globally) occurs through heterosexual contact, and tuberculosis is the leading cause of death.

In the midst of this calamity, there have been remarkable successes at slowing the spread of HIV through preventive programs, including education, drug treatment, employment, and distribution of condoms and clean needles. In Uganda, education programs have decreased the number of sexually active teenagers and increased condom use. Knowing that the presence of other sexually transmitted diseases (STDs) substantially increases the risk of transmitting HIV, officials in Tanzania implemented an STD treatment program which led to a 42% reduction in the incidence of HIV. Aided by the WHO, the Thai government began a major campaign for public education and condom use by prostitutes; as a result, prevalence among commercial sex workers and their clients decreased between 1993 and 1997. Many of these public health programs must make difficult choices. Breast-feeding, for instance, can transmit infection from a mother to a child. However, most infected women in developing countries remain unaware of their infection. Even if they did know, they would have to choose between the risk of breast-feeding and the risk of infant formula with a contaminated water supply.

Health officials believe that vaccines will ultimately provide the best solution for the long-term control and prevention of HIV in developing countries. An ideal vaccine would be safe, cheap, and stable enough for mass vaccination campaigns; it would provide long-lived protection; and it would be active against the diverse subtypes of HIV. Such a vaccine remains the Holy Grail of AIDS research: Despite more than 15 years of research, there has been little success. Researchers predict that a vaccine will not be available for many years; some even confess that the task might be impossible. However, work continues with the hope that even a partial success would be valuable: Even if it did not prevent infection, a "therapeutic vaccine" which strengthened a victim's response to the infection would be of tremendous value.

The greatest frustration of health officials in developing countries is that the powerful therapies which are now available in developed countries, particularly HAART, are far too expensive to be available to 95% of all people with HIV. Faced with limited resources, some officials have argued that they should shift their focus from HIV to tuberculosis (TB): Although the underlying disease would go unchecked, treatment of TB could improve health and prolong lives at much less cost. Others have sought to adapt lower cost versions of existing treatment programs. However, such research, as did a 1997 trial of a shorter and cheaper regimen of AZT to prevent maternal–fetal transmission of HIV, became embroiled in fierce controversy over whose ethical guidelines should regulate international health research. Such angry confrontations among researchers united by their desire to reduce the suffering created by HIV demonstrate the complicated scientific, social, and moral problems created by the epidemic.

As the end of its second decade of AIDS nears, it has attained a complicated status characterized by a series of striking disparities. Medical research and public health efforts have produced dramatic successes in some areas, whereas the virus spreads, effectively unchecked, in other areas. HIV has been contained in developed countries, but it afflicts some minority populations at a rate 10 times that in the general population. At the same time, HIV has moved from defined risk groups to the general populations of many developing countries. It will continue to spread, especially in Asia, in the next decade. Millions of people now infected with HIV will develop AIDS. At every level, AIDS has been an epidemic created by, and starkly reflecting, inequalities within and between countries: Poverty creates dangerous vulnerabilities to HIV, and AIDS exacerbates poverty. The same inequalities which create the epidemic also hinder responses to it. Although patients in wealthy countries have access to powerful treatments, the vast majority of victims never will: Scientific success has only exposed economic inequality. This raises difficult questions of health and social justice. In the next decades, as efforts are made to manage disparities in incidence and access to treatment in both the United States and abroad, AIDS will continue to lay bare the structures and tensions in society.

## See Also the Following Articles

ECONOMIC CONSEQUENCES OF INFECTIOUS DISEASES • EMERGING INFECTIONS • SEXUALLY TRANSMITTED DISEASES • SYPHILIS, HISTORICAL

## Bibliography

AIDS Education Global Information System (AEGIS). *http://www.aegis.com*.

Farmer, P. (1992). "AIDS and Accusation: Haiti and the Geography of Blame." Univ. of California Press, Berkeley.

Fee, E., and Fox, D. M. (Eds.) (1988). "AIDS: The Burdens of History." Univ. of California Press, Berkeley.

Fee, E., and Fox, D. M. (Eds.) (1992). "AIDS: The Making of a Chronic Disease." Univ. of California Press, Berkeley.

Gao, F., Bailes, E., Robertson, D. L., *et al.* (1999). Origin of HIV-1 in the chimpanzee *Pan troglodytes troglodytes*. *Nature* **397**, 436–441.

Garrett, L. (1994). Hatari: Vinidogodogo (Danger: A very little thing): The origins of AIDS. *In* "The Coming Plague: Newly Emerging Diseases in a World out of Balance" (L. Garrett, Ed.), pp. 281–389. Penguin, New York.

Grmek, M. D. (1990). "History of AIDS: Emergence and Origins of a Modern Pandemic" (R. C. Maulitz and J. Duffin, Trans.). Princeton Univ. Press, Princeton, NJ.

HIV InSite: *http://hivinsite.ucsf.edu*.

Lurie, P., and Wolfe, S. M. (1997). Unethical trials of interventions to reduce perinatal transmission of the human immunodeficiency virus in developing countries. *N. Engl. J. Med.* **337**, 853–856.

Mann, J. M., and Tarantola, D. (1996). "AIDS in the World II: The Global AIDS Policy Coalition." Oxford Univ. Press, New York.

Shilts, R. (1987). "And the Band Played on: Politics, People, and the AIDS Epidemic." St. Martin's, New York.

Treichler, P. (1987). AIDS, homophobia, and biomedical discourse: An epidemic of signification. *October* **43**, 31–70.

Smith, R. A. (Ed.) (1998). "Encyclopedia of AIDS: A Social, Political, and Scientific Record of the HIV Epidemic." Fitzroy Dearborn, Chicago.

Watney, S. (1989). Missionary positions: AIDS, "Africa," and race. *Critical Q.* **31**(3), 45–63.

# Airborne Microorganisms and Indoor Air Quality

Linda D. Stetzenbach and Mark P. Buttner

*University of Nevada, Las Vegas*

I. Microorganisms and Indoor Air Quality
II. Sources of Microbial Contaminants Indoors
III. Monitoring for Airborne Microorganisms

## GLOSSARY

**bioaerosol** An airborne suspension of microorganisms, microbial by-products, and/or pollen.
**building-related illness** Specific adverse health reaction resulting from indoor exposure to a known pollutant or contaminant.
**endotoxin** Component of the cell wall of gram-negative bacteria that can cause adverse health effects.
**microbial volatile organic compounds** Metabolic by-products of microbial metabolism.
**mycotoxin** Toxin associated with fungus.
**sick building syndrome** Random symptoms of illness reported by building occupants when no causative agent has been identified.

**AIRBORNE MICROORGANISMS,** including bacteria, algae, fungi, viruses, and protozoa, are passively transported from one place to another. When these organisms proliferate in indoor environments there is potential for exposure and subsequent adverse health effects for building occupants. Although indoor air quality has been expressed as a problem of modern buildings, concern for the presence of microbial contaminants indoors has been known since ancient times. For example, details of how to rid a dwelling of unwanted contamination are recorded in Chapter 14 of Leviticus in the Bible. Historically, this concern was limited to the prevention of disease transmission by infectious organisms. Today, opportunistic and non-pathogenic organisms, fragments of microbial cells, and microbial metabolites that may result in adverse health effects and allergic reactions are also studied. Numerous microbial sources and reservoirs are present in indoor environments, creating the potential for amplification of surface-associated organisms. These organisms can be aerosolized and transmitted through the air, resulting in exposure to building occupants.

## I. MICROORGANISMS AND INDOOR AIR QUALITY

Numerous factors have been cited as contributing to poor indoor air quality. Environmental tobacco smoke, comfort parameters (temperature and humidity), chemicals (e.g., radon, carbon monoxide, and carbon dioxide), particulate matter, and microorganisms are often linked with occupant complaints. Exposure to airborne contaminants indoors can be a significant health issue because the average human inhales approximately 10 m³ of air per day and spends approximately 22 hr a day in indoor environments.

The excessive reporting of vague, random symptoms such as headache, lethargy, tight chest, fatigue, dizziness, burning eyes, sinus difficulty and flu-like symptoms associated with occupancy of a building has been categorized as sick building syndrome. In contrast, building-related illness occurs when there is a case of specific disease manifested by building occupants as a consequence of exposure to a specific agent in the indoor environment. Legionnaires' disease is an example of building-related illness because this disease has a known etiologic agent (*Legionella pneumophila*) with a defined clinical profile readily diagnosed by a physician. Illnesses classified as sick

*Encyclopedia of Microbiology, Volume 1*
SECOND EDITION

**116**

Copyright © 2000 by Academic Press
All rights of reproduction in any form reserved.

building syndrome are difficult to diagnose because there is no easily recognized agent and no definitive clinical symptoms.

## A. Microorganisms

The microorganisms associated with indoor air quality complaints include viruses, bacteria, fungi, algae and free-living parasites.

### 1. Viruses

Viruses are submicroscopic (0.01–0.3 $\mu$m) non-cellular genetic elements consisting of nucleic acid surrounded by a protein coat. Viruses require a living host for replication. Outside of a host cell viruses are metabolically inert because they have no biosynthetic function and no respiratory function. Unlike other microorganisms, viruses do not increase in number on surfaces in the indoor environment. Air serves as a dispersal mechanism to carry virus particles from one infected individual to another. Many viruses, such as mumps, measles, polio, and chicken pox, are transmitted human to human through the air and casual contact. Numerous cold and flu viruses are produced in the nose and throat of infected persons and these viruses can then be expelled with talking and coughing. Hantavirus is a newly recognized organism that can cause severe pneumonia and death when transmitted to humans via aerosolized virus secreted in mouse urine and feces.

### 2. Bacteria

Bacteria are single-celled microorganisms approximately 0.5–2 $\mu$m in size. Bacteria are ubiquitous in nature and have self-directed biosynthesis so they can multiply indoors on many surfaces. Several bacteria may cause illness in building occupants. Table I lists some examples of airborne bacterial contaminants associated with adverse health effects indoors. The three predominant groups of bacteria in the environment are gram-positive cocci, gram-positive bacilli, and gram-negative bacilli.

#### a. Gram-Positive Cocci

Gram-positive cocci, which include the genera *Micrococcus*, *Staphylococcus*, and *Streptococcus*, comprise approximately 85–90% of culturable microorganisms in air samples. Gram-positive cells are frequently isolated because they have thick cell walls and many contain carotenoid pigments which increase their survival in the air. However, many gram-positive cocci are normal flora of the skin and mucous membranes so they are readily present in occupied indoor environments without associative disease.

#### b. Gram-Positive Bacilli

Gram-positive bacilli are also very common in indoor environments, especially in dirty and dusty spaces. These bacteria are commonly isolated in soil and form spores that are resistant to environmental

---

*TABLE I*
**Airborne Bacterial Contaminants Associated with Adverse Health Effects in Indoor Environments**

| Bacterial contaminant | Indoor sources | Illness |
|---|---|---|
| Endotoxin (gram-negative bacilli) | Water spray humidification systems, humidifier reservoirs, dust | Headache, fever, cough, wheezing |
| *Haemophilus influenzea* | High-density living conditions | Meningitis |
| *Legionella pneumophila* | Cooling towers, condensers, showerheads, hot water heaters | Legionnaires' disease, Pontiac fever |
| *Mycobacterium tuberculosis* | High-density living conditions | Tuberculosis |
| *Mycoplasma pneumoniae* | High-density living conditions | Pneumonia |
| *Neisseria meningitidis* | High-density living conditions | Meningitis |
| *Staphylococcus* | Skin, wounds | Eye and ear infections |
| *Streptococcus* | Skin, wounds | Throat and respiratory infections |

stresses. The majority of gram-positive bacilli have little or no pathogenic potential with the notable exception of *Bacillus anthracis,* which causes anthrax. Anthrax is a concern for animal handlers ("wool-sorter's disease") and as an agent for biological warfare.

### c. Gram-Negative Bacilli and Endotoxin

Gram-negative bacilli are ubiquitous in water but are less common in air samples collected for culture. These cells are more fragile and susceptible to stresses encountered during aerosolization, transport through the air, and sampling. However, gram-negative bacilli have been isolated in high concentrations in agricultural settings, manufacturing or metal working facilities, waste-water treatment plants, and in buildings with contaminated air-conditioning systems, cooling towers, and humidification units.

A previously unreported bacterium caused numerous cases of pneumonia and resulted in several deaths in Philadelphia during the 1976 American Legion convention. The illness was called Legionnaires' disease and was not transmitted person-to-person but rather via a contaminated air-handling system. The organism causing the disease, *Legionella pneumophila,* has since been identified as a naturally occurring waterborne aerobic gram-negative bacillus. Pathogenic and non-pathogenic strains of *Legionella* spp. often associate with sediment, algae, waterborne parasites, and other waterborne bacteria in a synergistic relationship that provides resistance to

environmental stresses and water treatment practices. In recent years, reported cases of Legionnaires' disease have been linked to aerosolization of the organism from shower spray heads, humidifiers, and cooling units. Exposure to *L. pneumophila* also may result in an non-pneumonic illness, Pontiac fever, which has a higher incidence of morbidity but a lower mortality rate than Legionnaires' disease.

Endotoxins, lipopolysaccharide complexes of the gram-negative bacterial cell wall, are an additional health concern. Endotoxins can be released when gram-negative cells grow, die, or are lysed and may cause ventilatory impairment when inhaled. Byssinosis, a chronic lung disorder, has been associated with endotoxin in cotton dust related to exposure in cotton carding and processing. Endotoxins also have been suggested as causes of humidifier fever.

### 3. Fungi and Mycotoxin

Fungi are non-photosynthetic and non-motile microorganisms that have extensive intracellular compartmentalization. Generally, fungi comprise <10% of the airborne microbial population but they may cause allergic, infectious, or toxigenic reactions in exposed populations (Table II). Fungi release reproductive spores ranging in size from 2 to 200 $\mu$m into the environment by active or passive means depending on the genus. Cladosporium, often cited as the most common airborne fungus, has recently been shown to cause allergic reactions. The spores of numerous other allergenic fungi are also dispersed

#### TABLE II
#### Airborne Fungal Contaminants Associated with Adverse Health Effects in Indoor Environments

| Fungus | Indoor sources | Illness |
| --- | --- | --- |
| *Alternaria alternata* | Flooring materials, dusty surfaces | Allergic reactions |
| *Aspergillus fumigatus* | Soil, moldy vegetation, composts | Aspergillosis |
| *Blastomyces dermatitidis* | Soil, old buildings | Blastomycosis |
| *Cladosporium herbarum* | Painted surfaces, window sills | Allergic reactions |
| *Coccidioides immitis* | Desert soil, dust storms | Coccidioidiomycosis, valley fever |
| *Cryptococcus neoformans* | Pigeon excreta | Meningitis |
| *Fusarium* spp. | Wetted surfaces | Allergic reactions, toxicosis |
| *Histoplasma capsulatum* | Bird and bat excreta | Histoplasmosis |
| *Penicillium* spp. | Drier margins of wetted surfaces | Allergic reactions, toxicosis |
| *Stachybotrys chartarum* | Wetted cellulose | Toxicosis |

in the air, notably *Alternaria, Aspergillus,* and *Penicillium.* Adverse health effects ranging from mild allergic symptoms to asthma can be induced by contact of allergenic spores with sensitive mucosa. The allergenicity or toxigenicity of some fungi is present even when the fungus is not viable.

Toxigenic fungi produce metabolic products which are called mycotoxins. These chemicals generally have a high molecular weight so they are not volatilized in the air but are an integral part of the fungus. Mycotoxins can cause severe adverse health effects in man. Aflatoxins are mycotoxins that are produced by *Aspergillus flavus* and *A. parasiticus.* They are potent liver carcinogens most often seen in agricultural products (e.g., peanuts) and are rarely found in offices or homes. Toxigenic *Stachybotrys chartarum (atra)* readily grows in indoor environments on wetted cellulose (e.g., ceiling tiles and paper lining of wallboard) and has been associated with reports of illness. Research studies have demonstrated that the mycotoxins are found in the spores. Inhalation exposure to *S. chartarum* spores in mice produces toxicosis with low numbers of toxigenic spores resulting in severe lung effects. Unfortunately, this fungus does not compete well with other fungi on isolation medium commonly used for indoor air surveys and may be undetected during monitoring if only culture-based methods are used.

### 4. Thermophilic Actinomycetes

Airborne thermophilic actinomycetes are organisms with an optimal growth temperature ≥40°C. These microorganisms are ubiquitous in compost, hay, and municipal garbage and have been associated with pulmonary symptoms described as "farmer's lung" disease. *Micropolyspora faeni* and *Thermoactinomyces vulgaris* are thermophilic actinomycetes shown to cause allergic pulmonary disease and hypersensitivity pneumonitis.

### 5. Parasites

Free-living parasites (e.g., *Naegleria fowleri,* and Acanthamoeba) are unicellular, colorless, and motile. These microorganisms obtain nutrients by ingestion and are common in surface-waters and soils, especially during storm run-off. The cyst stage is resistant to environmental stress and is commonly transmitted via fecal contamination of water. Cysts have also been found in dust. Contamination of contact lenses with dust-laden *Acanthamoeba* cysts has resulted in severe corneal damage and inhalation of *N. fowleri* has resulted in death of bathers in contaminated hot-springs.

### 6. Algae

Algae are photosynthetic, single-celled organisms that are common to fresh and marine waters, runoff water, and soils. Algae may proliferate in these environments and become aerosolized during splash or wind erosion. Algae are also common inhabitants of aquariums and poorly maintained decorative fountains in which they may become airborne via bursting bubbles and agitation. Aerosolization of algae may result in allergic reactions of sensitized individuals.

## B. Microbial Volatile Organic Compounds

Bacteria, algae, and fungi produce microbial volatile organic compounds (MVOCs) as metabolic by-products. The specific MVOCs produced are dependent on substrate and environmental conditions but are generally emitted in low concentrations ($ng/m^3$). MVOCs have been associated with offensive odors and cited as the cause of occupant complaints of headaches, nausea, and skin and eye irritation. *Pseudomonas, Aspergillus, Fusarium, Penicillium,* and actinomycetes are known MVOC emitters in indoor environments.

## II. SOURCES OF MICROBIAL CONTAMINANTS INDOORS

The air quality in buildings is influenced by the outdoor environment, the construction and operation of the building, building materials and furnishings, and occupants and their activities.

## A. Outdoor Sources

Airborne microbial contaminants are drawn into buildings from the outdoor environment and dispersed. Sources of outdoor bioaerosols include plant surfaces, wind-blown soil, lakes and rivers, marine waters, and beach sediments. Agricultural practices such as tilling and harvesting release organisms from soil and crops. Additional input of microorganisms to outdoor air occurs during wastewater treatment.

## B. Building Design and Operation

### 1. Air-Handling Systems

#### a. Heating, Ventilation, and Air-Conditioning Systems

Building heating, ventilation, and air-conditioning (HVAC) systems are complex mechanical networks designed to control the temperature and humidity inside buildings. Generally, the outdoor air is filtered and then passed through cooling coils, heating devices, and humidification units depending on the design of the system. The air is distributed by a series of supply ducts to the interior spaces of the building. Air is recollected in rooms and hallway passages through return air ducts or ceiling plenum systems and recycled. In many HVAC systems up to 90% of the air in a building is recycled, with the remaining air supplied from the outdoor environment. Recycled air may contain high concentrations of airborne microorganisms due to microbial growth in the building materials and furnishings and poor exchange with outside air. Under suitable environmental conditions, fungal and bacterial cells can grow in the ductwork and on filters resulting in increased airborne counts. Water condensation collection areas and water-spray systems are potential sources for the amplification and growth of algae, bacteria, and parasites that could become aerosolized and dispersed throughout the building. Proper design, operation, and maintenance of building HVAC systems can significantly reduce the potential for growth and distribution of airborne microbial contaminants.

#### b. Evaporative Cooling Systems

Evaporative cooling systems operate by blowing air through water-soaked fibers. These systems are commonly used in homes in the southwestern desert climates of the United States where the relative humidity is low and the daytime temperatures are high. Evaporatively cooled residences may have air ex-change rates 10 times higher than traditional air-conditioned rooms because large volumes of outside air are imported through the system. The evaporative cooling system is a low-cost, energy-efficient alternative to traditional air-conditioning systems. However, the increased potential for transporting airborne microorganisms from the outdoor environment and contamination of the water-soaked pads by microorganisms which may then become aerosolized indoors has raised questions regarding the impact of evaporative systems on indoor air quality.

#### c. Portable Systems

Portable humidifiers, ventilators, and cool-mist vaporizers aerosolize water droplets in a fine mist. These units are designed to increase humidity of indoor environments and assist pulmonary function for patients with respiratory illness. However, bacteria, fungi, algae, and free-living amoebas can proliferate in the water reservoirs of these systems and be aerosolized with the mist. Regular preventative maintenance by users is required to prevent biocontamination of the water reservoirs.

### 2. Indoor Building Materials and Furnishings

Although air-handling systems may be a significant source for indoor air microbial contaminants, other building materials and furnishings may also provide niches for growth of microorganisms.

Drop-ceiling tiles that have been wetted due to leaking pipes in plenum areas are primary sites for microbial growth, especially the toxigenic fungus *Stachybotrys*. Painted surfaces such as walls and ceilings have also been shown to provide sites for the growth of fungi, especially *Cladosporium*.

Carpeting is used in buildings to muffle sound, cushion traffic, moderate cold floors, and enhance decoration of the living or working space. However, carpets and other flooring materials collect dust, pet dander and hair, and other debris. Without proper maintenance, carpet, ceramic and vinyl tile, and wooden floors can provide an ideal environment for the growth of bacteria and fungi. These organisms can then be readily dispersed into the air with human activity such as walking, vacuuming, and mopping.

Kitchen and bathroom areas of residences are primary sites for bacterial contamination. *Escherichia coli, Citrobacter freundii,* and *Klebsiella pneumoniae* have been isolated in high numbers from wet areas in indoor environments, especially around sink areas, refrigerator drip pans, and bathroom surfaces. *Pseudomonas* and *Bacillus* species are frequently isolated in drier areas. Although the majority of these organisms were isolated during surface sampling, the potential for dispersal into the indoor air is evident.

## C. Occupants

Numerous bacteria are present in the nose and mouth and on the skin, clothing, and hair of building occupants. Human activity results in increased numbers of airborne bacteria, and coughing is a major means of dispersal and transport of upper respiratory tract flora into the air. High occupancy rates in buildings have been shown to correlate with high indoor bacterial concentrations compared to outdoors, especially when air-handling system ventilation rates are low.

Viruses are found in indoor environments because of the activity of infected occupants. Respiratory viruses are released with coughing and talking. They can then be inhaled and deposited in the oropharynx of other people in the building where they may cause infections.

## III. MONITORING FOR AIRBORNE MICROORGANISMS

Monitoring for bioaerosols may be accomplished by a variety of methods to determine the culturable or total concentrations of microorganisms or to quantitate a specific antigen, toxin, or other metabolite. Sampling requires an efficient method to remove the organisms or metabolites from the air and a collection matrix suitable for analysis. The resulting data are expressed as the number of organisms or grams of metabolite per unit volume of air.

## A. Sampling Instruments

### 1. Forced Air-flow Samplers

A variety of sampling methods rely on mechanically induced air flow to collect airborne micro-

organisms onto nutrient agar, an adhesive-coated surface, liquid buffer, or a filter.

### a. Impactor Samplers

Total count impactor samplers such as the Burkard personal impactor sampler (Fig. 1) collect airborne particles through a slit design onto an adhesive-coated glass slide. Analysis is limited to detection by microscopy and is used for monitoring of fungal spores and pollen.

Culturable impactor samplers collect organisms onto an agar surface followed by incubation of the sample and determination of numbers of colony-forming units per cubic meter of air sampled (CFU/m$^3$). Culturable slit impactor samplers operate by rotating an agar plate under a slit. These samplers offer time discrimination of the bioaerosol concentration as the organisms are deposited onto the agar surface over a known period of time. The Andersen

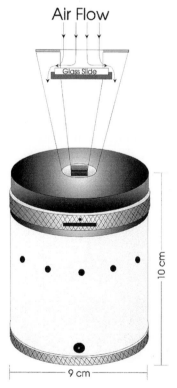

**Fig. 1.** Burkard personal volumetric air sampler for glass slides (courtesy of Paula Jacoby-Garrett, UNLV).

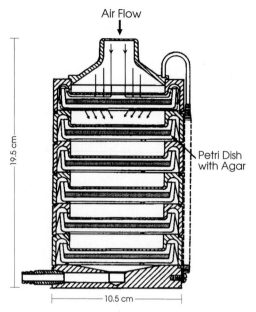

**Fig. 2.** Andersen six-stage impactor air sampler (courtesy of Shirley Burns and Paula Jacoby-Garrett, UNLV).

single-stage sampler (Fig. 2) and the multistage sampler (Fig. 3) are examples of impactor samplers that operate with an external vacuum pump attachment directing air through precision-drilled holes. For the multistage sampler, microorganisms are deposited onto an agar plate at the stage corresponding to their particle size. Unfortunately, agar surfaces may become overloaded when high bioaerosol concentrations are encountered or rapid-growing fungi are present. Falsely low counts may occur when clumps of organisms are dispersed as a single droplet and are deposited in the same location on the agar surface so they grow as a single colony.

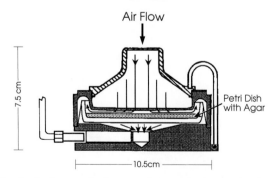

**Fig. 3.** Andersen single-stage impactor air sampler (courtesy of Shirley Burns and Paula Jacoby-Garrett, UNLV).

### b. Impinger Samplers

Impinger samplers, such as the AGI-30 (Fig. 4), operate by drawing air into a liquid collection fluid. The liquid buffer can then be used for a variety of analytical techniques such as culture analysis, assay by total count, biochemical, and molecular biological techniques. The buffer can be diluted prior to culturing to avoid overloading in high-density situations, and aliquots of the buffer sample can be plated onto different types of media to enhance the recovery of injured or fastidious organisms.

### c. Filtration Samplers

Collection of bioaerosols onto filters provides a means to sample for longer periods of time. However, filter sampling with a dry matrix filter material is not widely used with culture-based analysis due to the loss of viability with desiccation. Gelatin filters have been shown to minimize desiccation of bacterial cells and virus. Filtration can be used to sample stress-resistant organisms such as fungal spores or for assays not dependent on viability.

## 2. Passive/Depositional Sampling

Passive sampling, such as open petri dishes with culture medium or glass slides covered with a sticky film, relies on the settling out of particles from the

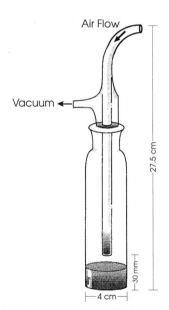

**Fig. 4.** All-glass impinger (AGI-30) (courtesy of Shirley Burns and Paula Jacoby-Garrett, UNLV).

air. This type of sampling, which has been widely used for pollen and large particulates, is not recommended for small particles such as bacterial cells and many fungal spores because they may remain suspended and not be collected. In addition, passive sampling methods do not permit quantitation of particles per unit volume of air.

## B. Sampling and Analysis Methods

Air sampling and analysis may be performed using traditional culture and microscopy-based methods or recently developed molecular and chemical methods.

### 1. Culture-Based Methods

Culture-based methods rely on growth of the organisms following collection and assume that the organisms will grow and produce classical characteristics within a specified time period. However, airborne microorganisms are stressed during aerosol transport and may be not respond to traditional culture techniques.

#### a. Viruses

Routine monitoring for airborne viruses is rarely done because of difficulties in sampling and analysis. However, if analysis by cell culture is available, sampling can be conducted using impactor samplers with tryptic soy agar plates. The agar is removed and blended with a viral culture medium for cell culture analysis. Buffer from high-volume liquid samplers and all-glass impingers can also be inoculated into cell culture. Buffer-moistened or gelatin filters have been used, but in all cases the samples must remain moist because desiccation will inactivate viruses.

#### b. Bacteria

Airborne bacteria are typically cultured from impactor and impinger samplers using a general nutrient medium such as tryptic soy agar amended with an anti-fungal agent such as cycloheximide to minimize fungal growth. Incubation temperatures are commonly 28–32°C for 2–5 days. The use of enrichment, selective, or differential media is usually not recommended due to poor recovery of stressed cells.

#### c. Fungi

Sampling for airborne fungi is routinely performed using impactor samplers. Impingement is generally not recommended because some fungal spores are hydrophobic and may not be retained in the collection fluid. Filter sampling followed by elution of spores from the filter material allows dilution of the sample in locations where high airborne concentrations are present and permits extended sampling periods. Filtration sampling can also be used with cell culture to establish cytotoxicity of mycotoxin.

A variety of media are used for culture of airborne fungi, including malt extract, rose bengal, Sabouraud glucose and Sabouraud dextrose, potato dextrose, and corn meal agars. Incubation at 23°C for 3–5 days is used for mesophilic fungi. Isolation of thermophilic fungi is usually conducted at >40°C.

#### d. Algae

Although airborne algae may be a significant allergen in indoor air, monitoring for these organisms is currently not routine. Samples for algae may be taken using liquid impingement as described for bacteria, but sampling of sources in which the algae are concentrated and/or growing is often more productive. Samples of house dust diluted in buffer can be inoculated onto a nutrient medium with a soft agar overlay to quantify algal cells per gram of dust.

#### e. Parasites

Building water reservoirs and standing water near air-handling system intakes are the most likely sites for the detection of free-living amoebae indoors. Andersen impactor samplers and liquid impinger samplers have been used for collection of airborne amoebae cysts in combination with plaque assay for detection.

### 2. Microscopy

Microscopic procedures do not discriminate between culturable and nonculturable microorganisms but can be used to rapidly assess microbial contamination without the requirement for growth of the organism. Viruses are too small to be detected by light microscopy but they can be viewed with electron microscopy. High detection limits and lack of specificity are major problems with the use of light microscopy-based methods for airborne bacteria. To improve detection, microscopic examination of liquid impingement samples for bacterial contaminants is often accompanied by filter concentration and staining of the specimen with an antibody-specific reagent or a fluorescent dye such as acridine orange.

Bioaerosols collected with slide impaction samplers and stained with lactophenol cotton blue are commonly used with microscopic examination to identify and enumerate the concentrations of airborne fungal spores. Microscopy is helpful in detecting fungi that are difficult to culture or for spores that can elicit an adverse health effect when nonviable, such as *Alternaria*. Although readily recognizable spores can be identified to the genus level, many spores are similar in appearance and expertise is required for accurate identification.

### 3. Biotechnology-Based Assays

Biotechnology methods of analysis of samples collected using filtration or impingement can enhance the detection and quantitation of airborne microbial contaminants without the requirements of culture or microscopy.

#### a. Gene Amplification

Polymerase chain reaction (PCR) technology provides a means for detecting specific genes of a target microorganism without the requirements for culture. PCR products are detectable by gel electrophoresis or molecular probes. PCR has shown increased selectivity and sensitivity in bacterial assay compared to culture, with detection completed in a few hours. Reverse-transcriptase PCR has similarly been successful in amplification of viral RNA. Accurate, rapid, and quantitative assessment of microbial contaminants with PCR has been developed using fluorescent probes. The limitations of this technology are in selection of gene sequences unique for a particular microbial contaminant of interest and interference of PCR by inhibitors in the sample.

#### b. Immunoassay

Immunoassay methods allow direct counting of organisms using labeled antibodies which bind specifically to the target organism. Immunoassay relies on development of antigen-specific antibodies combined with fluorescent, radioactive, or enzymatic detection methods. Immunoassay can also be used for monitoring microbial antigen and by-products of microbial metabolism without the need to detect a living cell.

### 4. Biochemical Assay

Biochemical assays are used for detection and quantitation of microbial constituents such as endotoxin, ergosterol, and $\beta$-1,3 glucan. These assays provide information on the presence of cellular constituents but do not identify the genus and species of organism that produced them.

The *Limulus* amoebocyte lysate assay is the preferred method for detecting endotoxin because the biological activity of endotoxin is not dependent on cell viability. This assay is used for air samples collected by filtration and impingement and for water and settled dust samples.

### 5. Chemical Assay

#### a. Mycotoxin

Analytical chemistry methods such as high-performance liquid chromatography are used to determine chemical constituents of fungal extracts. Extracts can be prepared from culture samples or spores. Numerous mycotoxins may be present in a sample, thus requiring expertise and quality assurance standards for accurate analysis.

#### b. Microbial Volatile Organic Compounds

A low-flow pump and chemical sorbent tubes are used to collect air samples for volatile organic compounds. Analysis is typically performed using gas chromatography with mass spectrophotometry.

### See Also the Following Articles

AEROSOL INFECTIONS • BIOMONITORS OF ENVIRONMENTAL CONTAMINATION • LIPOPOLYSACCHARIDES

## Bibliography

Burge, H. A. (1995). "Bioaerosols." Lewis, Boca Raton, FL.

Buttner, M. P., Willeke, K., and Grinshpun, S. (1997). Sampling for airborne microorganisms. *In* "Manual of Environmental Microbiology" (C. J. Hurst, G. Knudsen, M. McInerney, M. V. Walter, and L. D. Stetzenbach, Eds.), pp. 629–640. ASM Press, Washington, DC.

Cox, C. S., and Wathes, C. M. (1995). "Bioaerosols Handbook." Lewis, Boca Raton, FL.

Stetzenbach, L. D. (1997). Introduction to aerobiology. *In* "Manual of Environmental Microbiology" (C. J. Hurst, G. Knudsen, M. McInerney, M. V. Walter, and L. D. Stetzenbach, Eds.), pp. 619–628. ASM Press, Washington, DC.

# Alkaline Environments

### W. D. Grant

*University of Leicester*

### B. E. Jones

*Genencor International BV Delft*

I.   The Genesis of Soda Lakes and Soda Deserts
II.  Alkaliphile Diversity in Soda Lakes and Soda Deserts
III. Element Cycles in Soda Lakes
IV.  Soda Lakes in the Past

## GLOSSARY

**alkaliphile**  Organism with a pH optimum for growth in excess of pH 8; obligate alkaliphiles are incapable of growth at neutrality, and alkalitolerant organisms are capable of growth at high pH but are also capable of growth under non-alkaline conditions.

**evaporite**  Residue of salts left behind after brines evaporate to dryness.

**haloalkaliphile**  Organism with a pH optimum for growth in excess of pH 8 and a requirement for >15% w/v NaCl in the growth medium.

**halophilic archaea**  Aerobic, red-pigmented, obligately halophilic (i.e., a requirement for >15% w/v NaCl in the growth medium) archaea belonging to the order Halobacteriales.

**permineralization**  Preservation of organic material by infiltration of mineral-bearing ground-waters.

**soda lake**  Alkaline lake in which the alkalinity is due to large amounts of $Na_2CO_3$ (or complexes of this salt).

**STABLE ALKALINE ENVIRONMENTS** (pH >10) are not common and are caused by an unusual combination of topographical, geographical, and climatic conditions that mitigate against the significant buffering capacity of atmospheric $CO_2$. Many man-made unstable alkaline environments are produced by industrial processes, including cement manufacture and food processing, which introduce alkali [usually NaOH

or $Ca(OH)_2$] into the environment. $Ca(OH)_2$-dominated ground-waters are also occasionally naturally produced by the low-temperature weathering of the calcium-containing minerals olivine and pyroxene, which release $Ca^{2+}$ and $OH^-$ into solution under reducing conditions because of the concomitant product of hydrogen. Such alkaline waters have a very low buffering capacity due to the low solubility of $Ca(OH)_2$ when separated from solid-phase $Ca(OH)_2$.

Soda lakes and soda deserts represent the major type of naturally occurring highly alkaline environment and, as the name implies, are characterized by the presence of large amounts of soda [$Na_2CO_3$, usually present as natron ($Na_2CO_3 \cdot 10H_2O$) or trona ($Na_2CO_3 \cdot NaHCO_3 \cdot 2H_2O$)]. These environments, unlike the others, have substantial buffering capacity and are extremely stable, with pH values of up to or greater than 12.0—probably the most alkaline habitats on earth.

Alkaliphiles are defined as organisms that grow at alkaline pH with pH optima for growth in excess of pH 8 (usually between 9 and 10), with some being capable of cultivation at pH values >11. Obligate alkaliphiles are incapable of growth at neutrality and generally will not grow at pH values <8. Alkalitolerant organisms are capable of growth at alkaline pH but have pH optima for cultivation in the acid or neutral regions of the pH scale.

Alkaliphiles are widely distributed in almost all environments, including soils and deep marine sediments, even in those that would not be considered to be particularly alkaline. It is assumed that in such environments, transient alkaline sites are generated by biological activity, allowing survival and limited growth of a small alkaliphile population.

"Normal" soils, waters, and sediments together with the man-made environments and high-$Ca^{2+}$ ground-waters generally yield a restricted range of alkaliphile types, notably endospore-forming bacilli, which probably do not proliferate significantly *in situ*. Soda lakes and soda deserts, on the other hand, constitute the major natural alkaliphile habitat, yielding a much more diverse population of alkaliphiles.

## I. THE GENESIS OF SODA LAKES AND SODA DESERTS

Soda lakes and soda deserts are widely distributed (Table I) but are often located in inaccessible continental interiors which has hindered their detailed and systematic study. The best studied soda lakes are those of the East African Rift Valley, where detailed

**TABLE I**
**Worldwide Locations of Soda Lakes and Deserts**

| Continent | Country | Location |
|---|---|---|
| North America | Canada | Manito |
| | USA | Alkali Valley, Albert Lake Lenore, Soap Lake, Big Soda Lake, Owens Lake, Borax Lake, Mono Lake, Searles Lake, Deep Springs, Rhodes Marsh, Harney Lake, Summer Lake, Surprise Valley, Pyramid Lake, Walker Lake, Union Pacific Lakes (Green River), Ragtown Soda Lakes |
| Central America | Mexico | Lake Texcoco |
| South America | Venezuela | Langunilla Valley |
| | Chile | Antofagasta |
| Europe | Hungary | Lake Feher |
| | Former Yugoslavia | Pecena Slatina |
| Asia | Siberia | Kulunda Steppe, Tanatar Lakes, Karakul, Chita, Barnaul, Slavgerod, Lake Baikal region, Lake Khatyn |
| | Armenia | Araxes Plain Lakes |
| | Turkey | Lake Van, Lake Salda |
| | India | Lake Looner, Lake Sambhar |
| | China | Outer Mongolia, various "nors"; Sui-Yuan, Cha-Han-Nor and Na-Lin-Nor; Heilungkiang, Hailar and Tsitsihar; Kirin, Fu-U-Hsein and Taboos-Nor; Liao-Ning, Tao-Nan Hsein; Jehol, various soda lakes; Tibet, alkaline deserts; Chahar, Lang-Chi; Shansi, U-Tsu-Hsein; Shensi, Shen-Hsia-Hsein; Kansu, Ning-Hsia-Hsein, Qinhgai Hu |
| Africa | Libya | Lake Fezzan |
| | Egypt | Wadi Natrun |
| | Ethiopia | Lake Aranguadi, Lake Kilotes, Lake Abiata, Lake Shala, Lake Chilu, Lake Hertale, Lake Metahara |
| | Sudan | Dariba Lakes |
| | Kenya | Lake Bogoria, Lake Nakuru, Lake Elmenteita, Lake Magadi, Lake Simbi, Crater Lake (Lake Sonachi), Lake Oloidien |
| | Tanzania | Lake Natron, Lake Embagi, Lake Magad, Lake Manyara, Lake Balangida, Basotu Crater Lake, Lake Kusare, Lake Tulusia, El Kekhooito, Momela Lakes, Lake Lekandiro, Lake Reshitani, Lake Lgarya, Lake Ndutu, Lake Rukwa North |
| | Uganda | Lake Katwe, Lake Mahenga, Lake Kikorongo, Lake Nyamunuka, Lake Munyanyange, Lake Murumuli, Lake Nunyampaka |
| | Chad | Lake Bodu, Lake Rombou, Lake Dijikare, Lake Monboio, Lake Yoan |
| Australia | | Lake Corangamite, Red Rock Lake, Lake Werowrap, Lake Chidnup |

limnological and microbiological investigations have been carried out over many years.

The formation of soda lakes has much in common with athalassohaline (not derived from sea-water) salt lakes, with the major difference that soda lakes contain carbonate (or carbonate complexes) as the predominant anion. Like salt lakes, soda lakes require a closed drainage basin with a restricted outflow plus rates of evaporation that exceed inflow so that salts may accumulate by evaporative concentration. The surrounding rocks must be high in $Na^+$ and also be deficient in $Ca^{2+}$ and $Mg^{2+}$. In all aquatic systems, $CO_2$-charged surface waters generate a $HCO_3^{2-}/CO_3^{2-}$ solution of minerals reflecting the surrounding geology. In closed basins, in which intense evaporative concentration occurs, one of the determining features in the genesis of the final pH of the brine is the amount of $Ca^{2+}$ (and to a lesser extent $Mg^{2+}$) (Fig. 1). If the molarity of $Ca^{2+}$ always exceeds that of $CO_3^{2-}$, as in sea-water, neutral brines develop.

The chemistry of all brine development is complex and undoubtedly influenced by special local factors; for example, the athalassohaline Great Salt Lake is more alkaline than marine salterns because the composition is influenced by earlier evaporites. The Dead Sea is $Mg^{2+}$-rich and slightly acidic as a consequence of the influence of earlier evaporites and the precipitation of minerals that generate $H^+$ during the evaporative process. Where the concentration of $HCO_3^{2-}/CO_3^{2-}$ greatly exceeds that of $Ca^{2+}$ and $Mg^{2+}$, these cations are removed from solution as insoluble carbonates, and alkalinity develops as a consequence of the shift in the $CO_2/HCO_3^{2-}/CO_3^{2-}/OH^-$ equilibrium as evaporative concentration progresses (Fig. 1), with the $Na^+$-dominated surrounding geology producing an alkaline soda ($Na_2CO_3$) brine with pH values up to pH 12. It also follows that these brines are virtually devoid of $Ca^{2+}$ and $Mg^{2+}$, an unusual situation for the aquatic environment. In the course of the formation of the alkalinity, other ions also

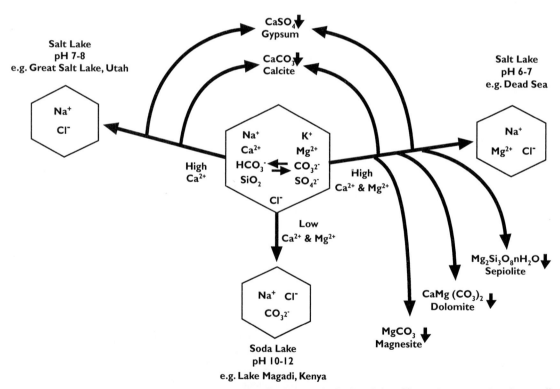

**Fig. 1.** Schematic representation of the genesis of saline and alkaline lakes [from Grant, W. D., Gemmell, R. T., and McGenity, T. J. (1998). Halophiles. *In* "Extremophiles: Microbial Life in Extreme Environments" (K. Horikoshi and W. D. Grant, Eds.), pp. 93–132. Copyright © 1998 Wiley–Liss. Reprinted with permission of Wiley–Liss, Inc., a subsidiary of John Wiley & Sons, Inc.].

concentrate, notably $Cl^-$, making soda lakes somewhat saline depending on the degree of concentration.

In certain soda lakes, calcium-rich ground-waters from distant sites seep into the alkaline lake water, giving rise to localized calcite ($CaCO_3$) precipitation in the form of columns or structures. These "tufa" columns may be of considerable size. Mono Lake in California exhibits impressive formations of these structures. Similar structures have been described where cyanobacteria contribute to further permineralization. Stromatolithic structures such as these were widespread in the Precambrian period and it has been argued that Precambrian oceans may have been soda oceans since this period predates the widespread mobilization and ubiquitous deposition of $Ca^{2+}$ by eukaryotic marine algae.

The Great Rift Valley running through East Africa is an arid tropical zone in which tectonic activity has created a series of shallow depressions. In the Kenyan–Tanzanian section of the Rift Valley, the bedrock is composed of alkaline trachyte lavas laid down during the Pleistocene period. These sodium-dominated lavas contain significant amounts of carbonate and have very low calcium and magnesium levels, allowing standing bodies of water to concentrate into caustic alkaline brines with pH values ranging from 8.5 in the most dilute lake to >12 in the most concentrated. The salinity of these lakes varies from approximately 5% (w/v) total salts in the northern lakes (Bogoria, Nakuru, Elmenteita, and Sonachi) to saturation in parts of the Magadi–Natron basin in the south. Chemical analyses showing the major ions present in these lakes are shown in Table II.

The majority of the dilute lakes have pH values of 10–10.5 with the exception of Oloidien, a more dilute lake, which has a pH of 8.5. The saturated lakes of the Magadi–Natron area have pH values >11.5, probably >12, although it is technically difficult to measure very high pH values in the presence of large amounts of NaCl.

These extreme pH environments, despite being so apparently hostile, support dense populations of microorganisms. Due to high ambient temperatures and high daily light intensities, combined with the almost unlimited supply of $CO_2$ from the carbonate-charged waters, soda lakes are the most productive natural aquatic environments on earth and are unusual in that the productivity is usually exclusively due to prokaryotes. The less saline lakes are usually dominated by vast blooms of alkaliphilic cyanobacteria resulting in gross photosynthetic rates of more than 30 g $O_2$ $m^{-2}$ $day^{-1}$ (approximately 11g C $m^{-2}$ $day^{-1}$—more than 10 times the average rate for the aquatic environment), whereas the hypersaline lakes of the Magadi–Natron area support both blooms of cyanobacteria and alkaliphilic anoxygenic phototrophic bacteria. The primary productivity of these phototrophic prokaryotes drives all the biological processes in the soda lake environment.

## II. ALKALIPHILE DIVERSITY IN SODA LAKES AND SODA DESERTS

Soda lakes are dominated by prokaryotic microbial populations and these organisms represent many taxonomic groups. Table III lists examples of taxonomic

***TABLE II***
**Chemical Analysis of Rift Valley Soda Lake Waters[a]**

| Lake | $Na^+$ | $K^+$ | $Ca^{2+}$ | $Mg^{2+}$ | $SiO_2$ | $PO_4^{3-}$ | $Cl^-$ | $SO_4^{2-}$ | $CO_3^{2-}$ | pH |
|---|---|---|---|---|---|---|---|---|---|---|
| Elmenteita | 195.7 | 3.6 | 0.07 | <0.004 | 2.9 | 0.03 | 65.1 | 2.0 | 68.0 | 10.5 |
| Nakuru | 326.1 | 5.6 | 0.15 | <0.004 | 3.3 | 0.15 | 57.5 | 0.5 | 198.3 | 10.5 |
| Bogoria | 795.7 | 6.8 | 0.19 | 0.008 | 2.0 | 0.17 | 115.5 | 1.1 | 516.7 | 10.5 |
| Sonachi | 140.4 | 9.0 | 0.05 | 0.008 | 2.1 | 0.04 | 12.4 | 0.8 | 90.0 | 10.0 |
| Oloidien | 8.7 | 1.8 | 0.28 | 0.65 | 1.0 | 0.003 | 4.8 | 0.5 | <10.0 | 8.5 |
| Magadi | 7000.0 | 57.0 | <0.01 | <0.01 | 14.9 | 1.82 | 3154.9 | 17.5 | 3900.0 | >11.5 |
| Natron | 4521.7 | 43.7 | 0.04 | 0.03 | 3.1 | 4.21 | 1464.8 | 1.7 | 2666.7 | >11.5 |

[a] Modified from Jones *et al.* (1994). All concentrations given in mM.

**TABLE III**
**Taxa from Soda Lakes**

| *Groups known to be present* | *Examples of validly named species* |
| --- | --- |
| Bacteria | |
|   Cyanobacteria | *Spirulina platensis* |
| | *Cyanospira rippkae* |
|   Gram-positive bacteria (high G + C) | |
|     Actinomycetes | *Bogoriella caseilyticus* |
|     Micrococci/Arthrobacters | *Dietzia natronolimnaois* |
|   Gram-positive bacteria (low G + C) | |
|     Bacilli | |
|     Clostridia | *Tindallia magadii* |
|     Haloanaerobes | *Natroniella acetigena* |
|   Proteobacteria | |
|     Sulfur oxidizers | |
|     Nitrifiers | *Nitrobacter alkalicus* |
|     Sulfate-reducing bacteria | *Desulfonatronovibrio hydrogenovorans* |
| | *Desulfonatronum lacustre* |
|     Anoxygenic phototrophic bacteria | *Ectothiorhodospira mobilis* |
| | *Halorhodospira halophila* |
|     Halomonads | |
|     Enterics/vibrios/aeromonads | |
|     Pseudomonads | |
|   Spirochaetes | *Spirochaeta alkalica* |
| | *Spirochaeta asiatica* |
|   Thermotogas | |
| Archaea | |
|   Halobacteria | *Halorubrum vacuolatum* |
| | *Natrialba magadii* |
| | *Natronobacterium gregoryi* |
| | *Natronomonas pharaonis* |
| | *Natronococcus occultus* |
| | *Natronococcus amylolyticus* |
|   Methanogens | *Methanosalsus oregonensis* |
| | *Methanosalsus zhilinaeae* |

groups containing prokaryotes isolated from soda lakes.

## A. Phototrophs

One of the striking features of many soda lakes is their color—various hues of green or red due to permanent or seasonal blooms of microorganisms. In the moderately saline lakes, cyanobacteria are the main contributors to primary production, usually a predominance of the filamentous species *Spirulina platensis*, although *Cyanospira, Chroococcus, Synech-*ococcus, and *Synechocystis spp.* are occasionally the principal species in some lakes. Vast populations of the lesser flamingo (*Phoeniconaias minor*) are supported by these algal blooms. It has been calculated that the population at Lake Nakuru, which may exceed 1 million birds, can consume approximately 200 tons of cyanobacteria per day. Densities of up to 14,000 *Spirulina* filaments ml$^{-1}$ have been recorded. In hypersaline lakes such as Lake Magadi, it is uncertain which organisms are responsible for the primary production. Cyanobacterial blooms do occasionally occur after prolonged rainfall has diluted surface waters; organisms such as *Spirulina platensis* are not particularly halophilic. It is possible that halophilic anoxygenic phototrophic bacteria of the genus *Halorhodospira* are responsible for at least a part of the primary productivity in very saline lakes. Less halophilic anoxygenic phototrophic bacteria of the related genus *Ectothiorhodospira* are also present in the more dilute lakes, sometimes producing red blooms.

## B. Aerobes

Alkaliphilic aerobic organotrophic bacteria are abundant in the more dilute soda lakes. Viable counts reveal a remarkably constant population over the year of $10^5$–$10^6$ ml$^{-1}$, with total counts indicating $10^7$–$10^8$ ml$^{-1}$. The dominant bacterial populations depend on variables such as conductivity, alkalinity, and phosphate and nitrogen levels. Many isolates have been subjected to phenotypic, chemotaxonomic, and phylogenetic analysis. A majority of isolates are gram-negative bacteria—representatives of the $\gamma 3$ subgroup of the Proteobacteria related to members of the Halomonadaceae family, whose members are characteristic of neutral terrestrial and marine saline environments although the alkaliphiles represent new taxa. Other gram-negative isolates are related to *Pseudomonas* group 1, whereas others are only peripherally associated with typical aquatic bacteria such as *Aeromonas* and *Vibrio* spp.

There is greater diversity among gram-positive isolates found in both the high G + C and low G + C divisions. Many low G + C isolates are associated with the *Bacillus* spectrum, although distinct taxa are present. High G + C isolates include new taxa associated with the genera *Dietzia, Arthrobacter, Terrabacter,* and *Nesterenkonia* and also actinomycetes, at least one of which has been classified in a new genus *Bogoriella*. Gram-positive isolates in particular are of interest to the biotechnology industry because of the battery of extracellular enzymes that they produce, and at least one alkali-stable detergent cellulase derived from a soda lake isolate is currently on the market.

A quite different population of prokaryotes is present in the concentrated brines of the very saline soda lakes and soda deserts throughout the world. These brines and soda flats are often characteristically red in color due to extensive blooms of microorganisms. The organisms most commonly cultured are both profoundly halophilic and alkaliphilic and are members of the archaeal halophile (halobacterial) lineage. These haloalkaliphilic archaea were originally classified in the genera *Natronococcus* and *Natronobacterium* but have recently been reclassified as *Natronoccus, Natronobacterium, Natrialba, Natronomonas,* and *Halorubrum* spp. Occasionally, haloalkaliphilic *Bacillus* spp. related to the *Bacillus* spp. from more dilute lakes are isolated. In common with other extreme environments, analysis of DNA extracted on site from these very saline sites reveals other distinct archaeal lineages yet to be brought into culture.

## C. Anaerobes

Soda lake muds are black and anoxic, implying the presence of sulfate-reducing bacteria (SRB). Geochemists have postulated SRB activity to explain the relative depletion of sulfate in soda lake brines. SRBs have been isolated from Lake Magadi and classified in a new genus *Desulfonatronovibrio,* although they show optimal activity at relatively low pH (9.5) and salt concentrations (3% w/v), more appropriate for the more dilute lakes. Alkaliphilic strict anaerobes that are associated with the *Clostridium* spectrum have been isolated from both moderately hypersaline and profoundly hypersaline soda lakes, representing new taxa that show optima for growth that match the environmental conditions of the isolation site. Distantly related organisms also isolated include *Natrionella* spp. Alkaliphilic and strictly anaerobic spirochaetes are also known to be present in soda lakes on at least two continents.

There is evidence of methanogenesis in soda lakes world-wide, and many methanogens have been isolated and assigned to the genus *Methanohalophilus* (*Methanosalsus*) as a separate genus within the *Methanomicrobiales*. In common with methanogens from other sulfide-rich sites, the preferred substrates for growth are methyl compounds such as methanol and methylamine.

Finally, the Rift Valley is a volcanically active region and many of the soda lakes are fed by less alkaline hot springs which may be boiling. Isolates of thermoalkaliphilic anaerobes related to members of the *Thermotogales* that grow at up to 78°C and up to pH 10.5 have been made from areas where the springs mix with the lake waters.

## III. ELEMENT CYCLES IN SODA LAKES

Although we do not know in detail all the aspects of the microbial ecosystem in soda lakes, it is possible to make predictions regarding the roles played by some of the groups in the cycling of nutrients since there are parallels with the better studied neutral salt lake systems.

The phototrophs already described are certainly responsible for primary production in soda lakes, supporting a dense population of aerobic and anaerobic organotrophs. As a consequence of the nutrient-rich habitat that they inhabit, organotrophic isolates are very biochemically reactive, hydrolyzing many polymers and utilizing a wide range of sugars and amino acids as growth substrates. The monomers produced by the hydrolysis of complex polymers presumably form the substrates for the organotrophic anaerobes that are known to ferment a variety of

simple compounds to volatile fatty acids. These are presumably consumed by alkaliphilic acetogenic bacteria such as *Natrionella acetigena* related to members of the *Haloanaerobiales,* although details of acetogenesis are scant for soda lakes compared with other anoxic environments. Methanogens in soda lakes are mainly obligately methylotrophic, growing on substrates such as methanol and methylamine derived from the anaerobic digestion of organic material in soda lake sediments. Methane oxidation in soda lakes is recorded in central Asian soda lakes and has also been noted in the Rift Valley.

In addition to the vigorous cycling of carbon, there is also an active sulfur cycle. The role of *Ectothorhodospira* and *Halorhodospira* spp. in the carbon cycle has already been noted. These bacteria also use reduced sulfur species as electron donors for photosynthesis, generating elemental sulfur and finally sulfate. The sulfur cycle is completed by SRBs such as *Desulfonatronovibrio hydrogenovorans* and *Desulfonatronum lacustre*. These organisms do not compete with alkaliphilic methanogens since hydrogen is the preferred electron donor for sulfate reduction. The sulfur cycle also has an aerobic component since lithoautotrophic alkaliphilic sulfur oxidizers have

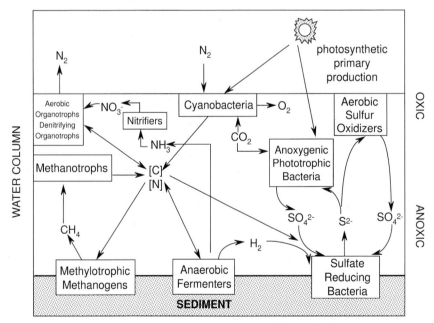

***Fig. 2.*** A simple model for nutrient cycles in soda lakes (modified from Jones *et al.,* 1998).

been isolated from Siberian and Kenyan soda lakes, representing new taxa within the Proteobacteria.

*Spirulina* and *Cyanospira* spp. are known to be capable of nitrogen fixation and a considerable number of the organotrophic bacteria, notably the alkaliphilic halomonads, reduce nitrate to nitrite and/or denitrify to molecular nitrogen. One would expect organotrophic activity to generate ammonia, although at alkaline pH ammonia is volatile and tends to be lost from the system. A recent example of an ammonifying organism has been named *Tindallia magadii*. Lithoautotrophic nitrifying bacteria are also known to be present in soda lakes, thus completing the cycle. Figure 2 summarizes what is known about element cycles in soda lakes.

## IV. SODA LAKES IN THE PAST

Although alkaline lakes are confined to specific geographic regions, they comprise more than 80% of all inland waters by volume, and soda lakes have existed throughout the geological record. One of the largest fossil soda lakes is the Green River formation in Wyoming and Utah which is between 36 and 55 million years old. Fossil soda lakes of even greater age are implied from the secondary characteristics of some geological formations such as the 2.3-billion-year-old Ventersdorf formation in South Africa. Present-day soda lakes are recent. Lake Magadi in its present form is probably 10,000 years old, although it is derived from a much older (800,000 years), less alkaline and saline lake that had characteristics similar to the more dilute northern Rift Valley soda lakes. The northern lakes are thus in an early phase of evolution and Lake Magadi represents a later stage in a development that has taken place over a significant period of time.

It has been argued that soda lakes have had a significant role in the generation of prokaryote diversity in the past. It is possible that the weathering of rocks in the Archaean era could have generated vast soda oceans, and modern equivalents of Precambrian stromatolites are recorded in the soda lake environment. There is considerable phylogenetic diversity among soda lake communities, and the metabolic diversity is sufficient to maintain and rapidly evolve an autonomous microbial community. If prokaryotes did evolve in ancient soda lakes, this raises important questions about ancestral lineages and indeed perhaps about the early abiogenic chemistry.

### See Also the Following Articles

Extremophiles • Methanogenesis • pH Stress • Water-Deficient Environments

### Bibliography

Duckworth, A. W., Grant, W. D., Jones, B. E., and van Steenbergen, R. (1996). *FEMS Microbiol. Ecol.* **19**, 181–191.

Grant, W. D., Mwatha, W. E., and Jones, B. E. (1990). *FEMS Microbiol. Rev.* **75**, 235–270.

Grant, W. D., Gemmell, R. T., and McGenity, T. J. (1998). Halophiles. *In* "Extremophiles: Microbial Life in Extreme Environments (K. Horikoshi and W. D. Grant, Eds.), pp. 93–132. Wiley–Liss, New York.

Hardie, L. A., and Eugster, H. P. (1970). *Mineral. Soc. Am. Spec. Papers* **3**, 273–296.

Jones, B. E., Grant, W. D., Collins, N. C., and Mwatha, W. E. (1994). Alkaliphiles: Diversity and identification. *In* "Bacterial Diversity and Systematics" (F. G. Priest, B. J. Tindall, and A. Ramos-Cormenzana, Eds.), pp. 195–230. Plenum, New York.

Jones, B. E., Grant, W. D., Duckworth, A. W., and Owenson, G. G. (1998). *Extremophiles* **2**, 191–200.

Zavarzin, G. A. (1993). *Microbiology* **62**, 473–479.

Zhilina, T. N., and Zavarsin, G. A. (1994). *Curr. Microbiol.* **29**, 109–112.

# Amino Acid Function and Synthesis

## Larry Reitzer
### The University of Texas at Dallas

## GLOSSARY

**assimilation**  The incorporation of inorganic compounds, such as ammonia and sulfate, into organic intermediates of cellular metabolism.

**attenuation**  A mechanism of gene expression that senses the availability of an amino acid by the extent of tRNA charging. A low level of an amino acid prevents formation of a transcriptional terminator before the first structural gene of an operon. A high level of the amino acid results in formation of the terminator.

**end-product repression**  A mechanism of transcriptional control in which the product of a reaction sequence contributes to the repression of the pathway.

**feedback inhibition**  The inhibition of enzyme activity by a product of a reaction or a pathway. The first enzyme of a pathway is usually the only target of such control.

**nitrogen limitation**  The slower nitrogen assimilation that results from utilization of a single nitrogen source other than ammonia.

**stringent response**  A response controlled by guanosine tetraphosphate that balances the demand for the protein synthesis with the synthesis of protein precursors.

**THE PATHWAYS OF AMINO ACID SYNTHESIS** are essential for growth and can comprise a significant fraction of a bacterium's metabolic activity. Knowledge of the regulation of these pathways provides significant insight into the regulation of cell growth. Amino acids are not only essential protein precursors but also precursors for numerous other crucial compounds, such as polyamines, *S*-adenosylmethionine, pantothenic acid, and nucleotides. Amino acids are also the immediate products of ammonia assimilation, and these products are essential nitrogen donors for the synthesis of other intermediates. This article presents an overview of amino acid synthesis, with an emphasis on the functions of the amino acids, the biosynthetic pathways and their regulation, and the interrelationships of the amino acids in *Escherichia coli*. Because of this broad perspective, individual reactions, enzymes, and the genes that specify these enzymes are frequently not discussed, although all known mechanisms of regulation are considered. This article begins with an estimate of the requirements for the individual amino acids for cellular biosyntheses. The complex mechanisms of nitrogen assimilation are then considered within the context of glutamine and glutamate synthesis. The sections that follow describe the families of amino acids, which are grouped to emphasize the metabolic interrelationships between the amino acids.

## I. CELLULAR REQUIREMENTS FOR AMINO ACIDS

Figure 1 summarizes the precursors and provides an overview of the relationships between the amino

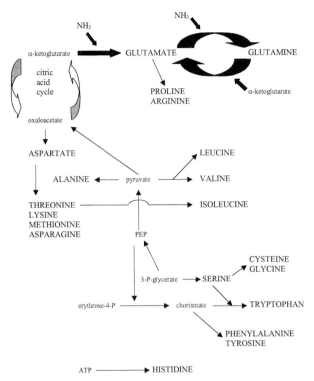

**Fig. 1.** Amino acid precursors and relationships between amino acids.

acids. Table I provides a quantitative description of the amino acid composition of total cellular protein, the use of amino acids as precursors for other compounds, and utilization of amino acids as nitrogen donors for cells grown in a glucose–ammonia minimal medium. For nitrogen-limited growth, glutamine provides most, if not all, the nitrogen for glutamate. In this situation, glutamine synthetase is the most active enzyme involved in amino acid synthesis. The data in Table I should be considered to be approximations, but they do provide some indication of the quantitative importance of each amino acid.

## II. GLUTAMATE AND GLUTAMINE

### A. Functions of Glutamine and Glutamate

The syntheses of glutamine and glutamate are the primary mechanisms for the assimilation of inorganic nitrogen into organic nitrogen. Glutamate and gluta-

mine donate their nitrogens for the synthesis of all nitrogenous compounds in the cell, except for the very few compounds that directly incorporate ammonia during their synthesis. Glutamate provides approximately 72% of the cell's nitrogen, mostly via reversible transaminations (Table I). Glutamine provides approximately 28% of the nitrogen, which is used for synthesis of histidine, tryptophan, asparagine, glutamate, purines, pyrimidines, amino sugars, and *p*-aminobenzoate (Table I).

Glutamate is the precursor for proline, arginine, and polyamines. It is also an osmotically regulated anion that can restore pH when $K^+$ accumulation increases the internal pH. Both glutamate and glutamine can be used as sole nitrogen sources but are not good carbon sources for *Escherichia coli*.

### B. Enzymes of Glutamine and Glutamate Synthesis and Their Functions

Glutamine synthetase (GS) is the only enzyme that catalyzes glutamine formation, but there are two enzymes that synthesize glutamate: glutamate dehydrogenase (GDH) and glutamate synthase, which aminate α-ketoglutarate with ammonia and glutamine's amide, respectively (Fig. 2).

These enzymes not only synthesize essential amino acids and nitrogen donors but also assimilate nitrogen from the environment. Ammonia is the preferred nitrogen source because it supports the fastest growth rate. However, *E. coli* and *Salmonella typhimurium* can also utilize several amino acids and nucleotide bases as sole nitrogen sources. Metabolism of these nitrogen sources limits growth and induces proteins that transport and catabolize nitrogenous compounds to generate ammonia and possibly glutamate. The genes activated during nitrogen limitation are defined as nitrogen-regulated (Ntr) genes. Their function is to provide ammonia and sometimes glutamate for the synthesis of nitrogenous intermediates.

Either GS or GDH can be the major ammonia assimilatory enzyme (Fig. 2). It was thought that GDH assimilates ammonia when it is present at >1 m*M* because GS activity is low, and that GS assimilates low ammonia (<1 m*M*) because the $K_m$ of GDH

***TABLE I***
**Amino Acid Requirements**[a]

| Amino acid | Protein[b] | Precursors for other compounds | Nitrogen donation | Total |
|---|---|---|---|---|
| Glutamate | 250 | 810 | 7011 | 8071 |
| Aspartate | 229 | 1558 | 979 | 2765 |
| Glutamine | 250 | | 2058 | 2308 |
| Serine | 205 | 1319 | | 1524 |
| Glycine | 582 | 328 | | 910 |
| Alanine | 488 | 55 | | 543 |
| Threonine | 241 | 276 | | 517 |
| Leucine | 428 | | | 428 |
| Valine | 402 | | | 402 |
| Lysine | 326 | 28 | | 354 |
| Arginine | 281 | | | 281 |
| Isoleucine | 276 | | | 276 |
| Cysteine | 87 | 146 | | 233 |
| Asparagine | 229 | | | 229 |
| Proline | 210 | | | 210 |
| Phenylalanine | 176 | | | 176 |
| Methionine | 146 | | | 146 |
| Tyrosine | 131 | | | 131 |
| Histidine | 90 | | | 90 |
| Tryptophan | 54 | | | 54 |

[a] All data are $\mu$mol/g dried cells.

[b] Derived from Tables 1 and 2 in Chapter 3 of Neidhardt (1996), which should be consulted for assumptions and uncertainties.

for ammonia is high (approximately 2 m*M*). However, Helling (1998) has shown that GS is the primary enzyme of ammonia assimilation whenever energy is not limiting (Fig. 2A), and that GDH assimilates ammonia when energy is limiting (Fig. 2B). This arrangement is most beneficial during energy-limited growth since GDH-dependent ammonia assimilation does not consume energy but GS-dependent assimilation does consume energy. The pathway of glutamate synthesis necessarily parallels that of ammonia assimilation. Whenever GS is the primary route of ammonia assimilation, glutamate synthase must synthesize glutamate because glutamate is the major intracellular nitrogen donor (Fig. 2A).

Another function for GS can be deduced from the observation by Soupene *et al.* (1998) that nitrogen limitation induces an ammonia transport system that exchanges ammonia between the cell and the environment, i.e., it does not concentrate ammonia.

When the levels of ammonia and glutamine limit growth, as occurs during nitrogen limitation, a major function of the assimilatory GS is to metabolically trap ammonia and prevent leakage through this transport system and the membrane.

## C. Regulation of GS Activity and Synthesis

### 1. Feedback Inhibition and Covalent Adenylylation

Several nitrogenous intermediates control GS activity. Alanine, glycine, and serine compete with glutamate at the active site. Products of glutamine metabolism—histidine, tryptophan, CTP, AMP, carbamoyl-phosphate, and glucoseamine 6-phosphate—also inhibit GS, but these inhibitors appear to bind allosteric sites with the exception of AMP, which competes with ATP.

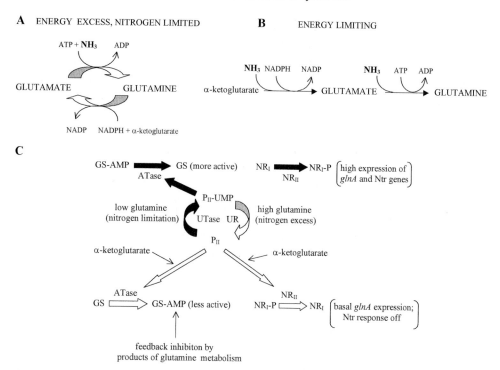

**Fig. 2.** Glutamine and glutamate synthesis, ammonia assimilation, and their control. (A) The reactions with energy excess. (B) The reactions during energy-limited growth. (C) The regulatory proteins that control GS adenylylation, GS synthesis, and the Ntr response: solid symbols, nitrogen limitation; open symbols, nitrogen excess.

GS from nitrogen-replete cells is more sensitive to feedback inhibition than GS from nitrogen-limited cells. The basis for this differential sensitivity is covalent adenylylation. GS from nitrogen-replete cells is more highly adenylylated than GS from nitrogen-limited cells. Adenylylation inactivates the modified subunit of the GS dodecamer, which reduces GS-specific activity, and sensitizes the unmodified subunits to feedback inhibition.

## 2. Control of Adenylylation

A three-protein regulatory cascade controls GS adenylylation (Fig. 2C). Jiang *et al.* (1998) have revised our understanding of the factors that control these proteins: Glutamine and α-ketoglutarate control their activities.

Glutamine, which senses nitrogen sufficiency, affects the regulatory cascade at two points. It is the only factor that affects the activity of the bifunctional uridylyltransferase/uridylyl-removing enzyme (UTase/UR). High glutamine senses nitrogen excess

and stimulates UMP removal from the regulatory protein $P_{II}$ (Fig. 2C, open arrows). Unmodified $P_{II}$ interacts with adenylyltransferase (ATase) and stimulates adenylylation of GS. Glutamine also allosterically stimulates the adenylyl transfer activity of ATase. Low glutamine, the sensor for nitrogen limitation, stimulates uridylylation of $P_{II}$, which not only prevents GS adenylylation but also actively promotes deadenylylation (Fig. 2C, solid arrows).

α-Ketoglutarate senses carbon sufficiency. It binds to unmodified $P_{II}$ and impairs the interaction with ATase. It essentially counters the effect of glutamine by favoring deadenylylation of GS, but only to the extent that $P_{II}$ is not modified (i.e., with moderate to high glutamine).

## 3. Regulation of glnA (GS) Expression and Ntr Genes

The complex *glnALG* operon codes for GS, nitrogen regulator II ($NR_{II}$; also called NtrB), and nitrogen regulator I ($NR_I$; also called NtrC). Two minor promoters ensure basal levels of the products of the operon. One of these promoters requires cyclic-AMP and its binding protein. The major promoter of the operon is utilized during nitrogen limitation, and its activity is controlled by the same regulatory proteins and environmental cues that regulate GS adenylylation. Low glutamine (nitrogen limitation) results in uridylylation of $P_{II}$, which is unable to interact with $NR_{II}$ (Fig. 2C, solid arrows). In this situation, $NR_{II}$ phosphorylates $NR_I$, which interacts with $\sigma^{54}$-containing RNA polymerase and stimulates transcription of *glnA* and other Ntr genes. High glutamine (nitrogen excess) results in the net dephosphorylation of $NR_I\sim P$ (Fig. 2C, open arrows). $\alpha$-Ketoglutarate and glutamate bind to unmodified $P_{II}$ and antagonize the effect of glutamine by inhibiting the dephosphorylation of $NR_I\sim P$.

### 4. Coordination of GS Activity, GS Synthesis, and the Ntr Response

GS-specific activity, *glnA* expression, and Ntr gene expression usually vary in parallel. Either all are high or all are low (Fig. 2C). However, they do not respond identically to changes in glutamine concentration. The adenylylation system senses glutamine at a higher concentration range, and it also responds to smaller changes in glutamine concentration. Therefore, during the transition to nitrogen-limited growth, GS adenylylation is affected before GS and other Ntr genes are induced. The obvious advantage of such regulation is speed. The first response to nitrogen limitation is to increase the specific activity of the available enzyme. The speed of adenylylation is also important in the transition from a nitrogen-poor to a nitrogen-rich environment since without adenylylation GS depletes the glutamate pool.

### D. The Enzymes of Glutamate Synthesis and Their Regulation

GDH and glutamate synthase both synthesize glutamate. GDH is not essential, although cells without GDH grow less well in carbon-limited medium. Very little is known about the control of GDH synthesis except that glutamate represses its synthesis by an unknown mechanism.

Glutamate synthase is an iron–sulfur-containing amidotransferase. The leucine-responsive protein (Lrp) is required for its synthesis. The function of such control is not apparent (see Section IX). Glutamate represses glutamate synthase by an unknown mechanism. Carbon limitation moderately represses glutamate synthase formation, which is consistent with the role for GDH during such growth.

A mutant lacking glutamate synthase fails to catabolize a variety of nitrogen sources such as arginine. However, growth with arginine represses glutamate synthase because arginine catabolism produces glutamate. These results imply that glutamate synthase is required for induction of the Ntr response. During the transition to a nitrogen-poor environment, glutamate synthase may either prevent a rapid accumulation of glutamine, which would shut off the Ntr response, or prevent a rapid depletion of glutamate.

## III. THE GLUTAMATE FAMILY: PROLINE AND ARGININE

### A. Proline

#### 1. Functions

Proline is not a precursor for other metabolites. However, at high environmental osmolality, proline serves to control cellular osmolality.

#### 2. Synthesis

The three enzymes of proline synthesis have been difficult to study since all the intermediates are unstable. The first two enzymes form a complex which phosphorylates and reduces glutamate to form $\gamma$-glutamic semialdehyde, which spontaneously cyclizes to L-$\Delta^1$-pyrroline-5-carboxylate. The third enzyme reduces this intermediate to proline. Both reductions require NADPH.

The enzymes of arginine synthesis provide an alternate route for formation of $\gamma$-glutamic semialdehyde (Fig. 3, dashed arrow). A block in the fourth step of arginine biosynthesis results in accumulation of $N$-acetylglutamic $\gamma$-semialdehyde, which can be deacetylated by the fifth enzyme of arginine synthesis to form $\gamma$-glutamic semialdehyde.

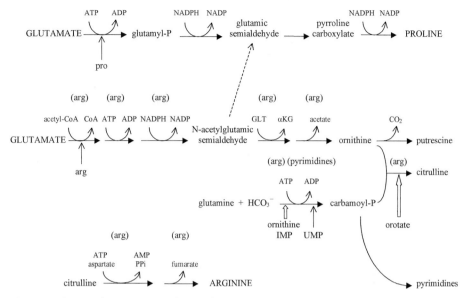

**Fig. 3.** Proline and arginine synthesis. The arrows under pathways show feedback inhibitors; the thick black arrow indicates stimulation of enzyme activity. Notations above the pathways indicate repressing effectors. arg, arginine; GLT, glutamate; $\alpha$KG, $\alpha$-ketoglutarate; pro, proline.

### 3. Regulation

The only control on proline synthesis is feedback inhibition of $\gamma$-glutamyl kinase by proline. The genes appear to be constitutively expressed. High osmolality, which results in proline accumulation, inhibits proline catabolism and enhances proline transport but is not known to affect proline synthesis.

## B. Arginine

### 1. Functions

Either arginine or ornithine, an intermediate in arginine synthesis, can be used to synthesize the polyamines putrescine and spermidine. The polyamine requirement is approximately 30% of that for arginine. Ornithine is also a precursor for the hydroxamate type of iron siderophores. Another arginine precursor, carbamoyl phosphate, is an essential precursor for pyrimidines. Arginine is catabolized as a nitrogen source in *E. coli* but not as a carbon/energy source. Arginine catabolism can protect *E. coli* against low extracellular pH.

### 2. Synthesis

The intermediates of arginine synthesis appear to be the same in all known bacteria, although there can be a slight variation in the reactions of the first and fifth steps. The first five reactions add an amino group to the $\delta$-carbon of glutamate to form ornithine. The first reaction acetylates glutamate's amino group, which prevents subsequent cyclization, and can occur by two distinct mechanisms: direct acetylation by acetyl-CoA (as in *E. coli*) or transacetylation with *N*-acetylornithine, which is also an intermediate in arginine synthesis. Phosphorylation, reduction, and addition of an amino group by transamination produces *N*-acetylornithine. The acetyl group is then removed either by deacetylation, as in *E. coli*, or by transacetylation, which recycles the acetyl group back to glutamate and forms the first intermediate of the pathway.

The last three reactions of arginine synthesis appear to be found in all organisms that synthesize arginine. The first of these requires carbamoyl phosphate, which is synthesized by a glutamine-dependent carbamoyl phosphate synthetase. Carbamoyl phosphate reacts with ornithine, forming citrulline. The last two steps of arginine synthesis amount to donation of aspartate's nitrogen to citrulline.

### 3. Regulation

There are two major sites of kinetic control: at the beginning of the pathway leading to ornithine and at the branch point where carbamoyl phosphate enters the biosynthetic pathway. Arginine inhibits the enzyme that acetylates glutamate. UMP inhibits carbamoyl phosphate synthetase, and ornithine and IMP prevent this inhibition. In addition, orotate, an intermediate in pyrimidine synthesis, activates ornithine carbamoyltransferase. These mechanisms balance the relative need for arginine and pyrimidines. (Section IX,A describes another mechanism that balances arginine and pyrimidine synthesis.) Other organisms, such as *Bacillus subtilis*, have two carbamoyl phosphate synthetases—one for pyrimidines and the other for arginine.

The major mode of transcriptional regulation in *E. coli* is repression by ArgR, which binds operator sites when bound with arginine. In *E. coli*, the arginine biosynthetic genes are not linked, and with only one exception all the genes have only one promoter. ArgR represses each to a differing extent. The gene for carbamoyl phosphate synthetase has two promoters—ArgR represses one, and pyrimidines repress the other. ArgR has a second, apparently unrelated function: It resolves plasmid dimers to monomers, which is required for maintaining copy number.

## IV. THE OXALOACETATE FAMILY: ASPARATE, ASPARAGINE, THREONINE, LYSINE, AND METHIONINE

### A. Aspartate and Asparagine

#### 1. Functions

Cells require a large amount of aspartate (Table I). It is the precursor for threonine, methionine, lysine, pyrimidines, pantothenate, and NAD. Aspartate is a nitrogen donor for arginine synthesis and for two reactions in purine synthesis. Aspartate, and not oxa-loacetate or malate, is a metabolic sensor of dicarboxylic acid availability. High aspartate inhibits dicarboxylic acid formation from PEP and also stimulates enzymes that convert dicarboxylic acids to PEP and pyruvate. In contrast, asparagine is a dead-end metabolite. For *E. coli*, neither aspartate nor asparagine are good carbon sources, but both can be degraded as sole nitrogen sources. Both amino acids are sources of fumarate, which can be used as a terminal electron acceptor during anaerobic respiration.

#### 2. Synthesis and Regulation

Glutamate-dependent transamination of oxaloacetate produces aspartate. Two enzymes can catalyze this reaction. Aspartate transaminase, specified by *aspC*, is quantitatively more important, and its synthesis is constitutive. The tyrosine–phenylalanine transaminase, the *tyrB* product, can also synthesize aspartate, and tyrosine represses its synthesis. Aspartate transaminase activity is very high, which suggests that its products and substrates are in equilibrium, and that mass action controls aspartate synthesis. Considering the numerous functions of aspartate, such regulation is appropriate.

An ammonia-dependent asparagine synthetase and a glutamine-dependent asparagine synthetase (AsnA and AsnB, respectively) catalyze the ATP-dependent amidation of aspartate. Eukaryotes only possess the latter. The functions of these enzymes have been most extensively studied in *Klebsiella aerogenes*. AsnB is required for growth in a nitrogen-limited medium presumably because there is insufficient ammonia for AsnA. During nitrogen-limited growth, AsnB, which has a low catalytic capacity, is approximately 5% of the soluble protein. When ammonia is available, AsnA presumably spares the need to synthesize AsnB.

Asparagine inhibits and represses both enzymes. In *K. aerogenes*, the two enzymes are reciprocally regulated. Nitrogen limitation represses AsnA and induces AsnB. The reverse is true for cells with excess nitrogen. Two regulators control the formation of AsnA. In *E. coli*, AsnC activates and asparagine antagonizes this activation; in *K. aerogenes*, Nac, a regulator induced by nitrogen limitation, represses. Control of AsnB synthesis has not been studied.

## B. Threonine, Lysine, and Methionine

### 1. Functions

Threonine is the precursor for isoleucine, and in unusual circumstances it can be the precursor for glycine and serine. Diaminopimelate, an intermediate in lysine synthesis, is an essential component of peptidoglycan. Numerous secondary metabolites are derived from intermediates in lysine synthesis in several organisms. Methionine is the precursor of *S*-adenosylmethionine (SAM), a donor for protein and nucleic acid methylations, for propylamino groups of polyamines, and for cyclopentenediol for tRNA modifications. Methionine is also an indicator of excess $C_1$-tetrahydrofolate derivatives, and it stimulates an enzyme that converts $N^{10}$-formyl-tetrahydrofolate to tetrahydrofolate.

### 2. The Common Pathway

The synthesis of these amino acids involves a single common pathway and three amino acid-specific pathways. The common pathway results in the synthesis of homoserine and starts with the phosphorylation of aspartate by aspartokinase, which produces $\beta$-aspartyl phosphate (Fig. 4). Two NADPH-dependent reductions, catalyzed by aspartic semialdehyde dehydrogenase and homoserine dehydrogenase, convert $\beta$-aspartyl phosphate to aspartate semialdehyde (the precursor for lysine) and then to homoserine (the precursor for threonine and methionine), respectively.

### 3. The Specific Pathways

The first reaction of lysine synthesis starts with condensation of aspartate semialdehyde with pyruvate to form a cyclic intermediate, which is reduced by NADPH to form tetrahydrodipicolinate (Fig. 4). In *E. coli*, tetrahydrodipicolinate is succinylated by succinyl-CoA, a nitrogen is added by glutamate-dependent transamination, and the blocking group is removed to produce ʟʟ-diaminopimelate. An epimerase converts ʟʟ-diaminopimelate to *meso*-diaminopimelate, which is decarboxylated to form lysine. The first two reactions of lysine synthesis are the same in all bacteria. Two variations of this pathway are present in other bacteria. In some organisms, tetrahydrodipicolinate is converted directly to *meso*-diaminopimelate, and in gram-positive organisms the blocking agent is an acetyl group. The synthesis of secondary metabolites and different requirements for cell wall components are thought to account for these variations.

Threonine is derived in two steps from homoserine (Fig. 4). Homoserine is phosphorylated, and threonine synthase catalyzes a complex reaction that converts the resulting homoserine phosphate to threonine.

Methionine is synthesized from homoserine in four steps (Fig. 4). Three complex reactions replace the hydroxyl group of homoserine with -SH, which produces homocysteine. Succinylation of the hydroxyl group by succinyl-CoA initiates these reactions in *E. coli*, whereas acetylation is employed in gram-positive organisms. Cysteine is the source of the reduced sulfur. The third enzyme of the pathway not only hydrolyzes the intermediate cystathionine but also hydrolyzes cysteine and serine. Serine inhibition of this reaction can result in a methionine requirement. In the fourth reaction, donation of a methyl group to the sulfur of homocystine generates methionine. The methyl donor is $N^5$-methyltetrahydrofolate, which is generated by reduction of $N^5$, $N^{10}$-methylene tetrahydrofolate. Two methionine synthases catalyze the final methyl transfer to homocystine: One is cobalamin dependent, whereas the other is cobalamin independent. *S*-adenosylmethionine is synthesized in one step from methionine and ATP.

### 4. Regulation

*Escherichia coli* has three aspartate kinases and two homoserine dehydrogenases—the first and third reactions of the common pathway, respectively. The homoserine dehydrogenases are part of the same polypeptide that contains aspartokinase. These isozymes are subject to different patterns of kinetic and transcriptional control, which ensures that an excess of one amino acid does not prevent synthesis of the others (Fig. 4).

Aspartokinase–homoserine dehydrogenase I is the major homoserine dehydrogenase activity, and it is threonine specific. It is understandable that it

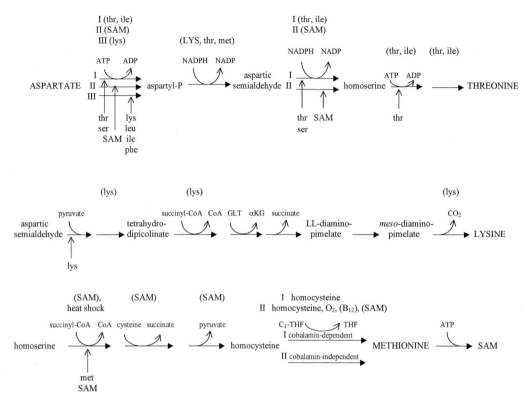

**Fig. 4.** Threonine, lysine, and methionine synthesis. Feedback inhibitors are shown beneath the pathway and transcriptional effectors above, with repressive effectors in parentheses. $B_{12}$, vitamin $B_{12}$; GLT, glutamate; ile, isoleucine; $\alpha$KG, $\alpha$-ketoglutarate; leu, leucine; lys, lysine; met, methionine; phe, phenylalanine; SAM, *S*-adenosylmethionine; ser, serine; THF, tetrahydrofolate; thr, threonine.

would be the major isozyme since threonine is also a precursor for isoleucine (Table I). Threonine allosterically inhibits its activity. Serine also inhibits this enzyme, and this is the basis for serine toxicity in some strains. Threonine inhibits the first enzyme specific to threonine synthesis, homoserine kinase. The *thrABC* operon codes for aspartokinase–homoserine dehydrogenase I and the two enzymes of the threonine-specific pathway, respectively. Isoleucine and threonine control its expression through an attenuation mechanism.

The only kinetic control of methionine synthesis is inhibition of the first methionine-specific enzyme, homoserine transsuccinylase, by methionine or SAM. Unlike the kinetic control, the transcriptional controls are surprisingly complex. The genes of methionine synthesis form the generally unlinked genes of the *met* regulon. The repressor MetJ bound with SAM, a product of methionine metabolism, represses

aspartokinase–homoserine dehydrogenase II of the common pathway and all the methionine-specific enzymes, except the cobalamin-dependent methionine synthase. MetR is a second regulator of the *met* regulon. MetR, which binds homocysteine, can either inhibit or stimulate transcription. Its most noticeable effect is the activation of the genes for the two methionine synthases. (MetJ and MetR also regulate *glyA*, which codes for serine hydroxy methyltransferase, an enzyme involved in synthesis of $N^5,N^{10}$-methylene tetrahydrofolate, which is required for methionine synthesis.) Homoserine transsuccinylase (encoded by *metA*) is thermolabile, and at high temperatures *metA* expression requires $\sigma^{32}$, which means that *metA* is a heat shock gene. Other regulatory proteins are also probably involved in the control of methionine synthesis.

Lysine inhibits aspartokinase III, which implies that it is specific for lysine. Leucine, isoleucine, and phenylalanine also contribute to this inhibition. Lysine also inhibits the first reaction of the specific pathway. Lysine represses aspartokinase III and aspartate semialdehyde dehydrogenase. The latter enzyme is also repressed by threonine and methionine, although lysine repression is by far the most significant. The genes of the lysine-specific pathway are not linked, and lysine represses only about half of the them; the others are constitutive. The mechanism of control has not been established for most of these enzymes. However, LysR, which binds diaminopimelate, activates expression of the gene for the last reaction of lysine synthesis, diaminopimelate decarboxylase.

## V. THE PYRUVATE FAMILY: ALANINE AND THE BRANCHED-CHAIN AMINO ACIDS

### A. Alanine

#### 1. Function

L-Alanine is the precursor for D-alanine, which is a major component of the cell wall. L-Alanine also binds to Lrp, a global regulator, and affects its activity.

#### 2. Synthesis

Alanine auxotrophs have yet to be isolated from *E. coli* and other enteric bacteria probably because multiple enzymes can catalyze alanine formation. One route of synthesis is undoubtedly from transamination of pyruvate, and two alanine-forming transaminases have been identified. The first (AvtA) uses valine and the second (AlaB) uses glutamate as a nitrogen donor. Alanine and leucine repress AvtA, but the mechanism of regulation has not been studied. Two labeling studies suggest a pyruvate-independent route of alanine formation, but this pathway has not been identified.

### B. The Branched-Chain Amino Acids

#### 1. Functions

Isoleucine, valine, and leucine are not precursors for other intermediates. However, one intermediate for valine and leucine synthesis, α-keto-isovalerate, is also a precursor for pantothenate. High α-ketobutyrate, which is an intermediate of isoleucine synthesis, is toxic and has been proposed to be an alarmone. The branched-chain amino acids are not known to be degraded by *E. coli*.

#### 2. Pathways

The first step specific to isoleucine synthesis is the deamination of threonine, which produces α-ketobutyrate (Fig. 5). Pyruvate is the corresponding α-keto acid precursor for both valine and leucine synthesis. Parallel pathways with shared enzymes then convert α-ketobutyrate and pyruvate to isoleucine and valine, respectively. Depending on the organism, two or three different acetohydroxy acid synthases decarboxylate pyruvate and transfer active acetaldehyde to either α-ketobutyrate or pyruvate. *Escherichia coli* K12 has isozymes I and III, whereas *Salmonella typhimurium* has isozymes I and II. (These enzymes differ in their substrate specificity and their sensitivity to feedback inhibitors.) This reaction creates a branch point at the α-carbon. The next enzyme reduces a ketone to an alcohol and transfers the branch point to the β-carbon. Dehydration, followed by transamination, results in formation of isoleucine and valine. Two different transaminases can transfer an amino group to the valine precursor. One of the valine transaminases, the *avtA* product, uses alanine as an amino donor.

Leucine is one methylene group larger than valine and has a branch point at the γ-carbon. The extra carbon is added by reactions similar to those catalyzed by three reactions of the citric acid cycle: citrate synthase, aconitase, and isocitrate dehydrogenase. The first intermediate of leucine synthesis, α-ketoisovalerate, is the last intermediate of valine synthesis. α-Ketoisovalerate is acetylated with acetyl-CoA, and the product, α-isopropylmalate, is converted to β-isopropylmalate by reaction similar to that catalyzed by aconitase. β-Isopropylmalate is then decarboxylated, forming α-ketoisocaproate, which acquires a nitrogen by transamination to produce leucine.

#### 3. Problems with Substrate Specificities

The hydrophobic branched-chain amino acids are structurally related, and proteins have only a limited

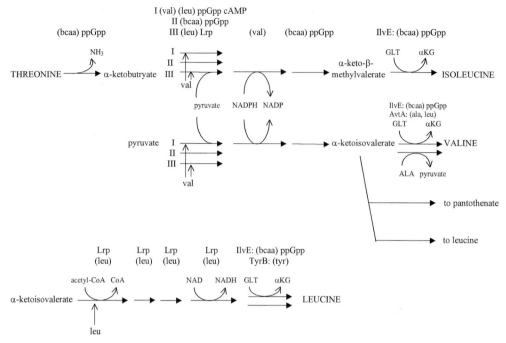

**Fig. 5.** Branched-chain amino acid synthesis. Feedback inhibitors are shown below the pathway and transcriptional effectors above, with repressing effectors in parentheses and activating effectors. ala, alanine; bcaa, the sum of leucine, isoleucine, and valine; cAMP, cyclic-AMP; GLT, glutamate; αKG, α-ketoglutarate; leu, leucine; tyr, tyrosine; val, valine.

ability to distinguish between them. This lack of specificity permits the sharing of the last four enzymes in the parallel pathways of isoleucine and valine synthesis. Furthermore, the *ilvC* product, acetohydroxy acid isomeroreductase (the second shared enzyme), not only reduces the acetohydroxy acid intermediates of isoleucine and valine synthesis but also reduces α-ketopantoate in the pantothenate biosynthetic pathway. Finally, isopropylmalate synthase, which acetylates α-ketoisovalerate, can also acetylate other α-keto acids such as pyruvate, especially during leucine starvation when the pool of α-ketoisovalerate is presumably low. The aminoacyl-tRNA synthetases are the only proteins that can discriminate between the branched-chain amino acids. Not suprisingly, elaborate mechanisms reduce the frequency of mischarging.

### 4. Regulation

Allosteric regulation controls the first committed step for each amino acid, but the allosteric regulation is complicated because of the metabolic interrelation-

ships and the shared enzymes. Isoleucine inhibits threonine deaminase, which is an isoleucine-specific enzyme. High valine, which indicates a high valine to isoleucine ratio, reverses this inhibition. Valine inhibits acetohydroxy acid synthases I and III, the first enzyme of valine synthesis and the second of isoleucine synthesis. This can cause an isoleucine deficiency and toxic accumulation of α-ketobutyrate. Isoleucine prevents α-ketobutyrate accumulation by inhibiting threonine deaminase. To maintain the proper ratio of isoleucine to valine in the absence of isoleucine, several enteric eubacteria contain the valine-insensitive acetohydroxy acid synthase II. *Escherichia coli* lacks this isozyme and apparently escapes valine toxicity because acetohydroxy acid synthase III prefers α-ketobutyrate compared to pyruvate. The major allosteric control of leucine synthesis is leucine inhibition of isopropylmalate synthase, which catalyzes the first committed step of leucine synthesis.

Several mechanisms regulate the formation of branched-chain amino acid enzymes. Attenuation controls the expression of 11 of the 15 genes—the effectors are shown above the pathways in Fig. 5. Lrp induces acetohydroxy acid synthase III and the *leuABCD* operon, which codes for the leucine biosynthetic enzymes. In contrast to these mechanisms of regulation, IIvY activates only one gene, *ilvC*, which specifies the third reaction of isoleucine synthesis. IIvY binds the acetohydroxy acids that are the substrates for IlvC. A final layer of regulation is activation by guanosine tetraphosphate (ppGpp) (Fig. 5)—growth in rich medium results in low levels of branched-chain amino acid enzymes.

## VI. SERINE, GLYCINE, AND CYSTEINE

### A. Serine and Glycine

#### 1. Functions

Serine is a precursor for cysteine, selenocysteine, tryptophan, glycine, and phospholipids. Glycine is a precursor for purines, pyridoxal, and heme-containing compounds. The conversion of serine to glycine and the cleavage of glycine generate $C_1$ units, which are required for the synthesis of purines, thymine, methionine, *S*-adenosylmethionine, histidine, and pantothenate and the formylation of the initiator tRNA$^{\text{Met}}$. Glycine is also an indicator of excess tetrahydrofolate: It inhibits an enzyme that converts $N^{10}$-formyl-tetrahydrofolate to tetrahydrofolate. It has been estimated that the serine–glycine pathway uses 15% of the carbon assimilated by glucose-grown cells.

L-Serine can be a sole carbon source, but only in the presence of leucine or glycine, which are required for induction of catabolic enzymes. L-Serine can be a sole nitrogen source, but only when methionine is in the medium. Glycine can also be a nitrogen source. Serine and glycine competitively inhibit glutamine synthesis, but the physiological significance of this inhibition has not been established.

#### 2. Pathways

NAD-dependent oxidation of the glycolytic intermediate 3-phosphoglycerate initiates the major pathway of serine synthesis (Fig. 6). Nitrogen is added to the resulting product, 3-phosphohydroxypyruvate, by glutamate-dependent transmination, thus forming 3-phosphoserine. (This transaminase also catalyzes a reaction in pyridoxine synthesis that does not involve intermediates in serine synthesis.) Dephosphorylation of 3-phosphoserine then produces serine. Serine hydroxy methyltransferase (SHMT) catalyzes the reversible conversion of serine to glycine and the formation of the $C_1$ carrier $N^5,N^{10}$-methylene tetrahydrofolate from tetrahydrofolate. The final reaction in this sequence is the oxidative cleavage of glycine by the glycine cleavage enzyme system (GCV), which produces ammonia, $CO_2$, and a second molecule of $N^5,N^{10}$-methylene tetrahydrofolate. This enzyme may seem unnecessary, but mutants deficient in GCV excrete glycine, which implies that it is active.

An alternate pathway synthesizes serine and glycine from threonine. Threonine is oxidized to form 2-amino-3-ketobutyrate, which is then cleaved to

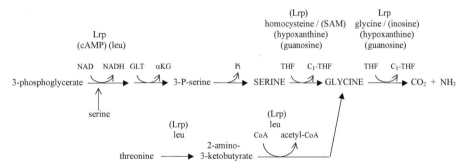

**Fig. 6.** Serine and glycine synthesis. The notation below the pathway indicates the feedback inhibitor. The notations above the pathway indicate repressive transcriptional effectors (in parentheses) and positive effectors. The slash between effectors indicates that the ratio is important for control. cAMP, cyclic-AMP; GLT, glutamate; $\alpha$KG, $\alpha$-ketoglutarate; leu, leucine; SAM, *S*-adenosylmethionine; THF, tetrahydrofolate.

acetyl-CoA and glycine. Serine is generated from the combined actions of the glycine cleavage enzyme, which produces a $C_1$ unit, and SHMT, which forms serine using the $C_1$ unit and a second molecule of glycine. Mutants deficient in SHMT require glycine, which implies that 3-phosphoglycerate is usually the major source of serine. The alternate pathway predominates only during carbon-limited growth in the presence of all three branched-chain amino acids and arginine.

### 3. Serine Toxicity

Serine toxicity, first discovered in the 1950s, is reversed by isoleucine and its precursors. Serine inhibits homoserine dehydrogenase I, which is required for isoleucine synthesis, for cells grown in a glucose–ammonia minimal medium. Serine is also toxic in nitrogen-limited medium, and methionine overcomes this inhibition. The basis for this toxicity appears to be serine-dependent inhibition of the third enzyme of methionine synthesis (Fig. 4). It is not known whether the differences in toxicity result from differences in strains or growth media. Not only is serine toxic but also the major product of serine catabolism is toxic—high pyruvate interferes with branched-chain amino acid synthesis.

### 4. Regulation

Serine allosterically inhibits 3-phosphoglycerate dehydrogenase, the first enzyme of the major serine pathway. Serine, glycine, or the products of $C_1$ metabolism do not affect the activity of any other enzyme of this pathway. In contrast, transcriptional regulation controls the synthesis of 3-phosphoglycerate dehydrogenase, SHMT, and GCV. The formation of the second and third enzymes of the serine pathway has not been extensively studied. The transcriptional regulation is extraordinarily complex and only partially understood. Curiously, serine is not involved. Hypoxanthine and guanine, products of $C_1$ metabolism, bind PurR, which then represses SHMT and GCV. Inosine, another product of $C_1$ metabolism, binds to another regulator, GcvA, which represses GCV formation. Glycine overcomes this repression and converts GcvA into an activator. Finally, $C_1$ sufficiency is sensed by a balance of homocysteine to

*S*-adenosylmethionine. These sensors control SHMT synthesis through MetR, an activator that binds homocysteine (a sensor of $C_1$ deficiency), and MetJ, a repressor that binds *S*-adenosylmethionine (a sensor of $C_1$ excess) and controls MetR synthesis. The leucine-responsive protein, Lrp, also controls these genes. Lrp in the absence of leucine tends to favor the primary pathway of serine and glycine synthesis. Lrp with leucine decreases the primary pathway, increases the secondary pathway, and increases serine catabolism.

## B. Cysteine

### 1. Functions

The synthesis of cysteine assimilates inorganic sulfur (Fig. 7). Cysteine is a precursor for glutathione, and it donates its sulfur for the synthesis of methionine and several cofactors. Cysteine can be degraded by organisms related to *E. coli*: *S. typhimurium* can degrade cysteine as a carbon source, and *K. aerogenes* can use cysteine as a nitrogen source. *Escherichia coli* is not thought to catabolize cysteine, even though it has enzymes to do so.

### 2. Pathways

The predominant mechanism of cysteine synthesis consists of two converging pathways. One branch reduces sulfate, the most abundant source of sulfur, to sulfide. Sulfate is initially activated by formation of the mixed anhydride, adenosine 5′-phosphosulfate, in a reaction that appears to be driven by GTP hydrolysis. The sulfate moiety is reduced to sulfite with thioredoxin or glutaredoxin as the reductant, and sulfite is then reduced to sulfide with NADPH as the reductant. NADPH-dependent sulfite reductase contains siroheme, a rare form of heme. The first reaction of the second branch of the pathway is catalyzed by serine transacetylase, which produces *O*-acetylserine from acetyl-CoA and serine. Sulfide reacts with *O*-acetylserine to form cysteine.

An alternate pathway involves thiosulfate as the source of sulfur. Thiosulfate can condense with *O*-acetylserine, forming *S*-sulfocysteine, which is proposed to be reduced to cysteine. This pathway may be required for the anaerobic synthesis of cysteine.

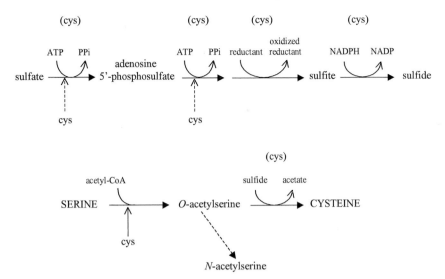

**Fig. 7.** Cysteine synthesis. The feedback inhibitor (solid arrow) and indirect inhibitor (dashed arrows) are shown below the pathway. The notations above the pathway indicate which enzymes are repressed indirectly by cysteine. cys, cysteine; PPi, inorganic pyrophosphate.

### 3. Regulation

Excess cysteine is toxic; therefore, sulfur incorporation is tightly regulated. A major point of control is cysteine inhibition of serine transacetylase. Allosteric control does not affect any other enzyme of either branch. However, the activities of the first two enzymes of sulfate reduction rapidly decay with low *O*-acetylserine, which prevents sulfate activation when cysteine is available.

Seven operons contain the 15 structural genes that are required for cysteine synthesis and the transport of sulfate and thiosulfate. Two of these genes are constitutively expressed: serine transacetylase, which synthesizes *O*-acetylserine, and the enzyme that synthesizes siroheme, which is required for other pathways. CysB, an activator of the LysR family, controls the expression of the other 13 genes. *N*-acetylserine is the inducer that binds CysB. *N*-acetylserine is believed to form spontaneously from *O*-acetylserine, and it is not known whether an enzyme assists this conversion (Fig. 7, dashed arrow). However, cysteine will prevent inducer synthesis. Sulfide or thiosulfate are anti-inducers which bind to CysB and block the effect of *N*-acetylserine binding. These regulatory mechanisms provide a hierarchy of sulfur sources that determine the extent of induction. Cysteine (assimilated sulfur) is the best sulfur source, and it prevents inducer synthesis. Sulfate, sulfite, and thiosulfate are moderately good sulfur sources that cause high levels of anti-inducers. Glutathione is a poor sulfur source that does not prevent inducer synthesis or cause a high level of an anti-inducer. It is the most derepressing sulfur source.

## VII. THE AROMATIC AMINO ACIDS

### A. Functions

Phenylalanine and tryptophan are not the precursors for other cellular metabolites, whereas tyrosine donates a carbon and a nitrogen for the thiazole unit of thiamine. Chorismate, the last common precursor for all three aromatic amino acids, is also a precursor for ubiquinone, menaquinone, folate, *p*-aminobenzoate, and enterochelin (a phenolic iron-binding siderophore). *Escherichia coli* can catabolize tryptophan as a carbon source and phenylalanine as a nitrogen source.

### B. Pathways

The first seven steps in the aromatic amino acid pathway, sometimes called the shikimate pathway (after the first identified intermediate), synthesizes chorismate, which is a precursor for all three amino acids (Fig. 8). The 10 carbons of chorismate are derived from erythrose 4-phosphate and two molecules of PEP. The next two steps of phenylalanine and tyrosine synthesis involve a different bifunctional enzyme (Fig. 8). The phenylalanine enzyme is a chorismate mutase–prephenate dehydratase that generates phenylpyruvate, which is transaminated to form phenylalanine. The tyrosine pathway contains a bifunctional chorismate mutase–prephenate dehydrogenase that produces 4-hydroxyphenylpyruvate, which forms tyrosine after transamination (Fig. 8). The *tyrB* product is the primary transaminase that catalyzes phenylalanine and tyrosine synthesis from phenylpyruvate and 4-hydroxyphenylpyruvate, respectively. The asparate transaminase, AspC, can also synthesize tyrosine and phenylalanine, and the transaminase for branched-chain amino acids, IlvE, can

generate phenylalanine. Tryptophan formation from chorismate requires phosphoribosylpyrophosphate, serine, and glutamine as a nitrogen donor (Fig. 8).

## C. Regulation

The only allosteric regulation of the shikimate pathway is directed at the three isozymes that catalyze the first reaction. A combination of phenylalanine and tyrosine regulates the activities of the two most active isozymes, whereas tryptophan controls the activity of the minor isozyme. In each case, the inhibition is incomplete, which permits synthesis of chorismate, a precursor for several other compounds. Phenylalanine, tyrosine, and tryptophan inhibit the first enzyme of each amino acid-specific pathway. Phenylalanine and tyrosine also inhibit the second reactions of their respective pathways; in fact, these end products inhibit the second reactions more

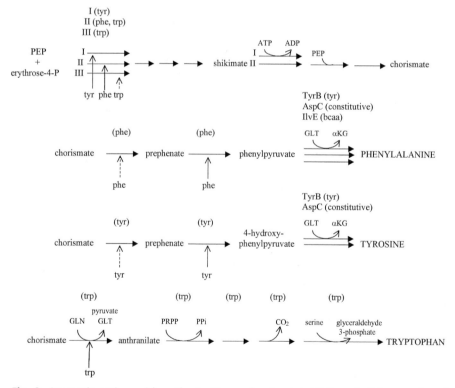

***Fig. 8.*** Aromatic amino acid synthesis. Strong feedback inhibitors (solid arrows) and weak inhibitors (dashed arrows) are shown below the pathways. The repressive effectors are shown above the pathways. bcaa, the sum of leucine, isoleucine, and valine; GLN, glutamine; GLT, glutamate; αKG, α-ketoglutarate; phe, phenylalanine; PPi, inorganic pyrophosphate; PRPP, phosphoribosylpyrophosphate; trp, tryptophan; tyr, tyrosine.

strongly. This is not surprising since a single bifunctional polypeptide catalyzes the first two reactions of each pathway. Finally, tryptophan inhibits anthranilate synthetase, the first reaction specific for tryptophan synthesis, and anthranilate inhibits the fourth reaction.

The transcriptional control of the aromatic amino acid pathways is mediated by TyrR, TrpR (complexed with tryptophan), and attenuation. TyrR is usually a repressor, although it does activate the genes for two transport proteins. TyrR represses when complexed with one of the three aromatic amino acids, although a particular gene may require a specific corepressor. TyrR represses two of the isozymes of the first step in the shikimate pathway, and TrpR represses the third. A combination of TyrR and TrpR represses the synthesis of shikimate kinase II (one of two such enzymes), which catalyzes the fifth reaction of the pathway. All the other enzymes of the shikimate pathways are produced constitutively, and each is encoded by only one gene. Such constitutivity may permit synthesis of some chorismate even with an excess of all three aromatic amino acids. This constitutivity contrasts with the regulation of all enzymes of the specific pathways, which are end-product repressed. Phenylalanine-mediated attenuation controls expression of the first gene of the phenylalanine pathway and, surprisingly, the gene for phenylalanyl-tRNA synthetase. TyrR controls the synthesis of the first gene of the tyrosine pathway (which codes for a bifunctional protein) and of *tyrB*, which codes for the phenylalanine–tyrosine transaminase. Finally, the well-studied *trp* operon is controlled by a combination of repression by TrpR and attenuation.

The entire *trp* operon is transcribed from one major promoter. A minor promoter transcribes *trpCB*—the products of these genes contain several tryptophans, and this promoter might ensure sufficient levels of these proteins during tryptophan starvation.

## VIII. HISTIDINE

### A. Functions

Histidine is not a precursor for other metabolic intermediates, and with only one exception intermediates in histidine synthesis serve no other purpose other than histidine formation. *Escherichia coli* cannot use histidine as a carbon source, although the related organism *Klebsiella aerogenes* can do so. *Klebsiella aerogenes* can also use histidine as its sole nitrogen source. *Escherichia coli* lacks this ability, but it can use histidine as a nitrogen source when a trace of aspartate is added.

### B. Biosynthesis and Its Regulation

A common pathway appears to exist in all organisms that synthesize histidine (Fig. 9). The nine-step pathway has many unusual reactions. Transfer of a phosphoribosyl group from phosphoribosyl pyrophosphate to N-1 of the purine ring of ATP initiates the pathway and provides all the carbon atoms. A glutamine-dependent amidotransferase and a glutamate-dependent aminotransferase provide the nitro-

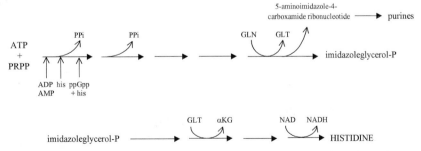

**Fig. 9.** Histidine synthesis. The feedback inhibitors are shown below the pathway. GLN, glutamine; GLT, glutamate; his, histidine; αKG, α-ketoglutarate; PPi, inorganic pyrophosphate; PRPP, phosphoribosylpyrophosphate.

gen required for the pathway. A curious feature of the pathway is the release of 5-aminoimidazole-4-carboxamide ribonucleotide, an intermediate in purine synthesis, which links histidine and purine synthesis. Failure to recycle this intermediate results in a significant decrease in purine pools and synthesis. Furthermore, overproduction of the pathway results in an adenine auxotrophy.

The activity of the first enzyme controls the flow of metabolites through the pathway. Histidine, guanosine tetraphosphate, and two indicators of a low-energy status (ADP and AMP) inhibit this reaction. Histidine is required for the inhibition by ppGpp. The rationale for such control is that it prevents needless histidine synthesis when growth is limited by starvation for another amino acid, which elevates ppGpp and activates expression of the *his* operon. Histidine also enhances the allosteric binding of ADP and AMP.

The eight genes of histidine synthesis form an operon, which has been extensively studied. ppGpp positively controls *his* operon expression and accounts for a 30-fold range of expression. An attenuation mechanism that senses the charging of tRNA$^{His}$ accounts for a 200-fold range of expression. There is a high basal expression of the *his* operon because exogenous histidine does not significantly affect the charging of tRNA$^{His}$ and because there is significant readthrough of the attenuation teminator, even with highly charged tRNA$^{His}$. The synthesis of histidyl-tRNA$^{His}$ is decreased by anaerobiosis, low osmolarity, several antibiotics, and positive supercoiling. These factors increase *his* operon expression. Factors that block addition of pseudouridine to tRNA$^{His}$ mimic the effect of histidine starvation because the unmodified tRNA$^{His}$ binds less well to codons and ribosomes stall. Histidine starvation also increases the amount of histidyl-tRNA synthetase, which can alter tRNA$^{His}$ charging, by an unknown mechanism.

The wealth of information concerning control of histidine synthesis results, in part, from the power of the available genetic systems. Positive selections exist for mutants with increased or decreased expression. Such genetic methods have permitted use of the *his* operon to study a variety of other basic phenomena, including gene duplications and mutagenesis.

## IX. GLOBAL EFFECTORS: THE STRINGENT RESPONSE AND Lrp

### A. The Stringent Response and Amino Acid Metabolism

The stringent response occurs when the demand for protein synthesis exceeds the availability of charged tRNAs, e.g., when cells are confronted with limitation for a single amino acid. When this happens, ppGpp accumulates and inhibits the synthesis of stable RNAs (tRNAs and rRNAs). The function of such control is to balance protein synthesis with the availability of precursors, i.e., charged tRNAs. Studies comparing *relA*$^+$ strains to *relA* mutants, which have diminished ppGpp, suggest that ppGpp stimulates the synthesis of glutamate, glutamine, the branched-chain amino acids, threonine, methionine, lysine, arginine, histidine, glutamate, and glutamine. Furthermore, mutants devoid of ppGpp are auxotrophic for arginine, all three branched-chain amino acids, histidine, methionine, phenylalanine, threonine, and some strains of glycine and lysine.

The stringent response and ppGpp affect the expression of several amino acid anabolic enzymes. Figure 10 summarizes the effects of the stringent response on amino acid synthesis and other metabolic pathways. The stringent response increases the enzymes of histidine and arginine synthesis and the common and specific pathways of methionine, lysine, threonine, and branched-chain amino acid

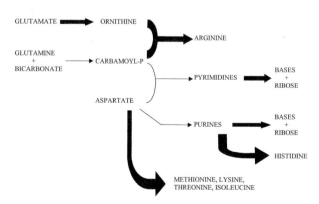

*Fig. 10.* The stringent response and the metabolism of amino acids and nucleotides. The stringent response stimulates some pathways (thick arrows) and inhibits others (thin arrows).

synthesis. These changes in gene expression simultaneously deplete nucleotides and drain common precursors away from nucleotide synthesis toward amino acid synthesis (Fig. 10). Enhanced histidine synthesis is known to deplete purines. The stringent response elevates the expression of several arginine enzymes, including the rate-limiting first enzyme, but it represses carbamoyl phosphate synthetase. The diminished synthesis of carbamoyl phosphate will impair pyrimidine synthesis, and ornithine accumulation will further divert the limiting carbamoyl phosphate away from pyrimidine synthesis. Finally, the elevation of methionine, lysine, and branched-chain amino acid enzymes may deplete aspartate, which is required for both pyrimidine and purine synthesis. Therefore, the stringent response increases the synthesis of amino acids at the expense of nucleotides (Fig. 10). This augments the direct effects of the stringent response, which inhibits nucleotide synthesis pathways and induces nucleoside degradation enzymes (Fig. 10). In summary, the stringent response rapidly balances the relative requirements for amino acids and nucleotides by simultaneously affecting several interconnected metabolic pathways.

## B. Lrp-Controlled Genes

Lrp controls the synthesis of at least 35 proteins. Lrp regulates the expression of genes whose products are generally involved in amino acid metabolism and pili formation. The most general themes of Lrp-dependent control involve enzymes that metabolize branched-chain amino acids, glutamate, serine, and glycine. Lrp can repress or activate gene expression. Leucine generally antagonizes repression or activation, although some Lrp-regulated genes are leucine insensitive. The following media or factors repress Lrp synthesis: rich medium, minimal medium with 1% Casamino acids, $\alpha$-ketoglutarate, the oxaloacetate family of amino acids, and pyruvate or acetate as the carbon source. A physiological theme is not obvious from either the proteins affected by Lrp or the factors that control Lrp synthesis.

### See Also the Following Articles

AMINO ACID PRODUCTION • CARBON AND NITROGEN ASSIMILATION, REGULATION OF • STRINGENT RESPONSE

### Bibliography

Helling, R. B. (1998). Pathway choice in glutamate synthesis in *Escherichia coli. J. Bacteriol,* **180**, 4571–4575.

Jiang, P., Peliska, J. A., and Ninfa, A. J. (1998). Enzymological characterization of the signal-transducing uridylyltransferase/uridylyl-removing enzyme (EC 2.7.7.59) of *Escherichia coli* and its interaction with the PII protein. *Biochemistry* **37**, 12782–12810.

Neidhardt, F. C. (editor-in-chief) (1996). "*Escherichia coli* and *Salmonella*: Cellular and Molecular Biology" (2nd ed., Chaps. 3, 14, 18, 23–33, 36, 39, 41, 43, 44, 77, 92, and 94). ASM Press, Washington, DC.

Soupene, E., He, L., Yan, D., and Kustu, S. (1998). Ammonia acquisition in enteric bacteria: physiological role of the ammonium/methylammonium transport B (AmtB) protein. *Proc. Natl. Acad. Sci. USA* **95**, 7030–7034.

# Amino Acid Production

**Hermann Sahm and Lothar Eggeling**

*Research Center Jülich*

I. Microbial Production
II. Enzymatic Production
III. Future Prospects

## GLOSSARY

**carriers/transporters** Membrane proteins that function to transport substances into or out of the cell through the cytoplasmic membrane.

**fermentor** A large growth vessel used to culture microorganisms on a large scale for the production of some commercially valuable products.

**immobilized cell** A cell attached to a solid support over which substrate is passed and is converted into product.

**metabolic engineering** The improvement of cellular activities by manipulation of enzymatic, transport, and regulatory functions of the cell with the application of recombinant DNA technology.

**regulation** Processes that control the activities or synthesis of enzymes.

**selection** Placing organisms under conditions in which the growth of those with a particular genotype will be favored.

**AMINO ACIDS** are simple organic compounds that contain one or more amino groups and one or more carboxyl groups. Amino acids are the building blocks of peptides and proteins, and they form many complex polymers. There are 20 protein-forming amino acids, all of which except glycine are optically active and occur as L-enantiomers. Eight of these protein-forming L-amino acids are essential for mammals. There are large demands for amino acids for use in the areas of food and feed additives and drug manufacturing. In medicine, amino acids are used for infusions and as therapeutic agents. Amino acid derivatives are also used in the chemical industry, such as in synthetic leathers, surface-active agents, fungicides, and pesticides. The whole market was estimated to amount to 1.5 million tons and have a value of approximately $3 billion in 1995: 38% for food, 54% for feed, and 8% for other applications. The market has increased steadily by approximately 5–10% per year. The production methods developed to date are chemical synthesis, protein hydrolysis, microbial production, and enzymatic synthesis. Whereas chemical synthesis produces a racemic mixture, which may require additional resolution, the latter procedures give rise to optically pure L-amino acids.

## I. MICROBIAL PRODUCTION

### A. Development of Amino Acid-Overproducing Strains

Many bacteria are capable of growing on a simple mineral salt medium containing ammonium, phosphate, and glucose as the sole carbon and energy source. From these simple nutrient components, these bacteria are able to synthesize all the compounds necessary for the living cell. Numerous analyses have indicated that the dry matter of a bacterial cell consists of approximately 60% protein, 20% nucleic acids, 10% carbohydrates, and 10% fat. Since the bacterial cell contains very large quantities of protein, it must be able to synthesize amino acids rapidly and efficiently. However, as a rule, only the amount of the various amino acids required for growth is formed in the bacterial cell (i.e., normally, the bacteria do not overproduce and excrete these

**TABLE I**
Analogs of Amino Acids Used for the Selection of L-Lysine-, L-Threonine-, or
L-Tryptophan-Overproducing Strains

| Lysine | Threonine | Tryptophan |
|---|---|---|
| S-(2-Aminoethyl)-L-cysteine | α-Amino-β-hydroxyvaleric acid | 5-Methyltryptophan |
| 4-Oxalysine | β-Hydroxyleucine | 4-Methyltryptophan |
| L-Lysine hydroxamate | Norleucine | 6-Methyltryptophan |
| 2,6-Diamino-4-hexenoic acid | Aminohydroxyvaleric acid | 5-Fluorotryptophan |
| 2,6-Diamino-4-hexenoic acid | N-Lauryl leucine | 6-Fluorotryptophan |
| ε-C-Methoylysine (2,6-diamino-heptanoic acid) | Norvaline | DL-7-Azatryptophan |
| δ-Hydroxylysine | N-2-Thienoylmethionine | 2-Azatryptophan |
| α-Chlorocaprolactam | 2-Amino-3-methylthiobutyric acid | 3-Inolacrylic acid |
| Trans-4,5-dehydrolysine | 2-Amino-3-hydroxyhexanoic acid | Indolmycin |

amino acids into the culture medium). As shown by biochemical and molecular biological studies, bacteria have regulatory mechanisms (repression and feedback inhibition through end products) that economically control the production and excretion of metabolites.

Thus, classical mutagenesis has been used to obtain strains which are able to overproduce a specific amino acid in large amounts. Regulatory mutants were obtained by selecting strains which are resistant to amino acid analogs. Some of these commonly used lysine, threonine, and tryptophan analogs are shown in Table I. Amino acid analog resistance may be due to derepression of the enzymes involved in the biosynthesis of amino acids or in the elimination of the allosteric control of biosynthetic key enzymes. Furthermore, the amount of amino acids synthesized via a branched pathway can be significantly increased by selecting auxotrophic strains such as those shown in Table II. To date, the applications of mutagenesis

and selection have been the most important techniques in the development of amino acid-overproducing microorganisms.

Recently, genetic engineering and amplification of relevant structural genes have become fascinating alternatives to mutagenesis and random screening procedures. Introduction of genes into organisms via recombinant DNA techniques is a powerful method for the construction of strains with desired genotypes. The opportunity to introduce heterologous genes and regulatory elements permits construction of metabolic configurations with novel and beneficial characteristics. Furthermore, this approach avoids the complication of uncharacterized mutations that are often obtained with classical mutagenesis of whole cells. The improvement of cellular activities by manipulation of enzymatic, transport, and regulatory functions of the cell with the application of recombinant DNA technology is a very promising method for obtaining highly productive amino acid-producing strains.

**TABLE II**
Amino Acid Production by
Auxotrophic Mutants

| Amino acid produced | Phenotype (auxotroph) |
|---|---|
| Tryptophan | Phe⁻, Tyr⁻ |
| Phenylalanine | Tyr⁻ |
| Tyrosine | Phe⁻ |
| Lysine | Hse⁻ |
| Homoserine | Thr⁻ |
| Valine | Leu⁻ |

## B. L-Glutamic Acid

Following the increasing demand for monosodium glutamate as a flavoring agent in the mid-1950s, a bacterium was isolated in Japan that excreted large quantities of the amino acid L-glutamic acid into the culture medium. This bacterium, *Corynebacterium glutamicum,* is a short, aerobic, gram-positive rod capable of growing on a simple mineral salt medium with glucose provided that biotin is also added. The production of L-glutamic acid is maximal at a critical biotin concentration of 0.5 $\mu$g/g of dry cells, which is suboptimal for growth. Excess biotin, which supports abundant growth, decreases the L-glutamic acid accumulation. Biotin is a prosthetic group for the enzyme acetyl-CoA carboxylase, an enzyme also involved in the biosynthesis of fatty acids. Thus, limited amounts of biotin cause changes of the fatty acid composition of the cell membrane. The total amount of fatty acids and the phospholipid content in glutamate-producing cells are only about half of those of nonproducers grown in a medium with excess biotin. Consequently, the lipid content of the cell membrane was thought to be involved in the regulation of the secretion of L-glutamic acid. Recently, it was demonstrated that L-glutamic acid is not secreted via passive diffusion but is secreted via a specific active transporter. The production rate of L-glutamic acid by *C. glutamicum* is correlated to the high secretion of this amino acid induced by limiting the supply of biotin.

In *C. glutamicum,* glucose is metabolized mainly via the glycolytic pathway into $C_3$ and $C_2$ fragments. The key precursor of L-glutamic acid is $\alpha$-oxoglutarate ($\alpha$-ketoglutarate), which is formed in the citric acid cycle and then converted to L-glutamic acid by reductive amination. The enzyme catalyzing this conversion is the NADP-dependent glutamate dehydrogenase. Strains used commercially for L-glutamic acid production have a very low $\alpha$-ketoglutarate dehydrogenase activity; thus, the intermediate $\alpha$-oxoglutarate is only partially further metabolized in the citric acid cycle, and is mainly converted into L-glutamic acid. Very little is known about the regulation of these two enzymes in *C. glutamicum.* Oxaloacetate is formed via the phosphoenolparuvate carboxylase and pyruvate carboxylase reactions (Fig. 1). Thus, *C. glutamicum* has two anaplerotic reactions for the conversion of the $C_3$ intermediates into oxaloacetate. The overall reaction for L-glutamic acid production from D-glucose is

$$C_6H_{12}O_6 + NH_3 + 1.5\,O_2 \rightarrow$$
$$C_5H_9O_4N + CO_2 + 3\,H_2O$$

Thus, the theoretical maximal yield is 1 mol of L-glutamic acid per mol of glucose metabolized. This represents a 100% molar conversion or 81.7% weight conversion of D-glucose to L-glutamic acid.

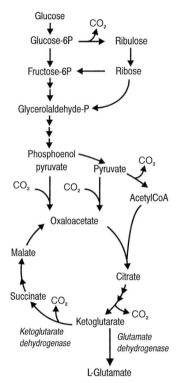

**Fig. 1.** Biosynthesis of L-glutamic acid in *Corynebacterium glutamicum* using glucose as the carbon source.

The L-glutamic acid production is carried out in stirred fermentors up to a size of 500 $m^3$. Provisions for cooling, dissolved oxygen measurement, and pH measurement and control (usually with ammonium) are required. A temperature between 30 and 35°C and a pH between 7.0 and 8.0 are optimal. The oxygen transfer rate is critical: A deficiency leads to poor glutamate yields, with lactic and succinic acids being formed instead, whereas an excess causes accumulation of $\alpha$-oxoglutaric acid. The yield of L-glutamic acid obtained after 2 or 3 days of incubation is on the order of 60–70% (by weight) of the sugar supplied, and the final concentration is approximately 150 g/l. The annual production exceeds 1 million tons, and the main use of this amino acid in the form of its monosodium salt is as a flavor enhancer in the food industry.

## C. L-Lysine

L-Lysine, an amino acid essential for human and animal nutrition, is mainly used as a feed supplement because it occurs in most plant proteins only in low concentrations. Furthermore, it has pharmaceutical applications in the formulation of diets with balanced amino acid compositions and in amino acid infusions. Currently, approximately 350,000 tons per year of L-lysine is produced using strains of *C. glutamicum* or subspecies. The wild-type strains of these bacteria do not secrete L-lysine into the culture me-

dium. High-yield strains were developed through mutation to auxotrophy and to antimetabolite resistance.

The pathway for the biosynthesis of L-lysine in *C. glutamicum* is illustrated in Fig. 2. A remarkable feature of *C. glutamicum* is its split pathway for the synthesis of L-lysine. At the level of piperideine-2,6-dicarboxylate there are two pathways for the conver-

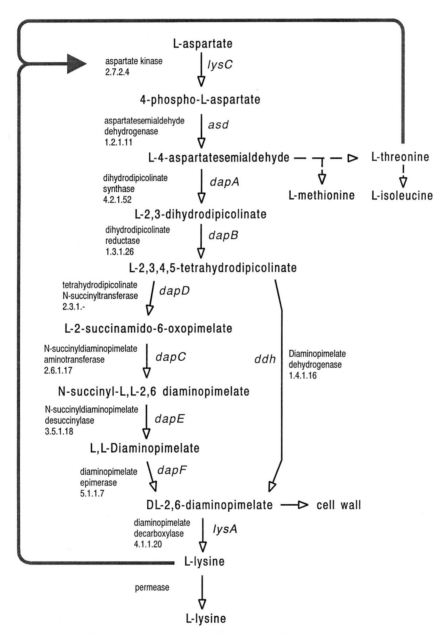

**Fig. 2.** The split pathway of L-lysine biosynthesis and its regulation in *Corynebacterium glutamicum;* arrows, feedback inhibition.

sion of this precursor into DL-2,6-diaminopimelate. This is the only known bacterium which has two parallel pathways for the synthesis of L-lysine. The first enzyme in L-lysine biosynthesis, aspartokinase, is regulated by concerted feedback inhibition by L-threonine and L-lysine. Hence, a homoserine auxotroph or a threonine and methionine double auxotroph of *C. glutamicum* diminisheses the intracellular pool of threonine, reduces its marked feedback inhibitory effect on aspartokinase, and promotes lysine overproduction (15–30 g/l). Another effective technique for obtaining L-lysine-producing strains is the selection of regulatory mutants. Growth of *C. glutamicum* is inhibited by an analog of L-lysine, aminoethyl-L-cysteine (AEC). This inhibition is markedly enhanced by L-threonine but reversed by L-lysine. This implies that AEC behaves as a false feedback inhibitor of aspartokinase. Some mutants, which are capable of growing in the presence of both AEC and L-threonine, contain an aspartokinase that is insensitive to the concerted feedback inhibition; therefore, L-lysine is overproduced (30–35 g/l). L-Aspartate used for L-lysine formation is formed from oxaloacetate by the anaplerotic reaction of phosphoenolpyruvate and pyruvate carboxylation. By combined overexpression of aspartokinase and dihydrodipicolinate synthase, L-lysine production can be increased by 10%.

In addition to all the steps considered so far, the secretion of L-lysine into the culture medium must also be noted. Secretion of L-lysine is not the consequence of unspecific permeability of the plasma membrane but rather is mediated by an excretion transporter that is specific for L-lysine. In *C. glutamicum*, L-lysine is excreted in symport with two OH⁻. The substrate-loaded transporter and the unloaded transporter carry different charges. The velocity of L-lysine excretion is thus influenced by several forces at different steps in the translocation cycle (i.e., by the membrane potential, the pH gradient, and the L-lysine gradient). This transporter is a system well designed for excretion purposes:

1. It has a high $K_m$ value for L-lysine (20 m$M$) at the internal (cytoplasmic) side, thus preventing unwanted efflux under low internal lysine concentration.

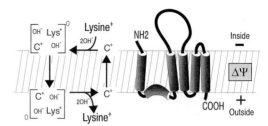

**Fig. 3.** Structure of the L-lysine exporter and the putative mechanism of L-lysine excretion in *Corynebacterium glutamicum*.

2. It is coupled to OH⁻ in a direction opposite to that of uptake systems (Fig. 3).

3. The unloaded carrier is positively charged; thus, the membrane potential is able to drive excretion of L-lysine (Fig. 3).

Recently, the gene for the lysine export carrier was cloned, and it was shown that this carrier is a small protein (25.4 kDa) with five transmembrane-spanning helices (Fig. 3).

In fed-batch culture, under optimized culture conditions a final concentration of approximately 170 g/l L-lysine can be obtained for the favorable mutants for L-lysine prodction, and the conversion rate relative to sugar used is approximately 40%. A typical L-lysine production curve is shown in Fig. 4; in addition to sugar, ammonium must also be fed. The conventional route of lysine down-stream processing is characterized by the the following:

1. Removal of the bacterial cells from the fermentation broth by separation or ultrafiltration

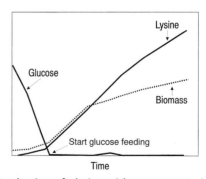

**Fig. 4.** Production of L-lysine with a mutant strain of *Corynebacterium glutamicum*; glucose is fed together with ammonium.

2. Absorbing and then collecting lysine in an ion exchange step

3. Crystallizing or spray drying as L-lysine hydrochloride

An alternative process consists of biomass separation, concentration of the fermentation solution, and filtration of precipitated salts. The liquid product contains up to 50% L-lysine base that is stable enough to be marketed.

Recently, a new concept for lysine production was introduced in which the L-lysine containing fermentation broth is immediately evaporated, spray dried, and granulated to yield a feed-grade product which contains L-lysine sulfate corresponding to at least 60% of L-lysine hydrochloride. Waste products usually present in the conventional L-lysine hydrochloride manufacture are avoided in this process.

In 1996, the price of L-lysine-HCl feed-grade was approximately $3 per kilogram. With the benefits provided by modern techniques, such as genetic engineering, for the useful design of metabolic pathways, and with the potentials of the fermentation technology, additional improvements in the L-lysine process should be realized. L-Lysine will continue to be the most attractive feed additive produced by fermentation.

## D. L-Threonine

Until 1986, L-threonine was used mainly for medical purposes, in amino acid infusion solutions, and in nutrients. It was manufactured by extraction of protein hydrolyzates or by fermentation using mutants of coryneform bacteria in amounts of hundreds of tons per year worldwide. The production strains were developed by classical breeding, auxotrophs, and resistance to threonine analogs such as $\alpha$-amino-$\beta$-hydroxy-valerate, and reached product concentrations up to 20 g/l. These strains possess deregulated pathways with feedback inhibition-insensitive aspartate kinase and homoserine dehydrogenase. During the past decade, strain developments has been very successful in both cases using conventional methods and recombinant DNA techniques, and strains of *Escherichia coli* have proved to be superior to other bacteria. Although the pathway of L-threonine bio-

synthesis in *E. coli* is much more regulated compared to that in *C. glutamicum,* new *E. coli* strains with excellent yield and productivity in threonine formation could be constructed by means of genetic engineering.

In *E. coli* the regulation of the biosynthesis of amino acids formed from L-aspartate is complicated since aspartate-$\beta$-semialdehyde and homoserine are common intermediates in the biosynthesis of L-threonine, L-isoleucine, L-methionine, and L-lysine. As shown in Fig. 5, phosphorylation of L-aspartate, the first reaction in the biosynthetic pathway of L-threonine, is catalyzed by three aspartokinase isoenzymes. One of these isoenzymes is inhibited by L-threonine and its synthesis is repressed by L-threonine and L-isoleucine. The second aspartokinase isoenzyme is repressed by L-methionine, and the third one is inhibited and repressed by L-lysine. Threonine biosynthesis occurs with aspartate-$\beta$-semialdehyde in three enzymatic steps which are encoded in *E. coli* by the *thrABC* operon. The *thrA* gene encodes a bifunctional enzyme with aspartokinase and homoserine dehydrogenase activities. The *thr* operon is under the control of a single promoter, which is bivalently re-

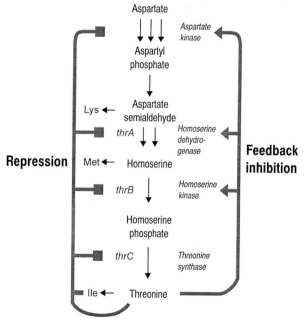

**Fig. 5.** Regulation of L-threonine biosynthesis in *Escherichia coli.* Only the regulation by L-threonine and L-isoleucine is shown.

pressed by L-threonine and L-isoleucine. In addition, L-threonine synthesis is regulated by feedback inhibition of the homoserine dehydrogenase and homoserine kinase.

Based on these data, there are two major targets for the design of L-threonine-overproducing strains (i.e., the prevention of L-isoleucine formation and stable high-level expression of the *thrABC* operon). Therefore, in one of the first steps of strain development chromosomal mutations were introduced, resulting in an isoleucine leaky strain which required L-isoleucine only at low L-threonine concentrations, but at high L-threonine concentrations growth was independent of the addition of L-isoleucine. There are several advantages to using this mutation. First, it prevents an excess formation of the undesired byproduct L-isoleucine. Second, it prevents the L-isoleucine-dependent premature termination of the *thrABC* transcription. Furthermore, the isoleucine leaky mutation has a positive selection effect on all the cells containing the plasmid with the threonine operon. To obtain very high activities of the *thrABC*-encoding enzymes, this operon was cloned from a strain in which the aspartokinase and homoserine dehydrogenase activities are resistant to L-threonine inhibition, and it was overexpressed. To prevent the degradation of L-threonine the gene *tdh*, which encodes the threonine dehydrogenase, was inactivated.

By continuous feeding of sugar these *E. coli* strains are able to produce more than 80 g/l L-threonine with a conversion yield of approximately 60%. The recovery of feed-grade L-threonine is simple: After the cell mass is removed from the culture broth by filtration, the filtrate is concentrated and the amino acid is isolated by crystallization. L-Threonine has been marketed successfully as a feed additive with a worldwide demand of more than 10,000 tons per year.

## II. ENZYMATIC PRODUCTION

### A. L-Aspartic Acid

L-Aspartic acid is produced industrially by an enzymatic process in which aspartase (L-aspartate ammonia lyase; EC 4.3.1.1) is used. This enzyme catalyzes the reversible interconversion between L-aspartate and fumarate plus ammonia. The equilibrium constant of the deamination reaction catalyzed by the enzyme is 20 mmol/l at 39°C and 10 mmol/l at 20°C; thus, the amination reaction is favored. Aspartase purified from *E. coli* is a tetramer with a molecular weight of 196 kDa and it has a strong requirement for divalent metal ions. Because the isolated enzyme is very unstable in solution, an immobilized cell system based on *E. coli* cells entrapped in polyacrylamide gel lattice was developed. Using this system, the half-life of the aspartase activity was increased to 120 days. Immobilization of the cells in $\kappa$-carrageenan resulted in remarkably increased operational stability; thus, a biocatalyst with a half-life of approximately 2 years was obtained (Table III). In addition, recombinant DNA-techniques have helped to im-

*TABLE III*
**Half-Life of Aspartase in *E. coli* Cells Immobilized Using Various Methods**

| Immobilization method | Aspartase activity (U/g cells) | Half-life (days) | Relative productivity (%)[a] |
|---|---|---|---|
| Polyacrylamide | 18,850 | 120 | 100 |
| Carrageenan | 56,340 | 70 | 174 |
| Carrageenan (GA)[b] | 37,460 | 240 | 397 |
| Carrageenan (GA + HA)[b] | 49,400 | 680 | 1498 |

[a] Considers the initial activity, decay constant, and operation period.
[b] GA, glutaraldehyde; HA, hexamethylene diamine.

prove aspartase-containing strains. Introduction of a plasmid with the *aspA* gene elevated aspartase formation in *E. coli* approximately 30-fold.

The production of L-aspartate by means of immobilized cells has been industrialized by using a fixed-bed reactor system. A continuous process enables automation and efficient control to achieve high conversion rates and yields. A column packed with the κ-carrageenan-immobilized cells produces 200 mmol L-aspartate per hour and per gram of cells; thus, in a 1-m³ column approximately 100 tons of L-aspartate can be produced in 1 month. In comparison to microbial amino acid production, the advantages of this enzymatic production method are higher product concentration and productivity. Furthermore, less by-products are formed; thus, L-aspartic acid can be easily separated from the reaction mixture by crystallization. In recent years, the market for L-aspartic acid has increased to approximately 10,000 tons per year due to the fact that this amino acid is a precursor for the production of the dipeptide sweetener aspartame (methyl ester of aspartyl-L-phenylalanine).

## B. L-Tryptophan

L-Tryptophan is one of the limiting essential amino acids required in the diet of pigs and poultry. A growing market for L-tryptophan as a feed additive is still developing, although many processes that have been proven on a production scale are available. However, high production costs have prevented a tolerable price level that would make it easier to introduce L-tryptophan as a bulk product.

The most attractive processes are based on microorganisms used as enzyme sources or as overproducers:

1. Enzymatic production from various precursors
2. Fermentative production from precursors
3. Direct fermentative production from carbohydrates by auxotrophic and analog-resistant regulatory mutants.

L-Tryptophan can be synthesized from indole, pyruvate, and ammonia by the enzyme tryptophanase (L-tryptophan indole-lyase; EC 4.1.99.1), which is normally responsible for degradation of this L-amino acid in bacteria. Based on the reverse reaction, indole can be almost quantitatively converted to L-tryptophan in the presence of an excess of ammonium. However, currently L-tryptophan is produced by using the enzyme tryptophan synthase (EC 4.2.1.20), which catalyzes the last step in the biosynthetic pathway of this aromatic amino acid. This bacterial enzyme is composed of two subunits, α and β. Two α-subunits and two β-subunits form an α₂β₂ complex that catalyzes the conversion of indole-3-glycerol phosphate plus L-serine into L-tryptophan, glyceraldehyde-3-phosphate, and water. Furthermore, each subunit also catalyzes its own specific reaction. Thus, the α-subunit converts indole-3-glycerol phosphate into indole and glyceraldehyde-3-phosphate and the β-subunit catalyses the synthesis of L-tryptophan from indole and L-serine. The three-dimensional structure of the tryptophan synthase complex shows that the active sites of neighboring α- and β-subunits are connected by a "tunnel" which provides a way for internal diffusion of indole between the two active sites and prevents indole from escaping from the active center.

In recent years, an enzymatic process for the production of L-tryptophan from indole and L-serine was established based on *E. coli* strains containing high amounts of tryptophan synthase (approximately 10% of the total protein). The precursor indole is available for a reasonable price. The second precursor L-serine is obtained from molasses, which is a by-product in the sugar beet industry. In addition to sucrose, molasses contains several L-amino acids (e.g., L-serine). To isolate the various compounds, molasses is fractionated by ion exclusion chromatography as shown in Fig. 6. The fractions containing L-serine are concentrated and this amino acid can then be used for the production of L-tryptophan. *Escherichia coli* cells with high tryptophan synthase activity are mixed with L-serine, and indole is added continuously at a concentration adjusted to 10 mM. Under these conditions, the precursors are quantitatively converted into L-tryptophan with a production rate of almost 75 g per liter per day.

The microbial conversion of biosynthetic intermediates such as anthranilic acid to L-tryptophan has also been considered as an alternative for production.

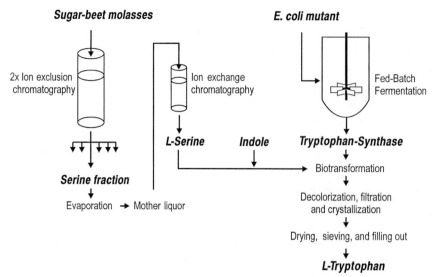

**Fig. 6.** Diagram of the enzymatic conversion of ʟ-serine (obtained from molasses) with indole to ʟ-tryptophan.

Strains of *Bacillus subtilis* and *Bacillus amyloliquefaciens* had final concentrations higher than 40 g/l ʟ-tryptophan with anthranilic acid. This process using anthranilic acid as a precursor has been commercialized. However, the manufacturer was forced to stop ʟ-tryptophan production using genetically modified strains derived from *B. amyloliquefaciens*. ʟ-Tryptophan produced using this process was not suitable because of the formation of by-products which cause a serious disease termed eosinophilia–myalgia syndrome. One of the problematic impurities, "peak E" was identified as 1,1'-ethylidenebis (ʟ-tryptophan), a product formed by condensation of one molecule of acetaldehyde with two molecules of tryptophan.

ʟ-Tryptophan production by direct fermentation from glucose has been studied using *E. coli*, *B. subtilis*, and *C. glutamicum* strains because of the knowledge of amino acid biosynthesis and regulatory mechanisms in these organisms. To obtain ʟ-tryptophan-overproducing organisms, it was necessary to remove the various regulatory mechanisms of this biosynthetic pathway. Also, in this case the classical techniques, namely, the selection of antimetabolite-resistant and auxotrophic mutants, were used. Furthermore, recombinant DNA techniques were used to increase ʟ-tryptophan overproduction, especially in strains of *C. glutamicum* and *E. coli*. One concept was realized successfully by amplification of the genes of the tryptophan operon together with *serA*, which codes for phosphoglycerate dehydrogenase. This key enzyme in ʟ-serine biosynthesis should provide enough ʟ-serine for the last step of ʟ-tryptophan synthesis. Currently, production strains are able to accumulate 30–50 g ʟ-tryptophan per liter with yields higher than 20% based on the carbon source.

## III. FUTURE PROSPECTS

The production of ʟ-amino acids by microbial and enzymatic procedures has both advantages and disadvantages. Starting materials for microbial processes are usually simple and cheap raw materials, such as sucrose or starch hydrolysate, but the desired ʟ-amino acids must be produced by complicated and time-consuming fermentation processes. Nevertheless, the microbial fermentation technology is key in the amino acid industry. Due to modern techniques such as metabolic engineering, together with new analytical methods (gene chip technology), additional improvement of the microbial processes is possible. Problems in ʟ-amino acid synthesis can be solved by amplification of genes coding for the limiting enzymatic steps. The recent discovery of the L-lysine secretion carrier provides new possibilities for increasing the overproduction of various L-amino acids. Furthermore, a thorough understanding of the various elements and mechanisms controlling the biosynthesis of an amino acid should make it possible to influence its rate of overproduction in a predictable way.

However, precursors for enzymatic processes are in general more expensive than the substrates used for microbial fermentations, but the procedures of the former are less time-consuming and more efficient than those of the latter. Thus, enzymatic methods will play an important role in the production of L-amino acids from favorable precursors by means of highly specific and readily available biocatalysts in efficient bioreactor systems. Alterations in the activity or stability of enzymes may also be possible by exchanging various amino acids or functional domains between various enzymes. Thus, using the DNA technique, for example, one could change the substrate specificity of an enzyme. Furthermore, the formation of chimeric enzymes by exchanging defined genetic cassettes responsible for specific protein domains provides an excellent opportunity to modify the specificity or the regulation of an enzyme in a purposeful manner.

## See Also the Following Articles

INDUSTRIAL FERMENTATION PROCESSES • STRAIN IMPROVEMENT

## Bibliography

Eggeling, L. (1994). Biology of L-lysine overproduction by *Corynebacterium glutamicum*. *Amino Acids* 6, 261–272.

Eikmanns, B. J. J., Eggeling, L., and Sahm, H. (1993). Molecular aspects of lysine, threonine, and isoleucine biosythesis in *Corynebacterium glutamicum*. *Antonie van Leeuwenhoek* 64, 145–163.

Esaki, N., Nakamori, S., Kurihara, T., Furuyoshi, S., and Soda, K. (1996). Enzymology of amino acid production. *In* "Biotechnology, Vol. 6. Products of Primary Metabolism" (M. Roehr, Ed.), pp. 503–560. VCH. Weinheim.

Kircher, M. (1998). Amino acids as feed additives. *SIM News* 48, 4–11.

Krämer, R. (1994). Secretion of amino acids by bacteria: Physiology and mechanism. *FEMS Microbiol. Rev.* 13, 75–94.

Krämer, R. (1996). Genetic and physiological approaches for the production of amino acids. *J. Biotechnol.* 45, 1–21.

Leuchtenberger, W. (1996). Amino acids—Technical production and use. *In* "Biotechnology, Vol. 6. Products of Primary Metabolism" (M. Roehr, Ed.), pp. 465–502. VCH, Weinheim.

Sahm, H., Eggeling, L., Eikmanns, B. J., and Krämer, R. (1995). Metabolic design in amino acid producing bacterium *Corynebacterium glutamicum*. *FEMS Microbiol. Rev.* 16, 243–252.

# Aminoglycosides, Bioactive Bacterial Metabolites

## Wolfgang Piepersberg

*Bergische University Wuppertal*

I. Structural Classes and Sources
II. Target Sites and General Effects on Cells
III. Biosynthetic Pathways and Genetics
IV. Clinical Relevance and Resistance
V. Perspectives

## GLOSSARY

**actinomycetes** High G + C branch of the gram-positive bacteria (including single-celled proactinomycetes).
**A-factor** Butyrolactone derivative regulating cell differentiation and secondary metabolism in some streptomycetes.
**aminocyclitol** A cyclitol with one or more hydroxyls substituted by amino groups.
**aminoglycoside** A low-molecular-weight (pseudo)saccharidic substance mainly based on aminated sugars.
**glycosidase inhibitors** Competitive inhibitors of hydrolases cleaving particular glycosidic bonds.
**mistranslation** Misreading of the genetic code on the ribosome due to wrong codon–anticodon pairing.
**translational inhibitors** Inhibitors of the translational apparatus, mainly the ribosome.

**SINCE THE DISCOVERY** of streptomycin in general screenings in 1942 by Waksman and his collaborators, aminoglycosides, especially the aminocyclitol–aminoglycoside antibiotics (ACAGAs), have become both indispensable chemotherapeutics and interesting targets of basic research. Also, recently some C7-(amino-)cyclitol-containing non-antibiotic substances active as glycosidase inhibitors have been introduced into clinical and agricultural use. For simplicity, in this article the term ACAG includes the broad range of structurally and biochemically similar polycationic nat-

ural products, even if individual compounds do not contain an aminocyclitol or an amino sugar. The current state of research and development (R&D) in the field is characterized by a reduced interest in screening and semisynthetic modification programs and by a continuing interest in improvements of clinical applications and in rapidly developing areas of biotechnological R&D programs, such as combinatorial biosynthesis. Also, future basic research efforts will focus on, for example, the analysis of the ecological role and evolutionary significance of aminoglycosides in nature. Here, a brief outline of the current state of knowledge on the main groups of ACAGs, examples for potential future applications, and some perspectives for a unifying view on the basics of the metabolism of secondary (amino-) sugars, (amino-)cyclitols, and their oligomers are provided.

## I. STRUCTURAL CLASSES AND SOURCES

The term "aminoglycoside" is not rational in the sense of chemical nomenclature and does not define a clearly limited systematic group of natural products. The classical aminocyclitol–aminoglycoside antibiotics (ACAGAs) are composed of both an (amino)-hexitol and one or more (amino-) sugar residue, such as in the antibacterial antibiotics of the following families: streptomycins, spectinomycins, 2-deoxystreptamine (2-DOS)-containing compounds (e.g., kanamycins, tobramycin, neomycins, gentamicins, and apramycin), and fortimicins (Fig. 1). Some non-antibiotics, such as the C7-cyclitol-containing glycosidase inhibitors of the families amylostatins and validamycins (Fig. 1), are also typical ACAGs. Also,

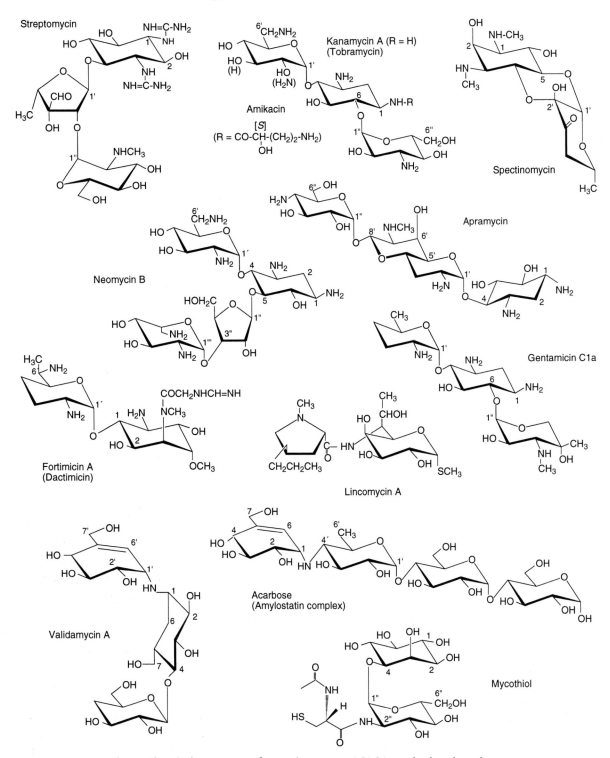

***Fig. 1.*** Chemical structures of some important ACAGAs and related products.

products of monomeric nature, such as modified sugars or cyclitols, occur as end products of secondary carbohydrate metabolism. The cyclitol precursors are either D-glucose or *sedo*-heptulose; sugar moieties are derived from C5- to C8-aldoses or -ketoses, mostly from D-glucose, D-glucosamine, or D-mannose. Other members of this variable group, when integrated in an extended but useful biochemical system, also may contain additional chemical groups, such as amino acids or nucleosides. Hence, some other groups of antibiotics containing similar aminosugar components, such as the lincosamides (lincomycin A in Fig. 1), are discussed in this article, whereas other groups of secondary metabolites with (amino-) sugar side chains, such as the aromatic polyketides, macrolides, and glycopeptides, are not.

The classical and newest members of the ACAG group of natural products are all from bacterial, typically actinomycete sources. Producers are members of the high-G + C gram-positive (actinomycete) genera *Streptomyces*, *Streptosporangium*, *Saccharopolyspora*, *Micromonospora*, *Dactylosporangium*, *Actinoplanes*, *Amycolatopsis*, and *Corynebacterium*, with a few exemptions in the low-G + C gram-positive bacilli (e.g., butirosin produced by *Bacillus circulans*) and the gram-negative *Pseudomonas* sp. (sorbistins). It should be noted that a variety of other natural compounds are structurally and biochemically related to ACAGAs, including the hexosamine-based lipo-oligosaccharidic Nod-factors and the so-called rhizopine N-methyl-*scyllo*-inoamine secreted by nodulating rhizobia. Despite the rare cases of production of diffusible carbohydrates in the gram-negative bacteria, these organisms produce a wide and variable range of cell-bound and carbohydrate-based extracellular substances which resemble oligomeric secondary metabolites, including lipopolysaccharides and other heteropolymeric polysaccharides. Also, these are obviously made by use of the same strain-specific and highly fluid gene pool used for the production of secondary carbohydrates.

Glycosidic and/or cyclitol-containing components that are very similar to the substructures of ACAGs also occur in several intra- or extracellular glycoconjugates of both archaeal and eukaryotic origin. Two examples are the glucosaminyl archaetidyl-*myo*-inositols formed by some methanogenic *Archaea* and the very similar core structure in the oligosaccharidic phosphatidylinositol protein anchors of glycoproteins attached to the outer surface of eukaryotes from trypanosomes to mammalian organisms. Interestingly, these share the content of non-acetylated glucosamine and the 1-phosphoryl-6-glucosaminyl *myo*-inositol core unit. These examples indicate that part of the biochemical component of aminoglycoside biosynthesis is disseminated throughout practically all major groups of organisms but is used for very different physiological means. Thus, the recently detected mycothiol may also be regarded as an ACAG (Fig. 1). It was a surprise that mycothiol is the general oxygen-protecting cocatalyst in the glutathion free actinomycetes and, therefore, the equivalent of glutathion in other organisms. However, it is not a typical secondary metabolite since it is not secreted and it is of primary metabolic function in all members of this group of bacteria. Its occurrence may explain the prevalence of ACAG production in actinomycetes since common precursor pools can be used.

## II. TARGET SITES AND GENERAL EFFECTS ON CELLS

In-depth research aimed at studying the target sites of ACAGAs has been mainly restricted to those substances used as chemotherapeutics, such as antibiotics and glycosidase inhibitors. Thus, the classical ACAGAs have been found to be translational inhibitors and to bind specifically to bacterial ribosomes (the 70S class of ribosomes compared to the 80S class in the eukaryotic cytoplasm). Also, their interaction with human cell systems concomitantly coming into contact with these substances during therapy has been studied, resulting in the finding that at least part of their measurable effects are based on an equivalent target site binding on the susceptible mitochondrial ribosomes which are of the 70S-type. In contrast, investigations of their effects in and ecological functions of the ACAGA-producing cells have not been carried out. Nevertheless, the results gained could give clues to the basic meaning of the natural functions of aminoglycosides and their evolutionary origin.

## A. Translational Inhibitors

The classic ACAGAs are obviously ligands optimized for their target sites; for example, pseudotrisaccharides, such as streptomycins, kanamycins, and gentamicins (Fig. 1), seem to be the optimal inhibitors of the translational machinery in the 30S subunits of bacterial ribosomes. They interact with 16S rRNA directly, and methylation of a single nucleotide out of approximately 1600 nucleotides in the 16S rRNA molecules completely suppresses the toxic and pleiotropic effects in the producers of several 2-DOS-containing and fortimicin-related ACAGAs (Table I). This finding indicates that all the diverse phenomena exerted are dependent on the specific interaction with a single target site.

The clinically used ACAGAs are classified into two functionally different groups: Most of them are bacteriocidal compounds (e.g., the streptomycins, fortimicins, and all 2-DOS aminoglycosides) and bacteriostatic inhibitors that have no effect on translational accuracy (e.g., spectinomycins). Their interaction with the small (30S) subunits of eubacterial ribosomes (eubacterial, mitochondrial, and plastidal

***TABLE I***

**Clinical Use of ACAGA, Mechanisms of Resistance, and Their Distribution in Clinically Relevant Bacteria and Producers of ACAGA** [a]

| Antibiotic | Clinical use | | Mechanisms of acquired resistance | Producing genera | Mechanisms of resistance |
| --- | --- | --- | --- | --- | --- |
| | *Organisms* | *Application* | | | |
| | | | *Naturally occurring ACAGAs* | | |
| Streptomycin | *My., Ye., Fr.* | im | RpsL, 16S(904), APH(3″), ANT(3″) | *Sm.* | APH(6), APH(3″) |
| Neomycin | | Top., Or. | AAC(6′), AAC(2′), AAC(3), APH(3′) | *Sm., M.* | AAC(3), APH(3′), (AAC(2′)?) |
| Paromomycin | | Top., Or. | AAC(6′), AAC(2′), AAC(3), APH(3′) | *Sm.* | AAC(3), APH(3′) |
| Lividomycin | — | — | AAC(6′), AAC(2′), AAC(3), APH(3′) | *Sm.* | AAC(3), APH(3′) |
| Ribostamycin | — | — | AAC(6′), AAC(2′), AAC(3), APH(3′) | *Sm.* | AAC(3), APH(3′) |
| Butirosin | — | — | AAC(6′), AAC(2′), AAC(3), APH(3′) | *B.* | AAC(3), APH(3′) |
| Kanamycin | | im | AAC(6′), AAC(2′), AAC(3), APH(3′) | *Sm.* | AAC(6′), 16S-MT (G1405) |
| Hygromycin B | — | — | APH(4) | *Sm., Sv.* | APH(7″), APH(?) |
| Tobramycin | GN, *Ps., St.* | im | AAC(6′), AAC(2′), AAC(3), APH(3′) | *Sm.* | AAC(3), AAC(2′), 16S-MT (A-1408) |
| Apramycin | GN | Vet. | AAC(3), AAC(1) | *Sm.* | 16S-MT (G-1405) |
| Gentamicin | GN, *Ps., St.* | im | AAC(6′), AAC(2′), APH(2″), ANT(2″), AAC(3) | *M.* | 16S-MT (G-1405) |
| Sisomicin | GN, *Ps., St.* | im | AAC(6′), AAC(2′), APH(2″), ANT(2″), AAC(3) | *M.* | 16S-MT (G-1405) |
| Fortimicin | GN | im | AAC(3), APH(2″)/AAC(6′) | *M.* | 16S-MT (G-1405) |
| Dactimicin | GN | im | AAC(3), APH(2″)/AAC(6′) | *Dact.* | 16S-MT (G-1405) |
| Istamycin | — | — | AAC(3), APH(2″)/AAC(6′) | *Sm.* | 16S-MT (A-1408) |
| Sannamycin | — | — | AAC(3), APH(2″)/AAC(6′) | *Sm.* | 16S-MT (A-1408) |
| Sporaricin | — | — | AAC(3), APH(2″)/AAC(6′) | *Sacch.* | 16S-MT (A-1408) |
| Spectinomycin | GN | im | ANT(9) | *Sm.* | APH(4) |
| Kasugamycin | — | — | | *Sm.* | AAC(?) |
| Lincomycin A | GP, GN-An | Or., im | 23S-MT | *Sm.* | 23S-MT, Ex. |
| *Semisynthetic ACAGAs* | | | | *Basic natural ACAGA* | |
| Amikacin | GN, *Ps., St.* | im | AAC(6′), APH(3′), ANT(4′)(4″) | | Kanamycin A |
| Netilmicin | GN, *Ps., St.* | im | AAC(6′), AAC(2′), AAC(3) | | Sisomicin |
| Isepamicin | GN, *Ps., St.* | im | AAC(3), ANT(4′)(4″) | | Gentamicin B |
| Dibekacin | GN, *Ps., St.* | im | AAC(6′), ANT(4′)(4″) | | Kanamycin B |
| Habekacin | GN, *Ps., St.* | im | AAC(6′), ANT(4′)(4″) | | Kanamycin B |
| Trospectomycin | *Ne.,* GN | im | ANT(9) | | Spectinomycin |
| Clindamycin | GP, GN-An | Or., im | 23S-MT | | Lincomycin A |

[a] Abbreviations used: GN, gram-negative aerobes without *Ps.*; GP, general gram-positives (including streptococci); GN-An, gram-negative anaerobes (e.g., *Bacteroides*); *Ps., Pseudomonas; St., Staphyloccocus; My., Mycobacterium tuberculosis; Ye., Yersinia pestis; Fr., Francisella tularensis; Ne., Neisseria gonorrhoeae; B., Bacillus; M., Micromonospora; Sm., Streptomyces; Sacch., Saccharopolyspora; Sv., Streptoverticillium; Dact., Dactylosporangium;* —, Not used; im, intramuscular; Top., topological; Or., oral; Vet., veterinary medicine; AAC, acetyltransferase; APH, phosphotransferase; ANT, nuleotidyltransferases (in parentheses is the position modified in the antibiotic molecule); RpsL, mutation in 30S ribosomal subunit protein S12; 16S(904), nucleotide exchange in position 904 of 16S rRNA; 16S-MT, 16S rRNA methyltransferase (in parentheses is the nucleotide in the RNA molecule); 23S-MT, 23S rRNA methylation; Ex., active drug export.

ribosomes), formed primarily by the 16S rRNA, is well established. The first group induces misreading of the genetic code and rapidly causes loss of all translational activity under sublethal and lethal doses, respectively, whereas compounds of the second group exert a "quasi-relaxed" (Rel$^-$) phenotype similar to the antibiotic chloramphenicol. An exception is hygromycin B, which shows functional traits of both groups but does not seem to induce translational ambiguity. The effects of the group 1 compound streptomycin on the ribosomal elongation cycle in wild-type, streptomycin-resistant or -dependent mutants in RpsL (ribosomal protein S12) of *Escherichia coli* are not fully understood. These seem to be associated with the extent of a GTP-hydrolysis idling reaction on cognate EF–Tu ternary complexes and may be interpreted as three ribosomal binding sites for tRNA and the functional interplay between ribosomal subunits in peptidyltransfer and translocation reactions. The individual primary binding sites for most of the classical ACAGAs on the 16S rRNA have been identified in various experiments. The specific interaction of spectinomycin (group 2) with 16S rRNA bases G-1064 and C-1192 has also been demonstrated. It is generally accepted that 16S and 23S rRNA are ribozymes that are catalytically active constituents of all ribosomes in both decoding and peptidyltransfer. The decoding process involves an interaction of a short RNA duplex (paired codon–anticodon) with the P and A sites of the 30S subunits which is impaired by the mistranslation-inducing ACAGAs. Thus, short RNA analogs of the 16S rRNA decoding site specifically interact with both of its RNA ligands, tRNA and mRNA, and ACAGAs in the absence of ribosomal proteins. All known bactericidal translational inhibitors among the aminoglycosides, though differentially binding, seem to interact with a single common domain in the decoding center of the 16S rRNA of bacterial ribosomes. In this context, it is interesting that some 2-DOS ACAGAs specifically inhibit the self-splicing mechanism of group I introns noncompetitively and with similar selectivity and affinities as in the translational process. This has been interpreted on the basis of splice site selection as being similar to ribosomal decoding, which involves triple-stranded RNAs. All these data resulted in the "molecular fossil hypothesis" of aminoglycoside evolution in a precellular RNA-world.

Effects other than direct interaction with the eubacterial ribosome have been suggested to be responsible for the lethality phenomenon of mistranslation inducing ACAGAs. In addition to severe impairment of the initiation and elongation phases of protein synthesis, two phenomena have been observed to be involved with lethality of ACAGAs. The uptake of ACAGAs into both gram-negative and gram-positive bacteria, in addition to a very rapid first electrostatic binding to negatively charged cell surfaces, shows two-step kinetics. The first phase is dependent on the $\Delta\Psi$ component of the proton motive force. The second phase, the killing phase, is characterized by exponential ACAGA accumulation due to a disturbance of membrane structure or the formation of membrane channels and is dependent on active translation. This is obviously an effect of misread proteins on the structure and function of complexes integral to the cytoplasmic membrane. The insensitivity of anaerobic bacteria in general to ACAGAs may be explained by the absence of the first phase of active uptake, due to too low $\Delta\Psi$ values; this effect is also exhibited by facultative anaerobes, such as *E. coli,* at low oxygen pressure, thus rendering cells resistant.

## B. Glycosidase Inhibitors

The non-antibiotic ACAGs of the amylostatin and validamycin families, which are used as therapeuticals or fungicides, do not act on cellular systems directly since their targets are mainly found among extracellular enzymes among the large family of glycosidases. Thus, acarbose (amylostatins) inhibits various $\alpha$-glucosidases both of microbial ($\alpha$-amylases, glucoamylases, and cyclodextrin glucanotransferases from bacteria and fungi) and mammalian origin, e.g., in the human intestine (saccharase, maltase, glucoamylase, and $\alpha$-amylase, but not isomaltase). Also, cytoplasmic maltases and binding protein-dependent uptake systems seem to be responsive in bacteria. Acarbose, in the presence or absence of oligomaltodextrins, interacts with $\alpha$-amylases and cyclodextrin glucanotransferases by forming new products, via transglycosylation, which are potent inhibitors of the same enzymes. Validamycins and trehazolin are specific inhibitors of trehalases, the allosamidins of chitinases.

## III. BIOSYNTHETIC PATHWAYS AND GENETICS

In contrast to other chemical groups of secondary metabolites, such as the polyketides and the non-ribosomally synthesized peptides, relatively few studies have investigated the genetics and biochemistry of the biosynthesis of this group of natural products. Only the streptomycins, the fortimicins, spectinomycin, kasugamycin, and acarbose have been studied in detail (Piepersberg, 1997; Piepersberg and Distler, 1997; Fig. 1). Also, the resistance mechanisms involved in self-protecting the producers have been investigated in many cases and found to be quite variable (Table 1). Biosynthesis of ACAGs follows different routes and basic design, especially for modification and condensing steps. The biochemistry of all of the biosynthetic pathways has not been completely elucidated.

### A. Cyclitol Pathways

The following basic mechanisms of cyclitol formation have been observed:

1. The fully substituted hexitols (i.e., derivatives of cyclohexane with a hydroxyl or amino group in each position) all seem to be derived from *myo*-inositol, which is not an essential metabolite in most bacteria but is in actinomycetes. This compound is synthesized from D-glucose-6-phosphate by D-*myo*-inositol-3-phosphate synthase, NAD$^+$-dependent intramolecular lyase (EC 5.5.1.4). Examples of (amino)-cyclitols synthesized from D-*myo*-inositol-3-phosphate are streptidine (in streptomycin), actinamine (in spectinomycin), the 1,4-*cis*-diaminocyclitols (in the fortimicins), and *myo*-inositol (in kasugamycin and mycothiol).

2. The C6- and C7-deoxycylitols, because they are precursors of 2-deoxystreptamine in the 2-DOS-ACAGAs or valienamine in amylostatins (acarbose) or validamycins, are synthesized by enzymes by the same mechanism that is used by the dehydroquinate synthase (EC 4.6.1.3), NAD$^+$-dependent, cyclizing phosphate lyases. They catalyze intramolecular aldol condensations yielding non-phosphorylated 1-keto-2-deoxy-cyclitols. The 2-deoxy-*scyllo*-inosose synthase of the neomycin-producing *S. fradiae* and the 2,5-*epi*-valiolone synthase of the acarbose-producing *Actinoplanes* sp. have been shown to use this mechanism.

### B. Streptomycins and Similar Compounds

The streptomycins (including spectinomycins and kasugamycin) were the first aminoglycosides to be studied. The genetics of their production have now been studied to some extent. The genes are localized in clusters in the respective genomes. In the *str/sts* gene clusters of *Streptomyces griseus* (streptomycin) and *S. glaucescens* (5′ hydroxystreptomycin), 27 and 23 genes have been described, respectively. Some genes have also been analyzed from spectinomycin- and kasugamycin-producing streptomycetes. In addition to biosynthetic genes, these gene clusters contain, genes for resistance, transport, and regulation. The gene for the D-*myo*-inositol-3-phosphate synthase was not found in the *str/sts* cluster. Streptomycins are composed of a *scyllo*-inositol-derived aminocyclitol (streptidine or bluensidine), a 6-deoxyhexose component ([dihydro-]streptose or 5′ hydroxystreptose), and an aminohexose derivative (*N*-methyl-L-glucosamine or derivatives thereof) (Fig. 1). Three aminotransferases of a new family of pyridoxalphosphate-dependent enzymes, called secondary metabolic aminotransferases (SMATs), are encoded in the *str/sts* cluster. One of these, StsC, is the L-glutamine:*scyllo*-inosose aminotransferase catalyzing the first transamination step in the pathway. Also, a characteristic step of biosynthesis is the amidinogroup transfer reaction forming the two guanidino groups in streptidine. The amidinotransferase StrB1 has been shown to contain a cysteine residue which covalently binds the amidinogroup in transfer reactions with arginine as the donor substrate. Enzymes StrD (dTDP-D-glucose synthase), StrE (dTDP-D-glucose-4,6-dehydratase), StrM (dTDP-4-keto-6-deoxy-D-glucose 3,5-epimerase), and StrL (dTDP-L-rhamnose synthase) catalyze the synthesis of dTDP-L-rhamnose, a putative precursor of dTDP-L-dihydrostreptose. Current knowledge on the pathway postulates production of the activated and fully modified intermediates, streptidine-6-phosphate, dTDP-dihydrostreptose, and NDP-N-methyl-L-glucosamine (condensation in this order) via a pseudodisaccharidic intermediate and its excretion in the form of streptomycin-6-phosphate. Outside the cells the active antibiotic becomes liberated from its inactive precursor by a specific phosphatase, StrK, which is also encoded in the production cluster. The regulation of streptomycin production in *S. griseus* by the bacterial hormone A-factor (a butyrolactone regulating both cell differentiation and secondary metabolism) is mediated via the activation of the pathway-specific activator StrR. The StrR protein in turn activates several operons in the *str/sts* cluster by binding to specific DNA boxes. Interestingly, the *str/sts* cluster of *S. glaucescens* contains some genes of NDP-sugar metabolism which do not seem to occur in the whole genome of *S. griseus*.

### C. 2-Deoxystreptamine-Containing ACAGAs

All the classical 2-DOS ACAGAs are biosynthetically homogenous in their early steps since they share the common pseudodisaccharidic intermediate paromamine; exceptions are hygromycin B and apramycin. Few details of the genetics and individual pathways have been published.

### D. Fortimicin Group

The fortimicin (astromicin)/istamycin group of compounds represents a third biosynthetically linked group. In the gene cluster of *Micromonospora olivasterospora* 13–15 genes involved in fortimicin production have been analyzed. A biosynthetic pathway forming a pseudodisaccharide from *scyllo*-inosamine and D-glucosamine which becomes extensively modified before excretion has been proposed.

### E. C$_7$-Aminocyclitol-Containing Compounds

The group of ACAGs containing a C$_7$-cyclitol moiety, called valienamine, are mostly glucosidase inhibitors because of their substrate analogy with oligoglucosides. The acarbose biosynthetic gene cluster has been identified and studied in detail in the producer *Actinoplanes* sp. In addition to genes for the cyclitol and 6-deoxyhexose branches of the pathway, a modifying enzyme, acarbose-7-phosphotransferase, and an enzyme for extracellular conversion of amylostatins, acarviosyltransferase (an α-amylase-related transglycosylase), are encoded in this cluster. The site and mode of maltose attachment to the pseudodisaccharide acarviose are unknown.

### F. ACAGA Resistance

Resistance in producers and related actinomycetes is frequently based on multiple mechanisms. It is mostly mediated by either the aminoglycoside-modifying enzymes phospho- (APH) and acetyltransferases (AAC), which clearly resemble those distributed in clinically relevant bacteria, or by target site modification (Hotta *et al.*, 1995; Table I). However, no nucleotidylyltransferases (ANTs) have been found in this group of organisms. Streptomycin resistance is mediated mainly by 6-phosphorylation [APH(6)] in the producers; *S. griseus* also bears an APH(3″)-encoding gene. Resistance is based on either or both AAC(6′) enzymes and 16S rRNA methyltransferases in the producers of gentamicins and kanamycins, whereas a combination of AAC(3) and APH(3′) enzymes protects the neomycin-type ACAGA-producing organisms. The 16S rRNA methyl transferases in the producers of kanamycins, gentamicins, and fortimicins modify either A-1408 (m$^1$A) or G-1405 (m$^7$G) at the decoding site. The latter type of resistance does not occur in pathogens.

## IV. CLINICAL RELEVANCE AND RESISTANCE

The clinical application of ACAGAs that are still in use is dominated by the susceptibility of target bacteria and patterns of acquired resistance, pharmacokinetics, and toxicity (Phillips and Shannon, 1997; Table I). Generally, because of their many adverse side effects, and those that also occur at the subclinical level, the ACAGAs are used only for special purposes in the therapy of severe infections. This is mostly the case for hospitalized patients in which a continuous control of the effects of these antibiotics can be practiced and especially the blood levels can be monitored. Serum concentrations of ACAGAs are measured by immunological tests based on substance-specific antibodies (e.g., EMIT). In clinical use, the naturally and semisynthetic members of the 2-DOS ACAGAs antibiotics are most important since they have strong potency against staphylococci and most gram-negative aerobes. These include the gentamicin family (C-complex, sisomicin, isepamicin, and netilmicin) and the kanamycin group (kanamycin A, tobramycin, amikacin, dibekacin, and habekacin). Other groups of ACAGAs are used only for the treatment of special infections, such as streptomycin as a second-choice regimen in the treatment of *Mycobacterium tuberculosis* or spectinomycins in curing penicillin-resistant *Neisseria gonorrhoeae*.

The ACAGAs are poorly absorbed from the gut when administered orally. Therefore, intramuscular injection is the typical form of administration. Cell and tissue penetration is very low. The polycationic compounds are mostly distributed via the extracellular water and bind to extracellular surfaces, which results in low excretion rates. The typically encountered toxic side effects of ACAGAs in man are oto- and nephrotoxicity. Neomycins (including paromomycins and lividomycins) are the most toxic substances and, therefore, in general are not used systemically but rather for topological infections on the skin or in cavities (e.g., bladder) or for oral prophylaxis and treatment of intestinal infections. Nephrotoxicity is primarily accompanied by membrane damage in the renal tubular cells. Damage of the renal structures and functions is not understood at the molecular level. Ototoxicity is mediated via different branches of the eighth nerve, thus creating damage of either vestibular or auditory functions. Nucleotide exchanges in the binding site of gentamicin in the 16S-type rRNA (12S rRNA) of mitochondrial ribosomes make them gentamicin hypersensitive. These patients carry an A to G mutation (G-1555) in 12S rRNA which seems to induce higher mistranslation rates in mitochondrial protein complexes. This phenomenon could indicate that the primary site of action of ACAGAs in mammalian cells is the same as that in bacterial cells.

Resistance in clinically relevant bacteria was among the first to be observed after introduction of antibiotic therapy (Hotta *et al.*, 1995; Phillips and Shannon, 1997; Table I). It is mediated mostly by aminoglycoside-modifying enzymes of three classes: APHs transferring the $\gamma$-phosphate group from ATP to hydroxyl groups, AACs transferring the acetate group from acetylcoenzyme A to amino groups, and ANTs transferring the adenylate or guanylate groups from ATP or GTP to hydroxyl groups. The enzymes described to date are further categorized by their substrate range and site of action in the individual compounds. For example, AAC(3)-I modifies position 1 of 2-DOS in gentamicins but not in kanamycins and neomycins, whereas AAC(3)-III also affects the latter compounds and AAC(3)-IV acetylates netilmicin and apramycin. The enzymes present in a particular clinical isolate can be predicted from their phenotypic substrate profiles when some chemically modified compounds are included on the list of tested inhibitors. Also, the host range of these mostly plasmid-transmitted resistance determinants is quite variable and differs largely for the gram-positive and gram-negative target pathogens. The occurrence of wide spread resistance determinants in clinical pathogens has diminished the efforts for finding new ACAGAs in most industrial screening programs for antibiotics.

## V. PERSPECTIVES

The changing policies in antibiotic use and the appearance of new and the reappearance of old infectious diseases caused by bacteria will make ACAGAs indispensable in the future. New semisynthetic derivatives could be synthesized by advanced carbohydrate chemistry. Also, new and useful ACAG-type enzyme inhibitors might be derived from screening assays using new target enzymes. The basic knowledge of the biochemistry and genetics of ACAGAs has already influenced many facets of biotechnological developments in secondary metabolite-producing microorganisms. Future efforts (e.g., in combinatorial biosynthesis) will also employ the variable tools provided by ACAGA producers.

## *See Also the Following Articles*

ACTINOMYCETES • ANTIBIOTIC BIOSYNTHESIS • LIPOPOLYSACCHA-RIDES • SECONDARY METABOLITES • *STAPHYLOCOCCUS*

## *Bibliography*

Hotta, K., Davies, J., and Yagisawa, M. (1995). Aminoglycosides and aminocyclitols (other than streptomycin). *In* "Biochemistry and Genetics of Antibiotic Biosynthesis" (L. Vining and C. Stuttard, Eds.), pp. 571–595. Butterworth-Heinemann, Boston.

Phillips, I., and Shannon, K. P. (1997). Aminoglycosides and aminocyclitols. *In* "Antibiotic and Chemotherapy" (F. O'Grady, H. P. Lambert, R. G. Finch, and D. Greenwood, Eds.), 7th ed., pp. 164–201. Churchill Livingstone, New York.

Piepersberg, W. (1997). Molecular biology, biochemistry, and fermentation of aminoglycoside antibiotics. *In* "Biotechnology of Antibiotics" (W. R. Strohl, Ed.), pp. 81–163. Dekker, New York.

Piepersberg, W., and Distler, J. (1997). Aminoglycosides and sugar components in other secondary metabolites. *In* "Biotechnology, Products of Secondary Metabolism" (H.-J. Rehm, G. Reed, H. Kleinkauf, and H. von Döhren, Eds.), 2nd ed. Vol. 7. pp. 397–488. VCH, Weinheim.

# Amylases, Microbial

**Claire Vieille, Alexei Savchenko, and J. Gregory Zeikus**

*Michigan State University*

I. Enzymes and Families
II. Microbiological Sources
III. Biochemistry
IV. Industrial Uses

## GLOSSARY

**pullulan**   A linear glucose polymer composed of maltotriose units joined by $\alpha$-1,6 linkages.

**starch**   An $\alpha$-glucan-based polymer containing a mixture of amylose and amylopectin (amylose accounts for 17–25% of the total, depending on the source). Amylose is a linear polymer of $\alpha$-1,4-linked glucose residues. Amylopectin is a polymer of $\alpha$-1,4-linked glucose residues branched at $\alpha$-1,6 positions ($\alpha$-1,6 linkages usually account for 4 or 5% of the glycosidic linkages, depending on the source).

**THE EXTENSIVE DIVERSITY IN CARBOHYDRATE STEREOCHEMISTRY**   is paralleled by a large variety of enzymes designed for their selective hydrolysis. Amylases or amylosaccharidases are part of this widespread group of enzymes—*O*-glycosyl hydrolases (EC 3.2.1) and hydrolyze starch and related $\alpha$-glucans, such as pullulan and glycogen. These $\alpha$-glucans are among the most abundant carbohydrates on Earth and are an important source of energy for animals, higher plants, and microorganisms. Amylases are thus implicated in a wide spectrum of biological processes.

Amylases are extensively used in industrial starch degradation and in the brewing, baking, and textile industries. Their broad applications make amylases a major product in the enzyme market and have led to the characterization of a large variety of these enzymes. These applications have also fueled intensive studies of these enzymes' structures and catalytic mechanisms: Their three-dimensional structures have been determined; their catalytic residues have been identified by mechanism-based labeling and by site-directed mutagenesis coupled with kinetic analysis; and the transition state was characterized using substrate analogs, kinetic analyses, and structural studies.

## I. ENZYMES AND FAMILIES

### A. Classes of Enzymes

The simplest classification for amylases is based on their modes of action: Exo-acting enzymes attack the polysaccharide non-reducing end, whereas endo-acting enzymes hydrolyze random glycosyl bonds within the polymer chain. Amylases are also classified according to their reaction mechanisms: Retaining enzymes perform hydrolysis while maintaining the $\alpha$-configuration of the resulting hydroxyl group, whereas inverting enzymes perform hydrolysis with inversion of the anomeric configuration from $\alpha$ to $\beta$. Amylases are typically named after their substrates and products specificities. The International Union of Biochemistry nomenclature of glycoside hydrolases is based on these criteria. Endo-acting, retaining enzymes, $\alpha$-amylases cleave random $\alpha$-1,4-glucosidic linkages in starch, glycogen, and related $\alpha$-glucans, producing mainly maltodextrins and branched oligosaccharides from starch. $\beta$-Amylases (EC 3.2.1.2) are exo-acting enzymes that hydrolyze starch $\alpha$-1,4-glucosidic linkages in an inverting mechanism to produce only $\beta$-maltose and $\beta$-limit dextrins. Their progressive action is stopped by $\alpha$-1,6 linkages in amylopectin, which explains the presence of $\beta$-limit dextrins among the products. Glucoamylases, another group of exo-acting, inverting enzymes (EC 3.2.1.3), active on $\alpha$-1,4 and $\alpha$-1,6 linkages, cleave starch (and, marginally, pullulan) from their non-reducing ends to produce $\beta$-glucose. Unable to degrade starch directly, $\alpha$-glucosidases hydrolyze short-chain oligosaccharides in an exo-fashion from their non-reducing ends into $\alpha$-glucose. Defined as debranching enzymes because of their specific activity on $\alpha$-1,6 but not on $\alpha$-1,4 linkages of amylopectin, endo-acting isoamylases and pullulanases differ in their substrate specificity. Isoamylases are active on amylopectin and glycogen but not on pullulan; pullulanases are active on amylopectin and pullulan but not on glycogen. The only product of pullulan hydrolysis by pullulanases is maltotriose. Pullulanases have been described in mesophilic bacteria and in a few moderately thermophilic bacteria. Two classes of pullulanases that cleave both $\alpha$-1,4 and $\alpha$-1,6 linkages have been identified. Amylopullulanases (APUs) cleave pullulan $\alpha$-1,6 linkages, producing only maltotriose, whereas neopullulanase mainly cleaves pullulan $\alpha$-1,4 linkages, producing panose (Glc–$\alpha$-1,6–Glc–$\alpha$-1,4–Glc). Since neopullulanase also cleaves some of the panose $\alpha$-1,6 linkages, it produces small amounts of glucose and maltose as coproducts of pullulan digestion. Both APU and neopullulanase cleave $\alpha$-1,4 linkages in starch, producing various oligosaccharides. With the exception of a few *Bacillus* APUs, neopullulanase and APUs (Mathupala *et al.*, 1993) contain a single catalytic site for the cleavage of both $\alpha$-1,4 and $\alpha$-1,6 linkages. Another class of pullulanase, isopullulanase (EC 3.2.1.57), cleaves pullulan $\alpha$-1,4 linkages to produce isopanose (Glc–$\alpha$-1,4–Glc–$\alpha$-1,6–Glc). Only one isopullulanase has been characterized. Cyclodextrin glycosyltransferases (CGTases) differ from $\alpha$-amylases in their product specificity: They produce cyclodextrins (CDs; circular $\alpha$-1,4-linked oligosaccharides of six to eight glucoses) from starch by a coupled hydrolysis–glycosyl transfer mechanism. Cyclodextrinases (CDases) mainly hydrolyze CDs but also degrade

pullulan and starch. Classifying new starch-degrading enzymes can be complicated: Recently characterized glycosyl hydrolases show broad substrate specificity, dual specificity for $\alpha$-1,4 and $\alpha$-1,6 linkages, and transglycosylation properties. Another problem with classifying amylosaccharidases based on their substrate specificity is that it fails to reflect their three-dimensional structural features.

## B. Amylase Families

Glycoside hydrolases are organized into families according to their sequence similarities (Henrissat and Davies, 1997). Two enzymes are assigned to the same family when their sequences can be aligned over their catalytic domains. The theory for this classification is that sequence-related enzymes have similar folds and catalytic mechanisms. Although this classification respects the enzymes's stereochemistries, it does not reflect substrate specificity. Enzymes with different substrate specificities can be found in the same family, indicating an evolutionary divergence to acquire new specificities. On the other hand, enzymes from different families can have the same substrate specificity, raising the possibility of convergent evolution. Among the 60 known sequence-based glycoside hydrolase families, families 13–15 and 57 contain amylases. $\beta$-Amylases and glucoamylases are the only representing enzymes of families 14 and 15, respectively. $\beta$-Amylases are organized into two subgroups, depending on their origin: plant and microbial $\beta$-amylases. Although sequence similarity inside each $\beta$-amylase subgroup is higher than that between the two subgroups, it is believed that microbial $\beta$-amylases share the same folding. Family 13 consists of a large group of amylases and related enzymes, encompassing approximately 20 different substrate specificities (Table I). This family is often called the $\alpha$-amylase family after the name of its major representing enzyme. Sequence databases contain several hundred family 13 enzyme sequences. Despite low overall sequence similarity (10%), family 13 enzymes share strict similarity in four sequence regions, which form this family's "fingerprints" (Table I). An $\alpha$-amylase from *Dictyoglomus thermophilum* was described in 1988 that was not similar to family

***TABLE I***
**Examples of Family 13 Enzymes and Their Conserved Regions**

| EC No. | Enzyme | Organism | Consensus regions[a] | | | |
|--------|--------|----------|------------|-----------|------------|-----------|
| | | | Region I | Region II | Region III | Region IV |
| 3.2.1.1 | α-Amylase | *Aspergillus niger* | 117 DVVANH | 202 GLRIDTVKH | 230 EVLD | 292 FVE--NHD |
| 3.2.1.10 | Oligo-1,6-glucosidase | *Bacillus cereus* | 98 DLVVNH | 195 GFRMDVINF | 255 EMPG | 324 YWN--NHD |
| 3.2.1.20 | α-Glucosidase | *Saccharomyces carlsbergensis* | 106 DLVINH | 210 GFRIDTAGL | 276 EVAH | 344 YIE--NHD |
| 3.2.1.41 | Pullulanase | *Klebsiella pneumoniae* | 590 DVVYNH | 661 GFRFDLMGY | 694 EGWD | 817 YVS--KHD |
| 3.2.1.68 | Isoamylase | *Pseudomonas amyloderamosa* | 291 DVVYNH | 370 GFRFDLASV | 416 EFTV | 502 FID--VHD |
| 3.2.1.1/41 | Amylopullulanase | *Thermoanaerobacter ethanolicus* | 488 DGVFNH | 593 GWRLDVANE | 626 ELWND | 698 LLG--SHD |
| 3.2.1.135 | Neopullulanase | *B. stearothermophilus* | 242 DAVFNH | 324 GWRLDVANE | 357 EIWHD | 419 LLG--SHD |
| 3.2.1.54 | Cyclodextrinase | *B. sphaericus* | 240 DAVFNH | 323 GWRLDVANE | 356 EIMHD | 418 LLG--SHD |
| 3.2.1.133 | Trehalose-6-phosphate hydrolase | *Escherichia coli* | 100 DMVFNH | 196 GLRLDVVNL | 251 EMSS | 320 FWC--NHD |
| 4.2.1.18 | Branching enzyme | *E. coli* | 335 DWVPGH | 401 ALRVDAVAS | 458 EEST | 519 FVLPLSHD |
| 4.2.1.19 | Cyclodextrin glycosyltransferase | *B. circulans* st. 8 | 135 DFAPNH | 225 GIRVDAVKH | 257 EWFL | 323 FID--NHD |
| 2.4.1.5 | Glucosyltransferase | *Streptococcus downei* | 915 DLVPNQ | 433 GVRVDAVDN | 475 EAWS | 542 FIR--AHD |

[a] Numbering of the amino acid residues starts at the N terminus of the mature proteins. Catalytic residues are underlined.

13 enzymes. Since then, four amylosaccharidases have been identified that are similar to the *D. thermophilum* enzyme: *Pfu* intracellular α-amylase, *P. furiosus* APU, and *Pyrococcus* KOD1 and *Thermococcus litoralis* 4-α-glucanotransferases. They have been grouped in glycosyl hydrolase family 57. Ongoing genome sequencing projects have identified three additional potential members of family 57 in *Aquifex aeolicus*, *Synechocystis*, and *P. horikoshi*.

## II. MICROBIOLOGICAL SOURCES

Amylosaccharidases are widespread in fungi, yeast, bacteria (including actinomycetes), and archaea (Table II) (Janecek, 1997). Most amylolytic microbes produce a liquefying, extracellular enzyme plus a saccharifying, intracellular enzyme (typically an α-glucosidase).

### A. Eukaryotic Sources

Among the amylolytic enzymes from eukaryotic microbes, the fungi enzymes have been best characterized. Rarely found in prokaryotes, glucoamylases are produced mainly by fungi, especially by *Aspergillus*, *Rhizopus*, and *Endomyces* species. The structures of *Aspergillus* α-amylases and glucoamylase are

known. Amylolytic yeasts and their amylosaccharidases are studied mostly in relation to their use in industrial fermentations, in particular for alcohol production.

### B. Bacterial and Archaeal Sources

Most bacterial amylosaccharidases have been characterized from gram-positive bacteria. The amylases produced by *Bacillus* species (i.e., *B. amyloliquefaciens*, *B. cereus*, *B. licheniformis*, *B. circulans*, and *B. subtilis*) cover a wide range of temperature and pH optima. *Bacillus* species also produce CGTases, β-amylases, pullulanases, APUs, and neopullulanase (Rüdiger *et al.*, 1995). CGTases are exclusively produced by bacteria (including *Bacillus*, *Klebsiella*, and *Micrococcus* strains). One of the most thermostable α-amylases was isolated from the mesophile *B. licheniformis*, which is a thermoduric organism that can withstand temperatures higher than 60°C. Most thermostable amylosaccharidases, however, have been characterized from thermoanaerobes—the more efficient starch hydrolyzers whose extracellular enzymes are usually active and stable in mild acidic conditions. With the exception of *Thermoanaerobacterium thermosulfurigenes* 4B, which produces an extracellular β-amylase, most thermoanaerobes (e.g., *Clostridium*, *Dictyoglomus*, *Thermoanaerobacter*, and

**TABLE II**
**Selected Microbial Sources of Starch-Degrading Enzymes**

| Enzyme | Microbial source |
|---|---|
| α-Amylase | *Alteromonas haloplanctis* |
| | *Aspergillus oryzae* |
| | *Bacillus licheniformis* |
| | *Pyrococcus furiosus* |
| | *Saccharomycopsis fibuligera* |
| | *Streptomyces hygroscopicus* |
| | *Thermococcus profundus* |
| β-Amylase | *Aspergillus oryzae* |
| | *Bacillus circulans* |
| | *Clostridium thermocellum* |
| | *Saccharomyces cerevisiae* |
| | *Thermoanaerobacterium thermosulfurigenes* |
| Glucoamylase | *Aspergillus awamori* |
| | *Rhizopus niveus* |
| | *Saccharomyces diastaticus* |
| Pullulanase | *Bacillus flavocaldarius* |
| | *Klebsiella pneumoniae* |
| Neopullulanase | *Bacillus stearothermophilus* |
| Amylopullulanase | *Bacillus* sp. KSM-1378 |
| | *Pyrococcus furiosus* |
| | *Thermoanaerobacter ethanolicus* 39E |
| Isoamylase | *Pseudomonas amyloderamosa* |
| CGTase | *Bacillus circulans* |
| | *Klebsiella pneumoniae* |
| | *Thermoanaerobacterium thermosulfurigenes* EM1 |
| CDase | *Bacillus coagulans* |
| | *Thermoanaerobacter ethanolicus* 39E |

*Thermoanaerobium*) liquefy starch with an extracellular APU. Hyperthermophilic amylolytic species have been described in the eubacteria Thermotogales (*Thermotoga maritima*) and in the archaeales Pyrodictiales (i.e., *Pyrodictium abyssum*) and Thermococcales (e.g., *Thermococcus profundus*, *T. litoralis*, *P. furiosus*, and *P. woesei*). Due to its particularly elevated growth temperature, *P. furiosus* has been thoroughly investigated for amylolytic enzymes. At least two extracellular *P. furiosus* amylosaccharidases, α-amylase and APU (Dong *et al.*, 1997), are responsible for starch reduction into oligosaccharides. Oligosaccharides are transported into the cells, in which they are degraded by an α-glucosidase. With optimal activity in the temperature range 100–125°C, thermophilic archaeal amylosaccharidases are the most thermostable amylolytic enzymes known.

## III. BIOCHEMISTRY

### A. Structural Properties

An increasing number of family 13 enzymes have been crystallized. Detailed information is available on the structures of several α-amylases, CGTases, and isoamylase (Janecek, 1997). These enzymes can have as many as five distinct structural domains. Three of them (A–C) are very similar in all family 13 enzymes, and it is accepted that all family 13 enzymes share similar catalytic sites and the same catalytic mechanism. Domain A is composed of eight parallel β strands surrounded by eight parallel α-helices. In this $(\beta/\alpha)_8$ barrel, loop $\beta3 \rightarrow \alpha3$ is very long and represents a second domain (domain B). The four family 13 fingerprint regions correspond to strands $\beta3$, $\beta4$, $\beta5$, and $\beta7$ and to the N-terminal ends of the following loops in the $(\beta/\alpha)_8$ barrel. These regions contain seven invariant residues that are involved in catalysis and substrate binding. Although domain B is an essential structural characteristic of family 13 enzymes, its sequence and length vary greatly. No common secondary structure elements exist in domain B. Isoamylase does not even contain a well-defined B domain. In this enzyme, loops $\beta3 \rightarrow \alpha3$ and $\beta4 \rightarrow \alpha4$ interact to form a globular cluster. In many family 13 enzymes, domain B's structure and its interaction with domain A are stabilized by a $Ca^{2+}$ ion. Most $\alpha$-amylases require $Ca^{2+}$ for optimal activity, and $Ca^{2+}$ has been shown to be essential for the folding of *Aspergillus oryzae* and porcine pancreatic $\alpha$-amylases. $Ca^{2+}$ is responsible for a significant increase in activity and/or thermostability of APU and pullulanase. *Bacillus licheniformis* $\alpha$-amylase contains a unique linear $Ca^{2+}-Na^+-Ca^{2+}$ metal array that directly affects the formation of the substrate binding site (Machius *et al.*, 1998). An additional $Ca^{2+}$ ion is located between domains A and C. Some bacterial and the mammalian $\alpha$-amylases are allosterically activated by a $Cl^-$ ion, located in close proximity to the active site. The C-terminal domain in most family 13 enzymes, domain C, is composed of $\beta$-strands arranged in a Greek key motif. Although its function in catalysis is unclear, domain C's presence is essential for substrate binding and activity. CGTases contain two additional C-terminal domains, domains D and E. Although domain D's function is unknown, domain E is involved in raw starch binding. Domain E is also found in glucoamylase and $\beta$ amylase (Janecek, 1997). With the exception of domain E, glucoamylase and $\beta$-amylase structures are not related to the $\alpha$-amylase structure. This result is not surprising since these two enzymes do not show any sequence similarity with the family 13 enzymes and since they have different catalytic properties. Isoamylase contains an additional N-terminal domain that has been identified only in branching and debranching enzymes (the F or G domains).

The three-dimensional structure of soybean $\beta$-amylase has been solved (Mikami *et al.*, 1993). It contains two domains: an $(\alpha/\beta)_8$ barrel and a small globular region formed by the long $(\alpha/\beta)_8$ barrel loops $\beta3-\alpha3$, $\beta4-\alpha4$, and $\beta5-\alpha5$. The two domains form a cleft that leads to the active site pocket. Eight conserved sequences (74 amino acid residues in total) were identified in $\beta$-amylases by multiple alignments. Five of these sequences start at the C terminus of strands $\beta4-\beta8$, and continue through the following loop. The three others are located in the $\beta1 \rightarrow \alpha1$ and $\beta3 \rightarrow \alpha3$ loops. According to the crystal structure of the soybean $\beta$ amylase complexed with inhibitors, the conserved regions (except loop $\beta3-\alpha3$) are involved in structural integrity, catalysis or substrate binding. Their location corresponds to that of homolog elements in other $(\beta/\alpha)_8$ barrel proteins. To date, only *T. thermosulfurigenes* $\beta$-amylase contains the starch-binding domain (or domain E) also present in CGTases (Janecek, 1997). The crystal structure of *Aspergillus awamori* glucoamylase is known (Aleshin *et al.*, 1992). In contrast to other amylases, the glucoamylase catalytic domain consists of an $(\alpha/\alpha)_6$-barrel, in which six parallel inner $\alpha$-helices are surrounded by six outer $\alpha$-helixes that run antiparallel to the inner ones. The five conserved sequences that shape the active site are located in $\alpha-\alpha$ connecting segments. The catalytic domain is followed by a starch-binding domain related to the E domain of CGTase.

## B. Reaction Mechanism

In both the retaining and the inverting mechanisms, hydrolysis occurs through a general acid catalysis mechanism that requires two critical residues: a proton donor and a nucleophile (McCarter and Withers, 1994). In retaining enzymes, one residue functions both as general acid and as general base, whereas another acts as the nucleophile. In inverting enzymes, one residue acts as a general acid and the other as a general base. Both glycosidase classes contain a pair of invariant carboxylic residues in the active site. In retaining enzymes, the two residues are located on the two opposite sides of the glycosidic bond to be cleaved and are separated by a distance of $\approx 5.5$ Å. In inverting enzymes, this distance is larger ($\approx 9.5$ Å) to accommodate a water molecule in addition to the substrate (Fig. 1) (McCarter and Withers, 1994).

Three conserved carboxylic acids are found in the active site of family 13 enzymes. According to *A.*

**INVERTING MECHANISM**

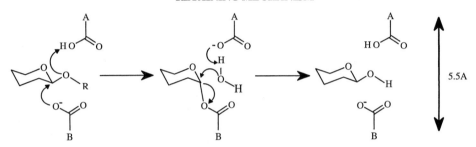

**RETAINING MECHANISM**

**Fig. 1.** Presumed inverting and retaining mechanisms for glycosyl hydrolases. (Top): Residue acting as acid catalyst; (bottom): residue acting as base.

*oryzae* and porcine pancreatic $\alpha$-amylase structures, residue Glu230 (nomenclature: *A. oryzae* enzyme) first donates a proton to cleave the glycosidic bond. A covalent bond then forms between the remaining sugar moiety and the catalytic nucleophile Asp206 (Kadziola *et al.*, 1998; McCarter and Withers, 1996). A water molecule hydrolyzes this intermediate in a second displacement reaction, in which the deprotonated Glu230 acts as a base catalyst. The third residue (Asp297) is believed to participate in catalysis by raising the p$K_a$ of Glu230 and by stabilizing the transition state. The difference in reaction products between CGTases and $\alpha$-amylases resides in the nature of the molecule attacking the intermediate. Hydrolysis occurs when a water molecule attacks the intermediate; transglycosylation occurs when the attack is performed by a substrate molecule.

## C. Specificity Differences

The overall topology of an amylase active site depends on the enzyme's mode of action. Active sites of the exo-acting enzymes glucoamylase and $\beta$-amylase show a pocket- (or crater-) type topology. Only the polysaccharide non-reducing extremity can bind the catalytic site. The depth and shape of the active site pocket reflects the number of subsites that contribute to substrate binding and to the length of the leaving group. In endo-acting enzymes (e.g., $\alpha$-amylases), the catalytic residues are located in an open cleft that allows random binding of the polymer chain.

In family 13, each $\alpha$-amylase produces a characteristic distribution of oligosaccharides from starch, each CGTase produces a characteristic distribution of CDs, and each CDase hydrolyzes one CD type preferentially. The same is true for other family 13 enzymes. A model for the structure of this family's substrate binding site has been proposed that accounts for the variations in product specificity (Fig. 2). The active center is composed of an association of a varying number of subsites, with each subsite interacting with one glucose ring of the substrate. A varying number of subsites and the substrate affinity of each of these subsites define the location and

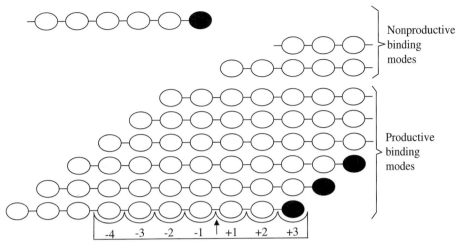

**Fig. 2.** Sugar-binding subsites in glycosyl hydrolases. By convention, the nonreducing end of the substrate is on the left and the reducing end is on the right. The cleavage site (between subsites −1 and +1) is indicated by an arrow. Solid ovals: nonreducing sugars.

specificity of the cleavage. While the subsite theory explains product length patterns, much less is known about the specificities for $\alpha$-1,4 versus $\alpha$-1,6 hydrolysis, $\alpha$-1,4 versus $\alpha$-1,6 transglycosylation, or even hydrolysis versus transglycosylation.

## IV. INDUSTRIAL USES

### A. Current Applications

Starch is an abundant, renewable feedstock that is easily processed in numerous industrial applications. Most industrial starch processes and amylosaccharidase applications involve starch hydrolysis into glucose, maltose, or oligosaccharides (Godfrey and West, 1996). Three types of enzymes are involved in the production of sugars from starch: endo-amylase ($\alpha$-amylase), exo-amylases ($\beta$-amylase and glucoamylase), and debranching enzymes (pullulanase and isoamylase). Starch bioprocessing usually involves two steps, liquefaction and saccharification, both of which are run at high temperatures. During liquefaction, starch granules are gelatinized in a jet cooker at 105–110°C for 5 min in aqueous solution (pH 5.8–6.2) and then partially hydrolyzed at $\alpha$-1,4 linkages with a thermostable $\alpha$-amylase at 95°C for 2 or 3 hr. The enzymes used for this process were isolated from *B. licheniformis* and *B. stearothermophi-*

*lus*. In the presence of 2–4 m$M$ Ca$^{2+}$, they are thermostable enough to resist denaturation at temperatures as high as 105°C. Temperature and pH controls are critical at this stage. If the gelatinization temperature decreases below 105°C, incomplete gelatinization occurs followed by filtration problems in the downstream process. If the gelatinization temperature increases higher than 105°C, $\alpha$-amylases are inactivated. The enzymes also inactivate at pHs below 5.5, and higher pH values cause by-product and color formation. After liquefaction, the pH is adjusted to 4.2–5.0, and the temperature is decreased to 55–60°C for the saccharification step. During saccharification (24–72 hr), the liquefied starch is converted into low-molecular-weight saccharides and ultimately into glucose or maltose. Glucose syrups (up to 95 or 96%) are produced using pullulanase and glucoamylase in combination, whereas maltose syrups (up to 80–85% maltose) are produced using pullulanase and $\beta$-amylase. Microbial amylosaccharidases usually possess better stability, wider range of optimal conditions (temperature and pH) for activity, and lower cost compared to their homologs from other origins. These advantages explain the preference for microbial amylases (when available) in most industrial applications.

The two major uses for starch and amylases are ethanol and high fructose corn syrup (HFCS) production. Starch is also processed into sugar syrups (i.e., glucose, maltose, or oligosaccharide syrups) used as feedstock in various fermentations (lysine, citric acid production, etc.). The synthesis of oligosaccharides (e.g., CDs and branched oligosaccharides) or glucoconjugates for the food and pharmaceutical industries is a high-value use of starch and amylases. In the textile industry, warp threads are strengthened during weaving by application of an adhesive size, usually based on starch, due to its low cost. After machining, the fabric is desized with bacterial thermostable amylases before dyeing. In baking, mostly involving cereal amylases, fungal and bacterial amylases are added to the flour in small quantities to help release the dextrins and fermentable sugars necessary for yeast metabolism. The presence of a thermostable amylase in baking products increases their storage time by preventing starch crystallization on cooling. Using bacterial amylases for conventional bread making, however, is restricted because of their high thermostability, which makes their inactivation difficult. Thermostable bacterial amylases from *B. subtilis* and *B. licheniformis* are used for "cooking" poorly modified malts during brewing. The former enzyme is also used together with a thermostable fungal β-glucanase from *Penicillium emersonii* for barley brewing. Pullulanases are used to produce beers with low carbohydrate content. A comparatively new application for amylolytic enzymes is their use in detergents for removing starch-containing stains.

## B. New Developments

High temperatures are required for both starch liquefaction and saccharification. Typically not water soluble, starch begins gelatinizing at temperatures near 100°C, thus becoming more accessible to hydrolysis by liquefying α-amylases. High temperatures increase starch solubility, allowing the liquefaction and saccharification processes to be run at higher substrate concentrations. The thermostabilities of *B. licheniformis* and *B. stearothermophilus* α-amylases depend on the presence of $Ca^{2+}$ ions. The last enzymatic step in HFCS manufacturing (i.e., glucose isomerization into fructose) uses glucose isomerase, an enzyme strongly inhibited by $Ca^{2+}$ ions. Devel-

oping a $Ca^{2+}$-independent, thermoacid stable α-amylase would allow bypassing the $Ca^{2+}$ requirement in the liquefaction step and the downstream ion-exchange step. Starch liquefaction can be improved by adding debranching enzyme, but with the exception of α-amylases, the enzymes currently used in industrial starch processing are not highly thermostable. Pullulanase, isoamylase, β-amylase, and glucoamylase (originating from *Klebsiella pneumoniae, Pseudomonas*, plants, and *Aspergillus niger*, respectively) are only marginally stable at 60°C. Characterization or engineering of thermoacid stable pullulanase, α-amylase, and glucoamylase would allow a temperature increase of the saccharification process and would result in many benefits: (i) higher substrate concentrations, (ii) limited risks of bacterial contaminations, (iii) increased reaction rates with a decreased operation time, (iv) lower costs for enzyme purification, and (v) longer fermentor half-life.

The use of amylases in detergents requires amylases that are active and stable at alkaline pHs (pHs optimal for proteases and lipases). *Bacillus licheniformis* and *B. amyloliquefaciens* amylases (currently used in detergents) are only partially active in these conditions. Engineering or characterizing new amylases that are optimally active at high pH should make amylases' use in detergents more efficient. Optimally active at temperatures near 0°C, psychrophilic enzymes (i.e., α-amylases, lipases, and proteases) can also be used in cold-temperature detergents. Several psychrophilic amylases have been characterized.

## See Also the Following Articles

ENZYMES IN BIOTECHNOLOGY • INDUSTRIAL FERMENTATION PROCESSES

## Bibliography

Aleshin, A., Golubev, A., Firsov, L. M., and Honzatko, R. B. (1992). Crystal structure of glucoamylase from *Aspergillus awamori* var. ×100 to 2.2-Å resolution. *J. Biol. Chem.* **267**, 19291–19298.

Dong, G., Vieille, C., Savchenko, A., and Zeikus, J. G. (1997). Cloning, sequencing, and expression of the gene encoding extracellular α-amylase from *Pyrococcus furiosus* and biochemical characterization of the recombinant enzyme. *Appl. Environ. Microbiol.* **63**, 3569–3576.

Godfrey, T., and West, S. (Eds.) (1996). "Industrial Enzymology" (2nd ed.). Macmillan, London.

Henrissat, B., and Davies, G. (1997). Structural and sequence-based classification of glucoside hydrolases. *Curr. Opin. Struct. Biol.* 7, 637–644.

Janecek, S. (1997). α-Amylase family: Molecular biology and evolution. *Prog. Biophys. Mol. Biol.* 67, 67–97.

Kadziola, A., Sogaard, M., Svensson, B., and Haser, R. (1998). Molecular structure of a barley α-amylase-inhibitor complex: Implications for starch binding and catalysis. *J. Mol. Biol.* 278, 205–217.

Machius, M., Declerck, N., Huber, R., and Wiegand, G. (1998). Activation of *Bacillus licheniformis* α-amylase through a disorder → order transition of the substrate-binding site mediated by a calcium–sodium–calcium metal triad. *Structure* 6, 281–292.

Mathupala, S. P., Lowe, S. E., Podkovyrov, S. M., and Zeikus, J. G. (1993). Sequencing of the amylopullulanase (*apu*) gene of *Thermoanaerobacter ethanolicus* 39E, and identification of the active site by site-directed mutagenesis. *J. Biol. Chem.* 268, 16332–16344.

McCarter, J. D., and Withers, S. G. (1994). Mechanisms of enzymatic glycoside hydrolysis. *Curr. Opin. Struct. Biol* 4, 885–892.

McCarter, J. D., and Withers, S. G. (1996). Unequivocal identification of Asp-214 as the catalytic nucleophile of *Saccharomyces cerevisiae* α-glucosidase using 5-fluoro glycosyl fluorides. *J. Biol. Chem.* 271, 6889–6894.

Mikami, B., Hehre, E. J., Sato, M., Katsube, Y., Hirose, M., Morita, Y., and Sacchettini, J. C. (1993). The 2.0-Å resolution structure of soybean β-amylase complexed with α-cyclodextrin. *Biochemistry* 32, 6836–6845.

Rüdiger, A., Sunna, A., and Antranikian, G. (1995). Natural polysaccharides degrading enzymes. *In* "Enzyme Catalysis in Organic Synthesis" (K. Dranz and H. Waldmann, Eds.), pp. 316–340. Weinheim.

# Anaerobic Respiration

## Robert P. Gunsalus

*University of California, Los Angeles*

## GLOSSARY

**anaerobic respiration** The ability to use electron acceptors other than oxygen to perform membrane-associated oxidation–reduction reactions for generating energy during anaerobic cell growth.

**ATP synthase** The membrane-bound enzyme that synthesizes ATP from ADP and inorganic phosphate, by utilizing the energy stored as membrane potential. Also known as the proton translocating ATPase.

**electron transport coupled phosphorylation** The process by which ATP is formed from ADP and inorganic phosphate as electrons are transferred from electron donors to electron acceptors.

**electron-transport pathway/chain** The set of proteins and cofactors that comprise the particular electron transport pathway.

**membrane potential** The pH and electrical gradients generated by the electron transport chains.

**redox coupled reaction** The combination of an oxidation reaction coupled to a reduction reaction that results in the release (or consumption) of free energy. **Oxidation** is defined as the withdrawal (or donation) of electrons from a chemical compound (e.g., NADH) and **reduction** is defined as the acceptance of electrons by a chemical compound (e.g., nitrate). An oxidation reaction is always coupled to a reduction of a chemical compound.

**ANAEROBIC RESPIRATION** represents the ability of a cell to perform membrane-associated oxidation–reduction reactions for the purpose of generating energy during anaerobic cell growth. There is considerable biochemical diversity for anaerobic respiration, depending on the bacterial species and the type of respiratory substrate present. In combination, the various respiratory reactions performed by all the bacteria in nature contribute to the recycling of many nutrients in the environment, including nitrogen, sulfur, iron, and carbon.

## I. THE ANAEROBIC RESPIRATORY PROCESS

Anaerobic respiration proceeds by a process much like respiration does under aerobic conditions. It requires the operation of an electron transport pathway/chain to generate energy. Because oxygen cannot serve as the electron acceptor, some other suitable oxidized organic or inorganic compound is used.

Regardless of whether respiration occurs aerobically or anaerobically, the respiratory process may be divided into two distinct components: (i) the energy released by the coupled oxidation–reduction reactions is used to create a cytoplasmic membrane potential. This is accomplished by the electron transport pathway reactions; (ii) the conversion of the membrane potential energy to ATP. This is accomplished by forming a phosphodiester bond from ADP and inorganic phosphate via the ATPase (i.e., ATP-synthase) enzyme. Electron transport-driven phosphorylation reactions generate all of the ATP made during by anaerobic respiration. Some additional

ATP molecules can sometimes be made by alternative substrate level phosphorylations involving fermentation reactions.

## II. HABITATS

Anaerobic respiration can occur in any habitat devoid of oxygen if suitable electron donors and acceptors are present to support cellular energy generation by electron transport-coupled phosphorylation reactions. Typical habitats include anoxic soils, lake and stream sediments, bogs, waste dumps and composts, as well as in the intestines of warm- and cold-blooded animals. The energy harvested by the cell during anaerobic respiration is then used to support other cellular processes that require energy consumption. These include the biosynthesis of cell precursors and their assembly into finished cell material, for transport of organic and inorganic nutrients into the cell, and for maintenance of cells during environmental stress.

Many species of microorganisms are capable of performing anaerobic respiration. Besides some obligate anaerobes that can obtain energy only by respiration, certain facultative aerobic and microaerophilic microbes can switch to an anaerobic respiratory growth mode. Additionally, certain types of photosynthetic bacteria, for example, the nonsulfur purple bacteria, can respire anaerobically when light is unavailable to support photosynthesis. Many of these microorganisms regulate their use of the alternative modes of energy generation in order to maximize growth (to be discussed).

## III. A SIMPLE ELECTRON TRANSPORT CHAIN

The anaerobic electron transport reactions are performed by a variety of distinct membrane-bound enzyme systems, commonly termed the **electron-transport chains** (or **respiratory pathways**). The electron transport chain couples the oxidation of the reduced electron donor (DH) with the reduction of an oxidized electron acceptor (A).

$$DH + A \rightarrow D + AH$$

Electron-transport chains consist of at least two enzyme complexes that are located in the cytoplasmic membrane of the cell, a dehydrogenase and a terminal oxido-reductase enzyme. In more complex electron-transport chains, additional enzymes or electron transfer proteins can be present in the membrane or cell periplasm. All enzymes are freely diffusible in the two-dimensional space of the cytoplasmic membrane. However, due to their size, the rate of protein diffusion is slow compared to the rate of electron transfer that is catalyzed by these enzymes.

A simple respiratory pathway (or electron transport chain) is shown in Fig. 1, where only two respiratory enzymes are employed to perform the coupled oxidation–reduction reactions. A quinone molecule (Q) is used to mediate the transfer of electrons from the electron donor reaction to the acceptor reaction.

In most cases, two electrons are transferred per reaction but sometimes there is a single electron transfer. In certain complex redox reactions that involve several enzymes, up to eight electrons can be transferred. The small lipophilic quinone in most anaerobic bacteria is menaquinone (MK), while in most aerobic bacteria, ubiquinone (Q) is used for electron transfer.

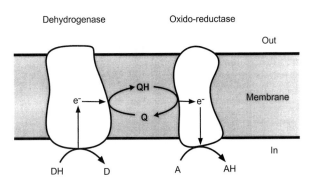

*Fig. 1.* A simple anaerobic respiratory pathway. The dehydrogenase enzyme extracts electrons and protons from the electron donor (DH) and passes them to the small lipophilic quinone (Q) that carries the electrons to the oxidoreductase for reduction of the electron acceptor (A).

## IV. DIVERSITY OF ELECTRON ACCEPTORS AND DONORS

Various anaerobic respiring microbes can use a variety of anaerobic electron acceptors (A). These include the inorganic compounds such as nitrate, nitrite, sulfate, sulfite, elemental sulfur, selenate, arsenate, and ferric iron. Some organic compounds, like fumarate, trimethylamine-*N*-oxide (TMAO), dimethyl-sulfoxide (DMSO), and $CO_2$, may also serve as electron acceptors by various species of microbes.

As the electron donor (DH), some microbes can use formate, hydrogen ($H_2$), hydrogen sulfide ($H_2S$), elemental sulfur, lactate, or alcohols like ethanol, in addition to the intracellular cofactor NADH. The type of electron acceptor or electron donor used by a particular microorganism depends on its genetic make-up (i.e., whether it possesses the requisite genes that encode each of the essential proteins or cofactors for a particular respiratory pathway).

Two examples of simple respiratory pathways are shown in Figs. 2A and 2B for the reduction of fumarate to succinate and for the reduction of nitrate to nitrite when NADH or formate is the electron donor (DH).

## V. ENERGY CONSERVATION

The amount of energy that can potentially be generated by a given respiratory pathway depends on the redox potentials of the electron donor (DH) and the electron acceptor (A) (Table I). For the reaction shown in Fig. 2A, the redox values for fumarate reduction coupled to NADH oxidation is favorable for energy harvesting. It yields about −68 kJ of energy per mole fumarate reduced. However, in reality, the cell cannot operate at 100% efficiency, so the actual energy harvest is less. The fraction of the energy that cannot be harvested by the cell is released as heat.

The calculation of free energy released by the coupled oxidation reduction reactions is shown following. It is based on the difference in the redox midvolt potentials for the donor and the acceptor compounds. The free energy value indicates the maximum amount of energy that can be obtained from

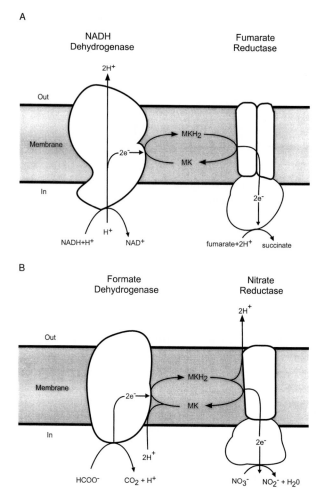

**Fig. 2.** Reduction of fumarate and nitrate by *E. coli.* (A) Fumarate reduction: the two membrane-bound enzymes involved in reduction of the electron acceptor fumarate to succinate, and where NADH is the electron donor, are fumarate reductase and NADH dehydrogenase. The active sites for each enzyme lie exposed to the cytoplasm of the cell. The two electrons extracted from NADH to yield NAD are transferred to menaquinone (MK) and then to fumarate reductase to reduce fumarate. Protons are simultaneously pumped to the cell exterior by the NADH dehydrogenase to create a membrane potential. (B) Nitrate reduction: the two membrane-bound enzymes involved in reduction of the electron acceptor nitrate to nitrite, and where formate is the electron donor, are nitrate reductase and formate dehydrogenase. The active sites for each enzyme lie exposed to the cytoplasm of the cell. The two electrons extracted from formate are transferred to menaquinone (or ubiquinone) and then to nitrate reductase. Protons are translocated by a proposed quinone shuttle mechanism by the formate dehydrogenase to create a membrane potential.

### TABLE I
**Oxidation Reduction Potentials of Respiratory Substrates and Products**

| Redox pair (ox/red) | $E_o'$ (mV) |
| --- | --- |
| $SO_4^{2-}/HSO_3^-$ | −516 |
| $CO_2$/formate | −432 |
| $H^+/H_2$ | −414 |
| $S_2O_3^{2-}/HS^- + HSO_3^-$ | −402 |
| $NAD^+/NADH + H^+$ | −320 |
| $CO_2$/acetate | −290 |
| $S^0/HS^-$ | −270 |
| $CO_2/CH_4$ | −244 |
| acetaldehyde/ethanol | −197 |
| pyruvate/lactate | −190 |
| dihydroxyacetone-P/glycerol-P | −190 |
| $HSO_3^-/S_3O_6^{2-}$ | −173 |
| $HSO_3^-/HS^-$ | −116 |
| menaquinone ox/red | −74 |
| $APS/AMP + HSO_3^-$ | −60 |
| fumarate/succinate | +33 |
| ubiquinone ox/red | +110 |
| $NO_2^-/NO$ | +350 |
| $NO_3^-/NO_2^-$ | +433 |
| $Fe^{3+}/Fe^{2+}$ | +772 |
| $O_2/H_2O$ | +818 |
| $NO/N_2O$ | +1175 |
| $N_2O/N_2$ | +1355 |

the redox reaction during standard conditions. The $\Delta E_o'$ value (given here in volts) is mathematically converted to the **Gibbs free energy** ($\Delta G'^o$) which has the dimension kJ/mol substrate

$$\Delta G'^o = -n \cdot F \cdot \Delta E_o' = -n \cdot 96.5 \cdot \Delta E_o' \text{ (kJ/mol)},$$

where n = number of electrons transferred, F = Faraday constant = 96.5 kJ/V, and $\Delta E_o'$ = difference in the midvolt potentials (in volts) for the acceptor and donor pairs. The $\Delta G'^o$ values for several anaerobic respiratory pathway reactions is presented in Table II to illustrate the amount of energy a bacterium may potentially harvest when using different electron acceptors.

*Coupling of Electron Transport to Proton Motive Force* The free energy ($\Delta G'^o$) of the reaction released by the electron transport process can be used to transport protons across the cytoplasmic membrane from the inside to the outside of the cell (e.g., vectoral proton movement). Some electron transport reactions can also result in scalar proton movement, where protons are consumed on the inside of the membrane and/or produced on the outside due to the chemical reaction. Since the cytoplasmic membrane is impermeable for protons, the protons are "trapped" on the outside of the cell. As a consequence, the pH on the outside of the cell becomes more acidic, whereas the pH in the interior of the cell becomes more alkaline. This pH difference across

### TABLE II
**Free Energy Released in Some Examples of Respiratory Metabolism in *E. coli***

| A | + DH | → | AH + D | $\Delta G'^o = -nF \Delta E_o'$ |
| --- | --- | --- | --- | --- |
| $O_2$ | + $NADH_2$ | → | $H_2O$ + NAD | $\Delta G'^o = -220$ kJ |
| $NO_3^-$ | + $NADH_2$ | → | $NO_2^-$ + NAD + $H_2O$ | $\Delta G'^o = -145$ kJ |
| DMSO | + $NADH_2$ | → | DMS + NAD + $H_2O$ | $\Delta G'^o = -92$ kJ |
| TMAO | + $NADH_2$ | → | TMA + NAD + $H_2O$ | $\Delta G'^o = -86$ kJ |
| fumarate | + $NADH_2$ | → | succinate + NAD | $\Delta G'^o = -68$ kJ |
| $NO_3^-$ | + formate | → | $NO_2^-$ + $CO_2$ + $H_2O$ | $\Delta G'^o = -167$ kJ |
| $NO_3^-$ | + G-3-P | → | $NO_2^-$ + glyceraldehyde | $\Delta G'^o = -120$ kJ |

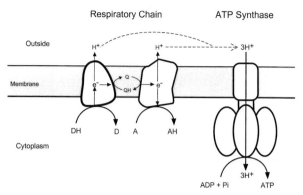

**Fig. 3.** ATP synthase. The membrane-bound ATP synthase forms ATP from ADP and inorganic phosphate by dissipating the cell membrane potential. This potential is represented by the proton gradient across the cytoplasmic membrane.

the cell cytoplasmic membrane is also referred to as **ΔpH** or **pH gradient**, and can be determined experimentally by use of a pH electrode.

Since protons are positively charged, a proton gradient also causes a charge difference (i.e., positive on the outside and negative on the inside of the cell). The difference in charge is referred to as $\Delta\Psi$ or **electrical membrane potential**. $\Delta\Psi$ can be experimentally determined by using lipophilic, positively charged radioactive molecules that can freely diffuse into the cell. The combined values of $\Delta$pH and $\Delta\Psi$ are defined as the **proton motive force** ($\Delta$p) or the **chemiosmotic membrane potential**.

The proton motive force is used to fuel ATP synthesis from ADP and inorganic phosphate via the membrane-bound **ATP synthase** (sometimes called an **ATPase**). This energy-consuming reaction requires three protons to make one molecule of ATP. The enzyme is remarkably similar among all organisms examined. This must reflect either the early evolution of this enzyme or the fact that those microbes that did not possess it acquired it by lateral gene transfer (Fig. 3).

## VI. DIVERSITY OF RESPIRATORY PATHWAYS

As mentioned previously, numerous types of oxidized inorganic and organic compounds can serve as electron acceptors (A) and can, thus, be used to support anaerobic respiration by different types of microbes. Some examples are shown in Table III. In many cases, the electron donor (DH) is NADH. However, a variety of other electron donors may be used, depending on the ability of the bacterial species to utilize a particular compound. A distinction should be noted between the reduction of compounds for respiratory purposes (i.e., dissimilatory) versus for cell biosynthetic needs (i.e., assimilatory).

**TABLE III**
**Examples of Anaerobic Respiration**

| Mode of respiration | Substrate | Product | Organisms |
|---|---|---|---|
| nitrate reduction | $NO_3^-$ | $NO_2^-$ | *Escherichia coli* |
| ammonification | $NO_3^-$ | $NH_3$ | *Klebsiella, E. coli* |
| dentrification | $NO_3^-$ | $N_2$ | *Pseudomonas, Paracoccus* |
| fumarate reduction | fumarate | succinate | *Wolinella* |
| TMAO reduction | TMAO | TMA | *Vibrio* |
| DMSO reduction | DMSO | DMS | *Escherichia coli* |
| sulfate reduction | $SO_4^{2-}$ | $H_2S$ | *Desulfovibrio* |
| sulfur reduction | sulfur | $H_2S$ | *Wolinella* |
| $CO_2$ reduction | $CO_2$ | $CH_4$ | *Methanobacterium* |
| selenate reduction | $SeO_4^{2-}$ | $SeO_3^{2-}$ | *Thauera* |
| iron reduction | $Fe^{+3}$ | $Fe^{+2}$ | *Geobacter* |

## A. Respiration by Dissimilatory Nitrate Reduction

Nitrate is one of the major anaerobic electron acceptors in nature. Depending on whether molecular $N_2$ or $NH_4^+$ is released as the end-product of respiration, two groups of nitrate-reducing bacteria may be defined as **denitrifiers** or as **nitrate ammonifiers**:

1. During denitrification, $NO_3^-$ is reduced to $N_2$. Denitrification is the only biological reaction that converts oxidized nitrogen back to molecular $N_2$. Thus, denitrification plays an important role in the nitrogen cycle on earth. Denitrifiers include the soil bacteria *Paracoccus denitrificans*, *Achromobacter xylosoxidans* (formerly, *Pseudomonas denitrificans*), *Thiobacillus denitrificans*, and many other bacterial species.

2. During nitrate ammonification, $NO_3^-$ is reduced to $NH_4^+$, rather than to $N_2$. $NH_4^+$ is then released into the environment. Nitrate ammonification is a feature of many facultative anaerobes, such as the enteric bacteria, *E. coli* and *Enterobacter aerogenes*, or strict anaerobes like the rumen bacterium, *Wolinella succinogenes*.

The source of electron donor used for nitrate reduction depends on the microorganism. Many bacteria use $NADH + H^+$ as the electron donor when they are grown on glucose. Other electron donors include hydrogen, formate, glycerol, lactate, and certain other substrates.

### 1. The Denitrification Pathway

Denitrification proceeds via several steps in which a total of five electrons are transferred from the electron donor substrate to a series of intermediates:

$$NO_3^- \xrightarrow[\text{nitrate reductase}]{2e^-} NO_2^- \xrightarrow[\text{nitrite reductase}]{e^-} NO \xrightarrow[\text{nitric oxide reductase}]{e^-} N_2O \xrightarrow[\text{nitrous oxide reductase}]{e^-} N_2$$

A specific enzyme catalyzes each step. The first step is catalyzed by membrane-bound molybdenum containing nitrate reductase enzyme. Nitrate reductases in denitrifying organisms are very similar to the nitrate reductases employed in nitrate ammonifying organisms.

The nitrite reductase enzyme from denitrifying bacteria produces NO as end-product, in contrast to the nitrite reductase from nitrate ammonifying organisms that reduces nitrite directly to $NH_4^+$ (see following). The enzymes contain either c- and d-type hemes or copper atoms as cofactors. The nitrite reductases of all denitrifier bacteria examined thus far are located in the periplasmic space of the cell.

Nitric oxide reductase, from *Paracoccus denitrificans*, is an integral membrane protein, whereas nitrous oxide reductase is again located in the periplasm of this and other denitrifying organisms. Because of the soluble nature of some of the enzymes, it is not clear whether all reactions of denitrification contribute to the generation of a proton motive force across the cytoplasmic membrane.

Under growth conditions where the electron donor is limiting, the intermediates $NO_2^-$, NO, and $N_2O$ can accumulate in the cell and be excreted into the environment. Thus, nitrogen oxides can reach the atmosphere not only as a result of oil and coal combustion, but also as a product of biological processes in soil and water.

### 2. The Nitrate Ammonification Pathway

Nitrate ammonification involves only two enzymes that catalyze the following reactions. Eight electrons are transferred to the nitrogen atom of nitrate to produce ammonia:

$$NO_3^- \xrightarrow[\text{nitrate reductase}]{2e^-} NO_2^- \xrightarrow[\text{nitrite reductase}]{6e^-} NH_4^+$$

The nitrate reductase is a membrane-bound, molybdenum-containing enzyme that catalyzes a 2-electron reduction of nitrate to nitrite.

Nitrite reductase enzyme contains cytochrome c as a prosthetic group, and it catalyzes the 6-electron reduction of nitrite to ammonium. In some bacteria, the nitrite reductase enzyme is localized to the cytoplasmic membrane. However, in other microorganisms, nitrite reductase is found either in the cytoplasm or in the periplasm of the cell.

## B. Respiration by Sulfate Reduction

Sulfate reduction to hydrogen sulfide is carried out by a distinct physiological group of bacteria called the "sulfate reducers." All sulfate reducing bacteria are strict anaerobes and include the gram-negative bacteria, *Desulfovibrio, Desulfobacterium*. Other sulfate reducers include the gram-positive *Desulfotomaculum* and the Archaeon *Archaoglobus fulgidus*. Sulfate reducers are widely distributed in nature and are found in anaerobic environments, including waterlogged soils, stream and lake sediments, and brackish and marine sediments. The smell of hydrogen sulfide gas produced by these organisms provides an indication of their presence. Various low molecular weight compounds can serve as electron donors (DH) for various members of the group: these include lactate, propionate, acetate, formate, fatty acids, methanol, ethanol, formate, and hydrogen, plus a variety of aromatic and aliphatic compounds.

Due to the very negative redox potential of the sulfate–sulfite couple, sulfate is not a suitable electron acceptor (Table I). Rather, **sulfate has to be activated prior to its reduction**. The enzyme ATP sulfurylase catalyzes this first energy-requiring step to form APS (adenosine-5-phosphosulfate):

$$ATP + SO_4^{2-} \rightarrow APS + PPi$$

The diphosphate is hydrolyzed by the enzyme diphosphatase. Two moles of ATP are required to regenerate ATP from AMP + 2 Pi. This initial reaction of the dissimilatory sulfate reduction pathway is identical to the distinct assimilatory process that provides the cell with sulfide for the biosynthesis of the sulfur-containing amino acids (i.e., cysteine and methionine) and coenzymes (lipoate, CoA).

The dissimilatory sulfate reduction pathway for APS reduction can proceed via two distinct pathways:

1. Some sulfate-reducing bacteria catalyze the reduction of APS to hydrogen sulfide via a series of free intermediates. The individual enzymes involved in these reduction steps have not yet been characterized in detail:

$$APS \xrightarrow[\text{APS reductase}]{2e^-} HSO_3^- \xrightarrow[\text{sulfite reductase}]{2e^-} S_3O_6^{2-}$$
$$\xrightarrow[\text{trithionate reductase}]{2e^-} S_2O_3^{2-} \xrightarrow[\text{thiosulfate reductase}]{2e^-} HS^-$$

2. In other bacteria, a distinct sulfite reductase catalyzes the 6-electron reduction of $HSO_3^-$ to form $H_2S$ without the release of free intermediates:

$$APS \xrightarrow[\text{APS reductase}]{2e^-} HSO_3^- \xrightarrow[\text{sulfite reductase}]{6e^-} HS^-$$

All enzymes involved in sulfate reduction are soluble enzymes and the coupling of sulfate reduction to the generation of a proton motive force across the cytoplasmic membrane is still not well understood. Several electron mediators (e.g., cytochrome c, cytochrome b, ferredoxins) have been invoked to transfer electrons from a membrane-bound dehydrogenase (e.g., lactate dehydrogenase, hydrogenase) via a small lipophilic cytochrome c to the APS reductase and the sulfite reductase to give sulfide.

## C. Respiration by Fumarate Reduction

Respiration by the reduction of fumarate to succinate is widely distributed among facultative anaerobic bacteria. The fumarate reductases that have been characterized thus far are membrane-bound and are similar in subunit structure and amino acid sequence. *E. coli* can reduce fumarate in a two-electron transfer reaction, using several alternative electron donors including NADH + H⁺ (Fig. 2A), H₂, glycerol-3-phosphate (G-3-P), lactate, or formate. For the latter compounds, NADH dehydrogenase is replaced by alternative enzymes that are specific for the particular electron donor (DH), for example, hydrogenase, formate dehydrogenase, or lactate dehydrogenase.

## D. Respiration by TMAO Reduction

TMAO or trimethylamine-*N*-oxide is a compound produced by many marine fishes for the purpose of osmotic balance. TMAO is reduced to trimethyl amine (TMA) by many bacteria for respiratory purposes. The membrane enzyme that performs this two-electron transfer reaction, TMAO reductase, couples to the menaquinone pool, just as fumarate reductase does (Fig. 2A).

## E. Respiration by DMSO Reduction

DMSO or dimethylsulfoxide is a compound resulting from the breakdown of certain plant materials. Like TMAO, it can also be reduced by many bacteria for respiratory purposes and yields dimethylsulfide. The membrane enzyme that performs this two-electron transfer reaction, DMSO reductase, couples to the quinone pool like fumarate reductase or nitrate reductase (discussed previously).

## F. Respiration by CO₂ Reduction

Biological reduction of carbon dioxide to methane gas occurs in many anaerobic habitats, due to the activity of a specialized group of microbes known as the methanogens, or the methane-producing Archaea. They employ a unique set of six cofactors to perform the eight-electron reduction of $CO_2$ when hydrogen gas is used as the electron donor. Some methanogen species can also use formate, methanol, methylamines, or acetate as an electron donor in place of hydrogen gas. While much is known biochemically about the individual steps of carbon reduction to methane, little is yet known about how the various oxidation reduction reactions are coupled to the cell membranes in order to form a membrane potential. In one instance, oxidation of one of the unique cofactors in these organisms is coupled to sodium ion-pumping to the outside of the cell. These organisms possess an ATP synthase enzyme that operates like those found in other bacteria for the conversion of the membrane potential energy ($\Delta p$) to chemical energy in the form of ATP (Fig. 3). In some instances, a sodium ion gradient is used to drive ATP formation.

## G. Respiration to Heavy Metals

Some bacteria are able to reduce the oxyanion forms of certain heavy metals, including selenium, tellurium, and arsenic compounds. In the case of selenium oxide reduction, selenate is used as an electron acceptor. The product, selenite, can subsequently be further reduced to the level of elemental selenium. Whereas selenate and selenite are soluble in water, elemental selenium is not. Thus, seletate-reducing bacteria can be used to bioremediate contaminated soils and waters by generating elemental selenium that is removed due to its insolubility.

## VII. REGULATORY ASPECTS

Anaerobic respiration occurs in preference to fermentation since the cell can generate more energy by the former strategy. Many microorganisms cannot accomplish both modes of growth due to their genetic makeup. However, those microbes that possess both metabolic abilities usually have multiple genetic regulatory circuits to ensure optimal energy-harvesting by the cell, depending on the availability of electron acceptors and other appropriate electron donors. This regulatory control prevents the unneeded synthesis of alternative respiratory and/or fermentative enzymes when a superior energy-generating pathway is used.

The ordered or hierarchical control of respiratory pathway use correlates with the amount of free energy ($\Delta G'^o$) released by the respective alternative respiratory pathways (Table III). For example, the intestinal bacterium *E. coli* differentially synthesizes the terminal oxido-reductases for reducing the alternative electron acceptors (A), in the order of $O_2 >$ $NO_3^- >$ DMSO $>$ TMAO $>$ fumarate. Only when respiration is not possible due to the lack of an acceptor, does the cell resort to the fermentation of simple sugars. In this situation, ATP can only be made by substrate level phosphorylation reactions, in contrast to oxidative phosphorylation reactions via the ATP synthase.

In *E. coli*, the synthesis of the enzymes involved in the alternative pathways for oxygen, nitrate, DMSO, and fumarate reduction are regulated primarily in response to the presence of oxygen and nitrate. Synthesis of enzymes needed for anaerobic respiration is suppressed during aerobic growth conditions, since respiration with oxygen as the electron acceptor is energetically superior. This control occurs at the level of gene transcription by the action of two global regulatory systems composed of the FNR and ArcA/ArcB proteins. When oxygen is absent from the cell's environment, FNR is converted into a transcriptional activator of genes that encodes the nitrate reductase respiratory enzymes, the DMSO reductase, and the fumarate reductase. It also serves as a positive regulator of several fermentation pathway genes in addition to regulating genes involved in formate and NADH utilization. Finally, FNR also modulates the production of several membrane transporters for uptake or excretion of substrates/waste products. If the cell encounters oxygen, FNR is inactivated by the loss of an essential iron sulfur center and is then unable to bind DNA to either activate or repress transcription.

The ArcA/ArcB two-component regulatory circuit operates independently of FNR as an anaerobic regulatory switch. ArcB is a membrane sensor–transmitter protein that detects the anaerobic state. It sends this signal to ArcA by phosphorylating it. This response-regulator protein then can bind to its DNA target sites to effect gene control. ArcA–phosphate may function as either a positive or negative regulator of gene expression, depending on the promoter it controls. It activates the transcription of the cytochrome d oxidase genes (*cydAB*) and represses the genes for cytochrome o oxidase (*cyoABCDE*), the TCA cycle genes that operate in part to provide NADH for respiratory purposes, and some accessory genes. The presence of the ArcA/ArcB and FNR anaerobic regulatory circuits in *E. coli* allows for the microaerobic control of the cytochrome oxidase genes and for the coordinate induction of the anaerobic pathway genes, which are switched on when the aerobic respiratory pathway genes are switched off.

The anaerobic expression of many anaerobic respiratory pathway genes in bacteria is further modulated in response to availability of nitrate in the cell environment. When present, this anion provides a signal to *E. coli* cells to further elevate expression of genes needed for nitrate respiration (e.g., the nitrate and nitrite reductase enzymes), and to repress expression of other genes that encode the alternative anaerobic respiratory pathways for DMSO reduction and fumarate reduction. Finally, several of the fermentation pathway genes are also switched off to prevent the cell from using this energy-poor mode of growth. The nitrate response in *E. coli* is provided by the Nar regulon, a somewhat unusual bacterial two-compo-

nent regulatory system. It employs two sensor–transmitter proteins, called NarX and NarQ, that can independently detect either nitrate (the major signal) or nitrite (a minor signal). Each transmitter then signals the two response-regulatory proteins, called NarL and NarP, that bind to their DNA target sites to activate or repress transcription. This control provides for the elevated synthesis of nitrate reductase and nitrite reductase in the cell, when nitrate is available. It also provides for the suppression of fumarate reductase, DMSO reductase, and several fermentation pathway genes, since these alternative energy harvesting pathways provide less energy than nitrate respiration (Table II).

## See Also the Following Articles

AEROBIC RESPIRATION • ENERGY TRANSDUCTION PROCESSES • NITROGEN CYCLE • SULFUR CYCLE

## Bibliography

Gennis, R., and Stewart, V. (1996). Respiration. *In* "*Escherichia coli* and *Salmonella*" (2nd ed.) (F. C. Neidhardt, ed.), pp. 217–261.

Gottschalk, G. (1986). "Bacterial Metabolism" (2nd ed.). Springer-Verlag Berlin, Heidelberg, New York.

Gunsalus, R. P. (1992). Control of electron flow in *Escherichia coli*: Coordinated transcription of respiratory pathway genes. *J. Bacteriol.* **174**, 7069–7074.

Harold, F. M. (1986). "The Vital Force: A Study of Bioenergetics." W. H. Freeman and Co., New York.

Stewart, V., and Rabin, R. S. (1995). Dual sensors and dual response regulators interact to control nitrate and nitrite responsive gene expression in *E. coli*. *In* "Two-Component Signal Transduction" (J. Hoch and T. J. Silhavy, eds.). ASM Press, Washington.

Thauer, R. K., Jungermann, K., and Decker, K. (1977). Energy conservation in chemotrophic anaerobic bacteria. *Bacteriol. Rev.* **41**, 100–180.

Zumft, W. G. (1997). Cell biology and molecular basis of denitrification. *Microbiol. Mol. Biol. Rev.* **61**, 533–536.

# Antibiotic Biosynthesis

## Haibin Liu and Kevin A. Reynolds
*Virginia Commonwealth University*

I. Aromatic Polyketide Antibiotics
II. Complex Polyketide Antibiotics
III. $\beta$-Lactam Antibiotics
IV. Nonribosomal Peptide Antibiotics

## GLOSSARY

**aglycon**  An organic molecule that can be glycosylated.
**ketosynthase**  An enzyme which produces a $\beta$-keto product by catalyzing a decarboxylative condensation between two substrates.
**macrolactone**  A lactone ring that typically contains 14 or more atoms.
**polyketide**  A carbon chain containing multiple keto groups on alternate carbon atoms.
**thioester**  Chemical entity formed by esterification of an organic acid with a thiol.

Since Alexander Fleming discovered penicillin from the fungus *Penicillium notatum* 70 years ago, thousands of new antibiotics have been isolated from microorganisms and many of them have been put into clinical or veterinary use. Antibiotics are secondary metabolites; that is, their biosynthesis is not essential for the growth of the host organism. Nevertheless, these structurally diverse compounds (for examples, see Fig. 1) exhibit a broad range of antimicrobial, anticancer, antiparasitic, antihypertensive, enzyme-inhibition, and immunosuppressive activities. Such a range of biological and pharmacological activities constitutes an indispensable resource for drug development and represents a major impetus for investigation into antibiotic biosynthesis.

Biosynthetic studies have revealed that antibiotics are derived from primary metabolic precursors. Examples of such precursors include the short-chain fatty acids (acetate and propionate) and amino acids found in polyketide and nonribosomal peptide antibiotics. In each case, specific biocatalysts (enzyme systems) have evolved to incorporate these precursors into a diverse range of structurally complex secondary metabolites (Fig. 1). Until recently, little was known about these enzymes and the genes encoding them. A scientific breakthrough came with the finding that in streptomycetes and other bacteria the genes required for synthesizing a particular antibiotic are clustered on chromosomal DNA, along with one or more antibiotic self-resistance genes. In the mid-1980s, a group of scientists led by David Hopwood successfully cloned the entire gene cluster of aromatic polyketide antibiotic actinorhodin from *Streptomyces coelicolor* and expressed it in another *Streptomyces* species. A few years later, two other research groups independently cloned and sequenced the structural genes of 6-deoxyerythronolide B synthase (DEBS), a modular polyketide synthase (PKS) responsible for synthesizing 6-deoxyerythronolide B (6-dEB), the aglycon of macrolide antibiotic erythromycin. The structural genes of L-$\delta$-(aminoadipoyl)-L-cysteinyl-D-valine (ACV; the tripeptide intermediate of $\beta$-lactam antibiotics) synthetase and many other nonribosomal peptide synthetases (NRPSs) have also been cloned and characterized.

Genetic and biochemical analyses of these antibiotic biosynthetic systems have been continuing and several generalizations can be drawn from these remarkable studies. First, antibiotic and other secondary metabolic processes not only utilize primary metabolic precursors but also adopt many of the catalytic

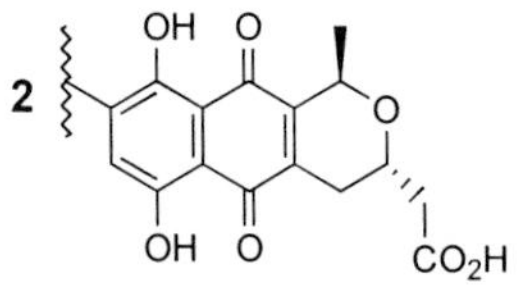

Actinorhodin (1)

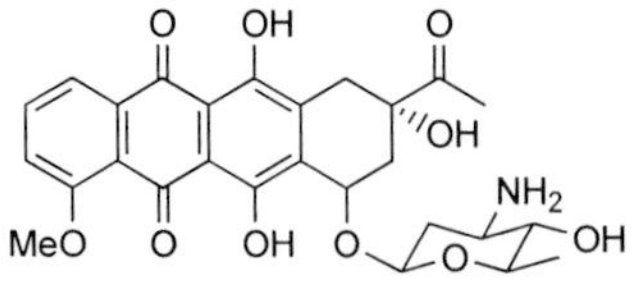

Daunorubicin (2)

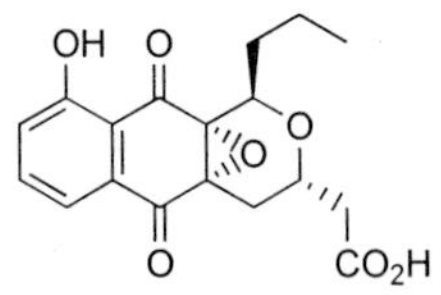

Frenolicin B (3)

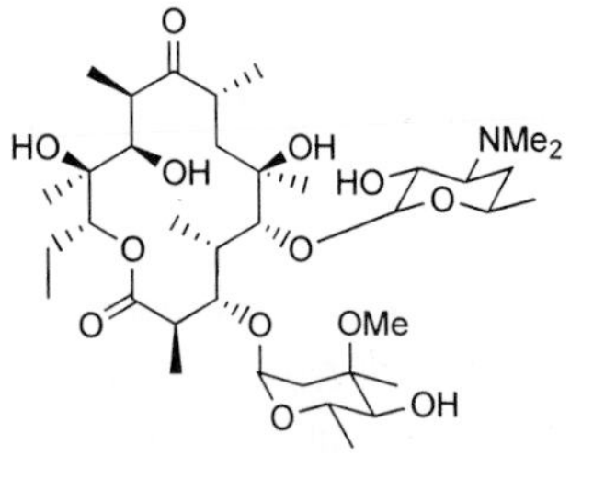

Erythromycin A (4)

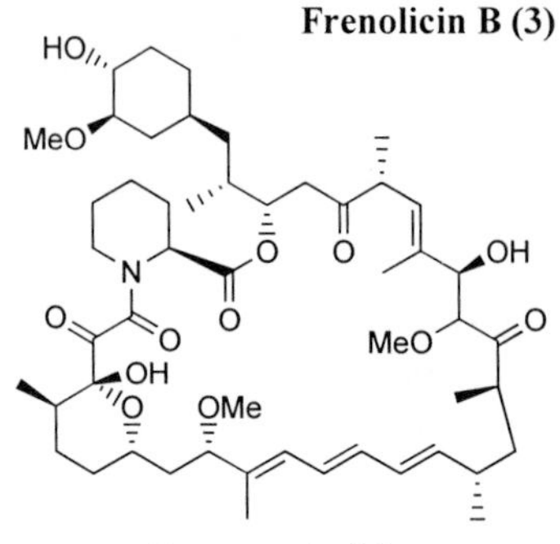

Rapamycin (5)

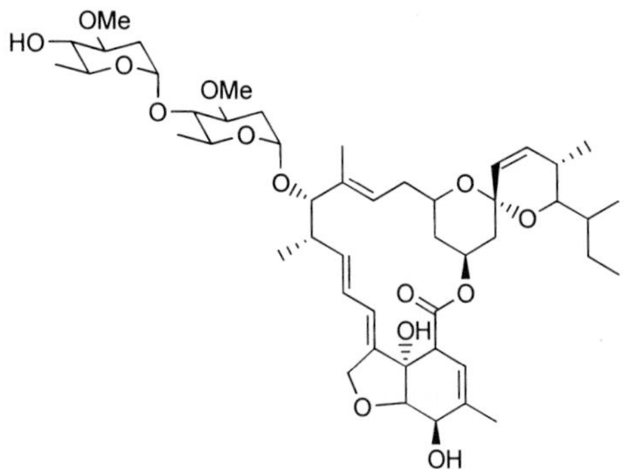

Avermectin B1a (6)

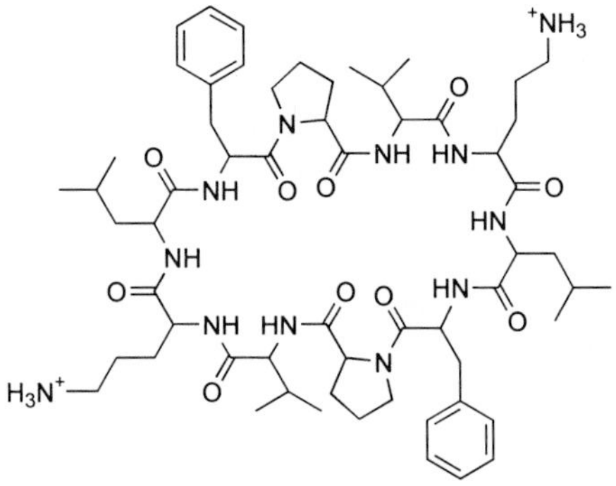

Gramicidin S (8)

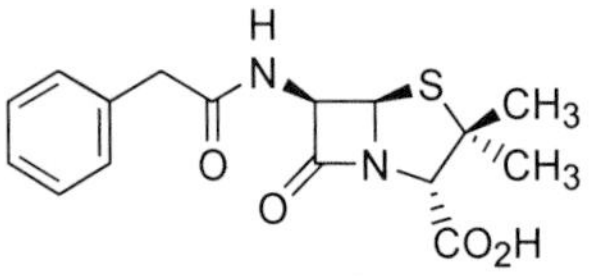

Penicillin G (7)

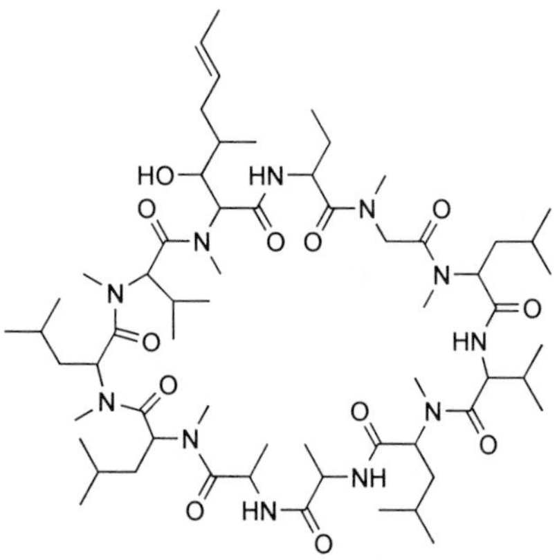

Cyclosporin A (10)

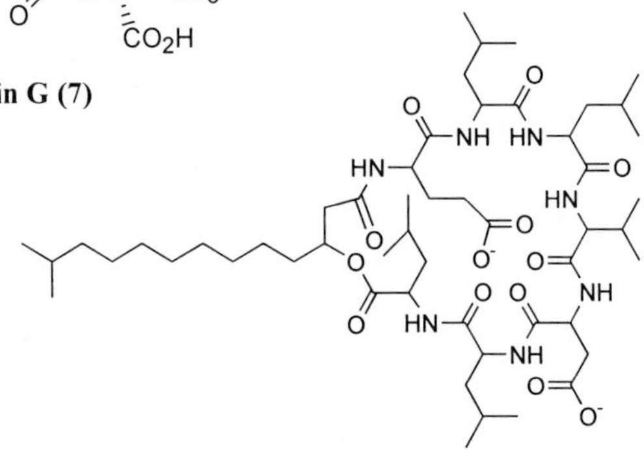

Surfactin (9)

*Fig. 1.* Structures of some polyketide (**1–6**) and nonribosomal peptide (**7–10**) antibiotics.

functions/enzyme activities of primary metabolism. An excellent example of this is the modular (type I) PKSs in which the enzyme activities normally involved in fatty acid biosynthesis are applied in a unique fashion for production of complex polyketide antibiotics. Second, the biocatalysts involved in secondary metabolism have evolved to ensure the fidelity of their products in a way that differs significantly from their counterparts in primary metabolism. A striking example is the well-established modular organizations of type I PKSs and NRPSs. In these multifunctional enzyme systems, the structure of a product is determined by the number of modules within a particular synthase/synthetase and the content of catalytic domains in each module. This is significantly different from DNA, RNA, and ribosomal polypeptide biosynthesis in which the structure of a product is dictated by a "modularized" template (DNA or RNA) rather than the biocatalysts.

Finally, antibiotic biosynthetic systems, at least the PKSs and NRPSs investigated to date, display a relatively relaxed specificity both in substrate recognition and in protein–protein interactions. Analogs of natural precursors are frequently recognized and processed to yield structurally modified products. Insertion, inactivation, substitution, and repositioning of certain enzymes and catalytic domains of an antibiotic biosynthetic system do not always abolish product formation but instead lead to the production of structurally novel compounds. These properties have provided the opportunity to engineer antibiotic and other secondary metabolite biosynthetic pathways, most prominently through genetic manipulation of the corresponding biosynthetic genes.

## I. AROMATIC POLYKETIDE ANTIBIOTICS

The structures in this group of antibiotics feature a multiple fused-ring aromatic system that, in many cases, forms a glycoside with one or more deoxysugar molecules (Fig. 1, **1–3**). This section discusses only the biosynthesis of the aromatic moiety of these polyketides. The most thoroughly investigated aromatic polyketide synthases studied to date are those involved in the biosynthesis of actinorhodin (**1**),

daunorubicin (**2**), frenolicin B (**3**), granaticin, and tetracenomycin C.

## A. Biosynthetic Studies

Before gene sequence data became available, two lines of biosynthetic studies had provided much of the insight into aromatic polyketide biosynthesis. On one hand, isotope-labeling experiments revealed that the aromatic framework of these antibiotics was derived from a polyketide intermediate that in turn was made from acetate (occasionally propionate) and malonate as the starter and extender units through a process analogous to fatty acid biosynthesis. Studies based on blocked mutants, on the other hand, helped to establish the sequence of reactions leading from the first detectable polyketide intermediate to the final fused aromatic ring product.

Biosynthetic studies, for example, have shown that in the case of actinorhodin (**1**), one acetate and seven malonate molecules are incorporated into the octaketide ($C_{16}$) carbon chain of its core structure. Seven different groups of blocked mutants, designated *act*I–VII, have also been characterized, many of which accumulated pathway-blocked shunt products (Fig. 2A, **11–15**). Through analysis of the structures of these shunt products and complementation between different groups of blocked mutants, the biosynthetic sequence was established as follows: *act*I → III → VII → IV → VI → V → actinorhodin (Fig. 2A).

In the actinorhodin and other aromatic polyketide biosynthetic processes, the $\beta$-keto groups of the nascent polyketide chain remain unreduced, although some of these groups undergo ketoreduction in the later stages of biosynthesis. This level of processing is in contrast to fatty acid biosynthesis, in which all the $\beta$-keto groups generated in successive elongation steps are fully reduced to methylene functionality through the actions of a ketoreductase, dehydratase, and enoyl reductase.

## B. Gene Cloning and Analysis

Several approaches for cloning biosynthetic genes of aromatic polyketide antibiotics have been used. One of the early approaches used to clone the PKS genes of actinorhodin (*act*), oxytetracycline (*otc*),

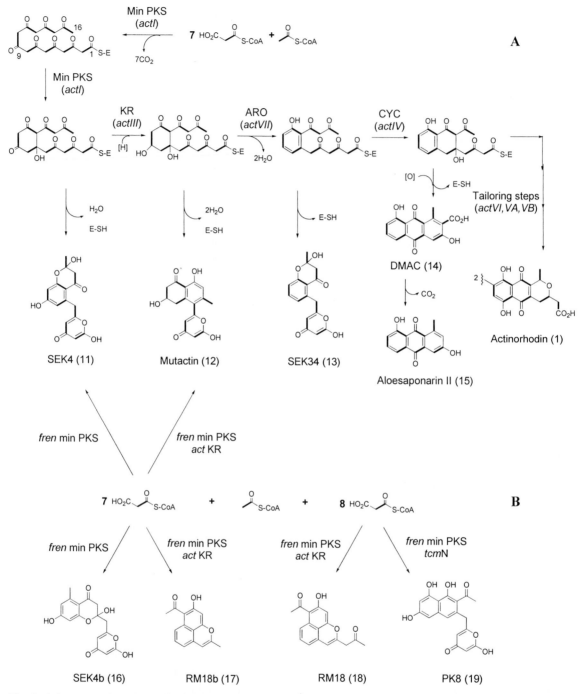

**Fig. 2.** (A) Proposed pathway for biosynthesis of the aromatic polyketide antibiotic actinorhodin (1). *act*I and *act*III–VII: genes that encode the actinorhodin (*act*) PKS and tailoring enzymes and have been mutated in different groups of pathway-blocked mutants. Min PKS, the *act* minimal PKS; KR, polyketide ketoreductase; ARO, aromatase; CYC, cyclase. (B) Production of six novel polyketide compounds by the *fren* minimal PKS, alone or in the presence of either *act* KR or the *tcm*N gene product (a "bifunctional" aromatase/*O*-methyltransferase).

and tetracenomycin (*tcm*) involved shotgun-cloning random fragments from a wild-type strain into pathway-blocked mutants and screening for restoration of antibiotic production through complementation. An alternative approach was based on the observation that antibiotic biosynthetic genes are often clustered with antibiotic self-resistance genes on the chromosome. In this approach, a library of DNA fragments from an antibiotic-producing organism were cloned into a sensitive surrogate host and resistant clones were then selected. Location of the resistance gene in this fashion could then lead to the identification of appropriate biosynthetic genes.

Once the sequence similarity between homologous genes from different systems was established, Southern hybridization using probes based on the already-known PKS genes (e.g., *act*I and *act*III) became the method of choice for cloning aromatic PKS genes from other antibiotic producers. To date, more than 20 aromatic PKS gene clusters from actinomycetes have been cloned and sequenced (Fig. 3A).

All the aromatic PKS gene clusters characterized to date have some similar organizational features (Fig. 3A). The type II nature (enzyme systems comprising dissociable monofunctional proteins) of these PKS genes is reflected in the resemblance of their components to those of type II fatty acid synthases (FASs) of bacteria and plants. A set of three genes, homologous to *act*I-ORF1, *act*I-ORF2, and *act*I-ORF3, respectively, are present in all aromatic PKS gene clusters and in most cases form a cluster in the following order: *act*I-ORF1 → *act*I-ORF2 → *act*I-ORF3. Sequence analysis has revealed that the proteins encoded by *act*I-ORF1 and *act*I-ORF2 strongly resemble the ketosynthase (KS and FabB) of *Escherichia coli* FAS. For this reason, *act*I-ORF1 and *act*I-ORF2 gene products and their homologs from other PKS systems are known as KS$\alpha$ and KS$\beta$. The KS$\beta$ subunits, however, lack the putative catalytic site for condensation (a consensus sequence involving a cysteine residue), and their role in polyketide biosynthesis is unclear, although a role as a chain-length factor (CLF) has been suggested from recombinant experiments. The *act*I-ORF3 gene encodes a protein that shows sequence similarity to the discrete acyl carrier protein (ACP) of the type II FASs of bacteria and plants. The three proteins encoded by *act*I-ORF1–3 [i.e., two ketosynthases (KS$\alpha$ and KS$\beta$) and an ACP] together form the so-called "minimal" PKS. This minimal PKS catalyzes successive decarboxylative condensations of malonyl ACP with an appropriate acyl-CoA/ACP starter unit to generate a polyketide chain.

In addition to *act*I-ORF1–3, another gene, the *act*III homolog, is found in the C-9-reduced octa-, nona-, and decaketide (e.g., actinorhodin, frenolicin, and daunorubicin) PKS gene clusters. This gene is thought to encode a discrete polyketide ketoreductase (KR) since its protein sequence shows strong similarity to several known oxidoreductases. The absence of an *act*III-like gene from the *tcm* cluster is consistent with the observation that tetracenomycin is formed without any of the $\beta$-keto groups of the nascent polyketide chain being reduced.

The functions of two other genes in the *act* cluster, *act*VII and *act*IV (and their homologs in other PKS gene clusters), could not be deduced from sequence analysis. However, their activities as an aromatase and cyclase, respectively, were subsequently established through recombinant experiments. The *act*VII product has been identified as a "didomain" protein with N- and C-terminal regions that resemble each other; both of these domains can function as a monodomain aromatase when expressed separately. A related but significantly different didomain gene, *tcm*N, is found in the *tcm* cluster. The product of *tcm*N has an N-terminal region homologous to that of *act*VII-encoded aromatase and a C-terminal region encoding an *O*-methyltransferase for a tailoring step in later stages of the biosynthesis.

## C. Genetic Manipulation of Aromatic Polyketide Synthases

Genetic engineering of aromatic PKSs has been extensively exploited. A special host-vector system was developed for this purpose and has been widely used in a variety of studies. This system involves *Streptomyces coelicolor* CH999 and plasmids derived from pRM5; CH999 strain is a derivative of actinorhodin producer *S. coelicolor* A3(2), from which the entire cluster of *act* genes has been deleted, and pRM5 is a *Streptomyces*–*E. coli* shuttle plasmid. One advantage of pRM5 is that genetic engineering of

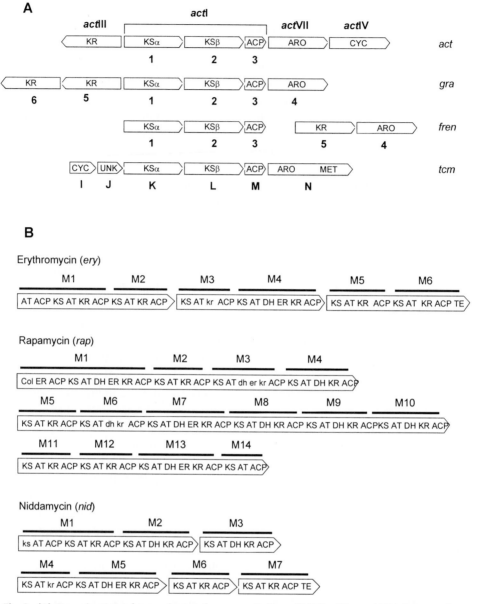

**Fig. 3.** (A) Organization of gene clusters for aromatic (type II) PKSs. KS$\alpha$ and KS$\beta$, ketosynthases $\alpha$ and $\beta$; ACP, acyl carrier protein; KR, ketoreductase; ARO, aromatase; CYC, cyclase; MET, *O*-methyltransferase; UNK, unknown function. The numbers or letters underneath each PKS gene cluster are the original symbols assigned to the corresponding open reading frames. (B) Modular organization of complex (type I) PKSs. KS, ketosynthase; AT, acyltransferase; DH, dehydratase; ER, enoylreductase; TE, thioesterase; Col, CoA ligase. Nonfunctional domains are indicated by lowercase letters. The individual PKS polypeptides are indicated as arrows.

PKS genes can be performed in *E. coli* prior to transformation into *S. coelicolor* CH999. An additional advantage is that it contains the *act*II-ORF4 gene, the natural pathway-specific activator of the *act* biosynthetic genes; its product activates transcription from *act*I and *act*III promoters in an appropriate and developmentally controlled fashion.

Using this host expression system, recombinant strains expressing either nonhybrid subsets or hybrid sets of aromatic PKS genes have been obtained and shown to produce a wide range of different chemical entities. Analysis of these structures has led to a greater understanding of the role of the individual PKS components. In a series of experiments, mutants of *S. coelicolor* CH999 carrying different subsets of *act* PKS genes were constructed and their polyketide products isolated and characterized (Fig. 2A). Expression of the minimal PKS gene set (*act*I-ORF1–3) led to the production of novel octaketide SEK4 (**11**), which resulted from a cyclization between C-7 and C-12, indicating that the *act* minimal PKS alone is sufficient to synthesize the nascent polyketide with both natural chain length and correct first ring cyclization. When *act*III was added to the minimal PKS gene set, the corresponding mutant was found to produce mutactin (**12**), which has the natural first ring closure but lacks the first ring aromatization and a correct second ring cyclization (compared to actinorhodin). This is consistent with the proposed function of *act*III as a polyketide ketoreductase which reduces the C-9 carbonyl to a hydroxyl group; reduction of C-9 carbonyl is thought to block spontaneous aromatization of the first ring. The addition of *act*VII to *act*I + *act*III to this system yielded the novel shunt product SEK34 (**13**), which has the correctly cyclized and aromatized first ring but still lacks a correct second ring cyclization. The function of *act*VII protein was therefore deduced as the first ring aromatase. The didomain nature of this protein is thought to be a reflection for the need of abstracting two water molecules to form the aromatic first ring. Finally, two additional shunt metabolites, 3,8-dihydroxy-1-methylanthraquinone-2-carboxylic acid (**14**) and aloesaponarin II (**15**), were found in the recombinant strain carrying the *act*I + *act*III + *act*VII + *act*IV gene set. These metabolites have the correct cyclized second ring, implying that the *act*IV

protein is a second ring cyclase. The results of these genetic engineering experiments are completely consistent with the biosynthetic studies based on various blocked mutants derived from random mutagenesis.

The catalytic functions of individual PKS gene products deduced from the *act* system have been reinforced and, in some cases, refined by recombinant studies involving other nonhybrid and, more important, hybrid aromatic PKS systems. Expression of the *tcm* minimal PKS gene set, for example, yielded a decaketide SEK15 (structure not shown), providing further evidence for the role of the minimal PKS in determining polyketide chain length (tetracenomycin is a decaketide). A separate line of studies involved constructing hybrid PKS systems through different combinations of *act*I-ORF1(KSα), -ORF2 (KSβ), and -ORF3 (ACP) homologous genes from the *act*, *gra*, *fren*, and *tcm* PKS gene sets. One finding from these studies is that chain length is controlled to some extent by the KSα and KSβ proteins. It is unclear if chain length control is provided solely by the KSβ, the so-called CLF.

Genetic manipulation of aromatic PKSs not only leads to an understanding of the role of the individual enzymes in the biosynthetic process but also results in the generation of structurally novel polyketide compounds. As previously discussed, recombinants carrying nonhybrid subsets of the *act* PKS genes were able to produce the previously unknown octaketides SEK4 and SEK34. "Combinatorial biosynthesis" based on hybrid PKS systems is more desirable in this context since the power of these systems to produce novel compounds is much greater. An example of this is illustrated in Fig. 2B in which simple combinations of the *fren* minimal PKS gene set alone or with either *act*III or *tcm*N yielded six novel polyketides. The products of the *fren* minimal PKS alone were octaketides SEK4 and SEK4b (**16**). In the presence of *act* KR, the resulting hybrid PKS produced two octaketides, mutactin and RM18b (**17**), and a nonaketide, RM18 (**18**). When *tcm*N was added to the *fren* minimal PKS gene set, nonaketide PK8 (**19**) was identified in the recombinant strain. Many additional combinatorial biosynthetic experiments using other aromatic polyketide synthase genes, particularly those involved in tetracenomycin biosynthesis, have generated many similar "unnatural" natural products.

### D. *In Vitro* Studies

Recently, the solution structure of the recombinant *act apo*-ACP has been solved by $^1$H nuclear magnetic resonance spectroscopy, and it is the first three-dimensional structure determined for any PKS component. The tertiary fold of *act apo*-ACP is highly similar to that of *E. coli* FAS ACP. However, the *act* ACP has buried hydrophilic amino acid residues, such as Arg72 and Asn79, which are not observed in the *E. coli* FAS ACP, and these are thought to be involved in stabilizing the growing polyketide chain. In recent studies, *in vitro* experiments using the purified minimal actinorhodin and tetracenomycin PKS have been carried out. In both cases, the KS$\alpha$ and KS$\beta$ copurified as either an $\alpha\beta$ dimer or an $\alpha_2\beta_2$ dimeric complex. Maximal activity in both reconstituted PKS systems was obtained if malonyl-CoA ACP transacylase (FabD) involved in fatty acid biosynthesis was included, supporting an earlier suggestion that this enzyme catalyzes the essential step of loading malonyl-CoA onto the ACP of an aromatic polyketide synthase. Nonetheless, it has been shown that a range of PKS ACPs have the capacity to self-malonate in the absence of FabD, and it is unclear which of these processes is physiologically relevant. Surprisingly, both purified PKS systems could not utilize the proposed acetyl-CoA starter unit but could use malonyl-CoA (presumably by decarboxylation of corresponding malonyl-ACP to acetyl-ACP).

### II. COMPLEX POLYKETIDE ANTIBIOTICS

Complex polyketide antibiotics represent a large and diverse group of natural products of which the basic structure is derived from a reduced polyketide carbon chain (Fig. 1, 4–6). Depending on the nature of individual biosynthetic systems, the polyketide chain may either cyclize through lactonization (macrolide antibiotics) or remain as a long acyl chain (polyether antibiotics). In macrolide antibiotics, the polyketide-derived macrolactone is frequently glycosylated with a range of deoxysugar molecules. Although this glycoslyation is often required for full biological activity of the polyketide, this section will focus on the biosynthesis of the polyketide moiety. Of the complex polyketides, biosynthesis of erythromycin (4) has been the most fully characterized from both a genetic and a biochemical perspective. Other macrolide antibiotic pathways, including those involved in rapamycin (5), avermectin (6), rifamycin, tylosin, and pikromycin biosynthesis, have been studied in a similar fashion.

### A. Biosynthetic Studies

Extensive labeling experiments using either stable or radioactive isotopes have revealed that the polyketide chain of macrolide and polyether antibiotics is made from a pool of small fatty acid building blocks, such as acetate, propionate, butyrate, and isobutyrate. Although a mechanistic relationship with fatty acid biosynthesis is obvious, the scenario is far more complicated. The structural diversity of macrolide and polyether antibiotics dictates that a complex polyketide synthase has to make at least the following biochemical choices: (i) starter units, ranging from simple straight and branched chain carboxylic acids to shikimate-derived or -related carboxylic acids; (ii) extender units, ranging from malonate to methylmalonate, ethylmalonate, even propylmalonate; (iii) the number of condensation cycles, ranging from 1 (in principle and as accomplished by genetic engineering) to more than 20; (iv) the degrees of reduction of $\beta$-keto group at each cycle, ranging from none to all the sequential reactions of ketoreduction, dehydration, and enoyl reduction; and (v) the stereochemistry introduced by incorporating 2-alkylmalonate extender units. Controlling such a complex biosynthetic process is beyond the capabilities of a simple synthase system such as that involved in fatty acid or aromatic polyketide biosynthesis.

Analysis of the carbon backbone of erythromycin reveals that the variations in both the stereochemistry of the alkyl side chains and the levels of processing of the $\beta$-keto group after each chain extension must occur. The choice of precursors, however, is limited to a propionyl-CoA starter unit and methyl malonyl-CoA for each extension step. Biosynthetic studies have revealed that a broader range of precursors are used in other cases. For instance, rapamycin and related immunosuppressants (e.g., FK506 and ascomycin) utilize a shikimate-derived substituted cyclohexanecarboxylic acid as a starter unit, a broad range extender unit, and lysine-derived pipecolic acid to terminate the polyketide chain extension process (Fig. 1).

The origins of other structural moieties of antibiotics and the sequence in which these are attached to the polyketide, in most cases, have been elucidated by labeling and complementation experiments. Specifically, in the case of 6-deoxyerythronolide B (6-dEB, **20**), the original polyketide-derived macrolactone of the erythromycin pathway, hydroxylation at C-6 by a P450 hydroxylase forms erythronolide B (Fig. 4, **21**). The next steps involve attachment of two deoxysugars, both synthesized via TDP-deoxyglucose; first L-mycarose at C-3 to yield 3-$\alpha$-mycarosylerythronolide B (**22**) and then desosamine at C-5 to generate erythromycin D (**23**), the first bioactive compound of the pathway. Erythromycin D is then converted to erythromycin A (**4**) through two additional reactions: C-12 hydroxylation by another P450 hydroxylase and C''-3 methylation by an O-methyltransferase (Fig. 4).

## B. Gene Cloning and Analysis

The first complex PKS gene cluster to be cloned and sequenced was that containing the structural genes of 6-deoxyerythronolide B synthase (DEBS). The process began with the identification of a segment of chromosomal DNA, *erm*E, from *Saccharopolyspora erythraea,* the native erythromycin-producing organism, as an erythromycin self-resistance gene. The *erm*E fragment was used as a hybridization probe to clone erythromycin biosynthetic genes from the genome of *S. erythraea.* Through a complementation test against an original mutant that was blocked in the synthesis of 6-dEB, a region that spanned 35 kb on the chromosome was identified as both essential and sufficient for synthesizing the erythromycin aglycon, 6-dEB. Sequencing and analysis of this 35-kb region revealed for the first time the "modular" organization of complex polyketide synthases.

The erythromycin PKS gene set consists of three large (~10 kb each) open reading frames designated *eryAI*, *eryAII*, and *eryAIII*, each encoding a giant (~350 kDa each), multifunctional protein named DEBS1, DEBS2, and DEBS3, respectively (Figs. 3B and 4). Each DEBS protein carries 8–10 domains (28 domains total) with considerable sequence similarity to the individual enzymatic domains of the vertebrate type I FASs. As exemplified by animal FAS, vertebrate type I FASs are a family of large, multifunctional proteins that carry all the enzyme activities required for fatty acid biosynthesis in one polypeptide. Unlike in vertebrate type I FASs, in which one set of 7 catalytic domains is iteratively used, the 28 domains in DEBS are noniterative and are grouped into six "modules," two modules per protein: modules 1 and 2 in DEBS1, modules 3 and 4 in DEBS2, and modules 5 and 6 in DEBS3. Each of these modules carries its own set of catalytic domains and is responsible for catalyzing one particular cycle of condensation and reduction. All six modules contain three essential domains involved in condensation, i.e., KS, acyltransferase (AT), and ACP. Depending on the degree of reduction of the $\beta$-keto group at each cycle, an individual module may also contain none (module 3, carrying a dysfunctional KR domain), one (modules 1, 2, 5, and 6), two or all (module 4) of the following catalytic domains: KR, dehydratase (DH), and enoylreductase (ER). In addition to these domains, module 1 also carries an AT–ACP "loading domain" near the N-terminal end of DEBS1; module 6, on the other hand, contains a thioesterase (TE) "off-loading domain" at the C-terminal end of DEBS3. The genetic order of individual modules and proteins is the same as the functional order of their activity in the biosynthesis of 6-dEB (Fig. 4).

Based on the modular organization of DEBS, a step-by-step mechanism for 6-dEB biosynthesis is proposed (Fig. 4). Initiation occurs with AT of the "loading domain" which binds the propionyl-CoA (starter unit) and transfers it to the 4'-phosphopantetheine (4'-PP) arm of the adjacent ACP domain and then to the active-site cysteine residue of the KS domain in module 1. In addition, the AT domain of module 1 binds methylmalonyl-CoA (extender unit) and transfers it to the ACP domain of the same module. The first decarboxylative condensation then oc-

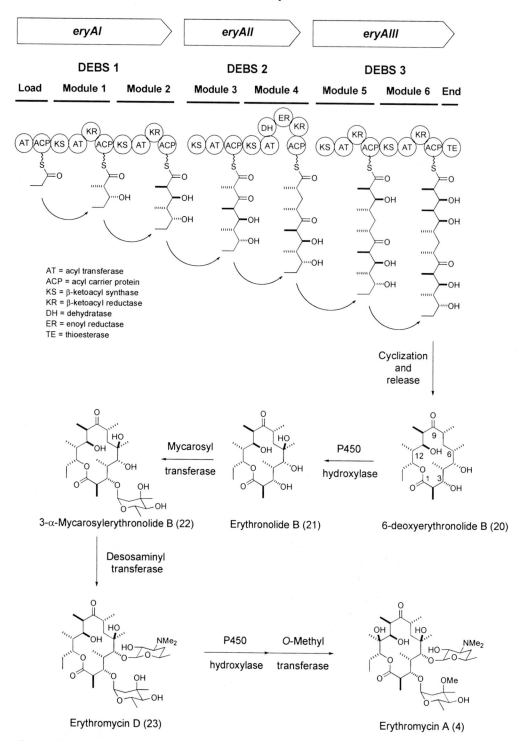

AT = acyl transferase
ACP = acyl carrier protein
KS = β-ketoacyl synthase
KR = β-ketoacyl reductase
DH = dehydratase
ER = enoyl reductase
TE = thioesterase

3-α-Mycarosylerythronolide B (22)

Erythronolide B (21)

6-deoxyerythronolide B (20)

Erythromycin D (23)

Erythromycin A (4)

**Fig. 4.** The "assembly-line" model for biosynthesis of 6-deoxyerythronolide B (6-dEB, **20**) by the modular erythromycin PKS (DEBS) and the postpolyketide pathway leading from 6-dEB to erythromycin A (**4**).

curs with transfer of the starter to the extender unit, resulting in the formation of the five-carbon acyl chain carrying a β-keto group. The KR domain in module 1 then reduces the β-keto group to a hydroxyl functionality. Since no other reductive domains are present in module 1, the diketide is transferred to the KS domain of module 2 and then condensed to the second methylmalonyl extender on the cognate ACP domain.

The process continues in this manner through the remaining enzymatic domains of the DEBS proteins, leaving either a keto, hydroxyl, or methylene group at each β-carbon position depending on the catalytic domains each module carries, until the extended polyketide chain reaches the TE domain at the end of module 6. This domain releases the 15-carbon acyl chain from the DEBS3 and forms 6-dEB (20) through a lactonization between the C-13 hydroxyl and the C-1 carboxylate. During the entire process, the growing acyl chain presumably remains covalently bound to the DEBS proteins and in essence functions as an assembly line. Such a biosynthetic system is efficient because intermediates do not need to diffuse from one module or active site to the next. The unique architecture of the modular polyketide synthase also permits utilization of different extender units at each elongation cycle and accommodates selective reduction of the β-keto groups.

Since the discovery of the DEBS genes, several other modular PKS gene sets have also been cloned and sequenced, either completely or in part, including those for rapamycin (5), avermectin (6), spiramycin, tylosin, FK506, niddamycin, rifamycin, and pikromycin. In all cases, modular organizations similar to those of the DEBS genes were revealed. Two sets of these PKS genes, *rap* and *nid*, are schematically shown in Fig. 3B together with the DEBS genes. Sequence analysis of these PKS gene sets has led to additional findings about modular PKSs. First, the genetic order of individual synthase proteins is not always the same as the functional order of their activity: The corresponding PKS genes can be transcribed either divergently (as in *rap* PKS) or convergently (as in *avr* PKS). Second, the number of modules in a synthase protein varies from one to as many as six (as in *rap* PKSs). Third, based on sequence alignment results, various AT domains cluster into two groups:

one includes all malonate-loading AT domains and the other all methyl- and ethylmalonate-loading AT domains. Finally, certain modular PKSs contain loading and termination domains that differ from those observed in DEBS. For instance, the *rap* PKS loading domain consisting of enzymatic functions resembling a CoA ligase, an enoylreductase, and an ACP is thought to activate, reduce, and transfer the dihydroxycyclohexenyl starter unit to the KS domain of the first module. There is also no TE domain at the end of the last module of the *rap* PKS, consistent with the assumption that the polyketide chain has to be moved to another enzyme which catalyzes the formation of an amide bond between the polyketide and pipecolic acid.

## C. Genetic Manipulation of Modular Polyketide Synthases

A variety of genetic changes have been introduced into the DEBS genes, ranging from a change of a single nucleotide pair to the deletion of large DNA segments, and from swapping of homologous sequences to insertion of foreign DNA fragments and the creation of truly hybrid modular polyketide synthases. These changes have been directed either at individual domains or at entire modules and have resulted in loss, gain, or change of catalytic functions. In most cases, such changes yielded structurally novel polyketide compounds and have provided insight into the mechanism of modular PKSs.

Two genetic systems have been developed and used in most studies. The first system involves *S. erythraea*, the native erythromycin-producing organism, whereas the second utilizes the *S. coelicolor* CH999/plasmid pCK7 host–vector system. The *S. erythraea* system presents more technical problems but has the capacity to yield glycosylated, and hence potentially bioactive, products owing to the presence of postpolyketide enzymes. The *S. coelicolor* CH999/pCK7 system, in contrast, significantly simplifies genetic operations but produces unglycosylated polyketide compounds.

Some examples of the genetic manipulations of DEBS using these systems are shown in Fig. 5 and are briefly described in the following sections.

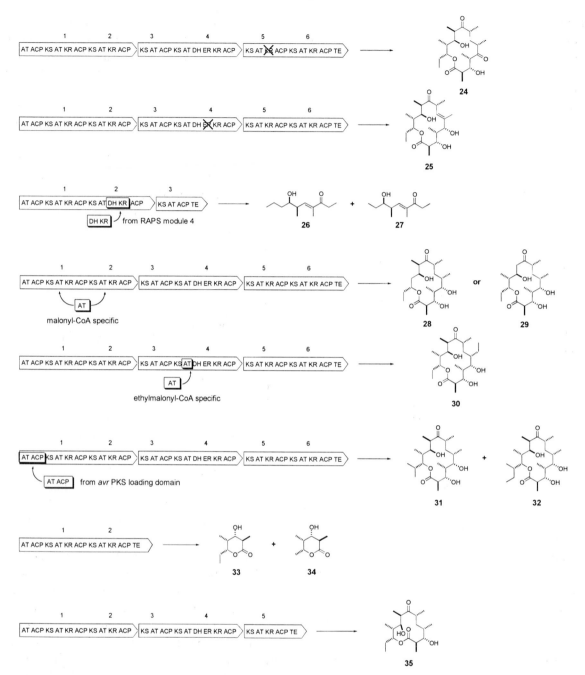

***Fig. 5.*** Genetic manipulations of DEBS genes and the novel erythromycin-related polyketide compounds produced by host strains carrying the altered DEBS genes. The genetic changes shown include inactivation, insertion, substitution, deletion, and repositioning of various catalytic domains. See the Fig. 3B figure legend for abbreviations.

## 1. Changes in β-Carbonyl-Processing Functions

The first changes introduced into the DEBS genes were inactivation of the KR domain in module 5 and the ER domain in module 4, respectively (Fig. 5). Both changes were made in the chromosome of *S. erythraea*. To inactivate the KR domain, a DNA segment of 813 bp (271 amino acids) was deleted from its NH₂ end, leaving the reading frame intact. The resulting mutant produced the expected 5,6-dideoxy-5-oxoerythronolide B (**24**). Inactivation of the ER domain was accomplished by the introduction of a four-base-pair change into its coding sequence, causing two adjacent glycine residues in the putative NADPH binding site to be substituted to the sequence of serine–proline. The resulting strain produced, as predicted, a novel erythromycin analog with a double bond at the C-6 position (**25**). These results indicated that the modular PKSs are tolerant to changes not only in their own architecture but also in the structure of the nascent polyketide chain. It should be noted, however, that attempts to generate structurally modified products through inactivation of the only DH domain (in module 4) were unsuccessful. In a study employing the *S. coelicolor* CH999/pCK7 system, the KR domain of module 2 in a construct carrying DEBS1 + module 3 + TE was replaced with the DH–KR didomain of module 4 of the rapamycin PKS. The resulting strain produced the acyclic tetraketides **26** and **27**, both of which contain a double bond in their structure as specified by the DH domain (Fig. 5).

## 2. Changes in Extender Units

All six AT domains (not including the first AT domain at the NH₂ terminus of DEBS1) in DEBS bind methylmalonyl-CoA. In a study employing *S. erythraea*, three malonyl-CoA-specific AT domains from other PKSs, designated RAPS AT14, VenAT2, and "Hyg" AT2, were used to replace the AT domains in modules 1 and 2 of DEBS (Fig. 5). The resulting mutants were found to produce either 12-desmethylerythromycin (**28**; for module 1 replacements) or 10-desmethylerythromycin (**29**; for module 2 replacements), indicating that malonyl-CoA, instead of the methylmalonyl-CoA extender unit, was incorporated at the expected positions. In a later study involving the same system, the AT domain in module 5 of the niddamycin PKS which specifies for ethylmalonyl-CoA (based on analysis of the niddamycin structure) was used to replace the AT domain in module 4 of DEBS (Fig. 5). At first, no production of the predicted 6-desmethyl-6-ethylerythromycin A (6-ethylErA) (**30**) was detected in the constructed mutant. However, the mutant did produce 6-ethyl-ErA when butyrate precursors were added to the medium. Further investigation revealed that the overexpression of crotonyl-CoA reductase, an enzyme catalyzing the reduction of crotonyl-CoA to butyryl-CoA, in the mutant could substitute for the exogenic addition of butyrate.

## 3. Changes in Starter Units

In *S. erythraea*, the natural starter unit for erythromycin synthesis is propionyl-CoA. Recently, the AT–ACP loading domain of DEBS was replaced with the AT–ACP loading domain of the avermectin PKS, resulting in the production of erythromycin analogs with isobutyrate or 2-methylbutyrate starter unit (Fig. 5, **31** and **32**). Since the loading domain of the avermectin PKS is known to have broad substrate specificity (it accepts more than 40 alternative small branched-chain fatty acids as starter units), a range of erythromycin analogs are expected to be generated with this mutant.

## 4. Changes in Polyketide Chain Length

Extensive studies have been performed for this category of genetic changes, both in *S. erythraea* and in the *S. coelicolor* CH999/pCK7 system. Most of the studies involved the deletion of large fragments of DNA and the repositioning of the TE domain. Mutants carrying DEBS1 + TE, DEBS1 + module 3 + TE, and DEBS1 + DEBS2 + module 5 + TE, respectively, were constructed and all yielded the expected products: triketides (**33** and **34**), tetraketides, and hexaketides (**35**), respectively (Fig. 5). These results indicated that modules and proteins of DEBS involved in early steps of the biosynthesis could function in the absence of those catalyzing later steps. The mutant carrying DEBS1 + TE, owing to its simple protein composition, has been used in many *in vitro* and *in vivo* studies.

## D. *In Vitro* Studies

All three DEBS proteins have been purified. Active *in vitro* systems have been developed using either the recombinant three-component (DEBS1–3) PKS or the engineered DEBS1 + TE protein. In an *in vitro* study using purified DEBS1–DEBS3 proteins, it was demonstrated that only the 2*S* and not the 2*R* stereoisomer of $^{14}$C-labeled methylmalonyl-CoA attached to the active sites of all the AT domains of the PKS subunits. This finding provides evidence for the use of only the 2*S* stereoisomer in chain extension of 6-dEB synthesis and suggests a racemization in the second, fifth, and sixth condensation cycles to give the *R* configurations found in 6-dEB. Two lines of biochemical studies involving either limited proteolysis or mutant complementation have led to the establishment of the dimeric structure of the modular PKSs.

## III. *β*-LACTAM ANTIBIOTICS

Classical *β*-lactam antibiotics, including penicillins (7), cephalosporins (40), and cephamycins (41), were among first bioactive natural products to be discovered from microorganisms and, despite the development of other families of antibiotics, still constitute a large fraction of antibiotics in clinical use. The core structure of these antibiotics is a two-fused ring heterocyclic system that is originally derived from a common tripeptide precursor, L-*δ*-(aminoadipoyl)-L-cysteinyl-D-valine (ACV). Although the biosynthetic pathway for *β*-lactam antibiotics has long been established, the enzyme catalyzing the first step of the biosynthesis (i.e., the formation of ACV) has only recently been identified as structurally and functionally related to the NRPSs.

### A. Biosynthetic Studies

Extensive biochemical studies have revealed that penicillins, cephalosporins, and cephamycins are derived from a common biosynthetic pathway (Fig. 6). An essential step in this pathway is the biosynthesis of the tripeptide ACV (36) by the enzyme ACV synthetase using L-*α*-aminoadipic acid, L-cysteine, and L-

valine as biosynthetic precursors. The next common step involves cyclization of ACV to form isopenicillin N (37) catalyzed by isopenicillin N synthase. The pathway diverges at this point in different producing organisms. In *Penicillium chrysogenum* and *Aspergillus nidulans,* the *α*-aminoadipate arm of isopenicillin N is removed and replaced with phenylacetic acid to form penicillin G (7). In other organisms, isopenicillin N undergoes epimerization and ring expansion to yield deacetoxycephalosporin C (DAOC; 39), which is then elaborated to either cephalosporin C (40) (*Cephalosporium acremonium*) or cephamycin C (41) (*Streptomyces clavuligerus*) through several additional enzyme-catalyzed steps.

The synthesis of tripeptide ACV has long been the subject of biochemical studies. ACV as the immediate precursor of isopenicillin N was established by the finding that a crude cell lysate of *C. acremonium* converted labeled ACV into isopenicillin N and penicillin N, with the former as the major product. The enhanced synthesis of ACV in the presence of agents that selectively inhibit protein synthesis indicated that ACV was synthesized by a mechanism independent of ribosomes. Studies using *C. acremonium* cell-free extracts demonstrated that ACV synthesis was $Mg^{2+}$–ATP dependent, presumably involving adenylation of individual amino acids. Although a D-configured valine (D-valine) was found in ACV, it was shown that only L-valine, and not D-valine, functioned as the substrate for ACV synthesis, suggesting an epimerization at either the di- or tripeptide level.

### B. Gene Cloning and Analysis

The first biosynthetic gene clusters for *β*-lactam antibiotics were cloned by screening the cosmid library of the chromosomal DNA of a producing organism for the ability to either restore antibiotic production in a pathway-blocked mutant or cause antibiotic synthesis in a nonproducing surrogate host. Many other gene clusters have subsequently been cloned through hybridization experiments using fragments of the thus-identified *β*-lactam biosynthetic genes as probes. In most cases, the genes required for the biosynthesis of a particular *β*-lactam antibiotic have been found to form a single cluster in which the putative ACV synthetase and isopenicillin N synthase genes, designated *pcb*AB and *pcb*C, respectively, are ubiquitously present. Depending on the nature of the final product, an individual cluster also contains genes encoding enzymes involved in the later stages of the biosynthetic pathway (Fig. 6).

The structural relationship of the ACV synthetase gene with other NRPS genes (Fig. 7) as revealed by sequence analysis was unexpected because for many years ACV was thought to be synthesized in an analogous fashion to glutathione biosynthesis. Although the enzymes responsible for synthesizing glutathione are two separate, monofunctional proteins, all the

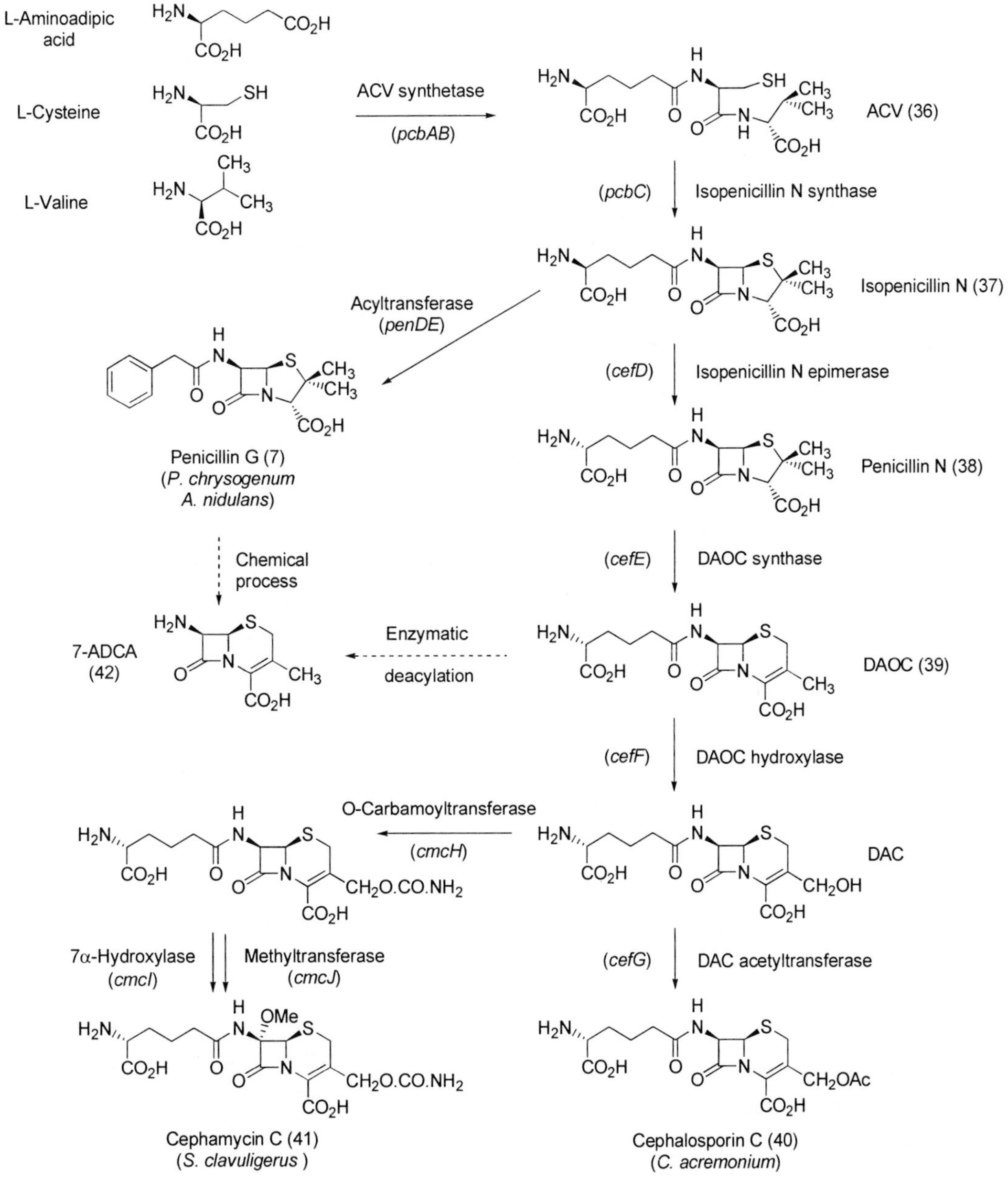

**Fig. 6.** Biosynthetic pathways for penicillins, cephalosporins, and cephamycins. Production of 7-amino-deacetoxycephalosporanic acid (7-ADCA), either by a chemical process using penicillin G as the starting material or through enzymatic deacylation of DAOC, is also shown. ACV, L-$\delta$-(aminoadipoyl)-L-cysteinyl-D-valine; DAOC, deacetoxycephalosporin C; DAC, deacetylcephalosporin C.

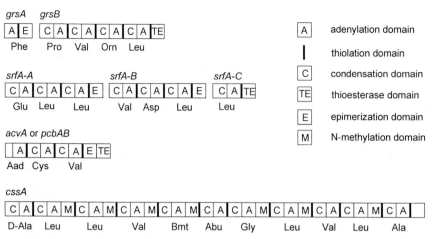

**Fig. 7.** Schematic presentation of the modular organization of nonribosomal peptide synthetases encoded by the bacterial operons *grs* [gramicidin S (**8**)] and *srfA* [surfactin (**9**)] as well as the fungal genes *acvA* or *pcbAB* [ACV (**36**)] and *cssA* [cyclosporin A (**10**)]. Orn, ornithine; Bmt, (4R)-[(E)-2-butenyl-4-methyl-L-threonine]; Abu, L-α-amino butyric acid.

known synthetases involved in nonribosomal peptide biosynthesis have been established as modularly organized, multifunctional polypeptides (see Section IV). Analogous to other NRPSs, the inferred primary sequence of the ACV synthetase gene exhibits three-fold internal homology with three distinct modules (Fig. 7). The three modules all contain adenylation (A) and thiolation (T) domains, presumably for activating and acylating amino acid substrates. The second and third modules also carry a condensation (C) domain at their NH₂ ends, consistent with the peptide bond formation at these stages of the biosynthesis. The epimerization (E) domain present in the third module apparently catalyzes the epimerization of L-valine to D-valine at the peptide stage. Finally, the putative thioesterase (TE) domain found at the C-terminal end of ACV synthetase is probably involved in the release of ACV from the enzyme.

## C. Genetic Manipulation of β-Lactam Biosynthetic Genes

Interest in genetic manipulation of β-lactam biosynthetic genes has been in large part focused on strain improvement and pathway engineering. In a study on cephalosporin C production, a high-level producing strain of *C. acremonium* was found to accumulate penicillin N (**38**) in its fermentation broth. The assumption that this was caused by a rate-limiting DAOC synthase (DAOCS) reaction was tested by introducing into this strain additional copies of the previously cloned *C. acremonium* DAOCS gene (Fig. 6). Many of the resulting transformants exhibited a 50% increase in cephalosporin C production.

7-Aminodeacetoxycephalosporanic acid (7-ADCA; **42**) is a precursor for several clinically important cephalosporins and is currently produced from penicillin G through chemical ring expansion followed by enzymatic deacylation (Fig. 6). Fermentative production of DAOC, which can then be enzymatically deacylated to 7-ADCA, is of interest since the chemical process uses large quantities of expensive, environmentally undesirable solvents. One approach to this problem has been to introduce the isopenicillin N epimerase gene (*cef*D) from *Strep-tomyces lipmanii* and the DAOCS gene (*cef*E) from *S. clavuligerus* into the penicillin high producer *P. chrysogenum*. Stable transformants producing detectable levels of DAOC were obtained in this manner. It has been suggested that additional increases in the levels of DAOC may be accomplished by blocking conversion of isopenicillin N to penicillin G by deletion of appropriate *pen*DE genes.

## D. *In Vitro* Studies

ACV synthetase has recently been isolated from *A. nidulans, C. acremonium,* and *S. clavuligerus* as a large multifunctional protein, providing firm evidence for the proposal that ACV is synthesized in a manner similar to that for nonribosomal peptide antibiotics. Biochemical studies using the purified ACV synthetase have confirmed many of the early findings about ACV biosynthesis, such as the use of only the L-isomer of the three amino acids and the $Mg^{2+}$–ATP dependence of the process. Some surprising new aspects, such as the formation of the C-terminal dipeptide L-cysteinyl-D-valine even in the presence of L-aminoadipic acid, have also been revealed by these studies.

Recently, the crystal structure of isopenicillin N synthase, both in the absence and the presence of ferrous iron and ACV, has been determined. A mechanism for penicillin formation based on the structure has been proposed. According to this mechanism, the formation of isopenicillin N begins with the ligation of ACV to the iron center (formed by binding of one Asp, two His and one Gln residues with the metal iron) of the enzyme, creating a vacant iron coordination site. Subsequently, dioxygen binds into this site, followed by removal of the requisite hydrogens from ACV by iron-dioxygen and iron-oxo species.

## IV. NONRIBOSOMAL PEPTIDE ANTIBIOTICS

Synthesized by a common mechanism independent of ribosomes, this group of antibiotics is structurally distinct from ribosomal-derived peptides/polypeptides. First, the amino acid precursors used to make nonribosomal peptides are exceedingly diverse, including pseudo, nonproteinogenic, hydroxy, N-methylated, and D-configured amino acids. Second, the backbone of nonribosomal peptides can assume a range of acyclic, cyclic, and cyclic branched structures that can be further elaborated by acylation, glycosylation, or heterocyclic ring formation. Structures of some nonribosomal peptide antibiotics are shown in Fig. 1, including gramicidin S (**8**), surfactin (**9**), and cyclosporin A (**10**).

## A. Biosynthetic Studies

Much of the knowledge concerning NRPSs was obtained from early biosynthetic studies, particularly those that focused on gramicidin S, tyrocidine, and linear gramicidin, produced by different strains of *Bacillus brevis.* For example, it was established based on the results of ATP–PPi and ATP–AMP exchange reactions that a two-step mechanism is required for activation of individual amino acids. In the first step, the cognate amino acid is activated as aminoacyl adenylate at the expense of $Mg^{2+}$–ATP. In the second step, an enzyme-bound thiol moiety reacts with the aminoacyl adenylate to form an aminoacyl thioester and AMP as products. Evidence for the formation of enzyme-bound aminoacyl thioesters includes the sensitivity of peptide synthesis to the thiol-blocking agent N-ethylmaleamide and the recovery of radioactive label from the trichloracetic acid precipitated synthetases after incubation with ATP and [14]C-labeled amino acids. The origin of the enzyme-bound thiol moieties was thought to be the cysteine residues at the active sites. It is now widely accepted, based on sequence analysis results, that these groups are in fact from the 4′-phosphopantetheine (4′-PP) arms covalently attached to peptide synthetases.

## B. Gene Cloning and Analysis

Numerous bacterial and fungal genes encoding NRPSs have been cloned, sequenced, and partially characterized. Strategies used for cloning these genes include complementation of pathway-blocked mutants, hybridization to the oligonucleotide probes derived from peptide synthetase gene fragments, and probing of expression libraries with antibodies raised against peptide synthetases. In addition, polymerase chain reaction (PCR) technology has recently been utilized to directly amplify NRPS genes from the genomic DNA by using degenerate oligonucleotide primers corresponding to the strictly conserved motifs in peptide synthetases.

Structural organizations of several bacterial and fungal NRPSs as revealed by the translated sequences of their cognate genes are shown in Fig. 7. Strikingly, all the NRPSs characterized to date are, without exception, multifunctional enzymes and show the modular organization analogous to that of the type I polyketide synthases (see Section II). Each module carries a set of catalytic functions (domains) required for activation, acylation, and, if applicable, modification of the cognate amino acid. The number of modules in a NRPS is the same as the number of amino acid precursors used to build the corresponding peptide antibiotic. In bacteria, these modules are unevenly distributed among several peptide synthetases, whereas in fungal systems all modules are integrated into a single polypeptide.

Adenylation (A), thiolation (T), condensation (C) and thioesterase (TE) functional domains are found within all NRPSs (Fig. 7). An A domain and a T domain are required for each module. The A domains, approximately 550 amino acids in length, represent an essential mechanistic core of an NRPS. They are responsible for recognition and activation of amino acid substrates. It is the specificity of these A domains that dictates the primary structure of the peptide antibiotic to be made. The T or peptidyl carrier protein domains are approximately 100 amino acids in length. Their function is similar to that of ACP in modular PKSs; they are the sites of 4′-PP cofactor binding and substrate acylation. The next functional domains of NRPSs, i.e., the C domains, are found between consecutive modules. The role of the C domains in peptide bond formation (polymerization) was first proposed based on their locations in NRPs and has recently been verified through recombinant experiments. The TE domains, either integrated into or associated with NRPSs, are thought to catalyze the release of peptide chain from the synthetase systems. In addition to these functional domains, two modifying domains, designated epimerization (E) and N-methylation (M) domains, have been found in the NRPSs whose peptide product contains D-configured or N-methylated amino acids (Fig. 7).

## C. Genetic Manipulation of Nonribosomal Peptide Synthetases

Compared to modular PKSs, reports on genetic manipulation of NRPSs to produce novel peptide compounds have been relatively limited. In a recent

study, the substrate specificity of a peptide synthetase was successfully changed at the genetic level. The target enzyme was surfactin synthetase 3 (SrfA-C; Fig. 7), which normally integrates L-leucine at the position 7 in the cyclic lipopeptide antibiotic surfactin (Fig. 1, 9). SrfA-C is a single-module synthetase carrying the four functional domains in the order of C-A-T-TE (Fig. 7). By using a two-step recombination method, a series of hybrid *srfA-C* genes were introduced into the chromosomal SrfA-C site of a surfactin-producing strain of *Bacillus subtilis*. These hybrid *srfA-C* genes were constructed by integrating the coding regions of various [A-T] modules of bacterial and fungal origin between the original C and TE domains of *srfA-C*. Such hybrid genes would encode SrfA-C derivatives (C-[A-T]-TE) with altered substrate specificity, as determined by the heterologous adenylation domain. Mutants of *B. subtilis* carrying the hybrid *srfA-C* genes were found to produce structurally modified surfactin analogs as expected.

## D. *In Vitro* Studies

One of the most significant advances in this category has been the determination of the crystal structure of the adenylation domain, designated PheA, of gramicidin S synthetase 1 (GrsA) in a complex with AMP and L-phenylalanine. Folded into a large N-terminal and a smaller C-terminal subdomain, the structure was found to have an overall topology highly similar to the crystal structure of firefly luciferase, although the two proteins share only 16% identity in their primary sequences. It was argued that the adenylation domains of other peptide synthetases would have a very similar structure. Analysis of the crystal structure of PheA revealed that almost all the core motifs (the best conserved short amino acid sequences designated A1–A10) of the A domain are positioned around the active site where the substrates are bound. In particular, the hydrophobic L-Phe binding pocket is located in the region between the core motifs A3 and A6, which consist of seven aliphatic amino acids. This finding provides an opportunity to rationally alter substrate specificity, and thereby the structure of the peptide antibiotic, through site-directed mutagenesis.

## See Also the Following Articles

<small>Polyketide Antibiotics • Secondary Metabolites</small>

## Bibliography

Cane, D. E. (Ed.) (1997). Polyketide and nonribosomal poly-peptide biosynthesis [Special issue]. *Chem. Rev.* **97**, 2463–2705.

Cane, D. E., Walsh, C. T., and Khosla, C. (1998). *Science* **282**, 63–68.

Hopwood, D. A., and Sherman, D. H. (1990). *Annu. Rev. Genet.* **24**, 37–66.

Hutchinson, C. R., and Fuji, I. (1995). *Annu. Rev. Microbiol.* **49**, 201–238.

Katz, L., and Donadio, S. (1993). *Anuu. Rev. Microbiol.* **47**, 875–912.

Leadlay, P. F. (1997). *Curr. Opin. Chem. Biol.* **1**, 162–168.

Martin, J. F. (1998). *Appl. Microbiol. Biotechnol.* **50**, 1–15.

Mootz, H. D., and Marahiel, M. A. (1997). *Curr. Opin. Chem. Biol.* **1**, 543–551.

Strohl, W. R. (Ed.) (1997). "Biotechnology of Antibiotics" (2nd ed.). Dekker, New York.

# Antibodies and B Cells

## Ian M. Zitron

*William Beaumont Hospital, Royal Oak, MI*

## GLOSSARY

**antigen** A molecule that can be specifically bound by antibodies.

**apoptosis** Programmed cell death. A death pathway which involves the activation of cellular enzymes and results in the death of the cell by organellar disruption, while the plasma membrane remains intact, preventing the release of cellular contents. Morphologically, apoptotic cells show nuclear condensation, swollen mitochondria, and membrane blebs. An end-stage event is the degradation of nuclear DNA by an activated cellular endonuclease. The engagement of Fas (CD95) on the B cell by Fas ligand (FasL) on a different cell is one pathway by which apoptosis can be induced; Fas-independent induction of apoptosis also occurs.

**class II MHC antigens** Cell membrane glycoproteins that are crucial to immune regulation. They are expressed on macrophages, dendritic cells, and B cells, where they form an integral part of the complex in which peptide antigens are presented to T helper cells.

**cluster of differentiation (CD) antigen** As cells develop, they express a variety of molecules which are identifiable by specific antibodies. Some of these antigenic molecules are unique to a particular cell type, while others are shared by a number of cell types. In an attempt to standardize nomenclature, many of these molecules have been given CD numerical designations. Over 100 CD antigens have been defined.

**combinatorial joining** The process by which a relatively small number of gene segments can be recombined to give a large number of full-length, functional genes. This is the mechanism by which diversity is generated in the variable region genes for both immunoglobulins and T cell receptors. Also applied to the independent assortment of full-length heavy and light chains, such that the variable regions of any heavy chain and any light chain can associate to form a combining site. In all cases, the principle is the same: Assume that a complete molecule is composed of two components, $a$ and $b$; let the available number of each be $n_a$ and $n_b$; then the total number of possible complete molecules is given by the product ($n_a \times n_b$).

**complement** A system of plasma proteins. These proteins function as a cascade and, when antibodies of certain classes are bound to the surface of a cell, they can initiate the cascade, which results in the lysis of that target cell. The process is called complement fixation. The antibody-dependent form of this is called the classical pathway; other, antibody-independent pathways, the alternate and Mannan-binding lectin pathways, also exist.

**determinant or epitope** Antigen or immunogen are designations usually applied to large molecules. From the perspective of the lymphocytes, however, neither of these words is sufficiently precise, since the antigen-specific receptors of a single cell are capable of binding only a small region on the larger molecule. An individual small region of a molecule to which an antibody can bind is called a determinant or epitope. These can be either sequential or conformational.

**germinal centers (GC)** Sites of B cell proliferation and somatic hypermutation (see following), found in spleen and lymph nodes after immunization. Germinal centers are also the sites in which memory B cells are generated and class-switching occurs.

**hapten** In order to form an antigen–antibody complex that will precipitate, both the antibody and the antigen used must be at least bivalent. A hapten is a small, monovalent molecule that may be bound by specific antibody but that will not form a precipitating complex. Hapten molecules are also capable of inhibiting precipitate formation when added to a mixture of antibody and bivalent antigen.

**hybridoma**   Somatic cell hybrid formed between a normal B cell and a B cell tumor called a myeloma. The normal B cell provides the genetic information to produce a particular antibody, while the myeloma cell provides immortality. These characteristics combine to yield a cell that can be grown long-term in tissue culture or as a tumor in animals. In each case, the result is a system that produces large amounts of homogeneous antibody.

**immunogen**   A molecule that is capable of eliciting an immune response when introduced into an immunologically naive animal.

**memory**   The ability of the immune system to respond faster and more vigorously to the second (or third) exposure to an antigen, compared to its response to the first, or primary, exposure. This phenomenon is due to the generation of populations of memory cells at the time of primary immunization.

**opsonization**   Coating of an antigen, either by antibody alone or antibody plus complement components. These greatly increase phagocytosis by cells of the reticuloendothelial system.

**phagocytic cell or phagocyte**   From the Greek, meaning "eating cell." A designation given to cells such as macrophages (large eaters), which can engulf and destroy particles, such as bacteria. The engulfment process is called Phagocytosis.

**phenotype**   The collective expression of the genome. In the context of B cell development, this is usually used to indicate the set of expressed molecules which define a particular stage of development.

**RAG (Recombination Activating Genes) genes**   The protein products of these genes catalyze the DNA recombinations that give rise to the variable domains of immunoglobulin chains and, therefore, form the specific binding sites on antibody molecules. These genes are expressed only in cells of the lymphocytic lineage, during their early development. They also perform a similar function in developing T cells, where they are responsible for DNA rearrangements leading to the expression of the T cell receptors.

**repertoire**   The total number of distinct binding sites that a individual organism can generate either in antibody or T cell receptor combining sites.

**somatic mutation (hypermutation)**   A process in which mutations are introduced into the DNA encoding the variable domains of antibody chains. Takes place after stimulation of the B cells by antigen and requires the activity of helper T cells. The mutations preferentially occur in the variable regions and have the effect of changing the specificity and binding strength of the antibody molecules. This, coupled with a selection process, results in a population of B cells, and, therefore, antibody molecules, which bind the antigen more tightly, resulting in the more rapid and efficient clearance of pathogens or their products. The process results in what is called affinity maturation. Since the mutation rate observed in the variable domains is several orders of magnitude higher than that generally seen in mammalian DNA, it is often referred to as hypermutation.

**specific(ity)**   The ability to identify unambiguously. In the context of immunity, this is reflected in the ability of the system to discriminate between different antigens. The antigens may be significantly different, e.g., influenza and poliomyelitis viruses; or they may be very similar, e.g., human blood group substances A and B, which differ only in an amino ($-NH_2$) group on the terminal monosaccharide.

**titer**   A measure of the concentration of specific antibodies in a serum sample. This is frequently expressed as the reciprocal of the highest dilution of the serum at which specific antibodies can be detected.

**ANTIBODIES AND B CELLS**   form the humoral arm of the immune system, the function of which is to provide a defense against foreign substances, such as bacteria, virus particles, and toxins in the extracellular compartment. B cells are lymphocytes which are found in the tonsils, spleen, and lymph nodes, and circulating in the blood. Antibodies are glycoproteins secreted by B cells. When a foreign substance enters the body, a small fraction of the B cells bind it, by virtue of specific membrane receptors. The binding event activates these B cells and initiates a process which results in the high-rate production of antibodies that appear in the serum, interstitial fluids, and mucous secretions. The antibodies produced have binding sites of the same specificity as the B cells and these bind the foreign substance, resulting in its elimination.

The issues considered in this article are the structure, function, and genetics of antibodies; the origin and development of B cells prior to the introduction of foreign substances; activation events and their consequences for B cells; pathological states directly involving B cells; and the uses of antibodies in microbiology and medicine.

## I. INTRODUCTION

In response to the introduction of foreign substances, such as viral or bacterial infection, the acquired immune response is capable of mounting two separate and distinct effector responses. These are designated humoral and cell-mediated immunity (CMI). The names have their historical origins in a nineteenth-century dispute between two schools, the "Humoralists" and "Cellularists." The former held the view that soluble "humors" (which we now know to be antibodies) were the principal protective factors. In contrast, the latter argued that protection was largely the domain of cells, in particular, phagocytic cells. We now know that that both schools were correct and that protective immunity is a consequence of the activity of lymphocytes, in collaboration with other cells. Both humoral immunity and CMI contribute to immune protection, with one or the other of these being more efficient, depending upon the insult or pathogen introduced into the body. The humoral immune response is the focus of this article.

A description of the immune response should begin with the Clonal Selection Hypothesis, originally proposed by Macfarlane Burnet. Briefly, Burnet proposed that, during the development of the immune system, many independent clones (families) of lymphocytes arise. The members of each clone are characterized by the expression of plasma membrane receptors of a single antigen-binding specificity. The developmental steps leading up to receptor expression are independent of, and occur prior to, any encounter with the antigen(s) for which the receptors show specificity; that is, the process is antigen-independent. Consequently, when an immunogenic substance is introduced, lymphocytes bearing receptors which can bind to epitopes on it are already present within the pool of cells. The lymphocytes with receptors having the best fit for the foreign molecule are selected for response and become activated, as a consequence of the receptor binding events. Those lymphocytes which are not selected by antigen remain

quiescent. Figure 1 depicts Clonal Selection. In the upper half of the illustration, two receptor structures, R1 and R2, are capable of binding the antigen, permitting clonal selection to occur. When the identical receptors are confronted with different antigens, binding fails to occur and the cells remain unstimulated. Specificity and memory are defining characteristics of the immune system, (see Glossary). Memory is very much like that observed in the functioning of the nervous system: the ability to recognize, and respond to, the second (or third, etc.) exposure to a foreign substance in a way which is both quantitatively and qualitatively different from the response to the first, or primary, exposure. Both specificity and memory are crucial for the effective function of B cells and, together, they form the underlying basis for the efficacy of vaccination and long-term immune protection.

The ability to distinguish between self and non-self and to react against the latter may be identified

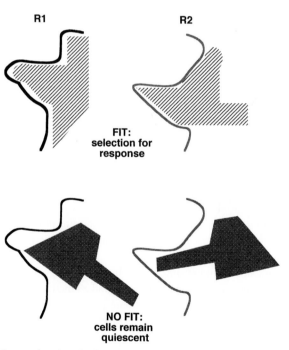

**R1**          **R2**

**FIT:
selection for
response**

**NO FIT:
cells remain
quiescent**

*Fig. 1.* The clonal selection hypothesis, originally proposed by Macfarlane Burnet. The antigen-binding sites on two receptors, R1 and R2, have distinctive shapes. Only when antigen fits the combining site is the B cell clone selected for response. If the same receptor structures are presented with antigen to which they do not bind, the cells remain quiescent.

as early in evolution as sponges. Thus, a possible evolutionary precursor of the acquired immune response appeared very early. Studies of invertebrates have shown that the immunity they manifest appears to resemble CMI, rather than humoral immunity. It is only when one reaches the vertebrates that humoral immunity per se is identifiable. Examining vertebrates, fish have been shown to express only one class of immunoglobulin, which resembles a mammalian class called IgM. Diversification of other heavy chain classes occurred later in evolution, with birds, frogs, and toads having three classes. The immune systems of mammals have evolved to produce five heavy chain classes with, depending upon the species, varying numbers of subclasses.

B cells arise from precursor cells in the bone marrow. Upon completion of development, mature B cells emigrate to the spleen, lymph nodes, and other secondary lymphoid organs where, should they encounter the foreign substance for which their receptors are specific, they become activated from their resting state to become the effector cells of humoral immunity. Their secreted products, antibodies, are the effector molecules of the humoral immune response. Within a population of lymphocytes, one can identify individual lineages and subpopulations by the presence of characteristic plasma membrane molecules. B cells are most readily identified by the presence of membrane immunoglobulin (mIg) molecules, the receptors by which activation is initiated and which are responsible for the specificity of the humoral response. The binding specificity of an individual B cell's mIg receptors is identical to that of the first antibodies which that clone of B cells will secrete. This ensures the continuity of antigen-binding specificity between the initiating event at the B cell surface and the systemic protection provided by the secreted antibodies.

## II. ANTIBODIES

### A. Function

The function of antibodies is to bind antigens and mediate their removal from the organism. The array of antigens to which antibodies can be produced is enormous and includes bacteria and their toxins, virions, parasites and soluble proteins, carbohydrates, lipids, and nucleic acids. Because antibodies are large, globular molecules, they cannot penetrate living cells and their protective function is restricted to the extracellular milieu. This milieu includes the plasma and the interstitial fluids, which contain antibodies secreted by the systemic immune system. In addition, the mucosal immune system functions in parallel to protect the mucosal surfaces of the body, which include the gastrointestinal, respiratory and urogenital tracts, the eye, and glandular tissues, such as the mammary glands.

As will be described in greater detail, each antibody molecule has two or more antigen-binding sites, which are responsible for the specific capture of the antigen. The sites are located in the so-called variable regions of the molecule, which comprise around 30% of the total mass. Comparison of variable region amino acid sequences between different antibodies show, as the name suggests, enormous variability. This is reflected in the large number of distinct, specific sites, estimated to be $10^8$–$10^9$, which can be made by the immune system. The remainder of the molecule is made up of the constant regions. The heavy-chain constant regions (see Fig. 2) are responsible for the biological functions of the molecule, which include complement fixation, opsonization, and the ability of some antibody classes to cross the placenta to provide protection to the developing fetus *in utero*.

### B. Structure

All antibodies are proteins of the class immunoglobulins. The words "antibody" and "immunoglobulin" are not synonymous, although they are frequently used interchangeably. While all antibodies are immunoglobulins, and we believe each immunoglobulin is an antibody with the capacity to bind a specific ligand, the problem is that the universe of potential ligands is so enormous that the latter statement is untestable. Consequently, the word "antibody" should be used only when the binding specificity is known, while the word "immunoglobulin" refers to the entire class of proteins, regardless of whether one knows the binding specificity.

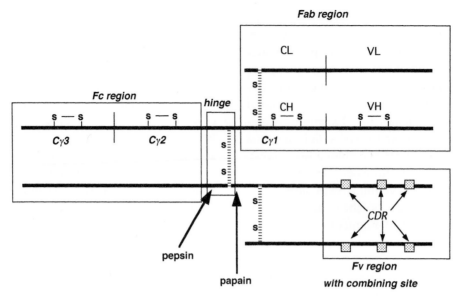

**Fig. 2.** Stick diagram of the basic, four-chain IgG molecule. The two halves of each molecule are identical, each consisting of one heavy and one light chain, shown by thick, solid lines. The chains are linked by disulfide bonds, shown as hatched vertical lines. The heavy and light chains each consist of two regions, a variable region (labeled, respectively, VH and VL) and a constant region (labeled CH and CL). Each variable region contains three stretches of amino acid sequences called the complementarity determining regions (CDRs). In the intact molecule, or an antigen-binding fragment derived therefrom, the VH and VL fold together such that the CDRs come together to form a surface which makes contact with the antigen molecule, effecting binding. The three boxed regions shown (labeled Fab, Fv, and Fc) are fragments which can be obtained by enzymatic digestion. While an Fab or Fv fragment is monovalent, i. e., has only one binding site, the four-chain Ig molecule is bivalent.

The structure of IgG was solved by Edelman and Porter. Edelman showed that reduction and alkylation of IgG gave rise to two molecules of different sizes: H and L chains. Porter used digestion with pepsin and papain to demonstrate bivalency of antigen combining sites and the relative homogeneity of the Fc region. Fab, antigen-binding fragment; Fv, variable fragment; Fc, crystallizible fragment.

Immunoglobulins are glycoproteins with a common structural organization, based upon a four-chain assembly of two large (heavy, or H) and two small (light, or L) chains, the chains being held together by interchain disulfide bonds; this is often referred to as the basic $H_2L_2$ unit (Fig. 2). The studies defining the structure of IgG were performed by Porter and Edelman, working independently; for their work, they shared the Nobel Prize in 1972. Within each $H_2L_2$ unit, the two H chains are identical to each other, as are the two L chains. Each chain itself is built of smaller units, approximately 110 amino acids in length, designated domains. An immunoglobulin domain has characteristic features, including a $\beta$-pleated sheet structure held together by an intradomain disulfide bond. A full-length L chain contains two domains, while an H chain has 4 or 5.

Sequencing of purified H and L chains from many different immunoglobulins has revealed that, in each chain, the N-terminal domains show enormous sequence diversity; these are the variable (V) domains. In contrast, the remainder of each chain shows relatively limited diversity, when the immunoglobulins are obtained from a single species; these are the Constant (C) domains of the molecule. With respect to function, antibody molecules demonstrate exquisite specificity of binding to their particular antigen. The antigen-binding function is the property of the combining sites, each of which is composed of one H chain variable domain (abbreviated VH) and one L chain variable domain (abbreviated VL). The two V domains fold together, forming a surface complementary to the antigen. More detailed examination of V domain amino-acid sequences revealed that, within each, there are three stretches which show even greater sequence diversity, when many different Ig chains are aligned. These were originally designated "hypervariable" regions. Kabat hypothesized that these were the sections of the V regions which formed the binding site proper and actually made contact with the antigen. He proposed the name "complementary determining regions" (CDRs) for them, since he predicted that they would prove to be the amino-acid residues which formed a surface complementary to the antigen. This prediction has been borne out by a number of experimental approaches. The tremendous sequence diversity observed in V regions explains much of the ability of the immune system to generate a large number of distinct combining sites (of the order of $10^8–10^9$). Processes at two distinct stages permit the B cell population to express this repertoire of combining sites. During the development of B cells from precursors, the genes for full-length Ig chain V regions are assembled by the combinatorial joining of smaller gene segments present in the germ line. These recombinations are catalyzed by the products of the RAG genes. A second level of diversification occurs within the germinal center (GC), subsequent to antigen and helper T cell stimulation of the mature B cell. Dividing GC B cells accumulate mutations, leading to changes in antibody binding specificity. The mutations are found preferentially in the Ig V region-encoding DNA, as opposed to the C region sequences. The rate of mutation is several orders of magnitude higher than that seen in the genomes of other somatic cells. The process is referred to as "somatic hypermutation." Antigens are held in the combining site by a large number of noncovalent, short-range interactions. These include electrostatic forces, hydrophobic interactions, hydrogen bonds, and Van der Waal's forces. The total binding strength is the sum of these. Since the forces are noncovalent,

antibody–antigen interactions are reversible and can reach an equilibrium position, which can be described by the Law of Mass Action. When a monovalent hapten is used to measure binding, each combining sites acts independently and the binding strength measured is termed "affinity." Antibody combining sites have affinities in the range $10^5–10^{11}$ liters/mole. Use of a multivalent antigen for measurement gives the antibody's "avidity," a reflection of binding by more than one combining site.

Each $H_2L_2$ unit contains two identical binding sites, i.e., the molecule is bivalent. In many antibodies, the stretch of the H chain in the region of the H–L disulfide bond is very flexible, forming the hinge region. Pathogens often have multiple copies of particular proteins or carbohydrates on their surfaces and the bivalency of the antibody and the flexible hinge region permit a single antibody to bridge two pathogens, such as virus particles. This starts the formation of immune complexes of antibody plus antigen. Phagocytic cells, such as macrophages, remove such complexes from the body, degrading both the antibody and the pathogen. Phagocytosis is more efficient for complexes containing multiple antibody molecules, since phagocytes bind the aggregated heavy chain constant region domains. Thus, the bivalency of the antibody and the flexible hinge contribute to the efficiency of a constant region-mediated event. Other biological properties, such as the fixation of complement and the ability to cross the placenta are also properties of the C regions of the H chains. Both sequencing and serological studies have shown that there are a limited number of classes of immunoglobulins: five H chain classes in mammals, with different numbers of subclasses depending upon the species. The individual classes of H chains are designated by (lower case) letters of the Greek alphabet, with the class of the complete immunoglobulin molecule being indicated by its corresponding (upper case) English alphabet equivalent. For example, immunoglobulins of the IgG class have $\gamma$(gamma) heavy chains. The class and biological properties of an immunoglobulin molecule are dictated solely by the H chain C region. However, two classes of L chain C region, $\kappa$ and $\lambda$, are also identifiable. Some of the characteristics of immunoglobulins are shown in Table I.

*TABLE I*
**Characteristics of the Immunoglobulin Heavy Chain Classes**[a]

| Immunoglobulin | Heavy chain class | Molecular form (kDa) | Molecular mass | Predominance |
|---|---|---|---|---|
| IgM | $\mu$ | $(\mu_2 L_2)_5$[b] | 900 | Primary responses |
| mIgM | $\mu$ | $\mu_2 L_2$ | 180 | Plasma membrane of B lineage cells from immature to mature, virgin stage |
| IgG | $\gamma$[c] | $\gamma_2 L_2$ | 160 | Anamnestic responses; highest concentration of Ig classes in serum; membrane receptor on IgG memory cells |
| IgA | $\alpha$ | $(\alpha_2 L_2)_2 / SC$[d] | 320 | Secretions (some serum) |
| IgE | $\varepsilon$ | $\varepsilon_2 L_2$ | 200 | Found on mast cells; lowest serum concentration of any of the Ig classes |
| IgD | $\delta$ | $\delta_2 L_2$ and $\delta L$ | 185 | Mature, virgin B cells; very low serum concentration |

[a] In addition to the heavy chain classes, there are two classes of light chains: $\kappa$ and $\lambda$. Each of the heavy chain classes may associate with either one of the light chain classes.

[b] The pentameric, secreted IgM molecule is held together by a small protein molecule, called J chain. This is synthesized by the antibody-producing cell, in addition to the chains of the IgM. J chain is also found in other polymeric molecules, such as dimeric IgA.

[c] Subclasses of heavy chains exist. For example, in the mouse, there are four $\gamma$ subclasses, designated $\gamma 1$, $\gamma 2a$, $\gamma 2b$, and $\gamma 3$. The Ig molecules in which these appear are called, respectively, IgG1, IgG2a, IgG2b, and IgG3.

[d] To enter secretions, IgA must be transported across an epithelial surface. The transport mechanism involves an additional molecule, called secretory component (SC), which is produced by the epithelial cells.

## C. Genetics

In B cells, immunoglobulin genes undergo the physical rearrangements of DNA which permit antibody production, while, in other cell types, they exist in the unrearranged, germ line configuration. DNA rearrangements occur in an ordered manner as B cells develop from precursors. Three different chromosomes bear genes encoding Ig chains; one locus each for H (human chromosome 14), $\kappa$ (human chr. 2), and $\lambda$ (human chr. 22). Independent rearrangements can be identified in each locus. Each locus contains discrete sets of gene segments. In the H chain cluster, there are three such sets, V segments, D segments, and J segments, as well as the constant region genes. The $\kappa$ and $\lambda$ clusters each contain V segments and J segments and constant region genes. During B cell development, rearrangements occur which assemble genes for full-length Ig chains from individual components. The first published experiments describing this were by Tonegawa; for this work, he was awarded the Nobel Prize in 1987. The variable domain of the heavy chain protein is encoded by three gene segments, one from each of V, D, and J pools. These are brought together by

recombination to a position immediately 5' to the $\mu$ chain constant region DNA. These events produce a gene which encodes a full-length H chain protein. This depicted in Fig. 3. The diversity in VH regions is an outcome of combinatorial association, because there are multiple individual segment genes. In a single locus, then, the potential number of full length V domain genes is the product of the numbers of genes for each of the individual segments. For example, the human VH locus has been estimated to contain 51 functional VH segments, 30 DH, and 6 JH. These have the potential to give rise to >9000 combinations from a germ line pool of 87 gene segments. A similar process occurs during rearrangement at the light chain eoci, again generating considerable diversity. Since an antibody-combining site is composed of a VH and a VL domain, the total number of potential germ line-encoded combining sites is the product (VH × VL). The total number of sites is, in fact, far greater than this. Additional mechanisms, such as imprecise joining during recombination, N-regions in the H chain (see following) and the ability of the D segment genes to be read in all 3 frames represent aspects of germ line diversification, while postactivation somatic hypermutation acts upon re-

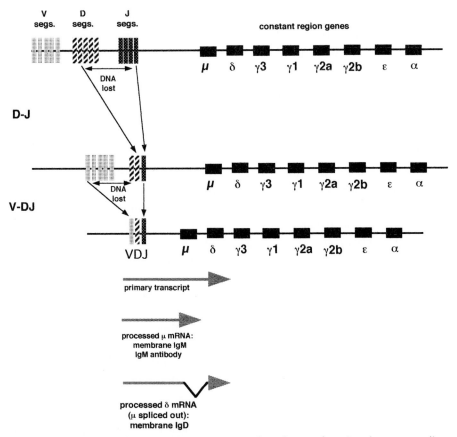

**Fig. 3.** Recombination between gene segments gives rise to a functional gene encoding a VH domain. The H chain locus contains multiple V, D and J segment genes. The first recombination brings a D segment and a J segment gene together, with loss of intervening DNA. The second event recombines in a V segment gene with, again, loss of intervening DNA. This results in an assembled VDJ upstream of the first H chain constant region gene, C$\mu$. The primary RNA transcript from this is able to give rise to both IgM and IgD by alternative processing.

arranged genes, changing the specificity and affinity of the antibodies produced.

DNA rearrangements can be identified by comparing B cell DNA with DNA from a tissue such as placenta. If placental DNA is digested with restriction endonucleases and the sizes of DNA fragments determined by Southern blotting and the use of hybridization probes for individual gene segments, one can see patterns characteristic of the unrearranged, germ line organization. If DNA from B cells is isolated and manipulated in parallel, the same probe shows hybridization to DNA fragments of different sizes, indicating that the target gene is present in a different context. The recombination events are catalyzed by

two proteins, designated RAG-1 and RAG-2; RAG is the acronym for "recombination activating gene."

B cells are, in common with all other somatic cells, diploid and contain two copies of each of the immunoglobulin gene loci. However, an individual B cell expresses only one combining site in its Ig molecules. That is, only one H chain locus (of two) and one L chain locus (of four) are expressed. This is termed "allelic exclusion." Successful rearrangement on one chromosome suppresses rearrangement of the allelic genes on its homolog, For Ig H chains, successful rearrangement to form a VH domain gene excludes the other H chain. For L chains, however, successful rearrangement of one locus excludes not only its homolog, but the other two L chain loci. Thus, if a full length Vκ gene is assembled, rearrangements in the other Vκ and both Vλ loci are prevented.

# III. B CELLS

## A. Antigen-Independent Development

All of the cellular elements of the blood and lymphoid system originate from pluripotential, hematopoietic stem cells. These cells are self-renewing, in that they can divide and give rise to daughter cells identical to the parent or, alternatively, give rise to cells which become progenitors committed to any one of the four developmental lineages found in blood and lymphoid tissue: erythroid, lymphocytic, granulocyte/macrophage, and megakaryocyte/platelet. The direction of commitment appears to be under the control of growth factors, which direct cellular development along particular pathways. The lymphoid progenitors give rise to both B cells and another, distinct, lymphocyte population, the T cells. The organ sites at which lymphocyte development occurs are referred to as the primary lymphoid organs. B cells are produced continuously throughout life. In adult mouse bone marrow, the rate of local production is around $5 \times 10^7$ cells/day; in humans, it is about 1000-fold higher. However, of this massive production, only 2–5% of the cells successfully emigrate to the periphery. The losses are probably due to failed recombinations in the Ig loci and the negative selection of B cells with mIg receptors specific for self components, both of which lead to cell death. Nonetheless, the B cell repertoire is continuously turning over, providing the potential for new antibody species to be generated throughout life.

Studies of B cell development were initiated by work performed in birds, which possess a discrete organ, the Bursa of Fabricius, located just above the cloaca, in which B cell development occurs. Removal of the Bursa immediately upon hatching renders birds incompetent for humoral immunity, without affecting their ability to mount CMI. One of the origins of the name "B cells" is from the word "bursa." Ontogenetic studies in birds showed that cells developing in the bursal follicles stained positively with fluorescein-conjugated antibodies specific for the Ig heavy-chain classes. The earliest mIg-positive cells bore mIgM only (referred to, hereafter, as mIgM-positive cells). As development proceeded, mIgG-positive cells could be identified and, finally, mIgA-positive cells. The sequential relationship between the various mIg-bearing populations and their ability to secrete antibodies of those classes was defined by showing that injection of anti-μ antibodies eliminated all humoral responses, presumably by their destructive effects on the mIgM-bearing cells. In contrast, injection of anti-γ antibodies left intact the ability to make IgM, but abolished the ability to make IgG and IgA. As might be expected, administration of anti-α abolished IgA production, but spared IgM and IgG. These experiments, thus, demonstrated that the mIgM-positive cells gave rise to the mIgG-bearers and that these gave rise to the mIgA-positive B cells, explaining the sequential appearance of the heavy chain classes.

The work in birds led to similar studies in mammals. However, in the absence of a discrete organ comparable to the Bursa, it was necessary to ask whether a mammalian bursa-equivalent existed, or whether B cell development occurred at multiple sites. These studies have shown that the site of B cell ontogeny varies according to the stage of mammalian development. Lymphocyte production in the early embryo occurs first in the yolk sac. As development proceeds, the fetal liver predominates, followed by the spleen during the neonatal period. Finally, the bone marrow becomes the primary lymphoid organ for B cell development in the post-neonatal mammal.

### 1. Discrete Development Steps in the Bone Marrow

Most studies of B cell development have been carried out with mouse cells. The following description summarizes results obtained in the mouse. Where comparable studies have been performed with cells from other species, the pattern of development has been found to be very similar, although some elements of the nomeclature may differ. Work performed in a number of laboratories has defined the sequence of events which occurs as cells mature along the B cell pathway and allowed investigators to determine the factors which regulate the process.

Instrumental to these studies have been the development and refinement of *in vivo* and *in vitro* systems, in which cells from the primary lymphoid organs can be grown and examined as they develop, coupled with the availability of monoclonal antibodies (see Section V), which recognize specific cell surface molecules. The various stages of development are recognized by the sets of molecules which the cells express and, from the pre-B cell stage onwards, the DNA rearrangements in the Ig gene loci, which have been described. The general scheme is that of a tightly regulated sequence, starting with a precursor cell and progressing through pro-B cell, pre-B cell, immature and, finally, mature, virgin B cell. The word "virgin" is used to denote a cell which is immunocompetent, but has not yet encountered antigen. Figure 4 presents a diagram of the stages in B cell development. For each stage, there is an indication of the DNA rearrangements and some of the proteins expressed. The cell's response to antigen exposure is also shown.

The first cell in the scheme, the pro-B cell, may be recognized by its membrane expression of two molecules, designated CD45R and heat-stable antigen (HSA), and the nuclear enzyme terminal deoxynucleotide transferase (TdT). The Ig loci in the DNA are unrearranged, in their germ line configuration. Expression of CD45R and HSA is maintained through the subsequent stages of development, while TdT is expressed only transiently, beginning in the pro-B cell and ending once rearrangements in the H chain locus are complete. TdT catalyzes the noncoded addition of nucleotides to the 3′ ends of DNA strands. In B cells, the recombining gene segments in the H chain provide substrates and this results in noncoded regions (*N*-regions) at the segment junctions in VH. CD19, which functions as a co-receptor with mIg on the mature cell, also appears at this time.

The next stage of development, the pre-B cell, is the first in which the Ig gene loci show DNA rearrangements, catalyzed by RAG-1 and RAG-2 proteins. The RAG genes are expressed only briefly and,

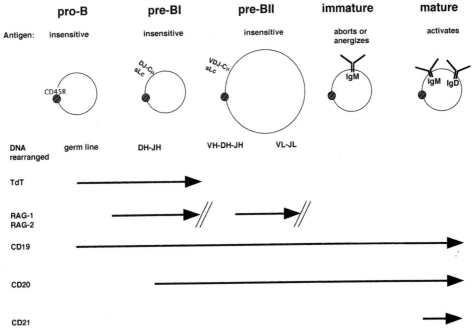

**Fig. 4.** A generalized scheme of antigen-independent B cell development. Development proceeds from left to right. Pre-BI and -BII cells are antigen-insensitive, but the expressed surrogate L chain (sLc)-containing structure is essential for progression to the next stage. Cell division occurs at the pre-BII stage. Cells are antigen-insensitive until they first express mIgM, at the immature stage. At this point, antigen contact results in tolerance. Mature B cells respond to antigen either by induction or by becoming tolerant.

at this point, catalyze recombination in the VH locus before being turned off. At the level of protein expression, pre-B cells may be subdivided into two stages: pre-BI and pre-B-II. Cells with successful (in-frame) DJ recombinations are the pre-BI cells, and these express a pre-B cell receptor comprising the protein products of a rearranged D–J–C gene associated with what are called surrogate light chains (sLC), which are produced from unrearranged loci. Pre-BII cells are those in which successful V-to-DJ recombination has occurred. These express the ($\mu$/sLC) complex on their plasma membranes. Should rearrangement be unsuccessful at either of these stages, the cell dies, since expression of the pre-B receptor is essential for progression. Unlike authentic mIg, pre-B receptors have no clonally distributed antigen-binding activity, but they are presumably capable of binding a molecule (or molecules) necessary for continued development. Pre-BII cells proliferate and it is at this stage that population expansion occurs for 3–5 cell cycles, after which proliferation ceases. The RAG genes are then re-expressed, this time catalyzing rearrangement at the light-chain loci. Cytoplasmic $\mu$ and light chains, both of which are derived from rearrangements, are detectable at this point, since sLC is no longer expressed. Immature B cells, the next developmental step, are the first cells in the scheme at which membrane expression of the clone's authentic receptor occurs. This makes the cells both antigen-specific and -sensitive. It is important to recognize that there is no constraint, or selection, operating on the recombination events in VH or VL. In real terms, this means that antigen binding sites may be generated which recognize self components. Should these clones of B cells develop into antibody-producing cells, autoantibodies and pathological sequelae would be likely. However, the biology of immature B cells is such that binding of specific antigen by their mIgM results in tolerance to that antigen. Immature B cells exposed to high levels of specific antigen undergo apoptosis, or programmed cell death. Since these events all occur in the bone marrow, the antigens to which immature B cells are most likely to be exposed are self antigens present at high local concentration. The induction of apoptosis in immature cells consequent to binding of antigen represents negative selection of self-reactive cells. Additionally, by the immature B cell stage, all B cells show membrane expression of class II MHC molecules, which are essential for recognition of antigenic peptides by helper T cells (see following).

The final step in the pathway is the appearance of mature, virgin B cells. The principal change which occurs here is the co-expression of a second mIg class, mIgD. Mature B cells, then, have the phenotype mIgM$^+$D$^+$. On an individual cell, the mIgM and mIgD have the same binding specificity. The mIg's are identical in their entire light chains and in the variable regions of their heavy chains; they differ only in their heavy chain constant regions. The molecular mechanism by which immunoglobulins of these two distinct classes can be expressed on a single cell involves alternative pathways for processing a long primary messenger RNA transcript (see Fig. 3). These cells also express CD21, a molecule which acts as a receptor for fragments of complement and which, on human B cells, is the site to which Epstein–Barr virus (EBV) binds. Mature, virgin B cells migrate from the primary lymphoid organ to the periphery where they are ready for encounter with antigen and, under the appropriate circumstances, the elaboration of a humoral response. The lifespan of these cells once they have entered the periphery is relatively short, only on the order of a few days, if they do not undergo selection by antigen encounter. The mechanisms responsible for the limited lifespan of unstimulated, mature B cells are unknown. Since new B cells are continuously being generated in the primary lymphoid organs, over a short period of time, B cells encompassing the entire repertoire enter the peripheral compartment and are available to mount a protective immune response.

None of the events in B cell ontogeny leading to mature B cells depends upon the presence of nonself antigens. However, this is not to suggest that external influences are irrelevant to the process of B cell development. A number of growth and maturational signals have been identified which are involved in driving B cell ontogeny. These include signals via the c-kit protein tyrosine kinase on the B cell precursor and the necessity for at least two T cell products, Interleukin-3 (IL-3) and Interleukin-7 (IL-7). Developing B cells express functional receptors for growth factors from a point very early in the lineage and binding of growth factors to these is crucial for successful development.

## 2. *B1 Cells: A Unique Subpopulation with an Autoreactive Bias*

The previous section dealt with the development of those B cells which are found in the spleen and lymph nodes. There is, however, an additional subpopulation of B cells with a unique anatomical localization and set of characteristics. These cells are B cells, as shown by their immunoglobulin gene rearrangements and the presence of membrane Ig. However, they differ from the more conventional splenic and lymph node B cells by their expression of the membrane molecule designated CD5. CD5 was originally described as being a unique marker of T lymphocytes, so the observation that it was also expressed on a population of mIg-positive lymphocytes was somewhat surprising. There is, however, no doubt that the population identified is, indeed, a true B cell population, albeit with some characteristics which distinguish its members from the B cells found in the secondary lymphoid organs. To distinguish between the subpopulations, the CD5+ cells are designated B1; the B cells which develop in bone marrow and populate spleen and lymph nodes are designated B2 cells. Some of the characteristics which distinguish B1 and B2 cells are shown in Table 2.

A potentially important functional significance for the B1 cells has been suggested by two lines of evidence. The first involved examination of the antibodies produced by them, which showed that a significant proportion of the antibodies were specific for self determinants, i.e., had the potential for being autoantibodies. The second line involved mice with a specific mutation, called Motheaten (*me*), which profoundly affects immune function. While the mutation affects both B and T cells, mice with this mutation have only B1 cells. Examination of the antibodies synthesized by motheaten B cells showed that these were also strongly skewed towards the representation of autoreactive binding sites. Thus, it may be that the B1 population represents a reservoir for many of the autoantibodies which exist. Whether such autoantibodies are simply a potential source of pathology, or whether they have some subtle, autoregulatory function (Section III.B), is still unclear.

## B. Antigen-Dependent Events

Resting B cells are morphologically identifiable as small cells (in the so-called Go phase of the cell cycle) of about $7\mu$m diameter, which contain only a thin rim of cytoplasm. When an animal is immunized, the resting B cells are triggered to undergo both proliferation and differentiation. These events, ultimately, give rise to the terminally differentiated plasma cells which secrete antibodies. The recognition of antigen by a mature, virgin B cell has two possible outcomes: the cell can either be induced,

**TABLE II**
**Comparison of Murine B1 and B2 Subpopulations**

| | *B1 cells* | *B2 cells* |
|---|---|---|
| Membrane phenotype | | |
|   mIg expression | mIgM+ mIgD − or low | mIgM+ mIgD+ |
|   light chain usage | ~20% of peritoneal cavity $\mu$+ cells are $\lambda$+ | ~5% $\lambda$+ and 95% $\kappa$+ |
|   CD5/Mac-1 expression | positive | negative |
|   CD45R expression | positive | positive |
| Precursors located | | |
|   Fetus and newborn | liver | liver/spleen |
|   Adult | peritoneal cavity | bone marrow |
| Functional cells located | | |
|   Adult | peritoneal cavity | spleen/lymph nodes |
|   Lifespan | long and/or self-renewing | a few days unless stimulated by antigen |

initiating the events which lead to antibody production, or it can be tolerized. The principal factors which determine the outcome are the number and nature of the signals delivered to the cell. In brief, if only one signal is delivered by the binding of antigen by mIg, the outcome is tolerance. If, on the other hand, a mIg-mediated signal is accompanied by, or closely associated in time with, signal(s) from other cell types, the outcome is induction.

## I. Induction for Response

In this section, we will consider inductive events at three levels: first, the level of the whole animal; second, with respect to the cellular cooperation, which is obligatory for humoral responses to protein antigens; and, third, the cellular and biochemical events which occur in the B cells and which are initiated upon binding of antigen by the mIg receptors.

### i. Humoral Responses at the Whole Animal Level

Almost all immune responses are polyclonal and heterogeneous. That is, in response to the introduction of, say, a toxin molecule, many clones of lymphocytes are selected and respond. While some heterogeneity is due to differences in H or L chain classes or subclasses, the vast majority is in the combining sites. While the antibody population collectively binds to the whole protein, when an analysis is performed with fragments of the molecule, groups of antibody species may be identified, each binding to a distinct epitope. Complex antigens, thus, comprise a collection of individual epitopes. Often, one epitope is the target of the majority of the antibodies, a phenomenon termed immunodominance.

B cells are largely sessile and reside mainly in the primary follicles of the secondary lymphoid organs (spleen, lymph nodes, Peyers Patches) and the actual anatomic site of response is dictated by the route of entry of the immunogen. Immunogens entering the bloodstream directly are delivered to the spleen. Immunogens entering the tissues are delivered, via the afferent lymphatics, to the lymph nodes draining the immunization site; for example, an infection of a finger will lead to enlarged, tender lymph nodes in the elbow of that arm. These two routes of immuniza-

tion will activate components of the systemic immune system, leading to the sequential appearance of IgM, IgG, and IgA in the serum. In contrast, immunogens delivered to the GI tract, such as those in food, will be delivered to the Peyers Patches and will activate components of the mucosal immune system, leading to IgA in secretions. It should be emphasized that both B and T cells in the secondary organs are affected by the delivery of immunogen and that the events observed at the whole animal level result from the interplay of multiple cell types.

The response of an animal to its first exposure to a particular immunogen is, by definition, the primary response. Responses to subsequent encounters with the same antigen (secondary, tertiary, etc.) are grouped together under the heading of anamnestic, or memory, responses. This distinction is most clearly seen when a nonreplicating immunogen, such as a killed vaccine or a toxoid, is administered. In such a case, the primary and anamnestic responses, while following the same general pattern, show significant qualitative and quantitative differences (see Fig. 5). In terms of kinetics, both show a lag period between immunization and the appearance of detectable circulating antibody; in the primary response, this is about 7 days, whereas in memory responses, it is considerably shorter. This is followed by a phase of rapid increase in serum antibody concentration, leading to a plateau. The slope of the rising portion of the curve is steeper in memory responses than in primary response and the plateau level of serum antibody achieved is vastly greater in an anamnestic response. Finally, a decay phase is apparent in both, indicating the cessation of high-rate antibody production and the turnover of Ig molecules. The decay phase in a primary response is quite rapid, reflecting the relatively short half-life of serum IgM. In contrast, the decay phase for a memory response is very slow, with IgG antibodies being detectable for many years. In addition to the kinetic and quantitative differences, primary and memory responses are dominated by different classes of antibodies. The predominant class in the primary response is IgM. In contrast, memory responses, at least in the systemic immune system, are dominated by IgG antibodies, with some serum IgA being detectable. The sequential appearance of IgM, IgG, and IgA antibodies of the same

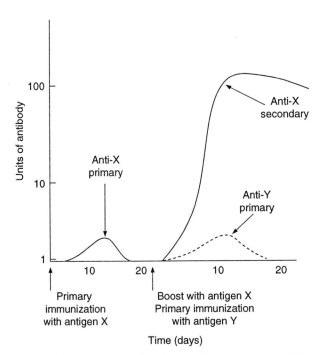

**Fig. 5.** Primary vs secondary humoral responses to a non-replicating immunogen. The responses differ in both magnitude and kinetics, as well as class of antibody predominating (see text); these differences reflect immunological memory. Immunization with a non-crossreacting antigen (Y) at the time of secondary immunization with X elicits a primary response to Y, indicating that the memory is antigen-specific.

binding specificity is called "class switching" and reflects genetic alterations within the clones of B cells responding to the immunogen.

The pattern of response to a replicating antigen, such as a pathogenic microorganism, differs in that the IgM response blends into the IgG so that, while IgM is still detectable in the serum, IgG appears and slowly increases in concentration. Concomitant with this, the IgM reaches a plateau and decays. This pattern reflects the continuing drive to the immune system by a replicating stimulus. The outcome, recovery or disease, depends upon whether the immune system can respond fast enough to overcome the increase in pathogen numbers.

Antibody affinity is a measure of the strength of antigen binding. In general, IgM responses are of lower affinity than IgG. Measurement of the distribution of affinities in an IgG response over a period of time shows that the average value rises. That is, the polyclonal IgG antibody population gradually shifts from a predominance of low affinity to higher affinity antibodies. This is called "affinity maturation." Affinity maturation is not seen in IgM antibodies. In physical terms, if one compares a low affinity antibody with one of high affinity, the former requires the presence of a higher concentration of antigen than does the latter for detectable binding to occur. In biological terms, if a humoral response is of low average affinity, then, due to the formation and clearance of antigen–antibody complexes, there will come a point at which the *in vivo* concentration of free antigen falls to a level at which essentially no binding occurs, even though free antigen may still be present. Thus, there will no longer be a protective effect of such antibodies. Teleologically, then, affinity maturation is advantageous because, as the average affinity of the IgG population rises, so the antibodies are able to bind and eliminate antigen at lower and lower residual antigen concentrations.

Primary immunization affects the B cell population in two ways. One is to elicit a largely IgM primary antibody response. The other is to generate a large population of memory (secondary) B cells, a process which occurs in the germinal centers of the lymphoid organs. During the proliferative phase of the response, both class switching (of H chain constant region genes) and somatic hypermutation of V regions occur. Both of these events depend upon the activity of Th cells interacting with the B cells.

A quite distinct route of immune stimulation that occurs through recognition of CpG (cytosine–phosphate–guanosine) motifs has recently been described. CpG dinucleotides are 10 times more frequent in bacterial DNAs than in vertebrate DNAs and, in the latter, most CpG dinucleotides are methylated on cytosine. DNAs containing unmethylated CpG are capable of rapidly stimulating cytokine production and acting as T cell-independent B cell mitogens, driving the B cells to proliferate and inducing the secretion of IL-6, which causes them to differentiate into IgM-secretors. They also act with mIg crosslinking as B cell co-stimulators. Activation by CpG-containing DNA is not restricted to B cells, being seen also in natural killer cells and, indirectly, on CMI. This may be an important aspect of immune protection, acting rapidly and efficiently to induce a polyclonal immune response in the event of bacterial infection.

### ii. Cellular Cooperation and the Role of CD4+ T Cells

Humoral responses to many immunogens have an absolute requirement for a population of T cells characterized by expression of the CD4 glycoprotein; these are the helper T (Th) cells. Such responses are described as thymus-dependent (TD). Almost all proteins and glycoproteins are TD immunogens. In contrast, substances have been identified which elicit humoral responses in the absence of Th cell activity; these are thymus-independent (TI) immunogens. Bacterial polysaccharides are good examples of TI immunogens. These are often large molecules which have repeating structural elements and this pattern of repeating structures is found in many TI immunogens. Another characteristic often associated with thymus-independence is mitogenicity, the ability of a substance to stimulate lymphocytes to respond without regard to the cells' specificity for antigen. That is, mitogens stimulate lymphocytes through mechanisms which bypass their antigen-specific receptors. TI immunogens are able to provide sufficient signals for the B cells to undergo the events leading to antibody secretion. However, humoral responses to TI antigens are largely IgM, showing limited class switching and neither affinity maturation nor the generation of B cell memory.

The interaction between B and Th cells in TD responses is constrained by the nature of the antigen-specific receptors on each cell type. Membrane Ig on B cells is able to bind free, native antigen, whereas the T cell receptor (TCR) binds peptide fragments only when they are presented in a complex with major histocompatibility antigens on antigen-presenting cells (APCs). For the CD4+ Th cells, the MHC molecules recognized are the class II molecules. B cells are able to function as extremely efficient APCs, since they express class II MHC. When antigen is bound by mIg, the complex is endocytosed and degraded in lysosomes. Peptides from the processed antigen become associated with newly synthesized class II MHC molecules and the complexes are delivered to the B cell surface. This permits what is called

cognate recognition of antigen-specific B cells by Th cells which have TCRs with specificity for the peptide-class II complex (Fig. 6). A series of interactions between B and Th cells ensues, which holds the cells in apposition and mediates signal delivery. In addition to recognition of peptide/MHC by TCR, these interactions include binding of (B cell) class II by CD4; recognition of B cell CD40 by the CD40 ligand (CD40L) on Th cells; and interaction between CD28 on the Th cells and a molecule designated B7 on B cells. As examples of the reciprocity of the interactions. TCR binding of the peptide/MHC complex provides one activation signal to the Th cell. However, a second, co-stimulatory signal is necessary; this is provided through CD28 binding of B7. Conversely, while mIg binding of antigen provides an activating signal to the B cell, co-stimulation is provided by the CD40L binding to CD40.

In addition to membrane interactions, Th cells help B cells (and other cell types) via secreted molecules called cytokines. These have no specificity for antigen, but function as local hormones in regulating immune responses. Cytokines have very short half-lives *in vivo*, of the order of seconds to minutes; consequently, they act mainly on the cells in the immediate environment. One of the most important cytokines involved in the B cell response is Interleukin-4 (IL-4), a multifunctional molecule which acts to increase expression of class II MHC, promote B cell proliferation and direct class switching. IL-4 is produced by a subpopulation of CD4+ cells, designated Th2, which have been shown to be of particular importance in humoral immunity. The result of B cell activation by antigen, in the context of cognate recognition by Th cells, sends the B cells down one of two parallel pathways. One leads to differentiation into plasma cells. The other is taken by B cells which enter follicles and form germinal centers (GCs). This pathway leads to the generation of memory B cells. Both affinity maturation and class switching occur in GCs and are Th cell-dependent processes. At a cellular level, affinity maturation results from a combination of positive and negative selection on the B cell population. As B cells proliferate, mutations occur in their immunoglobulin variable region genes at a higher rate than in other parts of their DNA, a phenomenon called hypermutation. A fraction of

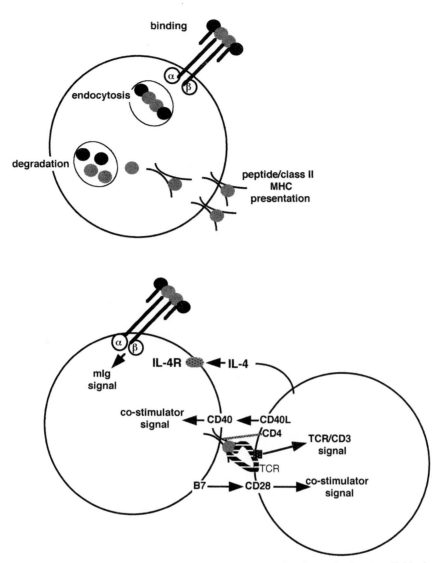

***Fig. 6.*** Cognate recognition between Th and B cells. (Upper) The B cell binds immunogen via its mIg receptors. The complex is internalized, degraded in lysosomes and peptide fragments presented on the B cell surface in association with class II MHC. (Lower) Antigen occupancy of mIg provides activating signal to B cell. TCR recognition of peptide/class II MHC provides activating signal (delivered through the CD3 complex). Activated T cell expresses CD40L; engagement of B cell CD40 by this provides a co-stimulatory signal to the B cell. Co-stimulator signal to T cell by recognition of B cell B7 by CD28.

these mutations results in cells which express mIg binding sites with higher affinity than the parental cell. Antigen is present at low levels on follicular dendritic cells in the GCs and only those B cells with high affinity mIg receptors are able to bind this and receive a mIg-mediated signal essential for survival. Proliferation and V region hypermutation depend upon both mIg binding and CD40–CD40L interactions, the latter providing co-stimulation to the B cells; this is the positive selection aspect. Those B cells which are unable to bind antigen because of low affinity combining sites receive only co-stimulation through CD40. This signal alone renders the cells susceptible to pro-apoptotic signals delivered, via cell surface Fas (CD95) protein, by activated T cells which express the Fas ligand; this is the negative selection process.

Heavy-chain class-switching also occurs in proliferating GC B cells and reflects irreversible changes in the H chain constant region of the DNA. The process has been described by a loop and excision model and is depicted in Fig. 7. The heavy-chain constant region genes are arrayed tandemly, on the 3′ side of the assembled VDJ. To the 5′ side of each of the heavy chain constant region genes, except $\delta$, there is a switch sequence; only the switch sequences immediately 5′ to the $\mu$ and $\gamma$1 constant region genes are shown (s$\mu$ and s$\gamma$1). Class-switching involves recombination in the region of the switch sequences: one upstream of the heavy-chain gene which the B cell is expressing prior to the switch (in this instance $\mu$); and the other upstream of the gene which the cell will express after the switch (in this instance $\gamma$1). The two switch sequences form a stem by complementary base pairing, the intervening DNA forming a loop. Class switching involves cutting at the stem and religation. The DNA which formed the loop is lost. The result of the process is to bring the VDJ 5′ to the heavy-chain constant region gene with which it will be expressed. In the illustration, the constant region genes for $\mu$, $\delta$, and $\gamma$3 have been lost and VDJ is immediately upstream of the $\gamma$1 constant region. Cytokines produced by Th cells have been shown to drive class-switching in distinct directions. For example, in the mouse IL-4, produced by Th2 cells, drives B cells to switch to IgG1 and IgE. Interferon-$\gamma$, a product of Th1 cells, drives B cells to IgG2a and IgG2b production. Transforming growth factor-$\beta$ may be particularly important in mucosal immunity, since it appears to be important in the switch to IgA production in human B cells.

### iii. Cellular and Biochemical Events

Immunoglobulins are integral membrane proteins with a hydrophobic membrane-spanning domain at the C-terminus. The final three C-terminal amino acids of both $\mu$ and $\delta$ are lysine–valine–lysine; these form the cytoplasmic domain for these two Ig classes. This minimal sequence suggests that other molecules

**A**

Heavy chain region organization in IgM producer

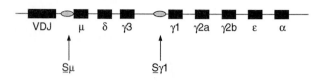

**B**

Stem and loop formation

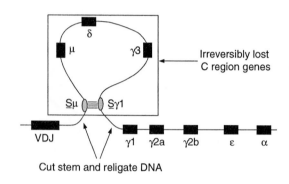

**C**

Heavy chain region organization in IgG1 producer

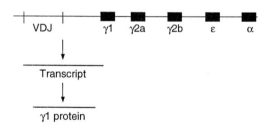

**Fig. 7.** The loop and excision model for class-switching in B cells. Panel (A) shows the assembled gene for the VH domain (VDJ) and the germ line organization of the constant region genes. Panel (B) shows a stem formed between the switch sequences (s) immediately upstream of $\mu$ and $\gamma$1. The constant region genes between these are on the loop. Panel (C) shows the organization of the locus after the stem has been cut and the DNA religated. An mRNA transcript initiating 5′ to VDJ would permit translation of a $\gamma$1 heavy chain, thus allowing the B cell to secrete IgG1.

may be associated with the transmembrane domains of the heavy chains and act as the proximal transducers. Biochemical analysis has shown that Ig H chains are noncovalently associated with disulfide-bonded heterodimers, now designated CD79. The individual chains have been called Ig-$\alpha$ and Ig-$\beta$. The B cell receptor (BCR), from the earliest stage of expression, is a molecular complex in which binding is the property of the H chain-containing component and the signal delivery is a function of CD79. The association with CD79 also holds for cells expressing mIgG, mIgE, and mIgA. The TCR also has seperate components which mediate specific recognition and signaling, as do a number of cytokine receptors.

In mature B cells responding to TD antigens, membrane Ig occupancy by antigen activates the resting lymphocyte from $G_0$ to the $G_1$ phase of the cell cycle. If this is coupled with the Th-mediated signals described earlier, the B cell is driven through several rounds of proliferation. The actively dividing B lymphoblast is about $12\mu$ in diameter and retains the appearance of a lymphocyte.

The first step in activation is the occupancy and cross-linking of mIgM or mIgD by antigen. The earliest events, on which all other signals in the mIg pathway depend, involve activation of, and catalysis by, protein tyrosine kinases (PTKs) of the src family of PTKs and another enzyme called syk. Phosphorylation on tyrosine residues, although representing only about 1% of total protein phosphorylation, has been shown to be crucial in a number of receptor systems. The cytoplasmic domains of both Ig-$\alpha$ and Ig-$\beta$ contain tyrosine-based activation motifs (TAMs), short sequences of amino acids containing two tyrosine residues which are substrates for PTKs. In the resting, unstimulated cell, the BCR complex is associated with a number of inactive PTKs. The earliest event after mIg occupancy is the activation, by autophosphorylation, of a PTK which, in its turn, phosphorylates the TAMs in Ig-$\alpha$ and Ig-$\beta$. The phosphorylated TAMs now recruit additional PTK molecules to the complex, where they are activated. The entire chain of PTK activity occurs rapidly after mIg occupancy and is the initiator of all subsequent downstream events in the mIg signaling pathway (for reviews, see Cambier *et al.*, 1994; Reth and Wienands, 1997). Other molecules on the B cell membrane, such as the CD19/CD21 complex and CD20, act as co-receptors, in that they appear to decrease the amount of antigen required for the mIg-mediated signal. They, too, contain sites for phosphorylation by, and binding of, PTKs and may act synergistically with the BCR.

CD45R, a molecule which appears early in B cell development, is a phosphotyrosine phosphatase, i.e., it specifically removes phosphate groups from tyrosine residues. This enzymatic activity probably acts in counterpoint to the action of PTKs, regulating the level of tyrosine phosphorylation and so modulating PTK-mediated events. The pathway from membrane to nucleus employed by the IL-4 receptor also employs PTKs, Janus kinases (JAKs). Two members of this family, JAK1 and JAK3, phosphorylate signal transducers and activators of transcription (STATs), which stimulate the production of specific mRNA species.

The signals which reach the nucleus are, therefore, derived from a number of pathways. As long as they represent both BCR and co-stimulator signals, integration results in the production of new mRNA species which drive the proliferation program. Among the new proliferation-associated transcripts detected in B cells are those of the cellular proto-oncogenes, *c-myc*, *c-jun*, and *c-fos*, the protein products of which are DNA-binding proteins, and bcl-2 which protects the cell from undergoing apoptosis.

The final step is the terminal differentiation into plasma cells (PCs). These are morphologically distinct from lymphocytes, being about $16\mu$ diameter, with an eccentrically placed nucleus and a cytoplasm full of rough endoplasmic reticulum and Golgi apparatus, consistent with the cell's function as a high-rate protein synthesizer. Differentiation is associated with exit from cycle and the expression of a different set of genes. An important signal for this is interleukin-6 (IL-6). In the primary B cell response, a striking change occurs in the processing of the primary mRNA for the $\mu$ heavy-chain. The resting cell expresses IgM as an integral membrane protein, with a hydrophobic transmembrane domain at its C terminus. The IgM secreted by plasma cells lacks this transmembrane domain, which is replaced by a different C terminus. This change in domains occurs by altern ate splicing patterns of the primary $\mu$ chain transcript, giving rise to two distinct mature mRNA species. During differentiation to either an IgM- or IgA-secreting PC, the gene for J chain is expressed. Serum IgM is secreted as a pentameric molecule $(\mu_2 L_2)_5$, while IgA is dimeric. J chain (J = joining) is a small protein produced by IgM- or IgA-secreting cells, which holds polymeric Ig's together through disulfide bonds.

PCs of the systemic immune system are found in the secondary lymphoid organs, where they survive for only a few days and, interestingly, in bone marrow in humans. At this latter site, they appear to be able to persist for long periods, continuing to secrete antibodies. PCs of the secretory immune system confront a logistic problem, however. The ultimate destination of their IgA product is the lumen of a glandular structure. The PCs are located on the basal side of the secretory epithelium, which necessitates transport of dimeric IgA (IgA–J–IgA) across an intact epithelial barrier with tight junctions between the cells. Passage of the IgA is by a process called transcytosis, which involves the polyimmunoglobulin receptor (pIgR) expressed on the epithelial cells. On the basal side of the epithelium, the pIgR binds to IgA and transports it through the cytoplasm of the epithelial cell, protecting it from degradation. The IgA is delivered to the luminal surface, where it is released with a fragment of pIgR still associated. This fragment is called "secretory place" and it is found in all IgAs in secretions.

## C. Termination of the Humoral Response

For the purpose of homeostasis, it is as important to turn B cells off as it is turn them on. A number of mechanisms exist for this (for a review of the topic, albeit with an emphasis on terminating T cell responses, see Van Parijs and Abbas, 1998). The first of these is decreasing antigen concentration, as a result of a successful humoral effector response. The very success removes the proximal drive for B cell activation through mIg and, indirectly, limits cognate recognition and co-stimulation by Th cells.

Soluble immune complexes, prior to clearance, form part of a negative feedback loop which regulates B cells. An immune complex with IgG antibodies is unlikely to have all of the determinants on the antigen occupied by antibody molecules. Unoccupied antigenic determinants may be recognized and bound by mIg molecules on antigen-specific B cells. This process might be expected to activate the B cells, as described earlier. However, the presence of the IgG in the immune complex permits recognition by the cell's FcγRs. Co-ligation of mIg and FcγR on the B cell delivers a strong negative signal, suppressing activation and proliferation. There is also evidence suggesting that the rate of spontaneous apoptosis may be increased. This provides a powerful and elegant mechanism of antigen-specific termination of response.

Regulatory T cells have also been shown to affect B cell responses. These may be a subpopulation of Th cells which secrete regulatory cytokines or which are able to induce apoptosis via Fas–FasL interactions. CD8+ cytotoxic T cells may also have a role in terminating B cell responses.

Finally, a mechanism, proposed by Jerne, depends upon the immunogenicity of antibody molecules themselves as the regulatory drive. The variable regions of antibody molecules bear determinants, called idiotypes, which can elicit antibodies in the animal undergoing the first (anti-antigen) response. Idiotypic determinants are the unique "signatures" of individual B cell clones, or sets of clones, and their antibody products. In experimental systems, anti-idiotypic antibodies can have profound regulatory effects on those B cells' expressing the appropriate idiotypes on their mIg. Possible mechanisms include steric hindrance of further antigen binding or interruption of signaling pathways. While the suggested mechanism is interesting, its importance in terminating polyclonal responses is uncertain.

## D. B Cell Tolerance

Tolerance is defined as antigen-specific unresponsiveness. It has been shown to occur in both B and T cells. The need for a process of tolerization (tolerance induction) comes from the mechanism by which diversity is generated in lymphocytes: the combinatorial joining of individual gene segments to yield the full-length variable regions of individual Ig molecules (and TCRs). The recombinational events and receptor expression occur without any extracellular signals dictating the repertoire which is generated. Thus, binding sites with specificity for self components may arise during the process. In addition, mutations accumulate in the Ig variable regions genes after antigen-driven triggering of B cells. These provide an additional source of self-reactive cells. Should self-reactive lymphocytes generated by either of these processes be allowed to respond in an uncontrolled manner, severe autoimmune disease might result (see Section IV.B.2). Tolerance mechanisms have evolved as one important way of limiting immune attack on self components.

B cells can become tolerized at either the immature or mature stage of development. Whole animal studies showed that the injection of deaggregated protein antigens could induce tolerance in B cells (and T cells), reflected in an inability to respond to a subsequent immunogenic dose of the same antigen. The tolerant state persisted in B cells for up to two months, reflecting effects on both the mature, peripheral cells and those maturing in the bone marrow. Subsequent *in vitro* studies showed, again, that both immature and mature cells could be tolerized, but the former were very much more susceptible than were the latter, as assessed by the concentration of tolerogen required in the cultures. At the cellular level, two mechanisms have been proposed by which lymphocytes become tolerized; these have been called clonal abortion (or deletion) and clonal anergy. In the former model, the cells are killed as a consequence of their interaction with the tolerizing molecule, whereas in the latter they persist but in an unresponsive state.

Genetic engineering techniques have been employed to construct transgenic mice, animals which have had genes introduced into their germ lines which encode and express proteins which are normally foreign to the host. This has allowed investigators to study the effects upon the immune system of protein molecules which behave, in terms of expression, as if they were self. Such an approach more accurately reflects the processes which occur naturally to prevent self-reactivity. This approach has confirmed that both immature and mature B cells can be tolerized and has shown that both mechanisms of tolerization, abortion and anergy, occur. One of the

factors dictating which of the two tolerization outcomes results appears to be the form in which the tolerizing epitope is presented. Membrane-associated molecules, which would presumably have an oligo- or polyvalent presentation and initiate a high level of mIg cross-linking, result in clonal abortion. In contrast, a soluble tolerogen, which would presumably be monovalent, gives rise to anergy. Regardless of the mechanism by which the tolerization occurs, the processes can be put into the context of the number of signals delivered to the cell. Tolerance results from the delivery of only one signal, through the mIg receptor, in the absence of other signals necessary for the B cell to continue through the activation process. This induces the cell to enter apoptosis. Anergic B cells persist and, although they are unresponsive to antigen, under certain conditions of stimulation, the anergic state can be reversed. The use of transgenic mice has permitted the identification of anergic B cells. Such cells have an unusual cell membrane phenotype with respect to mIg expression, with markedly reduced mIgM but essentially normal expression of mIgD.

## IV. PATHOLOGY

### A. Deficits: Immunodeficiencies

A number of immunodeficiencies are specific to the B cell compartment. The most profound of these is Bruton's X-linked agammaglobulinemia. The affected locus is the Bruton's tyrosine kinase (*Btk*) gene, located on the X chromosome. Hence, females (sex chromosome genotype XX) are carriers, whereas the affected individuals are males (sex chromosome genotype XY). The symptoms of the immunodeficiency become evident after 6 months of age, when the level of transplacental maternal IgG has declined, with a history of frequent and severe bacterial infections. This condition, incidentally, provides an "experiment of nature," which demonstrates the biological role of humoral immunity in providing protection against extracellular bacteria and their products. The immunodeficiency results from a failure in the maturation of B cells, such that very few mature B cells are present, development of the lineage being blocked at the pre-B cell stage. The result is the almost total absence of immunoglobulin from the serum.

The most common immunodeficiency detected is IgA deficiency, in which IgA production is diminished or absent. It occurs at a frequency of 1/400–1/800. IgA levels in both serum and secretions are affected. The deficiency is heterogeneous in presentation, with some patients being asymptomatic and being identified quite by chance. In contrast to Bruton's agammaglobulinemia, IgA deficiency does not reflect a defect in the development of mature B cells, but represents an undefined block in the production of IgA-producing plasma cells.

## B. Excesses

There are a number of situations in which the excessive or inappropriate production of antibodies can have pathological consequences. Among these are "immediate hypersensitivity" reactions and antibody-mediated autoimmune diseases.

### 1. Immediate Hypersensitivity (Allergic) Reactions

These are more commonly known as allergic reactions. They range in severity from allergic rhinitis, or "hay fever," with its symptoms of a stuffy nose and red, watering eyes, to hypersensitivity to insect venoms, which can lead to death within a few minutes of a sting. Specific antibodies of the IgE class are responsible for the reactions. Mast cells have on their membranes Fc receptors which avidly bind the Fc region of IgE. When antigen for which the mast cell-bound IgE is specific is introduced, the result is cross-linking of the IgE. Mast cells respond to this by becoming activated, which releases a variety of extremely potent, biological mediators. The immediate degranulation phase releases preformed mediators, predominantly histamine, which are stored in granules. This is followed by the release of newly synthesized molecules. The immediate release of histamine causes vasodilation, increased capillary permeability, and smooth muscle contraction. When the antigen is delivered locally to the mucosal surfaces of the eye and upper respiratory tract, such as occurs with pollen grains, then the symptoms of hay fever

result. Antigen delivered to the mast cells in the lower respiratory tract can lead to an asthmatic attack, with the characteristic wheezing and profound difficulty in breathing. Should the antigen is delivered by injection, which is what essentially occurs in the case of an insect sting, then a massive, systemic release of histamine can result, causing an anaphylactic reaction. Anaphylaxis can cause death within a few minutes.

All individuals make antigen-specific IgE. However, allergic individuals appear to make significantly higher quantities of this class of antibody. The control of class-switching in B cells, in particular, those events leading to IgE production, are being defined. IL-4 has been shown to be the principal drive to switching to IgE. The other regulatory events controling the amount of IgE produced are under study and it is not yet clear where in the sequence the dysregulated events occur in allergic individuals, giving rise increased IgE production.

### 2. Antibody-Mediated Autoimmune Diseases

While the protective function of the humoral immune response is against foreign molecules, conditions arise in which antibodies reactive to self-components are produced. These are termed autoantibodies. The presence of low-affinity IgM autoantibodies in serum is not abnormal and generally causes no detectable symptoms. However, there are instances in which high affinity IgG autoantibodies are produced and cause pathological effects; these are the antibody-mediated autoimmune diseases. There are a number of such diseases and they differ in the types of autoantibodies produced and, thus, the number and types of tissues affected. At one end of the spectrum is systemic lupus erythromatosus (SLE), a disease in which there is no obvious, single, organ-specific population of autoantibodies. Antibodies which react with self erythrocytes, DNA and RNA are all found in SLE patients. Myasthenia gravis (MG) is an organ-specific disease representative of the other end of the spectrum. In MG, the target molecule of the autoantibodies is the $\alpha$ chain of the nicotinic acetylcholine receptor and the antibodies disrupt neuromuscular transmission, leading to muscle weakness and easy fatigability.

## C. Malignancies

Tumors have been identified which are the malignant counterparts of cells throughout the B cell developmental scheme, from pre-B cells to plasma cells. Such tumors arise in man, but there are also animal models, particularly in mice and birds, which have been extensively studied. This work has been particularly instructive in revealing the role of cellular proto-oncogenes and how dysregulation of these can lead to malignancy.

Human B cell malignancies demonstrate dysregulation by chromosomal translocation. In this process, the proto-oncogene is activated by being moved to a different chromosome and being brought into proximity with one of the immunoglobulin gene loci. One example is seen in Burkitt's lymphoma, a B cell lymphoma prevalent in parts of Africa. Analysis of chromosome spreads from the malignant cells shows that, in about 90% of the cases, a translocation is identifiable involving chromosomes 14 and 8. In 5%, the translocation involves chromosomes 2 and 8; and in the final 5%, chromosomes 22 and 8 are involved. In humans, H chain is on chromosome 14, $\kappa$ on 2, and $\lambda$ on 22. The *c-myc* gene maps to chromosome 8. Translocation brings *c-myc*, a gene intimately involved in proliferation, into a chromosomal region which is open and active in B cells, causing unregulated expression. Follicular B cell lymphomas provide another example of translocation, in this case, involving chromosomes 14 and 18. This brings the *Bcl*-2 gene under the control of the H chain enhancer sequence, resulting in uncontrolled expression of the Bcl-2 protein, which prevents cells from undergoing apoptosis. The consequence is that cells which would normally die survive and continue to proliferate.

## V. B CELLS AND THEIR PRODUCTS IN MICROBIOLOGY AND MEDICINE

### A. Monoclonal Antibodies (Hybridomas)

As indicated earlier, serum antibody responses are polyclonal and heterogeneous. While advantageous for the survival of the intact organism, there are circumstances in which there is a need for highly purified, monospecific antibodies. Examples of this are the definition of cell populations by their (CD) antigen expression and clinically for diagnosis or therapy. In the 1970s, Kohler and Milstein devised a procedure to employ somatic cell hybridization to generate hybrid cell lines which could grow indefinitely in culture and produced only one species of antibody. These are monoclonal antibodies (MAbs), sometimes referred to as hybridomas. To produce MAbs, B cells are taken from an immunized mouse and somatic cell hybrids formed between these and myeloma cells which have been adapted to growth *in vitro*. The immune B cells provide both the genetic information for the synthesis of the desired antibody, as well as an enzyme required for surviving the selection procedure, while the myeloma cells provide immortality. The hybridization step is performed *in vitro;* any cells from the immune animal which fail to hybridize undergo apoptosis and die within a few days. The survivors, should there be no selective pressure applied, are either hybrids or myeloma cells which have not fused. A critical step in separating these two cell types is to kill the unhybridized myeloma cells, using standard selection procedures. Cells are seeded into tissue culture wells at limiting dilution (a procedure called "cloning") and each individual culture is then screened for the production of specific antibody. Those which are identified as being positive may be expanded and used as a source of monoclonal antibodies. Large-scale production can be achieved either in tissue culture or by growing the cells in mice.

MAbs are now being used for both diagnostic and therapeutic purposes. For the former purpose, tumor-specific MAbs can be labeled with tracer atoms, such as radioisotopes, and used for imaging studies to identify metastases. MAbs have also reached the clinic, recent examples of this being their use for posttransplant immunosuppression and the treatment of some cases of breast cancer, with a MAb directed to the cell surface product of the *her/neu* oncogene.

Most MAbs have been produced using B cells from immunized mice. The antibodies produced will, therefore, be of mouse origin. For research purposes, this presents no problem. However, when such antibodies are administered to humans, they elicit a strong immune response, ironically enough, a humoral response. The antimouse immunoglobulin antibodies are not only able to neutralize any subsequently administered mouse monoclonal antibodies, thus rendering them ineffective, but the immune complexes formed can themselves be potentially dangerous. Strategies have been devised to produce monoclonal antibodies which are less foreign to the intended recipient, one of which is to "humanize" the monoclonal antibodies. Immunoglobulins are strong immunogens across species barriers, but the binding specificity resides in only a relatively small percentage of the total molecular mass, the combining site proper. Using recombinant DNA techniques, investigators have isolated cDNA clones for the entire H and L chains of monoclonal antibodies of mouse origin and replaced various parts with the corresponding human DNA sequences. Such chimeric antibodies can then be re-expressed. The resulting monoclonal antibody retains the binding specificity of the original mouse antibody, while much of the molecule has now been rendered human and, thus, less strongly immunogenic to humans.

## B. Vaccines and Immunization

The active stimulation of the immune system, with the development of circulating antibodies and immunological memory, is the basis of vaccination. Vaccines have been strikingly effective in combating many infectious diseases. Among the best examples are smallpox, which has been eradicated worldwide, and poliomyelitis, the incidence of which has been markedly reduced in those countries with the economic ability to introduce large-scale immunization programs. Such programs, coupled with such public health measures as improved sanitation and drinking water supplies, are very cost-effective ways of maintaining and improving the health status of the population. Worldwide childhood immunization programs, which would cost only pennies per individual, might seem expensive in aggregate cost, given the number of individuals involved, but are well worth the expenditure in overall economic terms.

## C. Serological Diagnosis and Epidemiology

In the early stages of the infection of an unimmunized individual, the serum antibody titer to the pathogen is low. As antibodies are produced, they are able to neutralize the pathogen and their titer continues to rise. A classical and time-honored method for diagnosis is to compare the titers of serum samples taken from a patient during the course of the infection (an "acute" serum) and several weeks later, after recovery (a "convalescent" serum). An increase of fourfold or more in specific titer, from acute to convalescent sample, is taken as strong evidence of infection by the pathogen in question. In the case of bacterial infection, this might seem a somewhat academic point, if the organism can be cultured and identified. However, there are instances in which the organism cannot be identified at the time of infection and such serological evidence can only be obtained a significant time after the event. An example of such ex post facto diagnosis occurred after the identification of *Legionella pneumophila,* the organism causing Legionnaire's Disease. Some years previously, an outbreak of pneumonia had occurred in Pontiac, Michigan. The etiologic agent was not identified at the time. However, serum samples were stored and when the Legionella organisms were subsequently isolated, it became possible to demonstrate that organisms of this species had been responsible for the Pontiac episode.

## D. Bacteriophage Display: Antibodies without an Immune System

VH and VL genes have been isolated from the lymphocytes of immunized and unimmunized animals and cloned into filamentous bacteriophages. The fragments can be expressed singly, or together, fused to the minor coat protein, pIII. This permits expression of correctly folded antibody combining sites, or Fab fragments on the bacteriophage surface. Bacteriophage libraries have been constructed (analogous to combinatorial association of VH and VL in B cells) and selected with antigen (as in clonal selection), to isolate the rare bacteriophage particle expressing the desired combining site. The DNA from these particles can then be mutated in order to generate higher affinity mutants (somatic hypermutation). Finally, the antibody fragments can be either displayed on the bacteriophage surface or secreted by infected bacteria. This is an elegant system, the development of which has used the information obtained about the development and function of antibodies and B cells and employed it in a quite ingenious way. There are tremendous prospects for the use of this technology to generate antibody species for both research and clinical use.

## See Also the Following Articles

Antigenic Variation • Cellular Immunity • T Lymphocytes • Transgenic Animal Technology

## Bibliography

Ahmed, R., and Gray, D. (1996). Immunological memory and protective immunity: Understanding their relation. *Science* **272**, 54.

Ashman, R. F., Peckham, D., and Stuntz, L. L. (1996). Regulation of B cell apoptosis. *In* "Mechanisms of Lymphocyte Activation and Immune Regulation VI. Cell Cycle and Programmed Death in the Immune system" (S. Gupta & J. J. Cohen, eds.) p. 145. Advances in Experimental Biology and Medicine, **406**. Plenum Press, New York.

Cambier, J. C., Pleiman, C. M., and Clark, M. R. (1994). Signal transduction by the B cell antigen receptor and its coreceptors. *Ann. Rev. Immunol.* **12**, 457.

Cook, G. P., and Tomlinson, I. M. (1995). The human immunoglobulin VH repertoire. *Immunol. Today* **16**, 237.

de Kruif, J., van der Vuurst de Vries, A. *et al.* (1996). New perspectives on recombinant human antibodies. *Immunol. Today* **17**, 453.

Edelman, G. M. (1973). Antibody structure and molecular immunology. *Science* **180**, 830.

Goodnow, C. C. (1997). Balancing immunity, autoimmunity and self-tolerance. *Annals NY Acad. Sci.* **815**, 55.

Henderson, A., and Calame, K. (1998). Transcriptional regulation during B cell development. *Ann. Rev. Immunol.* **16**, 163.

Justement, L. B., Brown, V. K., and Lin, J. (1994). Regulation of B cell activation by CD45: A question of mechanism. *Immunol. Today* **15**, 399.

Krieg, A. M. (1996). An Innate immune defense machanism based on the recognition of CpG motifs in microbial DNA. *J. Lab. Clin. Med.* **128**, 128.

Melchers, F. (1997). B-lymphocyte-lineage cells from early precursors to Ig-secreting plasma cells: Targets of regulation by the myc/mad/max families of genes? *Curr. Top. Microbiol. Immunol.* **224**, 19.

Murakami, M., and Honjo, T. (1995). Involvement of B-1 cells in mucosal immunity and autoimmunity. *Immunol. Today* **16**, 534.

Osmond, D. G., Rolink, A., and Melchers, F. (1998). Murine B lymphopoiesis: Towards a unified model. *Immunol. Today* **19**, 65.

Porter, R. R. (1973). Structural studies of immunoglobulins. *Science* **180**, 713.

Rudin, C. M., and Thompson, C. B. (1998). B-cell development and maturation. *Seminars in Oncology* **25**, 435.

Tedder, T. F., and Engel, P. (1994). CD20: A regulator of cell cycle progression of B lymphocytes. *Immunol. Today* **15**, 450.

Tedder, T. F., Zhou, L., and Engel, P. (1994). The CD19/CD21 signal transduction complex of B lymphocytes. *Immunol. Today* **15**, 437.

Van Parijs, L., and Abbas, A. K. (1998). Homeostasis and self-tolerance in the immune system: Turning lymphocytes off. *Science* **280**, 243.

Winter, G., Griffiths, A. D., Hawkins, R. E., and Hoogenboom, H. R. (1994). Making antibodies by phage display technology. *Ann. Rev. Immunol.* **12**, 433.

# Antifungal Agents

### Ana Espinel-Ingroff

*Medical College of Virginia of Virginia Commonwealth University*

## GLOSSARY

**emerging fungal infections** Fungal infections caused by new or uncommon fungi.

**granulocytopenia/neutropenia** Acquired or chemically induced immunosuppression caused by low white blood cell counts.

**immunocompromised** Having a defect in the immune system.

**in vitro and in vivo** Describing or referring to studies carried out in the test tube and in animals, respectively.

**mycoses and mycotic infections** Diseases caused by yeasts or molds.

**nephrotoxicity** Damage to the kidney cells.

**opportunistic infections** Infections caused by saprophytic fungi or not true parasites.

**ANTIFUNGAL AGENTS** are naturally occurring or synthetically produced compounds that have *in vitro* or *in vivo* activity against yeasts, molds, or both. Fungi and mammalian cells are eukaryotes, and antifungal agents that inhibit synthesis of proteins, RNA, and DNA are potentially toxic to mammalian cells.

Fungi can be unicellular (yeasts) and multicellular or filamentous (molds) microorganisms. Some medically important fungi can exist in each of these morphologic forms and are called dimorphic fungi. Of the estimated 250,000 fungal species described, fewer than 150 are known to be etiologic agents of disease in humans. Most fungi associated with disease are considered opportunistic pathogens (especially the yeasts) because they live as normal flora in humans, lower animals, and plants and rarely cause disease in otherwise healthy individuals. Many fungi, on the other hand, are important plant and lower animal parasites and can cause damage to crops (wheat rust, corn smut, etc.) and to fruit (banana wilt), forest (Dutch elm disease), and ornamental trees and other plants. Historically, the potato famine, which was the reason for the great migration from Ireland to the Americas, was caused by a fungal infection (potato blight). At the same time, fungi and their products play an important economic role in the production of alcohol, certain acids, steroids, antibiotics, etc.

Due to the high incidence of toxicity among antifungal agents and the perception before the 1970s that the number of severe and invasive infections was low, only nine antifungal agents are currently licensed for the treatment of systemic fungal infections: the polyene amphotericin B and its three lipid formulations, the pyrimidine synthesis inhibitor

5-fluorocytosine (flucytosine), the imidazoles miconazole and ketoconazole, and the triazoles fluconazole and itraconazole. However, the number of fungal diseases caused by both yeasts and molds has significantly increased during the past 20 years, especially among the increased number of immunocompromised patients, who are at high risk for life-threatening mycoses. There are more antifungal agents for topical treatment and agriculture and veterinary use, and several agents are under investigation for the management of severe and refractory fungal infections in humans (Table I).

This article summarizes the most relevant facts regarding the chemical structure, mechanisms of action and resistance, pharmacokinetics, safety, adverse interactions with other drugs and applications of the established systemic and topical antifungal agents currently licensed for clinical, veterinary, or agricultural uses. A shorter description is provided for antifungal compounds that are in the last phases of clinical development, under clinical trials in humans, or that have been discontinued from additional clinical evaluation. The former compounds have potential use as therapeutic agents. More detailed data regarding these agents are found in the references.

## I. THE POLYENES

The polyenes are macrolide molecules that target membranes containing ergosterol, which is an important sterol in the fungal cell membranes. Traces of ergosterol are also involved in the overall cell cycle of fungi.

## A. Amphotericin B

Amphotericin B is the most important of the 200 polyenes. Amphotericin B replaced 2-hydroxystilbamidine in the treatment of blastomycosis in the mid-1960s. Two amphotericins (A and B) were isolated in the 1950s from *Streptomyces nodosus*, an aerobic bacterium, from a soil sample from Venezuela's Orinoco River Valley. Amphotericin B (the most active molecule) has seven conjugated double bounds,

an internal ester, a free carboxyl group, and a glycoside side chain with a primary amino group (Fig. 1A). It is unstable to heat, light, and acid pH. The fungistatic (inhibition of fungal growth) and fungicidal (lethal) activity of amphotericin B is due to its ability to combine with ergosterol in the cell membranes of susceptible fungi. Pores or channels are formed causing osmotic instability and loss of membrane integrity. This effect is not specific; it extends to mammalian cells. The drug binds to cholesterol, creating the high toxicity associated with all conventional polyene agents. A second mechanism of antifungal action has been proposed for amphotericin B, which is oxidation dependent. Amphotericin B is highly protein bound (91–95%). Peak serum of 1–3 $\mu$g/ml and trough concentrations of 0.5–1.1 $\mu$g/ml are usually measured after the intravenous (iv) administration of 0.6 mg/kg doses. Its half-life of elimination is 24–48 hr, with a long terminal half-life of up to 15 days.

Although resistance to amphotericin is rare, quantitative and qualitative changes in the cell membrane sterols have been associated with the development of microbiological resistance both *in vitro* and *in vivo*. Clinically, resistance to amphotericin B has become an important problem, particularly with certain yeast and mold species, such as *Candida lusitaniae, Fusarium* spp., *Malassezia furfur, Pseudallescheria boydii, Trichosporon beigelii,* and other emerging fungal pathogens.

The *in vitro* spectrum of activity of amphotericin B includes yeasts, dimorphic fungi, and most of the opportunistic filamentous fungi. Clinically, amphotericin B is considered the gold standard antifungal agent for the management of most systemic and disseminated fungal infections caused by both yeasts and molds, including endemic (infections caused by the dimorphic fungi, *Cocccidioides immitis, Histoplasma capsulatum,* and *Blastomyces dermatitidis*) and opportunistic mycoses. Although it penetrates poorly into the cerebrospinal fluid (CSF), amphotericin B is effective in the treatment of both *Candida* and *Cryptococcus* meningitis alone and/or in combination with 5-fluorocytosine. Current recommendations regarding daily dosage, total dosage, duration, and its use in combination with other antifungal agents are based on the type of infection and the

**TABLE I**
**Antifungal Agents, Mechanisms of Action, and Their Use**[a]

| Antifungal class | Antifungal target of action | Agent | Use |
|---|---|---|---|
| Polyenes | Membranes containing ergosterol | Amphotericin B (AMB) | Systemic mycoses[b,c] |
| | | Nystatin (NYS) | Superficial mycoses[b,c] |
| | | AMB lipid complex | Systemic mycoses intolerant or refractory to AMB |
| | | AMB colloidal dispersion | |
| | | Liposomal AMB | |
| | | Liposomal NYS | Under investigation |
| | | Pimaricin | Topical keratitis[b,c] |
| Phenolic benzyfuran cyclohexane | Microtubule aggregation and DNA inhibition | Griseofulvin | Dermatophytic infections[b] |
| Natural glutarimide | Protein synthesis inhibition | Cycloheximide | Laboratory and agriculture |
| Phenylpyrroles | Unknown | Fenpiclonil | Agriculture |
| | | Fludioxonil | |
| Synthetic pyrimidines | Fungal cytosine permeae and deaminase | Flucytosine | Systemic (yeasts) in combination with AMB[b,c] |
| | Ergosterol inhibition | Triarimol | Agriculture |
| | | Fenarimol | |
| Anilinopyrimidines | Enzyme secretion | Pyrimethanil | |
| | | Cyprodinil | |
| Azoles | Ergosterol biosynthesis inhibition | Imidazoles | |
| | | Clotrimazole | Topical, oral troche[b,c] |
| | | Econazole | |
| | | Isoconazole | |
| | | Oxiconazole | |
| | | Tioconazole | |
| | | Miconazole | *P. boydii* infections only and veterinary[c] |
| | | Ketoconazole | Secondary alternative to other agents and veterinary[b,c] |
| | | Enilconazole | Veterinary |
| | | Epoxiconazole | Agriculture |
| | | Fluquinconazole | |
| | | Triticonazole | |
| | | Prochoraz | |
| | | Triazoles | |
| | | Fluconazole | Certain systemic and superficial diseases[b,c] |
| | | Itraconazole | |
| | | Terconazole | Intravaginal |
| | | Voriconazole | Under investigation |
| | | SCH 56592 | |
| | | BMS-207147 (ER-30346) | |
| Allylamines | | Terbinafine | Superficial infections |
| | | Naftifine | Topical |

*continues*

*Continued*

| Antifungal class | Antifungal target of action | Agent | Use |
|---|---|---|---|
| Benzylamines | | Butenafine | Topical |
| Thiocarbamates | | Tolnaftate | Topical |
| | | Tolciclate | |
| | | Piritetrade | |
| Dithiocarbamates | Nonspecific | Mancozeb | Agriculture |
| | | Thiram | |
| Benzimidazoles and methylbenz-imidazole carbamates | Nuclear division | Carbendazim | Agriculture |
| | | Benomyl | |
| | | Thiophanate | |
| Morpholines | Ergosterol biosynthesis inhibition | Amorolfine | Topical |
| | | Fenpropimorph | Agriculture |
| | | Tridemorph | |
| Pyridines | | Buthiobate | Agriculture |
| | | Pyrifenox | |
| Echinocandins | Fungal $\beta$(1,3)-glucan synthetase inhibition | Papulocandins | None |
| | | Echinocandin B derivative LY 303366 | Under investigation |
| | | Pneumocandin derivatives Caspofungin L 743872 (MK-0991) | Under investigation |
| Pradimicins | Fungal sacharide (man-noproteins) | Pradamicin FA-2 (BMY 28864) | Under investigation |
| Benanomycins | | Benanomycin A | Under investigation |
| Polyoxins | Fungal chitin synthase inhibition | Polyoxin D | None |
| Nikkomycins | | Nikkomycin Z | Under investigation |
| Sordarins | Protein synthesis inhi-bition | GM 222712 | Under investigation |
| | | GM 237354 | |
| | | GM 211676 | |
| | | GM 193663 | |
| Cinnamic acid | Cell wall | Dimethomorph | Agriculture |
| Oomycete fungicide | Oxidative phosphory-lation | Fluazynam | Agriculture |
| Phthalimides | Nonspecific | Captan | Agriculture |
| | | Captafol | |
| | | Folpet | |
| Cationic peptides | Lipid bilayer of biologi-cal membranes | Natural peptides | |
| | | Cecropin | Under investigation |
| | | Indolicidin | |
| | | Synthetic peptides | Under investigation |
| Amino acid analogs | Amino acid synthesis in-terference | RI 331 | Under investigation |
| | | Azoxybacillins | |
| | | Cispentacin | |

[a] Only licensed, commonly used, and antifungals under clinical investigation are listed; see text for other antifungals.

[b] Clinical and veterinary use; other applications for use in humans only.

[c] A human product used in veterinary practice.

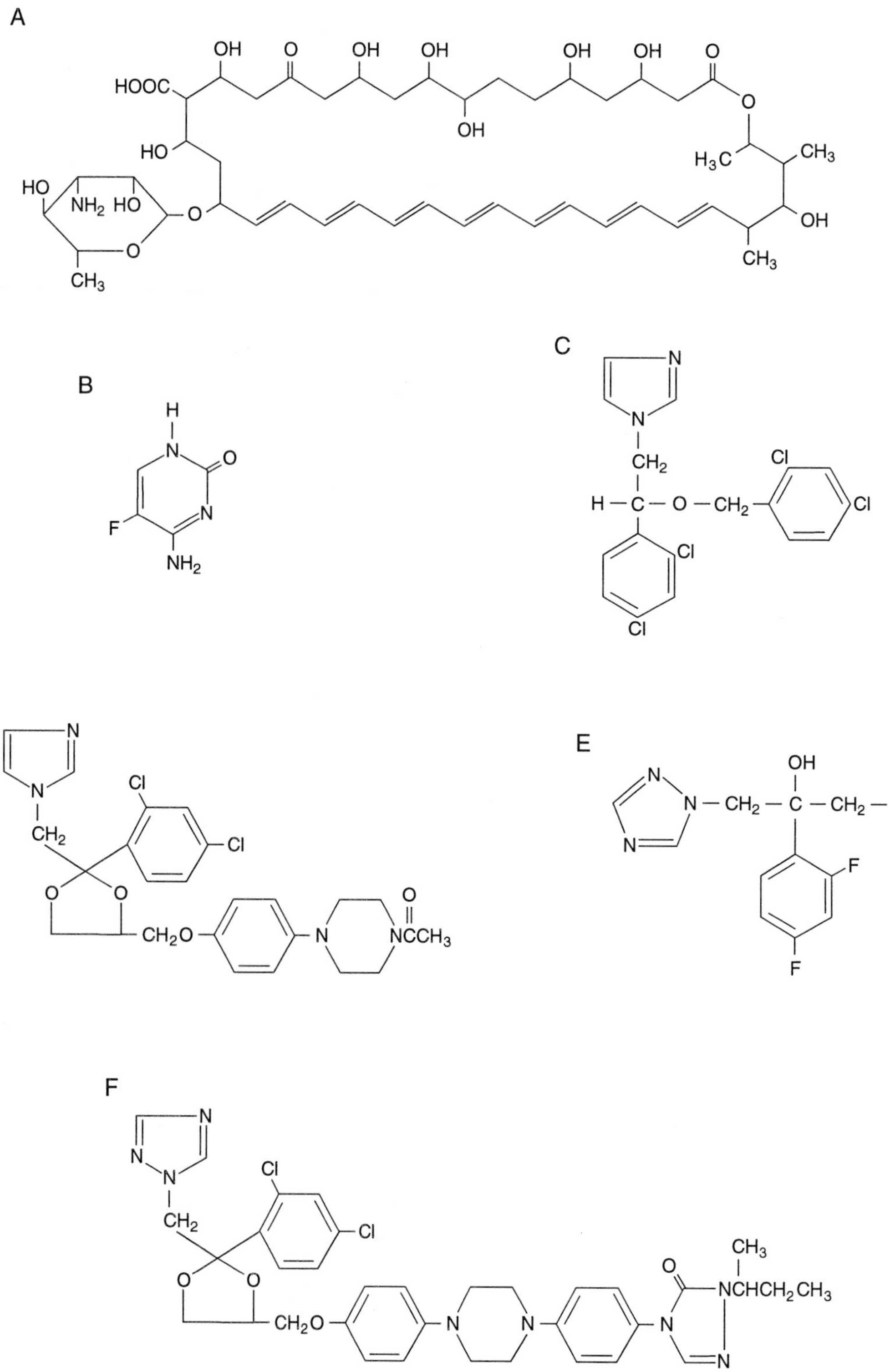

**Fig. 1.** Chemical structures of the systemic licensed antifungal agents: (A) amphotericin B, (B) 5-fluorocytosine, (C) miconazole, (D) ketoconazole, (E) fluconazole, and (F) itraconazole.

status of the host. Since severe fungal infections in the granulocytopenic host are difficult to diagnose and cause much mortality, empirical antifungal therapy with amphotericin B and other agents has improved patient care. Systemic prophylaxis for patients at high risk for invasive mycoses has also evolved. Toxicity is the limiting factor during amphotericin B therapy and has been classified as acute or delayed (Table II). Nephrotoxicity is the most significant delayed adverse effect. Therefore, close monitoring of renal function tests, bicarbonate, electrolytes including magnesium, diuresis, and hydration status is recommended during amphotericin B therapy. Adverse drug interactions can occur with the administration of electrolytes and other concomitant drugs. This drug is also used for the treatment of systemic infections in small animals, especially blastomycosis in dogs, but it is not effective against aspergillosis. Side effects (especially in cats) and drug interactions are similar to those in humans.

## B. Nystatin

Nystatin was the first of the polyenes to be discovered when it was isolated from *S. noursei* in the early 1950s. It is an amphoteric tetrane macrolide that has a similar structure (Fig. 2A) and identical mechanism of action to those of conventional amphotericin B. Although it has an *in vitro* spectrum of activity similar to that of amphotericin B, this antifungal is used mostly for the therapy of gastrointestinal (orally) and mucocutaneous candidiasis (topically). This is not only due to its toxicity after parenteral administration to humans and lower animals but also to its lack of effectiveness when given iv to experimental animals. It is used for candidiasis in small animals and birds and for otitis caused by *Microsporum canis.*

## C. Lipid Formulations

### 1. *Amphotericin B Lipid Formulations*

In an attempt to decrease the toxicity and increase

**TABLE II**
**Adverse Side Effects of the Licensed Systemic Antifungal Agents**[a]

| Side effect | Drug |
|---|---|
| Fever, chills | A, K |
| Rash | FC, K, I, FL |
| Nausea, vomiting | A, FC, K, I, FL |
| Abdominal pain | FC, K |
| Anorexia | A, K |
| Diarrhea | FC |
| Elevation of transaminases | FC, K, I, FL |
| Hepatitis (rare) | FC, K, I, FL |
| Anemia | A, FC |
| Leukopenia, thrombocytopenia | FC |
| Decreased renal function (azotemia, acidosis, hypokalemia, etc.) | A |
| Decreased testosterone synthesis | K (I, rare) |
| Adrenal insufficiency, menstrual irregularities, female alopecia | K |
| Syndrome of mineralocorticoid excess, pedal edema | I |
| Headache | A, FC, K, I, FL |
| Photophobia | K |
| Dizziness | I |
| Seizures | FL |
| Confusion | FC |
| Arthralgia, myalgia, thrombophlebitis | A |

[a] See Groll *et al.* (1998) for more detailed information. A, amphotericin B; FC, flucytosine; K, ketoconazole; Fl, fluconazole; I, itraconazole.

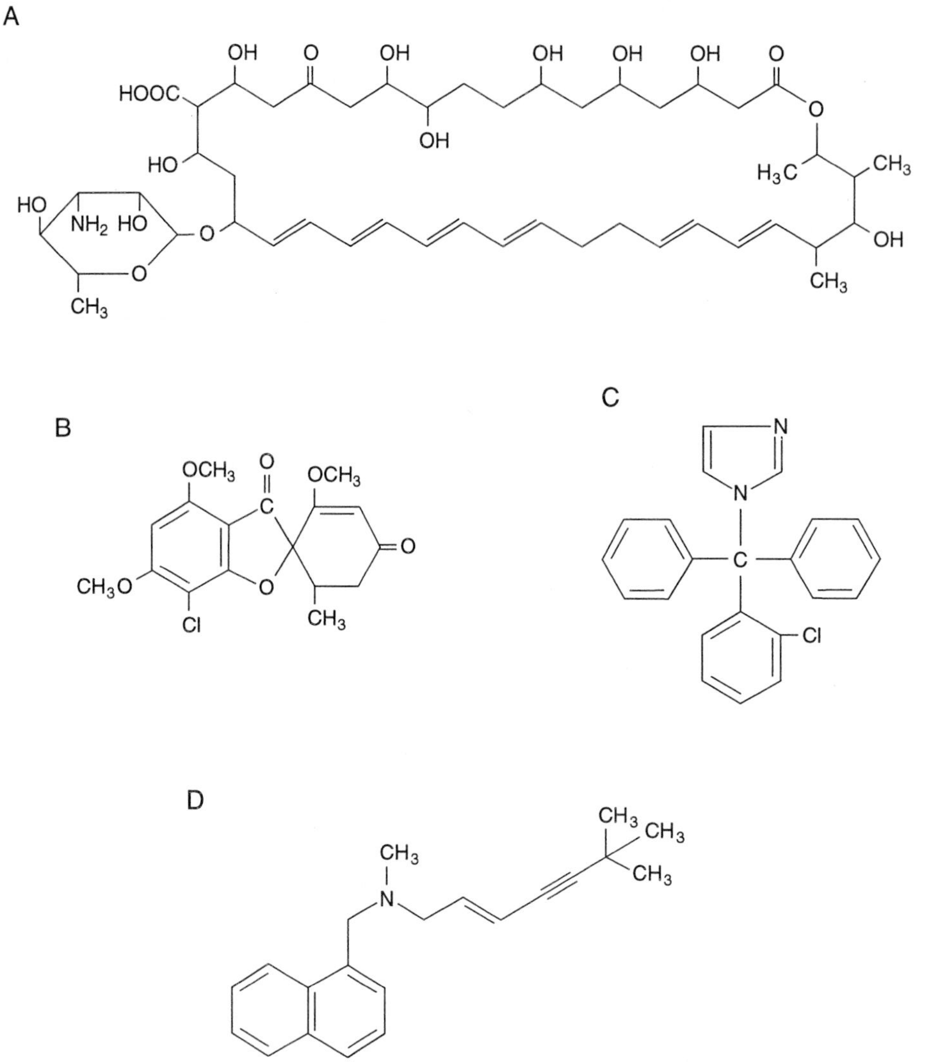

**Fig. 2.** Chemical structures of the most commonly used topical antifungal agents: (A) nystatin, (B) griseofulvin, (C) clotrimazole, and (D) terbinafine.

the efficacy of amphotericin B in patients with deep-seated fungal infections refractory to conventional therapy, several lipid formulations of this antifungal have been developed since the 1980s. These preparations have selective toxicity or affinity for fungal cell membranes and theoretically promote the delivery of the drug to the site of infection while avoiding the toxicity of supramaximal doses of conventional amphotericin B. The result is a reduction of human erythrocytes lysis; as a result, higher doses of amphotericin B can be safely used. Three lipid formulations of amphotericin B have been evaluated in clinical trials: an amphotercin B lipid complex, an amphotericin B colloidal dispersion, and a liposomal amphotericin B. However, despite evidence of nephrotoxicity reduction, a significant improvement in their efficacy compared to conventional amphotericin B has not been clearly demonstrated. Although these three formulations have been approved for the treatment of invasive fungal infections that have failed conventional amphotericin B therapy, not enough information is available regarding their pharmacokinetics, drug interactions, long-term toxicities, and the differences in both efficacy and tolerance among the three formulations. Also, the most cost-effective clinical role of these agents as first-line therapies has not been elucidated.

### a. Liposomal Amphotericin B

In the only commercially available liposomal formulation (ambisome), amphotericin B is incorporated into small unilamellar, spherical vesicles (60- to 70-nm liposomes). These liposomes contain hydrogenated soy phospatidylcholine and disteaoryl phosphatidylglycerol stabilized by cholesterol and amphotericin B in a 2:0.8:1:0.4 molar ratio. In the first liposomes, amphotericin B was incorporated into large, multilamellar liposomes that contained two phospholipids, dimyristoyl phosphatidylcholine (DMPC) and dimyristoyl phosphatidylglycerol (DMPG), in a 7:3 molar ratio (5–10% mole ratio of amphotericin B to lipid). This formulation is not commercially available, but it led to the development of commercial formulations.

### b. Amphotericin B Lipid Complex

Amphotericin B lipid complex contains a DMPC/DMPG lipid formulation in a 7:3 ratio and a 50% molar ratio of amphotericin B to lipid complexes that form ribbon-like structures.

### c. Amphotericin B Colloidal Dispersion

Amphotericin B colloidal dispersion contains cholesteryl sulfate and amphotericin B in a 1:1 molar ratio. This formulation is a stable complex of disk-like structures (122 nm in diameter and 4 nm thickness).

### 2. Liposomal Nystatin

In order to protect human erythrocytes from nystatin toxicity and thus make this drug available as a systemic therapeutic agent, nystatin has been incorporated into stable, multilamellar liposomes, which contain DMPC and DMPG in a 7:3 ratio. Although it has been demonstrated that the efficacy of liposomal nystatin is significantly superior to that of conventional nystatin and is well tolerated in experimental murine models of systemic candidiasis and aspergillosis (fungal infections caused by *Candida* spp. and *Apergillus* spp.), evaluations in human subjects are limited.

### D. Candicidin

Candicidin is a conjugated heptaene complex produced by *S. griseus* that is selectively and highly active *in vitro* against yeasts. It is more toxic for mammalian cells than either amphotericin B or nystatin; therefore, its use was restricted to topical applications for the treatment of vaginal candidiasis (infections by *Candida albicans* and other *Candida* spp.).

### E. Pimaricin

Pimaricin is a tetraene polyene produced by *S. natalensis*. It has a higher binding specificity for cholesterol than for ergosterol and, therefore, it is highly toxic for mammalian cells. The therapeutic use of pimaricin is limited to the topical treatment of keratitis (eye infections; also in horses) caused by the molds *Fusarium* spp., *Acremonium* spp., and other species.

## II. GRISEOFULVIN

Griseofulvin is a phenolic, benzyfuran cyclohexane agent (Fig. 2B) that binds to RNA. It is a product of *Penicillium janczewskii* and was the first antifungal agent to be developed as a systemic plant protectant. It acts as a potent inhibitor of thymidylate synthetase and interferes with the synthesis of DNA. It also inhibits microtubule formation and the synthesis of apical hyphal cell wall material. With the advent of terbinafine and itraconazole, the clinical use of griseofulvin as an oral agent for treatment of dermatophytic infections has become limited. However, it is frequently used for these infections in small animals, horses, and calves (skin only) as well as for equine sporotrichosis. Abdominal adverse side effects have been noted, especially in cats.

## III. CYCLOHEXIMIDE

This is a glutaramide agent produced by *S. griseus*. This agent was among the three antifungals that were reported between 1944 and 1947. Although cycloheximide had clinical use in the past, it is currently used as a plant fungicide and in the preparation of laboratory media.

## IV. PYRROLNITRIN, FENPICLONIL, AND FLUDIOXONIL

Pyrrolnitrin is the fermentation product of *Pseudomonas* spp. It was used in the past as a topical agent. Fenpiclonil and fludioxonil (related to pyrrolnitrin) were the first of the phenylpyrrols to be introduced as cereal seed fungicides.

## V. THE SYNTHETIC PYRIMIDINES

### A. 5-Fluorocytosine (Flucytosine)

The synthetic 5-fluorocytosine is an antifungal metabolite that was first developed as an antitumor agent, but it is not effective against tumors. It is an oral, low-molecular-weight, fluorinated pyrimidine related to 5-fluorouracil and floxuridine (Fig. 1B). It acts as a competitive antimetabolite for uracil in the synthesis of yeast RNA; it also interferes with thymidylate synthetase. Several enzymes are involved in the mode of action of 5-fluorocytosine. The first step is initiated by the uptake of the drug by a cell membrane-bound permease. Inside the cell, the drug is deaminated to 5-fluorouracil, which is the main active form of the drug. These activities can be antagonized *in vitro* by a variety of purines and pyrimidine bases and nucleosides. At least two metabolic sites are responsible for resistance to this compound: One involves the enzyme cytosine permease, which is responsible for the uptake of the drug into the fungal cell, and the other involves the enzyme cytosine deaminase, which is responsible for the deamination of the drug to 5-fluorouracil. Alterations of the genetic regions encoding these enzymes may result in fungal resistance to this drug by either decreasing the cell wall permeability or synthesizing molecules that compete with the drug or its metabolites.

5-Fluorocytosine has fungistatic but not fungicidal activity mostly against yeasts; its activity against molds is inoculum dependent. Clinically, the major therapeutic role of 5-fluorocytosine is its use in combination with amphotericin B in the treatment of meningitis caused by the yeast *Cryptococcus neoformans*. The synergistic antifungal activity of these two agents has been demonstrated in clinical trials in non-HIV-infected and AIDS patients. 5-Fluorocytosine should not be used alone for the treatment of any fungal infections. Therapeutic combinations of 5-fluorocytosine with several azoles are under investigation. The most serious toxicity associated with 5-fluorocytosine therapy is bone marrow suppression (6% of patients), which leads to neutropenia, thrombocytopenia, or pancytopenia (Table II). Therefore, monitoring of the drug concentration in the patient's serum (serial 2-hr levels post-oral administration) is highly recommended to adjust dosage and maintain serum levels between 40 and 60 $\mu$g/ml. Since the drug is administered in combination with amphotericin B, a decrease in glomerular filtration rate, a side effect of the latter compound, can induce increased toxicity to 5-fluorocytosine. Adverse drug interactions can occur with other antimicrobial and anticancer drugs, cyclosporine, and other therapeutic agents. Because of its toxic potential, 5-fluorocytosine should not be administered to pregnant women or animals. This drug has been used in combination with ketoconazole for cryptococcosis in small animals (very toxic for cats) and also for respiratory apergillosis and severe candidiasis in birds.

### B. Triarimol, Fenarimol, Pyrimethanil, and Cyprodinil

Triarimol and fenarimol are pyrimidines with a different mechanism of action than that of 5-fluorocytosine. They inhibit lanosterol demethylase, an enzyme involved in the synthesis of ergosterol, which leads to the inhibition of this biosynthetic pathway. Triarimol and fenarimol are not used in medicine but are used extensively as antifungal agents in agriculture.

The anilino-pyrimidines, pyrimethanil and cyprodinil, inhibit the secretion of the fungal enzymes that cause plant cell lysis. Pyrimethanil has activity (without cross-resistance) against *Botrytis cinerea* (vines, fruits, vegetables, and ornamental plants) and *Venturia* spp. (apples and pears), whereas cyprodinil has systemic activity against *Botrytis* spp. but only a preventive effect against *Venturia* spp.

## VI. THE AZOLES

The azoles are the largest single source of synthetic antifungal agents; the first azole was discovered in

1944. As a group, they are broad-spectrum in nature and mostly fungistatic. The broad spectrum of activity involves fungi (yeasts and molds), bacteria, and parasites. This group includes fused ring and N-substituted imidazoles and the N-substituted triazoles. The mode of action of these compounds is the inhibition of lanosterol demethylase, a cytochrome P-450 enzyme.

## A. Fused-Ring Imidazoles

The basic imidazole structure is a cyclic five-member ring containing three carbon and two nitrogen molecules. In the fused-ring imidazoles, two carbon molecules are shared in common with a fused benzene ring. Most of these compounds have parasitic activity (anthelmintic) and two have limited antifungal activity: 1-chlorobenzyl-2-methylbenzimidazole and thiabendazole.

### 1. 1-Chlorobenzyl-2-Methylbenzimidazole

The azole 1-chlorobenzyl-2-methylbenzimidazole was developed specifically as an anti-*Candida* agent. It has been used in the past in the treatment of superficial yeast and dermatophyte infections.

### 2. Thiabendazole

Thiabendazole was developed as an anthelmintic agent and has a limited activity against dermatophytes. It was also used in the past in the treatment of superficial yeast and dermatophytic infections. Thiabendazole has been used for aspergillosis and penicillosis in dogs.

## B. N-Substituted (Mono) Imidazoles

In this group, the imidazole ring is intact and substitutions are made at one of the two nitrogen molecules. At least three series of such compounds have emerged for clinical and agricultural use. In the triphenylmethane series, substitutions are made at the nonsymmetrical carbon atom attached to one nitrogen molecule of the imidazole ring. In the second series, the substitutions are made at a phenethyl configuration attached to the nitrogen molecule. The dioxolane series is based on a 1,3-dioxolane molecule rather than on the 1-phenethyl molecule. These series vary in spectrum, specific level of antifungal activity, routes of administration, and potential uses.

### 1. Clotrimazole

Clotrimazole is the first member of the triphenylmethane series of clinical importance (Fig. 2C). It has good *in vitro* activity at very low concentrations against a large variety of fungi (yeasts and molds). However, hepatic enzymatic inactivation of this compound, after systemic administration, has limited its use to topical applications (1% cream, lotion, solution, tincture, and vaginal cream) for superficial mycoses (nail, scalp, and skin infections) caused by the dermatophytes and *M. furfur,* for initial and/or mild oropharyngeal candidiasis (OPC; 10-mg oral troche), and for the intravaginal therapy (single application of 500-mg intravaginal tablet) of vulvovaginal candidiasis. Other intravaginal drugs require 3- to 7-day applications. This drug is also used for candidal stomatitis, dermatophytic infections, and nasal aspergillosis (infused through tubes) in dogs.

### 2. Bifonazole

Bifonazole is a halogen-free biphenylphenyl methane derivative. Bifonazole is seldom utilized as a topical agent for superficial infections, despite its broad spectrum of activity. Its limited use is the result of its toxic side effects for mammalian cells. Bifonazole is retained in the dermis for a longer time than clotrimazole.

### 3. Econazole, Isoconazole, Oxiconazole, and Tioconazole

Other frequently used topical imidazoles include econazole (1% cream), isoconazole (1% cream), oxiconazole (1% cream and lotion), and tioconazole (6.5% vaginal ointment) (Table I). As with clotrimazole, a single application of tioconazole is effective in the management of vulvovaginal candidiasis and as a nail lacquer for fungal onychomycosis (nail infections). Mild to moderate vulvovaginal burning has been associated with intravaginal therapy. Oxiconazole and econazole are less effective than terbinafine and itraconazole in the treatment of onychomycosis and other infections caused by the dermatophytes. Although topical agents do not cure onychomycosis as oral drugs do, they may slow down the spread of this infection. However, the recommended drugs for the treatment of onychomycosis are terbinafine (by dermatophytes) and itraconazole.

## 4. Miconazole

Miconazole was the first azole derivative to be administered intravenously for the therapy of systemic fungal infections. Its use is limited, due to toxicity and high relapse rates, to certain cases of invasive infections caused by the opportunistic mold, *P. boydii*. Since this compound is insoluble in water, it was dissolved in a polyethoxylated castor oil for its systemic administration. This solvent appears to be the cause of the majority of miconazole side effects (pruritus, headache, phlebitis, and hepatitis). On the other hand, miconazole is used for dermatophytic infections in large animals, fungal keratitis and pneumonia in horses, resistant yeast infections to nystatin in birds, and aspergillosis in raptors. However, safety and efficacy data are not available (veterinary use).

## 5. Ketoconazole

Ketoconazole was the first representative of the dioxolane series (Fig. 1D) to be introduced into clinical use and was the first orally active azole. Ketoconazole requires a normal intragastric pH for absorption. Its bioavailability is highly dependent on the pH of the gastric contents; an increase in pH will decrease its absorption, e.g., in patients with gastric achlorhydria or treated with antacids or $H_2$-receptor antagonists (Table III). This drug should be taken with either orange juice or a carbonated beverage.

Ketoconazole pharmocokinetics corresponds to a dual model with an initial half-life of 1–4 hr and a terminal half-life of 6–10 hr, depending on the dose. This drug highly binds to plasma proteins and penetrates poorly into the CSF, urine, and saliva. Peak plasma concentrations of approximately 2, 8, and 20 $\mu$g/ml are measured 1–4 hr after corresponding oral doses of 200, 400, and 800 mg. The most common and dose-dependent adverse effects of ketonazole are

**TABLE III**
**Adverse Interactions of the Licensed Systemic Azoles with Other Drugs during Concomitant Therapy[a]**

| Azole | Concomitant drug | Adverse side effect of interaction |
|---|---|---|
| K, FL, I | Nonsedating antihistamines, cisapride, terfenadine, astemizole | Fetal arrhythmia |
| K, Fl, I | Rifampin, isoniazid, phenobarbital, rifabutin, carbamazepine, and phenyton | Reduce azole plasma concentrations |
| K, Fl, I | Phenytoin, benzodiazepines, rifampin | Induces the potential toxicity levels of cocompounds |
| K, I | Antacids, $H_2$ antagonists, omeprazole, sucralfate, didanosine | Reduces azole absorption |
| K, Fl, I | Lovastin, simvastatin | Rhabdomyolysis |
| I | Indinavir, vincristine, quinidine, digoxin, cyclosporine, tacrolimus, methylprednisolone, and ritonavir | Induces potential toxicity cocompounds |
| Fl, I | Warfarin, rifabutin, sulfonylurea | Induces potential toxicity of cocompounds |
| K | Saquinavir, chlordiazepoxide, methylprednisone | Induces potential toxicity of these compounds |
| K | Protein-binding drugs | Increases the release of fractions of free drug |
| K | Cyclosporine A | Nephrotoxicity |

[a] See Groll *et al.* (1998) for more detailed information. K, ketoconazole; Fl, fluconazole; I, itraconazole.

nausea, anorexia, and vomiting (Table II). They occur in 10% of the patients receiving a 400-mg dose and in approximately 50% of the patients taking 800-mg or higher doses. Another limiting factor of ketoconazole therapy is its numerous and significant adverse interactions with other concomitant drugs (see Table III for a summary of the interactions of the azoles with other drugs administered to patients during azole therapy).

*In vitro*, ketoconazole has a broad spectrum of activity comparable to that of miconazole and the triazoles. However, due to its adverse side effects, its adverse interaction with other drugs, and the high rate of relapses, ketoconazole has been replaced by itraconazole as an alternative to amphotericin B for the treatment of immunocompetent individuals with non-life-threatening, non-central nervous system, localized or disseminated histoplasmosis, blastomycosis, mucocutaneous candidiasis, paracoccidioidomycosis, and selected forms of coccidioidomycosis. In noncancer patients, this drug can be effective in the treatment of superficial *Candida* and dermatophyte infections when the latter are refractory to griseofulvin therapy. Therapeutic failure with ketoconazole has been associated with low serum levels; monitoring of these levels is recommended in such failures. Ketoconazole also has been used for a variety of systemic and superficial fungal infections in cats and dogs.

### 6. Enilconazole

This is the azole most widely used in veterinary practice for the intranasal treatment of aspergillosis and penicillosis as well as for dermatophytic infections. The side effects are few.

### 7. Epoxiconazole, Fluquinconazole, Triticonazole, and Prochloraz

Epoxiconazole, fluquinconazole, and triticonazole are important agricultural fungicides which have a wider spectrum of activity than that of the earlier triazoles, triadimefon and propiconazole, and the imidazole, prochloraz, as systemic cereal fungicides. However, development of resistance to these compounds has been documented.

## C. The Triazoles

The triazoles are characterized by a more specific binding to fungal cell cytochromes than to mammalian cells due to the substitution of the imidazole ring by the triazole ring. Other beneficial effects of this substitution are (i) an improved resistance to metabolic degradation, (ii) an increased potency, and (iii) a superior antifungal activity. Although fluconazole and itraconazole are the only two triazoles currently licensed for antifungal systemic therapy, several other triazoles are at different levels of clinical evaluation (Table I).

### 1. Fluconazole

Fluconazole is a relatively small molecule (Fig. 1E) that is partially water soluble, minimally protein bound, and excreted largely as an active drug in the urine. It penetrates well into the CSF and parenchyma of the brain and the eye, and it has a prolonged half-life (up to 25 hr in humans). Its pharmacokinetics are independent of the route of administration and of the drug formulation and are linear. Fluconazole is well absorbed orally (its total bioavailability exceeds 90%), and its absorption is not affected by food or gastric pH. Plasma concentrations of 2–7 $\mu$g/ml are usually measured in healthy subjects after corresponding single doses of 100 and 400 mg. After multiple doses, the peak plasma levels are 2.5 times higher than those of single doses. The CSF to serum fluconazole concentrations are between 0.5 and 0.9% in both healthy human subjects and laboratory animals.

Fluconazole does not have *in vitro* or *in vivo* activity against most molds. Both oral and iv formulations of fluconazole are available for the treatment of candidemia in nonneutropenic and other nonimmunosuppressed patients, mucosal candidiasis (oral, vaginal, and esophageal), and chronic mucocutaneous candidiasis in patients of all ages. Fluconazole is the current drug of choice for maintenance therapy of AIDS-associated cryptococcal and coccidioidal meningitis. It is also effective as prophylactic therapy for immunocompromised patients to prevent both superficial and life-threatening fungal infections. However, since the cost of fluconazole is high and resistance to this drug can develop during therapy, fluconazole prophylaxis should be reserved for HIV-infected individuals or AIDS patients, who are refractory and intolerant to topical agents, or for patients with prolonged (>2 weeks) and profound neutropenia (<500 cells). Although the recommended dosage of fluconazole for adults is 100–400 mg qd, higher doses (>800 mg qd) are required for the treatment of severe invasive infections and for infections caused by a *Candida* spp. that exhibit a minimum inhibitory concentration (MIC) of >8 $\mu$g/ml. However, despite the fluconazole MIC obtained when the infecting yeast is either *Candida krusei* or *C. glabrata,* intrinsic resistance to these yeasts precludes its use for the treatment of such infections. In contrast to the imidazoles and itraconazole, fluconazole does not exhibit major toxicity side effects (2.8–16%). However, when the dosage is increased above 1200 mg, adverse side effects are more frequent (Table II). Fluconazole interactions with other concomitant drugs are similar to those reported with other azoles, but they are less frequent than those exhibited by ketoconazole and itraconazole (Table III). Fluconazole has been used to treat nasal aspergillosis and penicillosis in small animals and birds when topical enilconazole is not feasible.

### 2. Itraconazole

Itraconazole is the other commercially available oral triazole for the treatment of certain systemic mycoses. In contrast to fluconazole, itraconazole is insoluble in aqueous fluids; it penetrates poorly into the CSF and urine but well into skin and soft tissues; and it is highly protein bound (>90%). Its structure is closely related to that of ketoconazole (Fig. 1F), but itraconazole has a broader spectrum of *in vitro* and *in vivo* antifungal activity than those of both ketonazole and fluconazole. Similar to ketoconazole, itraconazole is soluble only at low pH and is better absorbed when the patient is not fasting. Absorption is erratic in cancer patients or when the patient is taking concomitant $H_2$-receptor antagonists, omeprazole, or antacids. Therefore, this drug should be taken with food and/or acidic fluids. Plasma peak (1.5–4 hr) and trough concentrations between 1 and 2.2 $\mu$g/ml and 0.4 and 1.8 $\mu$g/ml, respectively, are usually obtained after 200-mg dosages (capsule) as either single daily dosages (po or bid) or after iv administration (bid) for 2 days and qd for more days; these concentrations are also obtained in cancer patients receiving 5 mg/kg divided into two oral solution dosages.

Clinically, itraconazole (200–400 mg/day) has supplanted ketoconazole as first-line therapy for endemic, non-life-threatening mycoses caused by *B. dermatitidis, C. immitis,* and *H. capsulatum* as well as by *Sporothrix schenckii.* For more severe mycoses, higher doses are recommended and clinical resistance may emerge. It can also be effective as a second-line agent for refractory or intolerant infections to conventional amphotericin B therapy, e.g., infections by the phaeoid (dematiaceous or black molds or yeasts) fungi and *Aspergillus* spp. Although both the oral solution and the tablet are commercially available, the iv suspension is still under investigation. The oral solution is better absorbed than the tablet and has become useful for the treatment of HIV-associated oral and esophageal candidiasis, especially for those cases that are resistant to fluconazole. However, monitoring of itraconazole plasma concentrations is recommended during treatment of both superficial and invasive diseases: Drug concentration >0.5 $\mu$g/ml by high-performance liquid chromatography and >2 $\mu$g/ml by bioassay appear to be critical for favorable clinical response. Treatment with itraconazole has been associated with less adverse and mostly transient side effects (<10%) than that with ketoconazole (Table II), and these effects are usually observed when the patient takes up to 400 mg during several periods of time. Itraconazole has been used for the treatment of endemic mycoses, aspergillosis, and crytococcosis in dogs (especially blastomycosis), equine sporotrichosis, and osteomyelitis caused by *C. immitis* in large animals, but its use is minimal. No data are available regarding its side effects or drug interactions in animals.

### 3. Terconazole

Terconazole was the first triazole marketed for the topical treatment of vaginal candidiasis and superficial dermatophyte infections. Currently, it is only used for vulvovaginal candidiasis (0.4 and 0.8% vaginal creams and 80-mg vaginal suppositories).

## D. Investigational Triazoles

As fungal infections became an important health problem and resistance to established agents began to emerge, new triazoles were developed with a broader spectrum of antifungal activity. Early investigational triazoles, such as R 66905 (saperconazole), BAY R 8783, SCH 39304, and SCH 51048, were discontinued from further development due a variety of adverse side effects. Three triazoles are currently under clinical investigation (voriconazole, SCH 56592, and BMS-207147; Table I) and others are at earlier stages of development.

### 1. Voriconazole (UK-109496)

Voriconazole is a novel fluconazole derivative obtained by replacement of one triazole moiety by fluoropyrimidine and alpha methylation groups (Fig. 3A). In contrast to fluconazole and similar to itraconazole, voriconazole is non-water soluble. As do the other azoles, voriconazole acts by inhibiting fungal cytochrome P450-dependent, 14-$\alpha$-sterol demethylase-mediated synthesis of ergosterol. Voriconazole pharmacokinetics in humans are nonlinear. Following single oral doses, peak plasma concentrations were achieved after 2 hr and multiple doses resulted in a higher (eight times) accumulation. The mean half-life of elimination is about 6 hr. Voriconazole binds to proteins (65%), is extensively metabolized in the liver, and is found in the urine (78–88%) practically unchanged after a single dose. Voriconazole has an improved *in vitro* fungistatic activity and an increased potency against most fungi compared to those of fluconazole. It is fungicidal against some fungi, especially *Aspergillus* spp. However, less *in vitro* activity has been demonstrated for the opportunistic molds *Fusarium* spp., *Rhizopus arrhizus, S. schenckii,* and other less common emerging fungi. Studies in neutropenic animal models have demonstrated that voriconazole is superior to both amphotericin B and itraconazole for the treatment of certain opportunistic (especially aspergillosis) and endemic mycoses. This compound is under phase III evaluation for the treatment of invasive aspergillosis and infections refractory to established antifungal agents in humans. Its effectiveness as an empiric agent in neutropenia-associated candidemia is also under investigation. Although the drug has been well tolerated with only reversible side effects, information regarding the safety and drug interactions of this drug in immunocompetent and immunocompromised patients is limited. In small series of patients, both hepatic and visual side effects have been observed.

### 2. SCH 39304, SCH 51048, and SCH 56592

#### a. SCH 39304

SCH 39304 is an N-substituted difluorophenyl triazole with both *in vitro* and *in vivo* (oral and parental) activity for both yeasts and molds. Although preliminary clinical trials demonstrated that this compound was well tolerated by humans and had good pharmacokinetic properties, additional clinical development was precluded by the incidence of hepatocellular carcinomas in laboratory animals during prolonged treatment.

#### b. SCH 51048

SCH 51048 is a tetrahydrofurane-based triazole that has superior potency (orally) than that of SCH 39304 toward the target enzyme and good *in vitro* activity against a variety of fungi. Although animal studies demonstrated that this drug is also orally effective for the treatment of systemic and superficial yeast and mold infections, the slow absorption rate from the intestinal track due to its poor water solubility precluded its further clinical development.

#### c. Posaconazole (SCH 56592)

SCH 56592 is the product of a modification of the *n*-alkyl side chain of SCH 51048 which included a variety of chiral substituents. The *in vitro* fungistatic and fungicidal activities of SCH 56592 are similar to those of voriconazole and BMS-207147 and superior or comparable to those of the established agents against yeasts, the dimorphic fungi, most opportunistic molds including *Aspergillus* spp., the Zygomycetes, certain phaeoid fungi, and the dermatophytes. It has been demonstrated that SCH 56592 is superior to itraconazole for the treatment of experimental invasive aspergillosis in animals infected with strains of *Aspergillus fumigatus* with high and low itraconazole MICs. Similar results have been obtained for a variety

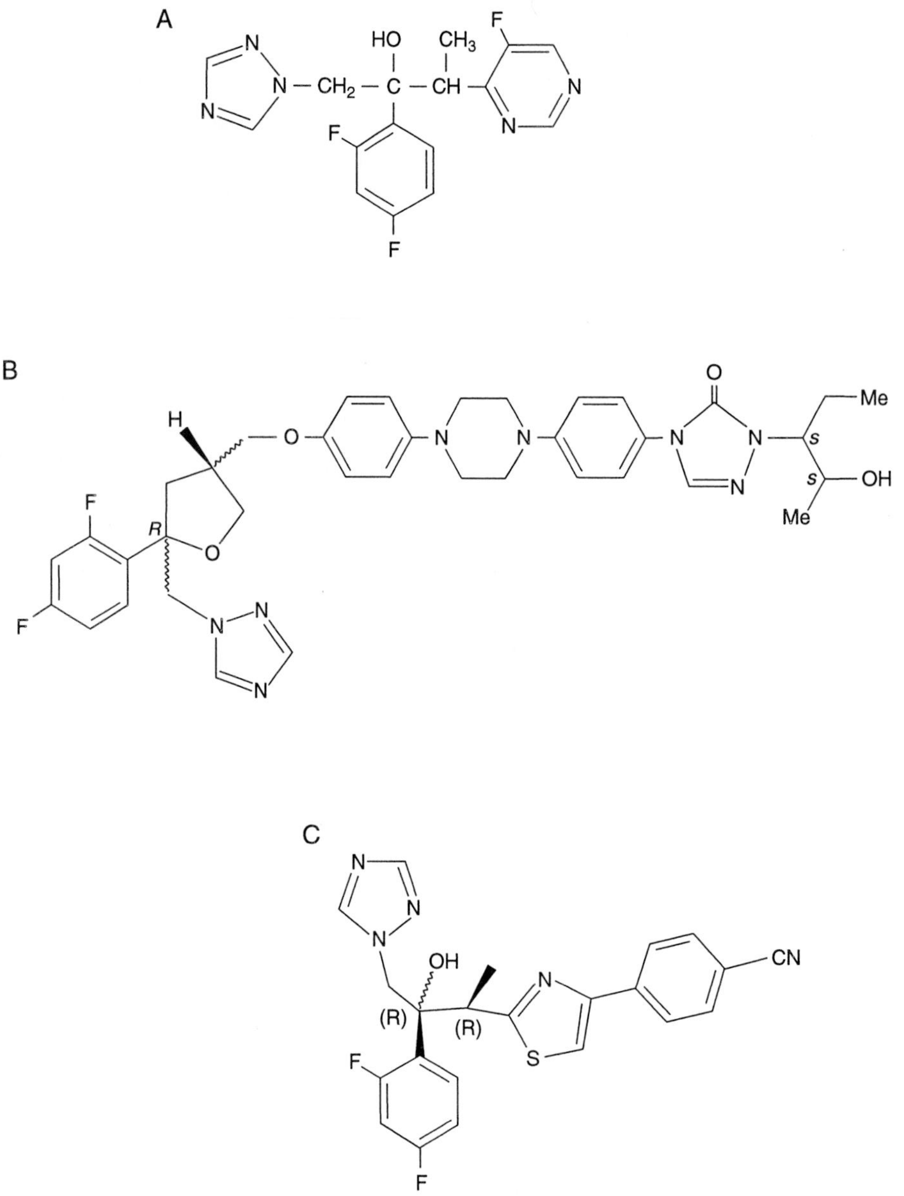

**Fig. 3.** Chemical structures of three triazoles under clinical investigation: (A) voriconazole, (B) SCH 56592, and (C) BMS-207147 (ER-30346).

of superficial and invasive infections in other animal
models. The pharmacokinetics of SCH 56592 has
been studied in laboratory animals and although drug
concentrations above both MIC and MFC (fungicidal) have been determined after a single po dose
at 24 hr, it has been demonstrated that plasma concentrations should be 5–10 higher than the MIC.
Also, its absorption from the intestinal tract is slow

and peak serum concentrations are achieved 11–24
hr after the actual dose. The clinical utility of this
compound has yet to be determined in clinical trials
in humans.

### 3. *Ravuconazole [BMS-207147 (ER-30346)]*

BMS-207147 is a novel oral thiazole-containing
triazole with a broad spectrum of activity against

the majority of opportunistic pathogenic fungi. The antifungal activity of this triazole against *A. fumigatus* appears to be enhanced by the introduction of one carbon chain between the benzylic *tert* carbon and thiazole substituents and the cyano group on the aromatic ring attached to the thiazole. BMS-207147 has a similar or superior *in vitro* activity compared to those of the other investigational and established drugs against most pathogenic yeasts, with the exceptions of *C. tropicalis* and *C. glabrata*. BMS-207147 also has good *in vivo* antifungal activity in murine models for the treatment of invasive aspergillosis, candidiasis, and cryptococcosis. BMS-207147 shows good pharmacokinetics in animals that is similar to that of itraconazole. This indicates that BMS-207147 is absorbed at levels comparable to those of itraconazole. However, the half-life of BMS-207147 (4 hr) is longer than that of itraconazole (1.4 hr) and similar to that of fluconazole. The potential use of BMS-207147 has yet to be determined in clinical trials in humans.

### 4. Saperconazole (R 66905)

Saperconazole is a lipophilic and poorly water-soluble fluorinated triazole; its chemical structure resembles that of itraconazole. Although both *in vitro* and *in vivo* antifungal activities were demonstrated against yeasts and molds and it was well tolerated during three clinical trials, this triazole was discontinued due to the incidence of malignant adrenal tumors in laboratory animals (long-term toxicity experiments).

### 5. BAY R 3783

This metabolite triazole was also discontinued from further clinical development due to the potential toxic effect during prolonged therapy.

### 6. SDZ 89-485

The antifungal activity of the D-enantiomer SDZ 89-485 antifungal triazole was demonstrated only in a few laboratory animal studies, and additional studies were not conducted with this compound.

### 7. D 0870

Although more *in vitro* and *in vivo* studies were conducted with D 0870 than with SDZ-89-485, and

D 0870 showed good antifungal activity, this drug was also discontinued by its original developers. The *in vitro* activity of D 0870 is lower than that of itraconazole against *Aspergillus* spp. but higher for the common *Candida* spp. Therefore, evaluation of this compound has been continued by another pharmaceutical company for the treatment of OPC in HIV-infected individuals. It has also shown activity against the parasite *Trypanosoma cruzei*.

### 8. T-8581

T-8581 is a water-soluble 2-fluorobutanamide triazole derivative. High peak concentrations (7.14–12 $\mu$g/ml) of T-8581 were determined in the sera of laboratory animals following the administration of single oral doses of 10 mg/kg, and the drug was detected in the animals sera after 24 hr. The half-life of T-8581 varies in the different animal models from 3.2 hr in mice to 9.9 hr in dogs. Animal studies suggest that the absorption of this compound is almost complete after po dosages. The maximum solubility of T-8581 is superior (41.8 mg/ml) to that of fluconazole (2.6 mg/ml), which suggests the potential use of this compound as an alternative to fluconazole for high-dose therapy.

T-8581 has shown potent *in vitro* antifungal activity against *Candida* spp., *C. neoformans,* and *A. fumigatus*. The activity of T-8581 is similar to that of fluconazole for the treatment of murine systemic candidiasis and superior to itraconazole for aspergillosis in rabbits. The safety of T-8581 is under evaluation.

### 9. UR-9746 and UR-9751

UR-9746 and UR-9751 are similar and recently introduced fluoridated triazoles that contain an N-morpholine ring, but UR-9746 has an extra hydroxyl group. The pharmacokinetics of these two compounds in laboratory animals has demonstrated peak concentrations (biological activity) of 184 (UR-9746) and 34 $\mu$g/ml (UR-9751) after 8 and 8–24 hr, respectively. A slow decline of these levels was seen after 48 hr. Chronic (19 days) doses of 100 mg/kg produced higher peak levels than single doses; two peaks were observed after 1 and 8 hr. However, the rate of decline of the drug after 24 hr was faster after multiple than after single doses. Superior *in vitro* and *in vivo* activity than that of fluconazole has been demonstrated with these compounds against *Candida* spp., *C. neoformans*, *H. capsulatum,* and *C. imitis.* Both antifungals lacked detectable toxicity in experimental animal infections Although UR-9751 MICs were fourfold higher than those of UR-9746, the *in vivo* activity in the animal model of systemic murine coccidioidomycosis was similar. Additional studies will determine the potential use of these compounds as systemic therapeutic agents in humans.

### 10. TAK 187 and SSY 726

Some *in vitro* and very little *in vivo* data are available for these new triazoles.

## VII. THE ALLYLAMINES

The allylamines act by inhibiting squalene epoxidase, which results in a decrease of the ergosterol content and an accumulation of squalene.

### A. Terbinafine and Naftifine

Terbinafine is the most active derivative of this class of antifungals. It has an excellent *in vitro* activity against the dermatophytes and other filamentous fungi, but its *in vitro* activity against the yeasts is controversial. It follows linear pharmacokinetics over a dose range of 125–750 mg; drug concentrations of 0.5–2.7 $\mu$g/ml are detected 1 or 2 hr after a single oral dose. Terbinafine has replaced griseofulvin and ketoconazole for the treatment of onychomycosis and other infections caused by dermatophytes (oral and topical). It is also effective for the treatment of vulvovaginal candidiasis. It is usually well tolerated at oral doses of 250 and 500 mg/day and the side effects (~10%) are gastrointestinal and cutaneous. The metabolism of terbinafine may be decreased by cimetidine and increased by rifampin.

### B. Naftifine

Pharmacokinetics and poor activity have limited the use of naftifine to topical treatment of dermatophytic infections.

## VIII. THE BENZYLAMINES, THIOCARBAMATES, AND DITHIOCARBAMATES

The benzylamine, butenafine, and the thiocarbamates, tolnaftate, tolciclate, and piritetrade, also inhibit the synthesis of ergosterol at the level of squalene. Their clinical use is limited to the topical treatment of superficial dermatophytic infections.

The Bordeaux mixture (reaction product of copper sulfate and lime) was the only fungicide used until the discovery of the dithiocarbamate fungicides in the mid-1930s. Of those, mancozeb and thiram are widely used in agriculture, but because they are only surface-acting materials frequent spray applications are required. Ferbam, maneb, and zineb are not used as much.

## IX. THE BENZIMIDAZOLES AND METHYLBENZIMIDAZOLE CARBAMATES

A great impact on crop protection was evident with the introduction of the benzimidazoles and other systemic (penetrate the plant) fungicides. These compounds increased spray intervals to 14 days or more. The methylbenzimidazole carbamates (MBCs; carbendazim, benomyl, and thiophanate) inhibit nuclear division and are also systemic agricultural fungicides. However, since MBC-resistant strains of *B. cinerea* and *Penicillium expansum* have been isolated, these compounds should be used in combination with N-phenylcarbamate or agents that have a different mode of action.

## X. THE MORPHOLINES

The morpholines interfere with $\delta$14 reductase and $\delta$7,$\delta$8 isomerase enzymes in the ergosterol biosynthetic pathway, which leads to an increase of toxic sterols and an increase in the ergosterol content of the fungal cell.

### A. Amorolfine

Amorolfine, a derivative of fenpropimorph, is the only morpholine that has a clinical application for the topical treatment of dermatophytic infections and candidal vaginitis.

## B. Fenpropimorph, Tridemorph, and Other Morpholines

Protein binding and side effects have precluded the clinical use of these morpholines, but they are important agricultural fungicides.

## XI. THE PYRIDINES

The pyridines are another class of antifungal agents that inhibit lanosterol demethylase.

## A. Buthiobate and Pyrifenox

These agents are important agricultural fungicides.

## XII. THE ECHINOCANDINS, PNEUMOCANDINS, AND PAPULOCANDINS

The echinocandins and papulocandins are naturally occurring metabolites of *Aspergillus nidulans* var. *echinulatus* (echinocandin B), *A. aculeatus* (aculeacin A), and *Papularia sphaerosperma* (papulocandin). They act specifically by inhibiting the synthesis of fungal $\beta(1,3)$-glucan synthetase, which results in the depletion of glucan, an essential component of the fungal cell wall.

## A. The Papulocandins

The papulocandins A–D, L687781, BU4794F, and chaetiacandin have *in vitro* activity only against *Candida* spp. but poor *in vivo* activity, which precluded clinical development.

## B. The Echinocandins

The echinocandins include echinocandins, pneumocandins, aculeacins, mulundo- and deoxymulundocandin, sporiofungin, vWF 11899 A–C, and FR

901379. The echinocandins have better *in vitro* and *in vivo* antifungal activity than the papulocandins. Pharmaceutical development has resulted in several semisynthetic echinocandins with an improved antifungal activity compared to those of the naturally occurring molecules described previously.

### 1. Cilofungin (LY 121019)

Cilofungin is a biosemisynthetic analog of the naturally occurring and toxic (erythrocytes lysis) 4-*n*-octyloxybenzoyl-echinocandin B. Although it showed good *in vitro* activity against *Candida* spp., this drug was discontinued due to the incidence of metabolic acidosis associated with its intravenous carrier, polyethylene glycol.

### 2. LY 303366

This is another semisynthetic cyclic lipopeptide which resulted from an increase of aromatic groups in the cilofungin side chain (Fig. 4A). It has high potency and oral and parental bioavailability. In laboratory animals, peak levels in plasma (5 or 6 hr) of $0.5–2.9$ $\mu$g/ml have been measured after single doses of 50–250 mg/kg. In humans, peak levels of 105–1624 ng/ml are measured after oral administrations of 100–1000 mg/kg; its pharmacokinetics is linear and the half-life is about 30 hr and is dose independent. Tissue concentrations are usually higher than those in plasma in animals.

LY 303366 has good *in vitro* activity against a variety of yeasts, including isolates resistant to itraconazole and fluconazole, and molds. This compound is not active against *C. neoformans* and *T. beigelii*; its MICs for certain molds are higher than those of the three new investigational azoles. However, its fungicidal activity against some species of *Candida* is superior to those of the azoles, which are mostly fungistatic drugs. LY 303366 has shown oral efficacy in animal models of systemic candidiasis and pneumocystis pneumonia. Although the drug is well tolerated up to 500-mg/kg doses, gastrointestinal adverse effects have been observed with 100-mg/kg doses in human subjects. Clinical trials in humans were conducted to assess the efficacy of LY 303366, but they were recently discontinued.

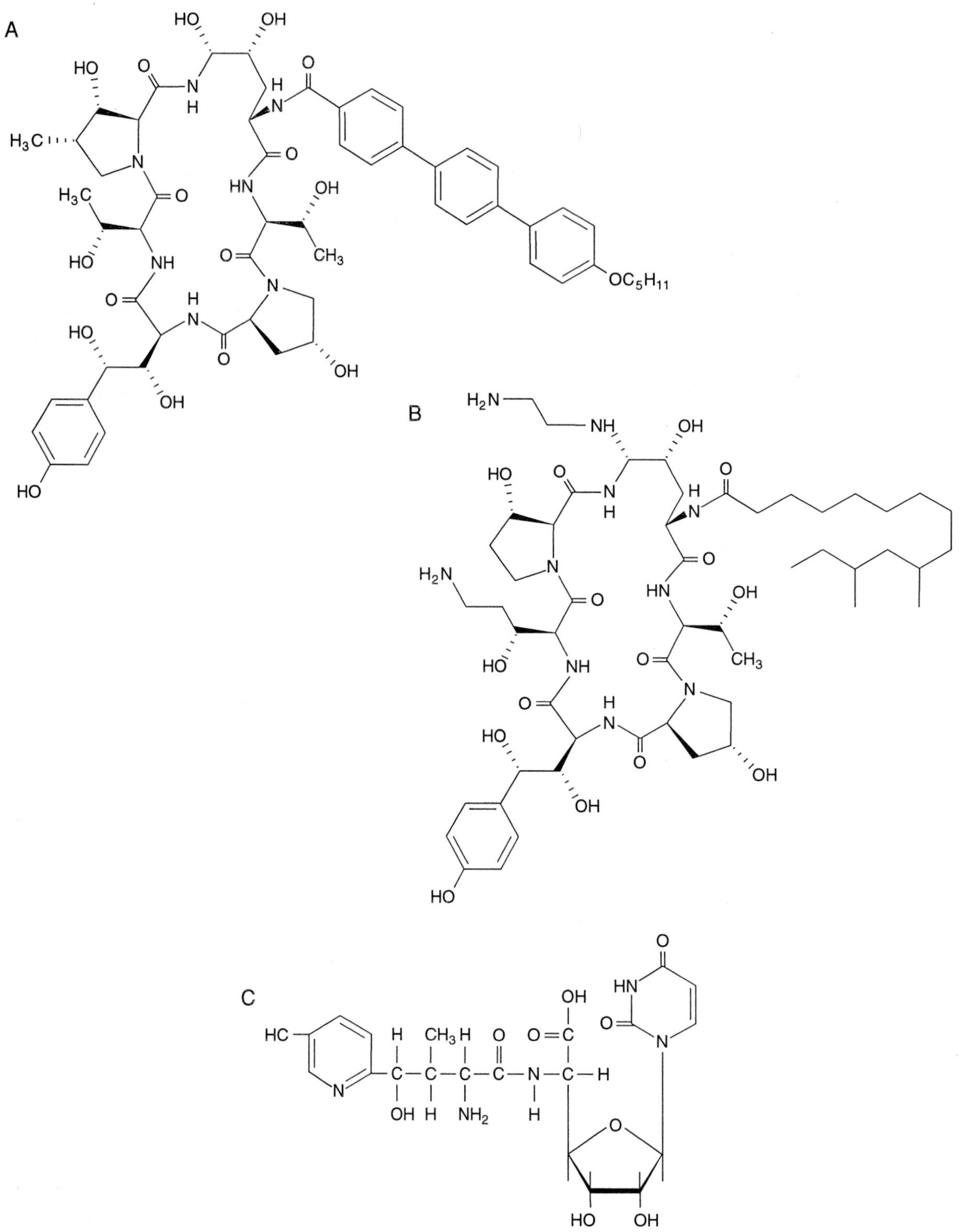

**Fig. 4.** Chemical structures of three echinocandin, pneumocandin, and nikkomycin agents under clinical investigation: (A) LY303366, (B) caspofungin (L 743872 or MK-0991), and (C) nikkomycin Z.

## C. Pneumocandin Derivatives

The pneumocandins have similar structures to those of the echinocandins, but they possess a hexapeptide core with a $\beta$-hydroxyglutamine instead of the threonine residue, a branched-chain $^{14}C$ fatty acid acyl group at the N-terminal, and variable substituents at the C-terminal proline residue. The pneumocandins are fermentation products of the mold *Zalerion arbolicola.*

Of the three naturally occurring pnemocandins (A–C), only A and B have certain antifungal activity *in vitro* and *in vivo* against *Candida* spp. and *Pneumocystis carinii* (in rodents), but they are non-water soluble.

### 1. L 693989, L 733560, L 705589, and L 731373

Modification of the original pneumocandin B by phosphorylation of the free phenolic hydroxyl group led to the improved, water-soluble pneumocandin B phosphate (L 693989). Further modifications of pneumocandin B led to the water-soluble semisynthetic molecules L 733560, L 705589, and L 731373. Although studies were conduced in laboratory animals, these molecules were not evaluated in humans.

## E. Caspofungin (MK-0991 or L 743872)

Caspofungin (Fig. 4B) is the product of a modification of L 733560 and has been selected for further evaluation in clinical trials in humans. As are the other semisynthetic pneumocandins, caspofungin is water soluble. Caspofungin is highly protein bound (97%) with a half-life that ranges from 5 to 7.5 hr and drug concentrations are usually higher in tissue than in plasma.

Caspofungin has fungistatic and fungicidal activities similar to those of LY 303366 against most *Candida* spp. and lower activity against the dimorphic fungi. It also has fungistatic *in vitro* activity against some of the other molds, especially *Aspergillus* spp. However, both LY 303366 and caspofungin pose difficulties regarding their *in vitro* laboratory evaluation and the data are controversial regarding their MICs for the molds. However, animal studies have demonstrated that this compound has good *in vivo* activity not only against yeast infections but also in murine models of disseminated aspergillosis and pulmonary pneumocystosis and histoplasmosis. The drug is not effective for the treatment of disseminated experimental infections caused by *C. neoformans.* In laboratory animals, the drug is mostly well tolerated, but histamine release and mild hepatotoxicity have been reported. Current clinical trials in humans for systemic candidiasis and refractory aspergillosis will determine its value as a therapeutic agent.

## XIII. THE PRADIMICINS AND BENANOMYCINS

The pradimicins and benanomycins are fungicidal metabolites of the *Actinomycetes,* but several semisynthetic molecules have also been produced. They act by disrupting the cell membrane through a calcium-dependent binding with the saccharide component of mannoproteins.

## A. Pradimicin A (BMY 28567) and FA-2 (BMY 28864)

The poor solubility of pradimicin A led to the development of BMY 28864, which is a water-soluble derivative of pradimicin FA-2. BMY 28864 appears to have good *in vitro* and *in vivo* activity against most common yeasts and *A. fumigatus.* Clinical trials in humans have not been conducted.

## B. BMS 181184

This compound is either a semisynthetic or biosynthetic derivative of BMY 28864. Although it was selected for further clinical evaluation due its promising *in vitro* and *in vivo* data, elevation of liver transaminases in humans led to the discontinuation of this drug.

## C. Benanomycin A

This compound has shown the best antifungal activity among the various benanomycins. Its great advantage compared to other new antifungals is its good *in vivo* activity in animals against *P. carinii*.

## XIV. THE POLYOXINS AND NIKKOMYCINS

The polyoxins are produced by *S. cacaoi* and the nikkomycins by *S. tendae*. The former compounds were discovered during a search for new agricultural fungicides and pesticides. Both polyoxins and nikkomycins are pyrimidine nucleosides that inhibit the enzyme chitin synthase, which leads to the depletion of chitin in the fungal cell wall. These molecules are transported into the cell via peptide permeases.

### A. Polyoxin D

Although this compound has *in vitro* antifungal activity against *C. immitis* (parasitic phase), *C. albicans*, and *C. neoformans*, it was not effective in the treatment of systemic candidiasis in mice.

### B. Nikkomycin Z

This compound appears to have both *in vitro* and *in vivo* activity against *C. immitis*, *B. dermatitidis*, and *H. capsulatum* as well as *in vitro* activity against *C. albicans* and *C. neoformans*. Studies to evaluate its safety have been conducted and clinical trials have been designed for the treatment of human coccidioidomycosis. These studies will determine its role as a therapeutic agent in humans.

## XV. THE SORDARINS

The natural sordarin GR 135402 is an antifungal fermentation product of *Graphium putredinis*. The compounds GM 103663, GM 211676, GM 222712, and GM 237354 are synthetic derivatives of GR 135402. *In vitro*, GM 222712 and GM 237354 have shown broad-spectrum antifungal activity for a variety of yeasts and molds.

## XVI. DIMETHOMORPH AND FLUAZINAM

Dimethomorph is a cinnamic acid derivative for use against *Plasmopara viticola* on vines and *Phytophthora infestans* on tomatoes and potatoes; it is not cross-resistant to phenylamides (systemic controllers of *Phycomycetes* plant infections). Fluazinam is used in vines and potatoes but also acts against *B. cinera* as an uncoupler of oxidative phosphorylation.

## XVII. THE PHTHALIMIDES

The discovery of captan in 1952 and later of the related captafol and folpet initiated the proper protection of crops by the application of specific fungicides. Captan is also used to treat dermatophytic infections in horses and cattle, but it causes skin sensitization in horses.

## XVIII. OTHER ANTIFUNGAL APPROACHES

### A. Natural and Synthetic Cationic Peptides

Cationic peptides provide a novel approach to antifungal therapy that warrants further investigation.

#### 1. Cecropin

Cecropin is a natural lytic peptide that is not lethal to mammalian cells and binds to ergosterol. Its antifungal activity varies according to the fungal species being challenged.

#### 2. Indolicidin

Indolicidin is a tridecapeptide that has good *in vitro* antifungal activity and when incorporated into liposomes has activity against experimental aspergillosis in animals.

#### 3. Synthetic Peptides

Synthetic peptides have been derived from the natural bactericidal-permeability increasing factor. They appear to have *in vitro* activity against *C. albicans*,

*C. neoformans,* and *A. fumigatus* and also show synergistic activity with fluconazole *in vitro*.

## B. Amino Acid Analogs

RI 331, the azoxybacillins, and cispentacin are amino acid analogs with good *in vitro* antifungal activity against *Aspergillus* spp. and the dermatophytes (RI 331 and azoxybacillins) and also good *in vivo* activity (cispentacin). RI 331 and the azoxybacillins inhibit homoserine dehydrogenase and the biosynthesis of sulfur-containing amino acids, respectively.

## See Also the Following Articles

ANTIVIRAL AGENTS • BACTERIOCINS • FUNGAL INFECTIONS • FUNGI, FILAMENTOUS

## Bibliography

Allen, D. G., Pringle, J. K., Smith, D. A., Conlon, P. D., and Burgmann, P. M. (1993). "Handbook of Veterinary Drugs." Lippincott, Philadelphia.

Clemons, K. V., and Stevens, D. A. (1997). Efficacies of two novel azole derivatives each containing a morpholine ring, UR-9746 and UR-9751, against systemic murine coccidioidomycosis. *Antimicrob. Agents Chemother.* **41**, 200–203.

Espinel-Ingroff, A. (1996). History of medical mycology in the United States. *Clin. Microbiol. Rev.* **9**, 235–272.

Espinel-Ingroff, A. (1998). Comparison of *in vitro* activity of the new triazole SCH 56592 and the echinocandins MK-0991 (L-743,872) and LY303366 against opportunistic filamentous and dimorphic fungi. *J. Clin. Microbiol.* **36**, 2950–2956.

Espinel-Ingroff, A., and Shadomy, S. (1989). *In vitro* and *in vivo* evaluation of antifungal agents. *Eur. Clin. Microbiol. Infect. Dis.* **8**, 352–361.

Espinel-Ingroff, A., White, T., and Pfaller, M. A. (1999). Antifungal agents and susceptibility tests. *In* "Manual of Clinical Microbiology" (P. R. Murray, E. J. Baron, M. A. Pfaller, F. C. Tenover, and R. H. Yolken, Eds.), 7th ed. ASM, Washington, DC.

Groll, A. H., Piscitelli, S. C., and Walsh, T. J. (1998). Clinical pharmacology of systemic antifungal agents: A comprehensive review of agents in clinical use, current investigational compounds, and putative targets for antifungal drug development. *Adv. Pharmacol.* **44**, 343–500.

Russell, P. E., Milling, R. J., and Wright, K. (1995). Control of fungi pathogenic to plants. *In* "Fifty Years of Antimicrobials: Past Perspectives and Future Trends" (P. A. Hunter, G. K. Darby, and N. J. Russell, Eds.). Cambridge Univ. Press: New York.

Sheehan, D. J., Hitchcock, C. A., and Sibley, C. M. (1999). Current and emerging azole antifungal agents. *Clin. Microbiol. Rev.* **12**, 40–79.

# Antigenic Variation

## Luc Vanhamme and Etienne Pays

*Free University of Brussels*

## GLOSSARY

**antigenic drift** Change of antigenic structure caused by amino-acid substitutions that result from the accumulation of random point mutations in the gene.

**antigenic shift** Change of antigenic structure resulting from random genetic reassortment between different sequences of nucleic acid.

**antigenic variation** Change of antigenic structure due to active specific mechanisms occurring at higher frequencies than random mutation rates.

**gene conversion** Replacement of a gene by the copy of another.

**phase variation** Switching on and off of the expression of a gene.

**ALL LIVING ANIMALS** result from the evolution of characters shaped by selective pressure. Pathogenic microorganisms (viruses, bacteria, fungi, and protozoans) obey these rules and have obviously been successful. Their success depends on their efficiency in invading, colonizing, and multiplying in their hosts. In order to survive long enough to be transmitted from one host to another, the parasites have to keep the host as healthy as possible and establish a balance between their needs and those of their host. In addition, they must escape elimination by the defenses of the host, particularly the immune system. For this purpose they have adopted different strategies, including concealment within the cells of the host, antigen shedding, and import or mimicry of host antigens. One of the most successful strategies is antigen variability. This generic term encompasses several phenomena of different names referring to more or less subtle differences. We will not enter into sterile discussions about definitions and only useful terms (antigenic variation, drift, and shift) have been defined in the glossary. This article will discuss the mechanisms underlying antigenic variability, namely, changing antigenic structures of surface molecules to allow adaptation to new conditions, including adaptation to changing extracellular environment (involving the support, nutrients, source of energy, osmolarity, pH, and temperature), the change of cell or host tropism, and escape from the attacks of the immune system. This article is not intended to be an exhaustive review of all cases of antigenic variability but rather focuses on the best known examples of this fascinating mechanism using African trypanosomes as a model.

## I. ANTIGENIC VARIATION IN PROTOZOANS

Although most protozoans performing antigenic variation (Fig. 1) are parasites, some free-living cells are also capable of surface variation. The protozoan parasites are responsible for millions of deaths yearly and therefore represent a major health problem throughout the world.

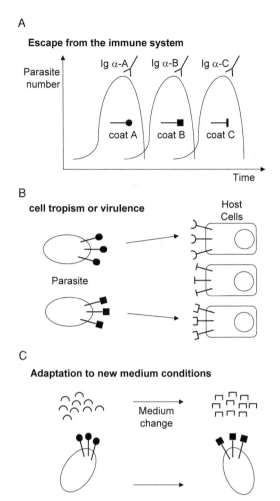

**Fig. 1.** Some adaptative functions of antigenic variation. (A) Successive waves of parasitemia resulting from the interplay between the parasite and its host: on the one hand, continuous expression of new surface coats by the parasite, and on the other hand synthesis of specific antibodies by the host. (B and C) The changes of surface components allow the parasites to recognize different host cell receptors and different nutrients, respectively.

## A. Trypanosoma brucei

### 1. The Disease and the Parasitic Life Cycle

African trypanosomes are flagellated protozoans of the group of kinetoplastidae and include *T. congolense*, *T. vivax*, *T. evansi*, *T. equiperdum*, and *T. brucei*. *Trypanosoma brucei* is the organism in which the molecular mechanisms underlying antigenic variation are best characterized. This organism is classi-

fied into three subspecies which are morphologically, biochemically, and genetically indistinguishable. *Trypanosoma brucei brucei* is the causative agent of nagana in cattle, whereas *T. brucei rhodesiense* and *T. brucei gambiense* are responsible for human sleeping sickness. These diseases are characterized by successive bursts of fever and culminate after several weeks or months when the parasite causes cachexia, migrates to the central nervous system, elicits neurological problems, and finally kills the host. Fifty million people are at risk for the sickness and probably more than 50,000 die yearly. The disease is currently taking such a heavy toll on cattle that it practically prevents raising livestock in central Africa.

*Trypanosoma brucei* proliferates in the bloodstream of its mammalian host as "slender" bloodstream forms and generates "stumpy" non-dividing forms. When ingested by a tsetse fly during a bloodmeal, stumpy forms differentiate into insect-adapted, procyclic forms which multiply in the midgut and eventually migrate in the salivary glands where they differentiate again into metacyclic forms. When reinoculated into the mammalian bloodstream these forms quickly differentiate into multiplying bloodstream slender forms (Fig. 2).

### 2. Stage-Specific Surface Antigens, Variant Surface Glycoprotein, and Procyclin

During all stages of its parasitic life cycle, *T. brucei* is covered with a coat containing one predominant species of protein. During the procyclic stage, the

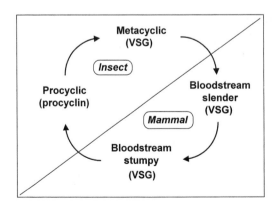

**Fig. 2.** The parasitic life cycle of *Trypanosoma brucei*. Stage-specific antigens are indicated in parentheses.

major surface component is procyclin, a glycosyl phosphatidylinositol (GPI)-anchored protein with a rod-shaped structure due to the presence of glutamine–proline repeats, several forms of which are known but not subject to antigenic variation. The different forms of procyclin probably play distinct roles during the trypanosome life in the fly, such as providing protection against proteolytic attack in the fly midgut and guidance and tropism toward specific host organs during the parasite journey in the insect. However, nothing is known about the way in which the relative expression of these different forms is regulated. During the metacyclic stage, procyclin is replaced by the variant surface glycoprotein (VSG), a GPI-anchored glycoprotein with an extended structure due to the folding of the N-terminal surface exposed domain in two antiparallel $\alpha$-helices. The tight association of $10^7$ molecules of this antigen over the entire cellular surface creates a dense wall which protects the parasite against lytic elements from the host. In addition to its function as a protective barrier, the VSG coat is also an extremely immunogenic antigen which is presented to the host to elicit a rapid antibody response. Metacyclic populations express more than 20 different VSGs, with each individual cell synthesizing only one. In the bloodstream, the majority of cells within the population exhibit a single type of VSG. However, this VSG is continuously subject to antigenic variation in a process which occurs spontaneously at a rate between $10^{-7}$ and $10^{-2}$ depending on the strains, and it does not require the presence of antibodies. When the population expressing a given VSG is destroyed by the immune response, it is replaced by the clonal expansion of individual cells which had previously switched to the expression of another VSG. Therefore, antigenic variation of the VSG continuously allows the parasite to escape antibodies whose synthesis was triggered by the VSG. This system typically exemplifies the complex interactions between parasites and their host for prolonged survival. Trypanosomes obviously trigger and use the antibody response against the VSG to continuously downregulate their population, an essential requisite to prevent premature death of the host and maintain long-lasting chronic infection, which is necessary to provide the opportunity of cyclical transmission by the fly to another host.

## 3. The Molecular Basis for the Developmental Control of Antigen Expression

In *T. brucei*, the genes for the major surface antigens are contained in three categories of expression sites. The procyclin gene transcription units are located in two diploid nontelomeric loci. These units are polycistronic and include two or three procyclin genes located immediately downstream from the transcription promoter together with several other cotranscribed genes. Metacyclic VSGs are transcribed from telomeric metacyclic expression sites (M-ESs). These sites harbor a monocistronic transcription unit containing only the VSG gene. There are approximately 25 metacyclic VSGs (and probably the same number of M-ESs) constituting a specific repertoire reexpressed each time metacyclic forms are generated. Bloodstream VSGs are transcribed from telomeric bloodstream expression sites (B-ES). There are approximately 20 B-ESs containing a single VSG gene located at the very end of the unit together with at least 8 other genes, termed ESAGs (expression site-associated genes), which are all under the control of a common transcription promoter located more than 40 kb upstream from the VSG gene (Fig. 3). Both procyclin transcription units and B-ESs are transcribed by a polymerase I-like RNA polymerase—an unusual feature for protein-encoding genes which are typically transcribed by RNA polymerase II. This particularity is probably linked to the need for a very high level of transcription since during the respective developmental stages in which they are synthesized the mRNAs encoding the surface antigens represent 5–10% of all mRNAs. It seems that the mechanisms controlling the expression of the genes for the stage-specific antigens operate downstream from transcription initiation. Transcription is initiated at all stages of the parasitic cycle but is only fully elongated at the appropriate stage. Moreover, the 3′ untranslated regions of the respective mRNAs influence the maturation and stability of these transcripts in a stage-specific way. These combined co- and post-transcriptional controls allow trypanosomes to meet the requirement for a very rapid switch of the expressed antigen when they are suddenly transmitted from host to vector or vice versa. In addition to this system, a burst of transcription initiation occurs in

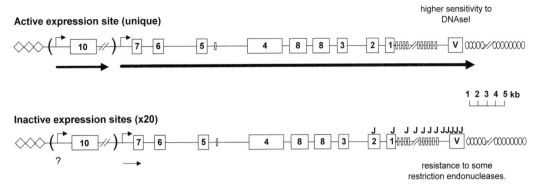

**Fig. 3.** Bloodstream VSG expression sites (B-ESs) of *Trypanosoma brucei.* Upstream from the transcription promoter(s) (bent arrows) are arrays of 50-bp repeats (lozenges) insulating the ES from the rest of the chromosome. In half of the ESs the promoter is duplicated, with an intervening 13-kb region encoding ESAG 10 (between brackets). The ESAGs and the VSG gene (open boxes numbered 1–8 and V) belong to a single transcription unit ending in telomeric repeats (open ellipses). A tandem array of 76-bp repeats (open bars) separates the ESAGs and the VSG gene. In the active ES, transcription is fully elongated (top, thick arrow), whereas in the inactive ESs elongation is abortive (bottom, light arrow).The active ES is more sensitive to digestion by DNAse I, indicating an open conformation of chromatin, whereas silent ESs are characterized by a partial resistance to digestion by some restriction endonucleases, due to the presence of the modified base J in their 3' terminal region.

M-ESs at the metacyclic stage to ensure expression of multiple VSGs in the population inoculated into the mammal.

## 4. The Molecular Basis for Antigenic Variation

The different B-ESs contain different VSG genes. However, only one ES is transcribed at any given time so that only a single VSG gene is expressed and the surface coat of the cell contains a single type of antigen. Therefore, antigenic variation can occur in two distinct ways: Either it results from transcriptional switching between the 20 available ESs, a process called *in situ* activation, or it is due to the replacement of the VSG gene in the single transcriptionally active ES (Fig. 4).

### a. In Situ Activation

This process is an enigma. The problem is understanding how only 1 of the 20 ESs is active at a time and how this selective activation is episodically transferred from one site to another. The only established fact about this phenomenon is that it does not require DNA rearrangement, even at the single base level. All B-ESs appear to be equipped with a potentially functional and complete promoter, and the up-

stream and downstream sequences do not contain elements required for transcription regulation. The control of differential expression between ESs seems to occur downstream from transcription initiation since transcription of several, if not all, ESs can be detected in cells even when only one VSG is expressed. Since the chromatin of the silent ESs is significantly less sensitive to exogenous and endogenous nucleases, it is probable that chromatin silencing by heterochromatinization (chromatin condensation) may be responsible for the inhibition of all ESs except one. This silencing resembles the position effect described for sub-telomeric genes in yeast since it is increased with proximity to the telomere. A modified base, $\beta$-glucosyl hydroxymethyluracil or J, was detected in silent telomeres and not in the active ES, but this modification may be more a consequence of heterochromatinization than a cause. A RNA elongation promoting factor present in limiting amount may be responsible for the selective derepression of a single ES at a time, although this hypothesis remains to be proven.

### b. Replacement of the VSG Gene

The replacement of the VSG gene in the active ES can occur by either gene conversion or telomeric

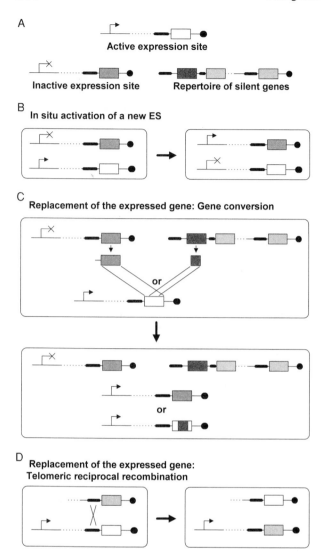

A
**Active expression site**

**Inactive expression site**          **Repertoire of silent genes**

B
**In situ activation of a new ES**

C
**Replacement of the expressed gene: Gene conversion**

or

or

D
**Replacement of the expressed gene:
Telomeric reciprocal recombination**

**Fig. 4.** Mechanisms of antigenic variation in *Trypanosoma brucei.* (A) Different loci involved in the process.(B–D) The three mechanisms of antigenic variation. See text for details. Solid circles, telomeric repeats; thick lines, 76-bp repeats; boxes, VSG genes; broken arrowed and crossed lines, promoters for active and inactive ESs, respectively.

reciprocal recombination. Both mechanisms are driven by homologous recombination facilitated by the sequence homologies shared between the ESs and/or the sequences flanking the VSG genes. Whereas reciprocal recombination is only observed occasionally, gene conversion appears to be the most commonly used mechanism for antigenic variation, at least after the initial period of the infection. In contrast to reciprocal recombination, gene conver-

sion is asymmetrical and consists of the replacement of the active gene by the copy of another (Fig. 4). The VSG gene recombining with that present in the active ES is derived from a repertoire of 1000 genes distributed in many telomeres, particularly of minichromosomes, as well as in tandem arrays on several chromosomes. Depending on the location of the homologous sequences used for recombination between the active VSG gene and its partner, very large or very short regions of the gene and the ES can be replaced by gene conversion. When the replacement involves short stretches, sequence reassortment within the coding region of the gene can lead to the generation of chimeric VSG genes, expanding the repertoire of antigenic variants. Moreover, it appears that the process of gene conversion can sometimes lead to point mutations, further contributing to the evolution of the antigenic repertoire.

## 5. *Programing and Evolution of VSG Repertoires*

The genetic mechanisms for antigenic variation provide the trypanosomes with a means to both organize the programing of VSG expression during chronic infection and rapidly alter the VSG repertoires.

The programing of early, intermediate, and late variants seems to be linked to the relative probability of gene expression. Alternative *in situ* activation of the different ESs, which occurs spontaneously and does not require any DNA rearrangement, seems to occur with high frequency during the early stages of the infection. Once this process is counter-selected by the presence of antibodies synthesized against the early variants, less probable DNA recombination targeted to the ES, either by reciprocal exchange or by gene conversion, can be selected. Since the probability of this recombination appears to be dependent on the level of sequence homology between the ES and the donor genes, VSG genes whose environment resembles that of the active gene are likely to recombine first. This is clearly the case for telomeric VSG genes, which are flanked by arrays of repeats also found in the telomeric VSG ESs. In particular, the telomeric repeats appear to favor the recombination with the ES. Nontelomeric VSG genes do not share high homology with the VSG ESs, which explains why this category of genes is usually expressed later. The respective number of 76-bp repeats present immediately upstream from these genes seems to dictate their relative order of expression, with those provided with many repeats recombining faster. Finally, nontelomeric VSG genes which are not flanked with sequences homologous to the ES, as well as pseudogenes which cannot be expressed as such, can only have access to the ES when the VSG gene present in the ES shows the necessary homology allowing for the recombination. This typically occurs late because the probability of its occurrence is less than that of earlier events, and it accounts for the frequent observation during chronic infection of mosaic VSG genes reassorted by segmental gene conversion involving several donors.

The rapid alteration, or hyperevolution, of the VSG repertoires can also be explained by considering the mechanisms for antigenic variation. Gene conversion is a powerful tool for the generation of new VSG genes by sequence reassortment, point mutation, or both. This happens continuously in the workshop composed of the VSG ES. Provided subsequent antigenic variation is driven by *in situ* activation, a new sequence generated in the ES can be stored in the repertoire since transcriptional inactivation of the ES where the new gene was constructed allows for its conservation, at least for a certain amount of time. Conversely, genes activated *in situ* are prone to rapid loss by gene conversion. Therefore, the alternation between gene conversion and *in situ* activation continuously modifies the repertoire of VSG genes through the gain and loss of different sequences.

### 6. Variation of ESAG-Encoded Receptors

The different B-ESs seem to share the structure depicted in Fig. 3, with some variation. First, in half the ESs the promoter is duplicated, with an intervening region of 13 kb which contains an additional ESAG. Second, although highly homologous, the ESAGs are not identical between ESs but show scattered point mutations. Finally, depending on the ES some ESAGs are either duplicated or deleted, and additional ESAGs can occasionally be found. Strikingly, several of these genes appear to code for surface-exposed proteins which are important for cellular growth. ESAG 10, which is located between the duplicated promoters and is thus only expressed in half the ESs, appears to encode a membrane transporter. ESAGs 6 and 7 encode a VSG-related heterodimeric receptor for serum transferrin, and ESAG 4 codes for a receptor-like transmembrane adenylate cyclase. The function of the other ESAGs remains a mystery, although most probably also code for surface proteins.

Because of the presence of additional genes in the ES, characters other than the VSG can be modified at antigenic variation. When a transcriptional switch to another ES occurs, a whole new set of genes is coexpressed with the new VSG. For example, the transferrin receptors encoded by ESAGs 6 and 7 from different ESs can show very different affinities for transferrin from various mammalian hosts. The functionality of these differences has been demonstrated. Trypanosomes that grow well in bovine serum do not behave similarly when grown in dog serum, in which they proliferate only after a lag period. Analysis of the trypanosomes obtained after this lag period revealed that these cells had switched to another ES which encodes a transferrin receptor with a higher affinity for dog transferrin. Therefore, the existence of several B-ESs provides the parasite with a means to store a collection of several receptors adapted to different mammalian hosts and *in situ* activation allows the selective expression of the set of genes which are the best adapted to the particular organism in which the parasite is inoculated. Another example concerns the SRA (serum resistance associated) gene, a special ESAG conferring resistance to a lytic factor contained in the human serum. This gene is present in only one ES in *T. brucei rhodesiense*, and activation of this ES allows the parasite to grow in man. In this case, the mechanism of *in situ* activation not only allows the parasite to undergo antigenic variation but also provides it with the most suitable means to survive in the host.

### 7. Invariant Antigens

Whereas the existence of multiple ESAGs constitutes a way for the parasite to alternatively express several variants for some crucial surface receptors, it is clear that many surface proteins whose function is to communicate with the host are not encoded in VSG ESs and are necessarily surface exposed and invariant. These proteins have to be sufficiently conserved to recognize invariant ligands and must be accessible to these ligands but not to the immune system. At least one way employed by the parasite to face this challenge is the sequestration of these molecules in a small specialized region of the plasma membrane termed the flagellar pocket. This region is an invagination of the plasma membrane located at the base of the flagellum which is totally inaccessible to the cells of the immune system while allowing diffusible molecules to enter. In this compartment the receptors and invariant surface components appear to be protected against efficient immune detection, perhaps through the presence of extended carbohydrate side chains of glycoproteins restricted to this particular location.

## 8. Conclusions

Trypanosomes are a typical example of parasites with high professional skills which have devised several ways to overcome the problems associated with their particular way of life. They are inoculated in the mammalian host as a population expressing multiple VSGs to minimize the possibility of premature elimination by the host antibodies. Because they can encounter multiple host species, they carry a collection of expression sites encoding receptors with different affinities for the same growth factor, and they select the best adapted ones at the beginning of infection. Once these first obstacles are crossed, the parasites continuously present new VSGs to the immune system, both to divert this system from recognizing crucial antigens and to use it as a way to downregulate their number, an indispensable condition to avoid premature death of the host and to support long-lasting infection. The system of VSG variation which involves alternative expression among 20 different ESs also allows a very fast evolution of VSG repertoires through the continuous creation, storage, and elimination of different genes.

## B. *Giardia lamblia*

Giardia is representative of one of the most ancient eukaryotic lineages, branching out before the acquisition of the mitochondrion. This flagellated protozoan inhabits the small intestine and is one of the most common parasites in humans. Giardiasis symptoms include diarrhea, intestinal cramping, nausea, and vomiting. The disease is propagated by cyst-infested feces, often contaminating drinking water.

The entire surface of this parasite, including the flagellum, is covered with an 18 nm-thick coat containing a major protein termed the CRP (cysteine-rich protein) or VSP (variable surface protein). This protein is extremely resistant to proteolysis and constitutes a protective barrier against the highly proteolytic environment in which the parasite develops. It has a high cysteine content (11 or 12%), no carbohydrate addition, and a putative transmembrane region. The CRP exhibits a variable size (50–200 kDa) due to the large variation observed in the number of repeated stretches of 65 amino acids. This variability accounts for the large heterogeneity found among and within parasite isolates. Although each cell expresses only one type of antigen, the parasite population developing in the host does not show the cyclical waves of parasitemia with one antigenic type regularly replacing the other as observed in trypanosomes but rather exhibits several CRP variants simultaneously. The antigen composition also evolves during the infection as some CRPs are positively selected and others progressively eliminated (Fig. 5). The rate of variation appears to vary enormously between isolates and between CRPs. Whether variation of the CRP is induced by antibodies is unclear. Whereas spontaneous variation of the CRP occurs during cell cultivation *in vitro*, the parasites developing in immunosuppressed mice do not show variation. It is possible that variation of the CRP is more relevant for

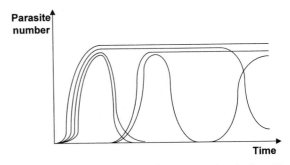

**Fig. 5.** Evolution of antigenic heterogeneity during *Giardia* infection. The curves represent populations expressing different CRPs coexisting, appearing, or disappearing at different stages of infection.

parasite adaptation to different host species or individuals than for avoiding the immune response of the host. The ability to express different CRPs would allow *Giardia* to maximize its chances of initiating an infection, no matter which host it meets, and the duration of the infection would depend on its ability to express the adequate CRP. However, the persistence of a CRP for a long period would trigger a specific immune response and promote its replacement by another variant.

The molecular basis for the variation of the CRP is poorly understood. CRPs are encoded by a repertoire of 30–40 genes, at least some of which are telomeric. There is only one gene expressed at a given time, and in at least one case switching of gene expression was linked to the loss of the gene previously expressed.

## C. Plasmodium

Malaria is a major health problem throughout the world. Each year, 400 million people develop the disease, which results in approximately 2 million deaths. It is caused by four different species of Plasmodium, a protozoan of the group of Apicomplexa. The infection by two species accounts for almost 95% of the cases. Malaria caused by *Plasmodium vivax* consists of relapsing fevers and is usually not lethal. Malaria caused by *Plasmodium falciparum* is associated with high mortality resulting from severe complications, such as nervous problems, respiratory failure, and anemia. These symptoms are due to parasite-induced clogging of infected erythrocytes in the capillaries of different organs or tissues.

Plasmodium is inoculated by Anophaeles mosquitoes and rapidly invades hepatocytes. After a development of approximately 10 days in the liver, the parasites invade and multiply in erythrocytes. The erythrocytes are ultimately lysed to release large numbers of parasites which invade other red blood cells. During the early intraerythrocytic (ring) stage of parasite development, the infected erythrocytes are present in the peripheral circulation, which results in the elimination in the spleen of these infected erythrocytes. Plasmodium has devised a mechanism to avoid this destruction. During the second half of the intraerythrocytic (trophozoite) stage, the infected

erythrocytes are retained on the walls of the capillaries due to the expression of a parasite-encoded molecule which mediates adherence to endothelial surface receptors. This protein, termed PfEMP1, is concentrated in "knobs" on the erythrocyte surface and is linked to the erythrocyte cytoskeleton. It is capable of binding to different receptors from the host, such as vascular cell adhesion molecule-1, intercellular adhesion molecule-1, endothelial leukocyte adhesion molecule-1, CD36, and thrombospondin. This adhesion not only prevents destruction of the infected cells in the spleen but also promotes cell clogging and, therefore, the pathology of malaria. Because of the diversity of receptors to which this antigen binds, many tissues and organs can be affected. Another consequence of the appearance of parasite adhesion molecules on the surface of the infected cells is the detection of these cells by the immune system, which triggers an efficient antibody response. This problem was solved by antigenic variation.

PfEMP1 has a molecular weight of 200–350 kDa and is encoded by a family of 50–150 genes termed *var* which are spread throughout the 14 chromosomes, many of which are found in subtelomeric regions. Molecular cloning has confirmed that proteins encoded by different genes bind to different host molecules. Analysis of steady-state and nascent RNAs indicated that whereas many *var* genes are transcribed in the early ring stage, only a single gene is expressed at the later trophozoite stage in which only one PfEMP1 protein can be detected at the surface of a single erythrocyte. These results point to a developmentally regulated transcriptional control restricting the expression to only one gene per cell. This appears to occur without major genomic rearrangement.

## D. Paramecium

*Paramecium tetraurelia* is a free-living ciliated protozoan. The plasma membrane of this organism is entirely covered with a 17- to 25-nm-thick coat made of a single type of protein, the surface antigen (SAg), which constitutes 3.5% of the total cellular protein amount. SAg is a GPI-anchored, 200- to 300-kDa polypeptide which contains a high proportion (>10%) of cysteines and is modified by carbohydrate addition. SAgs can be classified into at least 11 different serotypes. New phenotypes arise during cultivation, especially if culture conditions (temperature, pH, salt concentration, osmotic pressure, and food availability) are changed. Some changes to defined culture conditions give rise to the expression of predictable antigens, whereas other changes will trigger the appearance of a non predictable antigen. The exact significance of these adaptive changes is unclear.

Only one SAg is expressed at a time in a single cell. Genomic analysis showed that SAgs are encoded by single-copy genes, several of which are telomeric. Only one allele of the gene is expressed at a time. Antigenic variation does not require large chromosomal rearrangements (recombination or gene conversion) or finer rearrangements in the close vicinity of the expressed gene, but the length of the array of telomeric repeats appears to influence the relative production of specific mRNA (telomere position effect). Depending on the serotype gene, transcriptional and posttranscriptional controls have been found to modulate SAg expression. The transcriptional controls allowing for mutually exclusive expression of SAgs depend on sequence elements located in the beginning of the open reading frame of the genes. Posttranscriptional controls can involve selective RNA degradation since, during the transition from a given SAg to another, transcription of the previous SAg gene can be detected, whereas no mRNA accumulates.

## II. ANTIGENIC VARIATION IN FUNGI

### A. *Pneumocystis carinii*

Pneumocystis is an opportunistic pathogen and pneumocystis pneumonia is one of the main causes of mortality in AIDS patients. All attempts to detect this parasite in healthy humans have been unsuccessful. This organism is covered with a coating composed of a heterogeneous major surface protein (MSG), a 100- to 120-kDa cysteine-rich protein highly glycosylated with mannose. This protein is involved in attachment to the lung through binding to a mannose-binding protein, fibronectin, and surfactant protein A.

Populations grown in laboratory animals express several different MSGs simultaneously. MSGs are encoded by a family of 100 genes spread in tandem arrays in all 15 chromosomes, with some genes located at telomeres. All MSG mRNAs have in common the same 5' terminal sequence, the upstream conserved sequence, which is only found in a unique expression site that is telomeric. Therefore, full-size genes are expressed singly in a cell, and antigenic variation presumably occurs by gene conversion or reciprocal recombination targeted to this gene (Fig. 6). This is likely to occur at very high rate since several small focal colonies expressing different antigens are found in the same lung alveola.

### B. *Candida albicans*

In healthy humans, *Candida albicans* is found colonizing several organs or cavities, such as the vulva, vagina, mouth, esophagus, intestines, and the anus. However, in circumstances such as immunodepression these parasites can invade host tissues and severe systemic infections can develop. This behavior and the ability to colonize different organisms and organs are associated with very frequent ($10^{-5}$–$10^{-2}$ per gen-

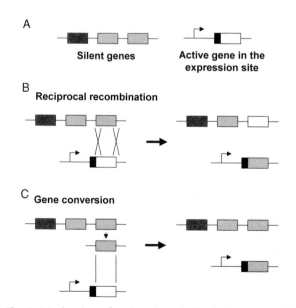

**Fig. 6.** Mechanism of antigenic variation in *Pneumocystis, Neisseria,* and *Borrelia.* The unique telomeric expression site is the only locus encoding the N-terminal region of the antigen (solid bar).

eration) changes between several phenotypes. These changes are extremely pleiotropic and affect variable combinations of antigenicity; colony morphology; cell shape, size, and ultrastructure; adherence; virulence; protein secretion; sugar metabolism; and resistance to drugs. Some of these changes can be obtained in culture by changing medium components, pH, or temperature. One of these changes, the white–opaque transition, has been studied in detail. In agreement with the observed pleiotropy which suggests a multifactorial change, protein electrophoresis and differential screening of cDNA libraries have demonstrated the phase-specific expression of a set of genes. Their localization on different chromosomes and the inability to detect major DNA rearrangements suggested a combinatorial regulation of this set of genes. Experiments using reporter genes under the control of phase-specific promoters and bandshift assays performed with probes from these promoters have supported the conclusion that the pleiotropic effects are obtained by an on/off switch of a master locus encoding a phase-specific transcription factor. This factor would be the key in the activation or repression of all the genes involved in the different aspects of the phenotype.

## III. ANTIGENIC VARIATION IN BACTERIA

### A. *Hemophilus influenzae*

*Hemophilus influenzae* is an agent of meningitis and respiratory tract infections. It represents a typical case of phase variation-regulated virulence. The presence of at least two components of the bacterial surface is indeed controlled by phase variation.

*Hemophilus influenzae* is found in fimbriated or non-fimbriated forms. Fimbriae are proteinic surface expansions which influence cell tropism. They favor adherence to some epithelial cell receptors and therefore determine the development of infection. Bacteria found in the body fluids of individuals are devoid of fimbriae, whereas bacteria isolated from infected mucosas are fimbriated. The fimbriae are accessible to the immune system, which can lead to the elimination of the bacteria. Proteins polymerized in fimbriae

are encoded in a locus containing two genes in divergent orientation separated by a common promoter. This promoter is composed of two stretches of 6 bp which recruit the RNA polymerase, separated by variable arrays of TA repeats. The efficiency of the promoter is strictly dependent on the distance between the two elements. For instance, it is inactive when 9 repeats are present, maximally active with 10 repeats, and moderately active with 11 repeats (Fig. 7).

*Hemophilus influenzae* can also be covered with a capsule of polysaccharides which confers increased virulence but allows recognition of the parasite by the immune system. The absence of capsule may improve the ability to bind and invade host epithelial cells. Loss or gain of the capsule is related to genetic changes in the *Cap* locus, which controls capsule synthesis (Fig. 8). In type B strains the loss of the capsule is related to a spontaneous deletion in the *bex-A* gene involved in the secretion of the capsular polysaccharide. This deletion is irreversible. Alternatively, production of capsule components can be increased by amplification of the genes involved in polysaccharide biosynthesis. Both events are related to the transposon nature of this locus, which is flanked by insertion elements capable of triggering amplification by recombination.

Another major component of bacterial capsules is the lipopolysaccharide (LPS). LPS has antiphagocytic properties and prevents complement-mediated lysis. It is subject to antigenic variation by loss or gain of

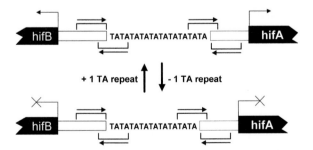

**Fig. 7.** Phase variation controlling the expression of fimbriae proteins in *Hemophilus influenzae*. Broken arrowed and crossed lines represent the transcriptional start sites of active and repressed promoters, respectively, whereas the brackets with arrows designate essential elements of the promoters and the solid boxes represent genes encoding fimbriae components.

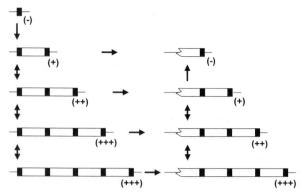

**Fig. 8.** Genetic changes of the locus controlling capsule expression in *Hemophilus influenzae*. See text for details. Solid boxes, insertion elements; open boxes, 18-kb transposons containing the genes involved in capsule expression. The break at the 5' end of some of the transposons represents a 1.2-kb deletion ablating most of the *bexA* gene and sequences involved in transposition. − and + refer to the level of capsule expression.

the core saccharide structure resulting from changes in expression of Lic proteins involved in their synthesis. These changes are in turn mediated by frameshifts in their open reading frames concurrently with changes in the number of internal CAAT repeats (Fig. 9). It is postulated that these changes occur through slipped-strand mispairing between repeats.

## B. *Neisseria*

This species is responsible for gonorrhea (*N. gonorrheae* or *N. gonococcus*) and meningitis (*N. meningitidis* or *N. meningococcus*). Adhesion to its substrate (cell tropism) and invasion are influenced

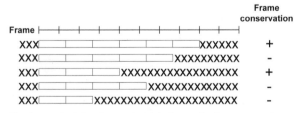

**Fig. 9.** Variation of protein translation by frame switching. The reading frame of the antigen gene is altered by increasing or decreasing the number of internal repeats (open boxes). This mechanism underlies variation of Lic proteins in *Hemophilus* (CAAT repeats) and Opa proteins in *Neisseria* (CTCTT repeats).

by several surface components, namely, the lipooligosaccharide (LOS; a special LPS), a capsule of polysaccharides, the opacity proteins Opa and pilins.

Meningococci exist in encapsulated or nonencapsulated forms. The capsula impairs the capability of Neisseria to adhere to host cells, an effect believed to be at least partially due to the masking of the Opa proteins present on the outer membrane of the cell. The Opa proteins are important in host cell invasion because they mediate attachment to epithelial cells and therefore determine virulence of the strain. They are encoded by 2–12 genes spread in different loci on the bacterial chromosome. These genes are very similar except for two hypervariable regions encoding the variant epitopes. All copies are constitutively transcribed but only some are translated. The variability of expression depends on a switch occurring at a rate of $10^{-2}$ per cell per generation. This switch places the protein sequence in or out of frame, resulting in the synthesis of either the correct protein or an irrelevant or truncated version. The determination of the reading frame depends on the loss or gain of CTCTT repeats which encode part of the hydrophobic leader sequence (Fig. 9). Therefore, phase variation turns on and off genes coding for antigens with different antigenic properties.

Pili are the only projections of the bacterial surface protruding through the capsule. They can mediate adherence to a variety of endothelial and epithelial cell types and this ability is modified by antigenic variation occurring at $10^{-4}$ or $10^{-3}$ per cell division. Pili consist of repeated subunit proteins of 18–24 kDa—the pilins. Only one or two genes (pilE for expressed) encode the full polypeptide and are efficiently transcribed, whereas a variety of other genes (pilS for silent) encode pilins devoid of the amino-terminal coding region and cannot be transcribed because they lack a transcription promoter.

Antigenic variation of pilins occurs by gene conversion targeted to the expressed genes, with the silent genes being used as donors (Fig. 6). This mechanism can generate more than 1 million variants but can also give rise to variants devoid of pili (pil-) through incorrect recombination or recombination with pseudogenes. A major contribution to gene conversion between pilin genes involves exogenous DNA from lysed cells, which naturally transforms living cells. In addition to these processes, carbohydrate addition also contributes to the variation of pili.

## C. *Borrelia*

Several species of these tick-borne bacteria are human pathogens. *Borrelia hermsii* causes relapsing fever, whereas *B. burgdorferi* is the agent of Lyme disease. This disease starts with mild flu symptoms but is followed by a chronic invasion of the perpipheral and central nervous system which is associated with various nervous symptoms and arthritis.

Both cases result in long-lasting infections due to continuous antigenic variation. The major immunogenic antigens are the VMP (*B. hermsii*) and the VLS (*B. burgdorferi*)—lipoproteins of 20–40 kDa encoded by a family of genes, only one of which is expressed at one time in a cell. Each wave of *B. hermsii* bacteremia expresses only one type of VMP, whereas during *B. burgdorferi* infection many subpopulations express different VLSs. The rate of variation is between $10^{-4}$ and $10^{-3}$ per cell per generation. The VMP genes (at least 26 in one strain) are located on linear plasmids and are kept silent except for a single one which is located in a telomeric expression site in the expression plasmid. Antigenic variation occurs by gene conversion or recombination targeted to the expression site using a silent gene from the same or from a different plasmid as that of the donor. Variation is increased by point mutations introduced in the expressed gene after the rearrangement. In the case of the VLS, the system is very similar except that all genes and the expression site appear to be contained in the same plasmid, and as in the case of Neisseria pilins (Fig. 6), the expression site is the only one to encode the N-terminal region of the protein.

Interestingly, as observed for metacyclic VSG genes in *T. brucei* the expression of some VMPs seems to be specific to the insect vector. This expression can be triggered *in vitro* by a temperature drop.

## D. *Streptococcus*

*Streptoccocus* is found as a commensal organism in 40% of the human population. However, in only 0.5% of the cases do severe diseases, such as pneumonia, meningitis, and septicemia, occur. In *S. pneu-*

*moniae,* the change from benign to aggressive phenotype sometimes occurs as a complication of a viral co-infection. The virus triggers cytokines to induce the expression of a platelet-activating factor receptor by lung epithelial cells, and this receptor is used by the bacteria to invade the cells. At this stage, the survival of *Streptococcus* is associated with the variation of the M protein, which possesses antiphagocytic properties but is the target of specific immunoglobulins. This protein is encoded by a single-copy gene and variation is achieved through either point mutations or recombinations between inexact repeats located within the gene. These rearrangements affect both the size of the protein and the nature of its antigenic determinants.

## E. *Salmonella*

*Salmonella* is a pathogenic member of the intestinal flora and causes enteric infections such as gastroenteritis and typhoid fever. These bacteria change their flagellar type by alternating the expression of different constitutive proteins, the flagellins, which are encoded by two genes, *H1* and *H2,* located in different regions of the genome. This occurs through regulated inversion (change of orientation) of a transcription promoter element of the *H2* gene (Fig. 10). Because the *H2* gene is followed by another cotranscribed gene encoding a repressor of the *H1* gene, *H2* is expressed and *H1* repressed when the *H2* promoter is in the "on" configuration, and *H1* is expressed when the *H2* promoter is in the "off" configuration. Enzymes involved in the rearrangement are all part of a multiprotein complex termed the invertasome

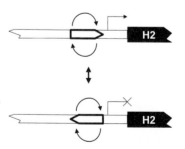

**Fig. 10.** Control of gene expression by promoter inversion in *Salmonella*. The invertase-controlled orientation of a transcriptional promoter element determines whether or not the gene encoding the H2 protein is transcribed.

and include a site-specific recombinase termed invertase as well as an enhancer-binding protein.

## IV. ANTIGENIC VARIATION IN VIRUSES

Many viruses undergo antigenic variation driven by the accumulation of mutations during viral infection. This mechanism, called antigenic drift, is thought to be due to low-fidelity copying by the RNA polymerases.

The best known examples are the HIV and influenza viruses. In both cases, the rapid and specific accumulation of mutations on the membrane or the external envelope of the virus allows them to escape neutralizing antibodies or cellular immunity and to elicit new waves of viremia. However, the role of antigenic variation may extend beyond the resistance to the immune response since, for instance, the parental viruses are often not eliminated and may persist together with the new variants. The ability of viruses to infect different cell types, which influences the success of infection and depends on interactions between viral envelope proteins and cell surface receptors, can be modulated by mutations in these proteins.

### A. HIV

The agent of AIDS is a retrovirus from the family of the lentiviruses. These viruses are retrotranscribed into DNA which is integrated in the genome of the host cell (macrophage or T lymphocyte) and serves as a template for the generation of new virus particles. HIV shows an extraordinary potential for diversity because most new isolates are different from previous ones. Variation mainly occurs in interspersed regions of a protein of the viral envelope, termed gp120, where mutations together with small deletions and insertions lead to amino acid substitutions. Particular attention has been directed at one the variable regions V3, which contains a major neutralizing epitope and is strain specific. In this case, the high rate of mutation could be ascribed to the very rapid rate of viral replication rather than to intrinsic tendency of the polymerase to generate mistakes.

### B. Influenza Virus

This RNA virus causes flu, a respiratory illness which periodically results in epidemics that can kill several million people (mostly the very young or the elderly). This virus is divided in three classes A–C on the basis of antigenic differences. Influenza virus performs both antigenic drift and antigenic shift.

Antigenic drift occurs in all three types. It mainly affects two surface proteins, neuramidinase (NA) and hemaglutinin (HA). The appearance of neutralizing antibodies allows the selection of minor antigenic changes that generate new variants with a frequency of $10^{-4}$ or $10^{-5}$.

Antigenic shift is due to the sequence reassortment of a RNA segment and leads to the appearance of new pandemic strains containing new variants of NA or HA. This mechanism only occurs in type A virus and has been attributed to its ability, as opposed to those of types B and C, to infect not only humans but also an animal reservoir. The shift would occur from genetic exchange between two different strains coinfecting the same animal host.

Therefore, the occurrence of yearly pandemic infections originates from the combination of two phenomenons—the genetic reassortment of a strain during coinfection of an animal host followed by adaptation to human hosts and escape from the immune response by amino acid substitutions.

## V. CONCLUSIONS

The variation of antigenic structures which allows the adaptation of microorganisms to the changing environment can be achieved through different genetic procedures, such as transcriptional (in)activation by position effect, DNA recombination targeted to antigen genes and/or to their promoter, error-prone copying of the antigen gene, and specific mRNA (de)stabilization. In fact, some of these procedures are also used by microbes to achieve other phenotypic changes, such as changing the mating type in yeasts (gene conversion) or sporulating in *Bacillus subtilis* (DNA excision). Note that DNA recombination, including gene conversion, is also used by metazoans to generate the antibodies that allow them to defend against microbial parasites and viruses. However, despite an apparent diversity, many of these mechanisms share common features. In many cases, antigenic variation occurs from the selective expression of a single or a few genes chosen from a repertoire of different variants; when this occurs, the expression site is frequently located in a telomere. The telomeric location of the expression site may tentatively be ascribed to the need for recombination within this site for antigenic variation. Telomeres are indeed well-known for being hot spots of DNA recombination, particularly homologous recombination, due to the presence of extensive arrays of repeats that are conserved between chromosomes and because of the abundance of G-rich stretches that are capable of forming quartet structures favoring pairing between double-stranded DNA molecules. Moreover, telomeric regions are relatively insulated from other regions of the chromosome so that in these regions recombination may be allowed to occur at high rate and on an extensive scale without perturbing the expression of other genes. These characteristics culminate in trypanosomes, which not only possess an extraordinary repertoire of more than 1000 genes for the variant antigen but also control the activity of a single expression site from a collection of 20 available sites. In addition, the presence within these expression sites of variant genes for surface receptors ensures an antigenic variation-coupled selection of the most appropriate set of receptors given the host in which the parasite is inoculated. No wonder the vaccine is not in sight.

## See Also the Following Articles

NATURAL SELECTION, BACTERIAL • *PLASMODIUM* • TRYPANOSOMES

## Bibliography

Borst, P., Bitter, W., Blundell, P. A., Chaves, I., Cross, M., Gerrits, H., Van Leeuwen, F., McCulloch, R., Taylor, M., and Rudenko, G. (1998). *Mol. Biochem. Parasitol.* **91**, 67–76.

Caron, F., and Meyer, E. (1989). *Annu. Rev. Microbiol.* **43**, 23–42.

Deitsch, K. W., Moxon, E. R., and Wellems, T. E. (1997). *Microbiol. Mol. Biol. Rev.* **61**, 281–293.

Dybvig, K. (1993). *Mol. Microbiol.* **10**, 465–471.

Fields, B. N., Knipe, D. M., Howley, P. M., Chanock, R. M., Melnick, J. L. L., Monath, T. P., Roizman, B., and Straus, S. E. (Eds.) (1996). "Fields Virology" (3rd ed.). Lippincott-Raven, New York.

Koomey, M. (1997). *Curr. Biol.* **7**, R538–R540.

Moxon, E. R., Rainey, P. B., Nowak, M. A., and Lensky, R. E. (1994). *Curr. Biol.* **4**, 24–33.

Nakamura, Y., and Wada, M. (1998). *Adv. Parasitol.* **41**, 63–107.

Nash, T. E. (1997). *Philos. Trans. R. Soc. London* **352**, 1369–1375.

Pays, E., and Nolan, D. P. (1998). *Mol. Biochem. Parasitol.* **91**, 3–36.

Reeder, J. C., and Brown, G. V. (1996). *Immunol. Cell Biol.* **7**, 546–554.

Vanhamme, L., and Pays, E. (1995). *Microbiol. Rev.* **59**, 223–240.

# Antisense RNAs

**Andrea Denise Branch**

*The Mount Sinai School of Medicine*

## GLOSSARY

**artificial RNAs**  RNA molecules expressed from genes that have been introduced into cells (transgenes) or RNA molecules synthesized in cell-free systems. The mode of action of artificial antisense RNAs is under active investigation. In some biological systems, artificial RNAs may themselves form double-stranded RNAs that mediate target-gene inhibition through novel mechanisms.

**complementarity**  A measure of the percentage of nucleotides in two sequences that are theoretically able to form Watson–Crick base pairs.

**cosuppression**  A type of posttranscriptional gene silencing in which transcripts of both an endogenous gene and an homologous transgene are synthesized and then degraded.

**homology-dependent viral resistance**  A form of posttranscriptional gene silencing in which viral RNAs are degraded in transgenic plants expressing RNAs homologous to viral RNAs, resulting in inhibition of viral replication and attenuation of virus symptoms.

**perfect double-stranded RNA (dsRNA) duplex**  A helical structure in which two segments from a single RNA molecule (an intramolecular duplex), or segments of two separate RNA molecules (an intermolecular duplex) in an anti-parallel orientation to each other form an uninterrupted series of Watson–Crick base pairs (C pairing with G; A pairing with U).

**posttranscriptional gene silencing**  A process through which specific RNAs are degraded posttranscriptionally, resulting in loss of expression of associated genes.

**ANTISENSE RNAs**  are RNA molecules that bind to a second, sense, RNA through complementary Watson–Crick base pairing of anti-parallel strands; RNA molecules that are at least 70% complementary to a second RNA for at least 30 nucleotides and thus have the potential for binding; or RNA molecules that are transcribed from the DNA strand opposite that of a second RNA. Antisense RNAs in gene therapy are complementary to target RNAs and are intended to eliminate the expression of specific genes; target RNAs may be either associated with diseases or with normal cellular functions. Naturally occurring antisense RNAs comprise a structurally and functionally diverse group that includes RNAs known to bind to their target RNAs and RNAs that simply contain sequences complementary to other previously identified RNAs.

In 1984, Izant and Weintraub thrust antisense RNA into the center stage of molecular research by proposing that artificial antisense RNAs could be used to eliminate the expression of specific target genes, offering an alternative to the labors of classical mutational analysis. Rather than producing random mutations and then screening for those affecting genes of interest, they suggested that mutants could be created at will by introducing antisense RNAs complementary to sense transcripts of selected genes. They envisioned antisense RNAs binding to messenger RNAs (mRNAs) or their precursors, forming duplexes, and thereby inhibiting gene expression. The promise of streamlined genetic analysis, and improved pharmaceutical agents, livestock, and crops stimulated tremendous interest in antisense technology in members of the research community and on Wall Street. However, artificial antisense RNAs have not always performed as intended. The molecular events responsible for their unexpected behavior are not yet known, but enough information has emerged to indicate that these events merit thorough investigation. To understand the properties of artificial antisense RNA and to gain a more complete understanding of RNA's regulatory functions, it is essential to study both naturally occurring and artificial antisense RNA. This collection of molecules includes RNAs known to alter the expression of their sense RNA counterparts and RNAs whose sequences appear to equip them to interact with their sense counterparts (i.e., RNAs that are at least 70% complementary to a second RNA for at least 30 nucleotides). Many natural and artificial antisense RNAs exist— far too many for each to be discussed here. Therefore, this article focuses on the principles governing their behavior. (Information about antisense oligomers composed of DNA is not included, but has been reviewed by the author.)

## I. INTRODUCTION

### A. Naturally Occurring Antisense RNAs Are Extremely Versatile

Antisense RNAs are best known for their ability to eliminate the expression of target RNAs by binding to complementary sequences. However, antisense RNAs do much more than turn off other genes. For example, in virus-infected mammalian cells, antisense RNA combines with sense RNA to form biologically active double-stranded RNA (dsRNA), which triggers the interferon (IFN) response. Other antisense RNAs are involved in RNA maturation. These molecules are often omitted from lists of antisense RNAs because they promote expression of their target RNAs, rather than inhibit it. However, there has never been a requirement for antisense RNAs to function as negative regulators of gene expression. The antisense RNAs involved in RNA maturation illustrate how complementary RNA sequences contribute to essential cellular functions. The guide RNAs of certain parasites bind to mitochondrial mRNA precursors through short complementary regions and direct upstream editing of the pre-mRNA. (RNA edit-

ing is any process leading to an alteration in the coding capacity of an mRNA, other than splicing or 3'-end processing). Similarly, small nucleolar RNAs (snoRNAs) bind to complementary regions of ribosomal RNA (rRNA) precursors, leading to methylase-mediated site-specific modification of the precursor.

Of the antisense RNAs on the frontiers of research, those transcribed from mammalian genes are among the most intriguing and in greatest need of further investigation. Based on evidence showing that certain of these RNAs down-regulate their targets— diminishing synthesis of sense RNA, interfering with pre-mRNA processing, and inhibiting sense RNA translation—it has generally been assumed that any newly discovered antisense RNA would also function as a negative regulator. However, recent data indicate that each RNA must be individually investigated. An antisense transcript of the Wilms's tumor gene (a gene imprinted under certain circumstances) appears to enhance expression of the sense RNA (Moorwood *et al.,* 1998). Concerning the range of possible antisense RNA functions, it is interesting to note that an antisense RNA to basic fibroblast growth factor mRNA is thought to serve in two capacities: to act as the mRNA for a highly conserved protein of its own and to down-regulate growth factor expression. Several additional antisense RNAs contain open reading frames and may specify proteins.

When interpreting a report of a newly discovered antisense RNA, particularly one detected in eukaryotic cells, it is important to remember that terminology in this part of the field permits a molecule to be designated an "antisense RNA" on the basis of sequence information alone. There is no requirement that the RNA bind to its sense counterpart or alter expression of the sense RNA in any way. Furthermore, throughout the entire antisense field, there is no requirement that sense and antisense RNAs be transcribed from opposite strands of the same DNA, and thus they are not necessarily exact complements of each other.

The looseness in antisense terminology could be problematic. However, it serves a useful purpose, increasing the chances that meaningful similarities will be recognized. Such similarities illustrate the principles governing the behavior of antisense RNAs. Examples are selected from three areas: prokaryotic systems, virus-infected mammalian cells, and artificial inhibitory RNAs. Antisense RNAs involved in RNA maturation, such as guide RNAs and snoRNAs, are not discussed further due to space limitations. However, the ability of guide RNAs to transfer genetic information is reflected in the function of the minus-strand viral RNAs, which are included; and the ability of snoRNAs to induce site-specific methylation is echoed in the gene-specific DNA methylation associated with some of the artificial inhibitory RNAs.

## B. Artificial RNAs Expanded the Antisense Field in Unexpected Directions

Some naturally occurring antisense RNAs are highly effective gene regulators. Their efficacy, and the conceptual simplicity of antisense-mediated gene ablation stimulated efforts to develop artificial antisense RNAs that could be used to inhibit specific genes in higher organisms and to confer resistance to micro-organisms. These efforts have already yielded commercial agricultural products, such as the transgenic Flavr Savr tomato. They have also revealed that it is sometimes possible to substitute a sense transcript for an antisense transcript and achieve the same level of target-gene inhibition. Because it is usually impossible for sense transcripts and their targets to form a perfect duplex containing more than about 7–12 bp, sense inhibition appears to be a manifestation of a novel regulatory pathway. It is important to learn the details of this pathway in order to gain insight into RNA function and to facilitate the development of more effective artificial RNAs for use in biotechnology and basic research.

## C. Despite the Diversity of Antisense RNAs, Four General Principles Account for Most Antisense Effects

The first principle is that, above all else, antisense RNAs are ribonucleic acids. As such, they are endowed with a unique combination of properties. RNAs can store and transmit genetic information, just as DNA can. Moreover, naturally occurring RNAs readily form intricate three-dimensional structures and can produce catalytic active sites. RNAs

are directly involved in protein synthesis at a variety of levels. Most RNAs are transcribed from DNA through a complex process involving *cis*-active promoter elements and many proteins. Nascent transcripts are converted into mature RNAs through an equally complex set of reactions. Regulation can occur at any of a number of points during transcription and subsequent processing. RNAs can be stable, or they can turn over rapidly. RNAs can readily move from the nucleus to the cytoplasm, and shuttle back and forth. They can form structural signals recognized by proteins, and they can interact with other nucleic acids through complementary base paring. These properties allow antisense RNAs to weave their way in and out of an enormous variety of cellular processes.

The second principle is that complementarity between an antisense RNA and a second nucleic acid is no guarantee that the two molecules will bind to each other. The tendency of antisense and target RNAs to form complexes, or to remain as separate molecules, is strongly influenced by their individual intramolecular structures. Potential nucleation sites can be prominently displayed, or virtually inaccessible. Complex formation is a bimolecular reaction whose rate is sensitive to concentration; the rate increases with increasing RNA concentration. The relationship between antisense RNA structure and function is illustrated most clearly by the antisense RNAs of prokaryotic systems, which are described in Sections II.A–B. Subcellular location also affects the probability that two RNAs will interact. Sense and antisense RNAs transcribed from the same genetic locus are more likely to encounter each other than RNAs transcribed from distant sites in the DNA. Similarly, two RNAs that accumulate in the same membrane-bound compartment are more likely to interact than those in separate compartments.

The third principle is that antisense activity is often mediated by proteins; these proteins must be identified and their modes of action characterized for antisense RNA function to be understood. Many different proteins bind to antisense RNAs and to the RNA–RNA duplexes they create. Depending on the protein and the nature of the duplex, binding can have a variety of effects. The same protein may catalyze a range of reactions, with the outcome determined by information encoded in the structure of the RNA–RNA duplex. Interactions between antisense RNAs and proteins are described in Sections II.D and III.C.

The fourth principle is that dsRNA can act as a signal. Mammalian cells recognize dsRNA as a sign that they, or their neighbors, are infected by a virus. Double-stranded RNA causes mammalian cells to enter an antiviral state. This response is mediated by a group of dsRNA-binding proteins, which make up a very sensitive dsRNA biosensor. There is growing evidence that dsRNA has symbolic value to cells from a variety of plants and animals. The potential of dsRNA to act as a signal is described in Sections III.A and IV.B–D and should be kept in mind when considering the possible biological effects of an antisense RNA.

### D. Summary

Antisense RNAs have many roles. They can act as negative regulators of gene expression, induce interferon, or direct RNA maturation. Antisense effects are strongly influenced by internal RNA structure and are often mediated by proteins. Artificial antisense RNAs have allowed new agricultural products to be developed and revealed unexpected roles of RNA in gene regulation.

## II. ANTISENSE RNAs IN PROKARYOTIC SYSTEMS: INHIBITION BY DIRECT BINDING TO TARGET RNAs

### A. The Copy Number of Plasmid ColE1 Is Regulated by RNA I, an Antisense Transcript

RNA I of the *Escherichia coli* plasmid ColE1 was the first regulatory antisense RNA to be discovered. In 1981, Lacatena and Cesareni reported that base pairing between complementary regions of RNA I and RNA II inhibits plasmid replication. Because this system illustrates many principles of antisense RNA action it is discussed in detail.

As is typical of antisense reactions, binding between RNA I and RNA II is a bimolecular process. Its rate is concentration dependent. The concentration

dependence of the RNA I–RNA II binding reaction is harnessed to achieve the desired biological effect—maintenance of plasmid copy number at a stable 10–20 copies per cell. Formation of the RNA I and RNA II complex inhibits plasmid DNA replication by preventing RNA II from maturing into the RNA primer required for DNA synthesis (for an excellent review of this system by a leading research group, see Eguchi, Itoh, and Tomizawa, 1991). RNA I is constitutively synthesized at a high rate and has a short half-life. Its concentration reflects the number of template DNA molecules. When copies of the plasmid are numerous, RNA I concentration is high, binding to RNA II is favored, and plasmid DNA synthesis is inhibited. Conversely, when the plasmid DNA concentration is low, RNA I concentration falls, and plasmid replication is stimulated. Because RNA I contains regions complementary to the RNA II molecules produced by related plasmids, it provides the basis for plasmid compatibility and incompatibility. RNA I has no coding capacity.

Synthesis of RNA II is initiated 555 bases upstream from the origin of DNA replication. RNA I is perfectly complementary to 108 bases at the 5′-end of RNA II and is transcribed from the same region of the genome, but in the opposite direction. RNA I must bind RNA II shortly after RNA II synthesis is initiated. If binding is delayed, the nascent RNA II transcript forms structures that render it resistant to inhibition by RNA I. This competition between formation of the RNA I–RNA II complex and the RNA II self-structure means that antisense activity requires rapid association.

RNA I and RNA II interact through an intricate process whose individual steps are predetermined by the structures of the two RNAs. As illustrated in Fig. 1, RNA I has three stem–loop structures and a short tail at its 5′-end. The loops contain seven bases. Figure 1 also depicts RNA II, in a conformation that may exist in nascent RNA II transcripts. The secondary structures of RNA I and RNA II maximize the chances that they will form a bimolecular complex. Three sets of complementary bases are exposed in single-stranded loops. Bases making up these potential nucleation sites are displayed in structures somewhat similar to those that project the bases of tRNA anti-codons toward the mRNA codons. During nu-

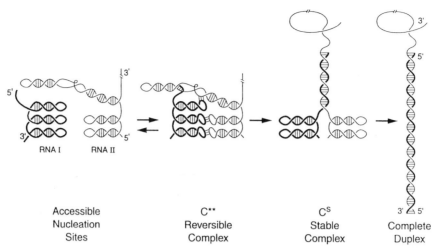

**Fig. 1.** Binding of ColEI RNA I to RNA II is a stepwise process. RNA I and RNA II interact through complementary sequences present in loops to form C**. Pairing between the 5'-end of RNA I and RNA II is followed by a series of structural changes that culminate in the formation of a stable complex, C$^s$. Finally, RNA I hybridizes to RNA II throughout its entire length. Adapted from Eguchi *et al.* (1991).

cleation, bases in corresponding loops of RNA I and RNA II interact weakly, evidently forming a limited number of bonds between bases in only one or two loops. The very unstable early intermediates can dissociate rapidly, or establish a "kissing complex," which can, in turn, produce the C** complex, a structure in which all three corresponding loops (reversibly) interact with each other.

The formation of C** can be facilitated by the plasmid-encoded protein, Rom (RNA-*one*-*modulator*), which binds to the kissing complex and reduces its equilibrium dissociation constant. The solution structure of a helix modeled after the RNA I–RNA II loop–loop helix was recently solved by nuclear magnetic resonance spectroscopy (Lee and Crothers, 1998). As expected from previous biochemical studies, all seven bases in the loops form complementary base pairs. The loop–loop helix partially stacks on the stem helices, producing a nearly linear structure. The loop–loop helix is bent toward the major groove, which is thereby narrowed. This bend, and phosphate clusters flanking the major groove, distinguish this helix from standard A-form RNA, perhaps accounting for the ability of Rom to recognize it. Conversion of C** to stable structures, such as C$^s$, begins with events occurring at the 5'-end of RNA I. If enough time elapses, the stable complexes convert

into full-length dsRNA molecules. However, inhibition can result from stable complexes formation itself and does not require the generation of a complete duplex. Any lengthy dsRNA regions that form are likely to be rapidly degraded by the endonuclease RNase III.

## B. Antisense RNAs in Prokaryotic Systems Have Many Features in Common

### 1. Antisense RNA Structure

RNA I is only the first example of the many well-characterized antisense RNAs in prokaryotic systems. Four other representative antisense RNAs are depicted in Table I and their modes of action are presented. Prokaryotic antisense RNAs are typically small (65–100 bases), stable, noncoding RNAs, whose secondary structures contain one or more stem-loops (see Table I). The loops usually contain 5–8 bases and often have sequences that are similar to each other. The stems of antisense RNA stem-loop structures often contain unpaired nucleotides at precise locations. These "imperfections" protect the RNAs from cleavage by dsRNA-specific ribonucleases and also reduce the stability of the stems,

***TABLE I***
**Representative Antisense RNAs of Prokaryotic Accessory DNA Elements and Bacterial DNA**

| System | Antisense RNA structure | Mode of action |
|---|---|---|
| **Plasmid** <br> Plasmid R1 <br> Antisense: CopA <br> (91 bases) <br> Target: CopT | *(stem-loop structure labeled* **CopA** *, 5′ sequence:* 5′-AU...ACGGUUUAAGUGGGC GUUUUUGCUU-3′*)* | CopA indirectly prevents synthesis of RepA, a protein required for plasmid replication, by pairing with CopT sequences in the polycistronic RNA that encodes RepA. Binding blocks the ribosome binding site of the *tap* gene, and prevents its translation, which is coupled to translation of the *repA* gene. Binding also yields duplexes which are RNase III substrates. |
| **Phage** <br> Bacteriophage λ <br> Antisense: oop RNA <br> (77 bases) <br> Target: cII mRNA | *(stem-loop structure labeled* **oop RNA** *, 5′ sequence:* 5′-GU CGCCUUAG UUUUA-3′*)* | oop RNA binds to (55) bases at the 3′-end of the cII portion of the cII-O mRNA, creating an RNase III cleavage site, destabilizing the cII message, and thereby enhancing the burst size during induction. |
| **Transposable element** <br> Insertion sequence IS10 <br> Antisense: RNA OUT <br> (70 bases) <br> Target: RNA-IN | *(stem-loop structure labeled* **RNA-OUT** *, 5′ sequence:* 5′-UUCG UAUCC-3′*)* | RNA-OUT binds to (35) nucleotides at the 5′-end of RNA-IN, transposase mRNA, preventing translation by blocking the ribosome binding site or by creating an RNase III cleavage site. Antisense inhibition increases as IS10 copy number increases, producing multicopy inhibition. IS10 is the mobile element of Tn10 (a tetracycline-resistance transposon). |
| **Bacterial chromosome** <br> *Escherichia coli* <br> Antisense: micF RNA <br> (93 bases) <br> Target: ompF mRNA | *(two stem-loop structures labeled* **micF RNA** *, 5′ sequence:* 5′-GCUAUCAUCAUUAACUUUAUUUAUUAC UUUACCCCUAUUUC UUUUUU-3′*)* | micF RNA is about 70% complementary to the 5′-end of ompF mRNA in the region of the ribosome binding site. Binding modulates production of OmpF, a major component of the *E. coli* outer membrane. |

allowing them to open up during binding to their target RNAs (Hjalt and Wagner, 1995).

### 2. Antisense and Target RNAs Associate through a Stepwise Binding Process

Antisense and target RNAs interact through a stepwise process that proceeds from nucleation to stable complex formation. This process has been studied extensively in three systems: RNA I and RNA II of the plasmid ColE1, CopA and CopT of the plasmid R1 (CopT occurs in repA mRNA; see Table I), and RNA-OUT and RNA-IN from the mobile genetic element IS*10*. The apparent second-order rate constants for pairing between these RNAs are in the range of $0.3-1.0 \times 10^6$ $M^{-1}$ $s^{-1}$. In the binding reactions between RNA I and RNA II and between CopA and CopT, loop–loop interactions between antisense and target RNAs nucleate binding and formation of the kissing complex. In the binding reaction between RNA-OUT and RNA-IN, the first bonds form between bases in the loop of RNA-OUT and the 5′-end of RNA-IN, an RNA thought to have a relatively open structure. Rapid association appears to be a general requirement for efficient antisense activity. Because they mediate this early and rapid association, the initial base pairs are far more important to the overall binding process than their thermodynamic contribution to the final complex would suggest. Early intermediates are rapidly replaced by complexes containing more intermolecular base pairs. The final outcome of antisense binding depends on the system. Effects include termination of transcription, destabilization, and inhibition of translation. All known prokaryotic antisense RNAs are negative regulators of gene expression, although according to Wagner and Simons, "mechanisms for positive control are quite plausible" (Wagner and Simons, 1994).

Most, but not all, antisense RNAs are transcribed from overlapping gene sequences. As indicated in Table I, mRNA-interfering complementary (micF) RNA is not closely linked to its target, ompF RNA. The duplex they form contains looped-out regions and noncanonical base pairs, in addition to conventional bonds (Delihas *et al.,* 1997). This duplex helps to establish the lower limit of complementarity for an antisense–target RNA pair. Within the duplex,

only 24 of 33 bases (73%) of micF RNA are Watson–Crick base-paired to nucleotides in ompF RNA.

## C. Bioengineers Hope to Use the Special Features of Naturally Occurring Antisense RNAs to Develop Effective Artificial Antisense RNAs

Engdahl and colleagues attempted to apply their knowledge of naturally occurring antisense RNAs to develop bioengineered antisense RNAs capable of inhibiting selected target genes (Engdahl *et al.,* 1997). They tested antisense RNAs containing a recognition element resembling the major stem-loop of CopA and either a segment complementary to the ribosome binding site of the target RNA or a ribozyme. None of their antisense RNAs inhibited the target genes by more than 50%. They concluded, "we still have too little insight into the factors that determine this property [the ability to rapidly associate] and, hence cannot yet tailor such structures to any chosen target sequence." However, their study and similar studies by other investigators are helping to identify the structural features needed to produce effective artificial antisense RNAs for use in bacterial systems.

## D. Proteins Often Mediate Antisense RNA Activity: RNase III Is a Prototypic dsRNA-Binding Protein

Important steps in several antisense systems are carried out by RNase III. Purified in 1968, RNase III was the first enzyme to be discovered that recognizes RNA–RNA duplexes as substrates. Like many other dsRNA-binding proteins, RNase III does not act exclusively on perfect duplexes. The varied interactions between RNase III and its substrates illustrate the range of functions that can be included in the repertoire of a single enzyme.

As illustrated in Fig. 2A, RNase III cleaves perfect RNA–RNA duplexes into short fragments averaging about 15 bases in length. Cuts are made across both strands of the duplex, at sites that are usually offset by one or two bases. This reaction shows no sequence

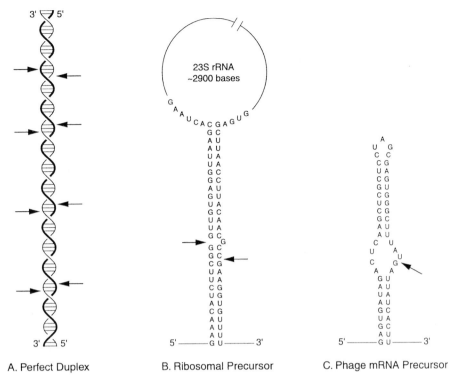

A. Perfect Duplex      B. Ribosomal Precursor      C. Phage mRNA Precursor

***Fig. 2.*** Structural features of dsRNA regions direct RNase III cleavage. RNase III cleaves perfect RNA–RNA duplexes into fragments averaging 15 base pairs in length (A). In addition, it cuts the 30S ribosomal RNA precursor at four positions, releasing intermediates that will become the mature ribosomal RNAs. The double-cleavage site in the region 23S region (Bram *et al.*, 1980) is shown (B). Finally, RNase III cleaves certain complex RNA structures, such as those in the bacteriophage T7 early mRNA precursor at single sites. These complex structures are typically depicted as "bubbles" because they are devoid of Watson–Crick pairs; however, it is likely that they contain a precise array of non-canonical bonds and are not open loops (C).

specificity. Certain complexes of antisense and target RNAs are degraded by such randomly placed double-cleavages. In contrast, the 30S rRNA precursor is cut at four precise bonds. The rRNA precursor folds into a structure with two large stems, one topped by the sequence of 16S rRNA, the other by 23S rRNA. RNase III cleaves each of these stems exactly twice at specific nucleotides, releasing rRNA intermediates. The stem flanking 23S rRNA is shown in Fig. 2B. The cleavage reactions carried out on the nearly perfect stems in the rRNA precursor resemble those carried out on perfect duplexes in certain respects, but not others. They are double-cleavages, but at predetermined locations. Surprisingly, RNase III also makes a series of precise cuts in the early mRNA precursor of bacte-

riophage T7 (Fig. 2C), even though this molecule contains no structures that bear an obvious similarity to perfect duplexes. Although the bacteriophage T7 cleavage sites lack the hallmark feature of dsRNA—a consecutive series of Watson–Crick bonds—they almost certainly contain noncanonical bonds that confer stability and allow them to fold into three-dimensional structures with features similar to dsRNA.

As a group, the RNase III cleavage sites demonstrate the subtlety of the interactions between dsRNA-binding proteins and RNA molecules. RNase III acts as a rampant random nuclease on dsRNA substrates. Duplexes are cleaved at multiple sites regardless of their sequence; yet RNase III makes precise cleavages at sequence-specific sites in certain RNA precursor molecules. The structure of the RNA dictates the outcome of encounters with RNase III. The ability of single-stranded RNAs to exploit and sometimes to thwart dsRNA-specific enzymes is a significant survival factor for viruses, as illustrated by bacteriophage T7, and by the mammalian viruses discussed in the next section.

## E. Summary

Naturally occurring antisense RNAs in prokaryotic systems are small, noncoding molecules whose structures facilitate rapid association with target RNAs. These antisense RNAs are much more than RNA molecules that happen to have sequences complementary to those of other RNAs. They are highly evolved machines designed to snare and entwine their targets. Inhibition can be a direct consequence of binding, or it can involve cellular proteins, especially endonucleases. RNase III is an endonuclease that cleaves RNA–RNA duplexes, such as those produced by certain antisense RNAs and their targets. Degradation is not the inevitable fate of an RNase III substrate. Depending on the structure of the duplex, RNase III can also introduce specific cleavages and promote RNA maturation.

## III. ANTISENSE RNAs IN VIRUS-INFECTED MAMMALIAN CELLS: SIGNALS OF DANGER

### A. dsRNAs Are Potent Inducers of Interferon and Activators of Antiviral Defenses

Because the interferon response is central to mammalian antiviral defense, few antisense molecules can compete for significance with those producing the dsRNAs that induce interferon and otherwise contribute to the antiviral state. Despite the technical obstacles that make these dsRNAs difficult to study, they are analyzed here because of their importance to mammalian survival and because they illustrate the ability of dsRNA to act as a signal. The protective power of an intact interferon response is demon-

strated by studies of transgenic mice deficient in either the type I or the type II interferon receptor. These mice rapidly succumb to viral infections that they would otherwise readily clear. For example, while the median lethal dose of intravenously administered vesicular stomatitis virus is normally in the range of $10^8$ plaque-forming units, mutant mice lacking the type I IFN receptor die within 3 to 6 days after receiving 30 to 50 units (Muller *et al.*, 1994). A functional interferon system raises the lethal dose of this virus 2 million-fold.

Mammalian cells have an extraordinarily sensitive mechanism for detecting dsRNA and for responding to dsRNA by synthesizing interferons. In 1977, Marcus and Sekellick reported that primary chick embryo cells are capable of responding to a single molecule of dsRNA. They exposed cells to defective interfering particles of vesicular stomatitis virus containing a covalently linked antisense–sense RNA molecule in a ribonucleoprotein complex. A single dsRNA molecule was presumed to form upon entry into the cell. Peak interferon titers were obtained in cultures incubated with 0.3 particles per cell. Both higher and lower doses of particles resulted in very marked reductions in interferon production, producing a bell-shaped dose–response curve. The data indicated that cells that attached two or more particles produced little or no interferon. Cells in the cultures exposed to the defective interfering particles entered a general antiviral state, as indicated by their resistance to a subsequent challenge with Sindbis virus. Control experiments ruled out the possibility that interferon induction was due to proteins in the particles.

In these experiments, cells responded to intracellular dsRNA. Cells also respond to exogenously applied dsRNA. This ability may allow cells to respond to dsRNA released from their moribund neighbors. A pharmaceutical form of dsRNA has been developed for intravenous delivery to virus-infected patients. When dsRNA acts as a danger signal, it is performing a function similar to that of unmethylated CpG-containing DNA. Such DNA is a strong immune stimulant and is interpreted by B-cells and cells of the innate immune system as a sign of microbial attack. Thus, two types of nucleic acid, dsRNA and unmethylated CpG-containing DNA, are central to mammalian defenses against infectious agents.

## B. Viruses Are Thought to Be the Source of Interferon-Inducing Antisense RNA and dsRNA, but Hard Evidence Is Very Difficult to Obtain

Conventional wisdom holds that the dsRNAs responsible for interferon induction are entirely of viral origin. However, as stated by Jacob and Langland, "Actually identifying the potential sources of dsRNA in infected cells has in fact been problematic over the years" (Jacobs and Langland, 1996). The replication intermediates of RNA viruses contain both plus and minus RNAs, and are obvious potential sources of dsRNA. DNA viruses could generate dsRNA by aberrant transcription or by transcription of overlapping genes encoded on opposite strands.

The lack of direct evidence concerning the identity of the interferon-inducing dsRNA reflects technical difficulties that make it nearly impossible to analyze the critical dsRNA molecules. Ironically, the cell's extreme sensitivity is a major problem; it sets a standard for dsRNA detection that existing molecular techniques cannot equal. RNA viruses generate relatively large quantities of complementary (minus) strands during the course of replication. Minus strands create a potential background problem because they can associate with sense strands during the extraction process. Particularly if the extraction is carried out in the presence of phenol, which catalyzes nucleic acid hybridization, the presence of viral dsRNA in extracts does not prove that it existed in cells.

Even when dsRNA can be shown to be present in cells, for example by the use of dsRNA-specific antibodies, questions remain about whether this dsRNA was accessible to the cell's dsRNA-sensing machinery. Magliano and colleagues demonstrated that the membrane-bound cytoplasmic vacuoles, called rubella virus "replication complexes," are virus-modified lysosomes (Magliano *et al.,* 1998). This compartmentalization may effectively hide the rubella virus dsRNA. Similar membranous structures have been described in other virus-infected cells. The sequestration of dsRNA may be a common viral defense strategy. Vaccinia virus, a DNA virus that produces large quantities of complementary transcripts, also produces proteins encoded by the E3L

gene that bind dsRNA. This countermeasure is effective. Although vaccinia virus produces dsRNA, it is relatively resistant to interferon unless the E3L gene is mutated. Moreover, interferon resistance can be restored to mutant vaccinia by supplying RNase III (Shors and Jacobs, 1997), the bacterial endonuclease which destroys dsRNA. The ability of vaccinia to replicate in cells expressing RNase III suggests that the viral dsRNA is not required by the virus, but rather is a side product. It would be interesting to know whether RNase III-producing cells support the replication of mammalian RNA viruses, or if the RNA to RNA replication cycle of such viruses render them sensitive to this endonuclease. The replication intermediates of RNA bacteriophage contain little if any exposed dsRNA and are not sensitive to RNase III *in vivo.*

The studies of rubella virus and vaccinia virus illustrate the general point that the stronger the evidence that viral dsRNA exists inside infected mammalian cells, the stronger the evidence that the dsRNA is obscured in some way. These experiments indicate that viruses produce very little dsRNA that is exposed to the interferon sensing machinery, and suggest that the RNAs reaching the dsRNA biosensor may not be mainstream viral RNAs required for replication. They also raise the possibility that viral dsRNA may not be the only sign cells use to detect viral infection. The high concentration of viral mRNA is a potential additional stigma. It has been proposed that higher plants have a surveillance system that recognizes and eliminates RNAs whose concentrations rise above threshold limits. This system has been associated with posttranscriptional gene silencing (see Section IV).

## C. Double-Stranded RNA-Binding Proteins Contribute to the Antiviral State

Double-stranded RNAs play two different roles in the interferon response. First, they stimulate interferon production and thus induce expression of at least 30 genes. Second, they interact with interferon-induced enzymes and thereby promote the antiviral state of the cell. Despite technical difficulties that impede direct analysis, it is possible to deduce some characteristics of these dsRNAs by studying the properties—length preferences, affinities, and concentrations—of the interferon-induced enzymes. Like dsRNA itself, at least one of these proteins, the interferon-induced RNA-dependent protein kinase (PKR), plays a dual role in the interferon response. PKR transduces the dsRNA signal, communicating to the nucleus that a virus is present. In addition, PKR and two other dsRNA-binding enzymes catalyze reactions that inhibit virus production.

### 1. The Interferon-Induced RNA-Dependent Protein Kinase, PKR

PKR levels have been measured in human Daudi cells. Each cell contains about $5 \times 10^5$ molecules in the cytoplasm (mostly associated with ribosomes) and $1 \times 10^5$ in the nucleus (mostly in the nucleolus). Following interferon treatment, the PKR concentration rises three- to fourfold, with almost all of the increase occurring in the cytoplasm. IFN-treated cells contain approximately one molecule of PKR for each ribosome (Jeffrey *et al.*, 1995). Ribosomes compete with dsRNA for binding to PKR (Raine *et al.*, 1998). Ribosome-bound PKR may constitute a reserve supply that can be rapidly deployed without the need for new RNA or protein synthesis.

PKR binds to and is activated by long dsRNA molecules. As is true for many interactions between dsRNA-specific enzymes and perfect duplexes, there is no discernible sequence specificity for the reactions between PKR and dsRNA. Duplexes shorter than 30 base pairs do not bind stably to PKR and do not activate the enzyme. Those longer than 30 base pairs bind with increasing efficiency, reaching a maximum at about 85 base pairs. The lack of sequence specificity allows the PKR to recognize dsRNAs regardless of their origins, satisfying a prerequisite for any broad-based antiviral response. The rather long optimal length of dsRNA makes PKR resistant to activation by the short and imperfect duplexes present in many cellular RNAs, including rRNAs. However, PKR's requirement for perfect duplexes is not absolute. Certain RNAs lacking extensive perfect duplexes activate PKR, including a cellular RNA recently identified by Petryshyn *et al.* (1997).

Binding to long dsRNA causes PKR to undergo an autophosphorylation reaction and become activated.

This process displays a marked concentration dependence: PKR is activated by low concentrations of dsRNA (in the range of 10–100 ng/ml), but higher concentrations are less and less effective, giving rise to a bell-shaped activation curve. The shape of this curve indicates that PKR is optimally activated by a particular ratio of dsRNA to PKR. It also suggests that virus-infected cells do not contain high concentrations of accessible dsRNA. If they did, the PKR defense system would not function efficiently.

Once it has been activated, PKR phosphorylates a number of proteins, most notably the translation initiation factor eIF-2. This phosphorylation inhibits protein synthesis, thereby diminishing virus production. In addition, PKR appears to transduce the dsRNA signal, at least in part, by phosphorylating I-κB, releasing and activating the transcription factor NF-κB. Analysis of the interferon response is progressing rapidly, producing a picture of an intricate combinatorial cascade in which PKR activation by dsRNA is an early event in a series of reactions that culminates in the antiviral state.

PKR is a highly effective antiviral agent. Accordingly, several viruses have evolved strategies for neutralizing it. One of the best characterized of the anti-PKR viral products, and the one with the closest ties to dsRNA, is VAI RNA of adenovirus. In cells infected with mutant viruses deficient in VAI RNA synthesis, PKR is activated and protein synthesis comes to a halt. VAI RNA is an abundant RNA ($10^8$ copies per infected cell) that is about 160 bases long. It has enough similarity to *bona fide* dsRNA to bind to PKR, but lacks the structural features required for activation. Thus, it competitively inhibits activation by dsRNA.

### 2. The 2′,5′-Oligo(A) Synthetases

The 2′,5′-oligo(A) synthetases are activated upon binding to dsRNA molecules. They then polymerize ATP into 2′,5′-oligo(A), which in turn activates RNase L (a normally latent endonuclease), leading to mRNA degradation. Constituitive expression of 2′,5′-oligo(A) synthetase has been shown experimentally to confer resistance to picorna virus infection.

In an attempt to determine the form of picorna virus RNA physically associated with the enzyme,

Gribaudo and colleagues analyzed RNAs co-precipitating with 2′,5′-oligo(A) synthetase extracted from encephalomyocarditis virus (EMCV)-infected HeLa cells (Gribaudo *et al.*, 1991). Precipitates contained both plus and minus EMCV RNAs. About 10% of the viral RNA was resistant to single-stranded RNA-specific ribonucleases, and thus potentially representative of preexisting dsRNA. However, the authors commented that this value might be "an overestimate resulting from the annealing of regions of complementary strands upon removing proteins which blocked the annealing." Providing further evidence that only a small percentage of the viral RNA was double-stranded *in vivo*, the synthetase prepared from these cells was not fully activated. Activation could be enhanced 20-fold by incubation with artificial dsRNA [poly(I)-poly(C)]. Because both adenovirus VAI RNA (Desai *et al.*, 1995) and heterogeneous nuclear RNA (Nilsen *et al.*, 1982) activate 2′,5′-oligo(A) synthetases *in vitro*, extensive regions of perfect duplex structure are clearly not required for synthetase activation. Plus and minus EMCV RNAs may have stable structural elements capable of partially activating the synthetase, particularly in cells primed to respond. Further study is needed to determine whether both duplexes (composed of plus and minus viral RNAs) and free viral RNAs contribute to synthetase activation in picorna virus-infected cells.

### 3. The dsRNA Adenosine Deaminase, dsRAD

The dsRNA adenosine deaminase, dsRAD, catalyzes the C-6 deamination of adenosine to yield inosine. Deamination reduces the stability of dsRNAs. In conjunction with a ribonuclease specific for inosine-containing RNA (Scadden and Smith, 1997), dsRAD may play a role in viral defense. However, its contribution to viral defense is not as clearly established as that of the PKR kinase and the 2′,5′-oligo(A) synthetases. Primarily a nuclear enzyme that is expressed in virtually all mammalian cells, dsRAD contributes to normal metabolism. It has also been implicated in the production of hypermutated measles virus RNAs during chronic infection of the central nervous system. Such chronic infection can lead to a fatal degenerative neurological disease, subacute sclerosing panencephalitis.

The substrate preferences of dsRAD are rapidly coming to light, and will clarify its biological functions when they are fully known. The deaminase has no clear *in vitro* sequence specificity for action on perfect dsRNA; however, some adenosines may be preferred. For maximum modification, intermolecular or intramolecular duplexes need to contain a minimum of 100 base pairs. From the standpoint of molecular structure, it is remarkable that this enzyme acts upon continuous duplex RNA. It is able to deaminate adenosines even though the C-6 amino group of adenosine lies in the deep and narrow major groove of standard A-form RNA, a space that is usually inaccessible to amino acid side-chains.

In addition to perfect duplexes, dsRAD acts on RNAs that lack extensive duplex structure. For example, it edits certain cellular pre-mRNAs, such as that of the glutamate-gated ion channel GluR. Like PKR and the 2′,5′-oligo(A) synthetases, dsRAD binds to adenovirus VAI RNA *in vitro* (Lei *et al.*, 1998). In a manner similar to the assistance RNase III lends to bacteriophage T7, dsRAD aids the human hepatitis delta agent by deaminating a specific adenosine residue and carrying out an RNA editing event essential for the survival of this viroid-like pathogen. Exhibiting an additional similarity to RNase III, dsRAD behaves like one type of enzyme when interacting with long dsRNA molecules, in this case acting as a very robust and vigorous deaminase while it functions as a highly selective editing enzyme when interacting with single-stranded RNAs that have specific structural elements.

The dsRNA adenosine deaminase is clearly an enzyme with important cellular functions, and it is sometimes exploited by pathogens. Its role in antiviral defense is less clearly established, but the fact that its level rises following interferon treatment suggests that dsRAD contributes to the antiviral state.

### D. Summary

Antisense RNAs play an important role in antiviral defenses by forming dsRNA. dsRNA is recognized by mammalian cells as a danger signal indicating that viral infection has occurred. A single molecule of dsRNA can induce interferon. Viruses often produce detectable amounts of dsRNA. However, in many cases, this dsRNA is obscured by other viral products. As a result, it has been difficult to pinpoint the actual dsRNA responsible for inducing the interferon response. Several cellular dsRNA-specific enzymes are induced by interferon and are thought to contribute to the antiviral state. Two of these enzymes degrade RNA, a third blocks protein synthesis. This enzyme, the PKR, also contributes to the antiviral state by setting off a cascade that activates interferon synthesis.

## IV. ARTIFICIAL RNAs, dsRNA, AND POSTTRANSCRIPTIONAL GENE SILENCING

### A. Artificial Sense, Antisense, and dsRNAs Place a Spotlight on Gene Silencing

Just as Rutherford was unprepared for what happened when he shot alpha particles at a thin sheet of gold, biologists were unprepared for what occurred when they engineered plants to express sense transcripts of the *chalcone synthetase A* (*chA*) gene (van der Krol *et al.*, 1990; Napoli *et al.*, 1990). In many plants, both the transgene and the endogenous homolog of the transgene were silent, or co-suppressed. Thus, an attempt to overexpress genes involved in pigment formation resulted in plants with white flowers. These plants, and many studied subsequently, exhibit posttranscriptional gene silencing (PTGS), a condition in which specific RNA molecules are degraded.

The examples of PTGS in plants involve many different genes, plant species, and DNA constructs. It is believed that PTGS could be produced in all plant species with most endogenous genes. Furthermore, PTGS can be used to confer virus resistance to transgenic plants expressing sense transcripts of viral genes. The RNA affected by PTGS may be the product of a transgene, an endogenous plant mRNA, or a viral RNA. According to Balcombe, who reviewed hypotheses concerning the pathway leading to PTGS, all mechanisms require the production of an antisense RNA (Baulcombe, 1996). Evidence reveals that PTGS also occurs in nematodes (Fire *et al.*, 1998). At

least in some cases, PTGS involves dsRNA molecules functioning as signals. In order to gain a full understanding of gene regulatory pathways and the biological role of RNA, it is critical to identify the molecular events leading to PTGS. To this end, PTGS is described here in three experimental settings.

### B. Homology-Dependent Virus Resistance Occurs in Transgenic Plants

Viral genes have been transformed into a wide range of plant species to obtain viral protection. Results of these experiments support a two-phase model of homology-dependent resistance. In the first phase, viral and transgene RNA concentrations rise. After their combined concentration exceeds a threshold (or for some other reason), a switch is triggered in a surveillance system and a factor capable of causing gene-specific RNA turnover is produced. Appearance of this factor—which is probably either a perfect or an imperfect RNA duplex—initiates the second (maintenance) phase. During the second phase, the factor moves from the inoculated leaf to other portions of the plant, causing systemic resistance (Voinnet and Baulcombe, 1997).

Like other forms of PTGS in plants, virus resistance is usually seen in only a fraction of the plants carrying a particular transgene. This variability suggests that PTGS results from a rare event. The level of virus resistance is also variable. In the most extreme cases, there is no detectable accumulation of the virus anywhere in the inoculated plant. In others, virus accumulates at least in the inoculated leaves. A plant showing intermediate resistance to tobacco etch virus (TEV) allowed the sequential events that take place during PTGS to be analyzed. This plant was initially susceptible to TEV and the transgene expressed high levels of viral sense transcripts. However, symptoms were attenuated in the (upper) leaves, which developed after inoculation. These new leaves contained little TEV RNA or RNA of the transgene. Such plants are said to have "recovered" (although the tissues showing "recovery" never developed symptoms in the first place) (Lindbo *et al.*, 1993; Goodwin *et al.*, 1996). This plant was resistant to challenge inoculation with a related virus, but was susceptible to infection by unrelated viruses, indicating that resistance was homology dependent.

Very similar events take place during certain natural viral infections, suggesting that homology-dependent virus resistance and natural resistance have common features. Ratcliff and colleagues demonstrated that *Nicotiana clevelandii* inoculated with tomato black ring nepovirus (strain W22) initially showed symptoms, and then recovered. Inoculated plants were resistant to challenge with a second inoculation of the same strain and were partially resistant to challenge with a related strain, BUK, which is 68% identical to W22. However, they were sensitive to an unrelated virus, potato virus X (Ratcliff *et al.*, 1997). Thus, in both homology-dependent virus resistance in transgenic plants and in certain natural viral infections, a factor is generated in highly infected tissues that moves to other parts of the plant, rendering them resistant. The specificity of these events strongly implicates a nucleic acid, almost certainly an RNA.

PTGS can be a two-way street, as illustrated by RNA viruses that have been engineered to contain inserts of nuclear genes. When such viruses replicate, they produce RNAs with sequences of the nuclear genes and they inhibit expression of the nuclear gene. For example, the upper leaves of *N. benthamiana* inoculated with a recombinant tobacco mosaic virus containing part of the *phytoene desaturase* gene displayed a photobleaching effect, indicating that the desaturate gene had been inhibited (resulting in the loss of carotenoid-mediated protection) (Kumagai *et al.*, 1995). Because the RNAs of plant viruses are thought to have a strictly cytoplasmic location, these results indicate that either all steps of PTGS can take place in the cytoplasm or that the RNAs interact with DNA during cell division following breakdown of the nuclear envelop.

Waterhouse and colleagues produced strong evidence that dsRNA can trigger PTGS. They showed that *N. tabaccum cv* W38 engineered to express dsRNAs of the potato virus Y (PVY) protease gene were much more likely to acquire virus immunity than plants expressing either sense or antisense transcripts of this gene (Waterhouse *et al.*, 1998). As they pointed out, the efficacy of their constructs, which were designed to produce dsRNA in which

both strands of the duplex originated from transgenes (rather than duplexes in which one strand originated from the transgene and the other strand was of viral origin), argues against conventional models of antisense action. Conventional models require pairing to take place between transcripts of transgenes and their targets, while the data of Waterhouse and colleagues indicate that constructs were much more effective when their transcripts were capable of forming dsRNA on their own. It will be interesting to learn what makes such constructs more effective than those expressing antisense RNA and to identify the cellular factors interacting with the dsRNA. Proteins will almost certainly be involved in this process. Changes at the DNA level, such as altered methylation, may also occur.

There are many reports of DNA methylation of transgenes associated with PTGS. For example, in tobacco plants displaying homology-dependent resistance and PTGS of a PVY transgene, the DNA of the transgene was methylated (Smith *et al.*, 1995). At the moment, the significance of DNA methylation is not clear. It may be a cause of homology-dependent PTGS, or it may be a consequence of it.

When one considers the impact RNA may have on DNA methylation patterns, it is interesting to consider the results of studies carried out on transgenic plants carrying defective viroid cDNAs. Viroids are circular RNAs that replicate through an RNA-to-RNA rolling-circle process in the nucleus. Inoculation of the transgenic plants with infectious viroid led to viroid replication and to specific methylation of the viroid cDNA sequences, even though this DNA was not the template for the viroid RNA (Wassenegger *et al.*, 1994). Unfortunately, because viroid-infected nuclei contain both free viroid RNA and viroid replication intermediates (which may have dsRNA segments of unknown length), these experiments do not reveal whether single-stranded viroid RNA or double-stranded viroid RNA induced the DNA methylation.

## C. Co-suppression of Nuclear Genes in Plants Involves RNA–RNA Duplexes

In studies paralleling those described above, Waterhouse and colleagues also compared the ability of various constructs to inhibit a $\Delta\beta$-glucuronidase (GUS) reporter gene in rice. Some constructs were designed to produce single-stranded RNA transcripts, others to produce dsRNA. Based on their results, they concluded that co-suppression, like homology-dependent virus resistance, is triggered by dsRNA (Waterhouse *et al.*, 1998). Their conclusion is consistent with observations made by many earlier investigators who found that PTGS is more likely to occur in plants containing two tandem copies of a transgene arranged as inverted repeats, an organization favoring the production of transcripts capable of forming dsRNA.

Despite the strength of the evidence implicating a perfect duplex as the PTGS trigger, Metzlaff and colleagues have developed a model that involves an imperfect duplex. Their model is based on the profiles of calcone synthetase-specific RNAs present in wild-type *Petunia* and in transgenic plants manifesting PTGS. They reported that white flowers of transgenic plants had little full-length poly(A)$^+$ *chsA* RNA, but instead had characteristic mRNA fragments. They proposed that a self-sustaining degradation cycle is set in motion when sequences from the 3′-portion of an "aberrant" *chsA* transcript bind to partially complementary sequences in a second *chsA* RNA molecule, causing it to be cleaved and to release a new 3′ fragment (Metzlaff *et al.*, 1997). Significantly, fragments similar to those in the white-flowering transgenic plants accumulate in the white portions of a nontransgenic *Petunia* (Red Star) whose flowers have purple-white patterned flowers. This result shows that co-suppression uses steps of a pre-existing control pathway. Eventually, the model proposed by Metzlaff and colleagues will need to be reconciled with the evidence that perfect dsRNA can trigger PTGS. A consistent model may emerge when the events leading to the production of the "aberrant" transcript are understood in greater detail.

Further studies are also needed to define the role of DNA methylation in gene silencing. DNA methylation has been studied in *Petunia* and *Arabidopsis* manifesting PTGS of the calcone synthetase gene. In purple *Petunia* flowers, an EcoRII site in the 3′-end of the endogenous genes only rarely contains a methylated cytosine, whereas in leaf DNA, these sites are frequently methylated. There is, therefore, a develop-

mentally regulated loss of methylation at these sites. In transgenic plants with white flowers, this developmental change does not occur, and these sites are frequently methylated (Flavell *et al.*, 1998). To determine whether methylation is required for PTGS, Furner and colleagues studied transgenic *Arabidposis* plants that carry a mutation in a gene required for DNA methylation. PTGS was reversed and expression of the *chs* transgene was restored in plants defective in DNA methylation, leading these investigators to conclude that "methylation is absolutely necessary" for PTGS (Furner *et al.*, 1998). Confirmation of this observation in another system will shed further light on the significance of DNA methylation.

## D. dsRNA-Induced Homology-Dependent Posttranscriptional Gene Silencing Takes Place in *Caenorhabditis elegans*

RNA interference in nematodes was discovered by Guo and Kemphues, who found that antisense and sense transcripts yielded identical results when used to block gene expression in the maternal germ line (Guo and Kemphues, 1995). Fire and colleagues later demonstrated that dsRNA mediates PTGS in nematodes and that these worms have a transport system that allows dsRNA-mediated interference to move across cell membranes. On a mole-per-mole basis, they found that dsRNA transcripts were about 100 times more potent than either antisense or sense transcripts. Their initial experiments involved the *unc-22* gene, which encodes an abundant but nonessential myofilament protein. They injected a mixture of sense and antisense transcripts covering a 742-nucleotide segment of *unc-22* into the body cavity of adults and observed robust interference in the somatic tissues of the recipients and in their progeny broods. Only a few molecules of dsRNA were required per affected cell, suggesting that the dsRNA signal may have been amplified.

Several genes have been tested for susceptibility to dsRNA-mediated interference in addition to *unc-22*. The following observations have been made (Montgomery *et al.*, 1998; Tabara *et al.*, 1998; Fire *et al.*, 1998). First, PTGS effects are usually similar to those of null mutants, indicating that the target gene has been fully and selectively inhibited. However, some expression of the target gene can occur in dsRNA-treated worms. In some cases, suppression occurs in only some cells. Second, mRNAs appear to be the targets of PTGS, rather than mRNA precursors. dsRNA segments corresponding to introns and promoter segments are not effective, as might be expected if precursors or the transcription process were the target. Furthermore, dsRNA covering upstream genes in polar operons have no effect on downstream genes, underscoring the conclusion that mRNAs, rather than precursors, are the target. In addition, cytoplasmic levels of target RNAs drop precipitously. Third, dsRNA-mediated interference is able to cross cellular boundaries. In fact, the dsRNA crosses cellular membranes so readily that it is possible to induce PTGS by feeding worms transgenic *Escherichia coli* expressing dsRNA covering the target gene (Timmons and Fire, 1998) or by soaking them in dsRNA—although neither of these approaches is as effective as microinjection. Fourth, PTGS passes into the $F_1$ generation; remarkably, Tabara and colleagues report that for certain genes, "interference can be observed to transmit in the germ line apparently indefinitely" (Tabara *et al.,* 1998).

## E. Summary

Growing evidence indicates that dsRNA is involved in gene regulation in higher organisms. In mammalian cells, dsRNA (whether applied exogenously or synthesized endogenously) induces interferon; in plants, dsRNA has been linked to homology-dependent virus resistance and to posttranscriptional gene silencing of both endogenous and transgenes; and in nematodes, dsRNA moves across cell boundaries and selectively inhibits gene expression. It was once thought that bioengineered antisense RNA would function by establishing Watson–Crick base pairs with target RNAs, thereby eliminating their function. It now appears that dsRNA mediates the effects of artificial RNAs in nematodes and in some cases of PTGS in higher plants. This dsRNA is evidently recognized by cellular factors that work in conjunction with it to destroy other RNAs of similar sequence. Most of the molecular intermediates of PTGS remain a mystery. However, DNA methylation frequently occurs during PTGS in plants and is thought to play an essential role by some investigators. When one considers the possible significance of PTGS for organisms other than vascular plants and worms, it is interesting to note that some of the mammalian genes that are subject to imprinting, a process associated with DNA methylation, express antisense transcripts (Ward and Dutton, 1998; Moorwood *et al.,* 1998; Rougeulle *et al.,* 1998; Reik and Constancia, 1997). As more studies are carried out on mammalian genes producing natural antisense RNA and on mammalian cells synthesizing artificial antisense RNAs, mechanistic ties to PTGS may become apparent.

## Acknowledgments

I thank Dr. Jose Walewski, Mr. Decherd Stump, and Ms. Toby Keller for help with the manuscript. This work was supported in part by NIDDK (grants R01-DK52071 and P01-DK50795, project 2), the Liver Transplantation Research Fund, and the Division of Liver Diseases research funds.

## See Also the Following Articles

ANTIVIRAL AGENTS • INTERFERONS • METHYLATION OF NUCLEIC ACIDS AND PROTEINS • PLANT DISEASE RESISTANCE

## Bibliography

Bass, B. L. (1997). RNA editing and hypermutation by adenosine deamination. *Trends Biochem. Sci.* **22,** 157–162.

Baulcombe, D. C. (1996). RNA as a target and an initiator of post-transcriptional gene silencing in transgenic plants. *Plant Mol. Biol.* **32,** 79–88.

Bram, R. J., Young, R. A., and Steitz, J. A. (1980). The ribonuclease III site flanking 23S sequences in the 30S ribosomal precursor RNA of E. coli. *Cell* **19,** 393–401.

Branch, A. D. (1998). A good antisense molecule is hard to find. *Trends Biochem. Sci.* **23,** 45–50.

Delihas, N., Rokita, S. E., and Zheng, P. (1997). Natural antisense RNA/target RNA interactions: Possible models for antisense oligonucleotide drug design. *Nat. Biotechnol.* **15,** 751–753.

Desai, S. Y., Patel, R. C., Sen, G. C., Malhotra, P., Ghadge, G. D., and Thimmapaya, B. (1995). Activation of interferon-inducible 2′-5′ oligoadenylate synthetase by adenoviral VAI RNA. *J. Biol. Chem.* **270,** 3454–3461.

Eguchi, Y., Itoh, T., and Tomizawa, J. (1991). Antisense RNA. *Annu. Rev. Biochem.* **60,** 631–652.

Engdahl, H. M., Hjalt, T. A., and Wagner, E. G. (1997). A two unit antisense RNA cassette test system for silencing of target genes. *Nucleic Acids. Res.* **25**, 3218–3227.

Fire, A., Xu, S., Montgomery, M. K., Kostas, S. A., Driver, S. E., and Mello, C. C. (1998). Potent and specific genetic interference by double-stranded RNA in Caenorhabditis elegans. *Nature* **391**, 806–811.

Flavell, R. B., O'Dell, M., and Metzlaff, M. (1998). Transgene-promoted epigenetic switches of chalcone synthase activity in petunia plants. *Novartis. Found. Symp.* **214**, 144–154.

Furner, I. J., Sheikh, M. A., and Collett, C. E. (1998). Gene silencing and homology-dependent gene silencing in arabidopsis: Genetic modifiers and DNA methylation. *Genetics* **149**, 651–662.

Goodwin, J., Chapman, K., Swaney, S., Parks, T. D., Wernsman, E. A., and Dougherty, W. G. (1996). Genetic and biochemical dissection of transgenic RNA-mediated virus resistance. *Plant Cell* **8**, 95–105.

Gribaudo, G., Lembo, D., Cavallo, G., Landolfo, S., and Lengyel, P. (1991). Interferon action: Binding of viral RNA to the 40-kilodalton 2′-5′-oligoadenylate synthetase in interferon-treated HeLa cells infected with encephalomyocarditis virus. *J. Virol.* **65**, 1748–1757.

Guo, S., and Kemphues, K. J. (1995). par-1, a gene required for establishing polarity in C. elegans embryos, encodes a putative Ser/Thr kinase that is asymmetrically distributed. *Cell* **81**, 611–620.

Hjalt, T. A., and Wagner, E. G. (1995). Bulged-out nucleotides in an antisense RNA are required for rapid target RNA binding in vitro and inhibition in vivo. *Nucleic. Acids. Res.* **23**, 580–587.

Izant, J. G., and Weintraub, H. (1984). Inhibition of thymidine kinase gene expression by anti-sense RNA: A molecular approach to genetic analysis. *Cell* **36**, 1007–1015.

Jacobs, B. L., and Langland, J. O. (1996). When two strands are better than one: The mediators and modulators of the cellular responses to double-stranded RNA. *Virology* **219**, 339–349.

Jeffrey, I. W., Kadereit, S., Meurs, E. F., Metzger, T., Bachmann, M., Schwemmle, M., Hovanessian, A. G., and Clemens, M. J. (1995). Nuclear localization of the interferon-inducible protein kinase PKR in human cells and transfected mouse cells. *Exp. Cell Res.* **218**, 17–27.

Katze, M. G. (1992). The war against the interferon-induced dsRNA-activated protein kinase: Can viruses win? *J. Interferon Res.* **12**, 241–248.

Kumagai, M. H., Donson, J., della Cioppa, G., Harvey, D., Hanley, K., and Grill, L. K. (1995). Cytoplasmic inhibition of carotenoid biosynthesis with virus-derived RNA. *Proc. Natl. Acad. Sci. U.S.A.* **92**, 1679–1683.

Lee, A. J., and Crothers, D. M. (1998). The solution structure on an RNA loop-loop complex: The ColE1 inverted loop sequence. *Structure* **6**, 993–1005.

Lei, M., Liu, Y., and Samuel, C. E. (1998). Adenovirus VAI RNA antagonizes the RNA-editing activity of the ADAR adenosine deaminase. *Virology* **245**, 188–196.

Lindbo, J., Silva-Rosales, L., Proebsting, W. M., and Dougherty, W. G. (1993). Induction of a highly specific antiviral state in transgenic plants: Implications for regulation of gene expression and virus resistance. *Plant Cell* **5**, 1749–1759.

Magliano, D., Marshall, J. A., Bowden, D. S., Vardaxis, N., Meanger, J., and Lee, J. Y. (1998). Rubella virus replication complexes are virus-modified lysosomes. *Virology* **240**, 57–63.

Malmgren, C., Wagner, E. G. H., Ehresmann, C., Ehresmann, B., and Romby, P. (1997). Antisense RNA control of plasmid R1 replication. The dominant product of the antisense RNA-mRNA binding is not a full RNA duplex. *J. Biol. Chem.* **272**, 12508–12512.

Marcus, P. I., and Sekellick, M. J. (1977). Defective interfering particles with covalently linked [+/−] RNA induce interferon. *Nature* **266**, 815–819.

Mathews, M. B., and Shenk, T. (1991). Adenovirus virus-associated RNA and translation control. *J. Virol.* **65**, 5657–5662.

Matzke, M. A., and Matzke, A. J. (1995). Homology-dependent gene silencing in transgenic plants: What does it really tell us? *Trends Genet.* **11**, 1–3.

Metzlaff, M., O'Dell, M., Cluster, P. D., and Flavell, R. B. (1997). RNA-mediated RNA degradation and chalcone synthase A silencing in petunia. *Cell* **88**, 845–854.

Mizuno, K., Chou, M. Y., and Inouye, M. (1984). A unique mechanism regulating gene expression: Translational inhibition by a complementary RNA transcript (micRNA). *Proc. Natl. Acad. Sci. U.S.A.* **81**, 1966–1970.

Montgomery, M. K., Xu, S., and Fire, A. (1998). RNA as a target of double-stranded RNA-mediated genetic interference in *Caenorhabditis elegans. Proc. Natl. Acad. Sci. U.S.A.* **95**, 15502–15507.

Moorwood, K., Charles, A. K., Salpekar, A., Wallace, J. I., Brown, K. W., and Malik, K. (1998). Antisense WT1 transcription parallels sense mRNA and protein expression in fetal kidney and can elevate protein levels *in vitro. J Pathol* **185**, 352–359.

Muller, U., Steinhoff, U., Reis, L. F., Hemmi, S., Pavlovic, J., Zinkernagel, R. M., and Aguet, M. (1994). Functional role of type I and type II interferons in antiviral defense. *Science* **264**, 1918–1921.

Napoli, C., Lemieux, C., and Jorgensen, R. (1990). Introduction of a chimeric chalcone synthase gene into petunia results in reversible co-suppression of homologous genes *in trans. Plant Cell* **2**, 279–289.

Nilsen, T. W., Maroney, P. A., Robertson, H. D., and Baglioni, C. (1982). Heterogeneous nuclear RNA promotes synthesis of (2′,5′)oligoadenylate and is cleaved by the (2′,5′)oligoadenylate-activated endoribonuclease. *Mol. Cell Biol.* **2**, 154–160.

Petryshyn, R. A., Ferrenz, A. G., and Li, J. (1997). Characterization and mapping of the double-stranded regions involved in activation of PKR within a cellular RNA from 3T3-F442A cells. *Nucleic Acids Res.* **25**, 2672–2678.

Proud, C. G. (1995). PKR: A new name and new roles. *Trends Biochem. Sci.* **20**, 241–246.

Raine, D. A., Jeffrey, I. W., and Clemens, M. J. (1998). Inhibition of the double-stranded RNA-dependent protein kinase PKR by mammalian ribosomes. *FEBS Lett.* **436**, 343–348.

Ratcliff, F., Harrison, B. D., and Baulcombe, D. C. (1997). A similarity between viral defense and gene silencing in plants. *Science* **276**, 1558–1560.

Reik, W., and Constancia, M. (1997). Genomic imprinting. Making sense or antisense? *Nature* **389**, 669–671.

Robertson, H. D. (1982). Escherichia coli ribonuclease III cleavage sites. *Cell* **30**, 669–672.

Rougeulle, C., Cardoso, C., Fontes, M., Colleaux, L., and Lalande, M. (1998). An imprinted antisense RNA overlaps UBE3A and a second maternally expressed transcript. *Nat. Genet.* **19**, 15–16.

Samuel, C. E. (1994). Interferon-induced proteins and their mechanisms of action. *Hokkaido Igaku. Zasshi.* **69**, 1339–1347.

Scadden, A. D., and Smith, C. W. (1997). A ribonuclease specific for inosine-containing RNA: A potential role in antiviral defence? *EMBO J.* **16**, 2140–2149.

Shors, T., and Jacobs, B. L. (1997). Complementation of deletion of the vaccinia virus E3L gene by the Escherichia coli RNase III gene. *Virology* **227**, 77–87.

Simons, R. W. (1988). Naturally occurring antisense RNA control—a brief review. *Gene* **72**, 35–44.

Smith, H. A., Powers, H., Swaney, S., Brown, C., and Dougherty, W. G. (1995). Transgenic potato virus Y resistance in potato: Evidence for an RNA-mediated cellular response. *Phytopathol* **85**, 864–870.

Smith, H. A., Swaney, S. L., Parks, T. D., Wernsman, E. A., and Dougherty, W. G. (1994). Transgenic plant virus resistance mediated by untranslatable sense RNAs: Expression, regulation, and fate of nonessential RNAs. *Plant Cell* **6**, 1441–1453.

Tabara, H., Grishok, A., and Mello, C. C. (1998). RNAi in *C. elegans:* Soaking in the genome sequencing. *Science* **282**, 430.

Timmons, L., and Fire, A. (1998). Specific interference by ingested dsRNA. *Nature* **395**, 854.

van der Krol, A. R., Mur, L. A., Beld, M., Mol, J. N., and Stuitje, A. R. (1990). Flavonoid genes in petunia: Addition of a limited number of gene copies may lead to a suppression of gene expression. *Plant Cell* **2**, 291–299.

Vanhée-Brossollet, C., and Vaquero, C (1998). Do antisense transcripts make sense in eukaryotes? *Gene* **211**, 1–9.

Voinnet, O., and Baulcombe, D. C. (1997). Systemic signalling in gene silencing. *Nature* **389**, 553.

Wagner, E. G., Blomberg, P., and Nordstrom, K. (1992). Replication control in plasmid R1: Duplex formation between the antisense RNA, CopA, and its target, CopT, is not required for inhibition of RepA synthesis. *EMBO J.* **11**, 1195–1203.

Wagner, E. G., and Simons, R. W. (1994). Antisense RNA control in bacteria, phages, and plasmids. *Annu. Rev. Microbiol.* **48**, 713–742.

Ward, A., and Dutton, J. R. (1998). Regulation of the Wilm's Tumour suppressor (WT1) gene by an antisense RNA: A link with genomic imprinting? *J. Pathol.* **185**, 342–344.

Wassenegger, M., Heimes, S., Riedel, L., and Sänger, H. L. (1994). RNA-directed de novo methylation of genomic sequences in plants. *Cell* **76**, 567–576.

Waterhouse, P. M., Graham, M. W., and Wang, M. B. (1998). Virus resistance and gene silencing in plants can be induced by simultaneous expression of sense and antisense RNA. *Proc. Natl. Acad. Sci. U.S.A.* **95**, 13959–13964.

# Antiviral Agents

### Richard J. Whitley

*The University of Alabama at Birmingham*

## GLOSSARY

**acyclic purine nucleoside analog** A molecule with the structure of the normal purine components of DNA or RNA but with the sugar ring cleaved open (acyclic).

**alanine amino transferase** An enzyme found in the liver and blood serum, the concentration of which is often elevated in cases of liver damage.

**anorexia** Aversion to food.

**antiretroviral agent** Any drug used in treating patients with human immunodeficiency virus (HIV) infection.

**antiviral resistance** The developed resistance of a virus to a specific drug.

**apnea** Failure to breathe; literally "without breath."

**aqueous humor** The fluid that fills the anterior and posterior chamber of the eye.

**bilirubin** A greenish compound formed in the liver from the degradation of the hemoglobin from degraded red blood cells.

**bioavailability** The property of a drug to be absorbed and distributed within the body in a way that preserves its useful characteristics; for example, it is not broken down, inactivated, or made insoluble.

**bronchial alveolar lavage** A procedure to obtain cells from the lining of the lung by collecting fluid "washings" of the passages in the lung.

**cardiomyopathy** Pathologic changes in the heart muscles.

**CD4** A specific type of white blood cell of the T-lymphocyte class.

**chemoprophylaxis** Preventive treatment with chemical agents such as drugs.

**chronic obstructive pulmonary disease** Any chronic condition which results in the blockage of the outflow of air from the lungs (e.g., emphysema).

**codon** A triplet of three consecutive nucleotide components in the linear genetic code in DNA or messenger RNA which designates a specific amino acid in the linear sequence of a protein molecule.

**condyloma acuminatum** Venereal warts.

**conjunctivitis** Inflammation of the conjuctiva or white of the eye.

**creatinine** An end-product of energy metabolism found in the blood in uniform concentration which is excreted by the kidney at a constant rate. Alterations of this rate are considered an indication of kidney malfunction.

**cytokine** One of a variety of proteins which has a regulatory effect on a cell.

**cytomegalovirus** A member of the herpesvirus family.

**digitalis toxicity** Toxicity from the effects of the drug digitalis, often taken for increasing the strength and efficiency of heart contractions. Toxic effects include irregular heartbeat, anorexia, nausea, vomiting, confusion, and disorientation.

**DNA hybridization** A method for comparing the similarity between DNA samples from different sources by the ability of identical or similar DNA single strands to form good "hybrids" composed of one strand from each of the two different samples.

**$EC_{50}$** Concentration of a drug which produces a 50% effect, e.g., in virus yield.

**enantiomer** One of a pair of organic chemicals which are structural mirror images.

**encephalitis** Inflammation of the brain.

**endosomes** Small, bag-like structures in the cytoplasm of cells which are involved in the uptake of material from the exterior of the cell.

**enterovirus** One of a group of viruses which infect the intestinal track.

**Epstein–Barr virus** A member of the herpesvirus family.

**esophagitis** Inflammation of the esophagus.

**hantavirus pulmonary syndrome** A pneumonia-like illness resulting from infection with hantavirus, a virus normally carried in rodents.

**hemagglutinin** Specific glycoprotein molecules on the surface of some viruses which have the property of binding to the surface of the red blood cells of some animal species. Because there are multiple binding sites, one virus can bind to two red cells causing them to clump (agglutinate).

**hematopoietic toxicity** Refers to toxic effects on the blood-forming tissues.

**hepatotoxicity** Liver toxicity.

**herpes labialis** Infection of the lips with herpesvirus; commonly called cold sores or fever blisters,

**hyperbilirubinemia** Abnormally high levels of bilirubin in the blood.

**hyperemia** Literally excess blood; flushed, reddened, and engorged with blood.

**hypocalcemia** Abnormally low level of calcium in the blood.

**hypotension** Low blood pressure.

**interferon** Any group of glycoproteins with antiviral activity.

**interstitial nephritis** An inflammation of the substance of kidney exclusive of the structure called the glomerulus.

**intramuscular** Refers to injection of a drug directly into the muscle for fast absorption.

**keratitis** Inflammation of the surface of the eye.

**leukopenia** Deficiency in circulating white blood cells.

**maculopapular** A skin rash characterized by slightly elevated, colored spots.

**maintenance therapy** Drug treatment given for a long time to maintain its effect after the condition has been controlled or to prevent recurrence.

**microsomes** Small bodies derived from the protein synthesis apparatus of the cell when the cell is violently disrupted, for example, by sonic shock waves or grinding with abrasives.

**monoclonal antibodies** Homogeneous antibodies produced (usually in cell cultures) by specialized white blood cells derived from a single cell (a clonal population) and hence of a single molecular form.

**monotherapy** Treatment with a single drug, contrasted with combination therapies with more than one drug at the same time.

**mucocutaneous** Refers to the skin where there is both exterior skin and mucus membranes, such as the borders of the mouth.

**myalgia** Aches and pains in the muscles.

**myelosuppression** Suppression of the production of the blood cells from the bone marrow.

**myoclonus** Rhythmic, rapid contractions of a muscle in response to stretching.

**nephrolithiasis** The presence of kidney stones.

**nephrotoxicity** Kidney toxicity.

**neuraminidase** An enzyme, present on the surface of some viruses, which catalyzes the cleavage of a sugar derivative called neuraminic acid.

**neuritis** Inflammation of the nerves.

**neuropathy** Pathological changes in the nervous system.

**neutropenia** Deficiency in circulating white blood cells of the neutrophil type.

**oral bioavailability** The rate and extent to which an active drug or metabolite enters the circulation by way of the gastrointestinal tract.

**orolabial** Refers to the mouth and lips.

**pancreatitis** Inflammation of the pancreas.

**papillomavirus** A group of viruses causing warts of various kinds.

**peptidomimetic** A molecule having properties similar to those of a peptide or short protein.

**pharmacokinetic** Refers to the rates and efficiency of uptake, distribution, and disposition of a drug in the body.

**phase III** The final stage in testing of a new drug, after determination of its safety and effectiveness, in which it is tested on a broad range, and large population of patients for comparison to existing treatments and to test for rare complications.

**photophobia** Sensitivity to, and hence "fear" of, light.

**picornavirus** A group of viruses with small RNA genomes, such as poliovirus.

**placebo** An agent used as a "control" in tests of drugs. The placebo is an agent without the specific effects of the drug under test and is used to determine to what extent any observed effects of the drug are due to psychological effects or expectations. It is usually given to some patients while the test drug is given to others, but neither group knows which agent it is receiving (the so-called "blind" design). Literally means "I please."

**pneumonitis** Inflammation of the lung tissue.

**polymerase chain reaction** A process that permits making, *in vitro*, unlimited numbers of copies of genes.

**polymyositis** Inflammation of muscles involving multiple muscles.

**prodrug** A drug that is given in a form that is inactive and must be metabolized in the body to the active form.

**prophylaxis** Prevention.

**protease** An enzyme that catalyzes the cleavage of proteins. In the case of HIV, a virus-specific protease is needed to cleave some of the virus coat proteins into their final, active form.

**protease inhibitor**   A substance that inhibits the action of enzymes.

**recombinant**   Produced by the methods and manipulations of biotechnology, specifically involving the joining of dissimilar DNA molecules, that is, recombining of genes.

**replication cycle**   The series of steps that a virus or cell goes through to multiply.

**reticulocytosis**   An increase in the number of immature forms of red blood cells (reticulocytes) in the blood-stream.

**retinitis**   Inflammation of the retina of the eye.

**respiratory syncytial virus**   An agent of lung disease, especially in children.

**rhinovirus**   The common cold virus.

**shingles**   Eruptive rash, usually in a girdle (*L. cingulus*; hence "shingles") distribution on the trunk, resulting from infection with varicella-zoster virus.

**stromal keratitis**   Inflammation of the deep layers of the cornea of the eye.

**subcutaneous**   Refers to injection of a drug just under the skin but not into the underlying muscle; a site for rather slow absorption of drug.

**superficial punctate keratopathy**   Fine, spot-like pathological changes in the superficial layer of the cornea of the eye.

**$t_{1/2}$**   The time for reduction of some observed quantity, for example, the blood concentration of a drug, by 50%.

**teratogenesis**   Production of fetal abnormalities by some agent.

**therapeutic index**   The numerical ratio of the concentration needed to achieve a desired effect in 50% of the patients and the concentration that produces unacceptable toxicity in 50% of the patients.

**thrombocytopenia**   Deficiency of platelets, the blood-clotting agents, in the blood.

**thymidine kinase**   An enzyme which catalyzes the transfer of a phosphoryl group from a donor such as adenosine triphosphate to the sugar (deoxyribose) component of the thymidine molecule, a building block of DNA.

**topical**   Refers to application of a drug directly onto the affected area, usually the skin (e.g., in ointment form).

**tubular necrosis**   Death of the tubule cells in the kidney.

**uveitis**   Inflammation of the iris or related structures in the eye.

**varicella**   Chicken pox.

**varicella-zoster virus**   A member of the herpesvirus family.

**viremia**   The presence of virus in the bloodstream.

**virion**   A complete virus, including the coat and nucleic acid core.

**zoster**   Infection with varicella-zoster virus which leads to skin lesions on the trunk (usually) following the distribution of the sensory nerves; commonly called shingles.

**zoster ophthalmicus**   Eye infection with varicella-zoster virus.

**ANTIVIRAL AGENTS**   are drugs that are administered for therapeutic purposes to humans with viral diseases. Importantly, many people are infected by viruses but only some develop disease attributed to these microbes. Antiviral agents used to treat these diseases are currently limited and only exist for the management of herpes simplex virus, varicella zoster virus, cytomegalovirus, hepatitis B, hepatitis C, human immunodeficiency virus, respiratory syncytial virus, human papillomavirus, and influenza virus-related diseases.

Only a few antiviral agents of proven value are available for a limited number of clinical indications. Unique problems are associated with the development of antiviral agents. First, viruses are obligate intracellular parasites that utilize biochemical pathways of the infected host cell. Second, early diagnosis of viral infection is crucial for effective antiviral therapy because by the time symptoms appear, several cycles of viral multiplication usually have occurred and replication is waning. Third, since many of the disease syndromes caused by viruses are relatively benign and self-limiting, the therapeutic index, or ratio of efficacy to toxicity, must be extremely high in order for therapy to be acceptable.

Fortunately, molecular biology research is helping solve two of these problems. Enzymes unique to viral replication have been identified and, therefore, distinguish between virus and host cell functions. Unique events in viral replication are sites which serve as ideal targets for antiviral agents; examples include the thymidine kinase (TK) of herpes simplex virus (HSV) or protease of human immunodeficiency virus (HIV). Second, several sensitive and specific viral diagnostic methods are possible because of recombinant DNA technology [e.g., monoclonal antibodies, DNA hybridization techniques, and polymerase chain reaction (PCR)]. This article will synthesize knowledge of the existing antiviral agents as it relates to both pharmacologic and clinical properties.

## I. THERAPEUTICS FOR HERPESVIRUS INFECTIONS

### A. Acyclovir and Valaciclovir

Acyclovir has become the most widely prescribed and clinically effective antiviral drug available to date. Valaciclovir, the L-valine ester oral prodrug of acyclovir, was developed to improve the oral bioavailability of acyclovir. Valaciclovir is cleaved to acyclovir by valine hydrolase which then is metabolized in infected cells to the active triphosphate of acyclovir.

### 1. Chemistry, Mechanism of Action, and Antiviral Activity

Acyclovir [9-(2-hydroxyethoxymethyl) guanine], a synthetic acyclic purine nucleoside analog, is a selective inhibitor of HSV-1 and -2 and varicellazoster virus (VZV) replication. Acyclovir is converted by virus-encoded TK to its monophosphate derivative, an event that does not occur to any significant extent in uninfected cells. Subsequent di- and triphosphorylation is catalyzed by cellular enzymes, resulting in acyclovir triphosphate concentrations 40–100 times higher in HSV-infected than in uninfected cells. Acyclovir triphosphate inhibits viral DNA synthesis by competing with deoxyguanosine triphosphate as a substrate for viral DNA polymerase, as illustrated in Fig. 1. Because acyclovir triphosphate lacks the 3′ hydroxyl group required for DNA chain elongation, viral DNA synthesis is terminated. Viral DNA polymerase is tightly associated with the terminated DNA chain and is functionally inacti-

vated. Also, the viral polymerase has greater affinity for acyclovir triphosphate than does cellular DNA polymerase, resulting in little incorporation of acyclovir into cellular DNA. *In vitro*, acyclovir is most active against HSV-1 (average $EC_{50} = 0.04$ $\mu$mg/ml), HSV-2 (0.10 $\mu$g/ml), and VZV (0.50 $\mu$g/ml). Epstein–Barr virus (EBV) requires higher acyclovir concentrations for inhibition, and cytomegalovirus (CMV), which lacks a virus-specific TK, is relatively resistant.

Acyclovir is available in topical, oral, and intravenous preparations. Oral formulations include a 200-mg capsule, a 800-mg tablet, and suspension (200 mg/5 ml) and absorption of acyclovir results in 15–30% bioavailability. After multidose oral administration of 200 or 800 mg of acyclovir, the mean steady-state peak levels are approximately 0.57 and 1.57 $\mu$g/ml, respectively. Higher plasma acyclovir levels are achieved with intravenous administration. Steady-state peak acyclovir concentrations following intravenous doses of 5 or 10 mg/kg every 8 hr are approximately 9.9 and 20.0 $\mu$g/ml, respectively. The terminal plasma time for a 50% decrease in drug concentration ($t_{1/2}$) is 2 or 3 hr in adults with normal renal function. Acyclovir is minimally metabolized and approximately 85% is excreted unchanged in the urine via renal tubular secretion and glomerular filtration.

Valaciclovir is only available as a tablet formulation and is metabolized nearly completely to acyclovir within minutes after absorption. Plasma levels of acyclovir, following 2 g of valaciclovir given three times a day by mouth, approximate 5 mg/kg administered every 8 hr intravenously. Both acyclovir and valaciclovir must be dose adjusted if renal impairment exists.

### 2. Clinical Indications
#### a. Genital Herpes
Initial genital HSV infection can be treated with topical, oral, or intravenous acyclovir. Topical application is less effective than oral or intravenous therapy. Intravenous acyclovir is the most effective treatment for first-episode genital herpes and results in a significant reduction in the median duration of viral shedding, pain, and time to complete healing (8 versus 14 days) but is reserved for patients with

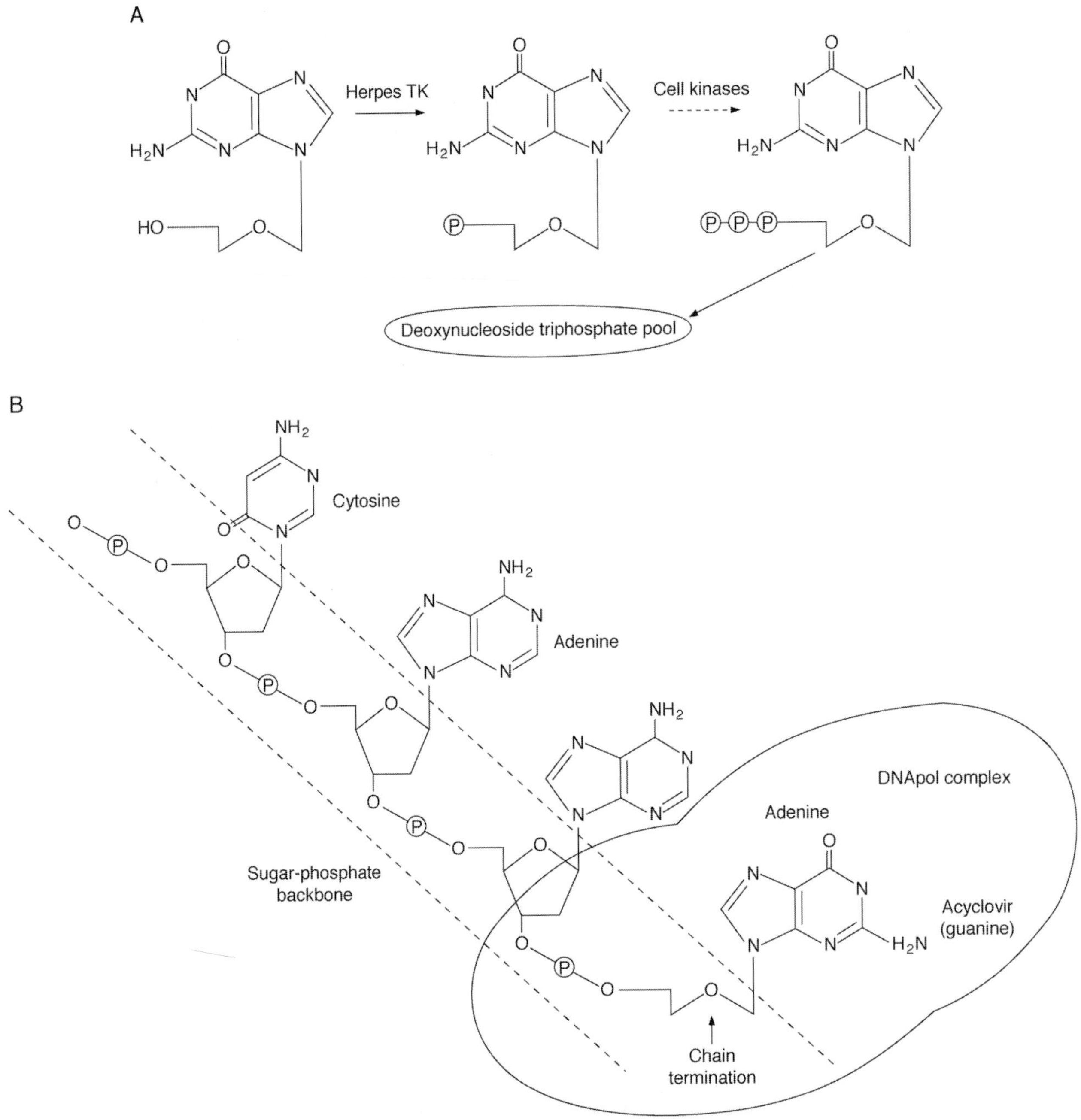

**Fig. 1.** The mechanism of action of acyclovir. (A) activation and (B) Inhibition of DNA synthesis and chain termination.

systemic complications. Oral therapy (200 mg five times daily) is the standard treatment. Neither intravenous nor oral acyclovir treatment alter the frequency of recurrences.

Recurrent genital herpes is less severe and resolves more rapidly than primary infection, offering a shorter time interval for successfully antiviral chemotherapy. Topically applied acyclovir has no clinically beneficial effect. Orally administered acyclovir (200 mg five times daily or 400 mg three times daily) shortens the duration of virus shedding and time to healing (6 versus 7 days) when initiated within 24 hr of onset, but the duration of pain and itching is not affected.

Oral acyclovir administration effectively suppresses frequently recurring genital herpes. Daily administration of acyclovir reduces the frequency of recurrences by up to 80%, and 25–30% of patients have no further recurrences while taking the drug. Successful suppression for as long as 3 years has been reported with no evidence of significant adverse effects. Titration of acyclovir (400 mg twice daily or 200 mg two to five times daily) may be required to establish the minimum dose that is most effective and economical. Asymptomatic virus shedding can continue despite clinically effective acyclovir suppression, resulting in the possibility of person-to-person transmission.

Valaciclovir therapy of recurrent genital herpes (either 1 g or 500 mg twice a day) is equivalent to acyclovir administered at either 200 mg three times daily or five times daily. It is also effective for suppression of recurrences when 1 g per day is administered.

### b. Herpes Labialis

Topical therapy for HSV-1 mouth or lip infections is of no clinical benefit. Orally administered acyclovir (200 or 400 mg five times daily for 5 days) reduces the time to loss of crust by approximately 1 day (7 versus 8 days) but does not alter the duration of pain or time to complete healing. Oral acyclovir therapy has modest clinical benefit but only if initiated very early after a recurrence.

### c. Immunocompromised Host

HSV infections of the lip, mouth, skin, perianal area, or genitals may be more severe in immunocompromised patients. Clinical benefit from intravenous or oral acyclovir therapy is documented as evidenced by a significantly shorter duration of viral shedding and accelerated lesion healing. Acyclovir prophylaxis of HSV infections is of significant clinical value in severely immunocompromised patients, especially those undergoing induction chemotherapy or organ transplantation. Intravenous or oral acyclovir administration reduces the incidence of symptomatic HSV infection from 70 to 5–20%. A variety of oral dosing regimens, ranging from 200 mg three times daily to 800 mg twice daily, have been used successfully.

### d. Herpes Simplex Encephalitis

Acyclovir therapy (10 mg/kg every 8 hr for 10–14 days) reduces mortality overall from 70 to 19%. Furthermore, 38% of acyclovir recipients returned to normal neurologic function.

### e. Neonatal HSV Infections

Acyclovir treatment of babies with disease localized to the skin, eye, or mouth yielded 100% survival, whereas 18 and 55% of babies with central nervous system (CNS) or disseminated infection died, respectively. For babies with HSV localized to the skin, eye, and mouth, 98% of acyclovir recipients developed normally 2 years after infection. For babies surviving encephalitis and disseminated disease, 43 and 57% of acyclovir recipients developed normally. The currently recommended intravenous dose is 10 mg/kg every 8 hr for 14–21 days.

### f. Varicella

Oral acyclovir therapy in normal children and adolescents with chicken pox shortens the duration of new lesion formation by about 1 day reduces total lesion count, and improves constitutional symptoms. Therapy of older patients with chicken pox (who may have more severe manifestations) is indicated, whereas treatment of younger children must be decided on a case-by-case basis.

Acyclovir therapy of chicken pox in immunocompromised children substantially reduces morbidity and mortality. Intravenous acyclovir treatment (500 mg/m$^2$ of body surface area every 8 hr for 7–10 days) improved the outcome, as evidenced by a reduction of VZV pneumonitis from 45 to <5%. Oral acyclovir therapy is not indicated for immunocompromised children with chicken pox; instead, treatment is with intravenous drug.

### g. Herpes Zoster

Intravenous acyclovir therapy of herpes zoster in the normal host produces some acceleration of cutaneous healing and resolution of pain—both acute neuritis and zoster-associated pain. Oral acyclovir (800 mg five times a day) administration results in accelerated cutaneous healing and reduction in the severity of acute neuritis. Oral acyclovir treatment of zoster ophthalmicus reduces the incidence of serious ocular complications such as keratitis and uveitis. Valaciclovir (1 g three times daily for 7–10 days) is superior to acyclovir for the reduction of pain associated with shingles.

The increased frequency of significant morbidity in immunocompromised patients with herpes zoster highlights the need for effective antiviral chemotherapy. Intravenous acyclovir therapy significantly reduces the frequency of cutaneous dissemination and visceral complications of herpes zoster in immunocompromised adults. Acyclovir is the standard therapy at a dose of 10 mg/kg (body weight) or 500 mg/m$^2$ (body surface area) every 8 hr for 7–10 days. Oral acyclovir therapy in immunocompromised patients with herpes zoster likely is effective but valaciclovir is presumably superior.

### 3. Antiviral Resistance

Resistance of HSV to acyclovir develops through mutations in the viral gene encoding TK via generation of TK-deficient mutants or the selection of mutants possessing a TK which is unable to phosphorylate acyclovir.

DNA polymerase mutants also have been recovered from HSV-infected patients. Acyclovir-resistant HSV isolates have been identified as the cause of pneumonia, encephalitis, esophagitis, and mucocutaneous infections, all occurring in immunompromised patients.

Acyclovir-resistant mutants have been described in the normal host but are uncommon. Acyclovir-resistant isolates of VZV have been identified much less frequently than acyclovir-resistant HSV but have been recovered from marrow transplant recipients and AIDS patients. The acyclovir-resistant VZV isolates all had altered or absent TK function but remained susceptible to vidarabine and foscarnet.

### 4. Adverse Effects

Acyclovir and valaciclovir therapies are associated with few adverse effects. Renal dysfunction can occur but is relatively uncommon and usually reversible. A few reports have linked intravenous acyclovir use with CNS disturbances, including agitation, hallucinations, disorientation, tremors, and myoclonus.

An Acyclovir in Pregnancy Registry has gathered data on prenatal acyclovir exposures. Though no significant risk to the mother or fetus has been documented, the total number of monitored pregnancies remains too small to detect any low-frequency teratogenic events.

## B. Cidofovir

### 1. Chemistry, Mechanism of Action and Antiviral Activity

Cidofovir, (S)-1-(3-hydroxy-2-phosphonomethoxypropyl) cytosine (HPMPC), is a novel acyclic phosphonate nucleoside analog, and is used to treat acyclovir and foscarnet-resistant HSV infections as well as CMV retinitis. The drug has a similar mechanism of action as the other nucleoside analog but employs cellular kinases to produce the active triphosphate metabolite. Activated HPMPC has a higher affinity for viral DNA polymerase, and therefore it selectively inhibits viral replication. The drug is less potent than ACV *in vitro;* however, *in vivo* HPMPC persists in cells for prolonged periods, increasing drug activity. In addition, HPMPC produces active metaboliets with long half-lives (17–48 hr), permitting once weekly dosing. Unfortunately, HPMPC concentrates in kidney cells 100 times greater than in other tissues and produces severe proximal convoluted tubule nephrotoxicity when administered systemically. Attempts to limit nephrotoxicity include coadministration of probenecid with intravenous hydration, synthesis of cyclic congener prodrugs of HPMPC and use of topical formulations. HPMPC has limited and variable oral bioavailability (2–26%) when tested in rats and, therefore, is administered intravenously.

### 2. Clinical Indications

Cidofovir is licensed for treatment of CMV retinitis and has been used to treat acyclovir-resistant HSV infection.

### 3. Resistance

The development of resistance with clinical use is uncommon; however, mutations in CMV DNA polymerase can mediate altered susceptibility.

### 4. Adverse Events

Nephrotoxicity is associated the cidofovir administration, occurring in up to 30% of patients. Oral probenecid administration accompanies intravenously administered HPMPC in order to prevent significant nephrotoxicity.

## C. Foscarnet

### 1. Chemistry, Mechanism of Action, and Antiviral Activity

Foscarnet, a pyrophosphate analog of phosphonoacetic acid has potent *in vitro* and *in vivo* activity against all herpesviruses and inhibits the DNA polymerase by blocking the pyrophosphate binding site, inhibiting the formation of the $3',5'$ phosphodiester bond between primer and substrate and preventing chain elongation. Unlike acyclovir, which requires activation by a virus-specific TK, foscarnet acts directly on the virus DNA polymerase. Thus, TK-deficient, acyclovir-resistant herpesviruses remain sensitive to foscarnet.

The oral bioavailability of foscarnet is poor; thus, administration is by the intravenous route. An intravenous infusion of 60 mg/kg every 8 hr results in peak and trough plasma concentrations which are approximately 450–575 and 80–150 $\mu M$, respectively. The cerebrospinal fluid concentration of foscarnet is approximately two-thirds of the plasma level.

Renal excretion is the primary route of clearance of foscarnet with >80% of the dose appearing in the urine. Bone sequestration also occurs, resulting in complex plasma elimination.

### 2. Clinical Indications

Foscarnet is licensed for the treatment of CMV retinitis as well as HSV and VZV disease caused by acyclovir- or penciclovir-resistant viruses. Administration of foscarnet at 60 mg/kg every 8 hr for 14–21 days followed by maintenance therapy at 90–120 mg/kg per day is associated with stabilization of retinal disease in approximately 90% of patients. However, as is with the case with ganciclovir therapy of CMV retinitis, relapse occurs.

Mucocutaneous HSV infections and those caused by VZV in immunocompromised host can be treated with foscarnet at dosages lower than that for the management of CMV retinitis. Foscarnet dosages of 40 mg/kg administered every 8 hr for 7 days or longer will result in cessation of viral shedding and healing of lesions in the majority of patients. However, relapses will occur which may or may not be amenable to acyclovir therapy.

### 3. Resistance

Isolates of HSV, CMV, and VZV have all been demonstrated to develop resistance to foscarnet both in the laboratory and in the clinical setting. Isolates of HSV which are resistant to foscarnet have $EC_{50}$ >100 $\mu g/ml$. These isolates are all DNA polymerase mutants.

### 4. Adverse Effects

Although foscarnet has significant activity in the management of herpesvirus infections, nephrotoxicity, including acute tubular necrosis and interstitial nephritis, can occur. Metabolic aberrations of calcium, magnesium, phosphate, and other electrolytes are associated with foscarnet administration and warrant careful monitoring. Symptomatic hypocalcemia and resultant seizures are the most common metabolic abnormality. Increases in serum creatinine will develop in one-half of patients who receive medication but usually are reversible after cessation. Other CNS side effects include headache (25%), tremor, irritability, and hallucinations.

## D. Ganciclovir and Val-Ganciclovir

### 1. Chemistry, Mechanism of Action, and Antiviral Activity

Ganciclovir [9-(1,3-dihydroxy-2-propoxymethyl) guanine] (Cytovene) has enhanced *in vitro* activity against all herpesviruses as compared to acyclovir, including an 8–20 times greater antiviral activity against CMV. Like acyclovir, the activity of ganciclovir in herpesvirus-infected cells depends on phosphorylation by virus-induced TK. Also like acyclovir, ganciclovir monophosphate is further converted to its di- and triphosphate derivatives by cellular kinases. In cells infected by HSV-1 or -2, ganciclovir triphosphate competitively inhibits the incorporation of guanosine-triphosphate into viral DNA. Ganciclovir triphosphate is incorporated at internal and terminal sites of viral DNA, inhibiting DNA synthesis. The mode of action of ganciclovir against CMV is mediated by a protein kinase, UL-97, that efficiently promotes the obligatory initial phosphorylation of ganciclovir to its monophosphate.

The oral bioavailability of ganciclovir is poor (5–7%). Peak plasma levels are approximately 1.0 $\mu$g/ml after administration of 1 g every 6 h. Intravenous administration of a standard dose of 5 mg/kg will result in peak and trough plasma concentrations of 8–11 and 0.5–1.2 $\mu$g/ml, respectively. Concentrations of ganciclovir in biologic fluids, including aqueous humor and cerebrospinal fluid (CSF), are less than plasma levels. The plasma elimination $t_{1/2}$ is 2–4 hr for individuals with normal renal function. The kidney is the major route of clearance of drug, and therefore, impaired renal function requires adjustment of dosage. Val-ganciclovir is orally bioavailable (approximately 60%) and is rapidly converted to ganciclovir after absorption. It is currently in clinical development.

### 2. Clinical Indications
#### a. HIV-Infected Patients

Ganciclovir has been administered to large numbers of patients with AIDS having CMV retinitis. Most patients (78%) experience either improvement or stabilization of their retinitis based on fundoscopic exams compared to historical controls. Induction therapy is usually at a dosage of 5.0 mg/kg twice a day given intravenously for 10–14 days. Maintenance therapy is essential. Median time to relapse for patients receiving no maintenance therapy averages 47 days. Maintenance therapy of 25–35 mg/kg per week significantly lengthens median time to relapse to 105 days. Virtually every patient treated will experience either a cessation or reduction of plasma viremia. Visual acuity usually stabilizes at pretreatment levels but rarely improves dramatically. Relapse occurs quickly in the absence of maintenance therapy but usually occurs eventually, even in patients receiving maintenance therapy (5 mg/kg for 5–7 days per week). The significance of bone marrow toxicity must be taken into consideration since 30–40% of patients develop neutropenia. Benefit has been reported with the use of ganciclovir for the treatment of other CMV infections, particularly in those involving the gastrointestinal tract.

Ganciclovir can be administered orally for prevention of CMV disease and retinitis in patients with AIDS. The utilization of ganciclovir at dosages of 1 g three to six times daily, following intravenous induction therapy, provides a sustained period prior to the next episode of reactivated retinitis at similar, albeit less (but not significantly less) intervals as when drug is given intravenously.

## b. Transplant Recipients

Prophylaxis and preemptive therapy of CMV infections in high-risk transplant recipients is common. Both prevention and therapy of CMV infection of the lung are amenable to ganciclovir therapy. Ganciclovir of CMV pneumonia in conjunction with CMV immune globulin is therapeutically beneficial. Ganciclovir has been administered in anticipation of CMV disease to bone marrow transplant recipients (preemptive therapy). Several clinical trials utilizing different designs (e.g., initiation of ganciclovir after engraftment versus at the time of documentation of infection by bronchial alveolar lavage but in the absence of clinical symptomatology) have established the effectiveness of ganciclovir in preventing CMV pneumonia and reducing mortality during the treatment period. The utilization of ganciclovir in these circumstances has support among transplant physicians; however, long-term survival benefit (>120 days) is not apparent.

## 3. Resistance

Resistance to CMV is associated with a deteriorating clinical course. Two mechanisms of resistance to ganciclovir have been documented: (i) The alteration of protein kinase gene, UL-97, reduces intracellular phosphorylation of ganciclovir, and (ii) point mutations in the viral DNA polymerase gene. Resistance is associated with decreased sensitivity up to 20-fold.

## 4. Adverse Effects

The most important side effects of ganciclovir therapy are the development of neutropenia and that of thrombocytopenia. Neutropenia occurs in approximately 24–38% of patients. The neutropenia is usually reversible with dosage adjustment of ganciclovir, including withholding of treatment. Thrombocytopenia occurs in 6–19% of patients.

Ganciclovir has gonadal toxicity in animal models, most notably as a potent inhibitor of spermatogenesis. It causes an increased incidence of tumors in the preputial gland of male mice, a finding of unknown significance. As an agent affecting DNA synthesis, ganciclovir has carcinogenic potential.

# E. Idoxuridine and Trifluorothymidine

## 1. Chemistry, Mechanism of Action, and Antiviral Activity

Idoxuridine (5-iodo-2'-deoxyuridine) and trifluorothymidine (trifluridine, Viroptic) are analogs of thymidine. When administered systemically, these nucleosides are phosphorylated by both viral and cellular TK to active triphosphate derivatives which inhibit both viral and cellular DNA synthesis. The result is antiviral activity but also sufficient host cytotoxicity to prevent the systemic use of these drugs. The toxicity of these compounds is not significant when applied topically to the eye in the treatment of HSV keratitis. Both idoxuridine and trifluorothymidine are effective and licensed for treatment of HSV keratitis. Topically applied idoxuridine or trifluorothymidine will penetrate cells of the cornea. Low levels of drugs can be detected in the aqueous humor.

## 2. Clinical Indications

Trifluorothymidine is the most efficacious of these compounds. These agents are not of proven value in the treatment of stromal keratitis or uveitis, although trifluridine is more likely to penetrate the cornea and, ultimately, may prove beneficial for these conditions.

## 3. Resistance

Little effort has been directed to evaluating HSV isolates obtained from the eye, in large part because of the difficulty in accomplishing this task.

## 4. Adverse Effects

The ophthalmic preparation of idoxuridine and trifluridine causes local irritation, photophobia, edema of the eyelids, and superficial punctate keratopathy.

## F. Penciclovir and Famciclovir

### 1. Chemistry, Mechanism of Action, and Antiviral Activity

A new member of the guanine nucleoside family of drugs is famciclovir [9-(4-hydroxy-3-hydroxy-methylbut-1-yl) guanine; Famvir], the prodrug of penciclovir. Penciclovir does not have significant oral bioavailability (<5%) but famciclovir is orally bioavailable (approximately 77%) and has a good therapeutic index for the therapy of both HSV and VZV infections. Famciclovir is the diacetyl ester of 6-deoxy penciclovir. When administered orally, it is rapidly converted to penciclovir. The spectrum of activity of penciclovir is similar to that of acyclovir. Penciclovir is phosphorylated more efficiently than acyclovir in HSV- and VZV-infected cells. Host cell kinases phosphorylate both penciclovir and acyclovir to a small but comparable extent. The preferential metabolism in HSV-and VZV-infected cells is the major determinant of its antiviral activity. Penciclovir triphosphate has, on average, a 10-fold longer intracellular half-life than acyclovir triphosphate in HSV-1, HSV-2, and VZV-infected cells after drug removal. Penciclovir triphosphate is formed at concentrations sufficient to be an effective inhibitor of viral DNA polymerase, albeit at a lower $K_i$ than that of acyclovir triphosphate. Both compounds have good activity against HSV-1, HSV-2, and VZV. The activity of penciclovir *in vitro*, like acyclovir, is dependent on both the host cell and the assay (plaque reduction, virus yield, and viral DNA inhibition). The mean penciclovir $EC_{50} \pm$ standard deviation for HSV-1 in MRC-5, HEL, WISH, and W138 cells is $0.4 \pm 0.2$, $0.6 \pm 0.4$, $0.2 \pm 0.2$, and $1.8 \pm 0.8$ $\mu$g/ml, respectively. For HSV-2, similar levels of activity in the identical cell lines are $1.8 \pm 0.6$, $2.4 \pm 2.5$, $0.8 \pm 0.1$, and $0.3 \pm 0.2$ $\mu$g/ml, respectively. These assays utilize a plaque reduction procedure. In virus yield reduction assays, inhibition of VZV replication in MRC-5 cells is between 3.0 and 5.1 $\mu$g/ml, values virtually identical to those of acyclovir. Penciclovir, like acyclovir, is relatively inactive against CMV and EBV. Penciclovir is also active against hepatitis B.

Conversion of famciclovir to penciclovir occurs at two levels. The major metabolic route of famciclovir is de-acetylation of one ester group as the prodrug crosses the duodenal barrier of the gastrointestinal tract. The drug is transported to the liver via the portal vein where the remaining ester group is removed and oxidation occurs at the sixth position of the side chain resulting in penciclovir, the active drug. The first metabolite which appears in the plasma is almost entirely the de-acetylated compound with little or no parent drug detected. Thus, the major metabolite of famciclovir is penciclovir. Pharmacokinetic parameters for penciclovir are linear over famciclovir oral dose ranges of 125–750 mg. Penciclovir is eliminated rapidly and almost unchanged by active tubular secretion and glomerular filtration by the kidneys. The elimination $t_{1/2}$ in healthy subjects is approximately 2 hr.

### 2. Clinical Indications

Famciclovir is available in an oral preparation. Penciclovir is available for topical therapy (Denavir).

#### a. Herpes zoster

Famciclovir (250, 500, or 750 mg three times a day) therapy is equivalent to the standard acyclovir treatment and superior to no therapy of herpes zoster for cutaneous healing, and in a subgroup analysis it accelerated resolution of pain (zoster-associated pain).

### b. Genital HSV Infection

Studies of patients with recurrent gential HSV infection (either intravenous penciclovir or oral famciclovir therapy) indicate beneficial effects in acceleration of all clinical parameter (e.g., pain, virus shedding, and duration). Famciclovir is given twice daily (125 or 250 mg twice daily for 5 days). Famciclovir therapy on recurring HSV infections of immunocompromised hosts also is effective as suppressive therapy.

### c. Herpes Labialis

Topical application of penciclovir (Denavir) accelerates lesion healing (1 day) and resolution of pain. It is available over-the-counter in many countries.

### 3. Resistance

Herpes simplex virus and VZV isolates resistant to penciclovir have been identified in the laboratory. These isolates have similar patterns of resistance as those of acyclovir. Namely, resistance variants can be attributed to alterations or deficiencies of TK and DNA polymerase.

### 4. Adverse Effects

Therapy with oral famciclovir is well tolerated, being associated only with headache, diarrhea, and nausea—common findings with other orally bioavailable antiviral agents. Preclinical studies of famciclovir indicated that chronic administration was tumorigenic (murine mammary tumors) and causes testicular toxicity in other rodents.

## G. Vidarabine

### 1. Chemistry, Mechanism of Action, and Antiviral Activity

Vidarabine (vira-A, adenine arabinoside, and 9D-arabinofuranosyl adenine) is active against HSV, VZV, and CMV. Vidarabine is a purine nucleoside analog that is phosphorylated intracellularly to its mono-, di-, and triphosphate derivatives. The triphosphate derivative competitively inhibits DNA-dependent DNA polymerases of some DNA viruses approximately 40 times more than those of host cells. In addition, vira-A is incorporated into terminal positions of both cellular and viral DNA, thus inhibiting elongation. Viral DNA synthesis is blocked at lower doses of drug than is host cell DNA synthesis, resulting in a relatively selective antiviral effect. However, large doses of vira-A are cytotoxic to dividing host cells.

The benefit demonstrated in initial placebo-controlled clinical trials of this drug was a major impetus for the development of antiviral therapies. However, because of poor solubility and some toxicity, it was quickly replaced by acyclovir in the physician's armamentarium. Today, it is no longer available as an intravenous formulation. Vidarabine should be recognized historically as the first drug licensed for systemic use in the treatment of a viral infection.

### 2. Clinical Indications

Vidarabine is only available as a topical formulation for ophthalmic administration.

### 3. Resistance

Studies of resistance to vidarabine have not been pursued.

### 4. Adverse Effects

Ocular toxicity consists of occasional hyperemia and increased tearing, both of low incidence.

## H. New Prospects for Therapy of Herpesviruses

Cyclobutyl compounds represent a new group of carbocyclic nucleoside analogs that provide broad-spectrum antiviral protection in experimental and animal studies. These agents have *in vitro* activity against resistant strains of HIV, HSV-1, CMV, HSV-2, VZV, and HIV-1. The nucleoside analogs terminate DNA chain elongation. Lubucovir, a member of the cyclobutyl class of drugs, was recently tested in placebo control phase II trials for HIV-infected patients with CMV. The drug exhibited linear kinetics at low doses, had good bioavailability (40%), and had a $t_{1/2}$ of 2 hr. The drug was tolerated as well as placebo. Only 1 of the 27 patients completing the study excreted CMV at the outset of the study; therefore, data are not available on the effect of lubucovir on CMV shedding. It is also under development for labial and genital HSV infection.

## II. THERAPEUTICS FOR RESPIRATORY VIRUS INFECTIONS

### A. Amantadine and Rimantadine

### 1. *Chemistry, Mechanism of Action, and Antiviral Activity*

Amantadine (1-adamantane amine hydrochloride; Symmetrel) is a tricyclic amine which is effective against all influenza A variants. Amantadine has a narrow spectrum of activity, being useful only against influenza A infections. Rimantidine is the $\alpha$-methyl derivative of amantadine ($\alpha$-methyl-1-adamantane methylamine hydrochloride). Rimantidine is 5- to 10-fold more active than amantadine and has the same spectrum of activity, mechanism of action, and clinical indications. Rimantadine is slightly more effective against type A viruses at equal concentrations. The mechanism of action of these drugs relates to the influenza A virus M2 protein, a membrane protein which is the ion channel for this virus. By interfering with the function of the M2 protein, amantadine and rimantidine inhibit the acid-mediated association of the matrix protein from the ribonuclear protein complex within endosomes. This event occurs early in the viral replicate cycle. The

consequences of this drug are the potentiation of acidic pH-induced conformational changes in the viral hemagglutinin during its intracellular transport.

Absorption of rimantadine is delayed compared to that of amantadine, and equivalent doses of rimantadine produce lower plasma levels compared to amantadine presumably because of a larger volume of distribution. Both amantadine and rimantadine are absorbed after oral administration. Amantadine is excreted in the urine by glomerular filtration and, likely, tubular secretion. It is unmetabolized. The plasma elimination $t_{1/2}$ is approximately 12–18 hr in individuals with normal renal function. However, the elimination $t_{1/2}$ increases in the elderly with impaired creatinine clearance. Rimantadine is extensively metabolized following oral administration, with an elimination $t_{1/2}$ which averages 24–36 hr. Approximately 15% of the dose is excreted unchanged in the urine.

### 2. *Clinical Indications*

Amantadine and rimantadine are licensed both for the chemoprophylaxis and treatment of influenza A infections. The efficacy of amantadine and rimantadine when used prophylactically for influenza A infections averages 70–80% (range, 0–100%), which is approximately the same as with influenza vaccines. Effectiveness has been demonstrated for prevention of both experimental (i.e., artificial challenge) and naturally occurring infections for all three major subtypes of influenza A. Because of a lower incidence of side effects associated with rimantadine, it is used preferentially. Rimantadine can be given to any unimmunized member of the general population who wishes to avoid influenza A, but prophylaxis is especially recommended for control of presumed influenza outbreaks in institutions housing high-risk persons. High-risk individuals include adults and children with chronic disorders of the cardiovascular or pulmonary systems requiring regular follow-up or hospitalization during the preceding year as well as residents of nursing homes and other chronic-care facilities housing patients of any age with chronic medical conditions.

These drugs are also effective for the treatment of influenza A. All studies showed a beneficial effect on the signs and symptoms of acute influenza as well as a significant reduction in the quantity of virus in respiratory secretions at some time during the course of infection. Because of the short duration of disease, therapy must be administered within 48 hr of symptom onset to show benefit.

### 3. Resistance

Rimantadine-resistant strains of influenza have been isolated from children treated for 5 days. There have been subsequent reports of rimantadine-resistant strains being transmitted from person to person and producing clinical influenza. Development of resistance of influenza A viruses is mediated by single nucleotide changes in RNA segment 7 which results in amino acid substitutions in the transmembrane of the M2 protein. Obviously, amantadine and rimantadine share cross-resistance.

### 4. Adverse Effects

Amantadine is reported to cause side effects in 5–10% of healthy young adults taking the standard adult dose of 200 mg/day. These side effects are usually mild and cease soon after amantadine is discontinued, although they often disappear with continued use of the drug. Central nervous system side effects, which occur in 5–33% of patients, are most common and include difficulty in thinking, confusion, lightheadedness, hallucinations, anxiety, and insomnia. More severe adverse effects (e.g., mental depression and psychosis) are usually associated with doses exceeding 200 mg daily. About 5% of patients complain of nausea, vomiting, or anorexia. Rimantadine appears better tolerated. Side effects associated with rimantadine administration are significantly less than those encountered with amantadine, particularly of the CNS. Rimantadine has been associated with exacerbations of underlying seizure disorders.

## B. Ribavirin

### 1. Chemistry, Mechanism of Action, and Antiviral Activity

Ribavirin ($\alpha$-methyl-1-adamantane methylamine hydrochloride) has antiviral activity against a variety of RNA and DNA viruses. Ribavirin is a nucleoside analog whose mechanisms of action are poorly understood and probably not the same for all viruses; however, its ability to alter nucleotide pools and the packaging of mRNA appears important. This process is not virus specific, but there is a certain selectivity in that infected cells produce more mRNA than noninfected cells. A major action is the inhibition by ribavirin-5'-monophosphate of inosine monophosphate dehydrogenase, an enzyme essential for DNA synthesis. This inhibition may have direct effects on the intracellular level of GMP; other nucleotide levels may be altered, but the mechanisms are unknown. The 5'-triphosphate of ribavirin inhibits the formation of the 5'-guanylation capping on the mRNA of vaccinia and Venezuelan equine encephalitis viruses. In addition, the triphosphate is a potent inhibitor of viral mRNA (guanine-7) methyltransferase of vaccinia virus. The capacity of viral mRNA to support protein synthesis is markedly reduced by ribavirin. Of note, high concentrations of ribavirin also inhibit cellular protein synthesis. Ribavirin may inhibit influenza A RNA-dependent RNA polymerase.

Ribavirin can be administered orally (bioavailability of approximately 40–45%) or intravenously. Aerosol administration has become standard for the treatment of respiratory synctial virus (RSV) infections in children. Oral doses of 600 and 1200 mg result in peak plasma concentrations of 1.3 and 2.5 $\mu$g/ml, respectively. Intravenous dosages of 500 and 1000 mg result in 17 and 24 $\mu$g/ml plasma concentrations, respectively. Aerosol administration of ribavirin results in plasma levels which are a function of the duration of exposure. Although respiratory secretions will contain milligram quantities of drug, only microgram quantities (0.5–3.5 $\mu$g/ml) can be detected in the plasma.

The kidney is the major route of clearance of drug, accounting for approximately 40%. Hepatic metabolism also contributes to the clearance of ribavirin. Notably, ribavirin triphosphate concentrates in erythrocytes and persists for a month or longer.

Likely, the persistence of ribavirin in erythrocytes contributes to its hematopoietic toxicity.

## 2. *Clinical Indications.*
### a. *Respiratory Syncytial Virus*
Ribavirin is licensed for the treatment of carefully selected, hospitalized infants and young children with severe lower respiratory tract infections caused by RSV. The vast majority of infants and children with RSV infection have disease that is mild and self-limited and are not candidates for ribavirin. Use of aerosolized ribavirin in adults and children with RSV infections reduced the severity of illness and virus shedding. In patients receiving 8 or more hours of continuous therapy, the mean peak level in tracheal secretions may be 100 times greater than the minimum inhibitory concentration preventing RSV replication *in vitro*. The use of ribavirin for the treatment of RSV infections is controversial and remains discretionary. It is under study for prevention of RSV pneumonia in bone marrow transplant recipients. Of interest, ribavirin is being administered intravenously to patients with presumed hantavirus pulmonary syndrome and chronic hepatitis C.

## 3. *Resistance*
Emergence of viruses resistant to ribavirin has not been documented.

## 4. *Adverse Effects*
Adverse effects attributable to aerosol therapy with ribavirin of infants with RSV include bronchospasm, pneumothorax in ventilated patients, apnea, cardiac arrest, hypotension, and concomitant digitalis toxicity. Pulmonary function test changes after ribavirin therapy in adults with chronic obstructive pulmonary disease have been noted. Reticulocytosis, rash, and conjunctivitis have been associated with the use of ribavirin aerosol. When given orally or intravenously, transient elevations of serum bilirubin and the occurrence of mild anemia have been reported. Ribavirin has been found to be teratogenic and mutagenic in preclinical testings. This drug is therefore, contraindicated in women who are or may become pregnant during exposure to the drug.

Concern has been expressed about the risk to persons in the room of infants being treated with ribavirin aerosol, particularly females of childbearing age. Although this risk seems to be minimal with limited exposure, awareness and caution are warranted. Furthermore, the use of a "drug salvage" hood is mandatory.

## 5. *Hepatitis C*
With interferon-$\alpha$, ribavirin is approved for combination therapy of chronic hepatitis C (see Section III.A).

## C. New Prospects for Therapy of Respiratory Viruses

Two new compounds are in late-stage clinical development for the treatment and prevention of influenza infections: zinamivir (4-guanodino-Neu5aAc2en) and GS4104. Both compounds are neuraminidase inhibitors; however, only GS4104 is orally bioavailable. Thus, zinamivir has to be administered by small particle spray. Phase III clinical trials of both medications suggest a beneficial risk therapeutic index.

## III. HEPATITIS AND PAPILLOMAVIRUS

## A. Interferons

### 1. *Chemistry, Mechanism of Action, and Antiviral Activity*
Interferons (IFNs) are glycoprotein cytokines (intracellular messengers) with a complex array of immunomodulating, antineoplastic, and antiviral properties. Interferons are currently classified as $\alpha$, $\beta$, or $\gamma$, the natural sources of which, in general, are leukocytes, fibroblasts, and lymphocytes, respectively. Each type of IFN can be produced via recombinant DNA technology. Binding of IFN to the intact cell membrane is the first step in establishing an antiviral effect. Interferon binds to specific cell surface receptors; IFN-$\gamma$ appears to have a different receptor from those of IFN-$\alpha$ and -$\beta$ which may explain the purported synergistic antiviral and antitumor effects sometimes observed when IFN-$\gamma$ is given with either of the other two IFN species.

A prevalent view of IFN action is that, following binding, there is synthesis of new cellular RNAs and proteins, particularly protein kinase R, which mediate the antiviral effect. Chromosome 21 is required for this antiviral state in humans no matter which species of IFN is employed. At least three of the newly synthesized proteins in IFN-treated cells appear to be associated with the development of an antiviral state: (i) 2′ 5′-oligoadenylate synthetase, (ii) a protein kinase, and (iii) an endonuclease. The antiviral state is not fully expressed until these primed cells are infected with virus.

Interferon must be administered intramuscularly or subcutaneously (including into a lesion such as a wart). Plasma levels are dose dependent, peaking 4–8 hr after intramuscular administration and returning to baseline between 18 and 36 hr. There appears to be some variability in absorption between each of the three classes of IFN and, importantly, resultant plasma levels. Leukocyte and IFN-$\alpha$ appear to have elimination $t_{1/2}$ of 2–4 hr. Interferon is inactivated by various organs of the body in an as yet undefined method.

### 2. Clinical Indications

#### a. Condyloma Acuminatum

Several large controlled trials have demonstrated the clinical benefit of IFN-$\alpha$ therapy of condyloma acuminatum which was refractory to cytodestructive therapies. Administration of $1.0 \times 10^6$ International Units (IU) of recombinant IFN-$\alpha$ led to significant benefit as evidenced by enhancing clearing of treated lesions (36 vs 17% placebo recipients) and by reduction in mean wart area (40% reduction vs 46% increase). In other well-controlled studies, either a similar rate (46%) or higher rates (62%) of clearance were reported. Notably, clearing responses of placebo recipients averaged 21 or 22%.

#### b. Hepatitis B

Hepatitis B DNA polymerase level, a marker of replication, is reduced with IFN therapy. Treatment with IFN-$\alpha$ in chronic hepatitis B has subsequently been investigated in several large, randomized, controlled trials. Clearance serum HBeAg and hepatitis B virus (HBV)–DNA polymerase occurs with treatment (30–40%).

#### c. Hepatitis C

The activity of IFN as a treatment of hepatitis C has undergone extensive evaluation. Interferon dosages have ranged from $1 \times 10^6$ to $10 \times 10^6$ IU three times weekly for 1–18 months. Of the placebo controls, only 2.6% normalize serum alanine amino transferase (ALT). In contrast, treatment led to serum ALT normalization in 33–45% of patients. Unfortunately, 50–80% of patients relapse. Recently, IFN-$\alpha$ has been administered with ribavirin. Concomitant therapy for 40 weeks resulted in sustained responses in more than 60% of patients.

### 3. Resistance

Resistance to administered interferon has not been documented although neutralizing antibodies to recombinant interferons have been reported. The clinical importance of this latter observation is unknown.

### 4. Adverse Effects

Side effects are frequent with IFN administration and are usually dose limiting. Influenza-like symptoms (i.e., fever, chills, headache, and malaise) commonly occur, but these symptoms usually become less severe with repeated treatments. At doses used in the treatment of condyloma acuminatum, these side effects rarely cause termination of treatment. For local treatment (intralesional administration) pain at the injection site does not differ significantly from that for placebo-treated patients and is short-lived. Leukopenia is the most common hematologic abnormality, occurring in up to 26% of treated patients. Leukopenia is usually modest, not clinically relevant, and reversible upon discontinuation of therapy. Increased alanine aminotransferase levels may also occur as well as nausea, vomiting, and diarrhea.

At higher doses of IFN, neurotoxicity is encountered, as manifested by personality changes, confusion, loss of attention, disorientation, and paranoid ideation. Early studies with IFN-$\gamma$ show similar side effects as those of treatment with and IFN-$\alpha$ and -$\beta$ but with the additional side effects of dose-limiting hypotension and a marked increase in triglyceride levels.

## B. Future Prospects

The following compounds are undergoing extensive evaluation in the treatment of HBV infections: famciclovir, lamivudine, adefovir dipivoxil, lobucavir, and BMS 200475. The latter three are the most active from controlled clinical trials. Lamivudine will likely be licensed early in the twenty-first century. Resistance to lamivudine does develop in a significant number of patients, prompting the evaluation of combination therapies.

## IV. PROSPECTS FOR ENTEROVIRAL THERAPIES

Pleconaril WIN 51711, a compound with activity against many rhinoviruses and enteroviruses, is the first compound for which data exist to define antiviral drug interaction with a virion at the atomic level. This compound is one of a class of compounds which resembles arildone, a drug known to inhibit uncoating of poliovirus. X-ray diffraction studies of WIN 51711 bound to rhinovirus 14 show that the compound adheres tightly to a hydropic pocket formed by VP1, one of the structural proteins of rhinovirus 14. These hydrophobic pockets were found in the VP1 proteins of poliovirus and meningovirus and may be common to all picomaviruses. Compounds such as WIN 51711 may lock into the conformation of the VP1 so that the virus cannot disassemble.

## V. ANTIRETROVIRAL AGENTS

### A. Reverse Transcriptase Inhibitors

#### 1. Zidovudine

#### a. Chemistry, Mechanism of Action, and Antiviral Activity

Zidovudine (3'-azido-2',3'-dideoxythymidine; azidothymidine and Retrovir) is a pyrimidine analog with an azido group substituting for the 3' hydroxyl group on the ribose ring. Drug is initially phosphory-

lated by cellular TK and then to its diphosphate by cellular thymidylate kinase. The triphosphate derivative competitively inhibits HIV reverse transcriptase and also functions as a chain terminator. Zidovudine inhibits HIV-1 at concentrations of approximately 0.013 $\mu$g/ml. In addition, it inhibits a variety of other retroviruses. Synergy has been demonstrated against HIV-1 when zidovudine is combined with didanosine, zalcitabine, lamiviudine, nevirapine, delavirdine, saquinavir, indinavir, ritonavir, and other compounds. It was the first drug to be licensed for the treatment of HIV infection and still is used in combination with other drugs as initial therapy for some patients.

Zidovudine is available in capsule, syrup, and intravenous formulations. Oral bioavailability is approximately 65%. Peak plasma levels are achieved approximately $\frac{1}{2}$–$1\frac{1}{2}$ hr after treatment. Zidovudine is extensively distributed with a steady-state volume of distribution of approximately of 1.6 liters/kg. Drug penetrates cerebrospinal fluid, saliva, semen, and breast milk and it crosses the placenta. Drug is predominately metabolized by the liver through the enzyme uridine diphosphoglucuronosyltransferase to its major inactive metabolite 3'-azido-3'-deoxy-5'-O-B-D-glucopyranuronosylthymidine. The elimination $t_{1/2}$ is approximately 1 hr; however, it is extended in individuals who have altered hepatic function.

#### b. Clinical Applications

Zidovudine was the first approved antiretroviral agent and, as a consequence, has been the most widely used antiretroviral drug in clinical practice. In monotherapy studies, zidovudine improves survival and decreases the incidence of opportunistic infections in patients with advanced HIV disease. Importantly, zidovudine decreased the incidence of transmission of HIV infection from pregnant women to their fetuses. However, its usefulness as monotherapy has been outlived.

Recently, zidovudine has been incorporated into multidrug regimens, including combinations with didanosine or zalcitabine which demonstrate a delay in disease progression and improved survival compared to zidovudine monotherapy; zidovudine plus didanosine and zidovudine plus lamivudine have also been shown to improve both outcome and important markers of disease, including CD4 counts and plasma HIV RNA levels.

Currently, three-drug combinations include the use of zidovudine with other reverse transcriptase inhibitors and nonnucleoside reverse transcriptase inhibitors and protease inhibitors. Triple-drug combinations offer enhanced therapeutic benefits, particularly as noted by survival and restoration of normal immune function.

### c. Resistance

Zidovudine resistance occurs rapidly after the onset of therapy. Numerous sites of resistance have been identified, with the degree of resistance being proportional to the number of mutations. The development of resistant HIV strains correlates with disease progression. The utilization of combination drug therapies delays the onset of resistance.

### d. Adverse Events

The predominant adverse effect of zidovudine is myelosuppression, as evidenced by neutropenia and anemia, occurring in 16 and 24% of patients, respectively. Zidovudine has been associated with skeletal and cardiac muscle toxicity, including polymyositis. Nausea, headache, malaise, insomnia, and fatigue are common side effects.

## 2. Didanosine

### a. Chemistry, Mechanism of Action, and Antiviral Activity

Didanosine (2′, 3′-dideoxyinosine; ddI and Videx) is a purine nucleoside with inhibitory activity against both HIV-1 and HIV-2. Didanosine is activated by intracellular phosphorylation. The conversion of 2′, 3′-dideoxyinsine-5′-monophosphate to its triphosphate derivative is more complicated than that with other nucleoside analogs because it requires addi-

tional enzymes, including a 5′ nucleotidase and subsequently, adenylosuccinate synthetase and adenylosccinate lyase. The triphosphate metabolite is a competitive inhibitor of HIV reverse transcriptase and is also a chain terminator. The spectrum of activity of didanosine is enhanced by synergism with zidovudine and stavudine as well as the protease inhibitors.

Didanosine is available in an oral formulation; however, it is acid labile and has poor solubility. A buffered tablet results in 20–25% bioavailability. A 300-mg oral dose achieves peak plasma concentrations of 0.5–2.6 $\mu$g/ml with a $t_{1/2}$ of approximately $1\frac{1}{2}$ hr. Drug is metabolized to hypoxanthine and is cleared primarily by the kidney.

### b. Clinical Indications

Didanosine is used in combination with other nucleoside analogs and protease inhibitors. In combination with zidovudine, improvement in both clinical outcome and immunologic markers of disease has been reported (CD4 lymphocyte counts).

### c. Resistance

As with zidovudine, mutations and reverse transcriptase appear promptly after administration of didanosine therapy, resulting in a 3- to 10-fold decrease in susceptibility to therapy.

### d. Adverse Effects

The most significant adverse effect associated with didanosine therapy is the development of peripheral neuropathy (30%) and pancreatitis (10%). Adverse effects of note include diarrhea (likely attributed to the phosphate buffer), headache, rash, nausea, vomiting, and hepatotxicty. Myelosuppression is not a component of toxicity associated with didanosine administration.

## 3. Zalcitabine

### a. Chemistry, Mechanism of Action, and Antiviral Activity

Zalcitabine (2′, 3′-dideoxycytidine; ddC and Hivid) is a pyrimidine analog which is activated by cellular enzymes to its triphosphate derivative. The enzymes responsible for activation of zalcitabine are cell cycle independent, and therefore this offers a theoretical advantage for nondividing cells, specifically dendritic and monocyte/macrophage cells. Zalcitabine inhibits both HIV-1 and HIV-2 at concentrations of approximately 0.03 $\mu$M. Synergy has been described between zidovudine and zalcitabine as well as with saquinavir.

The oral bioavailability following zalcitabine administration is more than 80%. The peak plasma concentrations following an oral dose of 0.03 mg/kg range from 0.1 to 0.2 $\mu$M and the $t_{1/2}$ is short (approximately 20 min). The drug is cleared mainly by the kidney, and therefore, in the presence of renal insufficiency a prolonged plasma $t_{1/2}$ is documented.

### b. Clinical Indications

Zalcitabine is used in combination with other reverse transcriptase and protease inhibitors. As with other nucleoside combinations, zidovudine and zalcitabine do not benefit patients to the same extent as combinations of zidovudine and didanosine. Currently, it is used as part of a two- or three-drug regimen in combination with zidovudine and saquinavir.

### c. Resistance

Zalcitabine-resistant HIV-1 variance has been documented both *in vitro* and *in vivo*.

### d. Adverse Effects

Peripheral neuropathy is the major toxicity associated with zalcitabine administration, occurring in approximately 35% of individuals. Pancreatitis can occur, but does so infrequently. Thrombocytopenia and neutropenia are uncommon (5 and 10%, respectively). Other zalcitabine-related side effects include nausea, vomiting, headache, hepatotoxicity, and cardiomyopathy.

### 4. Stavudine

### a. Chemistry, Mechanism of Action, and Antiviral Activity

Stavudine (2′, 3′-didehydro, 3′-deoxythymidine; d4T and Zerit) is a thymidine analog with significant activity against HIV-1, having inhibitory concentrations which range from 0.01 to 4.1 $\mu$M. Its mechanism of action is similar to that of zidovudine. It is either additive or synergistic *in vitro* with other combinations of both nucleoside and nonnucleoside reverse-transcriptase inhibitors.

The oral bioavailability of stavudine is more than 85%. Peak plasma concentrations of approximately 1.2 $\mu$g/ml are reached within 1 hr of dosing at 0.67 mg/kg per dose. Drug penetrates CSF and breast milk. Drug is excreted by the kidney unchanged and, in part, by renal tubular secretion.

### b. Clinical Indications

Stavudine has been studied both as monotherapy and in combination with other antiretroviral drugs. It is gaining increasing use as front-line therapy for HIV infection. Stavudine's clinical benefit is superior to that of zidovudine, particularly as it relates to increasing CD4 cell counts, slowing progression to AIDS or mortality.

### c. Resistance

The development of resistance on serial passage in the laboratory can be achieved. Cross-resistance with didanosine and zalcitabine has been identified by specific mutations for stavudine. The development of resistance in clinical trials has not been identified.

### d. Adverse Effects

The principal adverse effect of stavudine therapy is the development of peripheral neuropathy. The development of this complication is related to both dose and duration of therapy. Neuropathy tends to appear after 3 months of therapy and resolves slowly with medication discontinuation. Other side effects are uncommon.

### 5. Lamivudine

#### a. Chemistry, Mechanism of Action, and Antiviral Activity

Lamivudine is the (−) enantiomer of a cytidine analog with sulfur substituted for the 3′ carbon atom in the furanose ring [(−) 2′, 3′-dideoxy, 3′-thiacytidine; 3TC, Epivir]. It has significant activity *in vitro* against both HIV-1 and HIV-2 as well as HBV. Lamivudine is phosphorylated to the triphosphate metabolite by cellular kinases. The triphosphate derivative is a competitive inhibitor of the viral reverse transcriptase.

Lamivudine's oral bioavailability in adults is in excess of 80% for doses between 0.25 and 8.0 mg/kg. Peak serum concentrations of 1.5 $\mu$g/ml are achieved in $1-1\frac{1}{2}$ hr and the plasma $t_{1/2}$ is approximately 2–4 hr. Drug is cleared by the kidney unchanged by both glomerular filtration and tubular excretion.

#### b. Clinical Indications

Lamivudine is used in combination with other reverse transcriptase inhibitors and protease inhibitors. In combination with zidovudine, enhanced CD4 responses and suppression of HIV RNA levels occurs to a greater extent than with zidovudine monotherapy. The combination of zidovudine and lamivudine is without significant adverse event. Because of this degree it tolerability, it is widely used in clinical practice.

#### c. Resistance

With clinical therapy, resistance to lamivudine monotherapy develops rapidly. In large part, resis-

tance is mediated by amino acid change at codon 184, resulting in a 100- to 1000-fold decrease in susceptibility. The 184 mutation site, which is of importance, also occurs with didanosine and zalcitabine and appears to increase sensitivity to zidovudine, providing a logical basis for its combination with this agent.

#### d. Adverse Effects

Lamivudine has an extremely favorable toxicity profile. This may largely be attributed to the low affinity of lamivudine for DNA polymerase. At the highest doses of 20 mg/kg/day, neutropenia is encountered but at a low frequency. In pediatric studies, pancreatitis and peripheral neuropathies have been reported.

### 6. Future Prospects
#### a. Abacavir

Abacavir is a carbocyclic nucleoside antiviral agent. Currently, it is not licensed for the treatment of HIV infections of humans. The proposed dosage is 600–1200 mg daily. It is currently used with other nucleoside analogs and protease inhibitors in combination therapy. Significant reduction in viral load and an increase in CD4 count have been documented in patients receiving this medication. A hypersensitivity reaction has been documented with this compound which has been fatal in a few cases. The elimination $t_{1/2}$ is 1 to $1\frac{1}{2}$ hr.

## B. Non-nucleoside Reverse Transcriptase Inhibitors

### 1. Nevirapine

#### a. Chemistry, Mechanism of Action, and Antiviral Activity

Nevirapine (11-cyclopropyl-5,11-dihydro-4-methyl-6*H*-dipyrido[3,2-b:2′, 3′-e]; [1,4]diazepin-6-one and Viramune) is a reverse transcriptase inhibitor of HIV-1. Nevirapine is rapidly absorbed with a bioavailability of approximately 65%. Peak serum concentration is achieved approximately 4 hr after a 400-mg oral dose of 3.4 $\mu$g/ml. Nevirapine is metabolized by liver microsomes to hydroxymethyl-nevirapine. *In vitro*, synergy has been demonstrated when administered with nuceloside reverse transcriptase inhibitors.

### b. Clinical Indications

Nevirapine monotherapy is associated with a non-sustained antiviral effects at a dosage of 200 mg/day. Concomitant with this minimal effect is the rapid emergence of resistant virus, such that by 8 weeks all patients had evidence of viral resistance. Thus, drug can only be administered in combination with other antiretroviral agents. In combination with nucleoside reverse-transcriptase inhibitors, there is evidence of reduction in viral HIV RNA load as well as increasing CD4 counts.

### c. Adverse Effects

The most common adverse effects include the development of a nonpruritic rash in as many as 50% of patients who received 400 mg/day. In addition, fever, myalgias, headache, nausea, vomiting, fatigue, and diarrhea have also been associated with administration of drug.

### d. Resistance

Nevirapine resistance has been identified according to its binding site on viral polymerase. Specifically, two sets of amino acid residues (100–110 and 180–190) represent sites at which resistant mutations have occurred. Nevirapine monotherapy is associated with resistance most frequently appearing at codon 181. Because of the rapid appearance of resistance, nevirapine must be administered with other antiretroviral agents.

### 2. Delavirdine

$\cdot$CH$_3$SO$_2$–OH

### a. Chemistry, Mechanism of Action, and Antiviral Activity

Delavirdine (1-[5-methanesulfonamido-1*H*-indol-2-yl-carbonyl]-4-[3-(1-methylethylamino) pyridinyl]piperazine; Rescriptor) is a second-generation bis (heteroaryl) piperazine licensed for the treatment of HIV infection. It is absorbed rapidly when given orally to >60%. Delavirdine is metabolized by the liver with an elimination $t_{1/2}$ of approximately 1.4 hr. It has an inhibitory concentration against HIV-1 of approximately 0.25 $\mu$M. Inhibitory concentrations for human DNA polymerases are significantly higher.

### b. Clinical Indications

Reductions in plasma HIV RNA of more than 90% have been documented when delavirdine is administered such that trough levels exceed 50 $\mu$M. However, there is a rapid return to baseline over 8 weeks as resistance develops. As a consequence, delavirdine must be administered with either zidovudine or didanosine to have a more protracted effect.

### c. Adverse Effects

Delavirdine administration is associated with a maculopapular rash. Other side effects are less common.

### d. Resistance

Delavirdine resistance can be generated rapidly both *in vitro* and *in vivo* with the codon change identified at 236, resulting in an increase and susceptibility to >60 $\mu$M. Delavirdine resistance can also occur at codons 181 and 188, as noted for nevirapine administration.

### 3. Efavirenz

### a. Chemistry, Mechanism of Action, and Antiviral Activity

Efavirenz Sustiva [(*S*)-6-chloro-4-(cyclopropylethynyl)-1,4-dihydro-4-(trifluoromethyl)-2*H*-3,1-

benzoxazin-2-one; Sustiva and DMP266] is a non-nucleoside reverse transcriptase inhibitor which can be administered once daily. Activity is mediated predominately by noncompetitive inhibition of HIV-1 reverse transcriptase. HIV-2 reverse transcriptase in human cellular DNA polymerases $\alpha$, $\beta$, $\gamma$, and $\delta$ are not inhibited by efavirenz. The 90–95% inhibitory concentration of efavirenz is approximately 1.7–25 n$M$. In combination with other anti-HIV agents, particularly zidovudine, didanosine, and indinaver, synergy is demonstrated.

### b. Clinical Indications

Efavirenz is employed in combination with other antiretroviral agents indicated in the treatment of HIV-1 infection. Efficacy has been documented in the demonstration of plasma HIV negativity (<400 HIV RNA copies/ml) in approximately 80% of patients. Combination therapy has resulted in a 150-fold or greater decrease in HIV-1 RNA levels. Importantly, data have shown efficacy in children for both virologic and immunologic end points.

### c. Adverse Effects

The most common adverse events are skin rash (25%), which is associated with blistering, moist desquamation, or ulceration (1%). In addition, delusions and inappropriate behavior have been reported in 1 or 2 patients per 1000.

### d. Resistance

As with other non-nucleoside reverse transcriptase inhibitors, resistance appears rapidly and is mediated by similar enzymes.

## C. Protease Inhibitors

### 1. Saquinavir

### a. Chemistry, Mechanism of Action, and Antiviral Activity

Saquinavir (*cis*-N-tert-butyl-decahydro-2[2(R)-hydroxy-4-phenyl-3-(S)-([N-(2-quinolycarbonyl)-L-asparginyl] amino butyl)-4aS, 8aS]-isoquinoline-3[S]-carboxyamide methanesulfonate; Invirase) is a hydroxyethylamine-derived peptidomimetic HIV protease inhibitor. Saquinavir inhibits HIV-1 and HIV-2 at concentrations at 10 n$M$ and is synergistic with other nucleoside analogs as well as selected protease inhibitors.

Oral bioavailability is approximately 30% with extensive hepatic metabolism. Peak plasma concentrations of 35 mg/$\mu$l are obtained following a 600-mg dose.

### b. Clinical Indications

The clinical efficacy of saquinavir is limited by poor oral bioavailability but improved formulation (soft-gel capsule) will likely enhance efficacy. Currently, it is used in combination therapy with other nucleoside analogs, particularly zidovudine, lamivudine, zalcitabine, and stavudine.

### c. Adverse Effects

Adverse effects are minimal with no dose-limiting toxicities. Abdominal discomfort, including diarrhea and nausea, has been reported infrequently.

### d. Resistance

Resistance to saquinavir develops rapidly when it is administered as monotherapy. By 1 year, 45% of patients develop resistance at codon sites 90 and 48, resulting in approximately a 30-fold decrease in susceptibility.

### 2. Indinavir

### a. Chemistry, Mechanism of Action, and Antiviral Activity

{*N*-[2(*R*)-hydroxy-1(*S*)-indanyl]-5-[2(*S*)-(1,1-dimethylethlaminocarbonyl)-4-(pyridin-3-yl) methylpiperazin+++-1-yl]-4[s]-hydroxy-2[2]-phenylmethyl pentanamide; Crixivan} is a peptidomimetic HIV-1 and HIV-2 protease inhibitor. At concentrations of 100 nM, indinavir inhibits 90% of HIV isolates. Indinavir is rapidly absorbed with a bioavailability of 60% and achieves peak plasma concentrations of 12 $\mu$M after a 800 mg oral dose.

### b. Clinical Indications

Indinavir has been established as effective therapy for the treatment of HIV infection, particularly in combination with nucleoside analogs. At a dose of 800 mg per 8 hr, 80% of patients experience at least a 100-fold reduction in HIV-RNA levels, and in 50% of patients there is up to a 2 log reduction. In approximately 30% of patients plasma HIV RNA levels are reduced below 500 copies/ml with an associated increase in CD4 cell counts over baseline. In combination with zidovudine and lamivudine, a >2 log decrease in plasma RNA levels can be achieved for a majority of patients (more than 80%).

### c. Adverse Effects

Although indinavir is well tolerated, commonly encountered adverse effects include indirect hyperbilirubinemia (10%) and nephrolithiasis (5%).

### d. Resistance

Indinavir resistance develops rapidly with monotherapy and occurs at multiple sites. The extent of resistance is directly related to the number of codon changes in the HIV protease gene. Codon 82 is a common mutation in indinavir-resistant HIV isolates.

### 3. Ritonavir

### a. Chemistry, Mechanism of Action, and Antiviral Activity

Ritonavir (10-hydroxy-2-methyl-5-[1-methylethyl]-1[2-(1-methylethyl)-4-thiazo lyl]-3,6,dioxo-8,11-bis[phenylmethyl]-2,4,7,12-tetra azatridecan-13-oic-acid, 5-thiazolylmethylester, [5S-(5R, 8R, 10R, 11R)]; Norvir) is a symmetric HIV protease inhibitor which has exquisite activity *in vitro* against HIV-1 laboratory strains (0.02–0.15 $\mu$M). It is synergistic when administered with nucleloside analogs.

Oral bioavailability is approximately 80%, with peak plasma levels of approximately 1.8 $\mu$M after 400 mg administered every 12 hr. The plasma half-life is approximately 3 hr.

### b. Clinical Indications

Ritonavir is used for treatment of HIV infection in combination with nucleoside analogs. As monotherapy, a 10- to 100-fold decrease in plasma HIV RNA is achieved with a concomitant increase in CD4 cell counts of approximately 100 cells/mm³. Combination therapy results in a more significant decrease in HIV RNA plasma levels.

### c. Adverse Effects

Adverse effects include nausea, diarrhea, and headache, but all occur at a low frequency.

### d. Resistance

Resistance to ritonavir resembles that to indinavir. Mutations at codon 82 are the most common.

### 4. Nelfinavir

### a. Chemistry, Mechanism of Action, and Antiviral Activity

Nelfinavir [3S-(3R, 4aR, 8aR, 22 ' S, 3'S)]-2-[2'-hydroxy-3'-phenylthiomethyl-4'-aza-5'-ox-o-5'-(2″methyl-3'-hydroxyphenyl)pentyl]-decahydroisoquinoline-3-*N*-(tert-butyl-carboxamide methanesulfonic acid salt) is another peptidomimetic HIV protease inhibitor. Inhibitory concentrations of HIV-1 are in the range of 20–50 n*M*. Nalfinavir is orally bioavailable at approximately 40%, achieving peak plasma concentrations of 2 or 3 mg following a 800-mg dose every 24 hr. The drug is metabolized by hepatic microsomes.

### b. Clinical Indications

Nalfinavir is utilized in combination with nuceloside analogs. Monotherapy will achieve significant decreases in HIV RNA plasma levels up to 100-fold. Currently, the drug is used in combination with nuceloside analogs, particularly zidovudine, lamivudine, or stavudine, which results in 100- to 1000-fold reductions of HIV plasma RNA levels.

### c. Adverse Effects

Nelfinavir is well tolerated with mild gastrointestinal complication reported.

### d. Resistance

Cross-resistance to other protease inhibitors, particularly saquinavir, indinavir, or ritonavir, is not common. The most frequently demonstrated site of mutation is at codon 30.

### 5. VX-478

### a. Chemistry, Mechanism of Action, and Antiviral Activity

VX-478 is a hydroxyethylamine sulfonamide peptidomimetric with a structure identified as (3*S*)-tetrahydro-3-furyl *N*-(1*S*,2*R*)-3-(4-amino-*N*-isobutyl-benzenesulfonamido) - 1 - benzyl - 2 - hydroxypropyl carbamate. It is active at a concentration of 10–20 n*M*. The oral bioavailability is >70% and peak plasma concentrations of 6.2–10 $\mu$g/ml are achieved

after dosages of 600–1200 mg. The plasma half-life is 7–10 hr. Cerebrospinal fluid concentrations are significant.

### b. Clinical Indications

VX-478 is not licensed for the treatment of HIV infection; although it is anticipated to be so by the Year 2000.

### c. Adverse Effects

The drug is well tolerated without significant adverse events.

### d. Resistance

Resistance develops in the clinical setting following monotherapy; however, it is different than that of the other protease inhibitors. Sites at which resistance are more prone to occur include codons 50, 46, and 47.

## VI. SUMMARY

It is anticipated that many new compounds will be licensed for the treatment of viral disease because many are currently under development.

### Acknowledgments

Work performed and reported by the author was supported by Contracts NO1-Al-15113, NO1-Al-62554, NO1-Al-12667, and NO1-A1-65306 from the Antiviral Research Branch of the National Institute of Allergy and Infectious Diseases, a grant from the Division of Research Resources (RR-032) from the National Institutes of Health, and a grant from the state of Alabama.

### See Also the Following Articles

Enteroviruses • Influenza Viruses • Interferons • Recombinant DNA, Basic Procedures • Retroviruses

### Bibliography

Balfour, H. H., Jr. (1999). Antivirals (non-AIDS). *N. Engl. J. Med.* **340**, 1255–1268.

Beutner, K. R., Friedman, D. J., Forszpaniak C., *et al.* (1995). Valaciclovir compared with acyclovir for improved therapy for herpes zoster in immunocompetent adults. *Antimicrob. Agents Chemother.* **39**, 1547–11553.

Crumpacker, C. S. (1996). Ganciclovir. *N. Engl. J. Med.* **335**, 721–728.

Douglas, J. M., Critchlow, C., Benedetti J., *et al.* (1984). Double-blind study of oral acyclovir for suppression of recurrences of genital herpes simplex virus infection. *N. Engl. J. Med.* **310**, 1551–1556.

Dunkle, L. M., Arvin, A. M., Whitley, R. J., *et al.* (1991). A controlled trial of acyclovir for chicken pox in normal children. *N. Engl. J. Med.* **325**, 1539–1555.

Galasso, G., Whitley, R. J., and Merigan, T. C. (Eds.) (1989). "Antiviral Agents and Viral Diseases of Man." Raven Press, New York.

Richman, R., Whitley, F., and Hayden (Eds.) (1997). "Clinical Virology." Churchill Livingstone, New York.

Tyring, S., Barbarash, R. A., Nahlik, J. E., *et al.* (1995). Famciclovir for the treatment of acute herpes zoster. Effects on acute disease and postherpetic neuralgia: A rendomized, double-blind, placebo-controlled trial. *Ann. Intern. Med.* **123**, 89–96.

Whitley, R. J. (1998). Antiviral therapy. In "Infections Diseases" (S. L. Gorbach, J.G. Bartlett, and N. R. Blacklow. (Eds.), 2nd ed., pp. 330–350. Saunders, Philadelphia.

Whitley, R. J., and Gnann, J. (1992). Acyclovir: A decade later. *N. Engl. J. Med.* **327**, 782–789.

Whitley, R. J., Alford, C. A., Jr., Hirsch, M. S., *et al.* (1986). Vidarabine versus acyclovir therapy in herpes simplex encephalitis. *N. Engl. J. Med.* **314**, 144–149.

# Arboviruses

## Robert E. Shope

*University of Texas Medical Branch*

I. History
II. Concepts
III. Arbovirus Diseases
IV. Prevention and Control

## GLOSSARY

**arbovirus**  A virus transmitted biologically in nature in a cycle between vertebrate hosts and blood-sucking arthropods.

**extrinsic incubation**  In the arthropod, the time from infection of the vector to the time when the vector is first able to transmit the agent.

**host**  Any living animal in which the infectious agent subsists under natural conditions. A vertebrate reservoir host is essential for the long-term maintenance of the agent. An amplifying host serves tangentially to increase the natural pool of the agent available to arthropods, especially during epidemics. A dead-end host is infected but is not viremic and thus is not part of the basic maintenance cycle and cannot infect arthropods.

**intrinsic incubation**  In the vertebrate animal, the time from infection of the animal until viremia occurs at a level sufficient to infect an arthropod.

**transovarial transmission**  In the arthropod, the passage of the infectious agent through the egg to the progeny.

**viremia**  The presence of virus in the blood.

**zoonotic disease**  A human disease caused by an infectious agent transmitted to people from vertebrate animals.

**ARBOVIRUSES**  (*arthropod-borne viruses*) are viruses that are transmitted biologically in nature in a cycle between vertebrate hosts and blood-sucking arthropods. Some arboviruses are also maintained by vertical transmission through the arthropod egg and by venereal transmission in the arthropod. Mosquitoes, ticks, phlebotomine sand flies, and culicoid midges are the usual arthropod vectors. As a rule, the arthropod becomes infected on taking a blood meal from a viremic vertebrate. After a period of extrinsic incubation in the arthropod, the virus travels to the salivary gland and is transmitted by bite to a susceptible vertebrate host in which it multiplies and usually results in viremia. Some important diseases caused by arboviruses are yellow fever, dengue hemorrhagic fever, Japanese encephalitis, tick-borne encephalitis, Rift Valley fever, and Ross River disease.

## I. HISTORY

Yellow fever was the major arbovirus scourge of the eighteenth and nineteenth centuries in Africa and the Americas. Huge epidemics in Boston, New York, Philadelphia, and urban centers in the cities on the Gulf of Mexico and the lower Mississippi River valley were a serious impediment to colonization and economic development. Yellow fever was also largely responsible for the failure of initial attempts to construct the Panama Canal. In 1900, Major Walter Reed and his military colleagues, with the help of Cuban physician Carlos Finlay, discovered that the agent was transmitted by *Aedes aegypti* mosquitoes. In a series of dramatic experiments using U.S. Army volunteers, the Reed Commission also demonstrated that yellow fever was caused by a virus, that the virus was not transmitted by person-to-person contact or by contact with soiled bed clothes, and that the virus had to incubate in the mosquito for approximately 12 days before the mosquito could transmit it to

*Encyclopedia of Microbiology, Volume 1*
SECOND EDITION

another susceptible individual. These findings led to the dramatic control of yellow fever in Havana under the direction of Colonel William Gorgas, who used insecticides and environmental sanitation to rid Havana of the deadly mosquito. Gorgas then applied the same environmental sanitation techniques in Panama, thus controlling both yellow fever and malaria to facilitate the successful completion of the Panama Canal.

The Rockefeller Foundation and national governments in Central and South America supported similar successful campaigns in the urban centers. Eventually, *A. aegypti* was controlled and even eliminated in Brazil and some other South American countries. The dream, however, of ridding the world of yellow fever virus was squashed by the discovery after World War I that forest-dwelling monkeys and mosquitoes, both in Africa and in the Americas, could maintain a sylvan cycle of virus transmission not amenable to control by insecticides and environmental sanitation. In 1937, Max Theiler and Hugh Smith of the Rockefeller Foundation announced the successful use of the 17-D live attenuated yellow fever vaccine. Another vaccine developed by French scientists was also used effectively in Africa but resulted in encephalitis in a few recipients and was discontinued.

Meantime, during the 1930s the British in East Africa discovered Rift Valley fever virus, the cause of abortion and death in sheep and cattle and later recognized as a serious human hemorrhagic fever. At about the same time the cause of encephalitis in horses was recognized: eastern encephalitis in the eastern United States, Venezuelan encephalitis in northern South America, and western encephalitis in California and other western U.S. states. These viruses were later found to cause fever and encephalitis in people. The viruses of St. Louis encephalitis in the United States and Japanese encephalitis in Japan were also isolated in the 1930s. During World War II, Albert Sabin and coworkers discovered the viruses causing sandfly fever in the Mediterranean theater and dengue in the Pacific theater. Susumu Hotta in Japan independently discovered the virus of dengue.

The Rockefeller Foundation recognized that increasingly more diseases were being linked to mosquitoes, ticks, and sand flies. In 1953, the foundation initiated an ambitious program to discover and char-

acterize arboviruses throughout the world. In partnership with national governments, the Rockefeller Foundation established laboratories in South Africa, Nigeria, India, Egypt, Colombia, Brazil, Trinidad, and California. At the start, fewer than 20 arboviruses were known; 20 years later, with technological advances including the use of baby mice and tissue culture for isolation, more than 300 were known, and today more than 500 are recognized. This growth phase in the discovery of arboviruses was accomplished by a cooperative effort of many laboratories: the Institut Pasteur; the U.S. Army and Navy; U.S. universities at Cornell, Berkeley, and Wisconsin; the British Medical Research Council; the Japanese NIH; and the U.S. Centers for Disease Control. Most of these laboratories were formed into the network of arbovirus collaborating centers of the World Health Organization during the 1960s.

Currently, approximately 100 of the more than 500 known arboviruses cause human infection and disease. Human vaccines for yellow fever and Japanese encephalitis are available universally, and tickborne encephalitis vaccine is available in Europe. Dengue fever, with its severe form, dengue hemorrhagic fever, has become a major public health problem. The rapid increase in the prevalence and spread, especially in the Americas, is largely a result of the failure to control *A. aegypti* mosquitoes.

## II. CONCEPTS

### A. Cycles of Arbovirus Transmission and Pathogenesis

Arboviruses are transmitted from a viremic vertebrate to a susceptible vertebrate host by bite of a mosquito, tick, phlebotomine sand fly, or culicoid midge. These insects and ticks are infected and not merely contaminated by the virus. The infection is initiated in the lining cells of the arthropod midgut, from which the virus passes through the hemolymph or nerves to the salivary glands. The salivary glands are in turn infected, and the virus is excreted in the saliva when the arthropod feeds again. The period from initial infection until the tick or insect is able to transmit by bite is called the *extrinsic incubation period*. This period may be as short as 3 days but is usually 1 or 2 weeks.

Only the female arthropod (except for some ticks) takes a blood meal. Blood is needed for the development of eggs. The virus in the vertebrate animal usually replicates initially at the site of the bite, passes to the draining lymph nodes, and then is spread through the bloodstream to infect a target organ. The target may be the liver in the case of yellow fever and Rift Valley fever, the monocyte/macrophage cells in the case of dengue, or the brain in the case of the encephalitides. The time from infection of the vertebrate animal until viremia occurs at a level sufficient to infect an arthropod is called the *intrinsic incubation period*. This may be as short as 2 days or as long as 2 weeks. Thus, the entire cycle usually takes 2 weeks or longer. As a rule, the arthropod does not become sick and is not harmed by infection with an arbovirus. This rule also holds for many of the wild vertebrate reservoir hosts which remain healthy even though infected.

The cycle may be simple, involving only the arthropod and the vertebrate animal, the reservoir host. Most arboviruses have their basic maintenance in nature in such a cycle. The vertebrate animal may be people (dengue) or more often a bird (Japanese encephalitis), rodent (Venezuelan encephalitis), other wild animal, or even a domestic animal. Some arboviruses, such as LaCrosse encephalitis, can be maintained by transmission through the arthropod egg, a phenomenon called *transovarial transmission;* these viruses are also usually amplified by subsequent replication in a vertebrate animal. In addition to having a basic maintenance cycle, many viruses tangentially infect people and domestic animals. When these individuals have viremia in sufficient titer to infect arthropods, they are called *amplifying hosts*. When their viremia is low or absent, they may still develop disease and become *dead-end hosts*. These are vertebrate animals that are infected and diseased but, because they cannot infect mosquitoes, are not able to continue the cycle.

## B. Focality and Transport

Arboviruses occur in foci. Most arbovirus diseases are the result of zoonotic infections, i.e., infections of vertebrate animals transmitted to people. Their focality results from the limited distribution of the animal host and the arthropod. Those that are not zoonotic, such as dengue, have the distribution of the vector. In the case of dengue this is the *A. aegypti* mosquito distributed throughout the tropics. As a general rule, those arboviruses that are widely distributed have as hosts a wide range of animals, such as birds, domestic animals, and people. To establish infection in a new part of the world, the arbovirus not only needs to be transported but also needs to have an appropriate vector and vertebrate host and a receptive ecological niche in the new site. These infections are ecologically sensitive, and long-term changes in temperature and rainfall can make survival difficult for the arbovirus.

## C. Overwintering

Most arboviruses are seasonal according to the time of year when the vector is active. In temperate zones the virus must survive by overwintering; in the tropics there is comparable survival during dry periods. Some viruses, such as LaCrosse virus and Rift Valley fever virus, overwinter or survive dry periods in the mosquito eggs. For other arboviruses, such as the North American alphavirus and flavivirus encephalitides, it is not known where they hide out in the winter. Theories include passage of the winter in hibernating mosquitoes, latent infection of vertebrate animals, and reintroduction from the tropics by migrating birds or bats.

## III. ARBOVIRUS DISEASES

### A. Dengue and Dengue Hemorrhagic Fever

Dengue and its severe form, dengue hemorrhagic fever (DHF) are the most common arbovirus syndromes throughout the tropics. The World Health Organization recorded 2,512,123 DHF cases with 42,751 deaths in the 1980s, and the disease has spread and increased in incidence during the 1990s, especially in tropical America. There are four dengue serotypes (types 1–4). Infection with one serotype confers only short-lived protection against the others so that in endemic areas where two or more dengue viruses are circulating, sequential infections are common. The dengue viruses belong to the genus *Flavivirus* of the family Flaviviridae. The viruses are spherical, 43 nm in diameter, and have a single-stranded positive sense RNA genome.

Classic dengue fever is a self-limited febrile illness characterized by headache, muscle aches and pains, lymphadenopathy, and arthralgia. About half of the cases have a maculopapular non-pruritic rash. Fever usually lasts from 2 to 7 days and the fever curve may be saddle-backed. Some patients suffer mental depression during convalescence. The illness may be subclinical, especially in infants. DHF has onset like dengue fever, but on the second or third day the patient becomes irritable, somnolent, and may pass suddenly into shock. The skin becomes cool and clammy, the pulse pressure is narrowed, and hemorrhagic manifestations including petechiae, bleeding gums, and gastrointestinal hemorrhage ensue. The liver is enlarged and pleural and peritoneal fluid may be detected by X-ray and ultrasound. If supportive treatment is not instituted, 5–10% of patients with DHF and dengue shock syndrome die. Hallmarks of DHF are thrombocytopenia, a positive tourniquet test, and capillary leakage syndrome.

A major risk factor for DHF is infection with a second or third dengue serotype. The macrophage–monocyte series is the target for dengue virus infection. During sequential infection, dengue virus is complexed with subneutralizing antibody to the first infecting dengue virus. This complex is preferentially taken up by the monocyte following attachment to Fc receptor sites, and infection occurs by internalization of the complex. The process has been termed "immune enhancement." The infected monocyte is then presumed to elaborate cytokines which cause the capillary fragility, hemorrhage, and shock.

There is circumstantial evidence that the particular strain of infecting dengue virus is also a risk factor, i.e., that some strains are more virulent than others. Specifically, this would explain why dengue epidemics in Peru and other parts of South America are not associated with DHF despite the occurrence of sequential infection with different serotypes.

DHF in Southeast Asia is a disease of children. In such hyperendemic areas where all four dengue serotypes circulate, most children have already had secondary infections by age 12 years and adults are fully immune. In other settings, such as Santiago de Cuba in 1997, secondary infections were absent in children and common in adults. Under such conditions, DHF was an adult disease.

The vectors of dengue are *A. aegypti* and closely related mosquitoes. *Aedes aegypti* are domiciliary, breeding and living in and around houses in containers such as discarded tires, flower pots, and water storage jars. They feed preferentially on people and are day biters. Epidemics of dengue are usually associated with the rainy season but may also occur in dry areas where water is stored. The mosquito is limited in distribution to tropical and subtropical climates because it does not survive freezing weather. Historically, epidemics of dengue were common in the southern United States; however, today epidemics occur in Mexico just south of the border with the United States. Dengue infection is not common north of the Rio Grande River.

The vector was controlled until the 1970s in Latin America by insecticides and environmental sanitation by a program to prevent urban yellow fever. Since then, the mosquito has gradually and inexorably returned to major urban centers in Brazil, Peru, Colombia, Venezuela, Mexico, and other nations. As a consequence, dengue and DHF have emerged as the major arbovirus problem in tropical America.

## B. Yellow Fever

Although there is a very effective vaccine, hundreds of human yellow fever cases continue to occur each year as a result of persons exposed to forest mosquitoes in South America and Africa. Yellow fever is caused by a virus related to dengue in the *Flavivirus* genus. Urban epidemics caused by virus transmitted by *A. aegypti* mosquitoes have not occurred in South America for at least 40 years, but urban transmission continues in Nigeria. The urban vector is also found in Asia, but for reasons that are not clear yellow fever has never been reported there.

Yellow fever has a wide range of signs and symptoms. Infection may be inapparent or may be severe, leading to death in 30% or more of hospitalized patients. In its severe form, yellow fever has a sudden onset of fever, headache, malaise, and muscle aches; the pulse is characteristically slow in relation to the fever. Jaundice is common, hence the name of the disease. After approximately 5 days, the patient either improves and recovers or progresses to severe liver and kidney failure with bleeding from the stomach, nose, gums, and other body sites. Approximately 30% of jaundiced patients die. Mid-zonal hepatic necrosis is the characteristic lesion of yellow fever. The diagnosis can be made by isolation of the virus or viral nucleic acid from blood, by immunocytochemistry post-mortem, or by antibody studies.

Yellow fever virus is maintained in Africa in a forest cycle of nonhuman primates and *A. africanus, A. furcifer, A. taylori,* and related mosquitoes. People are infected when they enter the forest. In addition, *A. simpsoni* and other rural mosquitoes are infected by viremic monkeys coming out of the forest, and these mosquitoes then infect persons living near the jungle, who in turn initiate the urban *A. aegypti–*person cycle. In South America, *Haemagogus* mosquitoes are the forest vectors to monkeys, and people are infected when they enter the forest. Urban yellow fever has not been reported in the Americas in the past 40 years, but with the spread and rapidly increasing numbers of *A. aegypti,* there is an increasing risk of urban disease.

## C. Equine Encephalitis

Eastern, western, and Venezuelan equine encephalitis viruses infect horses and people in the Americas. The viruses are in the family Togaviridae, genus *Alphavirus.* Eastern equine encephalitis is distributed with its enzootic mosquito vector, *Culiseta melanura,* in swamp habitats along the eastern U.S. Atlantic and Gulf coasts and in the north central United States. A genetic variant of the virus found in Central and South America causes encephalitis in equines but rarely in people. Horses and humans in North America develop an acute fulminating encephalitis. The disease is most severe in the elderly and small children. Approximately 50% of human cases are

fatal, although in most years there are only one to three human cases. *Culiseta melanura* feeds almost exclusively on birds which maintain the basic bird–mosquito cycle. Humans are dead-end hosts and are probably infected by *Aedes* and other mosquitoes which have previously fed on viremic birds. Epidemiological evidence favors the theory that eastern equine encephalitis virus overwinters in enzootic swamp habitats and reappears each summer and fall in the same place. The mechanism of overwintering is not known.

Western equine encephalitis is distributed with its enzootic mosquito vector, *Culex tarsalis,* in western North America. The virus causes acute encephalitis in horses and humans, sometimes in large epidemics. The disease in humans is usually milder than eastern encephalitis; the case fatality rate is about 3%, but 10% of cases have sequellae, often manifest as subtle changes in behavior and intelligence. *Culex tarsalis* breeds in floodwater and is prevalent in irrigated fields. The enzootic cycle involves passerine birds, which are reservoir and amplifying hosts. People and horses are usually dead-end hosts. Like eastern encephalitis, western encephalitis is a summer–fall disease and the mechanism of overwintering is not known.

Venezuelan equine encephalomyelitis, as the name implies, is a disease primarily of South and Central America, but in 1971 the infection spread through Mexico and into the southern United States, causing encephalitis in approximately 1500 horses and fever and/or encephalitis in approximately 100 people. In addition, a genetic variant called Everglades virus is endemic in the Florida swamps, causing rare human encephalitis. The infection is maintained in nature in an enzootic cycle of *Culex (melanoconion)* spp. mosquitoes and forest rodents. Periodically, the virus emerges in Colombia and Venezuela from the enzootic cycle and becomes epizootic and epidemic. Major epidemics were recorded in 1962, 1971, and 1995, when thousands of human and equine cases were reported. Most human cases were self-limited fevers; approximately 4% involved the central nervous system and an estimated 20% of these died. There is genetic evidence that the epizootic form of the virus is a mutant of the enzootic form.

## D. St. Louis Encephalitis

St. Louis encephalitis is a flavivirus maintained in an enzootic cycle of birds and *Cx. tarsalis* in the western United States or *Cx. nigripalpus* in Florida. Its epidemiology is similar to that of western encephalitis virus, although cases occur later in the summer and rural epidemics of St. Louis encephalitis are usually limited to the southern United States. Urban epidemics in the central and eastern United States and Canada are vectored by *Cx. pipiens* or *Cx. quinquefasciatus*, mosquitoes that breed in water of high organic content such as urban sewage. The last major urban outbreaks in 1975 involved more than 1000 cases of encephalitis in Chicago and several other cities. The virus is detected in urban mosquitoes nearly every year in Houston, where the virus appears to be maintained during the winter by an unknown mechanism in focal areas. The virus infects all age groups, but only approximately 1% of infections lead to illness, and encephalitis is more common and more severe in persons over 60 years of age. The case fatality rate in the elderly approaches 6%. St. Louis encephalitis virus is closely related to mosquito-borne viruses that cause endemic and epidemic encephalitis in other parts of the world: Japanese encephalitis (Asia), Murray Valley encephalitis (Australia), and West Nile encephalitis (Middle East and Europe). These viruses, like St. Louis encephalitis, are transmitted by *Culex* mosquitoes and cycle enzootically in birds.

## E. LaCrosse Encephalitis

A group of closely related viruses, LaCrosse, California, trivittatus, Jamestown Canyon, and snowshoe hare in the family Bunyaviridae, are associated with rural endemic encephalitis in North America. The most common cause of endemic encephalitis in North America is LaCrosse virus, which causes a disease limited mostly to children. LaCrosse encephalitis is characterized by fever, headache, and altered consciousness. Convulsions can be a prominent sign. Most infections are inapparent and recovery is usually complete, although convulsions may recur. LaCrosse virus is maintained by the mosquito *A. triseri-*

*atus,* which breeds in hardwood tree holes and artificial sites such as discarded tires. The virus is passed transovarially, enabling the adult female mosquito to transmit immediately upon emergence. Virus is amplified in small rodents, especially chipmunks and squirrels. Cases are more common in males, and exposure in children is usually traced to playing in or near the woods.

## F. Colorado Tick Fever

Colorado tick fever is the most common tick-transmitted viral disease in North America. It occurs in the distribution of its tick vector, *Dermacentor andersoni,* throughout the Rocky Mountain states from April to June. Three to 6 days after the bite of the adult tick, there is sudden onset of fever with considerable malaise and sometimes a painful rash. Fever may be biphasic and in unusual cases is complicated by encephalitis, myocarditis, or bleeding tendency. Recovery is usually complete and death occurs in <0.5% of cases. The tick lives at elevations between 4000 and 10,000 feet and maintains an enzootic cycle of virus in ground squirrels and other small mammals. Persons at risk are campers, hikers, and mountain workers.

## G. Tick-Borne Encephalitis

Tick-borne encephalitis viruses include Russian spring–summer encephalitis, Central European tick-borne encephalitis, and Powassan virus. These are closely related flaviviruses prevalent in Asia and Europe, and in rare instances they are reported in North America (Powassan).

## H. Arboviral Arthritis

There are several other arboviruses that cause serious human diseases outside of the United States. Chikungunya and o'nyong-nyong viruses are alphaviruses prevalent in Africa and Asia (chikungunya), where they are associated with epidemics of fever and arthritis affecting thousands of persons. A closely related virus, Ross River, is the cause of epidemic polyarthritis of Australia and the Pacific Islands. The viruses are transmitted by *Aedes* and *Culex* mosquitoes, causing arthritis that is severe but invariably self-limited without mortality.

## I. Arboviral Hemorrhagic Fever

Two arboviruses in the family Bunyaviridae are associated with hemorrhagic fever. Rift Valley fever is limited to Africa, where it is linked with hepatitis and epizootic abortion in cattle and sheep and hemorrhagic fever, hepatitis, retinitis, and encephalitis in people. The largest recorded outbreak was in 1977 in Egypt, where an estimated 200,000 persons were sick and nearly 600 died. The virus is transmitted by *Culex* and *Aedes* mosquitoes and is believed to survive over dry seasons by transovarial transmission in the mosquito. The other virus is Crimean–Congo hemorrhagic fever, which is transmitted primarily by *Hyalomma* ticks in an epizootic cycle with small mammals and ground-dwelling birds and amplification in sheep and cattle. The disease has the distribution of its vector in Africa, the Middle East, and Eurasia. Persons at risk are shepherds, campers, military personnel, abattoir workers, and health care personnel, with the latter infected by aerosols generated from body fluids of infected patients. The case fatality rate is 15% or higher.

## J. Arboviruses Causing Undifferentiated Fever

There are at least 60 serologically discrete arboviruses that cause undifferentiated fever, sometimes with a rash. Most are known from study of less than 12 cases and their true significance is not known. Rarely are these diseases fatal. The viruses causing fevers are transmitted by ticks, mosquitoes, sand flies, or midges. Group C bunyaviruses are relatively common in the New World tropics and subtropics and are transmitted by *Culex* (*melanoconion*) spp. mosquitoes. Oropouche, another bunyavirus, is found in Brazil, Peru, Panama, and Trinidad and has caused urban epidemics involving thousands of cases. Oropouche virus is transmitted by culicoid midges.

## IV. PREVENTION AND CONTROL

Prevention and control of arbovirus diseases depend on intervention measures to interrupt the transmission cycle. The simplest of these is personal protection by use of repellents, bed nets, and clothing that keeps the arthropod from biting. In addition, the use of house screens and air-conditioning is often protective.

Vaccines are available generally for yellow fever and Japanese encephalitis; tick-borne encephalitis vaccine is distributed in Europe. Other vaccines for Venezuelan, eastern, and western encephalitis and Rift Valley fever are available only on an experimental basis. Vaccine development for most arbovirus diseases is not financially lucrative because of the limited clientele for any given vaccine. Dengue is an exception, and active commercial development of a tetravalent product is ongoing.

For most of the arbovirus diseases, the only practical method of control is to kill the vector or prevent breeding of the arthropod by environmental sanitation. In the past, there were notable successful campaigns to control *A. aegypti* with insecticides accompanied by destruction of the containers containing eggs and larvae. Insecticide resistance of these and other arthropods currently makes mosquito control problematic. Furthermore, expensive governmental controls and outright bans on some of the most effective pesticides have inhibited manufacturers from producing both old and new compounds. The prospects for control of arbovirus diseases by these means in the near future are dim.

One effective approach is to maintain surveillance and control the vector only when signs of an impending outbreak are detected. This is done for St. Louis encephalitis in several parts of the United States. Sentinel flocks of chickens are tested for seroconversion and/or mosquitoes are tested to detect virus. When likelihood of virus transmission is apparent, then intensive mosquito control is instituted locally on a focal basis. This sort of program conserves resources and has been successful in Florida, Texas, and California.

*See Also the Following Articles*

Lyme Disease • Surveillance of Infectious Diseases • Zoonoses

*Bibliography*

Benenson, A. S. (Ed.) (1995). "Control of Communicable Diseases Manual," 16th ed. American Public Health Association, Washington, DC.

Fields, B. N., Knipe, D. M., and Howley, P. M. (Eds.) (1996). "Virology," 3rd ed. Lippincott-Raven, New York.

Karabatsos, N. (1985). "International Catalogue of Arboviruses, Including Certain Other Viruses of Vertebrates," 3rd ed. American Society of Tropical Medicine and Hygiene, San Antonio, TX.

Shope, R. E., and Meegan, J. M. (1997). Arboviruses. *In* "Viral Infections of Humans" (A. S. Evans and R. A. Kaslow, Eds.), 4th ed., pp. 151–183. Plenum Medical, New York.

Theiler, M., and Downs, W. G. (1973). "The Arthropod-Borne Viruses of Vertebrates." Yale Univ. Press, New Haven, CT.

# Archaea

## Costantino Vetriani

*Rutgers University*

## Anna-Louise Reysenbach

*Portland State University*

## GLOSSARY

**Archaea** One of three domains of life. From the Greek *archaios* (ancient, primitive). Prokaryotic cells; membrane lipids predominantly isoprenoid glycerol diethers or diglycerols tetraethers. Formerly called archaebacteria.

**Bacteria** One of three domains of life. From the Greek *bacterion* (staff, rod). Prokaryotic cells; membrane lipids predominantly diacyl glycerol diesters. Formerly called eubacteria.

**Crenarchaeota** One of two kingdoms of organisms of the domain Archaea. From the Greek *crene-* (spring, fountain) for the resemblance of these organisms to the ancestor of the Archaea, and *archaios* (ancient). Include sulfur-metabolizing, extreme thermophiles.

**Eukarya** One of three domains of life. From the Greek *eu-* (good, true) and *karion,* (nut; refers to the nucleus). Eukaryotic cells; cell membrane lipids predominantly glycerol fatty acyl diesters.

**Euryarchaeota** One of two kingdoms within the domain Archaea. From the Greek *eurys-* (broad, wide), for the relatively broad patterns of metabolism of these organisms, and *archaios* (ancient). Include halophiles, methanogens, and some anaerobic, sulfur-metabolizing, extreme thermophiles.

**halophiles** From the Greek *halos-* (salt) and *philos* (loving). Includes organisms that grow optimally at high salt concentrations.

**hyperthermophiles** From the Greek *hyper-* (over), *therme-* (heat), and *philos* (loving). Includes organisms that grow optimally at temperatures warmer than 80°C.

**mesophiles** From the Greek *mesos-* (middle) and *philos* (loving). Includes organisms that grow optimally at temperatures between 20 and 50°C.

**methanogens** Strictly anaerobic Archaea that produce (Greek *gen,* to produce) methane.

**psychrophiles** From the Greek *psychros-* (cold) and *philos* (loving). Includes organisms that grow optimally at temperatures between 0 and 20°C.

**thermophiles** From the Greek *therme-* (heat) and *philos* (loving). Includes organisms that grow optimally at temperatures between 50 and 80°C.

**THE ARCHAEA** (formerly archaebacteria) represent one of the three domains of life as determined by Carl Woese and colleagues using phylogenetic analysis of the small subunit ribosomal RNA molecule (16S rRNA or 18S rRNA) sequences. These prokaryotes have many distinguishing characteristics, such as possession of membrane lipids composed predominantly of isoprenoid glycerol diethers or diglycerol tetraethers and the lack of peptigoglycan cell walls. In addition, it is generally accepted that the Archaea share some features in common with both of the other two domains, the Bacteria (formerly eubacteria) and Eukarya (formerly eukaryotes). Because the informational genes of Archaea resemble those of the Eukarya, archaeal gene equivalents are valuable tools for understanding processes common to both domains. Furthermore, since many Archaea thrive under extreme environmental conditions that are lethal to most organisms, such as high temperature and high salinity, they provide experimental models to study adaptations to extreme environments. For example, determining how the macromolecules of the extremely thermophilic Archaea maintain their structure and function at temperatures that denature the macromolecules of most organisms is of interest. From an evolutionary standpoint, since many of the Archaea represent some of the most deeply rooted lineages within the universal tree, the study of modern Archaea may offer valuable insights into the nature of the early evolution of life on Earth.

## I. TAXONOMY AND PHYLOGENY OF THE ARCHAEA

The Archaea exhibit considerable phylogenetic and physiological diversity. On the basis of their phylogenetic relationships, established through the comparison of 16S rRNA sequences, the Archaea comprise two kingdoms: the Crenarchaeota and the Euryarchaeota (Fig. 1). A third kingdom has been proposed (the Korarchaeota) based on 16S rRNA sequences obtained from thermal springs. The Crenarchaeota contain a group of microorganisms united primarily by an extremely thermophilic and sulfur-based metabolism. This kingdom includes sulfur-reducing microorganisms, such as *Thermoproteus* and *Pyrodictium,* and acidophilic, sulfur-oxidizing microorganisms, such as *Sulfolobus.* The Euryarchaeota include the mesophilic and thermophilic methanogens such as *Methanococcus* and *Methanopyrus;* the extreme halophiles such as *Halobacterium* and *Halococcus;* the sulfur-reducing, hyperthermophiles such as *Thermococcus* and *Pyrococcus;* the sulfate-reducing, hyperthermophilic genus *Archaeoglobus;* and the thermophilic wall-less acidophile *Thermoplasma.*

The recent application of 16S rRNA-based molecular techniques to survey natural environments has dramatically changed our perspective of the nature and diversity of Archaea. Crenarchaeota, once thought to be restricted to thermal environments, have been identified in a variety of temperate and cold environments, including marine, freshwater, and terrestrial ecosystems. These recent findings clearly indicate a ubiquitous distribution of Archaea and dispel the earlier idea that these microorganisms were confined to specialized ecological niches. In addition, 16S rRNA sequences obtained from a ther-

mal spring in Yellowstone National Park are sufficiently different from all other archaeal 16S rRNA sequences to warrant the proposal of a new kingdom within the Archaea (the Korarchaeota).

## II. CELL ENVELOPE OF THE ARCHAEA

### A. Archaeal Cell Walls

The outermost cellular constituent of prokaryotic organisms is the cell wall and it protects the cell from osmotic shock. Bacterial and archaeal cell walls have different chemical compositions. Almost all bacterial cell walls are composed of a polymer called peptidoglycan, whereas archaeal cell walls lack muramic acid and D-amino acids, the signature molecules of peptidoglycan. This renders Archaea resistant to action of lysozyme. In addition, the absence of murein in archaeal cell walls provides resistance to most antibiotics that inhibit bacterial cell wall synthesis, such as penicillin, cycloserine, vancomycin, and cephalosporin.

The cell walls of Archaea vary considerably. For example, in some methanogenic Archaea, such as *Methanobacterium, Methanobrevibacter,* and *Methanothermus,* the major cell wall component is pseudopeptidoglycan. Unlike peptidoglycan, pseudopeptidoglycan is composed of *N*-acetyltalosaminuronic acid instead of *N*-acetylmuramic acid; the glycosidic bond between amino sugars is a $\beta$ $(1 \rightarrow 3)$ bond instead of a $\beta$ $(1 \rightarrow 4)$; and the amino acids that cross-link the residues of *N*-acetyltalosaminuronic acid are all in the L form instead of the D form.

Archaea that lack pseudopeptidoglycan have cell walls consisting of polysaccharide, glycoprotein, or protein. By far the most common cell wall layer among the Archaea is the paracrystaline surface layer or S-layer, which is composed of hexagonally or tetragonally arranged protein or glycoprotein subunits. The proteins of *Halobacterium* cell walls contain a great excess of acidic amino acids, such as aspartic acid, and these negative charges serve to balance the abundance of positive charges due to the high concentration of sodium ions in the salty environment. In low $Na^+$ conditions, the negative charges of the amino acid carboxyl groups actively repel each other, eventually leading to cell lysis.

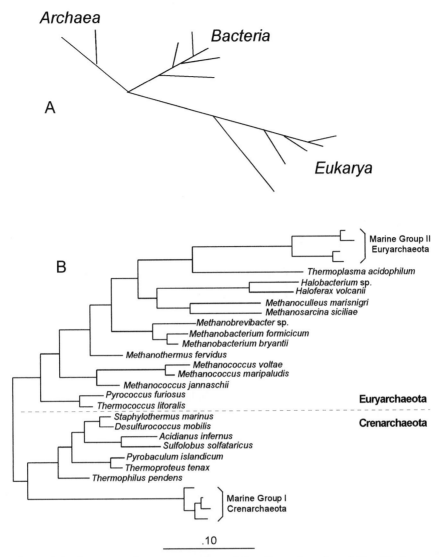

**Fig. 1.** (A) Diagrammatic representation of the three domains of life. (B) An un-rooted phylogenetic tree showing the relationships among the Archaea. Branch lengths (indicated by horizontal distances from nodes) are proportional to the evolutionary distances as determined by comparative analysis of 16S rRNA sequences. The scale represents the expected number of changes per sequence position. The tree was established using maximum likelihood analysis. Marine groups I and II Archaea were recovered directly from the environment as 16S rRNA genes.

The exception within the Archaea is *Thermoplasma*. All members of this genus are wall-less, resembling the mycoplasmas. The cell membrane of *Thermoplasma* is unique and serves to withstand both low pH and high-temperature conditions. The membrane contains lipopolysaccharides and glycoproteins. The lipopolysaccharide component is predomi-nantly tetraether lipids with glucose and mannose subunits.

## B. Archaeal Membranes

Archaeal cell membranes are chemically unique. They differ from bacterial cell membranes primarily in that they lack fatty acids and are composed of hydrocarbon moieties bonded by ether linkages to glycerol. In addition, the ester-linked fatty acids of Bacteria are linear, whereas the ether-linked hydrocarbons of Archaea are highly branched. The chirality of the glycerol moiety differs between the two domains. In the Bacteria the glycerol is in the R form and in Archaea it is in the L form. However, archaeal membranes are structurally arranged similar to membranes of Bacteria and Eukarya. The inner and outer polar surfaces (glycerol molecules) and the nonpolar interior tend to form lipid bilayers. Archaeal glycerol diether lipids form a true bilayer membrane, whereas glycerol tetraethers are arranged to form lipid monolayer membranes. The major difference is that in the monolayer membranes the hydrophobic moieties orient inward toward one another and are covalently linked. Lipid molayer membranes occur in certain methanogens and are widespread among hyperthermophilic Archaea and are thought to confer additional thermal stability.

Archaeol (diphytanylglycerol diether) is the predominant membrane core lipid in most methanogens and all extreme halophiles. In contrast, the cell membrane of hyperthermophilic Archaea and a few methanogens contain caldarchaeol, a dibiphytanyldiglycerol tetraether.

The production of ether-linked lipids in Archaea is so distinctive that they have been used as biomarkers for detecting fossilized Archaea in micropaleontological studies of rocks, sediment cores, and other ancient materials. The chemical differences between archaeal and bacterial lipids provide additional support for the evolutionary distance between the Archaea and Bacteria.

## III. ECOLOGY AND PHYSIOLOGY OF THE ARCHAEA

In general, the Archaea can be categorized into three general physiological types: (i) halophiles that inhabit highly saline environments and are characterized by a chemoorganotrophic, aerobic metabolism; (ii) methanogens that inhabit anaerobic environments and convert carbon dioxide and simple organic molecules to methane; and (iii) thermophiles that live at high temperatures and have a sulfur-based metabolism. However, recent molecular surveys of archaeal diversity have revealed that Archaea appear to thrive in other environments, such as temperate and low-temperature aerobic and anaerobic freshwater, marine, and benthic habitats. However, none of these newly discovered Archaea have been isolated in pure culture and their general physiological characteristics remain unknown or, at best, can be inferred by their ecological niche.

### A. Extremely Halophilic Archaea

#### 1. Habitats

The extremely halophilic Archaea inhabit highly saline environments, such as salt lakes, soda lakes, or inland seas such as the Dead Sea. Halophiles are also found in areas where salt is produced as a result of seawater evaporation (marine salterns) or associated with the surface of heavily salted foods such as certain fish or meats. Marine salterns may assume a reddish color indicative of the massive growth of halophilic Archaea containing carotenoids. Halophiles have also been found in highly alkaline environments such as soda lakes, where high pH values of 10–12 are mainly due to the dissolution of high levels of carbonate minerals from surrounding rocks. The salt requirement of halophilic organisms is very high and they usually grow at concentrations of NaCl above 1.8 $M$. However, most species require 2–4 $M$ NaCl for optimal growth, and the extreme halophiles can grow at 5.5 $M$ NaCl (32%), the saturation point for NaCl in water. Table I summarizes the characteristics and habitats of some halophilic Archaea.

#### 2. Physiology

The halophilic Archaea are obligate or facultative aerobes, although only a few are capable of growing anaerobically. Anaerobic growth at the expense of sugar fermentation and by anaerobic respiration linked to nitrate or fumarate reduction has been demonstrated in some *Halobacterium* and *Haloferax* isolates. All halophiles are chemoorganotrophs and most of them use amino acids or organic acids as carbon sources.

The mechanism by which these halophiles thrive in such an osmotically challenging environment has

***TABLE I***
**Characteristics of Some Halophilic Archaea**

| Genus | Morphology | Substrates | pH optimum | Optimum NaCl (M) | Habitat |
|---|---|---|---|---|---|
| *Halobacterium* | Rods | Amino acids | 5–8 | 3.5–4.5 | |
| *H. salinarum* | | | | | Isolated from salted fish, hypersaline lakes |
| *Haloferax* | Flattened disc | Amino acids, | 5–8 | 2.0–3.0 | |
| *H. volcanii* | or cup | $CH_2O$ | | | Originally isolated from the Dead Sea |
| *H. mediterranei* | shaped | | | | Salterns |
| *H. gibbonsii* | | | | | Marine salterns in Spain |
| *H. denitrificans* | | | | | Salterns in Baja California |
| *Haloarcula* | Irregular discs, | Amino acids, | 5–8 | 2.0–3.0 | |
| *H. vallismortis* | triangles, | $CH_2O$ | | | Death Valley, CA |
| *H. hispanica* | rectangles | | | | Marine salterns in Spain |
| *Halococcus* | Cocci | Amino acids | 5–8 | 3.5–4.5 | |
| *H. morrhuae* | | | | | Salted fish |
| *H. saccharolyticus* | | | | | Salterns |
| *Natronobacterium* | Rods | $CH_2O$, organic acids | 8.5–11 | 3.5–4.5 | |
| *N. gregoryi* | | | | | Highly saline soda lakes |
| *N. magadii* | | | | | |
| *Natronococcus* | Cocci | $CH_2O$ | 8.5–11 | 3.0–4.0 | |
| *N. occultus* | | | | | Highly saline soda lakes |

been best studied in *Halobacterium*. This halophile adapts to high salt concentrations by pumping large amounts of $K^+$ from the environment into the cell such that the concentration of $K^+$ inside the cell is greater than the concentration of $Na^+$ outside the cell. This mechanism allows *Halobacterium* to resist dehydration under conditions of high osmotic strength by using an inorganic ion to place the cell in a positive water balance with its surroundings.

Certain species of halophilic Archaea use light energy to synthesize ATP when oxygen partial pressure is too low to support respiration. In such conditions, halophiles such as *Halobacterium* synthesize and insert a protein called bacteriorhodopsin into their cytoplasmic membrane. This protein is conjugated to the carotenoid-like pigment, retinal, which adsorbs light at 570 nm, giving the protein a reddish-purple color.

Bacteriorhodopsin functions as a light-driven proton pump, converting light energy to electrochemical energy by pumping protons across the cell membrane. The resultant proton motive force is used for ATP synthesis and transport.

## B. Methanogenic Archaea

### 1. Habitats

Methanogenic Archaea are very sensitive to oxygen and inhabit strictly anaerobic environments such as anoxic sediments, marshes, waterlogged soils, rice paddies, protozoan hosts, and the digestive tracts of animals. They are responsible for biogenic methane and have been estimated to release $3–7 \times 10^{14}$ g of methane into the earth's atmosphere each year. Methanogens serve as the last step in the anoxic carbon cycle because they catalyze the terminal step in the mineralization of organic carbon to $CH_4$ and $CO_2$. Additionally, methanogens provide a good example for the process of syntrophy, whereby one organism's metabolic product is required as a substrate for another organism. For example, when the energies of the two reactions carried by a $H_2$-producing fatty acid-oxidizing bacterium such as *Syntrophomonas* and a $H_2$-consuming methanogen are coupled, the overall reaction is energetically favorable. This phenomenon is also referred to as interspecies hydrogen transfer.

Although methanogens are important components of anoxic environments such as the rumen, they are found in localized anaerobic microenvironments in habitats such as soils. Additionally, they have been found as endosymbionts of protozoa, such as the trichomonal protozoa associated with the termite hindgut. Methanogenesis is limited in sulfate-rich marine environments because the methanogens have to compete with sulfate reducers for $H_2$. Oxidation of $H_2$ with sulfate as the electron acceptor is thermodynamically more favorable than when $CO_2$ is the electron acceptor (as in methanogenesis). However, because some methanogens can use noncompetitive substrates (inaccessible to sulfate reducers), such as methanol, methylamines, and methionine, they are detected in some sulfate-rich environments. Additionally, thermophilic methanogens, such as *Methanococcus jannaschii,* have been isolated from deep-sea hydrothermal vents in which $CO_2$ and $H_2$ are abundant in the hydrothermal fluids.

## 2. *Physiology*

Methanogens reduce a variety of simple organic carbon substrates to methane, such as acetate, formate, carbon dioxide, methanol, and methylamines. When growing autotrophically, methanogens use molecular hydrogen to reduce carbon dioxide to methane in a multistep reaction. The carbon atom of $CO_2$ is carried through a series of cofactors (methanofuran, methanopterin, and coenzyme M) as it is reduced to $CH_4$ by electrons derived from $H_2$. These electrons are coupled to cofactors such as factor $F_{420}$, which serves as the electron donor in at least one of the steps of $CO_2$ reduction. The oxidized form of $F_{420}$ absorbs light at 420 nm and fluoresces blue-green. When reduced, the coenzyme becomes colorless. Using fluorescensce microscopy, the fluorescence of $F_{420}$ is a useful tool for preliminary identification of methanogens, although the closely related sulfate-reducing archaeon, *Archaeoglobus fulgidus,* has a similar cofactor that also autofluoresces when oxidized.

Methanogens convert carbon dioxide to organic carbon using the acetyl-CoA pathway, which is also used by homoacetogenic and sulfate-reducing bacteria. Methanogens obtain methyl groups for acetate biosynthesis from the methanogenic pathway, and the carboxyl group of acetate is derived from a second

molecule of carbon dioxide that is reduced to a carbonyl group by the carbon monoxide dehydrogenase enzyme complex. This mechanism differs from the pathways used by bacterial homoacetogens and sulfate reducers in that different cofactors are used. Thus, a similar biochemical mechanism for the reduction of $CO_2$ with $H_2$ may have arisen independently among Archaea and Bacteria. Growth of acetoclastic (acetate-degrading) methanogens is also tied to reactions of the acetyl-CoA pathway. In acetoclastic methanogens, acetate is used directly for biosynthesis and as an energy source. Table II summarizes the characteristics of some methanogenic Archaea.

## C. Extremely Thermophilic Archaea

### 1. *Habitats*

The name extreme thermophiles, or hyperthermophiles, encompasses a group of Archaea whose common characteristic is adaptation to extremely high temperatures (optimal growth temperatures $>80°C$). Most of the hyperthermophilic microorganisms described to date belong to the domain Archaea, and only members of the two bacterial orders, Thermotogales and Aquificales, have optimal temperatures for growth above $80°C$. Hyperthermophilic Archaea are generally restricted to environments in which geothermal energy is available, such as hot springs, solfataras, geothermally heated marine sediments, and submarine hydrothermal vents. These environments are rich in sulfur and sulfides, and consequently many of the thermophiles have a sulfur-dependent metabolism. Elemental sulfur is formed from geothermal $H_2S$ either by spontaneous oxidation of $H_2S$ with $O_2$ or through the reaction between $H_2S$ and $SO_2$. Terrestrial volcanic environments rich in sulfur (solfataras) may have temperatures up to $100°C$ and variable pH conditions, from alkaline to acidic (pH values $<1$ are not uncommon). Members of the *Sulfolobus* group inhabit acidic solfataras, whereas *Thermoproteus* and *Desulfurococcus* grow in mildly acidic conditions. Submarine volcanic environments include shallow (2–50 m) and deep-sea hydrothermal vents (to depths exceeding 3700 m), in which the pressure, even at shallow depths, can raise the boiling point of water sufficiently to select for organisms capable of growth above $100°C$.

***TABLE II***
**Characteristics of Some Methanogenic Archaea**

| Genus | Morphology | Substrates | Temperature optimum (°C) |
|---|---|---|---|
| **I** | | | |
| *Methanobacterium* | Long rods | $H_2 + CO_2$, formate | 35–40 |
| *Methanobrevibacter* | Short rods | $H_2 + CO_2$, formate | 30–38 |
| *Methanosphaera* | Cocci | Methanol $+ H_2$ | 36–40 |
| *Methanothermobacter* | Rods | $H_2 + CO_2$, formate | 55–70 |
| **II** | | | |
| *Methanothermus* | Rods | $H_2 + CO_2$; can also reduce $S^0$ | 83–88 |
| **III** | | | |
| *Methanococcus* (mesophilic sp.) | Irregular cocci | $H_2 + CO_2$, pyruvate $+ CO_2$, formate | 35–40 |
| *Methanococcus* (thermophilic sp.) | Irregular cocci | $H_2 + CO_2$ | 88 |
| **IV** | | | |
| *Methanomicrobium* | Short rods | $H_2 + CO_2$, formate | 40 |
| *Methanogenium* | Irregular cocci | $H_2 + CO_2$, formate | 30–57 |
| *Methanospirillum* | Spirilla | $H_2 + CO_2$, formate | 30–40 |
| *Methanoplanus* | Plate-shaped cells | $H_2 + CO_2$, formate | 32–40 |
| **V** | | | |
| *Methanosarcina* | Large irregular cocci | $H_2 + CO_2$, methanol, methylamines, acetate | 35–50 |
| *Methanolobus* | Irregular cocci in aggregates | Methanol, methylamines | 30–40 |
| *Methanohalobium* | Irregular cocci | Methanol, methylamines; halophilic | 50 |
| *Methanococcoides* | Irregular cocci | Methanol, methylamines | 23–35 |
| *Methanohalophilus* | Irregular cocci | Methanol, methylamines; halophilic | 26–36 |
| *Methanosaeta* | Long rods to filaments | Acetate | 35–60 |
| *Methanoculleus* | Coccus | $H_2 + CO_2$, formate | 37–60 |
| **VI** | | | |
| *Methanopyrus* | Rods in chains | $H_2 + CO_2$, hyperthermophilic, growth up to 110°C | 100 |

Archaea isolated from various submarine vent sites include the fermentative and sulfur-reducing organisms such as *Pyrococcus* and *Thermococcus*, sulfate-reducing organisms such as *Archaeoglobus*, and chemolithotrophic sulfur-dependent hyperthermophiles such as *Pyrodictium* and *Pyrolobus*, the latter representing a novel group of Archaea that extends the upper temperature limit for life to 113°C. Table III summarizes the characteristics and habitats of some extremely thermophilic Archaea.

## 2. Physiology

Extremely thermophilic Archaea can carry out a variety of respiratory processes, and in most cases elemental sulfur plays a key role as either an electron donor or an electron acceptor (Table IV). *Sulfolobus* grows in acidic solfataras in which it is an obligate aerobe capable of oxidizing $H_2S$ or $S^0$ to $H_2SO_4$ and using organic carbon or fixing $CO_2$ as a carbon source. A close relative of *Sulfolobus*, *Acidianus*, is a facultative aerobe and an obligate autotroph. *Acidianus* uses $S^0$ as the electron donor in the presence of $O_2$ or the electron acceptor in the presence of $H_2$. Furthermore, *Thermoproteus* and *Thermophilum* are strict anaerobes that can grow chemolithotrophically on $H_2$ or chemoorganotrophically on complex carbon substrates with $S^0$ as an electron acceptor.

*Pyrococcus* and *Thermococcus* are closely related hyperthermophiles that differ primarily in their optimal growth temperatures (100 and 88°C, respec-

**TABLE III**
**Characteristics of Some Hyperthermophilic Archaea**

| Genus | Morphology | Electron donor | Electron acceptor | Temperature (°C) | | | Optimum pH |
|---|---|---|---|---|---|---|---|
| | | | | Minimum | Optimum | Maximum | |
| Terrestrial hot springs isolates | | | | | | | |
| Sulfolobus | Lobed spheres | Organic, $S^0$, $H_2S$, $Fe^{2+}$ | $O_2$, $Fe^{3+}$ | 55 | 75–85 | 87 | 1–5 |
| Acidianus | Spheres | $H_2$, organic | $S^0$, $O_2$ | 65 | 85–90 | 95 | 2 |
| Thermoproteus | Rods | Organic, $H_2$ | $S^0$ | 60 | 88 | 96 | 6 |
| Thermofilum | Rods | Organic | $S^0$ | 70 | 88 | 95 | 5.5 |
| Desulfurococcus | Spheres | Organic | $S^0$ | 70 | 85 | 95 | 6 |
| Desulfurolobus | Lobed spheres | $H_2$ | $S^0$, $O_2$ | 65 | 80 | 87 | 2.5 |
| Pyrobaculum | Rods | $H_2$ | $S^0$ | 74 | 100 | 102 | 6 |
| Stygiolobus | Lobed spheres | $H_2$ | $S^0$ | 57 | 80 | 89 | 3 |
| Submarine hydrothermal vents isolates | | | | | | | |
| Pyrodictium | Disc shaped, connecting threads | $H_2$ | $S^0$ | 82 | 105 | 110 | 6 |
| Pyrococcus | Spheres | Organic | $S^0$ | 70 | 100 | 106 | 6–8 |
| Pyrolobus | Lobed cocci | $H_2$ | $S_2O_3^{2-}$, $NO_3^-$ | 90 | 105 | 113 | 5.5 |
| Thermodiscus | Disc shaped | Organic | $S^0$ | 75 | 90 | 98 | 5.5 |
| Staphylothermus | Spheres in clumps | Organic | $S^0$ | 65 | 92 | 98 | 6–7 |
| Thermococcus | Spheres | Organic | $S^0$ | 70 | 88 | 98 | 6–7 |
| Archaeoglobus | Cocci | $H_2$, lactate, organic | $SO_4^{2-}$, $S_2O_3^{2-}$ | 64 | 83 | 95 | 7 |

**TABLE IV**
**Examples of Energy-Yielding Metabolism in Hyperthermophilic Archaea**

| Energy-yielding reaction | Organism |
|---|---|
| $H_2 + S^0 \rightarrow H_2S$ | Pyrodictium, Thermoproteus, Pyrobaculum, Acidianus, Stygiolobus |
| $4H_2 + SO_4^{2-} \rightarrow H_2S + 4H_2O$ | Archaeoglobus |
| $H_2 + HNO_3 \rightarrow HNO_2 + H_2O$ | Pyrobaculum, Pyrolobus |
| $6H_2O + NO_3^- + 2\,FeCO_3 \rightarrow NO_2^- + H_2O + 2Fe(OH)_3 + 2HCO_3^-$ | Ferroglobus |
| $H_2 + 1/2O_2 \rightarrow H_2O$ | Pyrobaculum, Sulfolobus, Acidianus |
| $2S^0 + 3O_2 + 2H_2O \rightarrow 2H_2SO_4$ | Sulfolobus, Acidianus |
| Organic compound $+ S^0 \rightarrow H_2S + CO_2$ | Thermoproteus, Thermococcus, Desulfurococcus, Thermofilum, Pyrococcus |
| Organic compound $+ H_2SO_4 \rightarrow H_2S + CO_2$ | Archaeoglobus |
| Organic compound $+ O_2 \rightarrow H_2O + CO_2$ | Sulfolobus |
| Organic compound $\rightarrow CO_2 +$ fatty acids | Staphylothermus |
| Organic compound $\rightarrow CO_2 + H_2$ | Pyrococcus |
| $4H_2 + CO_2 \rightarrow CH_4 + 2H_2O$ | Methanopyrus, Methanothermus, Methanococcus |

tively). They are both obligate anaerobic chemoorganotrophs that utilize proteins and other complex organic mixtures and reduce $S^0$ to $H_2S$. *Pyrodictium* is a chemolithotrophic strict anaerobe and grows up to 110°C on $H_2$ and $S^0$. *Pyrolobus* is unusual in that it is capable of reducing both $NO_3^-$ and $S_2O_3^{2-}$ to $NH_4^+$ and $H_2S$, respectively, with $H_2$ as the electron donor. The only known hyperthermophilic archaeon capable of sulfate reduction is *Archaeoglobus*, which uses $H_2$, lactate, or complex organic mixtures as electron donors. Interestingly, factor $F_{420}$ and methanopterin, coenzymes involved in methanogenesis in methanogens, are also present in *Archaeoglobus*. Furthermore, 16S rRNA sequence data indicate that *Archaeoglobus* is phylogenetically related to certain methanogens. From an evolutionarily perspective, sulfate reduction by *Archaeoglobus* may have been a transitional type of metabolism in the diversification of Archaea from sulfur-respiring to methane-producing and halophilic phenotypes. A close relative of *Archaeoglobus* is *Ferroglobus*. This hyperthermophile can oxidize ferrous iron, hydrogen, or sulfide with nitrate as the electron acceptor. If hydrogen is used as the electron donor, *Ferroglobus* can also oxidize thiosulfate. It has been hypothesized that both ferrous iron and nitrate may have been present in the early hot Archaean ocean and could have supported the growth of *Ferroglobus*-like organisms.

## D. Global Distribution of the Archaea

Novel microbial isolates such as those described previously have traditionally been cultured, purified, and identified in the laboratory based primarily on their morphology, physiology, metabolism, and phylogeny. However, isolated strains may represent a minor fraction of the extant microbial diversity and microbiologists generally agree that more than 90% of the microorganisms in nature have resisted traditional cultivation methods. This problem has been alleviated in part through recovery of the universally conserved 16S rRNA genes directly from environmental samples. Traditionally, these genes are amplified by the polymerase chain reaction (PCR) from DNA extracted from the environment. The PCR products are sorted by cloning, and the unique cloned 16S rRNA genes are then sequenced. The

sequences are analyzed using a ribosomal sequence database, and their phylogenetic position is determined. This approach bypasses traditional cultivation methods and it is routinely used in surveys of microbial diversity. In general, the 16S rRNA genes do not provide information on the phenotypic and physiological characteristics of the organisms, and microbiologists rely both on traditional culture methods and the identification of functional genes to fully characterize them.

Recently, two significant discoveries regarding archaeal diversity were made using these phylogenetic-based techniques. An entire new lineage within the Archaea was identified from a thermal spring in Yellowstone National Park and proposed as a new kingdom within the Archaea, namely, the Korarchaeota. The second surprising discovery was that the Archaea are much more ubiquitous than previously thought and inhabit many environments considered to be devoid of Archaea or only restricted to methanogenic Archaea. Novel Archaea have been localized in a variety of temperate and cold environments, such as marine planktonic and benthic habitats, freshwater lakes, soils, terrestrial subsurface environments, and in association with several marine animals (Table V). In particular, members of the Crenarchaeota, whose representatives are all extreme thermophiles, were identified for the first time in temperate and cold environments. 16S rRNA sequence data revealed a wide phylogenetic diversity among the low-temperature Archaea, and their distribution in diverse environments suggests a wide range of ecological and physiological adaptations.

## IV. GENETICS AND MOLECULAR BIOLOGY OF THE ARCHAEA

### A. Genetic Organization

The genomes of the Archaea are composed of a circular chromosome ranging in size from approximately 1.1 to $3 \times 10^6$ base pairs. Archaeal genes are often organized in operons and prokaryotic-type polycistronic trancriptional units have been identified in genes from *Sulfolobus* and methanogens. For example, the genes for the three large subunits of

***TABLE V***
**Archaeal 16S rRNA Gene Sequences Detected in Temperate and Low-Temperature Environments**

| Habitat | Organism taxonomic position |
|---|---|
| Marine | |
| Atlantic Ocean | |
| Surface and deep waters (up to 1000 m) | Crenarchaeota, Euryarchaeota |
| Coastal and deep-sea sediments (12–4500 m) | Crenarchaeota, Euryarchaeota |
| Salt marsh | Euryarchaeota |
| Pacific Ocean | |
| Surface and deep waters (up to 3000 m) | Crenarchaeota, Euryarchaeota |
| Microbial mats, Loihi Seamount (980 m) | Crenarchaeota, Euryarchaeota |
| Antarctic Ocean | |
| Surface waters | Crenarchaeota, Euryarchaeota |
| Associated with marine animals | |
| Atlantic Ocean | |
| Gut of abyssal holothurian *Oneirophanta mutabilis* (4870 m) | Crenarchaeota |
| Digestive tract of fish | Crenarchaeota, Euryarchaeota |
| Pacific Ocean | |
| Tissues of sponge *Axinella mexicana* (10–20 m) | Crenarchaeon (*Cenarchaeum symbiosum*) |
| Freshwater | |
| Lakes Griffy, Lemon, and Lawrence, USA | |
| Sediments | Crenarchaeota |
| Lake Michigan, USA | |
| Sediments (101 m) | Crenarchaeota, Euryarchaeota |
| Terrestrial | |
| Soil | Crenarchaeota |
| Paddy field soil | Crenarchaeota |
| Soybean field soil | Crenarchaeota, Euryarchaeota |
| Subsurface | |
| Subsurface paleosol (188 m) | Crenarchaeota |
| Contaminated aquifer | Crenarchaeota, Euryarchaeota |
| Anaerobic digestor | |
| Wine distillation waste | Crenarchaeota, Euryarchaeota |

the RNA polymerase in *Sulfolobus acidocaldarius* are clustered in an operon in the same order as the corresponding genes in the *Escherichia coli* operon. As in Bacteria, archaeal rRNA genes are also arranged in 16S–23S–5S operons that appear to be cotranscribed into primary transcripts that must then be cleaved and processed to generate the mature rRNAs. A tRNA$^{Ala}$ gene resides in the spacer region between the 16S and 23S rRNA genes in most of the Euryarchaeota, whereas the spacers in most of the Crenarchaeota do not contain any tRNA genes. The 5S rRNA gene in most of the extreme thermophiles is frequently found outside the 16S–23S operon. *Thermoplasma acidophilum* is exceptional in that all three

rRNA genes are separated in the genome. Introns are usually considered eukaryal features; however, they are found within the 23S rRNA genes from *Desulfurococcus mobilis* and *Staphylothermus marinus* and in tRNA genes from *Halobacterium volcanii*, *Sulfolobus solfataricus*, and *Thermoproteus tenax*.

## B. Transcription and Translation

The DNA-dependent RNA polymerase, which synthesizes messenger RNA, is essential to all living forms and therefore it is considered to be quite ancient. The bacterial enzyme is relatively simple in structure and consists of a core enzyme with three subunits. In contrast, the eukaryal RNA polymerase is more complex and contains 7–12 subunits. The archaeal enzyme has a complex subunit pattern, and the subunits that have been sequenced are closer to the corresponding subunits of eukaryal RNA polymerase II and III than to those of the bacterial enzyme. Furthermore, the archaeal RNA polymerase is not inhibited by the antibiotic rifampicin, which at low concentrations inhibits the bacterial enzyme.

In prokaryotes, transcription initiation involves the binding of the RNA polymerase to a specific sequence on the gene called the promoter. The promoter directs the polymerase to the initiation site. The consensus sequence for the minimal archaeal promoter includes an AT-rich sequence, located between 32 and 25 base pairs upstream of the transcriptional start site. This sequence, named boxA or DPE (distal promoter element), resembles the eukaryal AT-rich region (TATA box) both in sequence and in position. The archaeal boxA sequence is common to protein-coding genes from Archaea and therefore can be considered a general feature of the domain. Like mRNAs in Bacteria, archaeal mRNAs do not have 5' end caps and often have Shine–Dalgarno ribosome binding sites. However, the locations of putative Shine–Dalgarno sequences relative to the translational initiation codon are variable in different members of the Archaea, and the upstream sequences of several highly expressed genes bear little resemblance to Shine–Dalgarno motifs.

Archaeal ribosomes are similar to those found in Bacteria, and they have the same sedimentation coefficients (namely, 5S, 16S, and 23S). However, some differences exist in the structure and composition between bacterial and archaeal ribosomes, which allow for phylogenetic sequence comparisons and result in different sensitivity to certain antibiotics. For example, chloramphenicol and streptomycin affect ribosome activity in Bacteria but have no adverse effect on protein synthesis in Archaea.

## C. DNA Replication

Several DNA-binding proteins and histone-like proteins have been isolated from Archaea. The DNA of *Thermoplasma acidofilum* is surrounded by a highly basic protein that organizes the DNA into globular particles. This organization resembles the nucleo-

somes of eukaryal cells. The DNA-binding protein, HTa, shares amino acid identity with both the eukaryal histones and the bacterial histone-like proteins of *E. coli*. A different DNA-binding protein, HMf, was isolated from the thermophilic methanogen *Methanothermus fervidus* and also shows significant amino acid sequence identity with eukaryal histones.

In bacterial nucleoproteins and in eukaryal chromosomes, DNA has a negative superhelicity as a result of topoisomerase activity. A novel class of topoisomerases has been identified in thermophilic Archaea (e.g., *S. acidocaldarius*). Since these enzymes catalyze positive supercoiling into the DNA, they have been referred to as reverse gyrases. Reverse gyrase activity appears to be widely distributed in hyperthermophiles. In addition to reverse gyrase, other DNA topoisomerase activities have been identified in hyperthermophilic Archaea, such as an ATP-independent type I topoisomerase which relaxes only negatively supercoiled DNA and an ATP-dependent type II topoisomerase which is able to relax both negatively and positively supercoiled DNA.

DNA polymerases from Archaea share similarities with both eukaryal and bacterial enzymes. DNA polymerases isolated from several Archaea, including *S. solfataricus, Halobacterium halobium,* and *Methanococcus vanniellii,* are sensitive to aphidicolin, an inhibitor of eukaryal α-type DNA polymerases. In contrast, this drug has no effect on the DNA polymerase activities of *S. acidocaldarius* and *Methanobacterium thermoautotrophicum,* whose enzymes more closely resemble those found in Bacteria. A DNA polymerase from the uncultivated psychrophilic symbiotic crenarchaeote, *Cenarchaeum symbiosum,* was isolated recently. This enzyme is heat labile, which lends credence to the proposed nonthermophilic phenotype of this uncultivated member of the Crenarchaeota.

## D. Molecular Adaptations to High Temperatures

Archaea exhibit a strong adaptive capacity to extremely high temperatures. Since microorganisms are isothermal, they have to develop strategies to avoid thermal stress. Thus, in order to survive at temperatures in excess of 100°C, hyperthermophiles have to adapt their cell inventory to function optimally at the temperatures in the niches they occupy. Many different mechanisms have been hypothesized by which hyperthermophiles can simultaneously retain stability and plasticity at high temperatures. Histone-like proteins may play an important role in thermophilic Archaea, protecting DNA against thermal denaturation and degradation. The DNA-binding proteins isolated from both *T. acidofilum* and *M. fervidus* stabilize double-stranded DNA molecules *in vitro* by increasing their melting temperatures. Furthermore, the presence of reverse gyrase activity in all hyperthermophilic Archaea and Bacteria (e.g., *Thermotoga*) that have been examined suggests that positive supercoiling may play a role in the stabilization of DNA molecules at high temperature. Additionally, *Pyrococcus furiosus* has a very efficient DNA repair system that has been suggested as a possible mechanism to maintain the integrity of chromosomes at high temperature.

An important mechanism of thermoadaptation is the biosynthesis of thermostable proteins and enzymes that maintain sufficient structural integrity to allow optimal catalytic efficiency at high temperatures. Recent studies on the structure of proteins from hyperthermophilic organisms revealed some of the characteristics commonly associated with protein thermostability. Thermostable proteins are often characterized by a very efficient packing density in the hydrophobic core of the molecule and shorter connecting elements (loops) between regions of secondary structure. Recently, the comparison of proteins from mesophilic organisms with their thermophilic homologs revealed a striking increase in the number of ionic interactions in the more thermostable proteins. Ionic interactions among monomers are thought to stabilize multimeric proteins at high temperatures. Overall, these characteristics lead to decreased flexibility in the polypeptide chain, a required feature that compensates for increased thermal fluctuations at high temperatures.

## V. EVOLUTION OF THE ARCHAEA

Archaea occupy a pivotal phylogenetic position between the two other domains of life, Bacteria and Eukarya. With the recent sequencing of the entire genomes of several Archaea and the extensive analysis of archaeal genes, it has become evident that archaeal genomes share bacterial and eukaryotic features. Although Archaea and Bacteria appear very similar in terms of general genome organization, many archaeal components of functions, such as the DNA replication, transcription, and translation, show greater similarity to eukaryotic homologs. Overall, Archaea are unique in having a combination of traits which were previously believed to be exclusive to either Bacteria or Eukarya. However, more genome sequences will be necessary to test hypotheses on possible evolutionary scenarios between the Archaea, Bacteria, and Eukarya.

Furthermore, hyperthemophilic Archaea have been proposed as analogs for the early life on Earth. If life arose and evolved on the anoxic, high-temperature, sulfur-rich early Earth, then the requirement of thermophilic Archaea for high-temperature environments and their predominantly anaerobic, sulfur-metabolizing phenotype suggest they are good analogs to test such a theory. Thus, the unusual enzymes and metabolic pathways of extant hyperthermophiles may represent remnants of the first organisms that evolved on Earth. Furthermore, phylogenetic analyses of 16S rRNA gene sequences suggest that hyperthermophilic Archaea evolve slowly, and that they represent the deepest branches of the Archaea. In contrast, halophilic Archaea and the newly discovered low-temperature Archaea appear to evolve much faster than the hyperthermophiles (Fig. 1).

## VI. CONCLUSION

The separate identity of the Archaea, as phylogenetically unique, is a relatively recent discovery. With the recent interest in extreme environments as sources of unusual organisms and as analogs for early evolution of life on Earth and other planets, the Archaea will most likely continue to unravel their secrets to science. As more entire genomes are sequenced, the relationships within the Archaea and between the Archaea and Bacteria and Eukarya will become clearer; then, what we currently know about this domain of life will only appear as the tip of the iceberg.

*See Also the Following Articles*

DNA Replication • Evolution, Theory and Experiments •
Extremophiles • Methanogenesis

*Bibliography*

Aravalli, R. N., She, Q. X., and Garrett, R. A. (1998). *TREE* **13**, 190–194.

Barns, S. M., Delwiche, C. F., Palmer, J. D., and Pace, N. R. (1996). *Proc. Natl. Acad. Sci. USA* **93**, 9188–9193.

Blöch, E., Burggraf, S., Fiala, G., Lauerer, G., Huber, G., Huber, R., Rachel, R., Segerer, A., Stetter, K. O., and Völkl, P. (1995). *World J. Microbiol. Biotechnol.* **11**, 9–16.

Brown, J. R., and Doolittle, W. F. (1997). *Microbiol. Mol. Biol. Rev.* **61**, 456–502.

Ciaramella, M., Cannio, R., Moracci, M., Pisani, F. M., and Rossi, M. (1995). *World J. Microbiol. Biotechnol.* **11**, 71–84.

DeLong, E. F. (1992). *Proc. Natl. Acad. Sci. USA* **89**, 5685–5689.

Fuhrman, J. A., McCallum, K., and Davis, A. A. (1992). *Nature (London)* **356**, 148–149.

Konig, H., and Stetter, K. O. (1989). Archaeobacteria. *In* "Bergey's Manual of Determinative Bacteriology" (J. T. Staley, M. P. Bryant, N. Pfennig, and J. G. Holt, Eds.), Vol. 3, pp. 2171–2173. Williams & Wilkins, Baltimore.

Madigan, M. T., Martinko, J. M., and Packer, J. (1997). "Brock Biology of Microorganisms," 8th ed. Prentice Hall, Upper Saddle River, NJ.

Vetriani, C., Maeder, D. L., Tolliday, N., Yip, K. S.-P., Stillman, T. J., Britton, K. L., Rice, D. W., Klump, H. H., and Robb, F. T. (1998). *Proc. Natl. Acad. Sci. USA* **95**, 12300–12305.

Woese, C. R., Kandler, O., and Wheelis, M. L. (1990). *Proc. Natl. Acad. Sci. USA* **87**, 4576–4579.

# *Arsenic*

## Dianne K. Newman

*California Institute of Technology*

## GLOSSARY

**arsenic geochemical cycle**  The transformations of arsenic from one chemical form to another that alter its mobility in the environment.

**As(III)**  Arsenite, inorganic; thermodynamically stable under reducing conditions, and present in minerals such as orpiment ($As_2S_3$). It is generally more toxic, soluble, and mobile than arsenate.

**As(V)**  Arsenate, inorganic; thermodynamically stable under oxic conditions, and present in minerals such as scorodite $[(Fe,Al)(AsO_4) \cdot 2H_2O]$.

**chemolithotrophic metabolism**  The use of an inorganic compound as an electron donor for energy metabolism.

**dissimilatory reduction**  Use of an inorganic compound, such as nitrate, Fe(III), or sulfate, as an electron acceptor in anaerobic respiration, resulting in the reduction of an element in that compound.

**ARSENIC**  is relatively abundant in the biosphere owing to contamination from a variety of anthropogenic sources in addition to its natural occurrence in minerals. Since the industrial revolution, arsenic has been discharged into waterways as a waste product of sulfuric acid manufacturing, sprayed onto soils as a pesticide, dispersed into the air during ore smelting, and distributed over the Earth through mining activities. Although human activities are estimated to release 50,000 tons of arsenic per year, simple weathering of igneous and sedimentary rocks (including coal) naturally releases nearly an equal amount of arsenic into the environment. The geochemical cycle of arsenic is controlled by a variety of chemical reactions, including oxidation–reduction, precipitation–dissolution, adsorption–desorption, and methylation. Strong evidence exists that microorganisms play an important role in these reactions. This article will focus primarily on the microbial contributions to the cycling of inorganic arsenic.

## I. INTRODUCTION

### A. Forms of Arsenic

Arsenic belongs to group V of the periodic table, along with nitrogen, phosphorus, antimony, and bismuth, and it has only one stable isotope in nature ($^{75}As$). It is a nonmetal, but because it resembles a metal in its elemental state it is sometimes called a "metalloid." The primary oxidation states of arsenic are V (arsenate), III (arsenite), 0 (arsenic), and $-III$ (arsine gas). The main chemical forms of these compounds in aqueous solution at pH 7.0 are $H_2AsO_4^-$ and $HAsO_4^{2-}$, $HAsO_2$, As, and $AsH_3$, respectively. Under oxidizing conditions (0.2–0.5 V), both anionic arsenate species predominate, whereas uncharged arsenite is the principal species in reducing environments (0–0.1V). The redox reaction between As(V) and As(III) is $0.5 H_2AsO_4^{2-} + 1.5 H^+ + e^- \leftrightarrow 0.5HAsO_2 + H_2O$ (pe° = 10.56). Elemental arsenic occurs rarely, and arsine is stable only under highly reducing conditions. Methylated forms, such as monomethylarsonic acid [MMAA(V)], dimethylarsinic acid [DMAA(V)], monomethylarsonous acid [MMAA(III)], and dimethylarsinous acid [DMAA(III)], can be synthesized by microorganisms and phytoplankton; arsenobetaine, arsenosugars, and other complex organic compounds are formed by lobsters, fish, and phytoplankton but contribute little to arsenic speciation in natural waters.

## B. Uses of Arsenic

Throughout the centuries, arsenic has been used for a variety of purposes from pigments to poisons. Although its toxicity is renowned, paradoxically one of the most important historical uses of arsenic has been medicinal. In ancient times, arsenic compounds were used to remedy ailments ranging from asthma to fear of ghosts (Azcue and Nriagu, 1994). In the late eighteenth century, Fowler's solution (1% potassium arsenite) became the most widely used medication for a variety of illnesses. Solutions of arsenic iodide and arsenic trichloride were recommended to treat rheumatism, arthritis, malaria, trypanosome infections, tuberculosis, and diabetes; in 1909 the discovery of Salvarsan (arsphenamine) made it the primary medicine for syphilis until the discovery of antibiotics in the 1940s. Today, arsenic is still used in some developing countries as an antisyphilitic drug and to treat trypanosomiasis (sleeping sickness). Recent reports suggest that arsenic may even be an effective therapy for acute promyelocytic leukemia, a rare blood-cell cancer.

Although arsenic continues to have medicinal applications, its more common modern uses are in the agricultural and industrial sectors. Arsenic is used in pesticides, insecticides, defoliants, wood preservatives, antifouling paints, feed additives, semiconductor chips (gallium arsenide is the primary alternative to silicon), and metal alloys.

## C. Toxicity

Arsenate is toxic because it acts as a phosphate analog, uncoupling oxidative phosphorylation and thereby inhibiting ATP synthesis; arsenite inhibits enzymes due to its strong affinity for sulfhydryl groups. Both the Environmental Protection Agency (EPA) and the International Agency for Research on Cancer (IARC) have classified arsenic as a human carcinogen based on multiple epidemiological studies showing evidence of carcinogenic risk by both inhalation and ingestion. Nevertheless, the health-based environmental regulation of arsenic is in a stage of transition and continues to be controversial. The EPA is reevaluating the current maximum contaminant level for As of 50 $\mu$g/l; the range under consideration is from 2 to 20 $\mu$g/l. Debate is centering on risk assessment, the practical detection limit, and the costs of treatment.

## II. OCCURRENCE AND MOBILITY OF ARSENIC IN THE ENVIRONMENT

### A. Basic Geochemistry

Arsenic is the twentieth most abundant element in the Earth's crust and is a component of more than 200 minerals. More than 99% of arsenic in the environment is present in rocks, resulting from the ease with which arsenic substitutes for S in crystal lattices of sulfur minerals or substitutes for Si, Al, or Fe in silicate minerals. Sedimentary rocks contain higher concentrations of arsenic than igneous or metamorphic rocks. For example, the average concentrations of arsenic in igneous rocks, limestone, sandstone, and shale are 1.5, 2.6, 4.1, and 14.5 ppm, respectively (Bhumbla and Keefer, 1994). Arsenic is widely distributed in nature, but it is particularly concentrated in sulfide-ore deposits. Other ores containing arsenic include copper, nickel, lead, cobalt, and gold. Typically, smelting of these ores produces arsenic trioxide, "white arsenic" ($As_2O_3$), the raw material used in industrial arsenic chemical production. Some typical minerals include arsenopyrite (FeAsS), native arsenic (As), realgar (AsS), orpiment ($As_2S_3$), loellingite (FeAs), niccolite (NiAs), enargite ($Cu_3AsS_4$), scorodite $(Fe,Al)(AsO_4) \cdot 2H_2O$, and olivenite ($Cu_2AsO_4OH$). Of these, arsenopyrite is the most abundant and is an important constituent of coal; the burning of fossil fuels is therefore an important pathway through which arsenic enters the environment.

After rocks, the most important reservoirs for arsenic are soils and the oceans. Arsenic is present in the continental crust at an average of 3 mg of As/kg, whereas the average concentration of arsenic in deep-sea sediments is significantly higher (approximately 40 mg/kg). The median worldwide concentration of arsenic in soil is 6 mg/kg, with a typical range of 0.1–40 mg/kg. Soils derived from or in proximity to sulfide-ore deposits may contain up to 8000 mg/kg, however, and arsenic concentrations in soils from polluted sites have been reported to be as high as 30,000 mg/kg. Arsenic is present as a trace element in geothermal reservoir fluids and hot springs in concentrations ranging from 0.1 to 10 ppm in most systems but up to 50 ppm in some As-rich systems. The average concentration in seawater is 2 $\mu$g/l (Andreae, 1979) and in fresh water 0.5 $\mu$g/l (Ehrlich, 1990).

## B. Arsenic Cycling in Fresh Water

On entering an aquatic body, arsenic may be exported to the sediments or cycle in surface waters. Arsenate adsorbs onto manganese and aluminum oxides at near-neutral pH, although adsorption onto iron oxides and hydroxides ($FeO_x$) predominates. Coprecipitation with $FeO_x$ may also occur, leading to the formation of the mineral scorodite. Arsenate removal by ferric iron is favored at slightly acidic pH and is important in lacustrine sediments. It is thought that such adsorption and co-precipitation bind aqueous arsenate to colloids and particles that sink from the water column to the sediments, consistent with observations that arsenic concentrations in sediments are usually much higher than those in the overlying water (Cullen and Reimer, 1989). Arsenite also adsorbs onto metal oxides but is observed in the field to be much more mobile than arsenate. Synthetic birnessite ($\delta$ $MnO_2$) has been shown to oxidize arsenite directly with the release of arsenate and Mn(II), with maximal rates of adsorption and release occurring at pH 4. Recently, clays such as kaolinite and illite have been shown to adsorb and enhance the oxidation of arsenite to arsenate, with arsenite adsorption maximized between pH 7.5 and 9.5. Organic matter is also known to affect arsenic's mobility: Humic acids (which are insoluble) strongly adsorb arsenic in the pH range 5–7, whereas fulvic acids (which are soluble) can increase its leaching and mobility.

Arsenic remains adsorbed to $FeO_x$ as long as the sedimentary environment is sufficiently oxidized. High inputs of organic carbon to the sediments, however, usually result in oxygen depletion and lowering of redox potentials, with the lowest potentials present in the deepest layers. Reduction of sedimentary $Fe(III)O_x$ solubilizes Fe(II) and releases adsorbed arsenic into pore waters. Dissimilatory Fe(III)-reducing microorganisms might contribute to this release because they are thought to be major catalysts of $Fe(III)O_x$ reduction in anoxic sediments. Pore-water arsenic that diffuses upward into oxidizing zones may reassociate with $FeO_x$ and reprecipitate, and internal arsenic cycling in sediments with sufficiently oxidized surface zones frequently results in the accumulation of arsenic just below the surface sediment layers (Cullen and Reimer, 1989). Desorbed arsenate that diffuses downward into sulfate-reducing zones may be reduced to arsenite and, under acidic conditions, precipitate as the arsenic sulfides $As_2S_3$ or AsS. Diagenetic sulfides control the distribution of arsenic in reduced, sulfidic sediments, but if physical disturbance moves the sediments to an oxidizing environment the arsenic is likely to be re-released into the water column. Chemolithotrophic sulfur-oxidizing bacteria may also assist this process and enhance the mobilization of arsenic.

## C. Arsenic Speciation in Seawater

Arsenate is the predominant form of arsenic in seawater, but arsenite is present at concentrations greater than those predicted by thermodynamic equilibrium, and methylated species such as MMAA(V) and DMAA(V) also occur. Current techniques for analyzing arsenic in seawater may not be capable of detecting all the arsenic species present; it is estimated that unidentified arsenic species may constitute 25% of the total. Nevertheless, the concentrations of arsenite and methylated species reach their maxima in the photic zone, coinciding with the maximum concentration of particulate chlorophyll, which implies that marine phytoplankton produce these arsenicals from arsenate. This production is thought to reflect a detoxification mechanism under conditions in which arsenate:phosphate ratios are high (>1). Bacteria also play a role in arsenic speciation in marine systems because they both oxidize and reduce arsenic in seawater (see Section III). It is not known whether the high non-equilibrium As(III) concentrations measured in the deep waters are maintained in a steady state by *in situ* reduction or if they represent the kinetically preserved remainder of As(V) reduction in the upper waters. In a study of arsenic speciation in interstitial water in sediments from the Santa Barbara Basin (Andreae, 1979), total arsenic concentrations were found to be lower in interstitial waters than in the overlying water, implying that adsorption or coprecipitation of arsenic onto solid phases had occurred. In these highly reducing sediments, no systematic increase of As(III) : As(V) was observed with depth, implying that arsenic speciation also may be kinetically controlled. Methylated species have been measured in interstitial waters of estuarine and marine sediments and are thought to be formed by microbial methylation occurring *in situ*. Biological demethylation of the methylarsinicals and the oxidation of As(III) serve to regenerate As(V) in seawater. Marine algae contain high levels of arsenic (up to >200 mg/kg dry weight); most of this arsenic is present as arsenic-containing ribosides, which are likely the primary sources of arsenobetaine that occurs in marine animals, although the biogenesis of arsenobetaine is not well understood.

## D. Arsenic Exposure

For most people living in the United States, inorganic arsenic exposure is primarily from food and water sources. The EPA estimates that the dietary intake of inorganic arsenic is approximately 14 mg/day, about 20% of total arsenic intake. This estimate is important because inorganic arsenic intake is of primary concern; organic arsenic in foods is less toxic than inorganic forms partly due to its rapid excretion. Organic forms of arsenic in seafood, for example, are trimethylated, and most are excreted unchanged. Marine crabs, lobster, shrimp, and cod typically con-

tain 10–40 mg As/kg based on fresh weight. In comparison, pickerel, catfish, coho salmon, and other freshwater fish, along with pork and beef, typically contain <1 mg As/kg (Pontius *et al.*, 1994). Arsenic concentration in groundwater is affected by local geochemistry. For example, public water supplies in Bangladesh are contaminated with naturally occurring arsenic that derives from the reductive dissolution of arsenic-rich iron oxyhydroxides, which in turn are derived from weathering of base-metal sulfides (e.g., arsenic-rich pyrites). Reduction is driven by high concentrations of sedimentary organic matter. Measured concentrations reach up to 1000 mg/l, which is higher than the recommended limit by the World Health Organization (10 mg/l).

## III. MICROBIAL TRANSFORMATIONS OF ARSENIC

### A. Oxidation

As early as 1918, bacteria from cattle-dipping tanks were reported to both oxidize and reduce arsenic. In a study of arsenite oxidation in seawater, noncolonial, heterotrophic bacteria were believed to be responsible for oxidizing 1.5 nmol/l/day. The apparent $K_m$ of arsenite oxidation was on average 107 $\mu M$ As(III), and a cooxidation mechanism was thought to control the process (Skudlark and Johnson, 1982). In some cases, arsenite oxidation may be coupled to energy generation, as shown by biochemical work on an arsenite-oxidizing strain of *Alcaligenes faecalis* from soil and studies of *Pseudomonas arsenitoxidans,* which can grow by using arsenite as the sole source of energy in chemoautotrophic metabolism. A recent field study of geothermal streamwaters in the eastern Sierra Nevada suggests that bacteria attached to aquatic macrophytes mediate the rapid arsenite oxidation measured in this system; efforts are currently under way to identify the organisms and the biochemical mechanisms they use to oxidize arsenite (Wilkie and Hering, 1998). In addition to aqueous arsenite, *P. arsenitoxidans* can attack the arsenic in arsenopyrite, and bacteria such as *Thiobacillus ferrooxidans* can oxidize arsenopyrite, orpiment, and enargite (Ehrlich, 1990).

## B. Reduction

Microbial reduction of arsenate is widespread; it has been found to occur in sewage, rumen fluid, compost, and a variety of freshwater and marine environments. Cell extracts of *Micrococcus lactilyticus* and whole cells of *M. aerogenes* are known to reduce arsenate to arsenite with $H_2$ as a reductant, various *Pseudomonas* ssp. and *Alcaligenes* ssp. reduce arsenate and arsenite to arsine, and whole cells and cell extracts of *Methanobacterium* strain M.o.H. can produce dimethylarsine from arsenate. The capacity of these bacteria to reduce arsenate, however, has not been linked to growth and is considered to be incidental to metabolism or part of a resistance mechanism. Two detoxification systems that have been extensively studied are those of *Escherichia coli* and *Staphylococcus* species. The enzymes and proteins involved in ridding the cell of arsenic are encoded by the *ars* operons. In the case of *E. coli*, this operon is located on the chromosome and on plasmid R773, and in the case of *S. aureus* and *S. xylosus* on plasmids pI258 and pSX267, respectively. The *ars* operons work by encoding proteins that reduce arsenate to arsenite and then export it out of the cell (Rosen *et al.*, 1994). Other organisms that contain homologous chromosomal operons to the *E. coli* chromosomal *ars* operon include *Pseudomonas aeruginosa* and members of the family Enterobacteriacea such as *Shigella, Citrobacter, Klebsiella, Enterobacter, Salmonella,* and *Erwinia* (Diorio *et al.*, 1995).

Recently, bacteria have been found that are able to grow using arsenate as the terminal electron acceptor in anaerobic respiration. This is consistent with thermodynamic calculations which show that arsenate reduction is energetically favorable: Given the same electron donor, the standard free energy generated when arsenate serves as the electron acceptor is less than that from nitrate, Mn(IV), and Fe(III) but more than that from sulfate. Arsenate reduction occurring in slurries of sediment from both freshwater and saline environments has been demonstrated to be linked to cellular energy generation because the respiratory inhibitors/uncouplers dinitrophenol, rotenone, and 2-heptyl-4-hydroxyquinoline N-oxide each blocked arsenate reduction. Other evidence for microbial arsenate respiration has been pro-

vided from studies with isolates that show growth to be proportional to the concentration of arsenate in the medium and that show that arsenate reduction stoichiometrically follows the oxidation of lactate, formate, and acetate. Although strict anaerobic conditions are normally used to isolate arsenate respirers, primary enrichments of these organisms can tolerate small amounts of oxygen; one isolate is known to be a microaerophile. Rates of arsenic reduction by arsenate-respiring bacteria have been found to be $2–5 \times 10^{-13}$ mol As/cell/day (Newman *et al.*, 1998).

Although these organisms share the capacity to grow on arsenate, they are phylogenetically and physiologically diverse. The isolates *Desulfotomaculum auripigmentum, Bacillus arsenicoselenatis,* and *Bacillus selenitireducens* belong to the gram-positive group of bacteria, whereas *Sulfurospirillum arsenophilus* and *Sulfurospirillum barnesii* belong to the epsilon subdivision of the Proteobacteria and *Chrysiogenes arsenatis* appears to be the first representative of a new deeply branching lineage of the domain Bacteria. *Wolinella succinogenes,* a close relative of the sulfurospirilla, can also use arsenate as a terminal electron acceptor. Although all strains utilize lactate as a carbon/energy source, they differ in the other substrates they can use as well as their alternative electron acceptors. *Chrysiogenes arsenatis,* for example, is the only arsenate-reducing bacterium isolated to date that can utilize acetate as the sole carbon and electron source; *D. auripigmentum* is the only bacterium of this group that can also reduce sulfate (which, in some cases, leads to the precipitation of $As_2S_3$). Growth of these organisms on arsenate is not restricted to the aqueous form: Both *S. arsenophilus* and *D. auripigmentum* have been shown to grow on ferric arsenate ($FeAsO_4 \cdot 2H_2O$).

To highlight the ability of these bacteria to use arsenate for anaerobic respiration, the molar growth yields ($Y_M$) for *Sulfurospirillum barnesii* strain SES-3, *S. arsenophilus* strain MIT-13, and *D. auripigmentum* strain OREX-4 have been calculated based on the published ability of these organisms to grow on arsenate or other inorganic oxidants in the presence of lactate. Table I shows that arsenate is an electron acceptor for these bacteria, and the growth achieved ($Y_M$) during arsenate respiration is approximately proportional to that predicted by the standard free energy ($\Delta G^{\circ\prime}$) to be gained when arsenate serves as the oxidant in a respiratory reaction. As can be seen in Table I, however, the pathway utilized by these organisms to respire arsenate is not always the same. For example, strains SES-3 and OREX-4 incompletely oxidize lactate to acetate, whereas MIT-13 completely oxidizes lactate to $CO_2$. Accordingly, the $\Delta G^{\circ\prime}$ to be gained from As(V) respiration when coupled to either incomplete or complete oxidation of lactate differs by more than a factor of 2, and the observed growth yields are correspondingly different.

The biochemical basis for respiratory As(V) reduction is just beginning to be understood (Newman *et al.*, 1998; Krafft and Macy, 1998). The enzymes used in this process, the respiratory arsenate reductases, appear to be fundamentally different from the enzymes responsible for arsenate resistance in *E. coli* and *S. aureus*, the ArsC enzymes. The respiratory arsenate reductase of *S. barnesii* is a multimeric integral membrane protein, with the molecular weight of the native complex exceeding 100 kDa; the respiratory arsenate reductase of *C. arsenatis* is a periplasmic heterodimer that consists of two subunits with molecular masses of 87 (ArrA) and 29 kDa (ArrB). The $K_m$ of strain *S. barnesii* is approximately 0.2 m$M$, and the $K_m$ of *C. arsenatis* is 0.3 mM. The arsenate reductases of *S. barnesii* and *C. arsenitis* appear to utilize cofactors such as molybdenum, iron, acidlabile sulfur, and zinc to pass electrons on to arsenate.

A b-type cytochrome is present in membranes of *S. barnesii* when it is grown on arsenate and may also be involved in electron transfer. Nitrate, sulfate, selenate, and fumarate cannot serve as alternative electron acceptors for the respiratory arsenate reductases, and the synthesis of the enzymes is regulated because arsenate must be present for them to be fully induced. In contrast, the ArsC enzymes are cytoplasmic monomers with molecular weights of approximately 15 kDa which utilize reduced dithiols for electron transfer and have a significantly higher $K_m$: *Staphylococcus aureus* is reported to have a $K_m$ of 2 mM (although a $K_m$ of 1 $\mu$M is claimed for the same enzyme but with a significantly lower $V_{max}$) and *E. coli* a $K_m$ of 8 mM.

## C. Methylation and Formation of Arsine

Methylation of both arsenate and arsenite is known to be carried out by bacteria and phytoplankton in both freshwater and marine environments. The first systematic study of the biological formation of arsines was performed by Gosio (1897), who reported that fungi gave off a strong garlic-like odor when they were grown in the presence of sodium arsenite. Later, this gas was shown to be trimethylarsine. According to a review by Cullen and Reimer (1989), arsenate is converted to monomethylarsine and dimethylarsine by *Achromobacter* sp. and *Enterobacter* sp. and to monomethylarsine, dimethylarsine, and

### TABLE I
**Calculated Molar Growth Yields on Arsenate Relative to Other Oxidants**

| Organism | Oxidant | $Y_M$ | $\Delta G^{\circ\prime}$ | Reaction |
|---|---|---|---|---|
| SES-3[a] | selenate | 11.5 | −347 | $2SeO_4^{2-} + 2H^+ + CH_3CHOHCOO^- \leftrightarrow 2HSeO_3^- + CH_3COO^- + CO_{2(g)} + H_2O$ |
| SES-3 | nitrate | 7.1 | −311 | $0.5NO_3^- + H^+ + CH_3CHOHCOO^- \leftrightarrow 0.5NH_4^+ + CH_3COO^- + CO_{2(g)} + 0.5H_2O$ |
| SES-3 | arsenate | 5.3 | −172 | $2HAsO_4^{2-} + 4H^+ + CH_3CHOHCOO^- \leftrightarrow 2HAsO_2 + CH_3COO^- + CO_{2(g)} + 3H_2O$ |
| SES-3 | thiosulfate | 2.1 | −48 | $0.5S_2O_3^{2-} + CH_3CHOHCOO^- \leftrightarrow HS^- + CH_3COO^- + CO_{2(g)} + 0.5H_2O$ |
| OREX-4[b] | arsenate | 5.5 | −172 | $2HAsO_4^{2-} + 4H^+ + CH_3CHOHCOO^- \leftrightarrow 2HAsO_2 + CH_3COO^- + CO_{2(g)} + 3H_2O$ |
| OREX-4 | sulfate | 2.3 | −89 | $0.5SO_4^{2-} + 0.5H^+ + CH_3CHOHCOO^- \leftrightarrow 0.5HS^- + CH_3COO^- + CO_{2(g)} + 0.5H_2O$ |
| MIT-13[c] | arsenate | 7.0 | −394 | $6HAsO_4^{2-} + 13H^+ + CH_3CHOHCOO^- \leftrightarrow 6HAsO_2 + 3CO_{2(g)} + 9H_2O$ |

*Note.* Calculations for $Y_M$ (g cell/mol lactate) assume a cell dry weight of $1.9 \times 10^{-10}$ mg/cell. Calculations for $\Delta G^{\circ\prime}$ (kJ/mol lactate) assume pH = 7; $PCO_2$ = 1 atm.

[a] Laverman *et al.* (1995). *Appl. Environ. Microbiol.* **61**, 3556–3561.

[b] Newman *et al.* (1997). *Arch. Microbiol.* **168**, 380–388.

[c] Ahmann *et al.* (1994). *Nature* **371**, 750.

trimethylarsine by *Aeromonas* sp. and *Nocardia* sp. Microbial demethylation of methylated arsenic species is believed to be important in regenerating As(V) in the oceans.

## IV. CONCLUSIONS

As arsenic inputs into the biosphere accelerate, understanding microbial interactions with arsenic will become increasingly important. From a bioremediation perspective, bacterial transformations of arsenic may have practical applications. For example, arsenate-reducing bacteria have been shown to be capable of mobilizing arsenic from the solid into the aqueous phase. In a recent study of metal(loid)-contaminated freshwater-lake sediments (Harrington *et al.*, 1998), most probable number estimates revealed that the densities of cultivable arsenate-reducing bacteria were approximately $10^4$ cells/g wet weight sediment. Furthermore, microcosms from these sediments were able to reduce more than 50% of added arsenate when stimulated by the addition of organic acids. If microbial communities such as these could be stimulated in *ex situ* bioreactors to mobilize arsenic from contaminated soil, the released arsenite could then combine with sulfide to form a precipitate such as $As_2S_3$ or be reoxidized (either biologically or chemically) to arsenate and removed by adsorption to ferric iron. More studies on the physiology, biochemistry, and ecology of arsenic-transforming microorganisms will help us understand to what extent and under which conditions these communities affect arsenic cycling in the environment as well as provide insights necessary to make effective use of these microbes in bioremediation.

### See Also the Following Articles

HEAVY METALS, BACTERIAL RESISTANCES • SELENIUM • SYPHILIS, HISTORICAL

### Bibliography

Ahmann, D., Roberts, A. L., Krumholtz, L. R., and Morel, F. M. M. (1994). Microbe grows by reducing arsenic. *Nature* **371**, 750.

Andreae, M. O. (1979). Arsenic speciation in seawater and interstitial waters: The influence of biological–chemical interactions on the chemistry of a trace element. *Limnol. Oceanogr.* **24**, 440–452.

Azcue, J. M., and Nriagu, J. O. (1994). Arsenic: Historical perspectives. *In* "Arsenic in the Environment" (J. O. Nriagu, Ed.), pp. 1–16. Wiley, New York.

Bhumbla, D. K., and Keefer, R. F. (1994). Arsenic mobilization and bioavailability in soils. *In* "Arsenic in the Environment" (J. O. Nriagu, Ed.), pp. 51–82. Wiley, New York.

Cullen, W. R., and Reimer, K. J. (1989). Arsenic speciation in the environment. *Chem. Rev.* **89**, 713–764.

Diorio, C., Jie, C., Marmor, J., Shinder, R., and DuBow, M. S. (1995). An *Escherichia coli* chromosomal *ars* operon homolog is functional in arsenic detoxification and is conserved in gram-negative bacteria. *J. Bacteriol.* **177**, 2050–2056.

Ehrlich, H. L. (1990). "Geomicrobiology," 2nd ed., pp. 250–266. Dekker, New York.

Ferguson, J. F., and Gavis, J. (1972). A review of the arsenic cycle in natural waters. *Water Res.* **6**, 1259–1274.

Harrington, J. M., Fendorf, S. E., and Rosenzweig, R. F. (1998). Biotic generation of arsenic(III) in metal(loid)-contaminated freshwater lake sediments. *Environ. Sci. Technol.* **32**, 2425–2430.

Krafft, T., and Macy, J. M. (1998). Purification and characterization of the respiratory arsenate reductase of *Chrysiogenes arsenatis*. *Eur. J. Biochem.* **255**, 647–653.

Laverman, A. M., Switzer Blum, J., Schaefer, J. K., Philips, E. J. P., Lovley, D. R., and Oremland, R. S. (1995). Growth of strain SES-3 with arsenate and other diverse electron acceptors. *Appl. Environ. Microbiol.* **61**, 3556–3561.

Newman, D. K., Kennedy, E. K., Coates, J. D., Ahmann, D., Ellis, D. J., Lovley, D. R., and Morel, F. M. M. (1997). Dissimilatory arsenate and sulfate reduction in *Desulfotomaculum auripigmentum* sp. nov. *Arch. Microbiol.* **168**, 380–388.

Newman, D. K., Ahmann, D., and Morel, F. M. M. (1998). A brief review of microbial arsenate respiration. *Geomicrobiol. J.* **15**, 255–268.

Pontius, F. W., Brown, K. G., and Chen, C.-J. (1994, September). Health implications of arsenic in drinking water. *J. Am. Water Works Assoc.*, 52–63.

Rosen, B. P., Silver, S., Gladysheva, T. B., Ji, G., Oden, K. L., Jagannathan, S., Shi, W., Chen, Y., and Wu, J. (1994). The arsenite oxyanion-translocating ATPase: Bioenergetics, functions, and regulation. *In* "Phosphate in Microorganisms" (A. Torriani-Gorini, E. Yagil, and S. Silver, Eds.), pp. 97–107. ASM Press, Washington, DC.

Scudlark, J. R., and Johnson, D. L. (1982). Biological oxidation of arsenite in seawater. *Estuarine Coastal Shelf Sci.* **14**, 693–706.

Wilkie, J. A., and Hering, J. G. (1998). Rapid oxidation of geothermal arsenic(III) in streamwaters of the Eastern Sierra Nevada. *Environ. Sci. Technol.* **32**, 657–662.

# Attenuation, Transcriptional

## Charles Yanofsky

*Stanford University*

## GLOSSARY

**antiterminator**  An RNA hairpin structure that generally contains several paired nucleotides that are essential for terminator formation. When these nucleotides are paired in the antiterminator they cannot participate in terminator formation.

**attenuator**  A short DNA region that functions as a site of regulated transcription termination.

**charged tRNA**  A transfer RNA bearing its cognate amino acid (e.g., Trp-tRNA$^{Trp}$).

**leader peptide**  A peptide encoded by the leader segment of a transcript.

**leader peptide coding region**  A short peptide coding region in the leader segment of a transcript.

**RNA-binding attenuation regulatory protein**  An RNA-binding protein that binds to a specific RNA sequence and, by so doing, either promotes or prevents formation of a transcription terminator.

**RNA hairpin structure**  A base-paired stem and loop structure that has sufficient stability to remain in the base-paired, hairpin configuration.

**terminator (factor-dependent)**  An RNA sequence usually causing transcription pausing that serves as a site of factor-dependent transcription termination.

**terminator (intrinsic)**  An RNA hairpin followed immediately by a sequence rich in U's. The terminator serves as a signal to RNA polymerase to terminate transcription.

**transcription pausing**  A temporary pause or delay in RNA polymerase movement on its DNA template.

**transcription pause structure**  An RNA hairpin which causes RNA polymerase to pause or stall during transcription.

**transcription termination**  Cessation of RNA synthesis and release of transcript and DNA template from RNA polymerase.

**transcriptional attenuation**  A mechanism used to regulate continuation vs termination of transcription.

**TRANSCRIPTIONAL ATTENUATION**  is the term used to describe a general transcription regulatory strategy that exploits various sensing events and molecular signals to alter the rate of transcription termination at a site or a site preceding one or more genes of an operon. Many mechanisms of transcriptional attenuation exist. Each regulates operon expression by responding to an appropriate molecule or event and determining whether transcription will or will not be terminated.

## I. OBJECTIVES AND FEATURES OF REGULATION BY TRANSCRIPTIONAL ATTENUATION

It is evident that an appreciable fraction of the genetic material of each organism is dedicated to regulating gene expression. The ability to alter expression provides the variability that an organism needs in order to initiate or respond to the many changes that are associated with or responsible for each physiological and/or developmental event. Initiation of transcription is perhaps the single biological act that is most often subject to regulation. There

*Encyclopedia of Microbiology, Volume 1*
SECOND EDITION

**339**

are numerous examples of "negative-acting" repressor proteins—proteins that inhibit transcription initiation by binding to their respective DNA operator site(s) within or in the vicinity of the regulated promoter. Similarly, there are many examples of "positive-acting" regulatory proteins that activate transcription by binding at specific DNA elements in the vicinity of the affected promoter. Both negative- and positive-acting regulatory proteins are commonly activated or inactivated by small or large molecules as well as by reversible processes, i.e., phosphorylation and dephosphorylation. However, transcription initiation is only one of several common metabolic events that may be modulated to alter gene expression. The two subsequent stages in transcription, transcript elongation and transcription termination, are also common targets for regulatory change. The principal advantages achieved by regulating these events is that different classes of molecules and different metabolic processes can participate in regulatory decisions. Thus, once transcription has begun, the nascent transcript is a potential target for a regulatory event. In addition, in prokaryotes, in which most transcripts are initially translated as they are being synthesized, components of the translation machinery may participate in regulatory decisions. By exploiting these additional targets, organisms have greatly increased their regulatory options. A separate objective may have been to devote as little unique genetic information as possible to a regulatory process. Accordingly, some of the transcriptional attenuation regulatory mechanisms that will be described use less than 150 bp of DNA to achieve gene- or operon-specific control. Often attenuation regulation is achieved using only the common cell components that participate in RNA and protein synthesis. In this article, I review the features of several examples of regulation by transcriptional attenuation.

## II. MECHANISMS OF TRANSCRIPTIONAL ATTENUATION

### A. Regulation of Termination at an Intrinsic Terminator

Many operons regulated by transcriptional attenuation contain a DNA region that specifies a RNA sequence that can fold to form a hairpin structure followed by a run of U's, a structure called an intrinsic terminator. Intrinsic terminators instruct RNA polymerase to terminate transcription. The region encoding the intrinsic terminator is located immediately preceding the gene or genes that are being regulated. The transcript segment before and including part of the terminator often contains a nucleotide sequence that can fold to form a competing, alternative hairpin structure called the antiterminator. The existence of this structure prevents formation of the terminator. Antiterminator and terminator structures generally share a short nucleotide sequence, which explains why prior formation of the antiterminator prevents formation of the terminator. Additional features of the nucleotide sequence preceding or following a terminator or antiterminator can influence whether these structures will form or act. The transcript segment preceding the terminator often contains sequences that allow the organism to sense a relevant metabolic signal and to respond to that signal by allowing or preventing antiterminator or terminator formation.

A variety of mechanisms are used to sense specific cell signals. In operons concerned with amino acid biosynthesis, ribosome translation of a peptide coding region rich in codons for a crucial amino acid is often used to sense the presence or absence of the corresponding charged tRNA. Depending on the location of the translating ribosome on the transcript, an antiterminator will or will not form. In another example, in an operon concerned with pyrimidine biosynthesis, coupling of RNA synthesis with translation is employed to sense the availability of a nucleotide needed for RNA synthesis. In some mechanisms, RNA-binding proteins regulate termination. These proteins bind to specific transcript sequences or structures and allow or prevent antiterminator or terminator formation. One common regulatory mechanism is designed to sense the relative concentrations of a charged and uncharged tRNA and, depending on which is in excess, induce formation of an antiterminator or terminator. It is evident from these and other examples that regulation of the formation of an intrinsic terminator is a common strategy used to alter operon expression.

## 1. Ribosome-Mediated Attenuation

Synthesis of most proteins requires not only the availability of all 20 amino acids but also these amino acids must be in their activated state, covalently attached to their respective tRNAs. As such, they are primed for participation in polypeptide synthesis. The intracellular concentration of each amino acid reflects a balance of several events, including rates of synthesis, utilization, import from the environment, and release from proteins by degradation. Occasionally, induction of a degradative pathway also affects the cellular level of an amino acid. The concentration of a specific charged tRNA also reflects several events, including the presence of the corresponding amino acid, its rate of charging onto tRNA, the availability of that tRNA, and use of that charged tRNA in protein synthesis. Other factors also affect the rate of protein synthesis, such as whether there are rare codons in the coding region being translated and whether all needed species of charged tRNA are available. The availability of free ribosomes and accessory molecules required for protein synthesis also has an impact on the rate of protein synthesis. Given these many variables, it is not surprising that so many attenuation mechanisms are used to sense and respond to specific cellular needs.

### a. The trp Operon of Escherichia coli

Transcription of the *trp* operon of *E. coli* is regulated by both repression and transcriptional attenuation. The initial event in regulation by attenuation is the formation of a RNA hairpin structure that directs the transcribing RNA polymerase molecule to pause after initiating transcription (Fig. 1, stage 1). This transcription pause provides sufficient time for a ribosome to bind to the ribosome binding site of a peptide coding region in the leader transcript and initiate translation (Fig. 1, stage 2). The moving ribosome in fact releases the paused polymerase, permitting resumption of transcription (Fig. 1, stage 3). Thereafter, transcription and translation proceed in unison. As the polymerase molecule transcribes the leader region, the translating ribosome moves along the transcript and reaches a segment that is capable of folding to form an antiterminator structure. However, whether or not this structure forms depends on the location of the translating ribosome. In a

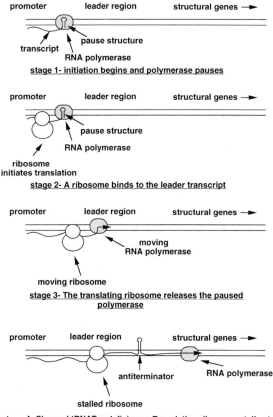

**Fig. 1.** Stages in ribosome-mediated transcriptional attenuation regulation of the *trp* operon of *E. coli*. Transcription initiation and pausing (stage 1), ribosome loading (stage 2), and initiation of translation and release of the pause transcription complex (stage 3) occur under all conditions. When a cell is deficient in tryptophan-charged tRNA$^{Trp}$ (stage 4), the translating ribosome stalls at either of the two Trp codons in the leader peptide coding region. Stalling permits the antiterminator to form; this prevents terminator formation, allowing transcription to continue into the structural genes of the operon. When a cell has sufficient charged tRNA$^{Trp}$ to support ongoing protein synthesis (stage 4 alternate), translation proceeds to the leader peptide stop codon. A ribosome at this position blocks formation of the antiterminator structure and permits the terminator to form and cause termination.

bacterium deficient in charged tRNA$^{Trp}$, the translating ribosome would stall over either of two adjacent Trp codons in the leader peptide coding region (Fig. 1, stage 4). Stalling would allow a downstream RNA segment to fold and form an antiterminator hairpin structure. As transcription proceeds, persistence of the antiterminator would prevent formation of the terminator since paired nucleotides at the base of the antiterminator must be free for terminator formation to occur. Under these conditions, transcription would continue into the structural genes of the operon. In a cell with adequate levels of charged tRNA$^{Trp}$ (Fig. 1, stage 4 alternate), the tandem Trp codons would be translated, and the translating ribosome would proceed to the leader peptide stop codon. At this position, the ribosome would block formation of the antiterminator and allow the terminator to form; hence, transcription would be terminated.

The leader regions of many bacterial operons, such as the *his, phe, leu, thr, ilvGMEDA,* and *ilvBN* operons, are organized much like that of the *trp* operon of *E. coli.* These operons appear to be regulated by the same mechanism, with only minor variations tailored to each operon's needs. Generally, the leader region sequence and organization reflects differences in regulatory requirements. For example, transcription of the *his* operon of *S. typhimurium* is regulated only by attenuation, unlike transcription of the *trp* operon of *E. coli* which is regulated by both repression and attenuation. The *his* operon's leader peptide coding region contains seven consecutive His codons. This organization allows greater sensitivity to changes in the cellular level of charged tRNA$^{His}$; a slight reduction is sufficient to delay ribosome movement through the His codon region. Any delay promotes antiterminator formation. An operon with a leader region that is organized differently is the *ilvGMEDA* operon of *E. coli.* Here, attenuation is regulated in response to the availability of three charged tRNAs those for tRNA$^{Ile}$, tRNA$^{Val}$, and tRNA$^{Thr}$. Codons for these tRNAs are arranged in the leader peptide coding region so that a deficiency of any of these charged species would promote antiterminator formation. Another operon regulated similarly is *pheST* of *E. coli.* This operon specifies the two polypeptides of phenylalanyl-tRNA synthetase. Translation of its leader peptide coding region containing five Phe co-

dons is used to regulate termination/antitermination. An interesting consideration that bears on *pheST* operon regulation is that the product of this operon, phenylalanyl-tRNA synthetase, is needed under all growth conditions.

### b. The pyrBI Operon of E. coli

Another well-studied example in which ribosome-mediated attenuation regulates transcription of an operon concerns the *pyrBI* operon of *E. coli.* When a cell has inadequate levels of UTP for RNA synthesis, the UTP deficiency triggers transcription antitermination in the leader region of this operon (Fig. 2). Continued transcription of the operon allows the cell to increase its rate of pyrimidine nucleotide synthesis. The *pyrBI* leader transcript has several features that explain its role in transcription regulation. It can fold to form alternative antiterminator and terminator structures. In addition, the leader segment contains the coding region for a leader peptide; this coding segment overlaps the antiterminator and terminator. The leader transcript also has several U-rich sequences which play a role in transcription pausing. When the UTP level is insufficient to sustain continued RNA synthesis, the polymerase transcribing the *pyrBI* operon stalls at these U-rich pause sites (Fig. 2, stage 1). Reduced polymerase migration allows sufficient time for a ribosome to bind to the transcript and move closely behind the polymerase (Fig. 2, stage 2). A translating ribosome at this position could prevent formation of the terminator structure; thus, transcription of the operon would continue (Fig. 2, stage 3). When a cell has an adequate level of UTP, the transcribing polymerase molecule moves through the pause sites rapidly and is positioned well ahead of the translating ribosome. This separation permits the terminator to form and cause transcription termination. Transcription of this operon is also regulated by an unrelated UTP-dependent mechanism.

### c. Other Examples

A related although different mechanism of ribosome-mediated transcription attenuation is used to regulate expression of the *ampC* operon of *E. coli.* The regulatory region of this operon, preceding *ampC,* encodes a leader transcript segment containing a ribosome binding site, adjacent start and stop codons,

## Cells deficient in UTP

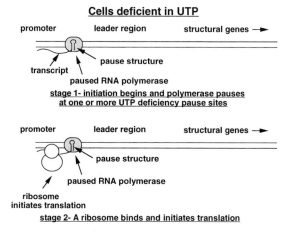

stage 1- initiation begins and polymerase pauses
at one or more UTP deficiency pause sites

stage 2- A ribosome binds and initiates translation

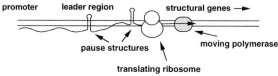

stage 3- The translating ribosome moves closely behind the
transcribing polymerase and prevents formation of the terminator

## Cells with sufficient UTP for rapid RNA synthesis

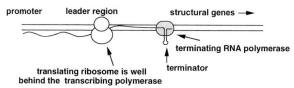

The transcribing polymerase pauses briefly, then moves well ahead of
the translating ribosome. The terminator forms, terminating transcription

***Fig. 2.*** Stages in transcriptional attenuation in the *pyrBI* operon of *E. coli.* When a cell is deficient in UTP, the RNA polymerase molecule that is transcribing the *pyrBI* operon leader region pauses at one or more UTP deficiency-dependent pause sites (stage 1). While the polymerase is paused a ribosome binds to the leader transcript and initiates translation (stage 2). When the polymerase is released, the translating ribosome moves closely behind the transcribing polymerase. Continued translation by this ribosome prevents formation of the terminator structure; thus, transcription continues into the structural genes of the operon (stage 3). When there are adequate levels of UTP to support rapid RNA synthesis (bottom) the transcribing polymerase pauses very briefly in the leader region and then continues transcription. The terminator sequence is formed well before the translating ribosome can approach this segment of the transcript. Terminator formation results in termination.

and a sequence that can form an intrinsic terminator. Expression of this operon is subject to growth rate regulation. During rapid growth, when the ribosome content per cell is high, a ribosome is likely to bind at the ribosome binding site in the leader segment and interfere with terminator formation. Under these conditions, transcription of the operon will continue. When the ribosome content per cell is low, the leader segment of the transcript is likely to be ribosome free for a period sufficiently long to allow the terminator to form and promote termination. An antiterminator is not used in this attenuation mechanism.

### 2. Binding Protein-Mediated Attenuation

In several operons regulated by transcriptional attenuation, specific RNA-binding proteins determine whether or not transcription will be terminated. These proteins recognize specific sites or sequences in a transcript and, by binding, regulate formation of an antiterminator or terminator. Well-studied examples include the *bgl* operon of *E. coli* and the *sac* operon of *Bacillus subtilis,* which are regulated similarly, and the *trp* and *pyr* operons of *B. subtilis,* which are regulated differently. The RNA-binding regulatory proteins that regulate transcription of these operons function much like the stalled ribosome in amino acid biosynthetic operons, as described previously.

### a. The bgl Operon of E. coli

The *bgl* operon of *E. coli*, *bglG–bglF–bglB*, is a three-gene operon encoding proteins required for the utilization of β-glucosides as carbon sources. The operon contains two independent sites of regulated transcription termination, the first before *bglG* and the second between *bglG* and *bglF*. The products of the first two genes of the operon, BglG and BglF, are necessary for regulation of this operon by attenuation. BglG exists in two forms: a phosphorylated, monomeric, inactive species and a dephosphorylated, dimeric, active (RNA-binding) species (Fig. 3). BglF is a membrane-bound phosphoenolpyruvate-dependent phosphotransferase. When BglF senses a β-glucoside, it phosphorylates the sugar and transports it into the cell. Substrate-activated BglF also dephosphorylates BglG, converting it into the active, RNA-binding dimeric form. In the absence of a β-

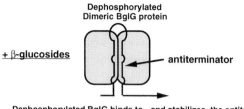

+ β-glucosides

Dephosphorylated BglG binds to - and stabilizes -the antiterminator, preventing formation of the terminator

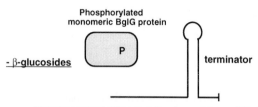

- β-glucosides

Phosphorylated BglG cannot dimerize and does not bind to RNA. This allows the terminator to form, promoting termination

**Fig. 3.** Protein-mediated transcriptional attenuation in the *bgl* operon of *E. coli*. In the presence of a β-glucoside carbon source the BglF protein phosphorylates the sugar and transports it into the cell (top). β-Glucoside-activated BglF also dephosphorylates the BglG protein. Dephosphorylated BglG dimerizes, and the dimer binds at one or both of the antiterminators in the transcript of the *bgl* operon, stabilizing the antiterminator structure. The existence of the antiterminator prevents formation of the terminator; thus, transcription proceeds. In the absence of a β-glucoside BglF phosphorylates BglG and the phosphorylated form remains as a monomer, incapable of binding to RNA (bottom). Under these conditions, the antiterminator is not stabilized, and the terminator forms, terminating transcription.

glucoside, BglF phosphorylates BglG, rendering it monomeric and inactive.

The transcript segment preceding *bglG* and *blgF* can fold to form either an antiterminator or a terminator structure. When BglG is dephosphorylated and active, it binds to and stabilizes the antiterminator (Fig. 3). Since the stem of the antiterminator contains bases that are part of the terminator, the terminator does not form. Nucleotides in the single-stranded loop region of each antiterminator as well as paired bases in the antiterminator stem appear to be the sites of BglG binding. BglG is believed to act similarly at the two antiterminators. When BglG is inactive and the *bgl* operon is being transcribed, terminator structures form in the transcript and terminate transcription (Fig. 3).

The *sacB* and *sacPA* genes of *B. subtilis*, genes concerned with sucrose utilization, appear to be regulated by a very similar antitermination/termination mechanism. The protein products of genes *sacY* and *sacT* regulate *sacB* and *sacPA* expression, respectively. The leader regions preceding *sacB* and *sacPA* specify RNA antiterminator structures that closely resemble those of the *bgl* operon. Dephosphorylation of SacY by SacX, in response to the presence of sucrose, leads to antitermination of transcription in the leader region preceding *sacB*. The proteins and sites involved in attenuation control in the *sac* and *bgl* systems are homologous.

### b. The trp Operon of B. subtilis

The leader segment of the transcript of the *trp* operon of *B. subtilis* can fold to form mutually exclusive antiterminator and terminator structures (Fig. 4). When a cell is deficient in tryptophan and

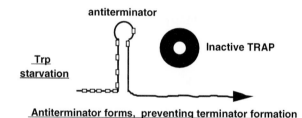

Antiterminator forms, preventing terminator formation

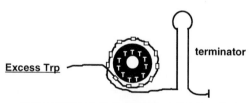

Active TRAP binds to the transcript, terminator forms

**Fig. 4.** Protein-mediated transcriptional attenuation in the *trp* operon of *B. subtilis*. When a cell is deficient in tryptophan the TRAP protein is not active, the leader region of the *trp* operon is transcribed, the antiterminator forms, and transcription continues into the operon (top). When a cell has sufficient tryptophan to support rapid growth, the TRAP protein is activated by bound tryptophan (bottom). Activated TRAP binds at U/GAG repeat sequences (small boxes) in the transcript segments located before and within the antiterminator. Bound TRAP essentially melts the antiterminator, allowing a sequence at the base of the antiterminator to exist in an unpaired form. This unpaired sequence participates in the formation of the terminator hairpin structure, which promotes termination.

the leader region of the operon is being transcribed, the antiterminator forms, preventing terminator formation and termination (Fig. 4). In the presence of excess tryptophan, an RNA-binding protein, TRAP (*trp* RNA-binding attenuation protein), encoded by the *mtrB* gene, binds tryptophan and becomes activated. Activated TRAP can bind to the *trp* operon leader transcript while it is being synthesized. The TRAP binding site consists of a series of U/GAG repeats located immediately preceding and including part of the antiterminator structure (Fig. 4). TRAP binding to the transcript prevents formation of the antiterminator, thereby promoting formation of the terminator. The 3D structure of TRAP has been described, and the residues in the protein principally responsible for RNA binding have been identified. The protein is doughnut shaped and consists of 11 identical subunits, each of which associates with a U/GAG sequence in the transcript. TRAP is believed to wrap the single-stranded leader transcript around its periphery and, by so doing, prevent formation of the antiterminator.

Tryptophan-activated TRAP also binds to a similar sequence of U/GAG repeats that precede the *trpG* coding region. *trpG* is the sole *trp* gene of *B. subtilis* that is not in the *trp* operon. *trpG* is located in a folate operon and specifies a bifunctional polypeptide that functions both in tryptophan and in folate biosynthesis. A TRAP binding site overlaps the *trpG* ribosome binding site; thus, TRAP binding inhibits translation of *trpG*. TRAP action therefore coordinates *trp* gene expression in the folate and tryptophan operons.

### c. The pyr Operon of B. subtilis

Another example of transcriptional attenuation mediated by a RNA-binding protein concerns regulated expression of the *pyr* operon of *B. subtilis*. This organism produces a novel uracil phosphoribosyltransferase, PyrR, that also functions as a RNA-binding transcription regulator. PyrR can bind at similar sites in three ~150-nt untranslated segments of the *pyr* transcript, each preceding a polypeptide coding segment and each containing a terminator. The first terminator precedes the first gene in the operon, *pyrR*, which in fact encodes this RNA-binding regulatory protein/enzyme. The second termina-

tor is located between *pyrR* and *pyrP*; *pyrP* encodes a uracil permease. The third terminator is located between *pyrP* and *pyrB*. *pyrB* specifies aspartate transcarbamylase. Each of the three untranslated segments of the transcript can fold to form an alternative antiterminator structure that can prevent formation of an intrinsic terminator. In addition, each untranslated transcript segment can form a third structure, earlier in the transcript, termed an anti-antiterminator. This structure includes part of the antiterminator; thus, its formation prevents formation of the antiterminator. When pyrimidines are plentiful PyrR binds to the nascent *pyr* operon transcript and stabilizes the anti-antiterminator stem-loop structure. Stabilization of this structure blocks formation of the antiterminator structure, promoting formation of the terminator and thereby causing termination. When cells are deficient in pyrimidines and PyrR is inactive the antiterminator prevents formation of the terminator, allowing transcription to continue. The three antiterminators are predicted to be the most stable of the several RNA structures. PyrR's RNA binding ability is responsive to the relative concentrations of UMP and PRPP, with bound UMP favoring RNA binding and bound PRPP preventing UMP binding and activation of the protein.

The 3D structure of PyrR of *B. subtilis* has been determined. The RNA sequences that are recognized have also been identified. Several bacterial species appear to produce homologs of PyrR and to regulate their *pyr* operons by the same or a similar mechanism.

The organization of the leader region of the *pur* operon of *B. subtilis* suggests that this operon is regulated by transcription termination/antitermination in response to changes in the availability of guanine nucleotides.

### d. The S10 Operon of E. coli

The 11-gene S10 ribosomal protein operon of *E. coli* contains a 172-base pair leader regulatory region which is used to achieve protein-mediated transcriptional attenuation. The S10 operon is regulated autogenously; that is, the product of one of its structural genes, protein L4, binds to the S10 leader transcript and regulates transcription termination. L4 binding also inhibits translation of coding regions of the operon. The transcript of the leader region forms multiple hairpin structures, two of which are essential for L4 activity. During transcription of the leader region RNA polymerase pauses after synthesizing one of these hairpins, a potential intrinsic terminator. Pausing at this site is enhanced *in vitro* by bound NusA protein and, most important, the pause complex is further stabilized by bound L4 protein. Enhanced stabilization of the terminator hairpin is believed to be responsible for efficient transcription termination. The leader RNA terminator structure, hairpin HE, participates in these events. An additional hairpin, HD, just preceding hairpin HE, also influences termination. How the structure HD is involved is not understood.

### 3. tRNA-Mediated Attenuation

#### a. tRNA Synthetase Operons of B. subtilis

In *B. subtilis* and other gram-positive bacteria, many operons encoding aminoacyl-tRNA synthetases, and some operons encoding amino acid biosynthetic enzymes, are regulated by tRNA-mediated transcriptional attenuation (Fig. 5). Each of these operons contains a leader region that specifies a transcript segment that can fold to form a complex set of structures, two of which are mutually exclusive and function as antiterminator and terminator. Translation is not used to choose between these alternative RNA structures. Rather, each leader RNA is designed to recognize the accumulation of an uncharged tRNA species as the signal to prevent termination. The crucial recognition sequence in leader RNA includes a single-stranded segment with a triplet codon, designated the specifier sequence (Fig. 5). The triplet specifier is located in a side bulge of a RNA hairpin structure. The specifier sequence is complementary to the anticodon of the tRNA that is a substrate of the tRNA synthetase that is being regulated. In amino acid biosynthetic operons regulated by this mechanism, this triplet codes for the amino acid that is synthesized by the proteins specified by the operon. A second tRNA binding site, termed a T box, located within a side bulge in the antiterminator, is complementary to nucleotides preceding the acceptor end of the tRNA (Fig. 3). The current regulatory model (Fig. 5) predicts that when an uncharged tRNA is plentiful, it binds to the speci-

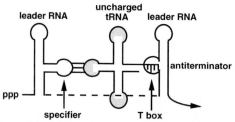

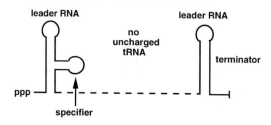

**Uncharged tRNA: tRNA binds to the specifier and T box sequence. Antiterminator forms, preventing termination**

**Charged tRNA: terminator forms, transcription terminates**

**Fig. 5.** Uncharged tRNA-mediated transcriptional attenuation in tRNA synthetase and amino acid biosynthetic operons of *B. subtilis* and other gram-positive bacteria. When a bacterial cell is defective in charging a tRNA with the corresponding amino acid, the uncharged tRNA pairs with the leader transcript of the operon specifying the tRNA synthetase that charges that amino acid. Two segments of the tRNA are believed to be involved in RNA–RNA pairing. One segment, the anticodon of the tRNA, is thought to pair with a complementary sequence in a side bulge in the leader transcript, called the specifier. The acceptor end of the tRNA is also believed to pair with the leader transcript. Its target is a single-stranded bulge sequence in the antiterminator, called a T box. Pairing of the uncharged tRNA at these two sites is proposed to stabilize an antiterminator structure, thereby preventing formation of the terminator (top). When the relevant tRNA is mostly charged, it cannot pair with the T box sequence. The leader RNA then folds to form the terminator structure, which terminates transcription (bottom).

fier and T box of an appropriate leader RNA, stabilizing the antiterminator and thereby preventing terminator formation. When the tRNA is charged, its acceptor end is blocked by an amino acid and thus it cannot pair with the T box. Under these conditions, the terminator will form, resulting in transcription termination. The charged tRNA apparently is still recognized because it competes with uncharged tRNA. Switching the codon in a leader RNA can change the specificity of the response. Although the events described only concern interactions between tRNA and leader RNA, unidentified factors may also participate.

## B. Regulation of Termination at a Factor-Dependent Terminator

In many bacterial species there is a second class of transcription termination sites—factor-dependent sites—at which a specific protein, Rho, interacts with RNA polymerase and causes termination. Rho-dependent termination requires an unstructured RNA segment as a site of Rho binding and a downstream RNA segment as a site of RNA polymerase pausing and termination. Accessory proteins that interact with RNA polymerase or with Rho also influence the termination process. Generally, once Rho binds to a transcript it migrates in the 3′ direction until it contacts a stalled polymerase. When it does, it can trigger the act of termination. Rho-dependent termination sites are not intrinsic terminators.

### 1. N Protein-Mediated Antitermination in Phage λ

The earliest studied and most thoroughly analyzed example of regulation by transcription termination/antitermination involves the action of the N protein of bacteriophage λ in mediating antitermination at sites of Rho-dependent termination in the phage genome. Regulation at these sites controls expression from major leftward and rightward phage promoters. N protein functions by interacting with RNA polymerase, forming an antitermination complex. This requires *cis*-acting transcript sites and sequences, called nut sites. These sites are composed of two elements, a BoxA sequence and a BoxB sequence. Box-B folds to form a hairpin loop structure. N associates with BoxB, and several host proteins associate with N and RNA polymerase in the formation of the antitermination complex. Other proteins in the complex either recognize the BoxA sequence or associate with N and the transcribing RNA polymerase complex. The fully formed N protein–RNA polymerase antitermination complex is resistant to the action of Rho. This antitermination complex can transcribe through intrinsic terminators as well as sites of Rho-dependent termination.

There are other examples, particularly in bacteriophage, in which specific viral proteins mediate antitermination events. In these instances, the mechanisms of antitermination vary somewhat from the mechanism attributed to the N protein. In addition, the ribosomal RNA operons of *E. coli* are known to be regulated by an antitermination mechanism that prevents Rho-dependent termination. This system has several features in common with N-mediated antitermination, including use of some of the same proteins and similar RNA binding sites.

### 2. Translation-Mediated Antitermination in the tna Operon

*Escherichia coli* and other bacteria contain operons that encode enzymes that can degrade specific amino acids, making them available as carbon and/or nitrogen sources. The tryptophanase (*tna*) operon of *E. coli* is one example. This operon encodes two polypeptides—one that degrades tryptophan and another that transports tryptophan into the cell. Transcription of the structural genes of this operon is subject to regulation by transcriptional attenuation. Transcription initiation in the operon is regulated by catabolite repression. Attenuation is mediated by a mechanism that involves tryptophan-induced transcription antitermination. The anititermination process prevents Rho from terminating transcription at specific sites in the leader region of the operon. The transcript of the leader region contains a short peptide coding region, *tnaC*, which has a single Trp codon. Synthesis of the 24-residue TnaC peptide, with its crucial Trp residue and certain other key residues, is essential for antitermination. In the presence of inducing levels of tryptophan the nascent TnaC peptide is believed to act in *cis* on the ribosome engaged in synthesizing the peptide, inhibiting its release at the leader peptide stop codon. Ribosome release at this stop codon is thought to be essential for termination since release is required to expose a presumed Rho entry/binding site in the vicinity of the *tnaC* stop codon. How the inducer tryptophan is recognized is not known, nor is it known how the leader peptide interacts with the translating ribosome to block its release at the *tnaC* stop codon.

## III. CONCLUSIONS

The transcriptional attenuation mechanisms described previously achieve operon-specific regulation by modifying one or more biological events that influence transcription termination. Use of these mechanisms greatly expands the regulatory capacity of each organism. An additional advantage is that these mechanisms permit a facile adjustment of the basal level of expression of an operon—expression in the absence of signals that regulate termination. Thus, variations in RNA structure, stability, or arrangement can establish an appropriate basal level of operon expression. In addition, as mentioned previously, some transcriptional attenuation mechanisms are economical because they require little unique genetic information. In eukaryotes there are several examples of regulated transcription delay with features resembling those of some of the attenuation mechanisms that were described.

### See Also the Following Article

TRANSCRIPTIONAL REGULATION IN PROKARYOTES

### Bibliography

Grunberg-Manago, M. (1996). Regulation of the expression of aminoacyl-tRNA synthetases and translation factors. *In* "Transcription Attenuation in *Escherichia coli* and *Salmonella*: Cellular and Molecular Biology" (F. Neidhardt *et al.*, Eds.), pp. 1432–1457. ASM Press, Washington, DC.

Hatfield, G. W. (1996). Codon context, translational step—Times and attenuation. *In* "Regulation of Gene Expression in *E. coli*" (E. C. C. Lin and A. S. Lynch, Eds.), pp. 47–65. Landes/Chapman & Hall, Austin, TX.

Henkin, T. M. (1996). Control of transcription termination in prokaryotes. *Annu. Rev. Genet.* **30**, 35–57.

Landick, R., Turnbough, C. L., Jr., and Yanofsky, C. (1996). Transcription attenuation. *In* "*Escherichia coli* and *Salmonella*: Cellular and Molecular Biology" (F. Neidhardt *et al.*, Eds.), pp. 1263–1286. ASM Press, Washington, DC.

Platt, T. (1998). RNA structure in transcription elongation, termination, and antitermination. *In* "RNA Structure and Function," pp. 541–574. Cold Spring Harbor Laboratory Press, Cold Spring Harbor, NY.

Roberts, J. W. (1996). Transcription termination and its control. *In* "Regulation of Gene Expression in *E. coli*" (E. C. C. Lin and A. S. Lynch, Eds.), pp. 27–45. Landes/Chapman & Hall, Austin, TX.

# *Autotrophic CO$_2$ Metabolism*

**Ki-Seok Yoon, Thomas E. Hanson, Janet L. Gibson, and F. Robert Tabita**

*The Ohio State University*

## GLOSSARY

**chemoautotrophy**  A type of biosynthetic metabolism in which cellular carbon is derived from inorganic carbon (CO$_2$), with the oxidation of inorganic electron donors providing the source of energy.

**chemoheterotrophy**  A type of metabolism in which cellular carbon is derived from organic carbon compounds, with energy derived from its oxidation.

**cyanobacteria**  A structurally diverse group of prokaryotes that perform oxygenic photosynthesis. Most cyanobacteria are obligate photoautotrophs in that they are incapable of growing in the dark with organic compounds as sources of carbon or energy. CO$_2$ is assimilated exclusively through the Calvin–Benson–Bassham reductive pentose phosphate pathway.

**facultative autotroph**  A versatile organism that is capable of utilizing either inorganic (CO$_2$) or organic carbon for biosynthetic metabolism.

**green nonsulfur photosynthetic bacteria**  A group of filamentous anoxygenic photosynthetic bacteria that use the 3-hydroxypropionate pathway of CO$_2$ fixation.

**green sulfur photosynthetic bacteria**  A metabolically limited group of anoxygenic photosynthetic bacteria that are obligately phototrophic and strictly anaerobic. Sulfide is the most common electron donor and CO$_2$ is assimilated via the reductive tricarboxylic acid cycle.

**photoautotrophy**  A type of metabolism in which cellular carbon is derived from inorganic carbon (CO$_2$), with photochemical light reactions providing the source of energy.

**photoheterotrophy**  A type of metabolism in which cellular carbon is predominantly provided by organic carbon, with photochemical light reactions providing the source of energy.

**purple nonsulfur photosynthetic bacteria**  A large metabolically diverse group of bacteria that carry out anoxygenic photosynthesis. Organisms within this group may grow via photoautotrophic or photoheterotrophic metabolism. These organisms may also grow via a type of anaerobic fermentation in the dark. They are all chemoheterotrophic and some can grow under chemoautotrophic conditions. The Calvin–Benson–Bassham reductive pentose phosphate pathway is the predominant pathway through which CO$_2$ is assimilated under photoautotrophic and chemoautotrophic growth conditions.

**AUTOTROPHIC CO$_2$ METABOLISM**  refers to the biochemical processes employed by certain microorganisms to convert oxidized CO$_2$ to usable organic carbon. Because all the building blocks of the cell must be synthesized from a simple and highly oxidized gas, this is a purely biosynthetic process. In addition, this type of metabolism is by definition autotrophic since all the organic carbon is derived from inorganic CO$_2$, with energy provided via light-dependent or light-independent reactions. In all cases, CO$_2$ is first "fixed" onto some acceptor molecule, followed by the subsequent metabolism of this CO$_2$–acceptor complex to intermediates that may then be incorporated into the various compounds required for growth. Finally, there is always a metabolic phase in the reaction pathway in which the CO$_2$ acceptor molecule is regenerated.

## I. THE IMPORTANCE OF AUTOTROPHIC CO$_2$ METABOLISM

Carbon dioxide is an important reactant for all living organisms. Therefore, this simple molecule partakes in many significant processes common to metabolism, including the biosynthesis of macromolecules and complex cell structures and the synthesis of several key metabolic intermediates of the cell. $CO_2$ may also be used as the sole source of carbon for a diverse and important group of organisms. Most important, as the most oxidized carbon compound found on Earth, this common and ubiquitous gas must be reduced before it can be assimilated. Thus, $CO_2$ fixation is an energetically expensive process that requires an exceedingly focused commitment by any organism to synthesize all the various reduced organic compounds required for life. In a global sense, biological $CO_2$ assimilation may thus be considered as a process that is diametrically opposite from the energy yielding metabolic schemes that result in $CO_2$ production from organic carbon. Obviously, the balance between the formation and breakdown of organic carbon in living cells is fundamental to life on Earth:

$$\text{Energy} + 2CO_2 + 8H \rightarrow (CH_2O)_2 + 2H_2O \quad (1)$$
$$\text{Energy} + 2CO_2 + 8H \leftarrow (CH_2O)_2 + 2H_2O \quad (2)$$

Indeed, when net $CO_2$ assimilation exceeds organic carbon degradation in any ecosystem [when the rate and extent of Eq. (1) exceeds that of Eq. (2)], environmental perturbations such as the eutrophication of natural bodies of water, as well as other manifestations of an abundance of organic carbon, are the unpleasant consequences. Likewise, if there are abnormally high ambient $CO_2$ levels [when the rate and extent of the processes depicted by Eq. (2) exceed those for Eq. (1)], a most dire situation also results. Since it is undoubtedly true that concentrations of $CO_2$ on Earth have steadily increased since the dawn of the industrial revolution, there is much interest in understanding factors that maximize biological $CO_2$ assimilation while maintaining the balance between carbon assimilation and degradation (Eqs. 1 and 2). In this article, the different strategies that microorganisms use to convert $CO_2$ to useful organic carbon compounds are discussed. In many instances, it will be apparent that this is a heavily regulated process, one in which diverse microbes have concocted elaborate scenarios to ensure that a constant flow of reduced organic carbon is produced from atmospheric $CO_2$. In addition to topical envi-

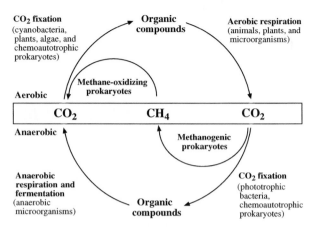

**Fig. 1.** Biotransformations of the carbon cycle and the organisms that participate.

ronmental issues of global warming and other aspects of carbon sequestration, $CO_2$ fixation is also important because it provides the fodder for living food chains on Earth, as a result of both light-dependent photosynthetic reactions and light-independent reactions characteristic of chemoautotrophic prokaryotes. Accordingly, much research is devoted to improving the potential for existing organisms to remove atmospheric $CO_2$ while maintaining the desired balance between $CO_2$ assimilation and organic carbon degradation. As shown in Fig. 1, several different types of organisms, and many diverse microbes, are involved with the cycling of carbon in the biosphere. Chemoautotrophic prokaryotes, both bacteria and archaea, along with phototrophic bacteria, cyanobacteria, eukaryotic algae, and plants all contribute to the removal and conversion of $CO_2$ to organic carbon. Figure 1 also indicates that $CO_2$ fixation occurs under both aerobic and anaerobic conditions and it is readily apparent that the delicate balance of the carbon cycle is maintained by the contribution of several different organisms.

## II. AUTOTROPHIC CO₂ FIXATION PATHWAYS

Currently, there are four known pathways by which autotrophic microorganisms use $CO_2$ as their sole source of carbon. In order of their discovery, these pathways are the Calvin–Benson–Bassham

(CBB) reductive pentose phosphate pathway, the reductive tricarboxylic acid (RTCA) cycle, the Wood–Lungdahl acetyl-CoA (AcCoA) pathway, and the hydroxypropionate (HPP) cycle. In several eukaryotic algae, there is a modified scheme in which four carbon products of $CO_2$ fixation play a role along with the CBB pathway.

## A. The Calvin–Benson–Bassham Pathway

The CBB pathway is probably responsible for the bulk of organic matter found on Earth because it is the predominant means by which oxygen-evolving photosynthetic organisms assimilate $CO_2$. These organisms include terrestrial and marine plants, eukaryotic algae, cyanobacteria, the picoplankton (including prochlorophytes), and several different diverse aerobic and anaerobic proteobacteria (Table I). In this pathway, $CO_2$ is assimilated by means of an interesting and important enzyme, ribulose 1,5-bisphosphate (RuBP) carboxylase/oxygenase (RubisCO). This protein is acknowledged to be the world's most abundant protein because it often comprises up to 50% of the total soluble protein in organisms that use the CBB pathway. If one considers that CBB $CO_2$ fixing organisms comprise the most prevalent biomass on Earth, the amounts of RubisCO must be enormous. Presumably, the large amounts of protein

that are required by organisms that use this pathway relate to the fact that this enzyme is an extremely poor catalyst, with a turnover constant ($k_{cat}$) of only $3–5 \, s^{-1}$. Mechanistically, the enzyme uses the enediol form of the unique phosphorylated keto sugar, RuBP (Fig. 2), as the $CO_2$ acceptor, resulting in the formation of a six-carbon intermediate that is then split to yield two molecules of 3-phosphoglyceric acid (3-PGA). Familiar enzymes of intermediary metabolism are then used as catalysts to further convert and reduce 3-PGA to other intermediates, with a requirement of ATP and reduced pyridine nucleotide. It is thus subsequent to the RubisCO step where much cellular energy and reducing equivalents are required. This "reduction" phase of the CBB scheme is then followed by a "regeneration phase" in which, after several steps, ribulose-5-phosphate (Ru-5-P) is formed. The other unique enzyme of the pathway, phosphoribulokinase (PRK), then catalyzes the ATP-dependent phosphorylation of Ru-5-P to form RuBP, the $CO_2$ acceptor (Fig. 2). This reaction completes the cycle. If one sums all the reactions of the CBB cycle, it can be demonstrated that one 3-carbon metabolite may be produced *de novo* from three $CO_2$ molecules while maintaining the cyclic nature of the pathway. In addition, it is apparent that for each $CO_2$ assimilated into organic carbon, there is an absolute requirement of two NAD(P)H and three ATP molecules. Clearly, this biosynthetic process requires a

***TABLE I***
**$CO_2$ Fixation Pathways in Nature**

| Phylogenetic kingdom | Energy source | $CO_2$ fixation pathway[a] |
|---|---|---|
| Eukarya | | |
|   Green algae | Light, organic carbon | CBB |
|   Red/brown/gold algae | Light, organic carbon | CBB, $C_4$/CBB |
|   Plants | Light | CBB, $C_4$/CBB |
| Bacteria | | |
|   Chemoautotrophic | Metal or $H_2$ oxidation | CBB, RTCA, AcCoA |
|   Phototrophic | Light, organic carbon, $H_2$ oxidation | CBB, RTCA, HPP |
|   Cyanobacteria | Light | CBB |
|   Prochlorophytes | Light | CBB |
| Archaea | $H_2$ oxidation, organic carbon, metal oxidation | AcCoA, RTCA, CBB? |

[a] CBB, Calvin–Benson–Bassham reductive pentose phosphate pathway; RTCA, reductive tricarboxylic acid cycle; $C_4$, primary $CO_2$ fixation via fixation onto $C_3$ carbon acceptor; $C_4$/CBB, combination of CBB and $C_4$ pathway; HPP, 3-hydoxypropionate pathway.

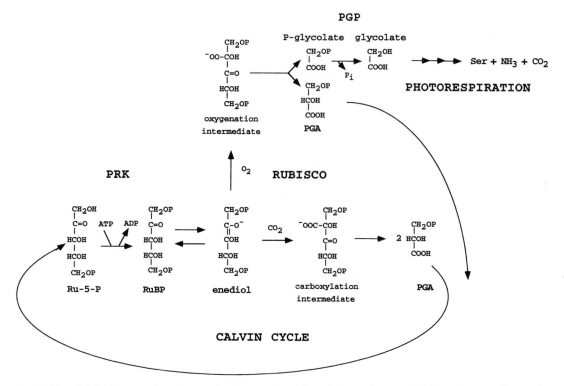

**Fig. 2.** The Calvin–Benson–Bassham reductive pentose phosphate pathway depicting the reactions catalyzed by the two unique enzymes of this pathway, RubisCO and PRK. RubisCO catalyzes both $CO_2$ and $O_2$ fixation reactions and is the first step of the competing pathways of photosynthetic carbon assimilation and photorespiratory carbon oxidation, leading to unique products and different metabolic consequences by PGA reduction and PG oxidation [via phosphoglycolate phosphatase (PGP)], respectively.

serious commitment by the cell. Another physiologically important issue is the ability of the enediol of RuBP to be attacked by compounds other than $CO_2$, particularly molecular oxygen. Thus, RubisCO catalyzes an internal monoxygenase reaction in which a unique product, 2-phosphoglycolate (PG), is produced from an oxygenated intermediate (Fig. 2). PG may be further oxidatively metabolized, eventually resulting in the release of $CO_2$ from the organism. This may be considered a wasteful type of metabolism for an organism that is trying to maximize the amount of $CO_2$ that can be converted to organic carbon. Thus, the same enzyme, RubisCO, serves as the first and key catalyst of two competing metabolic pathways, one important for $CO_2$ fixation and the other leading to $CO_2$ dissipation. There are several ways in which different organisms cope with competition for $CO_2$ and $O_2$ at the active site of RubisCO, including clever means to increase the local concen-

tration of $CO_2$. A highly active avenue of research is directed at elucidating the molecular basis by which some sources of RubisCO more efficiently catalyze the $CO_2$ fixation reaction so that organisms may be bioengineered to be more efficient in $CO_2$ assimilation (Tabita, 1995).

## 1. Molecular Regulation of the CBB Pathway

Until recently, research concerning the CBB cycle in bacteria was basically confined to biochemical and physiological investigations simply because genetic and molecular systems available to study phototrophic and chemoautotrophic bacteria were extremely limited. Recombinant DNA techniques greatly stimulated these studies, with the first endeavors directed toward cloning the genes encoding key enzymes such as RubisCO. Analysis of DNA sequences flanking the RubisCO genes in bacteria uncovered, in many cases, other CBB structural genes. These were found to be organized in large operons transcribed from a single promoter (Fig. 3). Neither the organization nor the content of the CBB operons appears to be conserved between organisms. Since RubisCO and PRK are the only enzymes unique to the CBB cycle, genes encoding all other CBB enzymes may be provided by heterotrophic counterparts from other metabolic pathways (Shively *et al.*, 1998). This is true for fructose bisphosphatase, transketolase, epimerase, aldolase, and glyceraldehyde phosphate dehydrogenase. It is also true, however, that enzymes encoded by genes of the *cbb* operons are different from their heterotrophic counterparts; exactly how they differentially function in $CO_2$ fixation is not understood. Although CBB gene redundancy is common among the proteobacteria, there appears to be no pattern regarding which genes are duplicated. In the chemoautotroph *Ralstonia eutropha* (*Alcaligenes eutrophus*), an entire *cbb* operon is duplicated. Since all genes are virtually identical, the duplication may simply serve to increase levels of enzymes through gene dosage. In contrast, in the nonsulfur purple photosynthetic bacterium *Rhodobacter sphaeroides*, two CBB operons differ not only with respect to gene content but also with respect to RubisCO coding sequences. Form I and form II RubisCO proteins of this organism are structurally and functionally distinct enzymes that are suited to different metabolic regimes. The diversity in content and gene arrangement of *cbb* operons probably reflects the evolutionary adaptation of individual organisms to the demands of unique environmental niches.

In contrast to the situation in proteobacteria, the RubisCO genes in cyanobacteria are not associated with the gene encoding PRK or any other CBB structural genes. However, in some cases the RubisCO coding sequences are linked to other genes related to $CO_2$ assimilation. These include genes involved in the transport and concentration of inorganic carbon and in the assembly of polyhedral inclusion structures known as carboxysomes. A gene encoding a homolog of the higher plant enzyme, RubisCO activase, is found adjacent to the RubisCO genes in some cyanobacteria (Fig. 3).

Facultatively autotrophic bacteria, versatile organisms that have the capacity to grow with $CO_2$ as the sole carbon source or with organic carbon as both carbon and energy source, have provided interesting systems to study the molecular regulation of $CO_2$ fixation (Gibson, 1995). This is simply because $CO_2$ assimilation is dispensable in these organisms, allowing for the facile isolation of mutants impaired in various aspects of $CO_2$ fixation. Thus, common procedures of chemical and transposon mutagenesis have been employed in photosynthetic and chemoautotrophic bacteria to obtain mutants defective in autotrophic growth. Site-directed mutagenesis with subsequent gene replacement has been used extensively to generate specific mutants in both CBB structural and regulatory genes, with the result that there is considerable knowledge of the molecular regulation of CBB-dependent $CO_2$ fixation in proteobacteria. In all such studies in facultative autotrophs, it was shown that *cbb* gene expression is tightly regulated. Organisms growing chemoheterotrophically on fixed carbon substrates do not synthesize RubisCO and PRK, the two enzymes unique to the CBB cycle. However, during autotrophic growth, in which $CO_2$ is the sole carbon source, RubisCO and other enzymes of the CBB cycle are synthesized to high levels. The molecular basis for *cbb* gene regulation has been an area of active study and it is known that the induction is mediated by a LysR-type transcriptional regulator called CbbR, which, as shown in Fig. 3, is the product of the divergently transcribed *cbbR* gene. In *R. sphaeroides*, the involvement of a global signal transduction pathway, centering on the two-component RegA/RegB system, was found to play an important role in regulating the expression of the *cbb* genes. The RegA/RegB system has also been shown to regulate expression of genes involved in photopigment synthesis, nitrogen fixation, and cytochrome assembly and is apparently able to integrate multiple cellular processes in response to the redox status of the cell. Although the RegA/RegB signal transduction system has also been shown to activate *cbb* gene expression in another nonsulfur purple photosynthetic bacterium, *R. capsulatus*, it is not known whether analogous systems are involved in the regulation of *cbb* operons from other bacteria.

Aside from studies on the transport of $CO_2$, cyanobacteria have generally proven more difficult for analysis of the control of $CO_2$ fixation. Knowledge of the

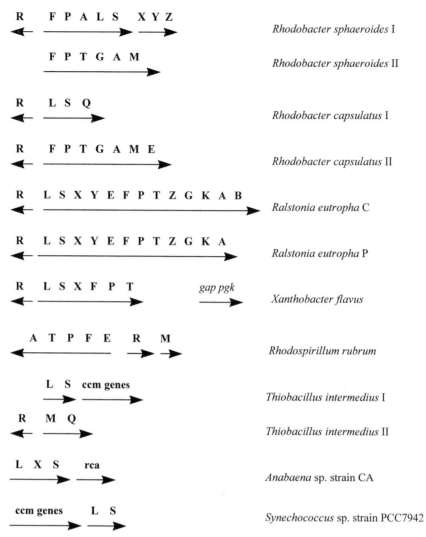

**Fig. 3.** Organization of genes of the CBB cycle in representative proteobacteria. Arrows refer to the direction of transcription, with the arrowhead delimiting the various gene clusters in proteobacteria comprising individual operons. In the proteobacteria, the form I RubisCO genes (*cbbLS*) are located in an operon with other CBB structural genes, as is the form II RubisCO gene (*cbbM*) (Gibson, 1995). These include fructose 1,6-sedoheptulose 1,7 bisphosphatase (*cbbF*), phosphoribulokinase (*cbbP*), aldolase (*cbbA*), phosphoglycolate phosphatase (*cbbZ*), transketolase (*cbbT*), glyceraldehyde phosphate dehydrogenase (*cbbG*), pentose 5-phosphate 3-epimerase (*cbbE*), phosphoglycerate kinase (*cbbK*), and genes of unknown function (*cbbX, cbbY, cbbQ,* and *cbbB*), although there is some evidence that CbbQ might mediate the proper folding of RubisCO. In all cases, transcription of the *cbb* operons is controlled by the product of the divergently transcribed *cbbR* gene. In cyanobacteria (*Anabaena* and *Synechococcus*), the RubisCO large and small subunit (*rbcLS*) genes are often juxtaposed but not cotranscribed with genes involved in the transport of inorganic carbon (the *ccm* genes), but *ccmK* is cotranscribed with *rbcLS* in certain marine cyanobacterial strains. Only in heterocystous *Anabaena* species, among cyanobacteria, is there evidence for a RubisCO activase-like gene (*rca*) downstream from the *rbc* genes but in a separate transcriptional unit. In *Anabaena,* the *rbcX* gene in cotranscribed with the *rbcLS* genes, and its product is required for maximizing the activity of recombinant RubisCO.

available regulatory mechanisms in these important organisms has thus generally lagged compared to that of the proteobacteria. In part, this is probably due to the fact that the CBB cycle is indispensable in these organisms and the structural genes are not linked (Tabita, 1994).

## B. The Reductive Tricarboxylic Acid Cycle

Several prokaryotes, both anaerobic and aerobic autotrophs, use the RTCA cycle to provide virtually all their organic carbon (Table I). This pathway has been shown to function in several phototrophic and chemoautotrophic bacteria and it plays an important role in the overall metabolism of archaea. Certainly, it is well appreciated that the oxidative citric acid cycle is used by most aerobic heterotrophic organisms for the oxidation of acetyl-CoA via citrate to yield $CO_2$ and $H_2O$, in which the eight reducing equivalents [H] formed during oxidative metabolism are consumed by different types of respiration. A reductive version of this pathway was first proposed to function as a means to assimilate $CO_2$ in anoxygenic green sulfur photosynthetic bacteria, in which novel ferredoxin-linked reactions were shown to reverse the essentially irreversible decarboxylation reactions of the oxidative citric acid cycle (Evans *et al.*, 1966). This type of pathway was eventually shown to be widespread among anoxygenic prokaryotes and it has also been shown to function in some aerobic autotrophs. As shown in Fig. 4, there are three key novel enzymatic reactions that allow enzymes of the oxidative tricarboxylic acid cycle to be used for the reductive assimilation of $CO_2$: ATP citrate lyase and the ferredoxin-linked $CO_2$ fixation enzymes, pyruvate synthase (PS) and $\alpha$-ketoglutarate synthase ($\alpha$-KGS). Basically, this pathway allows citrate to be formed from oxaloacetate, $2CO_2$, and 8[H]. Oxaloacetate is reduced to succinate via malate dehydrogenase, fumarase, and fumarate reductase. Succinate becomes activated to succinyl-CoA by the action of succinyl-CoA synthase, which requires the expenditure of one molecule of ATP. Two $CO_2$ fixation reactions are then employed; in one instance, a unique ferredoxin-dependent $\alpha$-KGS enzyme is used to carboxylate succinyl COA to $\alpha$-ketoglutarate. A normal

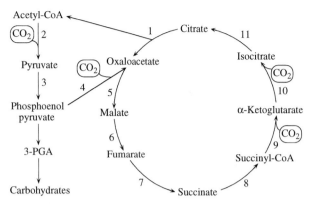

**Fig. 4.** The RTCA cycle of $CO_2$ assimilation, as exemplified by the green sulfur photosynthetic bacterium *Chlorobium tepidum*. Enzymes: 1, ATP–citrate lyase; 2, pyruvate synthase; 3, phosphoenolpyruvate synthetase; 4, phosphoenolpyruvate carboxylase; 5, malate dehydrogenase; 6, fumarase; 7, fumarate reductase; 8, succinyl-CoA synthetase; 9, $\alpha$-ketoglutarate synthase; 10, isocitrate dehydrogenase; 11, aconitase.

NADPH-dependent isocitrate dehydrogenase catalyzes the carboxylation of $\alpha$-ketoglutarate to isocitrate, which is converted via aconitase to citrate. ATP-dependent citrate lyase is a very important enzyme that allows this $CO_2$ fixation pathway to function in a cyclic manner. This enzyme, which requires 1 ATP per catalytic turnover, catalyzes the cleavage of citrate to acetyl-CoA and oxaloacetate. To replenish intermediates of the cycle, the acetyl-CoA is used as a substrate by the other key ferredoxin-dependent $CO_2$ fixation enzyme, PS. In addition, either pyruvate carboxylase or phosphoenolpyruvate carboxylase is used to convert three-carbon intermediates to oxaloacetate.

In summary, one complete turn of the RTCA cycle results in the assimilation of four molecules of $CO_2$ and the production of one molecule of oxaloacetate. The novel carboxylation reactions (PS and $\alpha$-KGS) employ reduced ferredoxin as electron donor:

$$\text{Acetyl-CoA} + CO_2 + Fd_{red}$$
$$\xrightarrow{\text{PS}} \text{pyruvate} + CoA + Fd_{ox} \quad (3)$$
$$\text{Succinyl-CoA} + CO_2 + Fc_{red}$$
$$\xrightarrow{\alpha\text{-KGS}} \alpha\text{-ketoglutarate} + CoA + Fd_{ox} \quad (4)$$

Reduced ferredoxin, which has a strong electronegative potential, is required to overcome the energy barriers suggested by the thermodynamically unfavorable carboxylation reactions. Thus, the biochemistry of these proteins, the role of iron–sulfur centers in the redox reactions required, and the overall regulation of catalysis are important areas of current research.

## 1. Molecular Regulation and Distribution of the RTCA Cycle Enzymes

Until recently, a suitable system to study the molecular regulation of the RTCA cycle was not available. However, it should be stressed that complete sequencing of microbial genomes has already yielded a great deal of information about autotrophic physiology, and more information is generated constantly. According to the National Center for Biotechnology Information (www.ncbi.nlm.nih.gov/PMGifs/Genomes/bact.html), as of January 15, 1999, there were 18 completely sequenced and annotated microbial genomes. Six genomes were completely sequenced and annotated, and another 12 completely sequenced but not yet annotated. An additional 35 genomes were in the process of being sequenced. Much of these data are accessible via the world wide web for similarity searches with nucleotide or protein sequences to identify homologous sequences of interest. These genomic sequences have all come from organisms that display different heterotrophic and autotrophic physiologies, including two that rely on the RTCA cycle for $CO_2$ assimilation—the chemolithoautotroph *Aquifex aeolicus* and the green sulfur phototroph *Chlorobium tepidum*. Genome sequencing has at least two important contributions to make to studies of the RTCA cycle. One is the identification and organization of genes encoding RTCA cycle enzymes by comparison to amino acid sequences of biochemically characterized proteins. The second is the identification of relatives of sequences homologous to those catalysts in non-RTCA cycle organisms, allowing studies of the evolution of the RTCA cycle as a whole.

The analysis of the *A. aeolicus* genome has identified candidate genes necessary for the RTCA cycle. Identification of *C. tepidum* genes corresponding to biochemically identified RTCA enzymes and accessory proteins is underway. *Chlorobium tepidum* is particularly interesting in that this organism is amenable to genetic manipulation and gene transfer, which will allow for the verification of sequence-predicted functions by mutation, complementation, and expression of mutant derivatives in a natural physiological context. Genes encoding the three diagnostic RTCA enzymes, ATP-dependent citrate lyase, PS, and α-KGS, are widely distributed in bacteria, archaea, and eukarya. PS and α-KGS also catalyze the reverse of the reactions depicted in Eqs. (3) and (4), such that these enzymes are also termed pyruvate : ferredoxin oxidoreductase (PFOR) or α-ketoglutarate : ferredoxin oxidoreductase (KGOR), respectively. Thus, in addition to $CO_2$ fixation, these enzymes are also important for the oxidation of pyruvate or α-ketoglutarate. In fact, PFOR and KGOR are representatives of an enzyme family that is widely distributed throughout the bacteria, archaea, and eukarya. The substrate specificity of the enzymes can vary and includes pyruvate, indolepyruvate, α-ketoglutarate, and α-ketoisovalerate. Their importance is indicated by their presence in the heterotrophic gastric pathogen *Helicobacter pylori,* in which genomic sequencing has uncovered two Fd oxidoreductases—one apparently specific for pyruvate and the other with an undefined substrate specificity. Finally, primitive amitochondriate eukaryotes, such as *Giardia lamblia, Entamoeba histolytica,* and *Trichomonas vaginalis,* possess PFOR. This enzyme apparently serves as an alternative to the pyruvate dehydrogenase complex of eukaryotes that possess mitochondria. In *H. pylori* and the amitochondriate eukaryotes, PFOR could be of significance as a drug target since this enzyme is not present in higher eukaryotes.

In the autotrophic methanogenic archaeon, *Methanobacterium thermoautotrophicum,* α-ketoisovalerate, indolepyruvate, pyruvate, and α-ketoglutarate : Fd oxidoreductases are proposed to function as anabolic enzymes to allow for synthesis of amino acids from acetyl-CoA produced by the acetyl-CoA/carbon monoxide dehydrogenase pathway (Wood–Ljungdahl pathway). Reduced Fd for these $CO_2$ fixation reactions is produced by the oxidation of $H_2$. Phylogenetic comparison of the sequences indicates that all KGORs and PFORs may have a single ancestor. The heterotetrameric organization characteristic of some proteins is thought to be ancestral and to have given rise to different subunit combinations by genetic recombination during the course of evolution. This seems to be supported by the fact that enzymes of similar subunit structure appear more similar to one another than to other types. Thus, genes that encode monomeric types of PFOR tend to form coherent groups when relationships between similarities of PFOR and KGOR genes are described as a phylogenetic tree. The same is true of dimeric, trimeric, and tetrameric types of Fd-linked oxidoreductases.

Regarding ATP citrate lyase, it is known that citrate lyases in general catalyze the cleavage of citrate to oxaloacetate and acetyl-CoA. There are two forms of the enzyme known: One enzyme form requires ATP (ATP–citrate lyase) and one does not. Citrate lyases that do not require ATP are involved in bacterial fermentative metabolism. As noted previously, ATP–citrate lyase serves as the closing reaction in the RTCA cycle and is also found in eukaryotes. Eukaryotic ATP–citrate lyases are involved in the production of acetyl-CoA for fatty acid and cholesterol biosynthesis. Human ATP–citrate lyase has attracted interest as a potential target site for drugs to treat diseases resulting in excess lipid production. Studies of the enzyme from green sulfur bacteria indicate that the RTCA cycle ATP–citrate lyase is similar to the eukaryotic enzyme in size and reaction mechanism. It remains to be determined whether this is the case in all organisms utilizing the RTCA cycle. No clear candidate ATP–citrate lyase gene was identified in the *A. aeolicus* genome; however, the activity has been detected in a related organism, *A. pyrophilus*.

## C. The 3-Hydroxypropionate Pathway

The most recently discovered autotrophic $CO_2$ fixation pathway is the HPP cycle, originally discovered in the facultatively autotrophic green photosynthetic bacterium *Chloroflexus aurantiacus*. The net product of the cycle is one molecule of glyoxylate produced by the fixation of two molecules of $CO_2$. The pathway starts at acetyl-CoA, which is carboxylated via acetyl-CoA carboxylase, yielding malonyl-CoA. This compound is then reduced to HPP (Fig.

5) and eventually secreted by *C. aurantiacus*, particularly when the organism is grown photoheterotrophically in the presence of propionate. The next steps involve the thioesterification of HPP to CoA followed by the reduction of the thioester in two steps to propionyl-CoA, which is then carboxylated to yield methylmalonyl-CoA, catalyzed by propionyl-CoA carboxylase. Methylmalonyl-CoA is converted to succinyl-CoA. Succinate is produced by a succinyl-CoA : malate CoA transferase and converted to malate, which can subsequently be utilized in the same reaction yielding malyl-CoA. Malyl-CoA is finally cleaved via a malyl-CoA lyase into glyoxylate (the net product) and acetyl-CoA (the initial $CO_2$ acceptor), thus completing the cycle. Both carboxylases require biotin and ATP and are known in other systems. Acetyl-CoA carboxylase is a ubiquitously distributed fatty acid synthesis enzyme, and propionyl-CoA carboxylase serves as a route of propionate assimilation in many organisms. Novel aspects of the pathway are the reduction of malonyl-CoA to propionyl-CoA via HPP and the shuttling of the CoA group from succinyl-CoA to malate. Many questions remain concerning this pathway, including questions about the regulation of the pathway during photoautotrophic, photoheterotrophic, and dark heterotrophic growth; the route of assimilation of glyoxylate into cellular material; and the distribution of this

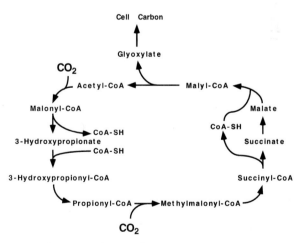

**Fig. 5.** The HPP pathway of $CO_2$ assimilation as exemplified by the green photosynthetic bacterium *Chloroflexus aurantiacus*. The key steps involved in $CO_2$ fixation are catalyzed by acetyl-CoA carboxylase and propionyl CoA carboxylase.

pathway outside of *C. aurantiacus*. There is evidence that other diverse organisms may use a version of this pathway. Currently, nothing is known about the regulation of the HPP pathway, nor is there any biochemical information available about the nature of the key catalyst.

## *See Also the Following Articles*

CARBON AND NITROGEN ASSIMILATION, REGULATION OF • GLYOXYLATE BYPASS IN *ESCHERICHIA COLI* • HETEROTROPHIC MICROORGANISMS

## *Bibliography*

Evans, M. C. W., Buchanan, B. B., and Arnon, D. I. (1966). A new ferredoxin dependent carbon reduction cycle in a photosynthetic bacterium. *Proc. Natl. Acad. Sci. U.S.A.* **55**, 928–934.

Gibson, J. L. (1995). Genetic analysis of CO₂ fixation genes. *In* "Anoxygenic Photosynthetic Bacteria" (R. E. Blankenship, M. T. Madigan, and C. E. Bauer, Eds.), pp. 1107–1124. Kluwer, Dordrecht.

Shively, J. M., van Keulen, G., and Meijer, W. G. (1998). Something from almost nothing: Carbon dioxide fixation in chemoautotrophs. *Annu. Rev. Microbiol.* **52**, 192–230.

Tabita, F. R. (1994). The biochemistry and molecular regulation of carbon dioxide metabolism in cyanobacteria. *In* "The Molecular Biology of Cyanobacteria" (D. A. Bryant, Ed.), pp. 437–467. Kluwer, Dordrecht.

Tabita, F. R. (1995). The biochemistry and metabolic regulation of carbon metabolism and CO₂ fixation in purple bacteria. *In* "Anoxygenic Photosynthetic Bacteria" (R. E. Blankenship, M. T. Madigan, and C. E. Bauer, Eds.), pp. 885–914. Kluwer, Dordrecht.

# Azotobacter

### Susan Hill and Gary Sawers

*John Innes Center*

I. Taxonomy of *Azotobacter*
II. Ecology of *Azotobacter*
III. The *Azotobacter* Life Cycle
IV. Genetics of *Azotobacter*
V. Physiology and Biochemistry of *Azotobacter*
VI. Agriculture and Applications

## GLOSSARY

**alginate**  A hydrated, viscous polysaccharide copolymer comprising variable amounts of $\beta$-D-mannuronic acid and $\alpha$-L-guluronic acid. Alginate is excreted from the cells of *Azotobacter* species, giving them a slimy glutinous appearance.

**conformational protection**  Protection from the deleterious effects of oxygen afforded to the nitrogenase enzyme of *Azotobacter* species by the Shethna or Fe–S II protein. The oxidized form of the Fe–S II protein interacts with nitrogenase by making direct protein–protein contacts thereby conferring protection.

**cyst**  A metabolically dormant vegetative *Azotobacter* cell that has differentiated to a form resistant to desiccation and damage by chemical agents.

**diazotrophy**  The ability of a microorganism to grow in the absence of a fixed nitrogen source by reducing dinitrogen in an ATP-dependent reaction to ammonia.

**iron–molybdenum cofactor**  The site of dinitrogen reduction in nitrogenase. The cofactor comprises a large iron–sulfur cluster, an atom of molybdenum, and a molecule of homocitrate. In alternative nitrogenases, the molybdenum atom can be replaced by vanadium or iron.

**nitrogen fixation**  The process whereby a microorganism reduces dinitrogen to ammonia.

**nitrogenase**  The metalloenzyme that catalyzes the ATP-dependent reduction of dinitrogen to ammonia.

**phyllocoenosis**  Association of a microorganism with the stem or leaves of a plant, which results in a mutual benefit to one or both of the partners.

**phyllosphere**  The leaves and stem of a plant that can be colonized by microorganisms.

**polyhydroxyalkanoate**  A polymer composed of repeating units of a hydroxylated alkane (e.g., polyhydroxybutyrate) which is composed of repeating units of $\beta$-hydroxybutyrate. These polymers can be composed of a mixture of two or more different monomers.

**polyploidy**  Possession of more than one copy of a chromosome.

**respiratory protection**  The process whereby the highly active respiratory chain of *Azotobacter* species intercepts oxygen, thus preventing it irreversibly inactivating nitrogenase.

**rhizocoenosis**  Association of a microorganism with the root system of a plant, which results in a mutual benefit to one or both of the partners.

**rhizosphere**  The immediate area surrounding the root system of a plant.

**AZOTOBACTER**  species are gram-negative, non-acid fast soil bacteria that have the capacity to fix molecular nitrogen. Biological nitrogen fixation is exclusive to bacteria and archaea.

First reports of the metabolism of dinitrogen appeared more than 130 years ago but it was near the turn of the century that free-living, nitrogen-fixing bacteria were first identified. In the mid-1890s, Winogradsky identified diazotrophic nitrogen fixation in the anaerobe *Clostridium pasteurianum*. Subsequently, Beijerinck in 1901 described an aerobic organism with a very high capacity to fix molecular nitrogen. This bacterium was given the generic name *Azotobacter* (nitrogen rod). Since its discovery, *Azotobacter* has intrigued scientists not only because of its remarkable capacity to fix nitrogen but also because it can do this in the presence of molecular oxygen. Paradoxically, the enzyme nitrogenase, which catalyzes the reduction of dinitrogen to ammonia, is extremely sensitive toward oxygen. Consequently, nitrogenase within the *Azotobacter* cell must somehow be protected from the deleterious effects of oxygen. It transpires that *Azotobacter* has an extremely efficient respiratory chain that affords the protection the nitrogenase enzyme requires to allow nitrogen fixation to proceed unhampered. Since nitrogen fixation is also an energy-demanding process, the extra ATP generated by growth in the presence of oxygen is of great benefit to these organisms. Combined physiological, biochemical, and genetic analyses on the heterotrophic diazotroph *Azotobacter* have therefore helped greatly in elucidating our understanding of biological nitrogen fixation.

## I. TAXONOMY OF *AZOTOBACTER*

*Azotobacter* is one of two genera in the family Azotobacteraceae; the other genus is *Azomonas.* They are obligately aerobic gram-negative chemoheterotrophs. The family Azotobacteraceae is a member of the gamma subdivision of the proteobacteria. The Azotobacteraceae appear to be most closely related to subgroup Ia of the nonfluorescent pseudomonads (e.g., *Pseudomonas stutzeri*). Prior to 16S rRNA sequence comparisons, the family had also included the genera *Beijerinckia* and *Derxia;* however, they have been removed and reclassified into the alpha and beta subdivisions, respectively, of the proteobacteria.

The genus *Azotobacter* comprises seven species (Table I), which can be distinguished on the basis of their morphology, motility, salt tolerance, and pigmentation. Diffusible pigments can be water soluble or water insoluble depending on the species and the growth conditions. The dark pigments resemble melanins and *A. vinelandii* produces azotochelin, in addition to other iron and molybdenum chelating compounds, which is responsible for the yellow-green appearance of the colonies.

With the exception of *A. paspali,* all members of the genus can utilize a relatively broad spectrum of carbohydrates, organic acids, and alcohols as carbon sources. None of the *Azotobacter* spp. are acid tolerant and they are rarely found in soils below pH 6.0. They all require the trace elements molybdenum or vanadium, which function as cofactors in the nitrogenase enzyme. They fix approximately 10 mg dinitrogen per gram of appropriate carbon source consumed. It has been estimated that diazotrophs fix between 1 and 3 kg of dinitrogen per hectare per year.

Some *Azotobacter* species are motile and have either polar or peritrichous flagella (Table I). All are pleiomorphic with cell shape depending on the growth conditions. Cells growing in the exponential phase generally have a rod-like structure (Fig. 1), with cells becoming more oval or coccoid in the

**TABLE I**
**Distinguishing Characteristics of the Various *Azotobacter* Species**

| Species | First described | Motility | Pigmentation[a] | Habitat | Morphology |
|---------|-----------------|----------|-----------------|---------|------------|
| A. armeniacus | 1964 | + | dark red + brown-black | soil | ovoid |
| A. beijerinckii | 1904 | − | none or yellow | soil | ovoid |
| A. chroococcum | 1901 | + | dark brown | soil | ovoid |
| A. nigricans | 1949 | − | dark brown | soil | ovoid |
| A. salinestris | 1991 | + | dark brown | saline soils | ovoid |
| A. paspali | 1966[b] | + | yellow-green/dark red | rhizosphere | long rods |
| A. vinelandii | 1903 | + | yellow-green/dark red | soil | rod/ovoid |

[a] Pigmentation includes soluble and insoluble pigments.
[b] *A. paspali* was initially classified as *Azorhizophilus paspali.*

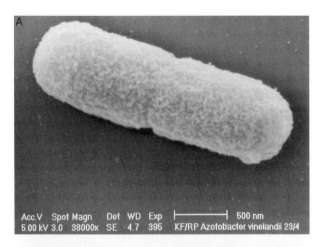

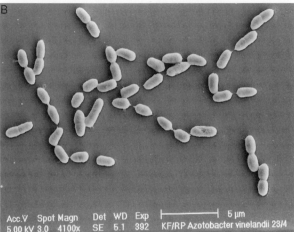

**Fig. 1.** Electron micrographs of vegetatively growing cells of *Azotobacter vinelandii*. Scale bar = 500 nm in A and 5 μm in B.

stationary phase of growth. Cells are often found in pairs or short chains (Fig. 1).

## II. ECOLOGY OF *AZOTOBACTER*

### A. Distribution in Soil

All *Azotobacter* are found in the soil and water habitats and are widely distributed, but probably more abundant in temperate regions. Although *Azotobacter* is very rare in polar regions, it has been isolated from tundra and it tolerates 0°C in soil well. In hot climates it is more abundant under wet than arid conditions and numbers are high in paddy fields.

Notably, however, numbers never exceed $10^4$/g of soil. Some isolates are halotolerant, with the exception of *A. salinestris* which exhibits an absolute salt requirement.

Due to their ability to fix molecular nitrogen, *Azotobacter* spp. can readily be isolated from soil samples by mixing a portion of the soil material with a carbon source (e.g., mannitol) and low concentrations of phosphate, calcium, and magnesium. It is important that the plate is well aerated and maintained in a moist environment, which can be achieved by placing the soil sample on a piece of filter paper in a petri dish. Incubation at 25–30°C will result in the appearance of slimy, opaque colonies after 3–5 days. Colonies of *Azotobacter* appear glutinous on plates due to the production of large amounts of diffusable exopolysaccharides.

*Azotobacter* species are ubiquitous in neutral to alkaline soils, with *A. chroococcum* being the most abundant species isolated from soil samples. Surprisingly, the occurrence of *A. vinelandii* in nature is rather limited, and little information is available on the distribution and habitat of *A. nigricans* or *A. armeniacus*. Unlike all other species of *Azotobacter*, *A. beijerinckii* favors slightly acidic soils and can tolerate low pH.

The recently isolated *A. salinestris* species has been isolated from saline environments in both Alberta, Canada, and in Egypt. Although this organism has a requirement for sodium ions, a concentration of 1 mM NaCl is sufficient to promote growth. The global distribution of this species thus remains to be established.

Salt-tolerant strains of *A. chroococcum* have been isolated; however, *Azotobacter* species in general do not exhibit a particular tolerance toward salt and consequently they are seldom found in environments with high salt content.

### B. Association with Plants

Two *Azotobacter* species have been shown to have associations with plants. These associations do not result in apparent physiological or morphological changes in either the bacterium or the plant and consequently can be distinguished from symbiotic relationships, for example, between *Rhizobium* species and pea or clover. The loose association between the plant and the bacterium does, however, result in a benefit to one or both partners. Such mutualistic associations have been referred to as biocoenoses. When the association occurs between the plant root system and the bacterium it is termed a rhizocoenosis, and when the leaf or stem is involved the term phyllocoenosis is used.

The first diazotrophic rhizosphere association to be identified involved *Beijerinkia* species and sugar cane. Subsequently, Döbereiner in 1961 described the first report of a rhizocoenosis involving *Azotobacter* and Bahia grass of the genus *Paspalum,* which are found only in tropical and sub-tropical regions. At the time it was not realized that the *Azotobacter* species was a new isolate, which was later named *A. paspali.* It was noted that *A. paspali* is always found associated with the rhizosphere of *Paspalum* species, although both plant and bacterium are able to grow in each other's absence. *Azotobacter paspali* is only found in association with *Paspalum* species and no other plant, indicating that host specificity plays an important role in this rhizocoenosis. The mutual benefit derived from this association is reflected in the fact that *Paspalum* species devoid of *A. paspali* in its rhizosphere grows more poorly than when *A. paspali* is present. The limited substrate spectrum of *A. paspali* may be the reason why it is only found in association with the rhizosphere of *Paspalum.*

Association of *A. paspali* with the plant rhizoshpere probably promotes plant growth, and inoculation of seedling hypocotyls and roots of several plant species with *A. paspali* results in marked improvements in plant growth and development and significantly increases the weight of both shoot and root systems. The major effect was observed as an increase in the surface area of the roots, but this proved to be dependent on inoculum size.

*Azotobacter chroococcum* is often found associated with the leaves of plants (phyllosphere) and a recent report described the isolation of *A. vinelandii* from the stems of lotus plants. No reports exist to indicate whether these associations are of benefit to the plant. Presumably, both *A. paspali* and *A. chroococcum* benefit from these associations through the high polysaccharide content of the plant and root exudates.

## III. THE *AZOTOBACTER* LIFE CYCLE

### A. Encystment

*Azotobacter* species undergo a simple form of differentiation whereby the vegetative cell forms a cyst. The ability of *Azotobacter* to form cysts distinguishes them from *Azomonas* species, which do not form cysts. The encystment process usually occurs in older cells at the end of exponential growth when the carbon source becomes limiting. Cysts are not classified as spores since the cell inside the cyst is similar to a vegetative cell, only it is metabolically dormant. Although they are not particularly heat resistant, cysts are more robust than vegetative cells and are resistant to physical and chemical agents. Generally, it is assumed that cysts remain viable in dry soil for more than 10 years, although it was reported by Abd-al-Malek and Ishac in the 1960s that they may remain viable for in excess of 2300 years.

Morphologically, the cyst comprises a central body, which is the vegetative cell, a cytoplasmic membrane, a cell wall of muramic acid, and two layers of polysaccharide and lipids, termed the intine and exine layers (Fig. 2). Both layers are composed of highly hydrated alginate, which counteracts desiccation. The intine layer is less dense, whereas the external exine layer is thick and laminated. The exine layer also contains several unusual lipids. Alginate is composed of alternating blocks of 1,4-linked β-

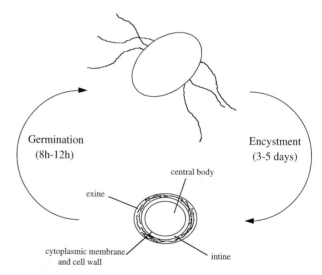

**Fig. 2.** The *Azotobacter* cell cycle.

mannuronate and 1,4-linked $\alpha$-guluronate. The presence of $Ca^{2+}$ ions aids formation of a gel network and, depending on their frequency of occurrence, polyguluronate forms ribbon-like molecules with increased flexibility (intine), whereas polymannuronate forms a more rigid structure (exine).

Cysts contain twice as much lipid compared to vegetative cells, 70% of which is present in the central body and approximately 25% is in the exine layer. The lipids are derived from $\beta$-hydroxybutyrate (BHB). They comprise resorcinolic and pyronic compounds with long-chain alkyl groups. The biosynthesis of these lipids is similar to that of polyketides, and they are also found in plants, fungi, *Mycobacteria,* and *Streptomyces* species.

Encystment can be induced either by growing vegetative cells in *n*-butanol or by transferring glucose-grown cultures to a medium containing polyhydroxybutyrate (PHB). Such treatments result in conversion of approximately 90% of the vegetative cells to cysts. It has been demonstrated that BHB is the inducer of cyst development. Significantly, BHB cannot be replaced by butyraldehyde or butyrate as the inducer.

Four hours subsequent to initiation of treatment with BHB or *n*-butanol, the cells lose their flagella and a final cell division occurs yielding two coccoid cells. Both cells become heavily encapsulated and shut down $N_2$ fixation, which involves high ATP expenditure, and slow down their metabolism. Completion of the encystment process occurs within 3–5 days.

Alginate synthesis is essential for cyst development and mutants unable to make alginate are unable to differentiate into cysts. An alternative RNA polymerase sigma factor called AlgU, which is a member of the $\sigma^E$ family of sigma factors, controls alginate synthesis.

## B. Germination

Germination can be triggered by incubation of cysts in a well-aerated, preferably $N_2$-free medium including a carbon source such as glucose, sucrose, or acetate (Fig. 2). There is a rapid initiation of metabolism indicating that the cysts most probably are in a state of metabolic "readiness." It is likely that stable mRNA molecules are present in the cysts, which facilitate the initiation of the germination process.

Germination of the cyst can be halted by inhibitors of protein, RNA or ATP synthesis, indicating that there is a temporal sequence of events controlling the germination process. The initial outgrowth occurs at approximately 4 hr after germination has commenced and is accompanied by DNA synthesis and the onset of $N_2$ fixation. Notably, no obvious cytological changes to the central body accompany germination. Finally, after approximately 8 hr the exine coat ruptures and the vegetative cell emerges.

## IV. GENETICS OF *AZOTOBACTER*

### A. Genome Size and Number of Chromosomes

The vast majority of genetic analyses in *Azotobacter* have been carried out with *A. vinelandii* or *A. chroococcum.* Laboratory strains of *A. vinelandii* have an advantage over *A. chroococcum* strains since, unlike the latter, they do not contain indigenous plasmids and can be readily transformed. The G + C content of *Azotobacter* DNA is in the range of 65–68 mol%.

Debate has occurred for many years concerning the DNA content of the *Azotobacter* cell. Results of recent scanning electron microscopy experiments estimated that the volume of the *A. vinelandii* vegetative cell is approximately 16 times greater than that of *Escherichia coli.* Surprisingly, the volume of an *A. vinelandii* cyst was calculated to be approximately the same as that of an *E. coli* cell. It has been demonstrated for the majority of cell types that a linear correlation between cell volume and DNA content exists. *Azotobacter* cells appear to be no exception, and various biochemical and biophysical techniques have clearly shown that the DNA content varies between 10 and 100 times that of the *E. coli* cell. By determining the size of DNA fragments derived from restriction enzyme digestion of the chromosome after separation by pulse-field gel electrophoresis, it has been estimated that the genome size of *A. vinelandii* is 4.5–4.7 Mbp. This is a range similar to that found for *E. coli.* To account for the large DNA content it must be assumed that *Azotobacter* is polyploid.

DNA hybridization experiments have demonstrated that the chromosomal content of the *A. vinelandii* cell can be as high as 80 or even 100 copies. Nevertheless, genetic experiments have revealed that recessive mutations can be expressed after only a small number of generations of outgrowth, and that introduction of a kanamycin resistance gene within the *nifY* gene resulted in all segregants retaining the resistance marker. These findings are not in accord with polyploidy. Flow cytometry experiments conducted with cells derived from various stages of growth have shown that the chromosome content of *A. vinelandii* changes dramatically during the growth cycle; however, this occurs only in rich medium. Thus, in the early exponential phase of growth the chromosome content is ~4 per cell, which is similar to that found in the growing *E. coli* cell. In the early stationary phase this can increase to >80 copies per cell. Dilution into fresh medium results in a rapid reduction in chromosome content. Polyploidy does not occur when the cells are grown in minimal medium, in which it appears that the chromosome content during the growth phase remains relatively constant. This raises the question, therefore, whether polyploidy has any significance outside the laboratory. It may simply be the result of an asynchrony between replication and cell division caused by growth in rich medium—a circumstance which will not occur in the environment. It is nonetheless intriguing to understand how gene expression, DNA turnover, chromosome packaging, and chromosomal segregation are controlled in polyploid cells.

## B. The Genetics of *nif*

For approximately the past 20 years, the genetics of *Azotobacter* has focused on the process of nitrogen fixation. Mutants defective in nitrogen fixation have been isolated using chemical mutagenesis and using standard methods, e.g., introduction of antibiotic-resistance cassettes or transposon mutagenesis. Gene transfer into *A. vinelandii* and *A. chroococcum* can be achieved by both conjugation and transformation and broad-host range plasmids can be stably maintained in these species. Moreover, heterologous DNA is stable in both strains, which is important in complementation studies.

In contrast to the situation in *Klebsiella pneumoniae*

in which the *nif* genes form a large cluster, in *Azotobacter* some of the genes are separate on the chromosome (Fig. 3). Nevertheless, a large proportion of the genes whose products are involved in ancillary functions, such as molybdenum–iron cofactor biosynthesis and insertion, as well as the nitrogenase structural genes form a large cluster spanning ~20 kb of the chromosome. The first three genes in the cluster, *nifHDK*, encode the structural components of the nitrogenase enzyme. The early identification of these genes allowed the construction of *A. vinelandii* mutants (Bishop, 1986) unable to synthesize nitrogenase. Remarkably, these mutants were still able to fix nitrogen, but only in the absence of molybdenum, indicating that *Azotobacter* had alternative nitrogenase enzymes that were functional without molybdenum. This finding confirmed an earlier discovery by Bishop's group (1980) that in the absence of molybdenum, vanadium was incorporated into a nitrogenase enzyme. It transpired that *A. vinelandii* has two sets of genes, termed *vnf* and *anf*, encoding alternative nitrogenase enzymes (Fig. 3). The H, D, and K proteins of each are highly similar to the corresponding NifH, D, and K subunits of molybdenum-containing nitrogenase. The Vnf enzyme utilizes vanadium instead of molybdenum, whereas the Anf enzyme is thought to incorporate iron. Although *A. paspali* also has genes similar to *vnf* and *anf*, *A. chroococcum* has only the *vnf* system. *Klebsiella pneumoniae* has only the molybdenum-dependent nitrogenase enzyme.

## C. Regulation of the *nif* Genes

A core of approximately 20 *nif* genes are necessary for nitrogen fixation. Due to the massive energy ex-

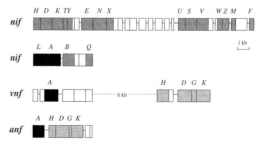

**Fig. 3.** Organization of the gene clusters encoding the molybdenum nitrogenase and the alternative vanadium (*vnf*) and iron (*anf*) nitrogenases of *Azotobacter vinelandii*.

penditure required to synthesize all these proteins, plus the energetic demands inherent in the nitrogen fixation process, it is crucial that expression of the *nif* genes is tightly controlled. Consequently, *nif* gene expression is regulated in response to many environmental factors, including oxygen, $NH_4^+$, the cellular energy status, and molybdenum.

Many genes are key to the regulatory process and among the most important is *ntrA*, which encodes the novel RpoN sigma factor. RpoN forms a complex with the core RNA polymerase and directs the complex to the *nif* promoters, which are characterized by having conserved sequences at $-12$ (GC) and $-24$ (GG) relative to the site of transcription initiation. RpoN is unusual for a sigma factor because it can bind specifically to promoters in the absence of core polymerase. Moreover, it has an absolute requirement for an activating protein to catalyze the transition from the closed promoter complex to the open, transcriptionally active, promoter complex. The transcriptional activator in *Azotobacter* is NifA and it binds to a specific DNA sequence that is located more than 100 bp upstream of the promoter. Once NifA has bound to the DNA and contacted the RpoN–RNA polymerase complex at the promoter, open complex formation is contingent on ATP or GTP hydrolysis, which is catalyzed by NifA. All RpoN-dependent promoters are positively activated and the study of *nif* gene transcription has proved paramount in defining the mechanisms underlying long-range promoter activation in prokaryotes.

In *Azotobacter*, the activity of NifA is controlled by the NifL protein. NifL and NifA are members of the two-component, sensor-regulator class of proteins. In contrast to other members of this family, however, phosphotransfer is not the means by which NifL (the sensor protein) controls the activity of NifA (the DNA-binding protein). Rather, NifL interacts directly with NifA, preventing it from binding productively to *nif* promoter DNA (Fig. 4).

NifL is a cytoplasmic flavoprotein with the bound flavin in the form of FAD. Dixon and colleagues (1996, 1998) have shown that NifL senses the redox status, the fixed nitrogen status, and the energy status of the cell. In the presence of high levels of oxygen the FAD moiety becomes oxidized, causing a conformational change in the NifL protein to occur which then captures NifA. Similarly, when the ATP : ADP

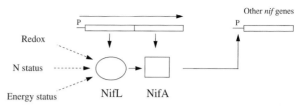

**Fig. 4.** Environmental signal transduction by the *Azotobacter vinelandii* NifL protein. The *nifLA* operon is expressed constitutively and, when associated with active NifL, NifA no longer is able to activate the expression of other *nif* genes. NifL becomes activated by oxygen, the presence of fixed nitrogen, or a low ATP : ADP ratio. P, promoter.

ratio is low, NifL binds ADP and this switches the protein to its inhibitory conformation. It appears that these signals are recognized by different parts of the protein. However, it is currently unclear whether the fixed nitrogen status is sensed by NifL directly or whether an intermediary protein transmits a signal to NifL. NifL and NifA are present in approximately equal proportions in the cell and this is achieved by cotranscription of the corresponding genes.

The *nifLA* operon is constitutively expressed in *Azotobacter* (Fig. 4). This contrasts the situation in *K. pneumoniae*, in which *nifLA* transcription is controlled by the NtrB/NtrC two-component pair. NtrB is responsive to the fixed nitrogen status and in the absence of $NH_4^+$, for example, phosphorylates NtrC, which in turn activates transcription of the *nifLA* genes. Moreover, NifA from *K. pneumoniae* does not bind or respond to ATP or ADP *in vitro*. Although *A. vinelandii* has an *ntrC* gene, it appears that NtrC is not involved in nitrogen fixation. Its role in regulating gene expression remains to be elucidated.

Other diazotrophs (e.g., *Bradyrhizobium japonicum*) do not have a NifL homolog, and it appears that the NifA protein responds directly to the $O_2/$ redox status and possibly also to the nitrogen status.

*Azotobacter vinelandii* also has two additional *nifA*-like genes, one of which is associated with the *vnf* operon and the other with the *anf* operon (Fig. 3). Neither has a corresponding *nifL*-like gene. Recent results using *lacZ* reporter fusions indicate that transcription of both *anfA* and *vnfA* is repressed in the presence of molybdenum, whereas that of *anfA* is also repressed by $NH_4^+$ and vanadium. This regulation correlates with the physiological requirement for the respective nitrogenase enzyme and is commensurate with AnfA and VnfA being positive activators of the *anfHDGK* and *vnfHDGK* operons, respectively.

### D. Molybdenum Regulation

Molybdenum is transported into *A. vinelandii* by a high-affinity transport system encoded by the *modABC* operon. The three Mod proteins comprise an ATP-binding cassette (ABC) transporter, in which ModA is a periplasmic molybdenum-binding protein, ModB is the integral membrane protein, and ModC is a peripheral ATP-binding protein. Directly upstream of the *modABC* operon is a gene called *modE*, whose gene product binds molybdenum and DNA. When molybdenum is present, ModE represses expression of the *modABC* operon and may also be involved in molybdenum-dependent control of *nif* gene expression. Recently, ModE has also been implicated in the molybdenum-dependent regulation of *anfA* and *vnfA*.

### E. Genetics of Alginate Production

Although genetic studies on *Azotobacter* species have mainly focused on *nif*, an increasing amount of effort has been invested in studies designed to elucidate the production of alginate and polyhydroxybutyrate. This has been driven primarily by commercial and medical interest. The biochemistry and genetics of alginate metabolism are very similar to those of *Pseudomonase aeruginosa*. At least 17 genes have been identified in *A. vinelandii* whose gene products are highly similar to the corresponding *P. aeruginosa* proteins. In *P. aeruginosa* more than 24 gene products have been identified that are directly involved in some aspect of alginate biosynthesis. It is anticipated that the additional genes are also present in *A. vinelandii*.

One protein of particular interest that has also been identified in *A. vinelandii* is AlgU. The AlgU protein is an alternative sigma factor of the $\sigma^E$ family and it is responsible for transcription of the various *alg* operons. Intriguingly, the activity of AlgU is held in check by anti-sigma factors called MucA and MucB. The activity and stability of the MucA and MucB proteins determine whether AlgU is released and can initiate alginate overproduction.

### F. Polyhydroxybutyrate

Since PHB is linked both to nitrogen fixation and to the encystment process interest has been directed toward understanding the genetic basis of PHB formation and degradation. PHB synthesis is regulated in response to the levels of environmental oxygen, and characterization of a recently isolated PHB⁻ strain of *A. vinelandii* identified a gene termed *ptsP*, whose product has a N-terminal domain which has similarity to the NifA protein, whereas the rest of the protein is similar to enzyme I of the phosphoenolpyruvate:glucose phosphotransferase system. The mutant is unable to make PHB and has reduced respiratory protection of nitrogenase under carbon-limiting conditions. This suggests that reduced electron flux to the respiratory chain means that oxygen cannot be removed quickly enough from the cytoplasm of the bacterium. An alternative interpretation of the data is that reduced ATP synthesis may make nitrogen fixation unfeasible. Regardless of the physiological reason for the reduction in nitrogen fixation, these findings reinforce the genetic link between nitrogen fixation, PHB synthesis, and encystment.

## V. PHYSIOLOGY AND BIOCHEMISTRY OF *AZOTOBACTER*

The majority of cellular reactions that occur in *Azotobacter* species are common to many organisms. In this section, in addition to dealing briefly with carbon and fixed-nitrogen metabolism, we shall concentrate on the extraordinary aspects of *Azotobacter* physiology and biochemistry, in particular, aerotolerant nitrogen fixation, respiration, and alginate biosynthesis.

### A. Carbon Metabolism

Like many gram-negative aerobic bacteria, *Azotobacter* species catabolize hexoses by the Entner–Doudoroff pathway. They also use the pentose phosphate, tricarboxylic acid, and glyoxylate cycles. As mentioned earlier, many carbon sources can be oxidized, including alcohols and organic acids, which reflects the large enzymic repertoire with which many aerobic heterotrophic bacteria are equipped. Preferred substrates include mannitol, sucrose, and fructose, although some species can utilize raffinose, trehalose, or galactose. None of these substrates can be fermented. However, it has been noted that *Azotobacter* does excrete partially oxidized carbon compounds, but only when the level of oxygenation is exceptionally high.

During oxygen limitation *Azotobacter* accumulates PHB, which acts as an electron sink to regenerate oxidized pyridine nucleotides, consequently permitting glucose metabolism and the TCA cycle to function. When oxygen becomes available PHB furnishes the cell with a readily degradable reserve of carbon and energy. The enzymes involved in PHB synthesis and breakdown are those common to all organisms that deposit granules of polyhydroxyalkanoates and include $\beta$-ketothiolase, $\beta$-hydroxybutyryl-CoA dehydrogenase, and $\beta$-hydroxybutyryl-CoA polymerase and depolymerase.

## B. Assimilation of Fixed Nitrogen

*Azotobacter* species assimilate combined nitrogen, such as ammonia or urea, using the standard enzymes glutamate dehydrogenase, glutamine synthetase, and glutamate synthase. They are also able to use a limited number of amino acids as nitrogen sources. Assimilatory nitrate and nitrite reductases have been identified in all species except *A. armeniacus* and *A. paspali*.

## C. Nitrogenase

### 1. Enzyme Reaction and Structure

The extreme oxygen sensitivity of nitrogenase has restricted its occurrence to microorganisms and only to those that are strict anaerobes or to those that have developed a means whereby the nitrogenase enzyme can be protected from the deleterious effects of oxygen. Thus, the physiology and biochemistry of the *Azotobacter* nitrogenase is of particular interest because the organism is a strict aerobe.

Nitrogenase catalyzes the ATP-dependent reduction of dinitrogen to ammonia according to the equation:

$$N_2 + 8\,e^- + 8\,H^+ + 16\,MgATP \rightarrow 2\,NH_3 + H_2 + 16\,MgADP + 16\,Pi$$

The low potential electrons required for the reduction of dinitrogen are derived from pyruvate in the case of *K. pneumoniae* and most likely from the respiratory chain in *Azotobacter*. Electrons are delivered to nitrogenase one at a time, and for each electron transferred the hydrolysis of minimally 2 MgATP molecules is required.

Resolution of the X-ray crystal structure of *A. vinelandii* nitrogenase in 1992 by the group of D. Rees resulted in a tremendous advance in nitrogenase structure–function research. The nitrogenase enzyme comprises two component proteins, termed the iron (or Fe) protein and the molybdenum–iron (or MoFe) protein. The Fe protein is a homodimer of relative molecular mass 60 kDa and is encoded by the *nifH* gene. Fe protein contains a single 4Fe–4S iron–sulfur cluster, which is required to deliver the electrons one at a time to the MoFe protein, where substrate reduction occurs. The MoFe protein is an $\alpha_2\beta_2$ heterotetramer of relative molecular mass 250 kDa that is encoded by the *nifD* ($\alpha$ subunit) and *nifK* ($\beta$ subunit) genes. The MoFe protein has two pairs of metalloclusters: the P cluster, which consists of eight iron atoms and seven or eight acid-labile sulfur atoms, and the FeMo cofactor, which consists of seven Fe atoms, nine sulfur atoms, and a single molybdenum atom. The Mo atom of the FeMo cofactor also has a homocitrate coordinated to it through its 2-hydroxy and 2-carbonyl groups. The FeMo cofactor is covalently attached to the $\alpha$ subunit via the thiolate of a cysteinyl residue at the Fe end of the cofactor and via a side chain N of a histidinyl residue at the Mo end of the cofactor.

In order for electron transfer from the Fe protein to the MoFe protein to occur, both component proteins must associate. Two molecules of ATP then bind to a site on the Fe protein, and upon hydrolysis the electron is transferred from the Fe–S cluster in the Fe protein to the P cluster in the MoFe protein. The electron is then transferred to the FeMo cofactor. In order for another round of ATP hydroysis and electron transfer to occur, the two component proteins must first dissociate and then reassociate. After multiple rounds of electron transfer, only then does substrate reduction occur.

Nitrogen probably binds to the molybdenum atom, where substrate reduction is also presumed to occur. Nitrogenase can also reduce a variety of dinitrogen-related compounds, most notably acetylene, which is used to assay the enzyme. Acetylene is reduced by two electrons to ethylene in the reaction. Substitution of molybdenum with vanadium yields an enzyme that catalyzes not only the two-electron reduction of acetylene to ethylene but also a four-electron reduction to ethane.

For every molecule of dinitrogen reduced, one molecule of hydrogen is also evolved. Studies with different mutants indicate that homocitrate plays an important function in hydrogen evolution.

## 2. Protection of Nitrogenase against the Deleterious Effects of Oxygen

Nitrogen fixation places a high energetic demand on the cell since for every molecule of dinitrogen reduced 16 molecules of ATP are expended. Moreover, the evolution of hydrogen is potentially also wasteful if it cannot be recaptured and reoxidized. Consequently, nitrogen fixation must be carefully controlled so that a balance is met between energy gain and expenditure. *Azotobacter* species have a distinct advantage over other nitrogen-fixing organisms because they are able to fix nitrogen aerobically, despite the fact that their nitrogenase enzyme is extremely oxygen sensitive. Thus, whereas in *K. pneumoniae* nitrogen fixation is inhibited when the dissolved oxygen concentration exceeds 30 nM, *A. vinelandii* species can fix nitrogen over a range of oxygen concentrations up to 225 $\mu M$. Clearly, there must be a very steep oxygen gradient between the medium and the nitrogenase enzyme. The large cell size of *Azotobacter* no doubt aids this, and it has also been suggested that compartmentalization of the nitrogenase enzyme within intracytoplasmic membrane structures may also help damage limitation. However, by far the most effective means by which *Azotobacter* prevents oxygen-dependent inactivation of the nitrogenase enzyme from occurring is through conformational and respiratory protection.

### a. Conformational Protection

It was noted that although nitrogenase from *Azotobacter* is very oxygen sensitive, crude extracts derived from *A. chroococcum* or *A. vinelandii* can be handled in air without the nitrogenase enzyme being inactivated. This is not the case for crude extracts derived from other nitrogen-fixing organisms. *Azotobacter* species have a small redox protein termed the Shethna protein or Fe–S II protein that forms a complex with the nitrogenase enzyme and is thought to change its conformation such that it is no longer susceptible to oxygen. The Fe–S II protein has been proposed to bind to nitrogenase when oxidized and to dissociate from the complex when reduced. The reaction is magnesium dependent. Synthesis of the Fe–S II protein is constitutive, which is possibly indicative of a further physiological function(s); however, it should be noted that synthesis of Fe–S II is enhanced during diazotrophy.

### b. Respiratory Protection

Although conformational protection is a passive process, *Azotobacter* species also have an active mechanism, termed respiratory protection, by which they protect the nitrogenase enzyme from oxygen. *Azotobacter* has one of the highest respiratory rates known and it is able to adjust its respiration to the oxygen supply. Moreover, and perhaps most significantly, it has the ability to uncouple respiration from ATP generation. This means that electron flow can be diverted to reduce molecular oxygen without being coupled to the generation of a proton gradient. This process protects the oxygen-sensitive nitrogenase by mopping up any free oxygen molecules. Clearly, although such a mechanism releases respiration from the constraints imposed by ADP supply, the consequence is that the cell has a very high maintenance energy requirement. As the oxygen concentration increases, the energy required to maintain nitrogen fixation increases. Thus, if carbon supply diminishes then nitrogen fixation also decreases due to insufficient electron flow to the respiratory apparatus.

In contrast to the situation in *K. pneumoniae* in which the electrons required for nitrogen reduction are derived from pyruvate, the actual source of electrons to nitrogenase in *Azotobacter* is unclear, although flavodoxin is the direct electron donor to the enzyme. It is known, for example, that mutations in the TCA cycle enzymes cause defects in nitrogen fixation; however, this could be the result of diminished electron flow from the TCA cycle to the many flavin-dependent dehydrogenases, which ultimately supply the electrons for reduction of molecular oxygen. It is interesting that the electron flow to nitrogenase represents only between 1 and 10% of the total electron flow, with the majority of the remainder going to the terminal oxidases.

## D. The Terminal Oxidases

In contrast to many so-called "strict" aerobes, *Azotobacter* does not appear to have any reductases for anaerobic electrons acceptors. In this sense, *Azotobacter* is a true obligate aerobe. Based on a kinetic analysis, however, it does have three high-affinity oxidases (Fig. 5). The highest $K_m$ of 4.5 $\mu M$ is clearly associated with a cytochrome *bd*-type oxidase related at the primary structural level to the equivalent enzyme from *E. coli*. Two additional high-affinity oxidases with $K_m$ values for oxygen of 0.33 and 0.016 $\mu M$ have been determined, but they have not been assigned to a specific oxidase. It is clear, however, that *Azotobacter* does have an energy-conserving cytochrome *o*-like oxidase, which is likely to be a heme-

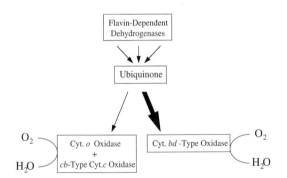

**Fig. 5.** The flow of electrons along the respiratory pathways of *Azotobacter vinelandii*. The cytochrome o-like enzyme (and possibly the *cb*-type cytochrome *c* oxidase) generates a proton gradient, whereas the cytochrome *bd*-type oxidase affords respiratory protection to the nitrogenase enzyme. The thick arrow signifies that the electron flow and the synthesis of the oxidase increase with increasing external oxygen concentration.

copper oxidase. A mutation in the gene encoding this enzyme still results in aerotolerant nitrogen fixation, indicating that it is not involved in respiratory protection of nitrogenase. Recently, a gene fragment was identified which has significant similarity to a Cco *cb*-type cytochrome *c* oxidase. It remains to be established whether the Cco and cytochrome *o*-like oxidases are distinct enzymes.

Much more is known about the cytochrome *bd*-type enzyme. The level of this oxidase increases with increasing oxygen concentration, which is in accord with what would be expected for an enzyme with a role in respiratory protection. The genes encoding the cytochrome *bd* enzyme are organized as they are in *E. coli* in a *cydAB* bicistronic operon.

Mutants unable to synthesize the oxidase are defective in aerotolerant nitrogen fixation, which is a phenotype expected of a protective enzyme. Moreover, as mentioned earlier, this enzyme can be uncoupled and electrons flow preferentially to it during aerobic nitrogen fixation. Thus, when the oxygen concentration increases there is a concomitant reduction in respiratory control characterized by the inability of either ADP or inorganic phosphate to stimulate oxygen uptake. This means that the electron flux is being diverted to the uncoupled cytochrome *bd* enzyme. Recent findings indicate, however, that the cytochrome *bd* enzyme can generate a proton potential, but it does so with a much reduced efficiency compared with the cytochrome *o*-like enzyme.

Directly upstream of the *cydAB* operon lies a gene called *cydR* that encodes a FNR-like transcription factor. Mutations in *cydR* enhance cytochrome *bd* synthesis, even at low oxygen concentrations. It appears that the CydR protein is a repressor of the *cydAB* operon and that it is responsive to the oxygen status.

## E. Alginate Biosynthesis

Alginate synthesis is stimulated by energy deprivation and thus correlates with the requirement for cyst formation. In addition to being crucial for the encystment process, alginate also plays an important role in biofilm formation.

Since polyguluronate has a more rigid structure

than polymannuronate, by controlling the degree of polymannuronate epimerization to polyguluronate the rigidity of the polymer can be controlled for the appropriate conditions. The high molecular mass of the polymer, together with its high negative charge, helps to ensure that it is highly hydrated and viscous. To improve its water-binding capacity further alginate is usually O-acetylated on the 2 or 3 position of the polymannuronate component.

The initial stages of alginate biosynthesis are similar to those of lipopolysaccharide biosynthesis and involve the removal of oxaloacetate from the TCA cycle and its conversion to fructose-6-phosphate (Fig. 6). Following activation of mannose-1-P through its conversion to GDP-mannose, the next committed step is the oxidation of GDP-mannose to GDP-mannuronate by GDP-mannose dehydrogenase. The precise sequence of events resulting in the polymerization and ultimate export of alginate is unclear. However, it is clear that polymerization occurs concurrently with export to the periplasm. Only in the periplasm do the epimerization at carbon-5 and the O-acetylation reactions occur. To date, five epimerase genes have been identified in *A. vinelandii*, all of which encode proteins with a signal sequence. The epimerization reaction is strongly influenced by the $Ca^{2+}$ concentration.

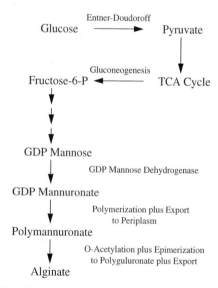

**Fig. 6.** The biosynthesis of alginate in *Azotobacter* species.

## VI. AGRICULTURE AND APPLICATIONS

*Azotobacter* and particularly its polymeric products polyhydroxyalkanoate and alginate have potential uses in the industrial, biotechnological, and medical fields.

### A. Use of *Azotobacter* in Agriculture

As early as 1930, Russian scientists added a material referred to as azotobacterin to seed crops in an attempt to improve growth and yields. Azotobacterin contained mainly *A. chroococcum*. Repeated attempts have been made using combinations of symbiotic and free-living diazotrophs, including *Azotobacter* species, to improve crop production, especially in countries in which soil quality is poor in nitrogen. The soil in the northwestern part of Egypt is particularly poor in nitrogen and is also high in calcium carbonate. Successful attempts at improving growth (27% increase in dry weight) of alfalfa (*Medicago sativum*) by inoculation with *Azotobacter* have been reported. One study in Egypt reported that *Azotobacter* improved wheat (*Triticum aestivum*) development. Although these are interesting findings, it nevertheless must be borne in mind that the commercial viability of these ventures is questionable since the growth and distribution of the organisms is an expensive operation.

### B. Polyhydroxyalkanoates

There is currently great interest in the development of polyhydroxyalkanoates as natural biodegradable thermoplastics. Depending on their composition, they can range in their chemical and tensile properties from extremely brittle to malleable. The use of genetically manipulable bacteria to produce these polymers has clear benefits. The hydrogen-oxidizing bacterium *Ralstonia eutropha* (formerly *Alcaligenes eutrophus*) is being studied extensively in this regard. *Azotobacter vinelandii* also produces PHB; however, it has proved difficult to find conditions which allow introduction of β-hydroxyvalerate (BHV) into the polymer, even by feeding cultures with the precursor valerate. The ability to produce PHB–PHV copolymers is critical in making useful plastic items. However, a recent study has shown that *A. salinestris* produces a poly(HB-co-HV) copolymer with approximately 90% PHB and 10% PHV. It has also been noted that BHV can be supplemented to cultures of *A. salinestris* and incorporated into the copolymer, indicating that polymers with differing composition can be generated.

## C. Alginate

Currently, all commercially used alginates are harvested from seaweeds. The major advantage of using seaweed is that the production costs are relatively low. Nevertheless, environmental concerns must increasingly be taken into consideration and alternative sources of alginate are being actively sought. Moreover, the use of bacteria to produce alginate offers the possibility of producing alginates with improved qualities and different properties. The properties of alginates are determined by the degree of polymerization and modification (e.g., acetylation) as well as monomer composition and its sequence. Through the judicious use of bacteria it should be possible to control all these parameters by manipulating both the genetic make-up of the organism and the fermentation conditions used to cultivate the bacterium.

Alginates are used in a variety of industrial and medical processes. In the food industry they are important as stabilizers and gelling agents, particularly in sauces, syrups, ice creams, and confectionery. Amongst a multitude of other functions, they are used as suspending agents in the paint and textile industries and in the production of ceramics. Medically, they are used in the immobilization of cells for the slow, sustained release of chemicals (e.g., insulin), and they are being used in wound healing.

Polymannurans are strong immunostimulants, and by constructing mutants unable to acetylate the polymer or epimerize it to guluronate it should be possible to generate strains that produce the pure polymer. The pure polymer can also be used as starting material for introducing chemical modifications *in vitro*. The acetylation of the polymannuran governs the extent of conversion to guluronate, which in turn determines the gelling properties of the alginate. Thus, isolating mutants with altered acetylation potential will produce variant forms of alginate with altered chemical properties. *Azotobacter vinelandii* has multiple epimerase isoenzymes, which also makes it an attractive target for genetic manipulation.

### See Also the Following Articles

Biological Nitrogen Fixation • Carbon and Nitrogen Assimilation, Regulation of • Soil Microbiology

### Bibliography

Hill, S. (1992). Physiology of nitrogen fixation in free-living heterotrophs. *In* "Biological Nitrogen Fixation" (G. Stacey, R. H. Burris, and H. J. Evans, Eds.), pp. 87–134. Chapman & Hall, London.

Kennedy, C. (1989). The genetics of nitrogen fixation. *In* "Genetics of Bacterial Diversity" (D. A. Hopwood and K. F. Chater, Eds.), pp. 107–127. Academic Press, London.

Merrick, M. J. (1992). Regulation of nitrogen fixation genes in free-living and symbiotic bacteria. *In* "Biological Nitrogen Fixation" (G. Stacey, R. H. Burris, and H. J. Evans, Eds.), pp. 835–876. Chapman & Hall, London.

Peters, J. W., Fisher, K., and Dean, D. R. (1995). Nitrogenase structure and function: A biochemical-genetic perspective. *Annu. Rev. Microbiol.* **49**, 335–366.

Poole, R. K., and Hill, S. (1997). Respiratory protection of nitrogenase activity in *Azotobacter vinelandii*—Roles of the terminal oxidases. *Biosci. Rep.* **17**, 303–317.

Postgate, J. R. (1982). "The Fundamentals of Nitrogen Fixation." Cambridge Univ. Press, Cambridge, UK.

Rehm, B. H. A., and Valla, S. (1997). Bacterial alginates: Biosynthesis and applications. *Appl. Microbiol. Biotechnol.* **48**, 281–288.

# Bacillus subtilis, Genetics

## Kevin M. Devine

*Trinity College, Dublin*

## GLOSSARY

**competence** Development of the ability to bind and internalize DNA from the medium.

**endospore** A metabolically quiescent cell that is resistant to desiccation, ultraviolet light, and other environmental insults.

**forespore** The cell compartment of the sporangium destined to become the spore.

**integrating plasmid** A plasmid that cannot replicate autonomously in a host bacterium. It can, however, establish itself by integration into the chromosome through recombination between homologous plasmid and chromosomal sequences.

**mother cell** The compartment of the sporangium which engulfs the forespore, synthesizes spore coat proteins, and lyses when the mature endospore is formed.

**polymerase chain reaction** Amplification of specific DNA sequences *in vitro* using oligonucleotide primers and thermostable DNA polymerase.

**sigma factor** A transcription factor which recognizes specific DNA sequences and directs RNA polymerase to initiate transcription at these sites.

**SOS response** A regulon that is induced to protect cells against DNA damage.

**sporangium** The developing bacterial cell.

**sporulation** The developmental process whereby the bacterial cell forms a quiescent spore.

**two-component system** A signal transduction system composed of a sensor kinase and a response regulator. The kinase is activated when it senses some environmental or nutritional parameter. It then activates the response regula-

tor, which alters gene expression in a manner that allows the bacterium to respond to the prevailing conditions.

**BACILLUS SUBTILIS** is an endospore-forming, gram-positive, rod-shaped bacterium. Several characteristics of *B. subtilis* have attracted intense interest and therefore it has become a model system for bacterial research. It produces enzymes that are widely used in the brewing, baking, and washing powder industries.

Because its products have traditionally been used in the food industry, *B. subtilis* is classified as a GRAS organism (generally regarded as safe) and is therefore a natural choice of host for the production of heterologous proteins using recombinant DNA methodology. *Bacillus subtilis* cells become naturally competent during the transition between exponential growth and the stationary phase of the growth cycle. Competent cells have the ability to bind and internalize DNA present in the medium. Therefore, although the regulation of competence development has attracted research interest, competence development has provided the means through which *B. subtilis* can be readily genetically manipulated. This has led to the development of sophisticated molecular techniques, primarily based on integrating plasmids and transposons, for genetic analysis.

Spore formation is a developmental process whereby a vegetative cell undergoes a series of morphological events to become a metabolically quiescent spore. This process involves temporal and spatial regulation of gene expression and communication between the forespore and mother cell of the sporangium. These features make spore formation in *B. subtilis* an attractive model system to study development. The complete genome sequence of *B. subtilis* was published in November 1997. This knowledge has greatly expedited research efforts in this bacterium. It has also revealed that the genome encodes many genes that cannot be assigned a function. The challenge now is to determine how these genes contribute to the cellular metabolism and physiology.

## I. CHARACTERISTICS OF *BACILLUS SUBTILIS*

### A. Taxonomy and Habitat

The genus *Bacillus* consists of gram-positive, endospore-forming, rod-shaped bacteria. There are more than 70 species, which display wide morphological and physiological diversity. Only 2 (*B. anthracis* and *B. cereus*) are known to be human pathogens. The defining feature of the genus is endospore formation. The genus is subdivided into six groups using a variety of morphological (particularly sporangial) and metabolic criteria. *Bacillus subtilis* belongs to group II, whose distinguishing features are (i) the formation of an ellipsoidal spore which does not swell the mother cell, (ii) the ability of cells to grow anaerobically with glucose as the carbon source in the presence of nitrate, and (iii) the production of acid from a variety of sugars.

The natural habitat of *B. subtilis* is the soil, but it is also found in fresh water, coastal waters, and oceans. The ubiquity of the bacterium is probably a consequence of endospore formation, which allows survival after exposure to even the most hostile environments. *Bacillus subtilis* is also associated with plants, animals, and foods and is found in animal feces. The significance of these associations is not clear. It is thought that its presence in feces is merely the result of ingestion and passage through the gut, whereas a synergistic relationship may exist with plants in which the bacterium enhances the supply of nutrients.

### B. Development of Competence

*Bacillus subtilis* cells become competent naturally. Competence is the ability to bind and internalize exogenous DNA from the medium. This capability develops during nutrient limitation when cells are in transition between exponential growth and the stationary phases of the growth cycle. Only 10% of the cell population becomes competent. The competent and non-competent fractions can be separated using renograffin gradients indicating that they are morphologically distinguishable. Competent cells can also be distinguished because they do not engage in either macromolecule or nucleotide synthesis and the SOS response is induced.

The mechanics of DNA binding and internalization have been established. DNA fragments of heterogeneous size adhere noncovalently to approximately 50 binding sites on the cell surface. DNA binding is not sequence specific. The DNA is then fragmented randomly. During internalization, one strand (chosen randomly) is degraded while the other is transported into the cytoplasm. Internalized DNA fragments are approximately 10 kilobases in size. The nature of the transforming DNA determines its fate: DNA that is homologous to the bacterial chromosome will form a heteroduplex with the chromosome leading to homologous recombination. Plasmid DNA will be established as autonomously replicating molecules.

### C. Enzyme and Antibiotic Production

*Bacillus* species produce a range of enzymes and antibiotics in response to nutrient limitation. The enzymes include proteases, amylases, cellulases and lipases. Production is maximal when cells are in the stationary phase of the growth cycle. Production of these enzymes is presumably a survival strategy to scavenge macromolecular energy sources when nutrient levels are low. Many of these enzymes are widely used in the food, brewing, and biological washing powder industries. Enzymes with useful properties, such as thermostability, activity over a wide pH range, activity in detergents and oxidizing environments, have been identified in many *Bacillus* species. The role of *B. subtilis* in the enzyme industry is two-fold: (i) Many *Bacillus* species are refractory to genetic analysis and *B. subtilis* is therefore the organism of choice to study the regulation of enzyme production and (ii) heterologous genes encoding enzymes with desirable properties can be cloned into

*B. subtilis* strains which have been manipulated to give high product yields.

*Bacillus* species also produce antibiotics when cells enter the stationary phase of the growth cycle. This is probably a strategy to limit bacterial competition for the energy sources liberated through macromolecular degradation by the scavenging enzymes. *Bacillus subtilis* produces a range of peptide antibiotics, including subtilin, surfactin, bacillomycin, bacilysin, and fengycin, that display a range of antibacterial and antifungal activities. Although the synthesis of these antibiotics and their role(s) in bacterial cell physiology and survival are academically interesting, they are not of great medical importance. They are synthesized by a variety of mechanisms: For example, subtilin is a lantibiotic (contains the modified amino acid lanthionine) which is produced ribosomally, whereas surfactin is produced by the multienzyme thiotemplate mechanism. The complete genome sequence (see Section II) has revealed many of the loci encoding enzymes for antibiotic synthesis: For example, *pks* encodes a polyketide synthase, *srf* encodes surfactin synthetase, and *pps* encodes a peptide synthetase. These three loci comprise 4% of the total genome length.

## D. Sporulation

*Bacillus subtilis* undergoes spore formation in response to carbon, nitrogen, or phosphate limitation. This process results in the formation of a metabolically quiescent cell that is resistant to desiccation, ultraviolet (UV) light, and other environmental insults. The process of sporulation involves temporal and cell type-specific regulation of gene expression, intercellular communication (between mother cell and forespore), morphological differentiation and programmed cell death (bacterial apoptosis). Such features are characteristic of more complex developmental systems. Sporulation in *B. subtilis* is therefore a simple developmental system amenable to genetic and biochemical analysis. The process requires 6–8 hr for completion and can be divided into seven stages (Fig. 1). At stage 0, the cell senses its environment and makes the decision to initiate sporulation. At stage II an asymmetric cell division has occurred, with the larger cell becoming the mother cell and

the smaller cell the forespore. At stage III, the mother cell has completely engulfed the forespore to produce a cell within a cell. A cell type-specific program of gene expression has been established in each compartment at this stage. A series of morphological changes occur between stages IV and VI that lead to the formation of the spore cortex and spore coat. At stage VI, the developing endospore becomes resistant to heat, UV light, and desiccation, and at stage VII the mother cell lyses and releases the mature dormant spore.

## II. THE COMPLETE GENOME SEQUENCE OF *B. SUBTILIS*

### A. Genome Organization

The complete nucleotide sequence of the *B. subtilis* genome was published in 1997. The circular genome is 4,214 kilobases in size and has an average G+C content of 43.5%. There are 10 regions which have a G+C content significantly lower than average and that correspond to known bacteriophage and bacteriophage-like elements. The origin and terminus of replication are almost perfectly diametrically opposed on the genome. The *B. subtilis* genome displays significant GT skew at third codon positions in common with many other bacteria. The leading strands have an excess of G (9%) and T (4%) over the lagging strands, and the position at which skew reversal occurs corresponds to the positions of the origin and terminus of replication. Approximately 87% of the genome is coding. More than 74% of all open reading frames and 94% of ribosomal genes are transcribed co-directionally with replication.

### B. Gene Composition

Fifty-three percent of genes are present in single copy. The remainder are present in multigene families, which range in size from those with 2 gene copies (568 genes are duplicated) to the ABC family of transporters that has 77 members. Multigene families present the opportunity for individual member genes to diverge and fulfill different functions and roles within the cell. In addition, individual members

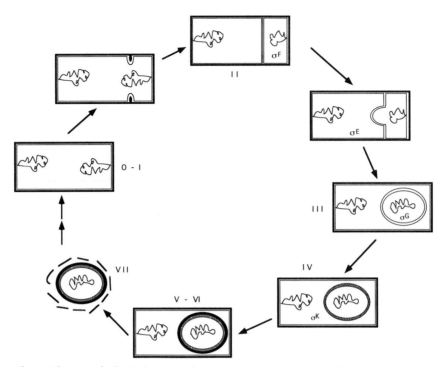

**Fig. 1.** The morphological stages of sporulation in *Bacillus subtilis*. The decision to sporulate has occurred (stages 0 and 1) with two chromosomes (wavy circles) located at opposite poles of the cell. An asymmetric cell division occurs (stage II) with a single chromosome positioned in each compartment. At this stage, SigmaF is activated only in the forespore (smaller) compartment. During engulfment of the forespore (stages II and III), SigmaE becomes active in the mother cell (larger) compartment. SigmaG becomes active on completion of engulfment (stage III). At stage IV, SigmaK is activated in the mother cell and a layer of cortex (stippled ellipse) surrounds the developing spore. Further morphological changes occur during stages IV–VI that include deposition of a coat (dark ellipse) outside the cortex. The mother cell lyses (stage VII), releasing the mature ellipsoid spore [from Stragier and Losick (1996) with permission, from the *Annual Review of Genetics*, Volume 30, © 1996, by Annual Reviews].

can have different regulatory signals so that they can be expressed under different environmental and nutritional conditions. Approximately 220 transcriptional regulators have been identified, including a family of 18 sigma factors (18 different types of promoter), a family of 34 two-component systems, 20 members of the GntR family, 19 members of the LysR family, and 12 members of the LacI family. It is evident, therefore, that *B. subtilis* has the potential to sense and respond to nutritional and environmental signals in a complex manner. This may be a reflection of the varied habitats in which *B. subtilis* can survive.

## C. Gene Identity

Approximately 58% of genes can be assigned an identity based either on functional analysis or extensive homology to a gene of known function. Therefore, the function of 42% of genes is unknown. This is a feature common to all genomes sequenced to date. Twelve percent of the unknown genes have homologs in other organisms. The large number of genes with unknown functions represents a formidable challenge to understanding the metabolism and physiology of *B. subtilis*. It is not clear why such a large number of genes were refractory to discovery by classical genetic analysis. It is probable that among this group are essential genes, redundant genes, and genes which participate in metabolic and physiological processes not yet discovered. Some of these questions will be resolved during the ongoing joint European–Japanese functional analysis project, the objective of which is to examine the expression of all genes of unknown function in *B. subtilis* by systematically inactivating each gene and testing the resultant mutant strain for a wide variety of phenotypes.

The intermediary metabolic pathways and the metabolic potential of a bacterium can be constructed from knowledge of the complete genome sequence. Analysis of this type shows that both the glycolytic and TCA cycles are complete and functional in *B. subtilis,* and the enzymes and regulator genes required for anaerobic growth with glucose as carbon source and nitrate as electron acceptor are also present. Anaerobic growth under these conditions has been experimentally verified.

## III. GENETIC METHODOLOGY IN *B. SUBTILIS*

The knowledge of the complete genomic sequence has had a profound effect on research on *B. subtilis.* This is manifest most clearly in the accelerated pace at which research is now done. The information in the complete genomic sequence is enhanced by three additional features: (i) Polymerase chain reaction techniques allow any chromosomal fragment to be rapidly amplified, (ii) the transformation frequency of *B. subtilis* is high, and (iii) there is a sophisticated range of integrating plasmids and transposons available for use in *B. subtilis.*

Integrating plasmids are the predominant and most versatile tool for genetic manipulation of the *B. subtilis* chromosome. The essential features of an integrating plasmid are (i) the inability to replicate autonomously in *B. subtilis,* (ii) the presence of a gene for selecting plasmid establishment in *B. subtilis,* and (iii) a segment of *B. subtilis* chromosomal DNA through which the plasmid can integrate into the chromosome by homologous recombination.

There are basically two types of integration events. When the transforming plasmid is circular, integration occurs by a single crossover event. When the transforming plasmid is linear, and contains two regions of homology with the chromosome, integration occurs by a double-crossover event that results in gene replacement. Incorporating additional genetic functions into the integrating plasmid can extend the repertoire of genetic manipulation. Such functions include reporter genes to generate transcriptional and translational fusions (e.g., $\beta$-galactosidase and chloramphenicol acetyl transferase to detect protein accumulation and green fluorescence protein to determine intracellular location), inducible promoters such as $P_{spac}$ (an IPTG-inducible system based on the *lac* operon of *Escherichia coli*), and site-specific recombination functions.

The details of these systems and the mechanisms through which specific genetic manipulations can be achieved using integrating plasmids are beyond the scope of this article. However, it is useful to illustrate the range of genetic analysis that can be performed using integrating plasmids. Any gene can be mutated through either insertional inactivation or deletion. Complementation analysis and the dominance or recessivity of specific mutations can be tested. Genetic loci can be inserted into heterologous sites to test whether they function in *cis* or in *trans*. The phenotype caused by overproduction of a gene product can be assessed by gene amplification. Similarly, amplification of a control region can be used to test for titration of repressors. Large chromosomal fragments can be deleted or inverted. Strains can be constructed with multiple deletions in non-contiguous chromosomal regions. Genes and/or their control regions can be mutated *in vitro* and reinserted into homologous or heterologous sites of the chromosome in single or multiple copy. The expression profile of a gene/operon can be established by generating transcriptional and translational fusions to reporter genes. Regulation at the transcriptional and post-transcriptional levels can be distinguished. Conditional expression of any gene can be effected by placing it under the control of an inducible promoter. This is particularly useful for analysis of essential genes.

## IV. GENETIC ANALYSIS OF *B. SUBTILIS*

An objective of bacterial research is to understand how individual processes are regulated and integrated within the cell. Two themes have emerged from the study of how post-exponential phenomena, such as competence development, enzyme production, and sporulation, are regulated: (i) Multiple signals detected by the cell are integrated by a signal transduction cascade which converges on a central regulator and (ii) the regulation of these processes overlaps so that entering one of these physiological states precludes activation of the other states.

## A. Two-Component Signal Transduction Systems

It is imperative that bacteria adapt their gene expression and metabolism to the prevailing conditions. Two-component systems comprise a family of proteins, found ubiquitously in bacteria, which sense environmental and nutritional conditions and effect appropriate metabolic and physiological responses. They are generally (but not always) composed of two proteins: a sensor kinase and a response regulator. The kinase detects a parameter(s) of the environment that results in enzyme activation. The active kinase autophosphorylates and then transfers the phosphate to the response regulator. Phosphorylation of the response regulator activates (or alters) its transcriptional activity. Thirty-four two-component systems have been identified in *B. subtilis,* suggesting great versatility and flexibility in its response to changing environmental and nutritional conditions. Three such systems, ComP–ComA, DegS–DegU, and the unusual phosphorelay KinABC–Spo0F–Spo0B–Spo0A, are involved in regulating the post-exponential phase phenomena of competence development, enzyme synthesis, and sporulation, respectively, in *B. subtilis.*

## B. Competence Development

The regulation of competence development can be divided into three stages: (i) sensing the environmen-

tal and nutritional conditions which trigger the process, (ii) the signal transduction pathway that integrates the signals, and (iii) activation of the transcription factor ComK. The composition of the growth medium is an important parameter in competence development. Cells do not become competent in rich medium. In defined medium supplemented with amino acids, competence develops when cells enter the stationary phase of the growth cycle. In defined glucose-minimal medium, cells become competent during exponential growth. Cell density is a second parameter to which competence development responds. This signal is mediated by peptide factors that accumulate in the medium as cells grow to high density. Two such peptides have been identified. Competence stimulating factor (CSF) is a small peptide that is secreted from the cell after signal sequence cleavage. The secreted peptide is further proteolytically processed and a pentapeptide is reimported into the cell through the oligopeptide transport system. The second peptide, ComX, is secreted from the cell by an unknown mechanism. Accumulation of both these peptides causes an increase in the level of phosphorylated ComA (ComA~P). ComX does this by stimulating the ComP kinase that specifically phosphorylates ComA, whereas CSF is thought to inhibit the activity of a phosphatase which dephosphorylates ComA~P. Phosphorylated ComA then activates expression of *srf,* the surfactin synthetase operon, leading to increased levels of ComS, the next regulator in the signal transduction cascade. ComS is encoded by a small gene (46 codons) located entirely within the much larger *srfA* gene. The reason for this unusual gene organization is not known, but it provides a link between the post-exponential growth phase phenomena of competence development and antibiotic production. ComS destabilizes a ternary protein complex composed of MecA, ClpC, and ComK leading to release of free ComK, which can then function as a transcription factor. ComK also activates its own expression leading to very high levels of the protein, thereby further committing cells to the competent state. The ComK regulon comprises the group of genes and operons encoding the proteins required for binding, fragmentation, and uptake of DNA. The *comF* operon encodes a helicase that is involved in unwinding transforming DNA. The *comG* operon encodes proteins homologous to (i) the pilin protein and proteins involved in pilin assembly, (ii) proteins involved in pullulanase secretion in *Klebsiella pneumoniae,* and (iii) proteins encoded by the *virB* operon of *Agrobacterium tumefaciens* which function to transfer T-DNA from the bacterium to the plant. It is interesting that the transfer of DNA into *B. subtilis* cells shares features with other systems designed to transfer both DNA and proteins across cell walls and membranes.

## C. Regulation of Enzyme Production

Production of extracellular enzymes occurs in response to nutrient limitation, and accumulation is observed when cells enter the stationary phase of the growth cycle. This is approximately the same growth period during which the cells become competent (see Sections I,B and IV,B). Although the regulatory pathways of these two physiological states overlap, it appears that enzyme production and competence development are alternate physiological states. The signals which trigger enzyme production (the nature of these signals is not precisely known) are sensed by the DegS kinase. Activation of the kinase leads to accumulation of phosphorylated DegU (DegU~P). DegU~P is a transcriptional activator which stimulates transcription of genes encoding the amylases, proteases, and glucanases produced when cells enter the stationary phase of the growth cycle. Two additional regulators, DegQ and DegR, are also required for enzyme production. DegU~P has an additional role in that it inhibits production of ComS, the regulator required for activation of the competence transcription factor ComK. Therefore, accumulation of Deg~P leads to stimulation of enzyme production and inhibition of competence development. In contrast, the non-phosphorylated form of DegU stimulates competence development. Phosphorylation of DegU therefore acts as a switch mechanism allowing cells to become competent (high levels of DegU) or to produce extracellular enzymes (high levels of DegU~P). The equilibrium between the phosphorylated and nonphosphorylated states will depend on the extent to which the kinase (which is responsive to nutritional and environmental conditions) is activated.

## D. Regulation of Sporulation

### 1. Initiation of Sporulation

The conditions that trigger sporulation include limitation of carbon, nitrogen, and phosphorous and high cell density. These signals, and perhaps others, are sensed and integrated by a signal transduction pathway which converges on the transcriptional regulator Spo0A. The critical parameter in the decision to sporulate is the level of phosphorylated Spo0A, the form of the protein required for transcriptional activation. The nonphosphorylated form of Spo0A has no known transcriptional activity, whereas high Spo0A~P levels are required for initiation of sporulation. The commitment to sporulate is reinforced by a positive autoregulatory loop whereby Spo0A~P activates transcription of the *spo0A* gene. Spo0A is unusual among two-component transcriptional activators in that it is phosphorylated indirectly by a so-called phosphorelay (Fig. 2). Spo0F is phosphorylated by sensor kinases in response to nutritional and environmental conditions. The phosphate is then transferred from Spo0F to Spo0A via the Spo0B phosphotransferase. The relative cellular levels of Spo0A and Spo0A~P are the result of competing kinase and phosphatase activities. There are at least three kinases which phosphorylate Spo0F that lead to a buildup of Spo0A~P in the cell. The precise nature of the nutritional and/or environmental signals that activate the kinases is not firmly established. There are also four phosphatases that function to lower the cellular level of Spo0A~P: RapA, RapB, and RapE specifically dephosphorylate Spo0F~P, whereas the Spo0E phosphatase specifically dephosphorylates Spo0A~P. It appears that cell density signals can be detected through these phosphatases by a quorum-sensing mechanism. There is a gene encoding a small peptide juxtaposed to the RapA and RapE phosphatase genes called *phrA* and *phrE,* respectively. The PhrA and PhrE peptides are secreted from the medium, processed, and reimported into the cell. This results in inhibition of Spo0F~P dephosphorylation by RapA and RapE and leads to an increase in the cellular level of Spo0A~P. The genetic evidence indicates that those conditions which favor competence development signal an inhibition of sporulation. For example, the high levels of Com~P that

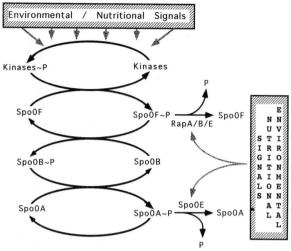

**Fig. 2.** The phosphorelay leading to formation of Spo0A~P. A variety of environmental and nutritional conditions (stippled arrows) are sensed by sensor kinases leading to their autophosphorylation. The phosphate group is then transferred from the kinase to Spo0F (to give Spo0F~P). It is subsequently transferred from Spo0F~P to Spo0A (to give Spo0A~P) by the phosphotransferase Spo0B. Phosphate groups can be drained from the phosphorelay at two points: (i) by dephosphorylation of Spo0F~P by any of three response regulator aspartate phosphatases (Rap A/B/E) and (ii) by dephosphorylation of Spo0A~P by Spo0E phosphatase. The phosphatase activities are also responsive to a distinct group of environmental and nutritional conditions (stippled arrows). The competing actions of the kinase and phosphatase activities determine the relative cellular levels of Spo0A and Spo0A~P.

direct competence development also lead to increased levels of RapA, which results in dephosphorylation of Spo0F. This leads to a decrease in cellular levels of Spo0A~P, thereby inhibiting sporulation. The AbrB regulator also provides a link between competence development, enzyme and antibiotic production, and sporulation. The level of AbrB varies throughout the growth cycle to ensure that cells can become competent, produce enzymes, or sporulate but cannot enter all three physiological states at the same time.

## 2. Regulation of Endospore Development
### a. Activation of SigmaF in the Forespore
Asymmetric septum formation in the sporangium is one of the first morphological events of endospore development (Fig. 1). At this stage (stage II) there are two complete chromosomes in the sporangium, each having been directed into one of the two compartments by a chromosome partitioning mechanism. When septum formation is complete, the fates of the two cells differ. The smaller compartment becomes the spore and the larger becomes the mother cell. Therefore, it is necessary to establish a separate program of gene expression in each compartment. The first step in this process is activation of expression of the operon encoding the transcription factor SigmaF by high levels of Spo0A~P. This operon is expressed before completion of septum formation and the SigmaF protein is therefore present in both compartments. However, it becomes active only in the forespore compartment. Three additional proteins, SpoIIAA, SpoIIAB, and SpoIIE, effect asymmetric activation of SigmaF. SpoIIAB is an anti-sigma factor that can bind either to SigmaF (making SigmaF inactive) or to SpoIIAA (allowing SigmaF to be transcriptionally active). The phosphorylation state of SpoIIAA determines whether SpoIIAB binds to SigmaF or to SpoIIAA. When SpoIIAA is phosphorylated, SpoIIAB binds to SigmaF preventing it from engaging in transcription; when SpoIIAA is not phosphorylated, it binds to SpoIIAB and SigmaF can now engage in transcription. The dephosphorylation of SpoIIAA is effected by SpoIIE, a phosphatase that is located in the asymmetric septum and dephosphorylates SpoIIAA only in the forespore (Fig. 3). This is a very clear example of morphological differentiation coupled with regulation of gene expression.

### b. Activation of SigmaE in the Mother Cell
A cell-type-specific pattern of gene expression, mediated by the SigmaE transcription factor, is established in the mother cell after SigmaF has been activated in the forespore (Fig. 1). SigmaE protein is also synthesized in the predivisional sporangium and is therefore present in both the forespore and the mother cell compartments. However, it is activated only in the mother cell. SigmaE is activated by cleavage of a small peptide from the amino terminus of the protein. The proteolytic cleavage is effected by SpoIIGA, a membrane-localized protease (Fig. 3). Genetic analysis has revealed that SigmaF must be activated in the forespore before SigmaE can be acti-

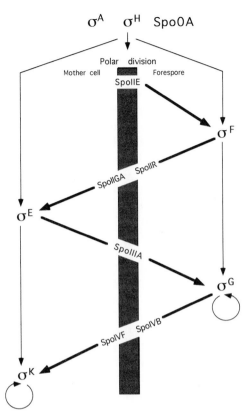

**Fig. 3.** Crisscross regulation of compartmental gene expression during sporulation. Transcriptional dependency is indicated by thin arrows: transcription of both the sigmaE- and sigmaF- encoding genes requires SigmaA, SigmaH, and Spo0A~P. The formation of the septum (shaded rectangle) between the forespore and mother cell compartments is also dependent on these three transcription factors. SigmaF is required for transcription of the sigmaG-encoding gene in the forespore and SigmaG positively autoregulates its own expression (arrowed circle). Likewise, SigmaE is required for transcription of the sigmaK-encoding gene, which also positively regulates its own expression. A second level of control operates at the level of the activities of these factors (thick arrows). The activity of SigmaF in the forespore is dependent on septum formation and the septum-linked SpoIIE protein. The activity of SigmaE is dependent on the activity of SigmaF through the septum-linked SpoIIGA and SpoIIR proteins. The activity of SigmaG is dependent on the activities of SigmaE in the mother cell and the activity of SpoIIIA, whereas the activity of SigmaK is dependent on the activity of SigmaG in the forespore and the activities of SpoIVF and SpoIVB [from Stragier and Losick (1996) with permission, from the *Annual Review of Genetics*, Volume 30, © 1996, by Annual Reviews].

vated in the mother cell. The basis of this requirement is that SigmaF is required to produce SpoIIR in the forespore (Fig. 3). SpoIIR is then secreted from the forespore into the intercompartmental space between forespore and mother cell where it binds to, and activates, the membrane-localized protease SpoIIGA. This protease then activates SigmaE, which effects the mother cell-specific program of gene expression.

### c. Activation of SigmaG and SigmaK in the Forespore and Mother Cell, Respectively

Separate programs of gene expression are first established in the two compartments by activation of SigmaE and SigmaF. These sigma factors are then replaced by two new compartment-specific sigma factors, SigmaG in the forespore and SigmaK in the mother cell. Production of the SigmaK protein is directed by the mother cell-specific SigmaE, whereas production of SigmaG is directed by the forespore-specific SigmaF. However, activation of SigmaG and SigmaK requires a signal from the other compartment (Fig. 3). Activation of SigmaG in the forespore requires gene products encoded by the *spoIIIA* operon which is transcribed by SigmaE in the mother cell. Activation of SigmaK in the mother cell is similar to activation of SigmaE. SigmaK must be proteolytically processed to become active. The protease is produced in the mother cell. However, the forespore produces a product (under SigmaG control) which is secreted into the space between the forespore and mother cell that is required for activation of the protease in the mother cell.

### d. Features of the Regulation of Endospore Formation

The establishment of temporal and cell-type-specific programs of gene expression in the forespore and mother cell compartments of the sporangium displays many interesting features. Activation of both SigmaE and SigmaF is coupled to the morphological event of asymmetric septum formation by locating SpoIIE and SpoIIGA in the septum. Temporal regulation of gene expression is effected by sequential activation of sigma factors. The timing of sigma factor activation and the coordination of gene expression in the forespore and mother-cell compartments are controlled by so-called crisscross regulation (Fig. 3). Activation of SigmaF in the forespore is required before SigmaE can be activated in the mother cell; SigmaE must be activated in the mother cell before SigmaG can be activated in the forespore, and SigmaG must be activated in the forespore before SigmaK can be activated in the mother cell (Fig. 3). Both SigmaE and SigmaK are activated in the mother cell by two similar (but not identical) signal transduction systems. In both cases, a signal is produced and secreted from the forespore to effect sigma factor activation in the mother cell.

## V. CONCLUSION

*Bacillus subtilis* is a very useful model organism for bacterial research. The complete genome sequence is known, it is amenable to genetic manipulation, and it exhibits many fundamental biological processes. Whole bacterial genomes can be sequenced with relative ease. However, only a small number of the bacteria are amenable to genetic manipulation. Therefore, the metabolic and physiological capabilities of these bacteria will have to be deduced from knowledge of their gene content coupled with research performed in model organisms such as *B. subtilis*. The large number of genes to which we cannot assign a function suggests that there is still much to be discovered in *B. subtilis*. It is likely, therefore, that *B. subtilis* will remain a primary focus of bacterial research.

## See Also the Following Articles

ENZYMES, EXTRACELLULAR • POLYMERASE CHAIN REACTION • SPORULATION • TWO-COMPONENT SYSTEMS

## Bibliography

Harwood, C., and Cutting, S. M. (Eds.), (1990). "Molecular Biological Methods for *Bacillus*." Wiley, Chichester, UK.

Kunst, F., *et al.* (1997). The complete genome sequence of *Bacillus subtilis*. *Nature* **390**, 249–256.

Sonenshein, A., Hoch, J., and Losick, R. (Eds.), (1993). "*Bacillus subtilis* and Other Gram-Positive Bacteria." American Society for Microbiology, Washington, DC.

Stragier, P., and Losick, R. (1996). Sporulation in *Bacillus subtilis*. *Annu. Rev. Genet.* **30**, 297–341.

# Bacteriocins

**Rolf D. Joerger and Dallas G. Hoover**

*University of Delaware*

**S. F. Barefoot, K. M. Harmon,
D. A. Grinstead, and C. G. Nettles Cutter**

*Clemson University*

I. Historical Aspects
II. Detection of Bacteriocins
III. Production and Purification of Bacteriocins
IV. Genetics, Molecular Properties, and Modes of Action of Select Bacteriocins
V. Application of Bacteriocins
VI. Future Directions

## GLOSSARY

**bacteriocin** Bacteriocidal peptide or protein produced by a bacterium.

**colicin** Bacteriocin produced by *Escherichia coli* or closely related enteric species.

**constitutive** Refers to continuously expressed or unregulated genes.

**indicator strain** Target organism sensitive to bacteriocin.

**inducible** Describes genes that are transcribed when an appropriate signal is present.

**lactic acid bacteria** Members of the genera *Lactococcus, Lactobacillus, Leuconostoc, Pediococcus,* and *Enterococcus* whose primary metabolic by-product is lactic acid.

**nisin** Bacteriocin produced by *Lactococcus lactis* subsp. *lactis*; has application in food preservation.

**open reading frame** Stretch of triplet codons that is not interrupted by a stop codon; likely a protein-coding region.

**operon** Collection of functionally related genes subject to common regulation and transcribed into a single messenger RNA molecule.

**plasmid** Self-replicating extrachromosomal DNA.

**promoter** DNA binding site for RNA polymerase; start signal for RNA synthesis.

**SOS response** Set of physiological responses induced by exposure of cells to conditions damaging DNA.

**BACTERIOCINS** are proteinaceous compounds of bacterial origin that are lethal to bacteria other than the producing strain. Normally, the cells producing the bacteriocin are immune to its antagonistic action and therefore might enjoy a competitive advantage over sensitive bacteria inhabiting the same ecological niche. Most of the information on bacteriocins comes from the study of colicins, bacteriocins produced by strains of *Escherichia coli* and closely related members of the Enterobacteriaceae; however, bacteriocins are widespread throughout the prokaryotic world and quite diverse in their chemical and physical properties. Applications of bacteriocins to improve food safety and for medical and veterinary purposes are being explored. Nisin, a bacteriocin produced by *Lactococcus lactis* subsp. *lactis,* has been approved for use as a food preservative in the United States and many other countries.

## I. HISTORICAL ASPECTS

The definition for the term bacteriocin has gradually changed since the first bacteriocin was discovered by Gratia in 1925. Called "principle V," it was produced by one strain of *Escherichia coli* and effective against another strain of *E. coli*. The term "colicine" was coined by Gratia and Fredericq in 1946, whereas "bacteriocine" was first used by Jacob and co-workers in 1953. The bulk of the early work on bacteriocins was concerned with colicins, and this explains why the key characteristics of the colicins were used to define bacteriocins in general. According to this definition, bacteriocins were protein-

**TABLE I**
**Bacteriocins from Gram-Negative Bacteria**

| Bacteriocin type | Molecular weight (kDa) | Producer | Examples |
|---|---|---|---|
| Colicin | 4–90 | *Escherichia coli* | Colicins A, B, D, E1–E7, Ia, Ib, K, L, M, N, V |
| Cloacin | 56 | *Enterobacter cloacae* | Cloacin DF13 |
| Microcin | <1–5 | *Escherichia coli* | Microcins A15, B17, C7, D15, D140, E492, H47, 15m |

aceous and bactericidal, they exhibited activity primarily against closely related species, they attached to specific cell receptors, and their genetic determinants were plasmid encoded. The definition also included that the synthesis of bacteriocins was lethal to the producer. The study of antibacterial proteins different from those of the colicin type has resulted in a broadening of the definition of bacteriocin. This term is now applied to any proteinaceous compound lethal to bacteria other than the producing strain. Generally, bacteriocins are given names according to the genus or species of the strain that produces them—for example, pediocins from *Pediococcus* and boticins from *Clostridium botulinum*.

Bacteriocins are a diverse group of proteins with different molecular structures and modes of action. Therefore, classification of bacteriocins proved difficult. Bacteriocins can be distinguished broadly, based on whether they originate from gram-negative or gram-positive bacteria. The differences in the structure of the bacterial cell wall of the two groups of bacteria appear to have resulted in the evolution of bacteriocins that are only active against similar bacteria within each group. Colicins, cloacin DF13, and microcins are examples of bacteriocins produced

by gram-negative bacteria (Table I). The bacteriocins of gram-positive bacteria, primarily those produced by lactic acid bacteria, have been separated into three major classes (Table II). This classification is mainly based on the molecular mass of the bacteriocins, and it does not distinguish mode of action.

## II. DETECTION OF BACTERIOCINS

The identification of a bacterial strain as a bacteriocin producer usually begins with the demonstration of inhibitory activity against another bacterial strain. Such antagonism between bacteria is a common phenomenon. As early as 1676, Antonie van Leeuwenhoek documented antibiosis, whereby the product from one microorganism inhibited growth of another. In 1877, Louis Pasteur and J. F. Joubert described the antagonistic effect of common bacteria from urine on *Bacillus anthracis;* however, demonstration of inhibition of one bacteria by another is not sufficient to establish a bacteriocin as a causative or contributing agent. Other inhibitors associated with bacteria and their metabolism may act alone or in combination to produce the same signs of inhibi-

**TABLE II**
**Classification of Bacteriocins from Gram-Positive Bacteria**

| Class | Characteristics | Examples |
|---|---|---|
| I | Lantibiotics: small (19–37 amino acids), heat-stable | Nisin, lacticin 481, lactocin S, carnocin UI49 |
| II | Small, heat-stable nonlantibiotics (<15 kDa) | Pediocin PA-1, diplococcin, lactacin B, lactacin F, leucocin A UAL 187, lactococcin A |
| III | Large, heat-labile proteins (>15 kDa) | Helveticin J, caseicin 80, lacticins A and B |

tion as do bacteriocins. These inhibitors include low-molecular-weight antibiotics, lytic agents, enzymes, bacteriophage, and metabolic by-products such as ammonia, organic acids, free fatty acids, and hydrogen peroxide. It is therefore necessary to ascertain the absence of such inhibitory compounds when assaying a culture supernatant for bacteriocin activity. Dialysis will remove low-molecular-weight inhibitors, such as antibiotics, ammonia, organic acids, and hydrogen peroxide. Careful adjustments of the pH of the medium to be assayed for bacteriocin activity can eliminate pH-mediated inhibition. Catalase has been used to eliminate hydrogen peroxide from solutions to be assayed.

Bacteriocin activity can be assayed on solid growth medium or in liquid culture. Despite inherent limitations, the screening for bacteriocin activity using solid growth media is well accepted, relatively easy, cost-effective, and, more important, usually an accurate reflection of inhibitory potential. A bacteriocin-producing strain is inoculated as a spot or streak on agar medium seeded with an indicator bacterium. Bacteriocin production is usually determined by comparing zones of inhibition around the site of inoculation after incubation. The zone of inhibition is the result of diffusion of the bactericidal protein through the agar medium preventing replication of the indicator organisms. The size of the zone of inhibition is related to the rate of diffusion of the bacteriocin and also to the rate of growth of the indicator bacteria. Unusually large zones may be due to slow growth of the indicator bacteria; small zones may be observed when the bacteria grow rapidly.

Deferred methods often are more sensitive than direct or simultaneous tests and allow separation of the variables of incubation time and conditions of incubation for the producing and indicator strains. An example of a deferred agar method is the Kekessy–Piguet assay, in which the producing and indicator strains can each be grown on different optimal media. In this method, the producing strain or test culture is spot inoculated onto solid media in a petri dish. After growth, the agar disk is aseptically dislodged with a spatula from the petri dish bottom and transferred to the dish lid by striking the inverted, closed dish onto the bench top until the agar flips down on the lid. A soft agar (0.7%) overlay seeded

with an appropriate concentration of indicator bacteria is then poured over the inverted agar. Following solidification and reincubation, bacteriocin-positive strains will display a halo of clearing in the lawn around their area of growth of the producing strain.

Cell-free growth supernatants can be examined for antagonistic activity in petri plates. For such an assay, wells are cut into agar medium seeded with indicator cells and the cell-free growth supernatant is placed into the wells. Another approach is to absorb the supernatant into sterile paper disks that can be placed onto seeded agar. After appropriate incubation, the plates are examined for zones of inhibition around the wells or paper disks.

One can measure growth of indicator bacteria in liquid medium containing different concentrations of bacteriocin. For example, dialyzed, cell-free growth extracts of the producing culture can be diluted with sterile growth medium and inoculated with indicator bacteria. The lag time, doubling time, and final turbidity are measured spectrophotometrically. Alternative methods to determine the growth and sensitivity to antimicrobial agents are also available, including the monitoring of changes in pH, redox potential, bioluminescence, impedance, electrical conductivity, or heat generation. Liquid-based assays are superior to agar-based tests when examining bacteriocins that do not diffuse well.

The titer of a bacteriocin preparation is usually determined using the reciprocal of the highest dilution causing a measurable degree of inhibition to an indicator strain under standardized conditions.

## III. PRODUCTION AND PURIFICATION OF BACTERIOCINS

### A. Conditions for Bacteriocin Production

Most of the knowledge concerning bacteriocin production stems from experiments with pure cultures of bacteriocin-producing strains. Little is known about the factors that play a role in bacteriocin production in "natural" environments. Such environments are characterized by intense competition with numerous other bacterial strains and species often under unfavorable conditions. Laboratory culture conditions that favor bacteriocin production vary from strain to strain and species to species. Some bacteriocins (e.g., plantaricin and a *Streptococcus salivarius* bacteriocin) are produced only on solid media suggesting that signals from close cell-to-cell or cell-to-surface contact are required for the induction of bacteriocin production. Such conditions also exist in natural biofilms. Other bacteriocins appear to remain cell bound or intracellular. How they are released in nature is unclear. In some cases, sonication or osmotic shock facilitate release of these bacteriocins from producer cells, allowing further study. Examples of these types of bacteriocins include a *Bacteroides fragilis* bacteriocin, marcescin JF246, staphylococcin 414, enterococcin EIA, and pesticin.

Many bacteriocins are released into the growth medium. Under laboratory conditions, it appears that some bacteriocins are produced constitutively, whereas others are produced on the onset of an inducing event. Exposure to agents that induce the SOS response, such as mitomycin C or ultraviolet (UV) light, is known to induce or increase the production of colicins. These inducing agents also promote the release of bacteriocins from certain strains of *Klebsiella, Vibrio, Pseudomonas, Bacillus megaterium, Clostridium,* and *Lactobacillus casei.* The importance of this inducibility in nature is not known, but it can be speculated that the production of a bacteriocin becomes increasingly advantageous whenever adverse conditions occur and long-term survival depends on the elimination of competitors.

Microcins and many bacteriocins from gram-positive bacteria are produced under laboratory conditions in broth or agar medium without any need for the addition of inducing agents. Sometimes bacteriocin recovery from the growth media is enhanced by culture under certain pH or nutritional conditions. For example, maximum production of lactacin B occurs when the producer cells are propagated in complex broth media at a constant pH of 6.0.

The molecular mechanisms by which bacteria regulate the production of bacteriocins are largely unknown: however, it has become increasingly obvious that regulatory circuits exist that respond to unknown signals from the environment. These signaling cascades regulate the level of transcription of the bacteriocin genes.

## B. Purification of Bacteriocins

Bacteriocins are, by definition, proteins. Therefore, assays for and purification and quantitation of bacteriocins utilize techniques established for these molecules. Usually, a combination of these biochemical techniques is required to achieve purification to homogeneity. The protocols are often established empirically, and the diversity of assay and purification strategies reflects the diverse nature of the bacteriocins encountered in the microbial world. Common steps in purification protocols include the preparation of a crude extract of the bacteriocin. In the simplest case, this means the recovery of the culture supernatant from a culture of producing cells. In some cases, bacteriocin-containing liquid is obtained from solid media by freeze-thawing and subsequent centrifugation of the medium. Cell-associated bacteriocins can be released by sonication or osmotic shock treatment. Intracellular bacteriocins can be recovered after lysis of the cells.

The crude extracts are then used as starting material for purification. Purification generally proceeds in several steps and involves a combination of techniques. The proteins in the extract can be concentrated by various means, such as filtration, lyophilization, or precipitation with salts such as ammonium sulfate or organic solvents such as acetone. For heat-stable bacteriocins, separation from most other proteins can be achieved by simple heat-induced precipitation of the heat-labile proteins. Bacteriocins that aggregate may require dissociation with detergents.

The concentrated crude preparations are then subjected to one or more fractionation techniques. Gel filtration, ion exchange chromatography, high-pressure liquid chromatography (HPLC), preparative isoelectric focusing, or solvent extraction techniques have been used for the purification of bacteriocins. The latter technique works well with some of the low-molecular-weight, heat-stable bacteriocins. Purification of lactacin F, on the other hand, was achieved by ammonium sulfate precipitation of proteins from the culture supernatant followed by gel filtration of the active fractions and reversed-phase HPLC.

Progress in purification and the final level of purity is often ascertained by SDS-polyacrylamide gel electrophoresis (SDS-PAGE). This technique, along with gel filtration, is also used to determine the molecular weight of bacteriocins. Sedimentation equilibrium analysis, thin-channel ultrafiltration, and dialysis in semipermeable membranes also provide size estimations and have been used in conjunction with gel filtration of SDS-PAGE.

## IV. GENETICS, MOLECULAR PROPERTIES, AND MODES OF ACTION OF SELECT BACTERIOCINS

The diverse nature of bacteriocins precludes but a few generalizations on their genetics, molecular properties, and modes of action. In contrast to some peptide antibiotics, such as bacitracin, which are synthesized by enzyme complexes and for which there are no gene sequences corresponding to the amino acid sequence of the final peptide, even very small bacteriocins are synthesized on ribosomes from messenger RNAs transcribed from genes located on plasmids or the bacterial chromosome. The bacteriocins are generally synthesized as precursors, consisting of a signal or leader peptide that is required for export of the bacteriocin from the producing cell and of the bacteriocin. The signal peptides are cleaved from the bacteriocin precursor during export from the cytoplasm of the bacteria. In addition to the bacteriocin gene or genes (in the case of bacteriocins consisting of two peptides), bacteria may harbor a range of genes that specify products involved in the regulation of bacteriocin production, in modification of bacteriocin peptides, and in export of the bacteriocins from the cytoplasm. Generally, genes specifying proteins conferring immunity to the bacteriocin of the producing cells are located in close proximity to the bacteriocin genes.

The molecular weight of the active bacteriocin proteins ranges from approximately 1 to more than 90 kDa. There are regions of the proteins that are required for binding to target cells and for the lethal action on these target cells. The mode of action of the bacteriocins varies considerably and includes inactivation of nucleic acids such as ribosomal RNA and destruction of membrane function.

## A. Bacteriocins Produced by Gram-Negative Bacteria

### 1. Colicins and Cloacin DF13

Examples of bacteriocins produced by gram-negative bacteria are the colicins and cloacin DF13 and a group of small bacteriocins, the microcins (Table I). The colicins are the most thoroughly studied bacteriocins from gram-negative bacteria, and their genetics, molecular structures, and modes of action are well documented. Colicins A, E1–E9, K, and N and cloacin DF13 are bacteriocins encoded on small multicopy plasmids which cannot promote their own transmission to other cells. The genetic determinants for colicins B, Ia, Ib, and M reside on large, low-copy plasmids that carry genetic information allowing their transmission to other cells. The gene encoding a particular bacteriocin is clustered with the gene encoding a protein that confers immunity to the particular bacteriocin. Except for colicins Ia, Ib, B, and M, the gene cluster also contains a third gene encoding a bacteriocin-release protein (BRP; also referred to as "kil protein" or "lysis protein"). The BRP protein is required for the secretion of the bacteriocin.

Some of the promoters of bacteriocin genes are activated by the SOS response, which is set in motion by exposure of cells to such agents as UV light or mitomycin C. The promoters of immunity genes of pore-forming bacteriocins allow constitutive expression, indicating that it is important to the cell to maintain a basic level of the immunity protein for continuous protection.

The bacteriocins are released from the producing cell only in the presence of active bacteriocin-release proteins and detergent-resistant phospholipase A in the outer membrane. The liberated bacteriocin is then able to interact with receptor sites on susceptible cells. Upon binding, the bacteriocin is thought to undergo structural changes that will allow its penetration through the outer membrane. After passage through the periplasmic space, the bacteriocin then penetrates the inner membrane and, depending on the nature of the bacteriocin, pores are formed or catalytic sites are exposed to targets in the cytoplasm of the cell.

Analyses of the structure of colicins and cloacin DF13 revealed significant similarities. These bacteriocins are elongated, single-peptide chains with three domains. The hydrophobic amino-terminal domain is important for the translocation of the bacteriocin across the cell envelope. The central domain is responsible for binding to specific receptors on the surface of susceptible cells. The carboxy-terminal domain mediates the lethal activity of the bacteriocin. Immunity proteins also interact with the carboxy-terminal domain. The lethal activity of the colicin-type bacteriocins is based on different mechanisms. Colicins E3, E4, and E6 and cloacin DF13 are active as RNases. Colicin E3 and cloacin DF13 cleave 16S rRNA at a specific site which causes the termination of protein synthesis. Colicins E2 and E7–E9 exhibit DNase activity. Colicins E1, A, B, Ia, Ib, K, and N form ion-permeable channels in the cytoplasmic membrane. Such channels may allow leakage of cations from the cytoplasma as well as other low-molecular-weight compounds such as ATP. Destruction of the electrical potential of the membrane will also occur. Colicin M inhibits the synthesis of peptidoglycan and lipopolysaccharide O antigens.

### 2. Microcins

Genetic determinants for production of most microcins are located on plasmids; however, chromosomal genes are also involved in the production process. This observation can be explained by the necessity of integrating bacteriocin synthesis with other cellular functions. The production of microcin B17 illustrates this point. Four plasmid-borne genes (*mcbA–D*) are required for microcin B17 synthesis. McbA, the product of the *mcbA* gene, is the precursor of microcin B17. The three other gene products are involved in the processing of the inactive precursor into an active form. Immunity is mediated by three plasmid-borne genes. The major promoter of the *MccB17* operon is growth-phase regulated (active in the stationary phase only) and depends on the product of the chromosomal *ompR* gene. (OmpR is involved in the production of outer membrane porin proteins.) Another promoter is responsible for low-level basal expression of *mcbD*. Transcription from both promoters presumably extends through the immunity genes. Immunity to MCCB17 is expressed constitutively throughout exponential and stationary phases. Another chromosomal gene product that affects transcription of the *MccB17* operon is MprA (*microcin production regulation*). MprA causes a reduction in production of *MccB17* by preventing transcription from the major promoter. Other chromosomal gene products may also affect *MccB17* production.

Although most colicins are between 23 and 90 kDa in size, microcins are generally <1 kDa. Therefore, these small proteins are stabile in heat and in the presence of chaotropic agents and organic solvents. Nevertheless, these bacteriocins exhibit similar modes of action as those of the colicins, namely, disruption of membrane potential and inhibition of protein or RNA synthesis.

## B. Bacteriocins of Gram-Positive Bacteria

### 1. Class I Bacteriocins (Lantibiotics)

These bacteriocins are characterized by the presence of lanthionine-type thioester bonds between certain side chains of amino acid residues of the protein. These modifications are introduced into the peptide posttranslationally. Nisin is a well-known member of this group of bacteriocins and is produced by strains of *Lactococcus lactis* subsp. *lactis*. Its structure is illustrated in Fig. 1. The name for this bacteriocin is derived from the term "group N inhibitory substance". (Group N refers to sero group N of bacteria classified as members of the genus *Lactococcus*.) Nisin consists of 34 amino acids; however, it is initially synthesized as prenisin, consisting of a 23-amino acid leader peptide and the 34-amino acid pronisin peptide (Fig. 2). Variants of nisin differing in 1 amino acid are known. Certain serine and threonine residues in the pronisin are converted to dehydroalanine and dehydrobutyrine through dehydration. Thioether bonds are then formed by reaction with the sulfhydryl groups of cysteine residues in the pronisin (lanthionine, Ala-S-Ala; $\beta$-methyllanthionine, Ala-S-Aba; Aba, aminobutyric acid). Follow-

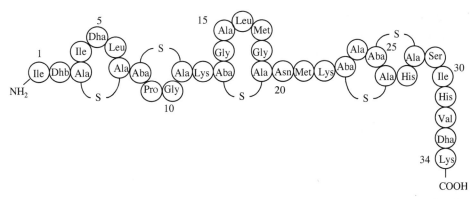

**Fig. 1.** Structure of nisin. Standard three-letter abbreviations are used for amino acids. Aba, aminobutyric acid; Dha, dehydroalanine; Dhb, dehydrobutytrin (redrawn from Kaletta and Entian, 1989).

ing these chemical modifications in the pronisin segment of prenisin, export and concomitant removal of the leader sequence yield active nisin. Normally, two nisin molecules form a dimer. This observation explains why early on the molecular weight of nisin was measured to be approximately 7 kDa rather than the approximately 3.500 kDa measured today.

The gene encoding prenisin (*nisA*) is part of a nisin gene cluster containing 11 genes that are responsible for nisin production (Fig. 2). This gene cluster is part of a conjugative transposable element that permits transfer of the nisin-producing capability to previously nonproducing strains. Two of the 11 genes, *nisR* and *nisK*, encode products of a two-component regulatory system, a response regulator and a sensor histidine protein kinase. The histidine protein ki-

nase, located in the cytoplasmic membrane, autophosphorylates upon interacting with an extracellular inducer molecule. The phosphate group is then transferred to a response regulator that serves as a regulator for the transcription of the bacteriocin gene. Interestingly, nisin regulates its own production via this signaling pathway.

Nisin and other lantibiotics act on the energy-transducing cytoplasmic membrane. The positively charged nisin binds to negatively charged components of the cell wall and membrane. Aggregation and insertion into the energized cytoplasmic membrane leads to the formation of a channel. This channel results in the dissipation of the membrane potential and the chemical gradient across the membrane, and it ultimately leads to cell death. Other lantibiotics

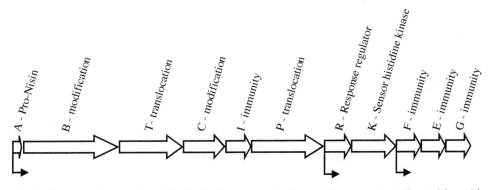

**Fig. 2.** The nisin A regulon of *L. lactis*. The organization of the genes is indicated by wide arrows. Above each arrow, the *nis* gene product and the function ascribed to the product are indicated. Promoters are marked by bent arrows (redrawn from Nes *et al.*, 1996, with kind permission from Kluwer Academic Publishers).

include subtilin from *Bacillus subtilis*, pep 5 from *L. lactis* subsp. *lactis,* and epidermidin from *Staphylococcus epidermiditis.* Their similar structure may reflect a common ancestry.

### 2. *Class II Bacteriocins*

This class of bacteriocins consists of small heat-stable membrane-active peptides that do not appear to contain lanthionines. Most commonly, the genetic determinants for these bacteriocins reside on plasmids, although a few cases of chromosomal location are known. The bacteriocin genes encode preforms of the bacteriocins consisting of leader peptides, required for translocation of the bacteriocin across the cytoplasmic membrane, as well as the bacteriocin. Next to or downstream from the bacteriocin gene, a gene encoding a protein conferring immunity is normally found. These immunity proteins are generally small peptides with approximately 50–150 amino acids. The genetic determinants for bacteriocin production can be part of relatively large gene clusters consisting of several operons. For example, a 16.5-kb chromosomally located gene cluster containing 22 open reading frames organized in five operons has been found in *Lactobacillus plantarum.* Some of these operons encode components of regulatory systems similar to those described previously for nisin. Figure 3 illustrates the regulatory system for class II bacteriocins. The inducer molecules, IF, interact with the histidine protein kinase, HK. The autophosphorylating histidine kinase in turn transfers the phosphate group, P, to the response regulator, RR. The phosphorylated protein activates the expression of several operons, including the bacteriocin operon. The mechanism by which environmental conditions such as cell density or nutritional status affect the concentration of the inducer molecules is largely unknown.

A division of the class II bacteriocins into subgroups IIa, -b, and -c has been proposed. Class IIa bacteriocins are pediocin-like bacteriocins with strong activity against the gram-positive bacteria belonging to the genus *Listeria.* Pediocins PA-1 and AcH are produced by *Pediococcus* species. These bacteriocins are synthesized as pro-pediocins from which the active pediocins are formed after cleavage of the leader peptide. Post-translational modification of pediocin AcH by intramolecular thioether linkage formation has been suggested. If confirmed, this would lessen the distinction between class I and class IIa bacteriocins. Other class IIa bacteriocins are produced by *Leuconostoc, Lactobacillus,* and *Enterococcus.*

Class IIb bacteriocins require the complementary action of two different peptides. Examples of this type of bacteriocin are lactacin F, lactococcin G, and plantaricin S. Class IIa and IIb bacteriocins are synthesized as probacteriocins, consisting of a leader sequence (double-glycine leader) with characteristic glycine–glycine residues located at the cleavage site between the leader peptide and the mature bacteriocin (Fig. 4). Secretion of class IIa and IIb bacteriocins is mediated by the ATP-binding cassette (ABC) transporter (ABC Trans. in Fig. 4), a protein that is localized in the membrane. It consists of a cytoplasmic domain with ATP-binding activity, a central membrane-spanning domain, and a second cytoplasmic domain with proteolytic activity responsible for cleavage of the leader peptide. For lactococcin A, the ABC transporter is encoded by *lcnC,* whose product,

⇓

```
Lactococcin A    M K N Q L N F N I V S D E E L S E A N G G   K

Lactacin F       M K - - - Q F N Y L S H K D L A V V V G G   R

Pediocin PA-1    M K - - - K I E K L T E K E M A N I I G G   K
```

***Fig. 3.*** N-terminal amino acid sequences of prebacteriocins. The arrow indicates the position where cleavage of the signal peptide from the bacteriocin occurs. The double-glycine residues at the cleavage site are highlighted (compiled from the following: lactococcin A, Holo *et al.,* 1991; lactacin F, Muriana and Klaenhammer, 1991; pediocin PA-1; Marugg *et al.,* 1992).

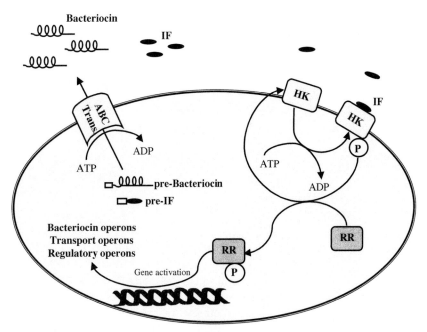

**Fig. 4.** Schematic depiction of transport of class II bacteriocins and signaling pathway leading to bacteriocin expression. IF, induction factor; HK, histidine kinase; P, phosphate; RR, response regulator; ABC Trans., ABC transporter system (modified from Nes *et al.*, 1996, with kind permission from Kluwer Academic Publishers).

C, is depicted in Fig. 5. In addition, the product of *lcnD* (D in Fig. 5) is also involved in transport and maturation of prolactococcin A from the cytoplasm (Fig. 5, In) through the membrane, M, and the cell wall, W, to the extracellular medium (Fig. 5, Out).

Divergicin A and acidicin B belong to class IIc. This class of small heat-stabile bacteriocins is secreted by the producing cells via a universal export pathway (signal peptide-dependent general export pathway or *sec*-dependent pathway). This pathway requires the presence of many gene products, especially the products of the *sec* genes. The extracellular bacteriocin is produced from the probacteriocin by cleavage of the signal peptide.

A common feature of class II bacteriocins is a high content of small amino acids such as glycine. Also, the peptides are strongly cationic with pI's in the range from 8 to 11. Related to their function as membrane-active compounds, these peptides also contain hydrophobic or amphiphilic regions. Proposed mechanisms for this membrane activity are illustrated in Fig. 5 for lactococcin A. The target cell for

the bacteriocin possesses receptors that are accessible to the bacteriocin. These receptors are thought to be blocked from interactions with the bacteriocin by immunity proteins (I) in bacteriocin-producing cells. Pore formation possibly occurs by one of two mechanisms. One model proposes that the binding of the bacteriocin opens a channel involving the receptor, through which cellular constituents can escape through the membrane with lethal results for the cell. An alternative mechanism proposed envisions that the receptor on the target cell functions to direct the pore formation by the bacteriocin molecules.

## C. Class III Bacteriocins

Caseicin 80, produced by *Lactobacillus casei* B80, and helveticin J, produced by *Lactobacillus helveticus* 481, are examples of large heat-labile bacteriocins. The molecular weights of these and some other bacteriocins from gram-positive bacteria (megacin A from *Bacillus megaterium* and bacteriocin BCN5 from *Clostridium perfringens*) are similar to those of some

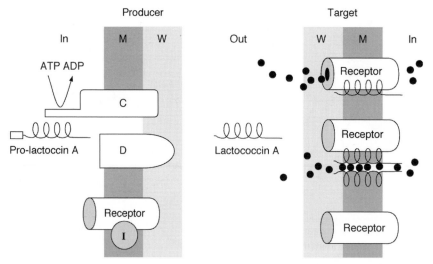

**Fig. 5.** Production of a class II bacteriocin and its effect on a target cell illustrated by the example of lactococcin A. In, inside the cytoplasmic membrane; M, cytoplasmic membrane; W, bacterial cell wall; Out, outside the cell, growth medium; C, LncC, a component of the ABC transporter system; D, LncD, a second component of the transport system; R, receptor for bacteriocin; I, immunity protein rendering receptor insensitive to lactococcin A action (redrawn from Kok *et al.*).

colicins; however, the genetic and molecular characterization of the class III bacteriocins from gram-positive bacteria is far behind that of the colicins. Helveticin J, a protein of approximately 37 kDa, is apparently encoded chromosomally, but location of class III bacteriocin determinants on plasmids appears to be the rule. An open reading frame is located upstream of the gene encoding helveticin J and appears to be part of an operon that includes the helveticin J gene. The function of the putative product of this open reading frame is not known. It is predicted to contain a leader sequence and it is speculated that it is secreted and might play a role in helveticin J immunity. The mode of action of the class III bacteriocins from the lactic acid bacteria is not known.

## V. APPLICATION OF BACTERIOCINS

### A. Nisin

Nisin is undoubtedly the most studied of the bacteriocins produced by gram-positive bacteria. It has found widespread commercial application since its

first use as a food preservative agent in 1951. Nisin has gained worldwide acceptance as a food additive, including in the United States in which nisin first received approval by the Food and Drug Administration for use in pasteurized processed cheese spreads in 1988. Since then, other American foods and food ingredients such as liquid whole egg formulations have included nisin.

Sometimes nisin is referred to as an antibiotic, and indeed, it does function in that manner; however, the term antibiotic is avoided when referring to nisin and other bacteriocins for use in foods. In the United States, therapeutic antibiotics are not permitted in foods. One reason for this ban is the common occurrence in humans of a severe allergic response to therapeutic antibiotics. It is estimated that 8% of the U.S. population is allergic to penicillin, but nisin has been consumed by people in cheese and other cultured dairy products for thousands of years with no known toxicological or allergic response. In part, this may be attributable to the breakdown of nisin by proteolytic enzymes during the digestive process. Also, nisin is not used therapeutically in human or veterinary medicine, and it is not used as an animal feedstuff additive or in growth promotion. Table III

### TABLE III
### Requirements for Bacteriocins Intended for Use as Food Preservatives

Proven safe for human consumption
Economically acceptable cost
Proven effective at relatively low concentrations
No detrimental effect on organoleptic characteristics of the food
Stable during storage and effective for the shelf life of the food
No medical uses

summarizes the requirements for bacteriocins intended for food use.

In the past, there was concern that nisin use might hide unsanitary manufacturing practices in the food industry; however, due to the narrow target spectrum of nisin (it is ineffective against gram-negative, rapidly growing, spoilage bacteria as well as molds), this is not an issue. In addition, the effectiveness of nisin against sensitive gram-positive bacteria depends on the bacterial load. The antibacterial effectiveness of nisin decreases as the population of microbiota in the food increases. It has been shown that although nisin is effective in extending the shelf life of canned soups, it has no efficacy when poor-quality starting ingredients are used.

There are five minor compositional variants of nisin: A–E. The commercially available preparation, Nisaplin, is a salted, diluted preparation of nisin A, the most biologically active of the nisins.

The solubility and stability of nisin depend on the pH of the aqueous solution. In solutions of dilute HCl at pH 2.5, its solubility is 12% and it may be autoclaved without loss of activity. The solubility decreases to 4% at pH 5.0. At neutral and alkaline pH, nisin is practically insoluble and irreversible inactivation occurs even at room temperature. In low-acid foods at pH 6.1–6.9 and in high-acid foods at pH 3.3–4.5, heating for 3 min at 121°C reduces the activity of nisin by 25–50%. Milk protects nisin from the effects of heat, but meat particles seem to increase sensitivity to heat. Although refrigerated, purified nisin in powdered form is stable indefinitely, nisin activity is gradually lost in refrigerated foods. A reason for its inactivation in foods is the susceptibility of nisin to $\alpha$-chymotrypsin and other endogenous proteolytic enzymes. Another factor is the presence of nisinase. Many lactic acid bacteria inactivate nisin by this dehydropeptide reductase. The presence of nisinase is a serious problem in cheese making and is a primary reason why nisin-producing cheese starter cultures cannot be used. Penicillinase at high levels has been reported to also inactivate nisin.

Nisin has no substantial effect against eukaryotic microorganisms and gram-negative bacteria, and the sensitivity of gram-positive bacteria varies. The organisms most sensitive to nisin are populations of *Lactococcus lactis* subsp. *cremoris,* whereas the closely related enterococci, such as *Enterococcus faecalis,* are most often resistant. Other asporogenous gram-positive bacteria that are normally inhibited by nisin include *Micrococcus, Staphylococcus, Corynebacterium, Listeria, Lactobacillus,* and *Mycobacterium.* Nisin is valuable in commercially prepared foods because of its activity against the clostridia and bacilli. The endospore-forming bacteria are major spoilage agents of foods, and the highly toxic pathogen, *Clostridium botulinum,* is of primary concern in food safety. *Bacillus coagulans* and *Bacillus stearothermophilus* (varieties of which produce the world's most heat-resistant spores) are extremely nisin sensitive. Small amounts of nisin increase the heat sensitivity of spores, which is why nisin treatment works well in thermally processed canned foods. Heat processing can be decreased because nisin makes the endospores more susceptible to the lethal effects of heat (e.g., thermal processing *D* values are reduced 50–60% by nisin).

The spores of the small-spored species of *Bacillus* are more sensitive to nisin than those of the large-spored species. For instance, *B. subtilis* spores (small) are inhibited by approximately 5 IU/ml of nisin, whereas *B. cereus* spores (large) require >100 IU/ml for inhibition. Nisin appears to block preemergence swelling of spores.

The spores of *Clostridium* (*C. sporogenes, C. butyricum,* and *C. bifermentans*) are significantly more sensitive to nisin than the vegetative cells. For *C. butyricum,* the sporicidal effect of nisin occurs after outgrowth is triggered. Nisin is more effective against type E than type A *C. botulinum.* The amounts of nisin used to inhibit outgrowth of *C. botulinum* spores range from 100 to 5000 IU/ml, depending on the variety of *C. botulinum* tested, the spore load, and the medium examined.

In vegetative cells, nisin acts as a cationic surfactant that adsorbs strongly to the cytoplasmic membrane, disrupting the membrane by inactivation of sulfhydryl groups and inducing cell lysis. Nisin blocks peptidoglycan synthesis at the cell wall. Resistant strains of *C. butyricum* have been shown not to adsorb nisin. This adsorption process is highly pH dependent.

Nisin is used as a food preservative in acidic foods and beverages in which nisin-sensitive, gram-positive bacteria require control. Nisin is very effective in cheeses, especially in pasteurized processed cheeses and cheese spreads. "Blowing" faults caused by *C. butyricum* and *C. tyrobutyricum* are effectively controlled in processed cheese products at ranges of nisin from 100 to >500 IU/ml, depending on water activity, pH, the levels of sodium chloride and phosphate salts, and the legal limits set by the country of product origin. The use of nisin allows processed cheese spreads to have higher moisture contents and lower levels of salts while maintaining product stability. For dairy products, nisin is often sold mixed with skim milk powder. In many less industrialized countries, in which the availability of refrigeration is limited, nisin is added to milk to increase its shelf life and safety. In Egypt, nisin-amended whole milks can maintain satisfactory quality for 21 days at 37°C with the heat treatment or pasteurization process reduced by 80%. The use of nisin with reduced heat treatment makes powdered milk available for reconstitution in those parts of the world in which water is unsafe and resources are scarce.

In Eastern Europe, nisin is added to canned vegetables. Companies in Poland and the former Soviet Union produce nisin for large-scale commercial use by canneries. The use of nisin significantly lowers energy consumption of the canning process and improves the texture, appearance, and nutritional quality of the products.

Due to its narrow antibacterial activity spectrum, nisin plays a valuable role in the manufacture of alcoholic beverages, in which lactic acid bacteria are important spoilage agents. Because it has no effect on fungi, nisin can be added to the alcoholic fermentation with no detrimental effects to commercial strains of wine or brewing yeast. Nisin inactivates the contaminating lactic acid bacteria of industrial yeast starter cultures so well that nisin treatment is replacing the traditional acid-washing techniques used to cleanse yeast strains because the use of nisin provides the cultures of *Saccharomyces cerevisiae* with improved viability and unchanged fermentative performance.

The development of nisin-resistant strains of *Leuconostoc oenos* has led to successful pure culture malolactic fermentation (conversion of malic acid to lactic acid) in nisin-amended wines in the presence of undesirable lactic acid bacteria. Naturally occurring lactic acid bacteria can cause spoilage of the wine as well as inconsistent malolactate fermentations, resulting in a less desirable product. The application of nisin in this manner allows less sulfur dioxide to be used in the wine to prevent bacterial spoilage. Sulfites are another group of food additives in which strong allergic reactions by consumers have been documented. Nisin has also been evaluated for use in fruit brandies and baked goods.

Nisin has been examined for use in meats as a possible alternative or adjunct to nitrite in cured products such as cooked ham. Nisin and nitrite apparently have an additive effect against clostridia in some model meat systems (e.g., cooked ham slurry) in which the nitrite level can be reduced to 40 ppm from the normally used 150 ppm without loss of preservative effect or color formation. However, reports in similar test systems have suggested instability of nisin in stored refrigerated meats. Recent work presents evidence that nisin does not work very well as a meat preservative.

In addition to issues of effectiveness, another important impediment for commercial use of nisin has been cost. In some instances, the application of nisin has not been as cost-effective as other methods of preservation.

## B. Other Bacteriocins for Use in Foods

In the marketplace, nisin is currently the only characterized or purified bacteriocin approved for use as a food additive; however, growth extracts of acidulating bacteria containing bacteriocins are used as food preservatives. Microgard is a commercial food additive that is a growth extract of *Propionibacterium freudenreichii* subsp. *shermanii*. Skim milk is fermented with the propionibacteria and then pasteurized to inactivate the culture. The antagonistic effect of Microgard is due to the metabolic by-products by the culture, including acids, bacteriocins, and diacetyl. It is marketed as a food preservative for use in such products as cottage cheese and fruit-flavored yogurt. Microgard has broad-spectrum activity against gram-negative bacteria, yeasts, and some molds. The shelf life of cottage cheese is extended 6–9 days using Microgard. Versions of Microgard have been developed that incorporate nisin as an active ingredient.

In the search for bacteriocins with commercial application as food preservatives, it is no mystery that bacteria with a long history of use in fermented foods or close beneficial association with humans are prime candidates in the screening for "new" bacteriocins. It is known that members of the genera *Lactobacillus*, *Pediococcus*, *Leuconostoc*, *Propionibacterium*, *Bifidobacterium*, and *Carnobacterium* synthesize bacteriocins and that *Lactococcus* produces other bacteriocins in addition to nisin. Many of these bacteriocins are inhibitory against the pathogen *Listeria monocytogenes*, the causative agent for listeriosis, a potentially lethal food-borne disease. *Listeria monocytogenes* is commonly found in raw, animal-derived foods, and it has relatively high resistances to extremes in temperature, pH, and salt concentrations. Therefore, these antilisterial bacteriocins from lactic acid bacteria could be considered safe, "natural" preservative agents; however, none of these bacteriocins are currently being commercially developed.

In general, bacteriocins from gram-positive bacteria have a wider spectrum of activity than bacteriocins from gram-negative bacteria. A broader activity spectrum represents a greater range of applications. That bacteriocins with a very broad activity spectrum may exist is suggested by experiments with a partially purified preparation of propionicin PLG-1 from *Propionibacterium thoeniii*. (A bacterium closely related to the propionibacteria that produce "eyes" in Swiss cheese.) The propionicin PLG-1 preparation was antagonistic not only against lactic acid bacteria and other gram-positive bacteria but also against several deleterious gram-negative bacteria, such as *Pseudomonas fluorescens*, *Pseudomonas aeruginosa*, *Vibrio parahaemolyticus*, and *Campylobacter jejuni*. In addition, propionicin PLG-1 inhibited genera of yeasts and molds, such as *Aspergillus*, *Candida*, *Saccharomyces*, and *Trichoderma*. Such antimicrobial versatility is highly desirable for a preservative because the microbiota present in foods and beverages is often unpredictable; a broad inhibitive effect is beneficial for maintenance or extension of shelf life for a range of products.

Bacteria such as *Staphylococcus aureus*, *Yersinia pestis*, *L. monocytogenes*, *C. botulinum*, *Streptococcus pyogenes*, and *Corynebacterium diphtheriae* all produce bacteriocins; however, given their established virulence as agents of severe human illness, the concept of using a by-product of their growth as an ingredient in a food or personal product is not acceptable. Hence the screening of food-grade bacteria for preservative compounds.

## C. Other Applications for Bacteriocins

Ambicin is a nontoxic bacteriocin formula that has been shown to kill bacteria that cause dental plaque on teeth and gums. It has been evaluated for intended use in mouthwash, toothpaste, soap, and other skincare applications. Its marketing strategy declares it to be a safe and natural alternative to antibiotics and chemical germicidals. It is also effective in the prevention of bovine mastitis, an infection of the udder of dairy cows that annually causes worldwide losses of approximately $35 billion. Ambicin is rapid acting, has a broad spectrum of activity, and leaves no toxic residue to contaminate milk supplies. In addition, it does not show the skin irritation commonly experienced with chemical germicidals, which can dry and crack the teat skin leading to persistent intramammary infections. The market for mastitis teat dips and sprays worldwide is estimated to be $130 million.

Bacteriocins have application in biotechnology as genetic markers and for maintenance of plasmid-bearing bacterial cells propagated in continuous culture. As genetic markers, genes for bacteriocin synthesis and immunity can substitute for antibiotic resistance markers that are currently predominantly used to tag or identify plasmids. Colonies made up of cells that harbor a bacteriocin gene-tagged plasmid and that were overlayed with an indicator strain will be encircled by zones of inhibition. Given the proliferation of antibiotic-resistant bacteria in the environment that threatens the efficacy of therapeutic antibiotics used to fight infection, the use of antibiotic resistance markers for selection of genetically engineered organisms is discouraged. This is especially true for food-related applications in which the possible transfer of antibiotic resistance to pathogens residing in the human intestinal tract could result in serious communicable disease resistant to the drugs used to control it.

Genetically engineered organisms harboring plasmids with desirable genes and antibiotic resistance markers are usually cultured in the presence of the corresponding antibiotics. This is done to ensure that only plasmid-bearing cells proliferate in the culture. Elimination of bacteria that have lost their recombinant plasmid is often essential since these plasmid-free cells can outgrow those that retain the plasmid. The success of large-scale industrial fermentations with recombinant bacteria whose desirable traits are encoded on plasmids critically depends on the biomass consisting of virtually only plasmid-bearing cells. Again, bacteriocin and the corresponding immunity genes can function as substitutes of antibiotic resistance markers on these plasmids because cells arising from plasmid loss during cell division will be killed by those cells retaining the plasmid, thus ensuring continued expression of the desired trait. It has been suggested that this kind of phenomenon is responsible for survival of such plasmids in natural environments.

## VI. FUTURE DIRECTIONS

The example of nisin illustrates the potential inherent in bacteriocins for applications as antimicrobials and preservatives; however, many significant obstacles to widespread use also exist. One of these obstacles is cost. Bacteriocins, even those of the low-molecular-weight variety, are expensive to produce from cultures. Frequently, the level of bacteriocin

that is found in cultures is too low to make the isolation of the bacteriocin commercially viable. Recombinant DNA technology is currently used to improve the yield of bacteriocins. Random or site-directed mutagenesis is applied to generate variants of known bacteriocins that demonstrate broader activity spectra and that are more stable than their wild-type counterparts.

To avoid the need to obtain purified bacteriocins as preservatives and antipathogenic compounds, the addition of bacteriocin-producing, food-grade bacteria directly to food products is being explored. This approach requires that bacteria are selected that produce an effective amount of bacteriocin in the "natural" food environment. Also, the bacteria, at the numbers required for sufficient bacteriocin production, have to be without affect on taste and appearance of the treated food.

Bacteriocins will probably rarely be a sufficient means to preserve or treat foods against pathogens; however, their use may reduce the need for undesirable additives such as salts or for prolonged heat treatments. In conjunction with physical treatments such as ultra-high pressure, or other natural preservatives, bacteriocins might have a more extensive role in the future.

## See Also the Following Articles

ABC Transport • Food Spoilage and Preservation • Lactic Acid Bacteria • Plasmids, Bacterial

## Bibliography

Abee, T., Krockel, L., and Hill, C. (1995). Bacteriocins: modes of action and potentials in food preservation and control of food poisoning. *Int. J. Food Microbiol.* 28, 169–185.

Delves-Broughton, J. (1990). *Food Technol.* 44, 100–117.

De Vuyst, L., and Vandamme, E. J. (Eds.) (1994). "Bacteriocins of Lactic Acid Bacteria." Blackie Academic & Professional (imprint of Chapman & Hall), London.

Holo, H., Nilssen, O., and Nes, I. F. (1991). Lactococcin A, a new bacteriocin from lactococcus lactic subsp. cremoris: isolation and characterization of the protein and its gene. *J. Bacteriol.* 173, 3879–3887.

Hoover, D. G., and Steenson, L. R. (Eds.) (1993). "Bacteriocins of Lactic Acid Bacteria." Academic Press, San Diego.

Kaletta, C., and Entian, K.-D. (1989). Nisin, a peptide antibiotic: cloning and sequencing of the nisA gene and post-translational processing of its peptide product. *J. Bacteriol.* **171**, 1597–1601.

Klaenhammer, T. R. (1993). *FEMS Microbiol. Rev.* **12**, 39–86.

Kok, J., Holo, H., van Belkum, M. J., Haandrikman, A. J., and Nes, I. F. Nonnisin bacteriocins in lactococci: Biochemistry, genetics, and mode of action. *In* "Bacteriocins of Lactic Acid Bacteria" (D. G. Hoover and L. R. Steenson, Eds.), pp. 121–150. Academic Press, San Diego.

Marugg, J. D., Gonzales, C. F., Kunka, B. S., Lederboer, A. M., Pucci, M. J., Toonen, M. Y., Walker, S. A., Zoetmulder, L. C. M., and Vandenbergh, P. A. (1992). Cloning, expression, and nucleotide sequence of genes involved in production of pediocin PA-1, and bacteriocin from Pediococcus acidilactici PAC1.0. *Appl. Environ. Microbiol.* **58**, 2360–2367.

Muriana, P. M., and Klaenhammer, T. R. (1991). Cloning, phenotypic expression, and DNA sequence of the gene for lactacin F, an antimicrobial peptide produced by Lactobacillus spp. *J. Bacteriol.* **173**, 1779–1788.

Nes, I. F., Diep, D. B., Havarstein, L. S., Brurberg, M. B., Eijsink, V., and Holo, H. (1996). Biosynthesis of bacteriocins in lactic acid bacteria. *In* "Lactic Acid Bacteria: Genetics, Metabolism and Applications" (G. Venema, J. H. J. Huis in 't Veld, and J. Hugenholtz, Eds.), pp. 17–32. Kluwer, Dordrecht.

Van der Wal, F. J., Luirink, J., and Oudega, B. (1995). Bacteriocin release proteins: mode of action, structure, and biotechnological application. *FEMS Microbiol. Rev.* **17**, 381–399.

# Bacteriophages

## Hans-Wolfgang Ackermann
*Laval University*

I. Isolation and Identification of Phages
II. Phage Taxonomy
III. Phage Occurrence and Ecology
IV. Phage Physiology
V. Phages in Applied Microbiology

## GLOSSARY

**bacteriophage**  Virus that replicates in a bacterium; literally "eater of bacteria."

**capsid**  Protein coat surrounding the nucleic acid of a virus.

**envelope**  Lipoprotein membrane surrounding a virus capsid.

**genome**  Complete set of genes in a virus or a cell; in viruses, it consists of either DNA or RNA.

**host range**  The number and nature of organisms in which a virus or group of viruses replicate.

**integrase**  Viral enzyme mediating the integration of viral DNA into host DNA.

**prokaryote**  Type of cell whose DNA is not enclosed in a membrane.

**restriction endonuclease**  Enzyme that recognizes a specific base sequence in double-stranded DNA and cuts the DNA strand at this site.

**superinfection**  Infection of a virus-infected host by a second virus.

**virion**  Complete infectious virus particle.

**BACTERIOPHAGES,** or "phages," are viruses of prokaryotes including eubacteria and archaebacteria. They were discovered and described twice, first in 1915 by the British pathologist Frederick William Twort and then in 1917 by the Canadian bacteriologist Félix Hubert d'Herelle working at the Pasteur Institute of Paris. With approximately 4650 isolates of known morphol-

ogy, phages constitute the largest of all virus groups. Phages are tailed, cubic, filamentous, or pleomorphic and contain single-stranded or double-stranded DNA or RNA. They are classified into 13 families. Tailed phages are far more numerous than other types, are enormously diversified, and seem to be the oldest of all phage groups.

Bacteriophages occur in more than 130 bacterial genera and many different habitats. Infection results in phage multiplication or the establishment of lysogenic or carrier states. Bacterial genes may be transmitted in the process. Some phages (e.g., T4, T7, I, MS2, fd, and fX174) are famous experimental models. Phage research has led to major advances in virology, genetics, and molecular biology (concepts of lysogeny, provirus, induction, transduction, eclipse; DNA and RNA as carriers of genetic information; and the discovery of restriction endonucleases). Phages are used in phage typing and genetic engineering, but high hopes for phage therapy have generally been disappointed. In destroying valuable bacterial cultures, some phages are nuisances in the fermentation industry.

## I. ISOLATION AND IDENTIFICATION OF PHAGES

### A. Propagation and Maintenance

#### 1. Propagation

On solid media, phages produce clear, lysed areas in bacterial lawns or, if sufficiently diluted, small holes called "plaques," each of which correspond to a single viable phage. In liquid media, phages sometimes cause complete clearing of bacterial cultures. Phages are grown on young bacteria during their logarithmic phase of growth, usually in conditions that are optimal for their host. Some phages require divalent cations ($Ca^{2+}$ and $Mg^{2+}$) or other cofactors. Phages are propagated by three types of techniques: (i) in liquid media inoculated with host bacteria, (ii) on agar surfaces with a monolayer of bacteria, and (iii) in agar double layers consisting of normal bottom agar covered with a mixture of soft agar (0.3–0.9%), phages, and bacteria. Phages are harvested after a suitable incubation time, generally 3 hr for liquid cultures and 18 hr for solid media. Phages from agar cultures are extracted with buffer or nutrient broth. Phage suspensions, or lysates, are sterilized (best by filtration through membrane filters of 0.45-nm pore size) and then titrated. Sterilization by chloroform or other chemicals is of questionable value.

### 2. Storage

No single technique is suitable for all phages. Many phages can be kept as lysates at 4°C or in lyophile, but others are quickly inactivated under these conditions. Lysates should be kept without additives such as thymol or chloroform. The best procedure seems to be preservation at −70°C with 50% glycerol. Phages may also be preserved in liquid nitrogen by drying on filter paper and, in the case of endospore-forming bacteria, by trapping phage genomes in spores. Ideally, any phage should be preserved by several techniques.

## B. Isolation of Phages

### 1. *Isolation from Nature*

All samples must be liquid. Soil and other solid material are homogenized and suspended in an appropriate medium. Solids and bacteria are removed usually by filtration, preceded or not by centrifugation. Very rich samples can be assayed directly on indicator bacteria. In most cases, phages must be enriched by incubating the sample in a liquid medium inoculated with indicator bacteria. The culture is then filtered and titrated and phages are purified by repeated cloning of single plaques. Large samples must be concentrated before enrichment. This is

done by centrifugation, filter adsorption and elution, flocculation, or precipitation by polyethylene glycol 6000. Adsorption–elution techniques may involve strongly acidic or alkaline conditions that inactivate phages.

### 2. *Isolation from Lysogenic Bacteria*

Many bacteria produce phages spontaneously. These phages may be detected by testing culture filtrates on indicator bacteria. It is generally preferable to induce phage production by mitomycin C, ultraviolet (UV) light, or other agents. A suspension of growing bacteria is exposed to the agent (e.g., 1 mg/ml of mitomycin C for 10 min or UV light for 1 min), incubated again, and then filtered. After mitomycin C induction, the bacteria should be separated from the agent by centrifugation and transferred into a fresh medium. Bacteriocins (see Section II.C), which are a source of error, are easily identified because they cannot be propagated and do not produce plaques when diluted.

## C. Concentration and Purification

Small samples of <100 ml are usually concentrated by ultracentrifugation (approximately 60,000 g in swinging-bucket rotors), followed by several washes of the sedimented phages in buffer. Fixed-angle rotors allow considerable reduction of the g force because large phages sediment at as little as 10,000 g for 1 hr. Further purification may be achieved by centrifugation in a CsCl or sucrose density gradient. For large samples, there are problems of contamination, aeration, and foaming. Preparation schedules are often complex: (i) pretreatment by low-speed centrifugation and/or filtration; (ii) concentration, mostly by precipitation with polyethylene glycol; and (iii) final purification in a density gradient or by ultracentrifugation.

## D. Identification

Phage identification relies greatly on the observation that most phages are specific for their host genus; however, enterobacteria, in which polyvalent phages are common, are considered in this context as a single "genus." Phages are first examined in the electron microscope. This usually provides the family diagnosis and often indicates relationships on the species level. If no phages are known for a given host genus or there are only phages of different morphology, the new isolate may be considered as a new phage. If the same host genus has phages of identical morphology, they must be compared to the isolate by DNA–DNA hybridization and/or serology. Further identification may be achieved by determining restriction endonuclease DNA cleavage patterns or constitutive proteins.

## II. PHAGE TAXONOMY

### A. General

D'Herelle thought that there was only one phage with many races, the *Bacteriophagum intestinale*. Early attempts at classification by serology, host range, and inactivation tests showed that phages were highly diversified, but these attempts proved premature. Modern taxonomy started in 1962 when a system of viruses based on the properties of the virion and its nucleic acid was introduced by Lwoff, Horne, and Tournier. In 1967, phages were classified into six basic types on the basis of morphology and nature of nucleic acid. Other types were later established, and this process is likely to continue if more archaebacteria and other "unusual" microbes are investigated for the presence of phages. The International Committee on Taxonomy of Viruses currently recognizes one order, 13 families, and 30 genera in phages. Their morphology is illustrated in Fig. 1 and their basic characteristics and hosts are listed in Tables I–V. The most important family criteria are type of nucleic acid, particle shape, and the presence or absence of an envelope. As in other viruses, family names end in *-viridae* and genus names in *-virus*. Species are designated by the vernacular names of their best known (or only) members (e.g., T4 or λ).

### B. Phage Families and Genera

#### 1. *Tailed Phages*

With approximately 4600 observations, tailed phages comprise approximately 96% of phages and

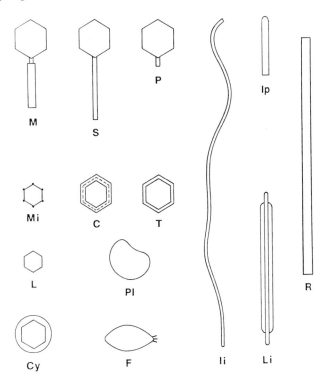

**Fig. 1.** Morphology of phage families. C, Corticoviridae; Cy, Cystoviridae; F, Fuselloviridae, Ii, Inoviridae, *Inovirus* genus; Ip, Inoviridae, *Plectrovirus* genus; L, Leviviridae; Li, Lipothrixviridae; M, Myoviridae; Mi, Microviridae; P, Podoviridae; Pl, Plasmaviridae; R, Rudiviridae; S, Siphoviridae; T, Tectiviridae. (modified from Ackermann, 1987, with permission of Blackwell Scientific Publications Ltd., Oxford, UK).

are the largest virus group known. They contain a single molecule of double-stranded (ds) DNA and are characterized by a tubular protein tail, a specialized structure for the transfer of phage DNA into host bacteria. Tailed phages have recently been given order rank and the name *Caudovirales*. They are classified into three families:

1. Myoviridae: phages with long complex tails consisting of a core and a contractile sheath (25% of tailed phages, six genera named after phages T4, P1, P2, Mu, SPO1, and ΦH);

2. Siphoviridae: phages with long noncontractile, more or less flexible tails (61%, six genera named after phages λ, T1, T5, L1, c2, ψM); and

3. Podoviridae: phages with short tails (15%, three genera named after T7, P22, and φ29).

***TABLE I***
**Main Properties and Frequency of Phage Families**[a]

| Shape | Nucleic acid | Family | Genus | Particulars | Example | No. of members[b] |
|---|---|---|---|---|---|---|
| Tailed | DNA, ds, L | Myoviridae | 6, see text | Tail contractile | T4 | 1128 |
| | | Siphoviridae | 6, see text | Tail long, noncontractile | λ | 2816 |
| | | Podoviridae | 3, see text | Tail short | T7 | 646 |
| Cubic | DNA, ss, C | Microviridae | *Microvirus* | Conspicuous capsomers | φX174 | 40 |
| | | | *Bdellomicrovirus* | | MAC-1 | |
| | | | *Chlamydiamicrovirus* | | Chp1 | |
| | | | *Spiromicrovirus* | | SV4 | |
| | DNA, ds, C, S | Corticoviridae | *Corticovirus* | Complex capsid, lipids | PM2 | 3? |
| | DNA, ds, L | Tectiviridae | *Tectivirus* | Double capsid, pseudo-tail, lipids | PRD1 | 16 |
| | RNA, ss, L | Leviviridae | *Levivirus* | | MS2 | 37 |
| | | | *Allolevivirus* | | Qβ | |
| | RNA, ds, L, M | Cystoviridae | *Cystovirus* | Envelope, lipids | φ6 | 1 |
| Filamentous | DNA, ss, C | Inoviridae | *Inovirus* | Long filaments | fd | 53 |
| | | | *Plectrovirus* | Short rods | L51 | |
| | DNA, ds, L | Lipothrixviridae | *Lipothrixvirus* | Envelope, lipids | TTV1 | 4 |
| | DNA, ds, L | Rudiviridae | *Rudivirus* | Stiff rods, no envelope, no lipids | SIRV1 | 2 |
| Pleomorphic | DNA, ds, C, S | Plasmaviridae | *Plasmavirus* | Envelope, no capsid, lipids | MVL2 | 5? |
| | DNA, ds, C, S | Fuselloviridae | *Fusellovirus* | Lemon shaped, envelope, lipids | SSV1 | 2? |

[a] Modified from Ackermann (1987) with permission of Blackwell Scientific Publications Ltd. C, circular, ds, double-stranded; L, linear, M, multipartite; S, supercoiled, ss, single-stranded.

[b] Excluding phage-like bacteriocins and known defective phages (computed August 25, 1998).

Classification of tailed phages into genera is still in its infancy. Phage capsids, usually named heads, are icosahedra or derivatives thereof. Capsomers are rarely visible. Elongated heads are relatively rare but occur in all three families. Heads and tails vary enormously in size and may have facultative structures such as head or tail fibers, collars, base plates, or terminal spikes (Fig. 2). The DNA is coiled inside the head. Its composition generally reflects that of the host bacterium, but it may contain unusual bases such as 5-hydroxymethylcytosine. Genetic maps are complex and include approximately 290 genes in phage T4 (possibly more in larger phages). Genes for related functions cluster together. Up to 40 proteins have been found in phage coats (T4). Lipids are generally absent, but have been reported in a few exceptional cases. Response to inactivating agents is variable and no generalization is possible. Despite the absence of lipids, about one-third of tailed phages are chloroform sensitive, making chloroform use in

phage isolation a dangerous procedure. Most properties of tailed phages appear as individual or species characteristics. Accordingly, genera have not been established, but approximately 250 species are cur-

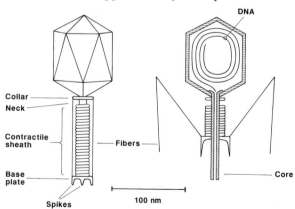

**Fig. 2.** Schematic representation of phage T4 with extended tail and folded tail fibers (left) and sectioned with contracted tail (right) (modified from Ackermann, 1985, with permission of Flammarion Médecine-Sciences, Paris).

**TABLE II**
**Dimensions and Physicochemical Properties**[a]

| Phage group or family | Virion | | | | | Nucleic acid | | |
|---|---|---|---|---|---|---|---|---|
| | Particle size (nm) | Tail length (nm) | Weight (MDa) | Buoyant density | Lipids (%) | Content (%) | Size (kbp or kb) | G + C (%) |
| Tailed phages | | | | | | | | |
| Average | 63[b] | 153 | 100 | 1.49 | — | 46 | 79 | 48 |
| Range | 38–160[b] | 3–825 | 29–470 | 1.4–1.54 | — | 30–62 | 17–745 | 27–72 |
| Microviridae | 27 | — | 7 | 1.39 | — | 26 | 4.4–6.1 | 44 |
| Corticoviridae | 60 | — | 49 | 1.28 | 15 | 13 | 9.0 | 43 |
| Tectiviridae | 63 | — | 70 | 1.29 | 15 | 14 | 15.2 | 51 |
| Leviviridae | 23 | — | 4 | 1.46 | | 30 | 3.5–4.3 | 51 |
| Cystoviridae | 75–80 | — | 99 | 1.27 | 20 | 10 | 13.4 | 56 |
| Inoviridae | | | | | | | | |
| Inovirus | 760–1950 × 7 | — | 12–23 | 1.30 | — | 6?–21 | 5.8–7.3 | 40–60 |
| Plectrovirus | 85–250 × 15 | — | | 1.37 | — | | 4.4–8.3 | |
| Lipothrixviridae | 400–2400 × 38 | — | 33 | 1.25 | 22 | 3 | 16–42 | |
| Rudiviridae | 780–950 × 20–40 | — | | 1.36 | — | | 33–36 | |
| Plasmaviridae | 80 | — | | | 11 | | 11.7 | 32 |
| Fuselloviridae | 85 × 60 | — | | 1.24 | 10 | | 15.5 | |

[a] Modified from Ackermann (1987) with permission of Blackwell Scientific Publications Ltd. Buoyant density is g/ml in CsCl; G + C, guanine-cytosine content; —, absent.

[b] Isometric heads only.

**TABLE III**
**Comparative Biological Properties**

| Shape | Phage group | Infection | | Adsorption | | Assembly | | Release |
|---|---|---|---|---|---|---|---|---|
| | | Nature | By | By | To | Site | Start | |
| Tailed | Caudovirales | V or T | DNA | Tail end | Cell wall, pili, capsule, flagella | Nucleoplasm, cell periphery | Capsid | Lysis |
| Isometric | Microviridae[a] | V | DNA | Spikes | Cell wall | Nucleoplasm | Capsid | Lysis |
| | Corticoviridae | V | DNA | Spikes | Pili | PM | Capsid | Lysis |
| | Tectiviridae | V | DNA | Pseudo-tail | Pili, cell wall | Nucleoplasm | Capsid | Lysis |
| | Leviviridae | V | RNA | A protein | Pili | Cytoplasm | RNA | Lysis |
| | Cystoviridae | V | Capsid | Envelope | Pili | Nucleoplasm | Capsid | Lysis |
| Filamentous | Inoviridae | | | | | | | |
| | Inovirus | S or T | Virion | Virus tip | Pili | PM | DNA | Extrusion |
| | Plectrovirus | S | Virion? | Virus tip | PM | PM | DNA? | Extrusion |
| | Lipothrixviridae | V or T | | Virus tip | Pili | | | Lysis |
| | Rudiviridae | S | Virion | Virus tip | Pili | | | |
| Pleomorphic | Plasmaviridae | T | DNA? | Envelope | PM | PM | DNA | Budding |
| | Fuselloviridae | T | | Spikes | | | | Extrusion |

[a] Data are for *Microvirus* genus only.

*Note.* Abbreviations used: PM, plasma membrane; S, steady state; T, temperate, V, virulent.

***TABLE IV***
**Occurrence and Frequency of Tailed and Cubic, Filamentous,
and Pleomorphic (CFP) Phages**[a]

| Volume and section | Bacterial group according to Bergey's Manual (Holt, 1990) | Phages | | |
|---|---|---|---|---|
| | | Tailed | CFP | Total |
| I | | | | |
| 1 | Spirochetes | 9 | | 9 |
| 2 | Spirilla and vibrioids | 40 | 9 | 48 |
| 4 | Gram-negative aerobic rods and cocci | 734 | 18 | 752 |
| 5 | Gram-negative facultatively anaerobic rods and cocci | 999 | 91 | 1090 |
| 6 | Gram-negative anaerobic rods | 26 | | 26 |
| 7 | Gram-negative sulfate or sulfur reducers | 2 | | 2 |
| 8 | Gram-negative anaerobic cocci | 4 | | 4 |
| 9 | Rickettsias and chlamydias | 2 | 2 | 4 |
| 10 | Mycoplasmas | 17 | 21 | 38 |
| 11 | Endosymbionts | 1 | | 1 |
| II | | | | |
| 12 | Gram-positive cocci | 1188 | | 1188 |
| 13 | Endospore formers | 575 | 9 | 584 |
| 14 | Gram-positive nonsporing regular rods | 283 | | 283 |
| 15 | Gram-positive nonsporing pleomorphic rods | 147 | | 147 |
| 16 | Mycobacteria | 77 | | 77 |
| 17 | Nocardioforms | 97 | | 97 |
| III | | | | |
| 18 | Anoxygenic phototrophs | 11 | | 11 |
| 19 | Cyanobacteria | 34 | | 34 |
| 20 | Chemolithotrophs | 2 | | 2 |
| 21 | Budding and/or appendaged bacteria | 112 | 8 | 120 |
| 22 | Sheathed bacteria | 1 | | 1 |
| 23 | Nonfruiting gliding bacteria | 32 | 2 | 34 |
| 24 | Myxobacteria | 16 | | 16 |
| 25 | Archaebacteria | 14 | 12 | 26 |
| IV | | | | |
| 26 | Actinoplanetes | 5 | | 5 |
| 29 | Streptomycetes | 122 | | 122 |
| 30 | Maduromycetes | 3 | | 3 |
| 31 | Thermomonosporae | 27 | | 27 |
| 32 | Thermoactinomycetes | 4 | | 4 |
| 33 | Other actinomycete genera | 6 | | 6 |
| Total | | 4590 | 172 | 4762 |

[a] Excluding phage-like bacteriocins and known defective phages; computed August 25, 1998. Based on a detailed computation published in 1996 (Ackermann, 1996).

**TABLE V**
**Host Range**

| Bacterial division | Phage group | Bacterial group or genus |
|---|---|---|
| Eubacteria | Caudovirales | Any (ubiquitous) |
| | Microviridae | Enterobacteria, *Bdellovibrio, Chlamydia, Spiroplasma* |
| | Corticoviridae | *Alteromonas* |
| | Tectiviridae | a. Enterics, *Acinetobacter, Pseudomonas, Thermus, Vibrio* |
| | | b. *Bacillus, Alicyclobacillus* |
| | Leviviridae | Enterics, *Acinetobacter, Caulobacter, Pseudomonas* |
| | Cystoviridae | *Pseudomonas* |
| | Inoviridae | |
| | *Inovirus* | Enterics, *Pseudomonas, Thermus, Vibrio, Xanthomonas* |
| | *Plectrovirus* | *Acholeplasma, Spiroplasma* |
| | Plasmaviridae | *Acholeplasma, Spiroplasma* |
| Archaebacteria | Caudovirales | Extreme halophiles and methanogens |
| | Lipothrixviridae | *Thermoproteus* |
| | Rudiviridae | *Sulfolobus, Thermoproteus* |
| | Fuselloviridae | *Sulfolobus* |

rently recognizable, mostly on the basis of morphology, DNA–DNA hybridization, and serology.

### 2. Cubic, Filamentous, and Pleomorphic Phages

This group includes 10 small phage families that correspond to approximately 4% of phages, differ greatly in nucleic acid nature and particle structure, and sometimes have a single member. Host ranges are mostly narrow (Table V). Capsids with cubic symmetry, with one exception, are icosahedra or related bodies. Filamentous phages, according to the current knowledge, have helical symmetry. Particles may or may not be enveloped. As in other viruses, the presence of lipids is accompanied by low buoyant density and high sensitivity to chloroform and ether.

#### a. Cubic DNA Phages

(1) *Microviridae*   The genus *Microvirus* includes the phage φX174 and related phages of enterobacteria and is characterized by large capsomers. Similar phages occur in taxonomically distinct bacteria such as *Bdellovibrio, Chlamydia,* and *Spiroplasma.*

(2) *Corticoviridae*   The only certain member of the family Corticoviridae is a maritime phage, PM2. Its capsid consists of two protein shells and a lipid bilayer sandwiched in between. Two similar, little known phages were isolated from seawater.

(3) *Tectiviridae*   Phages are characterized by a double capsid and a unique mode of infection. The outer capsid, which is rigid and apparently proteinic, surrounds a thick, flexible lipoprotein membrane. Upon adsorption to bacteria or chloroform treatment, this inner coat becomes a tail-like tube approximately 60 nm in length, obviously a nucleic acid ejection device. Tectiviruses of bacilli have apical spikes. Despite their small number, tectiviruses are found in widely different bacteria.

#### b. Cubic RNA Phages

(1) *Leviviridae*   Leviviruses resemble enteroviruses and have no morphological features. Most of them are plasmid-specific coliphages that adsorb to F or sex pili and have been divided, by serology and other criteria, into two genera. Several unclassified leviviruses are specific for other plasmid types (C, H, M, etc.) or occur outside of the enterobacteria family.

(2) *Cystoviridae*   The single member of the family Cystoviridae is unique in several ways. It is the only phage to contain dsRNA and RNA polymerase. The RNA is multipartite and consists of three molecules.

### c. Filamentous Phages

*(1) Inoviridae* The Inoviridae family includes two genera with very different host ranges and similarities in replication and morphogenesis that seem to derive from the single-stranded nature of phage DNA rather than from a common origin of these phages. Despite the absence of lipids, viruses are chloroform sensitive. The *Inovirus* genus includes 37 phages that are long, rigid, or flexible filaments of variable length. They are restricted to a few related gram-negative bacteria, sensitive to sonication, and resistant to heat. Many of them are plasmid specific. The *Plectrovirus* genus includes 16 isolates. Phages are short, straight rods and occur in mycoplasmas only.

*(2) Lipothrixviridae* This family includes four viruses of the archaebacterial genus *Thermoproteus*. Particles are characterized by the combination of a lipoprotein envelope and rodlike shape.

*(3) Rudiviridae* This family includes two viruses of different length, isolated from the archaebacteria *Sulfolobus* and *Thermoproteus*. Particles are straight rods without envelopes and closely resemble the tobacco mosaic virus.

### d. Pleomorphic Phages

*(1) Plasmaviridae* Only one member is known: *Acholeplasma* virus MVL2 or L2. It contains dsDNA, has no capsid, and may be considered a condensation of nucleoprotein with a lipoprotein envelope. Four similar isolates are known, but one them has been described as containing single-stranded DNA and the taxonomic status of all four is uncertain.

*(2) Fuselloviridae* This family has only one known member: SSV1, which is produced on induction by the archaebacterium *Sulfolobus shibatae*. Particles are lemon-shaped with short spikes at one end. The coat consists of two hydrophobic proteins and host lipids and is disrupted by chloroform. SSV1 has not been propagated for the absence of a suitable host. It persists in bacterial cells as a plasmid and as an integrated prophage (see Section IV.B.1). A possibly related droplet-shaped virus has been found in *Sulfolobus*.

## C. Plasmids, Episomes, and Bacteriocins

Plasmids are extrachromosomal genetic elements that consist of circular or linear dsDNA and replicate independently of the host chromosome. Certain prophages behave as plasmids, but phages and plasmids are sharply differentiated: contrary to plasmids, phages have a coat and genomes of uniform size, occur free in nature, and generally lyse their hosts. The term "episome" designates both plasmids and prophages that can integrate reversibly into host DNA. Bacteriocins are antibacterial agents that are produced by bacteria, require specific receptors, and kill other bacteria. High-molecular-weight or "particulate" bacteriocins are defective phages (e.g., contractile or non-contractile tails without heads). Low-molecular-weight or "true" bacteriocins are a mixed group of entities, including enzymes and phage tail spikes.

## D. Origin and Evolution of Bacteriophages

Phages are probably polyphyletic in nature and originated at different times. This is indicated by seemingly unbridgeable fundamental differences between most phage families and by their host ranges. Phages may have derived from cell constituents that acquired a coat and became independent [e.g., leviviruses from messenger RNA (mRNA) and filamentous inoviruses from plasmids]. Tailed phages are obviously phylogenetically related and may represent the oldest phage group. Their occurrence in eubacteria and archaebacteria suggests that they appeared before their hosts diverged, at least 3 billion years ago. Phage groups linked to aerobic bacteria may have emerged at the same time as or after the atmosphere became oxygenated by the activity of cyanobacteria. In some cases, nature repeated itself. Convergent evolution is evident in the pseudo-tails of tectiviruses and perhaps in the general resemblance of *Inovirus* and *Plectrovirus* phages.

Microviruses, tectiviruses, and leviviruses show little or no morphological differentiation, possibly because of constraints imposed by capsid size or because of the relatively young geological age of these phages. Inoviruses differentiated by elongation. By contrast, tailed phages are extremely diversified and probably had an eventful evolutionary history. In terms of structural simplicity and present-day frequency, the archetypal tailed phage from which the other types evolved is a *Siphovirus* with an isometric head. The diversification of tailed phages is attributed to point mutation and uniparental reproduction, which are found in all viruses, and two principal factors: modular evolution by exchange of genes or gene blocks and the frequency of lysogeny (see Section IV.B.1), which perpetuates prophages and makes them available for recombination with superinfecting phages. Other avenues are gene rearrangement (deletions, duplications, inversions, and transpositions) and recombination with plasmids or the host genome. On the other hand, morphological properties may be highly conserved and some phages appear as living fossils, indicating phylogenetic relationships of their hosts.

## III. PHAGE OCCURRENCE AND ECOLOGY

### A. Distribution of Phages in Bacteria

Phages have been found in more than 130 bacterial genera distributed all over the bacterial world: in aerobes and anaerobes; actinomycetes; archaebacteria; cyanobacteria and other phototrophs; endospore formers; appendaged, budding, gliding, and sheathed bacteria; spirochetes; mycoplasmas; and chlamydias (Table IV). Phage-like particles of the podovirus type have even been found in endosymbionts of paramecia. However, tailed phages reported in cultures of green algae and filamentous fungi are probably contaminants.

Most phages have been found in a few bacterial groups: enterobacteria (more than 800 phages), bacilli, clostridia, lactococci, pseudomonads, staphylococci, and streptococci. This reflects the availability and ease of cultivation of these bacteria and the amount of work invested. About half of phages have been found in cultures of lysogenic bacteria. Tailed phages predominate everywhere except in mycoplasmas. In archaebacteria, they have been found in halobacteria and methanogens but not in extreme ther-

mophiles. Siphoviridae are particularly frequent in actinomycetes, coryneforms, lactococci, and streptococci. Myoviruses and podoviruses are relatively frequent in enterobacteria, pseudomonads, bacilli, and clostridia. There must be phylogenetic reasons for this particular distribution.

### B. Phage Ecology

#### 1. Habitats

Phages have essentially the same habitats as their hosts; indeed, their most important habitat is the lysogenic bacterium because it protects prophages from the environment and frees them from the need to find new bacteria for propagation. In nature, phages occur in an extraordinary variety of habitats ranging from Icelandic solfataras to fish sauce, fetal calf serum, and cooling towers of thermal power stations. They are found on the surfaces and in normal and pathological products of humans and animals, on plants, and in food, soil, air, and water, especially sewage. Body cavities with large bacterial populations, such as intestines and rumen, are extremely rich in phages. According to their habitat, phages may be acido-, alkali-, halo-, psychro-, or thermophilic. These properties are not linked to particular phage groups but rather appear as individual adaptations. Psychrophilic phages are often temperature sensitive and occur frequently in spoiled, refrigerated meat or fish.

#### 2. Geographical Distribution

Except for phages from extreme environments, phage species generally seem to be distributed throughout the whole earth. This is suggested by (i) electron microscopical observations of rare and characteristical phage morphotypes in different countries and (ii) worldwide distribution of certain lactococcal phage species in dairy plants and of RNA coliphages in sewage. Unfortunately, most data are from developed countries.

#### 3. Frequency of Phages in Nature

Sizes of phage populations are difficult to estimate because plaque assays and enrichment and (most) concentration techniques depend on bacterial hosts; they therefore only detect phages for specific bacteria and environmental conditions. Consequently, phage titers vary considerably—for example, for coliphages between 0 and $10^9$/g in human feces and between 0 and $10^7$/ml in domestic sewage. Titers of actinophages in soil vary between 0 and $10^5$/g. Purely electron microscopic phage counts, which do not allow phage identification, indicate that total phage titers are between $10^4$ and $10^7$/ml in seawater and may attain $10^{10}$/ml in sewage and $10^9$/ml in the rumen.

### 4. Persistence of Phages in the Environment

Phage survival in nature is frequently studied with the aim of using phages as indicators of contamination. The principal experimental models are cubic RNA phages (MS2 and f2) because of their resemblance to enteroviruses, other coliphages ($\phi$X174 and T4), and cyanophages. The indicator value of phages has not been conclusively proven and still lacks a solid statistical basis, but considerable data on phage ecology have been obtained. Phages appear as parts of complex ecosystems including various competing bacteria. Their numbers are affected by factors governing bacterial growth, notably nutrient supply and, in cyanobacteria, sunlight. The lowest bacterial concentration compatible with phage multiplication seems to be $10^4$ cells/ml. In addition, phage counts are affected by association of phages with solids and colloids (e.g., clay), the presence of organic matter, the concentration and type of ions, pH, temperature, UV and visible light, the type of water (e.g., seawater), and the nature and phage sensitivity of bacteria. Finally, phage titers depend on intrinsic phage properties such as burst size (see Section IV.A.4) and host range. No generalization is possible and each phage seems to have its own ecology.

## IV. PHAGE PHYSIOLOGY

### A. The Lytic Cycle

The lytic cycle, also called vegetative or productive, results in the production of new phages. Phages undergoing lytic cycles only are virulent. Lytic cycles consist of several steps and show considerable variation according to the type of phage (Table III).

### 1. Adsorption

Phages encounter bacteria by chance and adsorb to specific receptors, generally located on the cell wall but also on flagella, pili, capsules, or the plasma membrane. Adsorption sometimes consists of a reversible and an irreversible stage and may require cofactors (see Section I.A.1).

### 2. Infection

In most phage groups, only the viral nucleic acid enters the host and the shell remains outside. The mechanism of this step is generally poorly understood. In the *Inovirus* genus and in cystovirus $\phi$6, the capsid penetrates the cell wall but not the plasma membrane. In phages with contractile tails, the cell wall is degraded by phage enzymes located on the tail tip. The sheath then contracts (Fig. 2) and the tail core is brought in contact with the plasma membrane.

### 3. Multiplication

The interval from infection to the release of new phages is called the latent period. It depends largely on the nature and physiological state of the host and varies between 20 min and 30–50 hr. After infection, normal bacterial syntheses are shut off or modified. Phage nucleic acid is transcribed into mRNA using host and/or phage RNA polymerases. The RNA of leviviruses acts as mRNA and needs no transcription. In tailed phages, gene expression is largely sequential. Host syntheses are shut off first and structural genes are expressed last. According to the current knowledge, replication of phage DNA and RNA is semiconservative; each strand of a double helix acts as a template for the synthesis of a complementary strand. In phages with single-stranded nucleid acid, double-stranded replicative forms are produced. In tailed phages, replication generally starts at fixed sites of the DNA molecule, is bidirectional, and it generates giant DNA molecules, or concatemers, which are then cut to fit into phage heads. Translation is generally poorly know in phages. Microviridae, Leviviridae, the *Inovirus* genus, and Fuselloviridae have overlapping genes that are translated in different reading frames, allowing the synthesis of different proteins from the same DNA or RNA segment. Lipids, if present, are of variable origin. Phospholipids are specified or regulated by phages and fatty acids seem to derive from the host.

The assembly of new phages is called maturation. Phage constituents assemble spontaneously or with the help of specific enzymes. In most phage families, the nucleic acid enters a preformed capsid; in others, the capsid is constructed around or co-assembled with the nucleic acid. In tailed phages, assembly is a highly regulated process with sequentially acting proteins and separate pathways for heads and tails, which are eventually joined together. The envelope of plasmaviruses is acquired by budding, but that of cystovirus $\phi6$ is of cellular origin. The assembly of tailed phages often results in aberrant particles, including giant or multi-tailed phages and structures consisting of polymerized head or tail protein, called polyheads, polytails, or polysheaths. Inoviruses produce particles of abnormal length. Leviviruses and some tailed phages produce intracellular crystalline inclusion bodies.

### 4. Release

Phages are liberated by lysis, extrusion, or budding. Lysis occurs in tailed and cubic phages and in the Lipothrixviridae. Bacterial cells are weakened from the inside and burst, liberating approximately 20–1000 phages (often 50–100). Exceptional burst sizes (up to 20,000) have been recorded in leviviruses. Extrusion, with phages being secreted through the membranes of their surviving hosts, is observed in inoviruses and fuselloviruses. Budding is found in plasmaviruses. Cells are not lysed and produce phages for hours. Progeny sizes for budding and extruded phages have been estimated to be 130–1000 per cell.

## B. The Temperate Cycle

### 1. Lysogeny

In phages called temperate, infection results in a special equilibrium between phage and host. The phage genome persists in a latent state in the host cell, replicates more or less in synchrony with it, and may be perpetuated indefinitely in this way. It behaves as a part of the bacterium. If this equilibrium breaks down, either spontaneously or after induction, phages are produced as they are in a lytic cycle.

A bacterium harboring a latent phage genome or prophage is called lysogenic because it has acquired the ability to produce phages. Polylysogenic bacteria may carry up to five different prophages. Defective lysogeny is the perpetuation of temperate phages that are unable to replicate and often consist of single heads or tails.

Most temperate phages are tailed, but some members of the *Inovirus* genus and the Lipothrixviridae, Plasmaviridae, and Fuselloviridae can also lysogenize (Table III). Lysogeny is near ubiquitous and occurs in eubacteria, including cyanobacteria, and in archaebacteria. Its frequency in a given bacterial species varies between 0 and 100% (often approximately 40%) according to the species, induction techniques, and number of indicator strains. Mitomycin C and UV light are the principal inducing agents (see Section I.B.2). Many others are known, notably antitumor agents, carcinogens, and mutagens. They often act by damaging host DNA or inhibiting its synthesis.

The $\lambda$ type of lysogeny is particularly well understood. After infection, the genome of coliphage $\lambda$ forms a circle and some $\lambda$ proteins are immediately synthesized. They direct the bacterial cell to make a choice between the lytic and the temperate cycle. If a certain $\lambda$ protein prevails, the $\lambda$ genome integrates via a crossover, mediated by an enzyme called "integrase," at a specific site of the host DNA. It is then replicated at every bacterial division, and the continued synthesis of the phage repressor protein maintains lysogeny and makes the bacterium immune against superinfection by related phages. Spontaneous or induced excision of the $\lambda$ prophage leads to normal phage replication. Some phages have several integration sites.

In the P1 type of lysogeny, the phage genome, though able to integrate, usually persists as a plasmid, perhaps in association with the plasma membrane. In the Mu type, the infecting DNA does not form circles and integrates at random at any site of the bacterial genome. The core domain of Mu integrase (transposase) resembles retrovirus integrase.

### 2. Pseudolysogeny and Steady-State Infections

In pseudolysogenic bacteria, only part of a culture is infected with phages and an equilibrium exists between free phages and noninfected, phage-sensitive bacteria. Phage-free strains can be obtained by simple cloning or by cultivating the bacteria in antiphage serum. In steady-state infections, the whole culture is infected, but cells are not lysed and produce phages continuously (see Section IV.A.4).

### 3. Transduction and Conversion

Transduction is transfer of host DNA by viruses and is normally a rare event. In generalized transduction, fragments of bacterial DNA are packaged by accident into phage heads and transferred to a new bacterium. Any host gene may be transferred and the implicated phages may be virulent or temperate. Specialized transduction is carried out by temperate phages that can integrate into host DNA (e.g., $\lambda$). If the phage DNA is not properly excised, bacterial genes adjacent to the prophage site may be packaged into phage heads along with normal genes. The resulting particle has a defective genome and may be nonviable. In conversion, bacteria acquire new properties through lysogenization by normal temperate phages. Conversion is a frequent event, affecting the whole bacterial population that has been lysogenized. The new properties are specified by phage genes and include new antigens, antibiotic resistance, colony characteristics, or toxin production (e.g., of diphtheria or botulinus toxin). They will disappear if the bacterium loses its prophage. Transduction and conversion are common in tailed phages; conversion to cholera toxin production has recently been found in the *Inovirus* genus.

## V. PHAGES IN APPLIED MICROBIOLOGY

### A. Therapeutic Agents, Reagents, and Tools

#### 1. Therapy and Prophylaxis of Infectious Diseases

Phage therapy started with high expectations and was strongly advocated by d'Herelle. Phages were, enthusiastically and uncritically, applied in many human and animal diseases and spectacular results were reported as well as failures. When antibiotics became available, phage therapy was practically abandoned. The main reasons were host specificity of phages and the rapid appearance of resistant bacteria. However, unbeknownst to researchers in the West, phage therapy was widely practiced in the former USSR until 1990 and surprisingly good results were reported in the 1980s from Poland. This suggests that phage therapy is a viable therapeutic alternative in antibiotic resistant pyogenic infections (wounds, abscesses, furunculosis, osteomyelitis, and septicemia). More basic research is needed, for example, on the inactivation of phages by body fluids. Phage prophylaxis of infectious diseases was also attempted. Despite encouraging results in cholera prevention, it is of historic interest only. Phage control of plant diseases has not been recommended.

#### 2. Identification and Classification of Bacteria

Early attempts to use phages for bacterial identification were abandoned because no phage lyses all strains of a bacterial species and no others. A few diagnostic phages are still used as screening agents in specialized laboratories, for example, for rapid identification of *Bacillus anthracis,* members of the genus *Salmonella,* or the serotype O1 of *Vibrio cholerae.* By contrast, phage typing is an important technique in epidemiology. In analogy with the antibiogram, bacteria are tested against a set of phages and subdivided into resistance patterns or phage types. Briefly, a continuous layer of bacteria is created on an agar surface, phage suspensions are deposited on it, and results are read the next day. Phage typing is invaluable for subdividing biochemically and serologically homogeneous bacterial species. In addition to international typing schemes for *Salmonella typhi* and *Salmonella paratyphi* B, there are typing sets for most human, animal, and plant pathogenic bacteria. Because of their host specificity, phages are also valuable tools in bacterial taxonomy. Phage host ranges provided a major argument in reclassifying *Pasteurella pestis* as an enterobacterium of the genus *Yersinia.*

#### 3. Genetic Engineering

Phages have made many contributions to recombinant DNA technology. Restriction endonucleases were first identified in a phage–host system and the DNA ligase of phage T4 is used to insert foreign DNA into viral or plasmid vectors. In addition, phages have several major applications:

1. Phage λ, derivatives of it, cosmids (hybrids between λ DNA and plasmids), phage P1, and "mini Mu" phages (derivatives of Mu containing the left and right ends of the Mu genome) are used as cloning vectors. Recombinant DNA (vector plus foreign DNA) is introduced into phage proheads. After completion of phage assembly, it can be injected into bacteria.

2. Filamentous coliphages of the *Inovirus* genus are used for DNA sequencing. Foreign DNA is introduced into the double-stranded replicative form of these phages. The same coliphages are also used to express proteins or peptides at their surface. The technique, called "phage display," is a powerful tool for the selection and cloning of antibody fragments.

3. Phage Mu DNA, which is able to integrate at random into any gene, is used to create mutations and to displace genes to other locations.

### 4. Other Applications

1. Destruction of unwanted bacteria in bacterial and cell cultures, milk, meat, and fresh water (e.g., of cyanobacteria in "algal blooms")

2. Assay of antivirals, disinfectants, air filters, and aerosol samplers

3. Detection of fecal pollution in water and of carcinogens, mutagens, and antitumor agents

4. Detection of *Listeria* bacteria in food using luciferase-marked phages

5. Tracing of water movements (surface water and aquifers)

### B. Phages as Pests

In industrial microbiology, phages may destroy valuable starter cultures or disrupt fermentation processes. Phage interference has been reported in various branches of the fermentation industry, notably in the production of antibiotics, organic solvents, and cheese. In the dairy industry, phage infection is considered as the largest single cause of abnormal fermentations and a great source of economic losses. Phages derive from raw material, plant environment, or phage-carrying starter cultures. They are disseminated mechanically by air and may persist for months in a plant. Phage control is attempted by (i) preventing contamination by cleanliness, sterilization of raw material, sterile maintenance of starter cultures, and use of phage-free starters; (ii) disinfection by heat, hypochlorites, UV light, and other agents; or (iii) impeding phage development by starter rotation, use of genetically heterogeneous starters, and phage-inhibiting media. A recently developed approach is to construct phage-resistant starters by genetic engineering.

### See Also the Following Articles

Bacteriocins • Dairy Products • Detection of Bacteria in Blood: Centrifugation and Filtration • Recombinant DNA, Basic Procedures

### Bibliography

Ackermann, H.-W. (1985). Les virus des bactéries. *In* "Virologie Médicale" (J. Maurin, Ed.). Flammarion Médecine-Sciences, Paris.

Ackermann, H.-W. (1987). Bacteriophage taxonomy in 1987. *Microbiol. Sci.* **4**, 214–218.

Ackermann, H.-W. (1996). Frequency of morphological phage descriptions in 1995. *Arch. Virol.* **141**, 209–218.

Ackermann, H.-W. (1998). Tailed bacteriophages—The order *Caudovirales. Adv. Virus Res.* **51**, 135–201.

Ackermann, H.-W., and DuBow, M. S. (1987). "Viruses of Prokaryotes," Vols. 1 and 2. CRC Press, Boca Raton, FL.

Calendar, R. (Ed.) (1988). "The Bacteriophages," Vols. 1 and 2. Plenum, New York.

Casjens, S., Hatfull, G., and Hendrix, R. (1992). Evolution of dsDNA tailed-bacteriophage genomes. *Sem. Virol.* **3**, 383–397.

Goyal, S. M., Gerba, C. P., and Bitton, G. (Eds.) (1987). "Phage Ecology." Wiley, New York.

Holt, J. G. (Editor-in-Chief) (1984, 1986, 1989, 1990). "Bergey's Manual of Systematic Bacteriology," Vols. 1–4. Williams & Wilkins, Baltimore, MD.

Klaus, S., Krüger, D., and Meyer, J. (1992). "Bakterienviren." Gustav Fischer Jena.

Maniloff, J., and Ackermann, H.-W. (1998). Taxonomy of

bacterial viruses: establishment of tailed virus genera and the order *Caudovirales*. *Arch. Virol.* **143**, 2051–2063.

Murphy, F. A., Fauquet, C. M., Bishop, D. H. L., Ghabrial, S. A., Jarvis, A. W., Martelli, G. P., Mayo, M. A., and Summers, M. D. (Eds.) (1985). "Virus taxonomy. Classification and nomenclature of viruses, sixth report of the International Committee on Taxonomy of Viruses". *Arch. Virol.* (Suppl. 10).

Smith, G. P. (1985). Filamentous fusion phage: Novel expression vectors that display cloned antigens on the virion surface. *Science* **228**, 1315–1317.

Zillig, W., Arnold, H. P., Holz, I., Prangishvili, D., Schweier, A., Stedman, K., She, Q., Phan, H., Garrett,, R., and Kristjansson, J. K. (1998). Genetic elements in the extremely thermophilic archaeon *Sulfolobus*. *Extremophiles* **2**, 131–140.

# Beer/Brewing

## Mark A. Harrison and Brian Nummer
*University of Georgia*

## GLOSSARY

**bottom-fermenting yeasts**   Yeasts used to produce the type of beer known as lager.

**chill-proofing**   Use of proteases to prevent haze development when beer is chilled to refrigerated temperatures.

**hops**   The dried flowers of the female *Humulus lupulus* plant that contribute flavor and antibacterial compounds to beer.

**malt**   Major raw material used in brewing that provides the appropriate substrate and enzymes needed to yield wort.

**top-fermenting yeasts**   Yeasts used to produce the type of beer known as ale.

**wild yeasts**   Yeasts that are present in the brewing process that were not introduced purposely nor tolerated for a specific purpose during brewing.

**wort**   Liquid that remains after mash is strained, containing soluble fermentable compounds.

**BEER**   is defined in the Bavarian Purity Law of Germany as a fermented alcoholic beverage made of malted cereals, water, hops, and yeast. This is the classical definition and has been enforced in Germany since the sixteenth century. Many countries, however, now allow additional substances to be used in this product. For instance, various enzymes and antifoaming agents are used by some brewers during the fermentation process. Others supplement expensive bar-ley malt with unmalted cereals such as corn, rice, or wheat which contribute to beer flavor while reducing processing costs.

Beer is generally subdivided into lagers and ales based on its geographic origin and history. For centuries the only beer known to all brewers was ale. During the fermentation of this beer a thick yeast foam rose to the surface. All too frequently the beer went sour, especially during warmer months. In the 1800s, German brewers observed that if beer could be kept at colder temperatures by brewing in the colder months or by using natural ice or caves, the beer soured less frequently. They also noticed that the yeast settled to the bottom of casks in the cold. This cold-storage method gave birth to "lager" beer in Germany. Lager beers are now traditionally fermented cool and aged cold for several weeks to several months. The yeast used in lager beers has adapted over time to ferment optimally at these temperatures. Ales, on the other hand, ferment at warmer temperatures and are aged only days. The yeast rises to the surface and is skimmed. Ales have remained the beer choice in England.

Classic examples of German lager beers are München-chener, Pilsener, Dortmunder, and Bock beer. All these beers are malty with a balance of hoppiness (bitterness). Color can vary from light (Helles) to dark (Dunkel). They usually contain 4.5–5% w/v alcohol, with bock containing 6% w/v. Examples of English ales are bitter, pale ale, porter, and stout. Bitter and pale ale are characterized by a copper color, full body, and elevated bitterness. Porter and stout are dark in color, contain roasted or burnt malts, and may or may not be bitter. Examples of German ales are weizenbier (wheat beer), alt, and kölsch.

There are other beer styles that do not clearly fit into the ale or lager category. Most of these beers are Belgian in origin and are spontaneously fermented, e.g., lambic.

## I. HISTORY OF BREWING

Evidence shows that brewing of beer was a popular practice in Mesopotamia before 6000 B.C. Beers offered people a flavorful alternative to drinking water and were often thought to possess therapeutic properties. Brewing beer became popular in other areas of the Middle East, including Ancient Egypt and Israel. Brewing practices had spread to Rome during Caesar's reign and into other parts of Europe. Over the centuries, it was discovered that the addition of hops and other spices would improve the flavor of beer. Since that time, hops have become essential in beer due largely to their contribution to the flavor and stability of beer.

Beer was made in North America by the colonists. During the sixteenth and seventeenth centuries, breweries were established in Virginia and New England. Barley did not prosper in the New England climate so a variety of unusual ingredients were fermented, including pumpkins, maple sugar, persimmons, and apples. Two factors contributed to the further development of the North American brewing industry. Pennsylvania was found to be a good barley and hop production area, and the immigration of Germanic and Dutch brewmasters bolstered the American industry.

During this entire period, brewing was basically a hit-or-miss process. Individuals experienced in brewing recognized that using old brewing vessels yielded better products than new ones. It is now realized that the cracks, crevices, and pores present in the older vessels, but lacking in the newer ones, harbored the yeasts and bacteria responsible for the fermentation. Several theories were developed in the nineteenth century in an attempt to explain the changes that occur during fermentation. Much of the debate centered around the issue of whether fermentation was a purely chemical process or a biological process. The issue was largely settled by Pasteur in the 1860s

and 1870s when he published reports concluding that fermentation was due to the actions of yeast.

In 1883, Emil Christian Hansen established the method of using pure yeast cultures to produce beer at the Carlsberg Brewery in Copenhagen, Denmark. He had demonstrated previously that the culture used in brewing was often a mixed culture and that the metabolism of wild yeasts caused many of the defects in improperly processed beer. Over the next several years, the practice of using pure yeast cultures to produce beer became more widely accepted. The purpose and function of yeast enzymes in the fermentation process was shown by Buchner in 1897. It was found that cell-free extracts contained enzymes that could ferment sugars.

## II. BREWING

The conversion of cereals into beer is not a direct process. The cereals used in beer production do not contain sufficient quantities of fermentable sugars. These cereals must first undergo modification during the malting and mashing steps to yield carbohydrates that yeast can convert during the fermentation step into ethyl alcohol and carbon dioxide. Freshly produced beer can then be aged for flavor development before it undergoes finishing steps which can include filtering, pasteurization, and packaging. Each of these steps will be examined more closely in the following sections and are shown in Fig. 1.

### A. Ingredients

The basic ingredients in beer are water, malted cereals, hops, and yeast. Water comprises 90–95% of the content of finished beer, and its quality can influence the flavor of beer. Barley is the most common cereal used in the Americas and Europe to produce malt, although small volumes of beer are made from other cereal grains. Better beers are produced with clean barley that was properly dried after harvest. Overheating barley during drying can lead to its becoming unacceptable for malting since its germination potential is adversely affected. Barley contains a high starch content suitable for conversion to fermentable carbohydrates and a sufficient protein

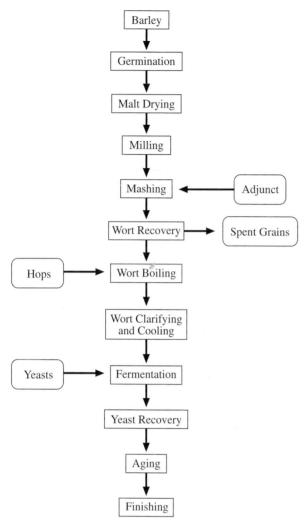

**Fig. 1.** Typical flow diagram for the brewing process.

content to support yeast growth and contribute to forming beer foam. In addition, it contributes unique flavor components. Hops are the dried flowers from the female hop (*Humulus lupulus*) plant and contribute flavor and antibacterial compounds to beer. Yeasts are the predominant fermentation organism used to make beer worldwide. In some instances, bacteria may contribute certain characteristics to some regional beers. Malt adjuncts, such as corn, rice, wheat, sorghum grain, soybeans, cassava, potatoes, sugars, and syrups, may be used in some formulations. The adjuncts are all starch- or sugar-containing substrates that contribute fermentable carbohydrates. They also contribute flavor characteristics to produce distinctive varieties of beers. Al-

though enzymes other than those in the malt and those contributed by the yeast are not needed to produce beer, some brewers use additional enzymes to impart desired characteristics to their product.

## B. Malting

The main objective of malting is to produce an ample supply of enzymes that degrade starch, proteins, fats, and other components of grain. The subsequent enzymatic changes provide fermentable sugars from starch and substances needed to support yeast growth (e.g., amino acids and fatty acids) from the other substrates. To produce malted barley, barley grains are first steeped in 10–15°C water and then germinated at 15–20°C for 3–7 days. After the barley germinates, the sprouts are removed, leaving a medium rich with $\alpha$ amylase, $\beta$ amylase, proteases, and their respective substrates. The malt is dried to approximately 5% moisture and ground. Grinding exposes the starchy endosperm of the grain which makes the carbohydrates more available.

## C. Mashing

During the mashing step, most of the nonsoluble, unfermentable carbohydrates and proteins are hydrolyzed into soluble fermentable materials by the enzymes present in the malt. To accomplish this, the ground malt is mixed with water and placed into a mash tun. To enhance protease action during the initial mashing period, the temperature of the mixture is maintained between 38 and 50°C. After a period of time, the temperature of the mix is increased to 65–70°C to enhance amylase activity. Within a few hours, the process is complete, and the temperature is increased to at least 75°C to inactivate the enzymes.

While the amylases are active, they degrade the starch contributed by the grain. The $\beta$ amylase splits off the disaccharide, maltose, from the amylose portion of the starch. Larger portions of starch are split off by yielding sections that are then acted on by $\beta$ amylase. The products that result from the action of the two amylases known as dextrins also undergo additional enzymatic changes. Branch linkages of the amylopectin portion of starch are broken by debranching enzymes while amyloglucoside removes single glucose residues from the dextrins. Alterations in the color are also noted (changing from light to dark amber) during mashing.

The normal pH of malt is approximately 5.8 and is not acidic enough for optimum enzyme activity. To achieve optimum activity, the pH can be reduced to approximately 5.2 for lager production. The pH is adjusted to be more acidic for ale production. Adjustment of the acidity, if desired, can be accomplished by addition of acid, usually lactic acid, or by bacterial fermentation. Although the lactic acid bacteria usually are undesirable contaminants, *Lactobacillus delbrueckii* has been used to accomplish this pH reduction in the past. This thermophilic bacterium converts sugars to lactic acid efficiently at temperatures of 42–51°C. Because the variety of microorganisms that can grow at these temperatures is small, it is easier to maintain a pure culture bacterial fermentation as well as to reduce the possibility of contamination by other microbes. Processors may find, however, that the bacterial modification requires much greater supervision and, if not controlled, may contribute to beer spoilage.

After the naturally-occurring and any added enzymes are inactivated, the solids settle out, leaving the wort. Wort contains the soluble compounds and is separated from the solids before it is transferred into the brew kettle. The spent grain can be used in animal feed.

The blend of grains used and the degree of enzymatic activity will influence the composition of the wort. These differences are some of the factors contributing to the characteristics noted in beers from different breweries.

## D. Wort Processing

Wort is usually boiled in the brew kettle along with added hops for up to 90 min. Boiling serves several purposes: It stops any further enzymatic action in the wort, causes any unhydrolyzed proteins to precipitate, extracts flavor compounds from the hops, and concentrates and sterilizes the wort. Among the compounds extracted from the hops are essential oils humulone ($\alpha$ bitter acid), lupulone ($\beta$ bitter acid), and tannin. Important flavor characteristics are contributed by the oils humulone and lupulone. In addition, humulone and lupulone have some antimicrobial properties. The wort is then separated from the spent hops, cooled rapidly, and placed into a fermentation vessel. The spent hops may be used in fertilizer.

Light beers are made by reducing the unfermentable dextrin content in wort before fermentation occurs. The enzyme glucoamylase is added to the wort to hydrolyze most of the dextrins to glucose. During fermentation the yeasts are able to ferment the glucose to alcohol. Thus, the amount of carbohydrates present that could contribute to the caloric content of the product is decreased.

## E. Fermentation

At this point in the process, the wort is inoculated with brewers' yeast and fermented. During fermentation, the yeast produces alcohol, carbon dioxide, and some additional flavor constituents. The inoculation step is also called other names, such as pitching and seeding.

The fermentation room must be maintained in a clean manner to reduce possible contamination problems, and it should be kept at a constant temperature and humidity to maintain the desired growth rate for the yeast. Fermentation vats can be glassed lined or constructed of wood, stainless steel, or aluminum. Wooden vats pose problems in cleaning and disinfecting that are not experienced with vessels constructed of any of the other materials.

The strain of yeast used depends on what type of beer is desired. Lagers are produced using bottom-fermenting yeasts, whereas ales are produced using top-fermenting yeasts. These yeasts have traditionally been referred to as *Saccharomyces carlsbergensis* (*uvarum*) and *S. cerevisiae*, respectively. Many brewers consider these as separate species, although fungal taxonomists do not recognize them as distinct species. Nevertheless, they do behave slightly different during the fermentation process.

The temperature of fermentation for lagers produced by the bottom-fermenting yeasts is usually in the range of 6–15°C and takes 7–12 days. During fermentation, the yeasts tend to flocculate and settle to the bottom of the fermentation vat. These yeasts can be collected from the bottom of the vat for reuse in subsequent fermentations. By varying the fermentation temperature, slightly different versions of lagers can be produced.

Ales are traditionally produced using top-fermenting yeasts and incubation temperatures of 18–22°C for 5–7 days. These yeasts tend to form small clumps of cells that are carried to the top of the fermenting liquid adsorbed to bubbles of carbon dioxide. These yeasts cells can be collected from the surface for reuse with the next fermentation batch.

Since the mid-1800s, the use of bottom-fermenting yeasts in closed fermentation vessels has increased world-wide. A corresponding decrease has occurred for top-fermenting yeasts in open fermentation vessels. In recent times the advantages of the closed fermenter have given rise to "bottom-fermenting" ale strains. These strains maintain the ale flavor characteristics and can be harvested from the bottom, eliminating the need for an open vessel and the risk of contamination.

Regardless of the type of beer made, a rapid decrease in pH during the fermentation will increase its stability and decrease potential problems of contamination. After fermentation, the pH of most lagers decreases from approximately 5.2–5.3 to approximately 4.1–4.2 and it decreases slightly more in ales. These acidic pHs assist in preserving the final product by inhibiting bacterial growth.

## F. Aging

At the end of fermentation, the "green beer" is separated from the sediment and transferred to aging vessels. Aging vessels have commonly been wooden (e.g., oak) or glass-lined steel tanks. The beer is aged by storage at 0–2°C for several weeks. Lagers are normally aged for slightly longer periods of time than ales. Aging allows the beer to develop its final flavor, color, and body characteristics. Clarification occurs to some extent as the yeasts, unstable proteins, and other suspended solids precipitate. Chemical changes occur that create a more mellow, smooth flavor.

## G. Finishing

After aging, beer undergoes several processing steps in preparation for distribution to the consumer. Some of these steps are optional, and some of the steps can be done by a variety of methods. The choice of the brewer depends on what type of finished product is desired. Most beers will be chill-proofed by the addition of proteases to prevent haze development by residual proteins when the product is kept at refrigerated temperatures. Most will also be clarified and filtered to remove remaining solids. The final carbon dioxide level will be adjusted to 0.45–0.52%. The most common carbonation method is to add carbon dioxide back into the product. An alternative way is to add freshly yeasted wort to the beer and allow a natural secondary fermentation. Packaging for beer includes cans, bottles, barrels, and kegs.

To increase the shelf life of canned or bottled beer, it is usually pasteurized. The majority of beer in the past several decades has received heat pasteurization (e.g., 60°C for 1520 min). Beer flavor can be adversely affected if the product is overheated. Thus, there has been and continues to be an interest in using an alternative pasteurization method. "Cold pasteurization" offers some advantages, such as less flavor loss due to heating and better energy efficiency. Cold pasteurization involves the use of chemical agents for preservation or filtration ("cold filtration") through membrane filters followed by aseptic packaging. Beer packaged in barrels or kegs is not pasteurized but must be chilled and stored under refrigeration temperatures to maintain maximum quality.

## III. BEER PROPERTIES

A myriad of beers are produced by different brewers. Properly brewed beers have flavor, color, and body characteristics dictated by the ingredients and yeast strain used, wort composition, and conditions for fermentation, aging, and finishing. Among the metabolites produced are ethanol, carbon dioxide, ethyl acetate, other esters, fusel alcohols, diacetyl, 2,3-pentanedione, various sulfur compounds, and amino acids and nucleotides from yeast cells. The type and proportion of these and other compounds in beer contribute the characteristics to a particular brew.

Beers also possess factors that aid in preservation of the product. Properly fermented and packaged beer has alcohol produced during fermentation, a relatively low pH, and a low redox potential, which inhibit a variety of spoilage microorganisms. Some compounds extracted from hops are inhibitory to gram-positive bacteria.

Acetic acid bacteria, lactic acid bacteria, coliforms, and wild yeasts often contaminate improperly processed beers. Growth of most contaminating microbes in beer is inhibited by the preservation factors associated with the product. For example, the anaerobic environment during fermentation of packaged beer inhibits the growth of the aerobic acetic acid bacteria. The coliforms are inhibited when the pH level of the beer is 4.3 or lower.

## IV. PROPERTIES OF BREWING YEASTS

### A. *Saccharomyces* Characteristics

The genus *Saccharomyces* is composed of ascosporogenous yeasts that produce ovoid, spherical, or elongate cells. *Saccharomyces* strains used in commercial brewing are diploid species. Reproduction by vegetative means occurs by multilateral budding, whereas sexual reproduction involves the formation of an ascus containing one to four spores. Members of this genus ferment sugars vigorously. Those strains that can yield significant amounts of ethanol by this metabolism are useful commercially.

This genus is a rather diverse group. Some of the growth characteristics for the species *S. cerevisiae* include minimum $a_w$ for growth of 0.90; minimum, optimum, and maximum temperatures for growth of 0–7, 20–30, and 40°C, respectively; and minimum and optimum pH for growth of 2.0–2.4 and 4.0–5.0, respectively.

The taxonomic classification of the yeasts commonly referred to as brewers' yeasts has been debated for many years. According to the most recent taxonomic references, both bottom yeasts and top yeasts are members of the species *S. cerevisiae*. It is estimated that there are probably more than 1000 strains of *S. cerevisiae*. Although the differences between strains are usually minor, they may be important to individual brewers. In older literature, the bottom yeasts were widely recognized as *S. carlsbergensis* and later as *S. carlsbergensis (uvarum)* or *S. uvarum*. These are still part of the terminology of the brewing

industry, and some brewers believe there are sufficient differences between strains to continue using these names.

### B. Factors Affecting Growth of Brewing Yeasts

During brewing, the goal is to maximize the production of desired metabolites of yeast growth while minimizing production of undesirable compounds and yeast biomass. By properly controlling various factors that influence yeast behavior, the brewer can achieve the desired end product. Factors that influence yeast metabolism include wort composition, oxygen level in the wort, inoculation rate, condition of yeast at pitching, the level of microbial contamination, wort pH, and temperature during fermentation. In addition, fermentation can be influenced by the fermenter design and whether a batch or continuous process is used. For example, there is evidence that continuous fermentation may be faster than batch fermentation and may reduce problems associated with handling the yeast culture. It may also prove to be more economical in many situations.

Yeasts growing in batch fermentations use the individual sugars in wort in a sequential order. Sucrose is the first used, followed by glucose, fructose, maltose, and maltotriose, although not all strains can fully use maltotriose efficiently. Ethanol and flavor compounds are among the compounds produced by carbohydrate metabolism. This metabolism also provides the energy to maintain growth. Yeasts also utilize the 19 amino acids normally present in wort in an orderly fashion. The metabolism of the amino acids is needed to maintain yeast nutrition and to contribute flavor to the product.

### C. Strain Development

Throughout the centuries, brewers have searched for yeast strains which will provide the best quality beer in an efficient manner. In the past, this has often been done by screening for the most suitable strain by trial and error or by forming hybrids of two strains with different desirable qualities and screening for a progeny strain with the desired capabilities. Not only are these methods time-consuming but also the resulting yeast may have both desirable and undesirable qualities from both parental strains. For example, substrate utilization may be improved but flavor traits may be adversely affected. Recently, use of molecular methods such as recombinant DNA techniques to improve yeast strains has become an option. The advantage of using the molecular methods is that alterations of single characteristics can be accomplished specifically.

The brewing industry is interested in modifying yeast behavior to accomplish several goals, including increasing the efficiency of fermentation by modifying the uptake and metabolism of wort components, improving the control of fermentation (e.g., the timing of late fermentation or yeast flocculation properties) and overall organoleptic quality of beer, developing new beers, and improving the value of by-products (e.g., spent yeasts).

Modification of some of these traits using molecular methods has been investigated with some success. Although some of these altered strains have been developed experimentally, currently there are few, if any, used in full-scale commercial operations. In an effort to produce "light" beers less expensively, strains have been developed that ferment more of the carbohydrates present in wort not fermentable by the normal strains. This alleviates the expense of using added enzymes to degrade these carbohydrates.

A second modification that has been accomplished concerns the degradation of $\alpha$ glucan. This substance causes filtration problems and forms precipitates and hazes in beer. Since use of genetically developed yeast can solve this problem, the expense of using an added enzyme to do the job is eliminated.

Strains with improved proteolytic capabilities have also been developed. These strains reduce the need to use added proteases to degrade the proteins in beer that are responsible for the haze that can develop when finished beer is refrigerated.

## V. SPOILAGE PROBLEMS OF BEER

### A. Range of Problems

Concern regarding the transmission of pathogens via beer is rare. In this aspect, beer is unlike most other food and beverage items. The lack of pathogen-related problems is due to the nature of the ingredients, processing methods, and characteristics of the final product.

Spoilage problems, however, can occur. A diverse group of microorganisms can present problems at various stages of brewing (Table I). The type of spoilage and the microorganisms responsible are influenced by the stage of processing and the characteristics related to the stage. Characteristics that affect spoilage include pH, alcohol content, the types of ingredients, the oxygen level of the product at particular stages, and the level of sanitation within the brewing environment. Wort just prior to fermentation is a rich medium for supporting microbial growth and is extremely susceptible to spoilage.

### B. Bacterial Spoilage

#### 1. Lactic Acid Bacteria

Species of *Lactobacillus* are among the most frequent and troublesome spoilage microorganisms of beer. They can cause spoilage problems at all stages of processing and even in the finished product. The lactobacilli can tolerate hop substances that are inhibitory to many other gram-positive bacteria. The taxonomy of lactobacilli encountered in beer is confusing and uncertain. One species characterized in the industry as *L. pastorianus* may be the most common beer spoiler. It is capable of decreasing the pH, producing diacetyl, and producing a ropy texture in beer. Diacetyl is a chemical which produces a buttery flavor that is undesirable in beer.

*Pediococcus damnosus* is one of five species of this genus encountered in brewery environments. This lactic acid bacterium, like the lactobacilli, is resistant to the inhibitory substances in hops. Some strains of this species can tolerate up to 10% (w/v) ethanol.

#### 2. Acetic Acid Bacteria

Species of *Acetobacter and Gluconobacter* can spoil beer primarily by converting ethanol to acetic acid. These bacteria are aerobic and are usually only associated with spoilage of beer exposed to air. The increased use of anaerobic conditions in modern breweries has decreased the frequency of problems related to these microorganisms.

***TABLE I***
**Microbial Spoilage of Beer**

| Microorganism | Stage of processing encountered | Problem |
|---|---|---|
| *Lactobacillus* spp. | Any stage | Off-flavors |
| | | Haze |
| | | Ropiness |
| | | Acidification |
| *Pediococcus* spp. | Inoculation | Off-flavors |
| | Fermentation | Haze |
| | Aging | Ropiness |
| | | Acidification |
| Acetic acid bacteria | Open fermenters | Off-flavors |
| | Packaging | Haze |
| | | Surface pellicles |
| | | Ropiness |
| *Hafnia protea* | Wort | Off-flavors |
| | Fermentation | Acidification |
| Other Enterobacteriaceae | Wort | Off-flavors |
|   *Bacillus* spp. | Wort | Off-flavors |
|   *Zymomonas* spp. | Packaging | Off-flavors |
|   *Pectinatus* spp. | Packaging | Off-flavors |
|   *Negasphaera* spp. | Bottled beers with pH >4.1 and <3.5% ethanol | Off-flavors |
| Wild yeasts | All stages | Off-flavors |
| | | Haze |
| Killer yeasts | Fermentation | Death of desired strain |
| | | Off-flavors |
| Molds | Raw barley spoilage | Gushing |
| | | Off-flavors |

## 3. Enterobacteriaceae

Although conditions suitable to support growth of most members of the Enterobacteriaceae are relatively few during the processing of beer, there are opportunities for some species to pose problems. The main concern is spoilage of wort before the decrease in pH and accumulation of ethanol that occurs during fermentation. Most enterics stop growing during early fermentation when the pH of wort decreases to <4.4 and when the ethanol content becomes >2% (w/v). A species that provides an exception to this behavior pattern is *Hafnia protea*. It has the capability to survive the fermentation changes to a degree and may become sufficiently associated with the yeast that it is passed via pitching to future fermentations.

## 4. Sporeformers

Although *Clostridium* species may be present on the raw ingredients of beer, these spore-forming microorganisms present no serious spoilage problems in the liquid phase once production commences. Spoilage of spent grains by *Clostridium* has been reported.

*Bacillus* species, however, have been encountered in spoiled beer. Since most, if not all, of the species within this genus are sensitive to hop components, the spoilage bacilli tend to be more problematic in the stages before the addition of hops to the wort.

## 5. Anaerobic Gram Negatives

Species of three genera of anaerobic, gram-negative bacteria have been recognized as spoilers. *Zymomonas* was first described in the 1930s and is unique to British breweries. The occurrence of spoilage problems due to this bacterium elsewhere in the world is rare. This organism produces hydrogen sulfide and acetaldehyde in beer.

*Pectinatus* and *Megasphaera* species were both described for the first time in the late 1970s. Both are unique to the brewing industry. *Pectinatus* species produce acetic acid, propionic acid, and hydrogen sulfide in beer, whereas species of *Megasphaera* produce primarily fatty acids and hydrogen sulfide.

### 6. Other Bacteria

Species of *Achromobacter, Alcaligenes, Flavobacterium, Acinetobacter,* and *Pseudomonas* are some of the other bacteria that have been associated with infrequent cases of beer spoilage. Many of these miscellaneous spoilage organisms are aerobic, intolerant of acid environments, and die once fermentation starts. Thus, the problems they can cause are limited to the mash and early wort stages.

## C. Fungal Spoilage

### 1. Wild Yeasts

Wild yeasts include any yeasts that are present in the brewing process that were not introduced purposely or tolerated for specific purposes in the development of the desired product. The taxonomy of the wild yeasts is confusing. There are probably more than 40 species that could be considered within this group. Problems due to wild yeasts include the production of undesired flavor compounds, including esters, acidic and phenolic substances, and fatty acids. They may also ferment the product beyond the desired end point due to their ability to ferment carbohydrates that the desired brewing yeast cannot utilize. Detection and identification of wild yeasts are important to brewers if they are to recognize the problem and take corrective action. Identification methods vary from biochemical classification to genetic methods, including DNA fingerprinting and gene probes.

### 2. Killer Yeasts

Killer yeasts can produce a toxic protein, or zymocide, that adversely affects the plasma membrane of other yeast species or strains. Members of several yeast genera are capable of producing this compound, including some *Saccharomyces* species. The major problem is the death of the desired fermentative yeast strains caused by the toxic protein. Thus, the product is not properly fermented. It has often been noted that killer yeasts can also produce phenolic off-flavors. Spoilage problems due to killer yeasts can occur in either batch or continuous fermentations but tend to be more common with the continuous process. This may be due to the slightly lower pH encountered in the early stages of continuous fermentation.

### 3. Molds

Mold contamination of barley is common by a variety of species; thus, it is important to handle barley properly to prevent spoilage prior to malting. Spoiled barley can adversely affect the malting process and can cause a problem known as "gushing" in the finished product. Gushing is the sudden release of carbon dioxide when a bottle or can containing beer made from mold-spoiled barley is opened.

## VI. SPOILAGE CONTROL

Controlling spoilage problems in the brewing industry is largely a matter of using the proper sanitation practices. Maintaining a clean, sanitized brewing environment will greatly reduce potential problems related to most of the environmental contaminants. Use of good quality water not only in the beer but also during cleaning and sanitizing is critical.

Using the proper processing practices is also important. Care must be used to maintain the purity of the yeast strain or strains used by a brewer. The brewer should ensure that the raw ingredients are of good quality and that the processing steps proceed as expected. It is also important for a brewer to be able to identify contamination problems early so corrective action can be taken and damage minimized.

## VII. OTHER TYPES OF BEER PROCESSING

### A. African Beers

The native beers of Africa have different ingredients and are brewed differently than the typical European or American beers. Rather than using barley in the malting step, sorghum, millet, or maize are used depending on the geographic location within Africa and the customary practice. Brewing in Africa originated in the home for personal or ceremonial uses, although it later expanded into commercial production. Fermentation of these beers is a two-stage process. First, a lactic acid fermentation softens the malt proteins, reduces the pH sufficiently to limit growth of bacterial pathogens, regulates starch conversion to sugar, and contributes to the body of the beer. The second step is a yeast fermentation that is initiated just prior to packaging the product. During distribution, there is an active yeast fermentation.

The finished product is unhopped with sour yogurt-like taste, has a pinkish-brown color, and normally contains 2 or 3% alcohol. It is opaque due to the high concentration of suspended solids and yeast cells. This product is actually thought of as a food rather than a beverage. These beers are highly susceptible to spoilage and have a shelf life that is usually less than 5 days. This limited shelf life is due to the wort not being boiled coupled with the fact that the final product characteristics (e.g., pH and alcohol content) are not sufficient to limit the growth of acid-tolerant spoilage bacteria.

## B. Home Brewing

It is possible to brew beer at home that may be of similar quality to that of commercially produced beers. Many supply stores sell the necessary ingredients and equipment, although normal kitchen utensils can be used for some of the needs. The processing steps that are used in home brewing are basically the same as those used commercially. There are naturally some limitations to home brewing that the commercial breweries are able to overcome. For example, in home brewing, excess yeast is usually not removed to the same degree and the storage temperature is usually not controlled as well to limit extended fermentation that can occur after packaging. Several books describe home brewing in detail.

### See Also the Following Articles

ACETIC ACID PRODUCTION • FERMENTED FOODS • LACTIC ACID BACTERIA • YEASTS

### Bibliography

Bamforth, C. (1998). "Beer: Tap Into the Art and Science of Brewing." Plenum, New York.

Banwart, G. J. (1990). "Basic Food Microbiology." Van Nostrand Reinhold, New York.

Cantarelli, C., and Lanzarini, G. (Eds.) (1989). "Biotechnology Applications in Beverage Production." Elsevier, London.

Haggblade, S., and Holzapfel, W. H. (1989). Industrialization of Africa's indigenous beer brewing. *In* "Industrialization of Indigenous Fermented Foods" (K. H. Steinkraus, Ed.), pp. 191–283. Dekker, New York.

Hough, J. S. (1985). "The Biotechnology of Malting and Brewing." Cambridge Univ. Press, Cambridge, UK.

Lawrence, D. R. (1988). Spoilage organisms in beer. *In* "Developments in Food Microbiology—3" (R. K. Robinson, Ed.), pp. 1–48. Elsevier, London.

Priest, F. G., and Campbell, I. (Eds.) (1996). "Brewing Microbiology" (2nd ed.). Chapman & Hall, London.

Rhodes, C. P., and Lappies, P. B. (Eds.) (1995). "The Encyclopedia of Beer." Holt, New York.

Spencer, J. F. T., and Spencer, D. M. (Eds.) (1990). "Yeast Technology." Springer-Verlag, Berlin.

Stewart, G. G. (1987). Alcoholic beverages. *In* "Food and Beverage Mycology" (L. R. Beuchat, Ed.), pp. 307–354. Van Nostrand Reinhold, New York.

# Beet Necrotic Yellow Vein Virus

## Renate Koenig and Dietrich-Eckhardt Lesemann

*Institut für Pflanzenvirologie, Mikrobiologie und Biologische Sicherheit*

## GLOSSARY

**ELISA (enzyme-linked immunosorbent assay)** A highly sensitive serological technique which is commonly used for the detection of viruses in infected plants. In the double-antibody sandwich variant of ELISA the virus particles are trapped in the wells of a plastic plate by means of virus-specific antibodies. Their binding is detected by means of virus-specific antibodies which are labeled with an enzyme. One enzyme molecule may convert large numbers of color-less substrate molecules into colored reaction products.

**immunogold labeling electron microscopy** Sensitive electron microscopical detection of the binding of antibodies to virus particles or other structures by means of gold-labeled second antibodies from another animal species.

**indicator plants** Plants which respond with conspicuous symptoms to the infection with a particular virus. In a local lesion host the infection with this virus remains localized.

**mechanical transmission of a virus** Transmission of a virus to a plant by mechanical contact. The transmission rate is greatly increased when sap from the infected plant is rubbed on the leaves of the not yet infected one.

**restriction fragment length polymorphism analysis** Electrophoretic analysis of the sequence-dependent sizes of the cleavage products obtained from dsDNAs [e.g., from polymerase chain reaction (PCR) products of viral cDNAs] by means of restriction enzymes. Used in combination with PCR for differentiating virus strains.

**single-strand conformation polymorphism analysis** The ssDNA obtained after heat denaturation of dsDNA

(e.g., from PCR products of viral cDNAs) may attain various sequence-dependent metastable conformations which confer different electrophoretic mobilities in polyacrylamide gels to them; used in combination with PCR for differentiating virus strains.

**tissue print immunoblotting** Sensitive serological test in which the freshly cut surface of parts of a plant is pressed first on an adsorbing filter membrane. The virus particles which are bound to the membrane are detected by means of enzyme-labeled antibodies. The enzyme converts an unstained substrate into a dark-colored insoluble reaction product.

**Western blotting** Proteins which are first separated electrophoretically in a polyacrylamide gel on the basis of their molecular masses are transferred, usually by means of an electric field, to a protein-binding membrane in which they are detected by means of enzyme-labeled antibodies. The enzyme converts an unstained substrate into a dark-colored insoluble reaction product indicating the location of the virus.

**BEET NECROTIC YELLOW VEIN VIRUS (BNYVV),** a soil-borne *Polymyxa betae*-transmitted rod-shaped virus, is the causal agent of sugar beet rizomania. This disease was first observed in the early 1950s in Italy and in the mid-1960s in Japan. The losses encountered during the early outbreaks of the disease were so severe that sugar beet growing had to be abandoned in various areas and many sugar factories, especially in Italy, had to shut down. The disease is now prevalent in the majority of the sugar beet growing areas worldwide, i.e., in most parts of Europe, Asia, and North America. Due to the availability of several newly bred resistant sugar beet varieties, losses have become less severe in many countries in the past decade. BNYVV also causes a severe disease in spinach, in which it produces pronounced leaf symptoms. Fodder beets may also become infected. This article summarizes the most important properties of BNYVV.

## I. BIOLOGICAL PROPERTIES

Beet necrotic yellow vein virus (BNYVV) has a narrow host range. Under natural conditions it mainly infects species in the genus *Beta* and spinach. It can be transmitted mechanically to the leaves of indicator plants such as *Chenopodium quinoa* and *Tetragonia expansa* in which it causes local lesions (Fig. 1). Systemic infections are produced in *Beta macrocarpa*.

Under natural conditions the virus is transmitted from the roots of diseased plants to those of healthy ones by the vector *Polymyxa betae*. In this vector the virus may persist indefinitely in the soil, which makes

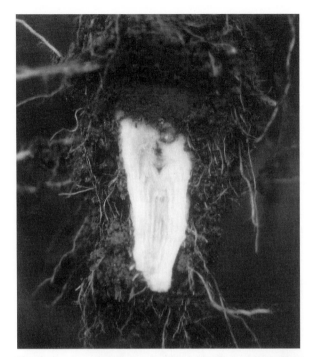

**Fig. 2.** Cross section through a BNYVV-infected sugar beet with pronounced beardedness. The tap root is very small and shows a pronounced discoloration of the vascular system. See color insert.

it practically impossible to eradicate the virus once it has become established in a field or an area. The name-giving symptom of rizomania (or "root madness") is a pronounced proliferation of small, readily necrotizing side roots ("beardedness") on early infected beets; the tap roots remain small and show a pronounced vascular browning (Fig. 2). Their sugar content is low. The upper parts of the beet plants are rarely invaded; if this happens, bright yellow lesions which sometimes become necrotic are formed on the leaves along the veins (Fig. 3). Because of this symptom, the name beet necrotic yellow vein virus has been given to the virus, which was first isolated from systemically infected leaves in Japan.

Growing resistant varieties has been the only successful means for minimizing yield losses due to the disease. Resistance genes used in breeding programs were found in various germplasm collections and also in *Beta maritima*. However, it is difficult to transfer resistance genes from the latter plant species to cultivated sugar beet by crossing. Genes for a complete immunity have not been found. Because the

**Fig. 1.** Local lesions formed by BNYVV on the indicator plant *Tetragonia expansa.*

**Fig. 3.** Sugar beet leaf systemically infected with BNYVV. See color insert.

resistant plants are invaded to a certain extent by the virus, resistance-breaking pathotypes may eventually be selected. Pronounced resistance, which is often RNA-mediated, has also been observed in genetically modified beets which contain the coat protein gene or other genes of BNYVV. However, no commercial varieties with genetically engineered BNYVV resistance have been put on the market.

## II. PROPERTIES AND COMPOSITION OF THE PARTICLES

BNYVV has nonenveloped, rod-shaped particles which are helically constructed with an axial canal (Fig. 4). They have predominant lengths of approximately 85, 100, 265, and 390 nm and diameters of 20 nm. The right-handed helix with a pitch of 2.6 nm has an axial repeat of four turns, involving 49 subunits of the major coat protein species which has a molecular weight of 20 kDa. Each coat protein subunit occupies four nucleotides on the RNA. Serological studies have provided information on the potential surface location of various parts of the amino acid sequence of the coat protein (see Section IV). Each particle contains one of the four or five different ssRNA species which make up the viral genome. There are no reports that the particles may contain lipids or carbohydrates.

## III. GENOME PROPERTIES

The linear positive-sense ssRNAs of BNYVV are capped at the 5′ end and, unlike the RNAs of all other plant viruses with rod-shaped particles, they are 3′ polyadenylated. RNAs 1 and 2 are sufficient to cause infections in experimental hosts such as *C. quinoa* and *T. expansa* to which the virus is transmitted by mechanical inoculation of the leaves. Isolates containing only RNA 1 and 2 produce pale green local lesions. The bright yellow lesions observed with fresh isolates (Fig. 1) are due to the presence of full-length RNA 3 in the inoculum.

Naturally infected sugar beets always contain RNAs 3 and 4 in addition to RNAs 1 and 2, and in some geographic regions they also contain RNA 5. The typical rizomania symptoms in beet are due to the presence of RNA 3 (Fig. 5). RNA 5 may modulate the type of symptoms formed; in the absence of RNA 3 it causes scab-like symptoms rather than root proliferations. RNA 4 has no pronounced influence on the symptoms in beet, but it greatly increases the transmission rate by *Polymyxa betae*. After mechanical transmission of BNYVV to test plants, RNAs 3–5 may become partially deleted or may be lost entirely.

RNA 1 (~6.7 kb) has only one large open reading frame (ORF) which codes for a posttranslationally cleaved protein (Fig. 6). In *in vitro* systems, translation may initiate at two sites: at the first AUG in the sequence at position 154 or at a downstream AUG at position 496. The resulting proteins of 237 and 220 kDa, respectively, both contain in their N-termi-

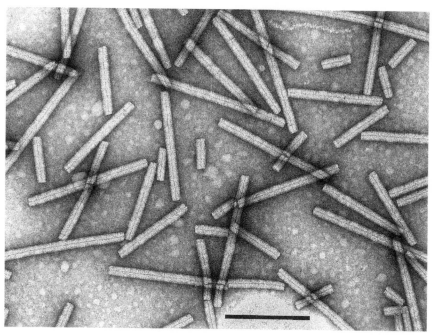

**Fig. 4.** Electron micrograph of BNYVV particles negatively stained with uranyl acetate. Bar, 200 nm.

nal part methyltransferase motifs (MetT), in their central part helicase (Hel) and papain-like protease motifs (Prot), and in their C-terminal part RNA-dependent RNA polymerase (RdRP) motifs. An assemble of such motifs is typically found in proteins involved in replication.

RNA 2 (~4.6 kb) contains six ORFs, i.e., the gene for the viral coat protein which is terminated by a suppressible UAG stop codon, the coat protein readthrough protein gene, a triple gene block (TGB) coding for proteins of 42, 13, and 15 kDa which

are involved in viral movement, and a gene coding for a 14-kDa cysteine-rich protein (Fig. 6). The N-terminal part of the readthrough portion of the coat protein readthrough protein is necessary for initiating encapsidation. It may be detected by means of specific antibodies on one of the extremities of freshly prepared particles, but it is readily cleaved off. The C-terminal part of the 75-kDa coat readthrough protein is essential for the transmission of the virus by its vector *P. betae.* The protein encoded on the 5'-proximal gene of the BNYVV TGB also contains

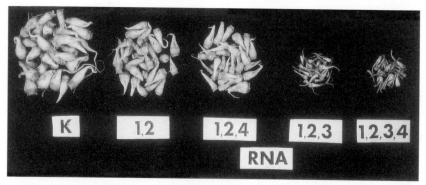

**Fig. 5.** Influence of BNYVV with various RNA compositions on the yield of mechanically inoculated sugar beets. K, the noninoculated control; the numbers refer to combinations of RNA species. See color insert. [From Koenig *et al.* (1991). *J. Gen. Virol.* **72,** 2243–2246.]

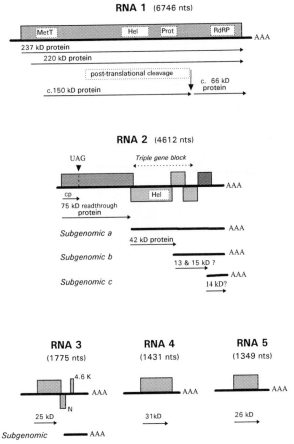

**Fig. 6.** Genome organization and translation strategies of BNYVV. For explanation see Section III.

helicase motifs. These motifs are also found in the respective TGB-encoded proteins of other viruses, e.g., hordei-, peclu-, potex-, and carlaviruses.

RNA 3 (~1.8 kb) has one major ORF coding for a 25-kDa protein. There is no evidence that the additional small ORFs present on RNA 3 are expressed under natural conditions. RNA 4 (~1.4 kb) has the coding capacity for a 31-kDa protein and RNA 5 for a 26-kDa protein (Fig. 6). The precise functions of these proteins are not known.

## IV. SEROLOGY

BNYVV particles are moderately to strongly immunogenic. ELISA has been extremely useful, not only for identifying the virus and following its spread into new areas but also in breeding programs for selecting

tolerant and partially resistant genotypes which may be identified by their low virus content. Tissue print immunoblotting has revealed an uneven distribution of BNYVV in infected sugar beet tap roots (Fig. 7). By means of immunogold-labeling electron microscopy, different binding sites (epitopes) for monoclonal antibodies (MAbs) were identified on the particles. Some MAbs were bound along the entire surface, whereas others were bound only on one extremity of the particles (Fig. 8). The ability of each of these MAbs to bind to a defined part of the amino acid sequence of the coat protein was determined by means of overlapping synthetic oligopeptides, and it has enabled the development of a structural model of BNYVV (Fig. 9). The C-terminal amino acids 182–188 are accessible on the entire length of the particles, whereas the N terminus (amino acids 1–<8) is accessible only on one extremity. On the opposite extremity epitopes are formed by amino acids 42–51 and 115–124. The region of amino acids 128–132

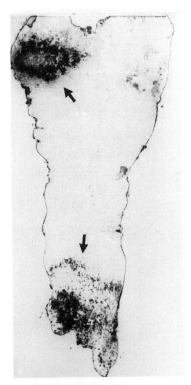

**Fig. 7.** Uneven distribution of BNYVV in a sugar beet tap root detected by means of tissue-print immunoblotting. Arrows indicate vein-infected zones. [From Kaufmann *et al.* (1992). *Arch. Virol.* **126**, 329–335.]

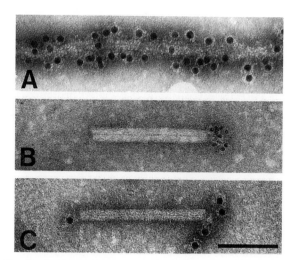

**Fig. 8.** Binding of monoclonal antibodies (MAbs) along the entire length of BNYVV particles (A), on one extremity only (B), and on both extremities (C). Binding on both extremities is observed only when the particles are treated with mixtures of MAbs which are specific for the opposite extremities of the particles. Bar, 100 nm.

can apparently not be reached by antibodies on the intact virus particles because the binding of the MAb specific for this region can be detected only on the denatured protein by means of Western blotting and not on the intact particles by means of immunogold-labeling electron microscopy. The C- and N-terminal epitopes of BNYVV coat protein are destroyed when the particles are treated with trypsin or plant proteases, but the gross particle morphology is not affected.

## V. STRAINS

By means of serology, no differences have been detected between BNYVV sources from various parts of the world. Molecular methods, such as restriction fragment length polymorphism, single-strand conformation polymorphism, and nucleotide sequence analyses did, however, reveal the existence of several strain groups. The A type is found in southern Europe and in The Netherlands whereas in France and Germany the B type is prevalent. The P type is restricted to a small area near the French town of Pithiviers (Fig. 10). Additional strain groups occur in Asia. The detection of various strain groups in Europe does not support an old hypothesis, ac-

**SDS-Stable Antigenic Regions of BNYVV Coat Protein**

**a) Location on the coat protein chain (determined by means of overlapping peptides)**

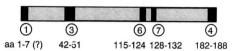

**b) Accessibility to antibodies on the virus particles (determined by means of immunogold electron microscopy )**

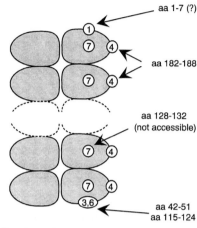

**Fig. 9.** Localization of epitopes 1, 3, 4, 6, and 7 on the coat protein amino acid chain (a) and on the virus particles by the combined use of overlapping synthetic peptides representing various parts of the amino acid chain and immunogold electron microscopy (b).

cording to which rizomania has spread from Italy, where it was first detected, to France and Germany and eventually to The Netherlands, because in Italy the A type is prevalent, in the upper Rhine valley in France and Germany the B type is prevalent, and in The Netherlands the A type is prevalent (Fig. 10).

## VI. CYTOPATHIC EFFECTS

Virions of most BNYVV isolates are scattered throughout the cytoplasm of infected cells or occur in aggregates. Either more or less dense masses of parallelly arranged particles or angle-layer arrays may be formed. Depending on the isolate only one or both types of aggregates occur. Membraneous accumulations of endoplasmic reticulum may also be found.

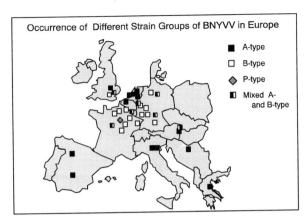

**Fig. 10.** Distribution of different strain groups of BNYVV in Europe.

## VII. TAXONOMY

Originally, BNYVV had been assigned to the genus tobamovirus, it was removed from this genus, as were several other viruses, because of its polypartite genome. The "out-grouped" viruses were then definitively or tentatively assigned to a new genus named furovirus (fungus-transmitted rod-shaped viruses) for which soil-borne wheat mosaic virus (SBWMV) is the type species. Recent sequence analyses, however, indicate that the original genus furovirus was very heterogeneous. Most of the other viruses which originally were assigned to this genus differ in their genome properties from SBWMV, which has a bipartite genome and a carmo-like movement protein encoded on a single gene. Since BNYVV has a different genome organization (see Section III and Fig. 6), it has been assigned to the newly established genus benyvirus (beet necrotic yellow vein virus). The only other virus in this genus is beet soil-borne mosaic virus, which has been found only in North America, where it is widespread.

Morphologically, the benyviruses are similar to other rod-shaped viruses, i.e., furo-, peclu-, pomo-, hordei-, tobra-, and tobamoviruses. The coat proteins of these viruses have many conserved residues (e.g., RF and FE in their central and C-terminal parts, respectively) which are presumably involved in the formation of salt bridges and determine the folding structures of these proteins. The possession of a TGB relates the benyviruses to the pomo-, peclu-, potex-, carla-, and alexiviruses. Conserved sequences are es-pecially found in the first and second TGB-encoded proteins of these viruses. Furo-, tobra-, and tobamoviruses lack a TGB. Benyviruses are differentiated from all other rod-shaped viruses by having only one large ORF for a replication-associated protein. This protein, which is cleaved posttranslationally, has methyltransferase, helicase- and RNA-dependent RNA polymerase motifs which show a higher degree of similarity to those of the caliciviridae (hepatitis virus E) and togaviridae (rubella virus) than to those of the other rod-shaped plant viruses. This suggests that the various parts of the genome of the benyviruses, like those of many other viruses, originated from different sources.

### Acknowledgment

We are grateful to the Deutsche Forschungsgemeinschaft for financially supporting our research on soil-borne viruses with rod-shaped particles.

### See Also the Following Articles

PLANT VIROLOGY, OVERVIEW • SOIL MICROBIOLOGY

### Bibliography

Asher, M. J. C. (1993). Rhizomania. *In* "The Sugar Beet Crop, Science into Practice" (D. A. Cooke and R. K. Scott, Eds.), pp. 311–346. Chapman & Hall, London.

Commandeur, U., Koenig, R., Manteuffel, R., Torrance, L., Lüddecke, P., and Frank, R. (1994). Location, size and complexity of epitopes on the coat protein of beet necrotic yellow vein virus studied by means of synthetic overlapping peptides. *Virology* **198,** 282–287.

Haeberlé, A. M., Stussi-Garaud, C., Schmitt, C., Garaud, J. C., Richards, K. E., Guilley, H., and Jonard, G. (1994). Detection by immunogold labelling of P75 readthrough protein near an extremity of beet necrotic yellow vein virus particles. *Arch. Virol.* **134,** 195–203.

Hehn, A., Fritsch, C., Richards, K. E., Guilley, H., and Jonard, G. (1997). Evidence for *in vitro* and *in vivo* autocatalytic processing of the primary translation product of beet necrotic yellow vein virus RNA 1 by a papain-like proteinase. *Arch. Virol.* **142,** 1051–1058.

Kaufmann, A., Koenig, R., and Lesemann, D.-E. (1992). Tissue print-immunoblotting reveals an uneven distribution of beet necrotic yellow vein and beet soil-borne viruses in sugarbeets. *Arch. Virol.* **126,** 329–335.

Kiguchi, T., Saito, M., and Tamada, T. (1996). Nucleotide

sequence analysis of RNA-5 of five isolates of beet necrotic yellow vein virus and the identity of a deletion mutant. *J. Gen. Virol.* 77, 575–580.

Koenig, R., Jarausch, W., Li, Y., Commandeur, U., Burgermeister, W., Gehrke, M., and Lüddecke, P. (1991). Effect of recombinant beet necrotic yellow vein virus with different RNA compositions on mechanically inoculated sugarbeets. *J. Gen. Virol.* 72, 2243–2246.

Koenig, R., Lüddecke, P., and Haeberlé, A. M. (1995). Detection of beet necrotic yellow vein virus strains, variants and mixed infections by examining single-strand conformation polymorphisms of immunocapture RT-PCR products. *J. Gen. Virol.* 76, 2051–2055.

Koenig, R., Haeberlé, A. M., and Commandeur, U. (1997). Detection and characterization of a distinct type of beet necrotic yellow vein virus RNA 5 in a sugarbeet growing area in Europe. *Arch. Virol.* 142, 1499–1504.

Putz, C., Merdinoglu, D., Lemaire, O., Stocky, G., Valentin, P., and Wiedemann, S. (1990). Beet necrotic yellow vein virus, causal agent of sugar beet rhizomania. *Rev. Plant Pathol.* 69, 247–254.

Richards, K., and Tamada, T. (1992). Mapping functions on the multipartite genome of beet necrotic yellow vein virus. *Annu. Rev. Phytopathol.* 30, 291–313.

Tamada, T., Kusume, T., Uchino, H., Kiguchi, T., and Saito, M. (1996). Evidence that beet necrotic yellow vein virus RNA-5 is involved in symptom development of sugarbeet roots. *In* "Proceedings of the Third Symposium of the International Working Group on Plant Viruses with Fungal Vectors," Dundee, Scotland, August 6–7, pp. 49–52.

# Biocatalysis for Synthesis of Chiral Pharmaceutical Intermediates

**Ramesh N. Patel**

*Bristol-Myers Squibb Pharmaceutical Research Institute*

## GLOSSARY

**asymmetric synthesis** Conversion of a prochiral compound into a chiral compound by a stereospecific reaction.

**chiral** Molecule with at least one chiral center; often called optically pure or enantipure molecule.

**chirality** Property of a molecule with carbon atoms to which four different ligands are bonded tetrahedrally. This gives a pair of stereoisomers per chiral carbon atom which exhibit mirror symmetry; however, they cannot be superimposed.

**enantiomers or optical isomers** Stereoisomers of molecules with one or more chiral centers, which are identical in chemical and physical property except for the rotation of plane-polarized light. Enantiomers differ in their biological, physiological, and pharmacological effects.

**+/− or d/l** Indicate the direction of rotation of plane-polarized light by a chiral compound. + or d, dextrorotatory; − or l, levorotarory.

**racemate** Equimolar mixture of enantiomers, which therefore no longer rotate plane-polarized light.

**stereoisomers** Molecules which are identical in all compositional matters (e.g., number, types of atoms, and chemical bonds) but differ in spatial orientation and some physical properties.

**RECENTLY,** much attention has been focused on the interaction of small molecules with biological macromolecules. The search for selective enzyme inhibitors and receptor agonists or antagonists is one of the keys for target-oriented research in the pharmaceutical industry. An increased understanding of the mechanism of drug interaction on a molecular level has led to increasing awareness of the importance of chirality as the key to efficacy of many drug products. It is now known that often only one stereoisomer of a drug substance is required for efficacy, and the other stereoisomer is either inactive or exhibits considerably reduced activity. Pharmaceutical companies are aware that, where appropriate, new drugs for the clinic should be homochiral to avoid the possibility of side effects due to an undesirable stereoisomer.

## I. INTRODUCTION

Chiral synthons can be prepared by resolution of racemates or asymmetric synthesis by either chemical or biocatalytic processes, with microbial cells or enzymes derived therefrom. The advantages of microbial- or enzyme-catalyzed reactions compared to chemical reactions are that they are stereoselective and can be carried out at ambient temperature and atmospheric pressure. These minimize problems of

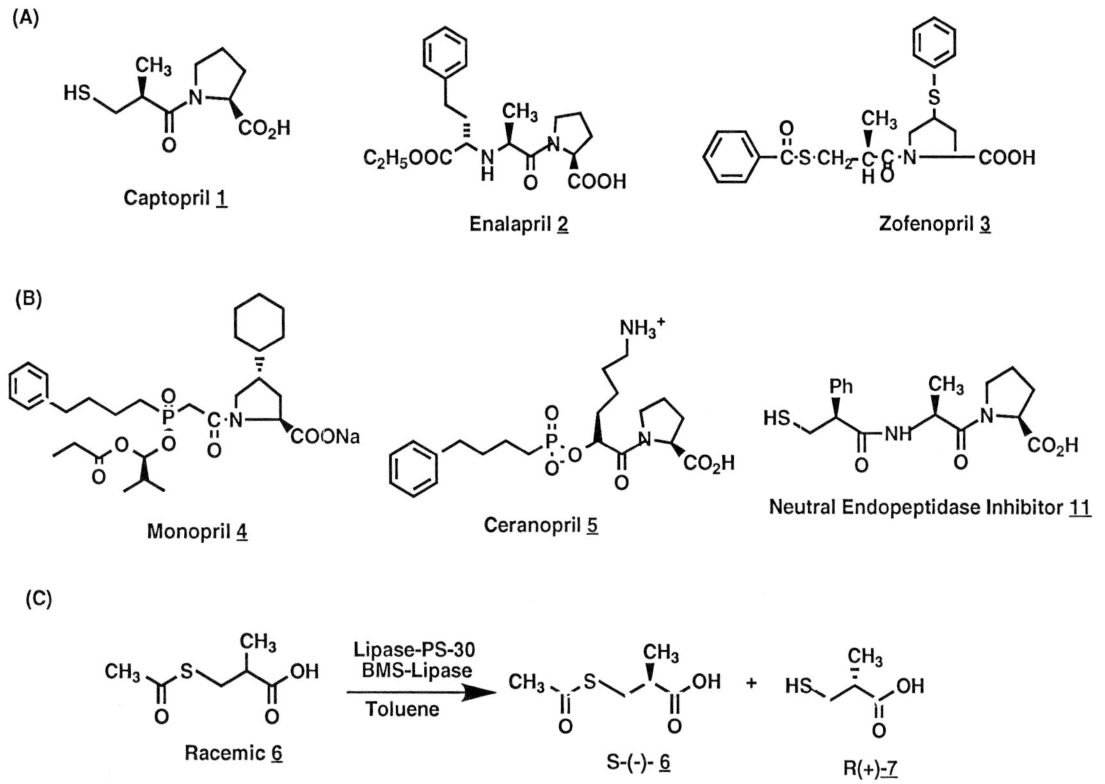

**Fig. 1.** (A) Angiotensin-converting enzyme inhibitors: captopril, **1**; enalapril, **2**; and zofenopril, **3**. (B) Angiotensin-converting enzyme and neutral endopeptidase inhibitors: monopril, **4**; ceranopril, **5**; and neutral endopeptidase inhibitor, **11**. (C) Synthesis of captopril side chain: stereoselective hydrolysis of thioester of 3-acylthio-2-methyl propanoic acid (**6**).

isomerization, racemization, epimerization, and re-arrangement which generally occur during chemical processes. Biocatalytic processes are generally carried out in aqueous solution; thus, the use of environmentally harmful chemicals in chemical processes and the disposal of solvent waste are avoided. Furthermore, microbial cells or enzymes derived therefrom can be immobilized and reused in many cycles.

## II. ANGIOTENSIN-CONVERTING ENZYME INHIBITORS (ANTIHYPERTENSIVE DRUGS)

Captopril is designated chemically as 1-[(2S)-3-mercapto-2-methylpropionyl]-L-proline (1). It is used as an antihypertensive agent through suppression of the renin–angiotensin–aldosterone system. Captopril and other compounds, such as enalapril

(2) zofenopril (3), monopril (4), and ceranopril (5) (Figs. 1A and 1B), prevent the conversion of angiotensin I to angiotensin II by inhibition of angiotensin-converting enzyme (ACE). The combined sales of ACE inhibitors for treatment of hypertension is in excess of $3 billion. The potency of captopril and other inhibitor of ACE depends critically on the configuration of the mercaptoalkanoyl moiety; the compound with the S configuration is about 100 times more active than its corresponding R-enantiomer. The required 3-mercapto-(2S)-methyl propionic acid moiety has been prepared from the microbially derived chiral 3-hydroxy-(2R)-methylpropionic acid, which is obtained by the hydroxylation of isobutyric acid. The use of extracellular lipases of microbial origin to catalyze the stereoselective hydrolysis of 3-acylthio-2-methylpropanoic acid ester in an aqueous system has been demonstrated to produce optically active 3-acylthio-2-methyl propanoic acid.

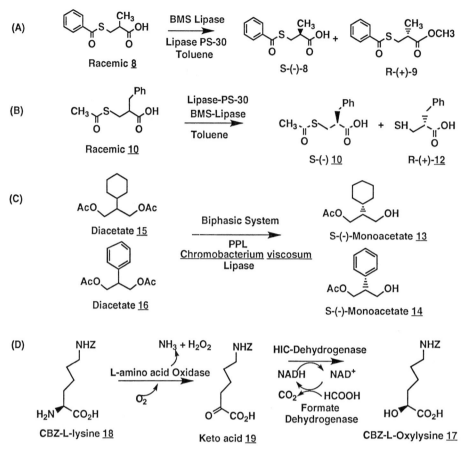

**Fig. 2.** (A) Synthesis of captopril and zofenopril side chain: stereoselective esterification of 3-benzylthio-2-methyl propanoic acid (**8**). (B) Synthesis of chiral synthon for neutral endopeptidase inhibitor: stereoselective hydrolysis of thioester of α-[(acetylthio)methyl] benzene propanoic acid (**10**). (C) Synthesis of chiral intermediates for monopril: asymmetric hydrolysis of 2-cyclohexyl-(**15**) and 2-phenyl-1,3-propanediol diacetate (**16**). (D) Synthesis of chiral synthon for ceranopril: biotransformation of CBZ-L-lysine (**18**) to CBZ-L-oxylysine (**17**).

The synthesis of the chiral side chain of captopril by the lipase-catalyzed enantioselective hydrolysis of the thioester bond of racemic 3-acetylthio-2-methyl propanoic acid (**6**) to yield S-(−)-**6** has been demonstrated. Lipase from *Rhizopus oryzae* ATCC 24563 (heat-dried cells) and lipase PS-30 in organic solvent system (1,1,2-trichloro-1,2,2-trifluoroethane or toluene) catalyzed the hydrolysis of the thioester bond undesired enantiomer of racemic **6** to yield desired S-(−)-**6**, R-(+)-3-mercapto-2-methyl propanoic acid (**7**), and acetic acid (Fig. 1C). The reaction yield of >24% (theoretical maximum 50%) and optical purity of >95% were obtained for S-(−)-**6** using each lipase.

In an alternate approach to prepare the chiral side-chain of captopril (**1**) and zofenopril (**3**), the lipase-catalyzed stereoselective esterification of racemic 3-benzoylthio-2-methylpropanoic acid (**8**) (Fig. 2A) in an organic solvent system was demonstrated to yield R-(+) methyl ester (**9**) and unreacted acid enriched in the desired S-(−) enantiomer (**8**). Using lipase PS-30 with toluene as solvent and methanol as nucleophile, the desired chiral side-chain S-(−)-**8** was obtained in 37% reaction yield (maximum theoretical yields is 50%) and 97% optical purity.

The S-(−)-α-[(acetylthio)methyl]benzene propanoic acid (**10**) [S-(−)-**10**] is a key chiral intermediate for the neutral endopeptidase inhibitor (11). The lipase-catalyzed stereoselective hydrolysis of thioester bond of racemic α-[(acetylthio)methyl] benzene-propanoic acid (10) in organic solvent yields R-(+)-α [(mercapto)methyl] benzene-propanoic acid (12) and S-(−)-10. Using lipase PS-30, the S-(−)-10 was obtained in 40% reaction yield (theoretical maximum 50%) and 98% optical purity (Fig. 2B).

The S-(−)-2-cyclohexyl-1,3-propanediol monoacetate (13) and the S-(−)-2-phenyl-1,3-propanediol monoacetate (14) are key chiral intermediates for the chemo-enzymatic synthesis of Monopril (4) (Fig. 2C), a new hypertensive drug which acts as an ACE inhibitor. The asymmetric hydrolysis of 2-cyclohexyl-1,3-propanediol diacetate (15) and 2-phenyl-1,3-propanediol diacetate (16) to the corresponding S-(−) monoacetate 13 and S-(−) monoacetate 14 by PPL and *Chromobacterium viscosum* lipase has been demonstrated. In a biphasic system using 10% toluene, reaction yield of >65% and optical purity of 99% were obtained for S-(−)-13 using each enzyme. S-(−)-14 was obtained in 90% reaction yield and 99.8% optical purity using *C. viscosum* lipase under similar conditions.

Ceranopril (5) (Fig. 1B) is another ACE inhibitor which requires chiral intermediate carbobenzoxy (CBZ)-L-oxylysine (17) (Fig. 2D). A biotransformation process was developed to prepare the CBZ-L-oxylysine.

Nε-carbobenzoxy (CBZ)-L-lysine (18) was first converted to the corresponding keto acid (19) by oxidative deamination using cells of *Providencia alcalifaciens* SC 9036 which contained L-amino acid oxidase and catalase. The keto acid 19 was subsequently converted to CBZ-L-oxylysine (17) using L-2-hydroxy-isocaproate dehydrogenase from *Lactobacillus confusus*. The NADH required for this reaction was regenerated using formate dehydrogenase from *Candida boidinii*. The reaction yield of 95% with 98.5% optical purity was obtained in the overall process.

## III. PACLITAXEL (ANTICANCER DRUG) SEMI-SYNTHESIS

Among the antimitotic agents, paclitaxel (Taxol; 20)—a complex, polycyclic diterpene—exhibits a unique mode of action on microtubule proteins responsible for the formation of the spindle during cell division. Paclitaxel is the only compound known to inhibit the depolymerization process of microtubulin. Various types of cancers have been treated with paclitaxel and the results in treatment of ovarian cancer and metastatic breast cancer are very promising. In collaboration with the National Cancer Institute, Bristol-Myers Squibb developed paclitaxel for treatment of refractory ovarian cancer. Paclitaxel was originally isolated from the bark of the yew, *Taxus brevifolia*, and has also been found in other *Taxus* species in relatively low yield. Taxol was initially obtained from *T. brevifolia* bark in approximately 0.07% yield. It required cumbersome purification of paclitaxel from the other related taxanes. It is estimated that approximately 20,000 pounds of yew bark (the equivalent of approximately 3000 trees) are needed to produce 1 kg of purified paclitaxel. Alternative methods for production of paclitaxel by cell suspension cultures and by semi-synthetic processes are being evaluated by various groups. The development of a semi-synthetic process for the production of paclitaxel from baccatin III (21) or 10-deacetylbaccatin III (22; 10-DAB) and C-13 taxol side-chain (23) provided a very promising approach. Paclitaxel, related taxanes, baccatin III, and 10-DAB can be derived from renewable resources, such as extract of needles, shoot, and young *Taxus* cultivars. The most valuable material in this mixture for semi-synthesis is the taxane "nucleus" component of baccatin III (21) (paclitaxel without the C-13 side-chain) and 10-DAB (paclitaxel without the C-13 side-chain and the C-10 acetate). Enzymatic conversion of taxanes to 10-DAB by cleavage of the C-10 acetate and the C-13 paclitaxel side-chain is a very attractive approach to increase the concentration of this valuable compound in yew extracts. By using selective enrichment techniques, we isolated two strains of *Nocardioides* that contained novel enzymes C-13 taxolase and C-10 deacetylase. The extracellular C-13 taxolase derived from filtrate of fermentation broth of *Nocardioides albus* SC 13911 catalyzed the cleavage of C-13 side-chain from paclitaxel and related taxanes, such as taxol C (24), cephalomannine (25), 7-β-xylosyltaxol (26), 7-β-xylosyl-10-deacetyltaxol (27), and 10-deacetyltaxol (28) (Fig. 3A). The intracellular C-10 deacetylase derived from fermentation of

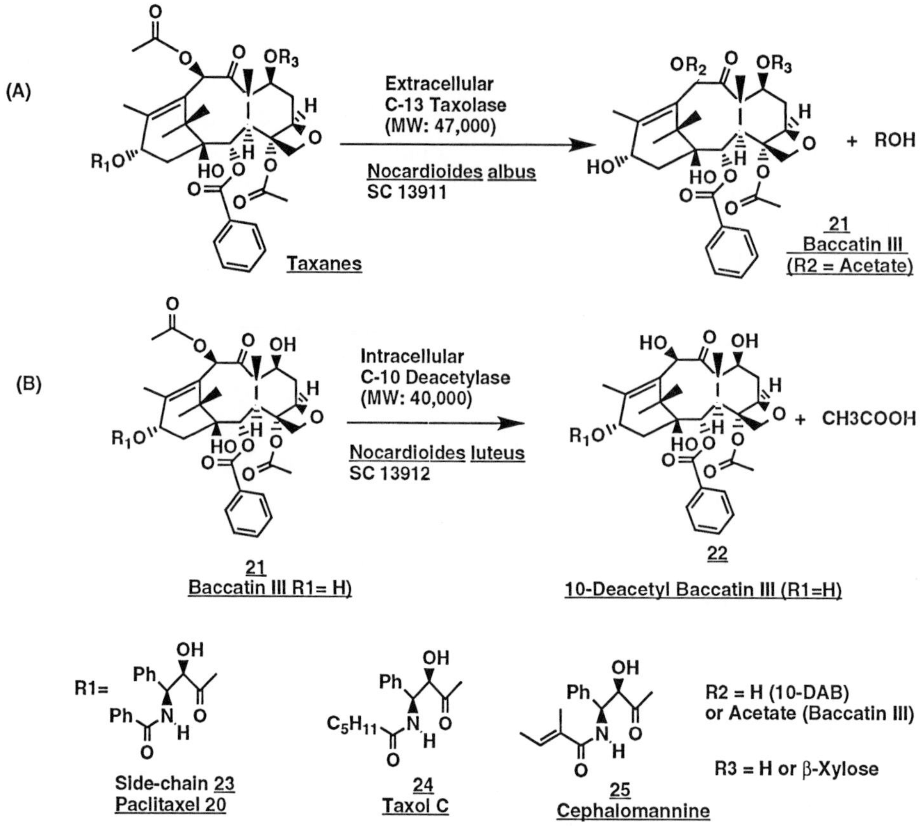

**Fig. 3.** (A) Hydrolysis of the C-13 side chain of taxanes by C-13 taxolase from *Nocardioides albus* SC 13911. (B) Hydrolysis of the C-10 acetate of taxanes by C-10 deacetylase from *Nocardioides luteus* SC 13912.

*Nocardioides luteus* SC 13912 catalyzed the cleavage of C-10 acetate from paclitaxel, related taxanes, and baccatin III to yield 10-DAB (Fig. 3B). Fermentation processes were developed for growth of *N. albus* SC 13911 and *N. luteus* SC 13912 to produce C-13 taxolase and C-10 deactylase, respectively, in 5000-liter batches. A bioconversion process was demonstrated for the conversion of taxol, related taxanes in extrtacts of *Taxus* plant cultivars, to a single-compound 10-DAB using both enzymes. In the bioconversion process, ethanolic extracts of the whole young plant of five different cultivars of *Taxus* were first treated with a crude preparation of the C-13 taxolase to give complete conversion of measured taxanes to baccatin III and 10-DAB in 6 h. *Nocardioides luteus* SC 13192 whole cells were then added to the reaction mixture to give complete conversion of baccatin III to 10-DAB. The concentration of 10-DAB was increased by

5.5- to 24-fold in the extracts treated with the two enzymes. The bioconversion process was also applied to extracts of the bark of *T. bravifolia,* resulting in a 12-fold increase in 10-DAB concentration. The enhancement of 10-DAB concentration in yew extracts was useful in increasing the amount and purification of this key precursor for the paclitaxel semi-synthetic process using renewable resources.

Among other taxanes in bark of the specific yew and taxus cultivars are 7-$\beta$-xylosyltaxanes. Using enrichment culture techniques, organisms capable of hydrolyzing 7-$\beta$-xylosyltaxanes were isolated. The best culture which catalyzed the cleavage of xylose from 7-$\beta$-xylosyltaxol (**26**) and 7-$\beta$-xylosyl-10-de-acetyltaxol (**27**) was identified as a strain of *Morexella* sp. Production of xylosidase was scaled-up from a to a 500-liter batch fermentation process. Cell suspensions of *Moraxella* sp. in 50 mM phosphate buffer (pH 7.0) gave complete conversion of 7-β-xylosyl-10-deacetyltaxol to 10-deacetyl-taxol (**28**) and 7-β-xylosyl-10-DAB (**29**) to 10. Various xylosyltaxanes [7-β-xylosyltaxol, 7-β-xylosylcephalomannine (**30**), 7-β-xylosyl-10-deacetyltaxol, 7-β-xylosyl-10-deacetylcephalomannine (**31**), 7-β-xylosyl-10-DAB, 7-β-xylosylbaccatin III (**32**), and 7-β-xylosyltaxol C (**33**); Fig. 4A] were converted to 10 DAB (for paclitaxel semisynthesis) by treatment with three enzymes: xylosidase (*Moraxella* sp.), C-13 taxolase (*N. albus*), and C-10 deacetylase (*N. luteus*) from microbial sources.

Another key precursor for the taxol semi-synthetic process is the preparation of chiral C-13 taxol side chain. Two different stereoselective enzymatic processes were developed for the preparation of chiral C-13 taxol side-chain synthon. In one process, the stereoselective microbial reduction of 2-keto-3-(*N*-benzoylamino)-3-phenyl propionic acid ethyl ester (**34**) to yield (2*R*,3 *S*)-(−)-*N*-benzoyl-3-phenyl isoserine ethyl ester (**35**) was demonstrated (Fig. 4B). After an extensive microbial screen, two strains of *Hansenula* were identified which catalyzed the stereoselective reduction of ketone (**34**) to the desired product (**35**) in >80% reaction yield and >94% optical purity. Preparative-scale bioreduction of ketone **34** was demonstrated using cell suspensions of *Hansenula polymorpha* SC 13865 and *Hansenula fabianii* SC 13894 in independent experiments. In both batches, a reaction yield of >80% and an optical purity of >94% were obtained for the desired alcohol isomer (**35**).

In an alternate process for the preparation of C-13 taxol side chain, the stereoselective enzymatic hydro-

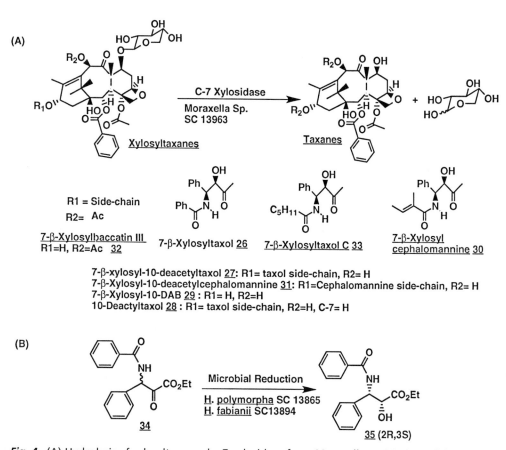

*Fig. 4.* (A) Hydrolysis of xylosyltaxanes by 7-xylosidase from *Morexella* sp. SC 13963. (B) Synthesis of paclitaxel side chain synthon: stereoselective reduction of 2-keto-3-(*N*-benzoylamino)-3-phenyl propionic acid ethyl ester (**34**).

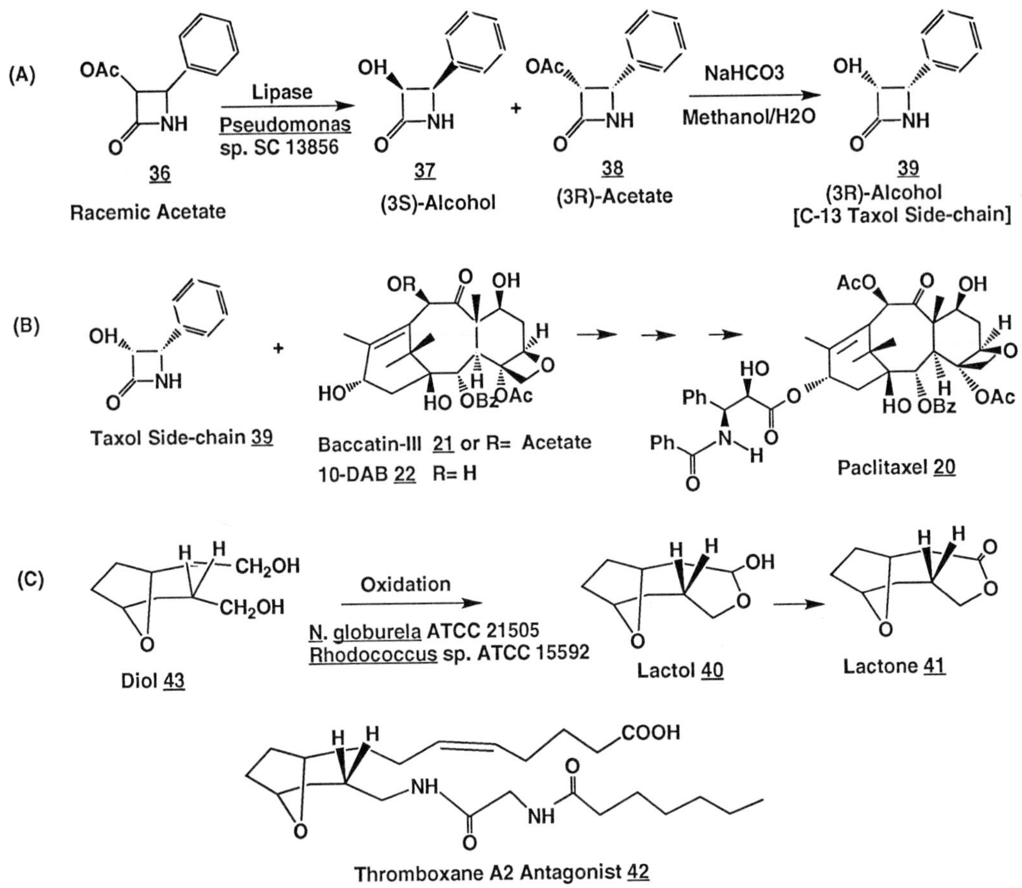

***Fig. 5.*** (A) Synthesis of paclitaxel side chain synthon: stereoselective hydrolysis of *cis*-3-(acetyloxy)-4-phenyl-2-azetidinone (**36**). (B) Semisynthesis of paclitaxel **20**: coupling of baccatin III (**21**) and paclitaxel side chain **39**. (C) Synthesis of chiral synthon for thromboxane A2 antagonist: stereoselective oxidation of (exo, exo)-7-oxabicyclo [2.2.1] heptane-2,3-methanol (**43**) to the corresponding lactol (**40**) and lactone (**41**).

lysis of racemic *cis*-3-(acetyloxy)-4-phenyl-2-azetidinone (36) to the corresponding (*S*)-(−)-alcohol (37) was carried out.

Lipase PS-30 from *Pseudomonas cepacia* (Amano International Enzyme Company) and BMS lipase (extracellular lipase derived from the fermentation of *Pseudomonas* sp. SC 13856) catalyzed hydrolysis of the undesired enantiomer of racemic **36**, producing *S*-(−)-alcohol (37) and the desired *R*-(+)-acetate (38) (Fig. 5A). Reaction yields of >96% and optical purities of >99.5% were obtained. The enzymatic process for the resolution of racemic acetate 36 was scaled up to 150 liters using each enzyme. From each reaction batch, 3-(*R*)-acetate 38 was isolated in 88–90 M% yield and 99.5% optical purity. 3-(*R*)-acetate 38 was chemically converted to 3-(*R*)-alcohol (39). The C-13 taxol side chain (35 or 39) produced by either the reductive or the resolution process could be coupled to bacattin III or 10-DAB after protection and nonprotection of each compound to prepare taxol using the semi-synthetic process (Fig. 5B).

## IV. THROMBOXANE A2 ANTAGONIST

Thromboxane A2 (TxA2) is an exceptionally potent pro-aggregatory and vasoconstrictor substance produced by the metabolism of arachidonic acid in blood platelets and other tissues. In addition to being a potent anti-aggregatory and vasodilator characteristics, it is thought to play a role in the maintenance of vascular homeostasis and contribute to the pathogenesis of a variety of vascular disorders. Approaches towards limiting the effect of TxA2 have focused on either inhibiting its synthesis or blocking its action at its receptor sites by means of an antagonist. The lactol [3a-(3aα, 4α, 7α, 7aα)]-hexahydro-4,7-epoxy-isobenzo-furan-1-(3*H*)-one (**40**) or corresponding chiral lactone (**41**) (Fig. 5) are key chiral intermediates for the total synthesis of TxA2 antagonist 1*S*-[1a, 2a (*Z*), 3a, 4a [[-7-[3-(1-oxoheptyl)-amine] acetyl] methyl]-7-oxabicyclo-[2.2.1] hept-2-yl]-5-heptanoic acid (**42**), a new cardiovascular agent useful in the treatment of thrombolic disease. The stereoselective oxidation of (exo, exo)-7-oxabicyclo [2.2.1] heptane-2,3-dimethanol (**43**) to the corresponding chiral lactol (**40**) and lactone (**41**) (Fig. 5C) by cell suspensions of *Nocardia globerula* ATCC 15592 and *Rhodococcus* sp. ATCC 15592 has been described. The reaction yield of 70 M% and optical purity of 96% were obtained for chiral lactone **41** after a 96-hr biotransformation process using cell suspensions of *N. globerula* ATCC 15592. An overall reaction yield of 46 M% (lactol and lactone combined) and optical purities of 96.7 and 98.4% were obtained for lactol **40** and lactone **41**, respectively, using cell suspensions of *Rhodococcus* sp. ATCC 15592.

The stereoselective asymmetric hydrolysis of (exo, exo)-7-oxabicyclo [2.2.1] heptane-2,3-dimethanol diacetate ester (**44**) to the corresponding chiral *S*(−)-monoacetate ester (**45**) (Fig. 6A) has been demonstrated with lipases. Lipase PS-30 from **P. cepacia** was most effective in asymmetric hydrolysis in obtaining the desired enantiomer of monoacetate ester. A reaction yield of 75 M% and optical purity of >99% were obtained when the reaction was conducted in a biphasic system with 10% toluene. The reaction process was scaled up to 80 liters (400 g of substrate) and *S*-(−)-monoacetate ester **45** was isolated in 80 M% yield with 99.3% optical purity and 99.5% chemical purity. The chiral monoacetate ester was oxidized to its corresponding aldehyde and subsequently hydrolyzed to give chiral lactol (Fig. 6A), which was used in chemo-enzymatic synthesis of thromboxane A2 antagonist.

## V. ANTICHOLESTEROL DRUGS

Chiral β-hydroxy esters are versatile synthons in organic synthesis, specifically in the preparation of natural products. The asymmetric reduction of carbonyl compounds reduced 4-chloro-3-oxobutanoic acid methyl ester (**46**) to *S*-(−)-4-chloro-3-hydroxybutanoic acid methyl ester (**47**) (Fig. 6B) by use of cell suspensions of **Geotrichum candidum** SC 5469. *S*(−)-**47** is a key chiral intermediate in the total chemical synthesis of **48** (Fig. 6D), a cholesterol antagonist which acts by inhibiting hydroxymethyl glutaryl CoA (HMG CoA) reductase. In the biotransformation process, a reaction yield of 95% and optical purity of 96% were obtained for S-(−)-**47** by glucose-, acetate-, or glycerol-grown cells (10% w/v) of *G. candidum* SC 5469. The optical purity of *S*-(−)-**47** was increased to 99% by heat treatment of cell suspensions (55°C for 30 min) prior to conducting the bioreduction of **46**. The stereoselective reduction of ethyl-, isopropyl-, and tertiary-butyl esters of 4-chloro-3-oxobutanoic acid and methyl- and ethyl esters of 4-bromo-3-oxobutanoic acid has been demonstrated by *G. candidum* SC 5469. A reaction yield of >85% and optical purity of >94% were obtained. NAD$^+$-dependent oxidoreductase (950 kDa), responsible for the stereoselective reduction of β-keto esters of 4-chloro- and 4-bromo-3-oxobutanoic acid, was purified 100-fold.

Recently, the stereoselective reduction of a diketone 3,5-dioxo-6-(benzyloxy) hexanoic acid, ethyl ester **49**, to (3*S*,5*R*)-dihydroxy-6-(benzyloxy) hexanoic acid, ethyl ester **50** (Fig. 6C), has been demonstrated. Compound **50** is a key chiral intermediate required for the chemical synthesis of [4-[4α, 6β(E)]]-6-[4,4-bis (4-fluorophenyl)-3-(1-methyl - 1*H* - tetrazol - 5 - yl) - 1,3-butadienyl] - tetrahydro - 4 - hydroxy - 2*H* - pyren - 2 - one, (compound *R*-(+)-**51**; Fig. 6D), a new anticholesterol drug that acts by inhibition of HMG CoA reductase. Among various microbial cultures evaluated for the stereoselective reduction of diketone **49**, cell suspensions of **Acinetobacter calcoaceticus** SC 13876 reduced **49** to **50**. The reaction yield of 85% and optical purity of 97% were obtained using glycerol-grown cells. Cell extracts of *A. calcoaceticus* SC 13876 in the presence of NAD$^+$, glucose, and glucose dehydroge-

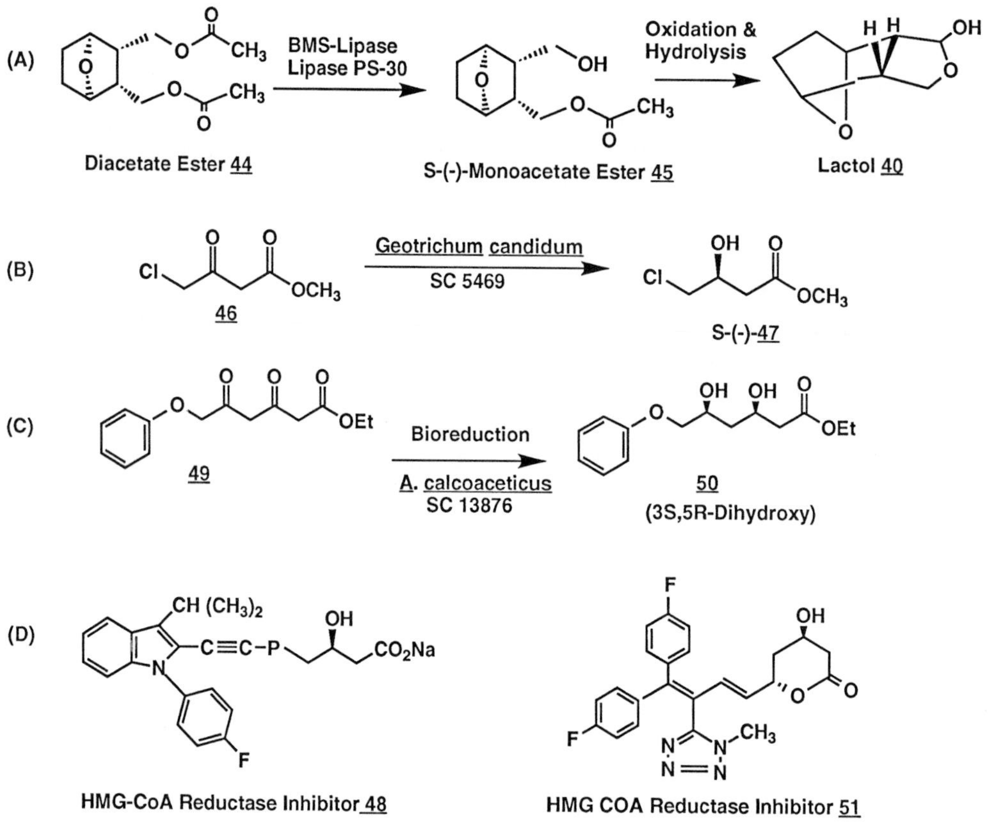

**Fig. 6.** (A) Synthesis of chiral synthon for thromboxane A2 antagonist: asymmetric hydrolysis of (exo, exo)-7-oxabicyclo [2.2.1] heptane-2,3-dimethanol diacetate ester (**44**) to the corresponding *S*-(−)-monoacetate ester **45**. (B) Synthesis of chiral synthon for anticholesterol drug **48**: stereoselective reduction of 4-chloro-3-oxobutanoic acid methyl ester **46**. (C) Synthesis of chiral synthon for anticholesterol drug **51**: stereoselective reduction of 3,5-dioxo-6-(benzyloxy) hexanoic acid ethyl ester **49**. (D) Structures of anticholesterol drugs **48** and **51** (HMG CoA reductase inhibitors).

nase reduced **49** to the corresponding dihydroxy compound **50**. The reaction yield of 92% and the optical purity of 99% were obtained at 10 g/liter substrate concentration.

Using a resolution process, chiral alcohol *R*-(+)-**51** was also prepared by the lipase-catalyzed stereoselective acetylation of racemic **51** in organic solvent. Lipase PS-30 (Amano International Enzyme Co.) and BMS lipase efficiently catalyzed the acetylation of the undesired enantiomer of racemic **51** to yield *S*-(−)-acetylated product **52** and unreacted desired *R*-(+)-**51** (Fig. 7A). A reaction yield of 49 M% (theoretical maximum 50 M%) and optical purity of 98.5% were obtained for **R**-(+)-**51** when the reaction was conducted using toluene as the solvent in the presence of isopropenyl acetate as the acyl donor at 4 g/liter

substrate concentration. In methyl ethyl ketone at 50 g/liter substrate concentration, a reaction yield of 46 M% and optical purity of 96.4% were obtained for *R*-(+)-**51**. The enzymatic process was scaled up to a 640-liter preparative batch using immobilized lipase PS-30 at 4 g/liter racemic substrate **51** in toluene as solvent. From the reaction mixture *R*-(+)-**51** was isolated in 35 M% overall yield with 98.5% optical purity and 99.5% chemical purity.

Pravastatin (**53**) and Mevastatin (**54**) are anticholesterol drugs which act by competitively inhibiting HMG CoA reductase. Pravastatin sodium is produced by two fermentation steps. The first step is the production of compound ML-236B by *Penicillium citrinum*. Purified compound was converted to its sodium salt with sodium hydroxide and in the second step was hydroxylated to Pravastatin sodium 53 (Fig. 7B) by *Streptomyces carbophilus*. A cytochrome P-450-containing enzyme system has been demonstrated from *S. carbophilus* to catalyze the hydroxylation reaction.

Squalene synthase is the first pathway-specific enzyme in the biosynthesis of cholesterol and catalyzes the head-to-head condensation of two molecules of farnesyl pyrophosphate (FPP) to form squalene. It has been implicated in the transformation of FPP into presqualene pyrophosphate (PPP). FPP analogs are a major class of inhibitors of squalene synthase. However, these compounds lack specificity and are potential inhibitors of other FPP-consuming transferases such as geranyl geranyl

pyrophosphate synthase. To increase enzyme specificity, analogs of PPP and other mechanism-based enzyme inhibitors have been synthesized. BMS-188494 (Fig. 7C) is a potent squalene synthase inhibitor effective as an anticholesterol drug. (*S*)-[1-(acetoxyl)-4-(3-phenyl)butyl]phosphonic acid (diethyl ester 55) is a key chiral intermediate required for the total chemical synthesis of BMS-188494. Compound 55 was prepared by the stereoselective acetylation of racemic [1-(hydroxy)-4-(3-phenyl)butyl] phophonic acid (diethyl ester 56) (Fig. 7C) using *Geotrichum candidum* lipase in tolune as solvent and isopropenyl acetate as acyl donor. A reaction yield of 38% (theoretical maximum 50%) and an optical purity of 95% were obtained for chiral acetate 55.

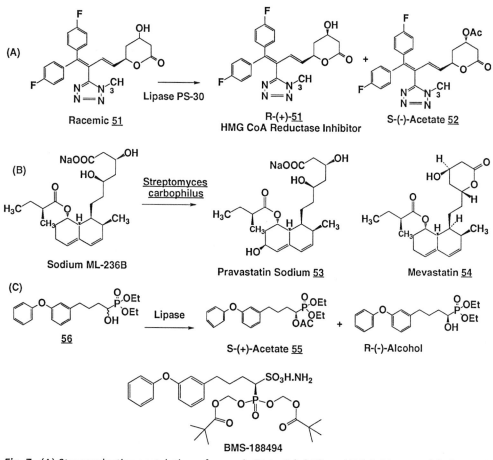

**Fig. 7.** (A) Stereoselective acetylation of recemic **51** to *S*-(−)-**52** and *R*-(+)-**51**, an anticholesterol drug. (B) Structures of Pravastatin and Mevastatin (anticholesterol drugs): stereoselective hydroxylation of ML-236 B to Prevastatin. (C) Preparation of chiral synthon for squalene synthase inhibitor BMS-188494: stereoselective acetylation of recemic **56** to *S*-(+)-acetate **55**.

## VI. CALCIUM CHANNEL-BLOCKING DRUGS

Dilthiazem (57), a benzothiazepinone calcium channel-blocking agent that inhibits influx of extra-cellular calcium through L-type voltage-operated calcium channels, has been widely used clinically in the treatment of hypertension and angina. Since dilthiazem has a relatively short duration of action, preparation of isosteric 1-benzazepin-2-one compounds led to the identification of 6-trifluoro-methyl-2-benzazepin-2-one derivative as a longer lasting and more potent antihypertensive agent. A key chiral intermediate, [(3R-cis)-1,3,4,5-tetra-hydro-3-hydroxy-4-(4-methoxyphenyl)-6-(trifluro-methyl)-2H-1-benzazepin-2-one] (58), was required for the total chemical synthesis of the new calcium channel-blocking agent [(cis)-3-(acetoxy)-1-[2-(di-

methylamino) ethyl]-1,3,4,5-tetrahydro-4-(4-meth-oxyphenyl)-6-triflutomethyl)-2H-1-benzazepin-2-one (59; Fig. 8B). A stereoselective microbial process (Fig. 8A) was developed for the reduction of 4,5-dihydro-4-(4-methoxyphenyl)-6-(trifluoromethyl)-1H-1benzazepin-2,3-dione (60) to chiral (58). Among various cultures evaluated, *Nocardia salmoni-color* SC 6310 catalyzed the efficient bioconversion of 60 to 58 in 96% reaction yield with 99.9% optical purity. A preparative-scale fermentation process for growth of *N. salmonicolor* and a bioreduction process using cell suspensions of the organism were demon-strated.

## VII. POTASSIUM CHANNEL OPENERS

The study of potassium (K) channel biochemistry, physiology, and medicinal chemistry has flourished,

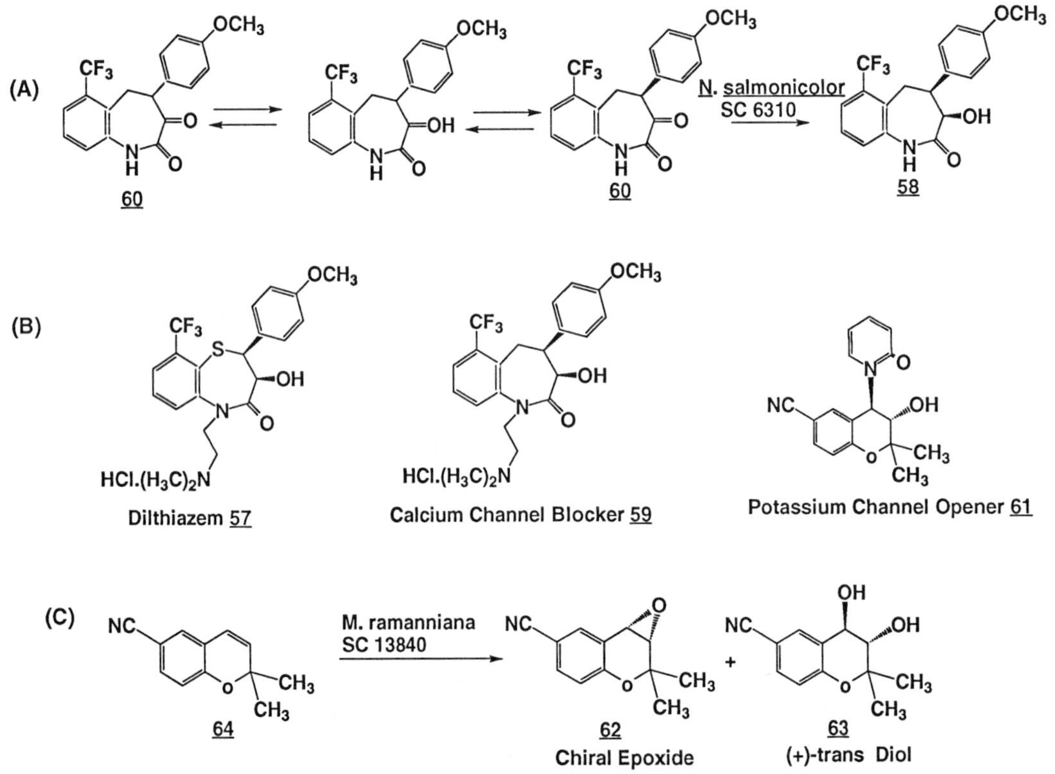

*Fig. 8.* (A) Synthesis of chiral synthon for calcium channel blocker **59**: stereoselective reduction of 4,5-dihydro-4-(4-methoxyphenyl)-6-(trifluoromethyl)-1H-benzazepin-2,3-dione (**60**). (B) Structures of dilthi-azem **57**, calcium channel blocker **59**, and potassium channel opener **61**. (C) Synthesis of chiral synthon for potassium channel opener **61**: oxygenation of 2,2-dimethyl-2H-1-benzopyran-6-carbonitrile (**64**) to the corresponding chiral epoxide (**62**) and (+)-*trans*-diol (**63**).

and numerous papers and reviews have been published in recent years. It has long been known that K channels play a major role in neuronal excitability and a critical role in the basic electrical and mechanical function of a wide variety of tissues, including smooth muscle, cardiac muscle, and glands. A new class of highly specific pharmacological compounds has been developed which either open or block K channels. K channel openers are powerful, smooth muscle relaxants with *in vivo* hypotensive and bronchodilator activity. Recently, the synthesis and antihypertensive activity of a series of novel K channel openers based on monosubstituted *trans*-4-amino-3,4-dihydro-2,2-dimethyl-2*H*-1-benzopyran-3-ol (61) (Fig. 8B) have been demonstrated. Chiral epoxide (62) and diol (63) are potential intermediates for the synthesis of K channel activators that are important as antihypertensive and bronchodilator agents. The stereoselective microbial oxygenation of 2,2-dimethyl-2*H*-1-benzopyran-6-carbonitrile (64) to the corresponding chiral epoxide 62 and chiral diol 63 (Fig. 8C) has been demonstrated using *Mortierella ramanniana* SC 13840. A reaction yields of 67 M% and optical purity of 96% are obtained for (+)-trans diol 63 in a single-stage process (fermentation/epoxidation) for the biotransformation of 63 in a 25-liter fermentor. In the two-stage process using a 3-liter cell-suspension (10% w/v, wet cells) of *M. ramanniana* SC 13840, the (+)-*trans* diol 63 was obtained with 76 M% yield and an optical purity of 96%. The reaction was carried out in a 5-liter Bioflo fermentor with 2 g/liter substrate and 10 g/liter glucose concentration. Glucose was supplied to regenerate NADH required for this reaction. From the reaction mixture, (+)-*trans* diol 63 was isolated with 65 M% (4.6 g) overall yield. An optical purity of 97% and a chemical purity of 98% were obtained for the isolated (+)-*trans* diol 63.

In an enzymatic resolution approach, chiral (+)-*trans* diol 63 was prepared by the stereoselective acetylation of racemic diol with lipases from *Candida cylindraceae* and *P. cepacia*. Both enzymes catalyzed the acetylation of the undesired enantiomer of racemic diol to yield monoacetylated product and unreacted desired (+)-*trans* diol 63. A reaction yield of >40% and an optical purity >90% were obtained using each lipase.

## VIII. ANTIARRHYTHMIC AGENTS

D-(+)-Sotalol is a beta-blocker that unlike other beta-blockers has antiarrhythmic properties and has no other peripheral actions. The $\beta$-adrenergic blocking drugs, such as propranolol and sotalol, have been separated chemically into the dextro and levo rotatory optical isomers, and it has been demonstrated that the activity of the levo isomer is 50 times that of the corresponding dextro isomer. Chiral alcohol (65) is a key intermediate for the chemical synthesis of D-(+)-sotalol (Fig. 9B). The stereoselective microbial reduction of N-(4-(2-chloroacetyl)phenyl)methane sulfonamide (66) to the corresponding (+)-alcohol (65) (Fig. 9A) has been demonstrated. Among the microorganisms screened for the transformation of ketone 66 to (+)-alcohol 65, *Hansenula polymorpha* ATCC 26012 catalyzed the efficient conversion with 95% reaction yield and >99% optical purity. Growth of *H. polymorpha* ATCC 26012 culture was carried out in a 380-liter fermentor, and cells harvested from the fermentor were used to conduct biotransformation. Cell-suspensions were supplemented with 12 g of ketone 66 and 225 g of glucose, and the reduction reaction was carried out at 25°C, 200 rpm, pH 7. Complete conversion of ketone 66 to (+)-alcohol 65 was obtained in a 20-hr reaction period. (+)-Alcohol 65 was isolated from the reaction mixture with a 70% yield and >99% optical purity.

## IX. ANTIPSYCHOTIC AGENTS

During the past few years, much effort has been directed toward understanding the sigma receptor system in the brain and endocrine tissue. This effort has been motivated by the hope that the sigma site may be a target of a new class of antipsychotic drugs. R-(+) compound 67 (BMY 14802) is a sigma ligand, has a high affinity for sigma binding sites, and has antipsychotic efficacy for treatment of schrizophenia. The stereoselective microbial reduction of keto compound 1-(4-fluorophenyl)-4-[4-[5-fluoro-2-pyrimidinyl)-1-piperazinyl]-1-butanone (68) to yield the corresponding hydroxy compound R-(+) BMY 14802 (66) (Fig. 9C) has been developed. Among

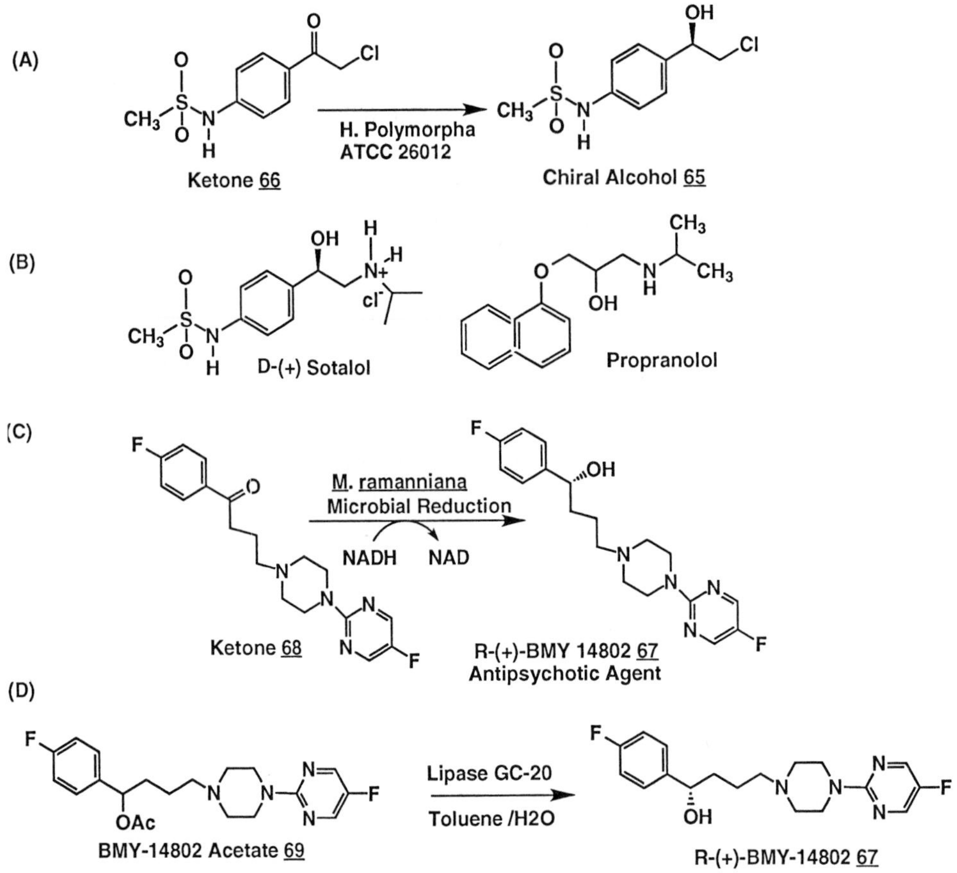

**Fig. 9.** (A) Synthesis of chiral synthon for D-(+)-sotalol: stereoselective reduction of *N*-(4-(2-chloroacetyl)phenyl)methane sulfonamide (**66**). (B) Structures of D-(+)-sotalol and propranolol. (C and D) Preparation of *R*-(+)-BMY 14802, an antipsychotic agent: (C) stereoselective reduction of 1-(4-fluorophenyl)-4-[4-(5-fluoro-2-pyrimidinyl)-1-piperazinyl]-1-butanone (**68**); (D) stereoselective hydrolysis of BMY 14802 acetate to *R*-(+)-BMY 14802.

various microorganisms evaluated, *M. ramanniana* ATCC 38191 predominately reduced compound **68** to *R*-(+)-BMY 14802. An optical purity of > 98% was obtained. In a two-stage process for reduction of compound **68**, cells of *M. ramanniana* ATCC 38191 were grown in a 380-liter fermentor and cells harvested were used for the reduction of ketone in a 15-liter fermentor using cell suspensions (20% w/v, wet cells). Ketone **68** was used at 2 g/liter concentration and glucose was supplemented at 20 g/liter concentration during the biotransformation process to generate NADH required for the reduction. After a 24-hr biotransformation period, approximately 90% yield (99.0% optical purity) of *R*-(+)-BMY 14802 was obtained.

A single-stage fermentation/biotransformation process was demonstrated for reduction of ketone **68** to *R*-(+)-BMY 14802 by cells of *M. ramanniana* ATCC 38191. Cells were grown in a 20-liter fermentor containing 15 liters of medium. After 40 hr of growth in a fermentor, the biotransformation process was initiated by addition of 30 g of ketone **68** and 300 g of glucose. The biotransformation process was completed in a 24-hr period, with a reaction yield of 100% and an optical purity of 98.9% for *R*-(+)-BMY 14802.

*R*-(+)-BMY 14802 has also been prepared by lipase-catalyzed resolution of racemic BMY 14802 acetate ester (**69**) (Fig. 9D). Lipase from *Geotrichum candidum* (GC-20 from Amano Enzyme Co.) catalyzed the hydrolysis of acetate **69** to *R*-(+)-BMY 14802 in a biphasic system with a 48% reaction yield and 98% optical purity.

## X. ANTI-INFECTIVE DRUGS

During the past several years, synthesis of $\alpha$-amino acids has been pursued intensely because of their importance as building blocks of compounds of medicinal interest, particularly anti-infective drugs. The asymmetric synthesis of $\beta$-hydroxy-$\alpha$-amino acids by various methods has been demonstrated because of their utility as starting materials for the total synthesis of monobactum antibiotics. L-$\beta$-Hydroxyvaline (**70**) is a key chiral intermediate required for

the total synthesis of orally active monobactum, Tigemonam (Fig. 10A). I have described the synthesis of L-$\beta$-hydroxyvaline from $\alpha$-keto-$\beta$-hydroxyisovalerate (**71**) by reductive amination using leucine dehydrogenase from *B. sphaericus* ATCC 4525 (Fig. 10A). NADH required for this reaction was regenerated by either formate dehydrogenase from *Candida boidinii* or glucose dehydrogenase from *B. megaterium*. The required substrate **71** was generated either from $\alpha$-keto-$\beta$-bromoisovalerate or from its ethyl esters by hydrolysis with sodium hydroxide *in situ*. In an alternate approach, the substrate **71** was also generated from methyl-2-chloro-3,3-dimethyloxiran-carboxylate and the corresponding isopropyl and 1,1-dimethyl ethyl ester. These glycidic esters are converted to substrate **71** by treatment with sodium

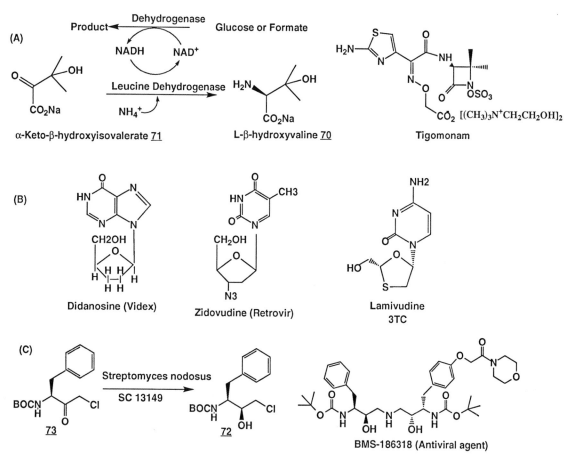

**Fig. 10.** (A) Synthesis of chiral synthon for tigemonam: stereoselective enzymatic reductive amination of $\alpha$-keto-$\beta$-hydroxyisovalerate (**71**) to L-$\beta$-hydroxyvaline (**70**). (B) Structures of antiviral agents didanosine, zidovudine, and lamivudine. (C) Synthesis of chiral intermediates for antiviral agent BMS-186318: stereoselective reduction of (1*S*) [3-chloro-2-oxo-1-(phenylmethyl)propyl] carbamic acid 1,1-dimethyl ester (**73**).

bicarbonate and sodium hydroxide. In this process, an overall reaction yield of 98% and an optical purity of 99.8% were obtained for L-$\beta$-hydroxyvaline.

## XI. ANTIVIRAL AGENTS

Purine nucleoside analogs have been used as antiviral agents. Lamivudine, zidovudine, and didanosine (Fig. 10B) are effective antiviral agents. Lamivudine, a highly promising candidate for HIV 2 and HIV 3 infection, is challenging to the synthetic chemist due to the presence of two acetyl chiral centers which both share the same oxygen atom. The use of cytidine deaminase from *Eschericha coli* has been demonstrated to deaminate 2'-deoxy-3'-thiacytidine enantio selectively to prepare optically pure (2'R-cis)-2'-deoxy-3'-thiacytidine.

Recently, we prepared the chiral intermediate (1S,2R) [3-chloro-2-hydroxy-1-(phenylmethyl)propyl] carbamic acid (1,1-dimethyl ester 72) for the total synthesis of an HIV protease inhibitor, BMS-186318. The stereoselective reduction of (1S) [3-chloro-2-oxo1-(phenylmethyl)propyl] carbamic acid (1,1-dimethylethyl ester 73) was carried out using *Streptomyces nodosus* SC 13149. A reaction yield of 80%, optical purity of 99.8%, and diastereomeric purity of >99% were obtained for chiral alcohol (72).

## *See Also the Following Articles*

Amino Acid Production • Antiviral Agents • Lipases, Industrial Uses

## *Bibliography*

Collins, A. N., Sheldrake, G. N., and Crosby, J. (Eds.) (1992/1995). "Chirality in Industry," Vols. 1 and 2. Wiley, New York.

Czuk, R., and Glanzer, B. I. (1991). Baker's yeast mediated transformations in organic chemistry. *Chem. Rev.* **96**, 556–566.

Jones, J. B. (1986). Enzymes in organic synthesis. *Tetrahedron* **42**, 3351–4303.

Kingston, D. G. I. (1991). The chemistry of taxol. *Pharm. Ther.* **52**, 1–34.

Patel, R. N. (1997a). Stereoselective biotransformations in synthesis of some pharmaceutical intermediates. *Adv. Appl. Microbiol.* **43**, 91–140.

Patel, R. N. (1997b). Use of lipases in stereoselective catalysis and preparation of some chiral drug intermediates. *Recent Res. Oil Chem.* **1**, 187–211.

Patel, R. N. (1998). Tour de pallitaxel: Biocatalysis for semisynthesis. *Annu. Rev. Microbiol.* **98**, 361–395.

Wong, C.-H., and Whitesides, G. M. (1994). "Enzymes in Synthetic Organic Chemistry." Tetrahedron Organic Chemistry Series, Vol. 12. Pergamon, New York.

# *Biocides*

## Mohammad Sondossi

*Weber State University*

**THE SIMPLEST DEFINITION OF A BIOCIDE** is evident from the terminology: *bio,* meaning life, and *cide,* referring to killing—an agent that destroys life. Therefore, any word with the suffix *cide* would be classified under the category of biocides. This broad literal meaning encompasses many other topics in this and other encyclopedias. The terms herbicide and insecticide indeed have biocidal activities. Therefore, the topic biocides has to be defined more narrowly in relation to specific subjects and applications.

## GLOSSARY

**biocidal agent** An agent that kills all living organisms.

**biocide** Primarily a chemical substance or composition used to kill microorganisms considered to be undesirable (i.e., pest organisms).

**biodegradation** A chemical breakdown of a substance into smaller molecules caused by microorganisms or their enzymes.

**biodeterioration** A physical or chemical alteration of a product, directly or indirectly caused by living organisms, their enzymes, or by-products, thereby making the product less suitable for its intended use.

**biostatic agent** An agent that inhibits or halts growth and multiplication of organisms. This means that when the agent is removed, the organism resumes growth and multiplication.

**deteriogenic organisms** The organisms that cause biodeterioration.

**minimal inhibitory concentration** The concentration of a particular biocide/antimicrobial agent necessary to inhibit the growth of a particular microorganism.

**selective toxicity** The ability of a chemotherapeutic agent (antibiotic, etc.) to kill or inhibit a microbial pathogen with minimal damage to the host at concentrations used.

Perhaps the most appropriate terminology for this topic drawn from common usage is "industrial biocides." It should be accepted that scientific terms can acquire new or multiple meanings according to common usage. It is of particular importance that terminologies used are consistent and descriptive of the activity of the agents involved. It is imperative to recognize that the terminology implies a specific use and the language used for labeling biocides may have legal consequences. However, the common usage changes the meaning of the terms and even the perception of the spectrum of their activities. Table I represents some of the common terms related to the control or suppression of microbial growth. According to the Environmental Protection Agency's (EPA) Office of Pesticide Programs, antimicrobial pesticide (a term used by the EPA) products contain approximately 300 different active ingredients and are marketed in several formulations: sprays, liquids, concentrated powders, and gases. Currently, more than 8000 antimicrobial pesticide products that are registered with the EPA are sold, constituting an approximately $1 billion market. The EPA estimates that the total amount of antimicrobial pesticide active

***TABLE I***
**Terminology Related to Control of Microbial Growth**

| Term | Definition | Comments |
| --- | --- | --- |
| Microbicide | An agent that kills microbes but not necessarily their spores | Usually a general term |
| Germicide | An agent that kills pathogens and many non-pathogens but not necessarily their spores | A general term |
| Bactericide | An agent that kills bacteria but not necessarily bacterial endospores | A general term |
| Fungicide | An agent that kills fungi (mold and yeast) but not necessarily their spores | A general term |
| Algicide | An agent that kills algae | A general term |
| Virucide | An agent that inactivates viruses | A general term |
| Sporocide | An agent that kills bacterial endospores and fungal spores | Sporocidal action is not to be equated to sporistatic action which results in inhibition of spore germination |
| Sanitizer | An agent that reduces the microbial contaminants to safe levels as determined by public health requirements | Usually used on inanimate objects and places where no specific pathogens are present or suspected and complete killing of all forms of microorganisms is not necessary |
| Disinfectant | An agent, usually chemical, commonly used on inanimate objects to destroy pathogenic and harmful organisms but not necessarily their spores | Widely used term, legal definition includes more details (relative to factors of time, temperature, percentage kill, concentration, etc.); may inactivate viruses |
| Antiseptic | Usually a chemical agent commonly applied to living tissue, skin, or mucous membrane to kill or inhibit microorganisms | Not considered safe for internal use |
| Preservative | An agent that prevents or preempts biodeterioration and spoilage of a product or material under storage conditions | A chemical or physical agent or process resulting in the act of preservation |
| Chemical sterilizer | A chemical agent that destroys all forms of life, including spores, and inactivates viruses | Sterilization is an absolute term and there are no degrees of sterilization |
| Bacteriostatic agent | An agent that inhibits growth and multiplication of bacteria but does not kill them | If the bacteriostatic agent is removed bacterial growth may resume |
| Fungistatic agent | An agent that inhibits growth and multiplication of fungi but does not kill them | If the fungistatic agent is removed fungal growth may resume |
| Antimicrobial pesticide | Substance or mixture of substances used to destroy or suppress the growth of undesirable (pest) microorganisms on inanimate objects and surfaces | This is the terminology used by the EPA and it encompasses all the antimicrobial agents fitting the definition under public health and nonpublic health categories |
| Antibiotic | A substance, usually produced by microorganisms, which in low concentrations inhibits the growth or kills disease-causing microorganisms | Synthetic and semisynthetic antibiotics are also available, usually used in treatment of disease; has selective toxicity |

ingredients used in 1995 was 3.3 billion lbs, accounting for 75% of all pesticides' active ingredients used. Antimicrobial pesticides, from a regulatory standpoint, are divided into public health products and nonpublic health products. The latter products are used to control microorganisms which cause spoilage, deterioration, or fouling of materials. Industrial biocides are classified under this category. They are chemical compositions used to control and prevent microbial biodeterioration and contamination of industrial/commercial material, systems, and products and/or to improve the efficiency of operation. The application of industrial biocides varies greatly depending on major use categories. Although biocides used in the preservation of cosmetics and personal care products are relevant to this article, they will not be discussed. The emphasis will be on nonpublic health-related topics. In the United States, cosmetics and toiletries are regulated under the Federal Food, Drug, and Cosmetic Act.

## I. HISTORICAL PERSPECTIVE

Current uses of biocides are aimed at the inhibition and control of undesirable microorganisms based on their antimicrobial action and the microbes' potential roles in biodeterioration, spoilage, and disease. However, even before the discovery of the microbial world by Antoni van Leeuwenhoek in 1674, many practices were used to preserve material, food, and animal and human bodies (mummification). Although early methods were effective, the scientific foundation of these practices was not understood until almost two centuries after van Leeuwenhoek's discovery. Drying and salting fish and meat was one of the earliest food preservation techniques developed. In cold climates, food could also be buried in snow or underground. An early version of surface sterilization was the practice of passing metal objects through fire to clean them. One of the first documented cases of chemical sanitation was practiced as early as 450 BC in the Persian Empire, where boiled water was stored in copper and silver containers. This allowed for a portable water supply that helped the Persian army in many military conquests. Medical applications of chemical sanitation include the use of mercuric chlo-

ride as a wound dressing by Arab physicians in the Middle Ages, the use of bleaching powder as a disinfectant by Alcock in 1827, the use of iodine by Davies in 1839, the use of chlorinated water for hand washing in hospitals by Semmelweis in the 1840s, and the use of phenol on surgical wounds by Lister in the 1860s.

It was not until after the mid-nineteenth century that quantitative and comparative antimicrobial efficacies of some compounds were established. For example, in 1875 Bucholtz determined the minimal inhibitory concentrations of phenol, creosote, salicylic acid, and benzoic acid against bacterial growth. These and other findings were followed by the introduction of hydrogen peroxide as a disinfectant by Traugott in 1893 and chlorine-releasing compounds in 1915 by Dakin. It is obvious that most of these findings and their applications were in the areas of medicine and public health. Here, the description of biocides is not in the context of the general definition based on antimicrobial activity but instead covers applications in more specific areas dealing with biodeterioration. The latter term has been in use for the past 30 years and is basically not present in most dictionaries, traditional printed material, or even recent electronic media. Hueck (1968) defined biodeterioration as any undesirable change in the properties of a material used by humans caused by the vital activities of organisms in which the material is any form of matter, with the exception of living organisms. The term biodeterioration is distinguished from biodegradation in having a more negative or harmful connotation. Where the material is known to be at risk, preventative measures can be taken. These measures could be based on many physical and chemical parameters affecting microbial growth and include the use of biocides. It should be mentioned that the term biocide is also a new term introduced in the past few decades. The range of materials used by man has changed dramatically in comparison to days when raw materials were used with minimal processing. Currently, complex and heavily processed materials, composites, and synthetic and semisynthetic materials are everywhere. Complex man-made environments and the materials used, combined with a wide range of biotic and abiotic parameters, provide abundant and ideal environments for the growth of microorganisms. The total cost of losses due to biodeterioration and spoilage is approximately $100 billion per year. When the costs of replacement of deteriorated material, remedial measures, and lost productivity are considered, the importance of preventative measures and the role of biocides is clear.

## II. CURRENT APPLICATIONS

There are many arbitrary categories of biocide applications in published articles and reference books. They have been grouped from an application aspect, with some differences. It should be noted that the use of a particular biocide is not restricted to any one group and may be used in different areas. One such summary of application categories could be assembled from articles, reviews, and reference materials as presented in Table II.

Another grouping based on areas of application is used by regulatory agencies (the EPA and the Food and Drug Administration). These groups can be divided into two categories based on the type of microorganism (pest) against which the biocide (antimicrobial pesticide) is used. First, public health antimicrobials are intended to control infectious microorganisms (to humans) in any inanimate environment. Disinfectants, sterilizers, sanitizers, and anti-

### TABLE II
### Selected Application Areas of Biocides

| | |
|---|---|
| Human drinking water disinfectants and purifiers | Paper and pulp |
| Freshwater algicide | Metalworking lubricants and hydraulic fluids |
| Swimming pools | Oil field operations |
| Animal husbandry | Fuels |
| Animal feed preservatives | Textiles |
| Food and beverage processing hygiene | Paint and paint film preservation |
| Food preservation | Wood preservation |
| Crop protection | Plastics |
| Hospital disinfectants | Resins |
| Hospital and medical antiseptics | Polymer emulsion, latex, adhesives, slurries |
| Pharmaceuticals | Tannery |
| Cosmetics | Museum specimens |
| Personal care disinfectants | Construction |
| Process cooling water | |

### TABLE III
### Antimicrobial Product Use Sites and Categories under Consideration by the EPA[a]

Agricultural premises and equipment[b]
Food handling/storage establishment premises and equipment[b]
Commercial, institutional, and industrial premises and equipment
Residential and public access premises[b]
Medical premises and equipment
Human drinking water systems[b]
Materials preservatives[b]
Industrial processes and water systems
Antifouling coatings
Wood preservatives
Swimming pools
Aquatic areas

[a] Major use categories are subdivided further based on exposure scenarios.

[b] Use of a biocide product on some sites in this category with direct or indirect food contact will be considered a food use and registration must be supported by data sufficient to support the establishment of a tolerance or exemption from the requirement of a tolerance under the Federal Food, Drug, and Cosmetic Act.

septics are included in this category. Second, the nonpublic health antimicrobial products are the products used to control growth of microorganisms causing deterioration, spoilage, and fouling of material, including growth of algae and odor-causing bacteria. Human exposure, product chemistry, and toxicology are considered in assigning antimicrobial agents into these main application categories.

In order to meet registration and data requirements, the EPA is currently considering classifying the antimicrobial products into 12 major use categories which are further subdivided based on exposure scenarios. The major categories are shown in Table III.

## III. EXAMPLES OF INDUSTRIAL BIOCIDES

Providing a complete list of registered industrial biocides is beyond the scope of this article and is not practically possible for many reasons. For example, in the United States most states require biocide registration after registration with the EPA. In addition to Canada, European countries, and Japan, many other countries have laws regulating biocide registration and use. Toxicological and environmental impact regulations vary worldwide and are reevaluated constantly. An extensive list of biocides with current and past use in North America and Europe is given in Table IV, although some have been discontinued, have use limitations, and may not be registered in some countries. Therefore, for updated information on industrial biocides, contacting biocide manufacturers and regulatory agencies is strongly recommended. Databases are available that indicate the name and location of the basic manufacturers of compounds as listed by CAS registration number. Most of the regulatory statuses can also be obtained from on-line databases and search engines.

## IV. CLASSIFICATION OF BIOCIDES

Classifying industrial biocides based on their chemical structures is not an easy task. Many review articles present group classifications and include a miscellaneous group whose members do not fit in any major class. Table V is a representation of this type of classification.

Biocides are sometimes also grouped based on their mode of action. This can be organized based on the target region of the microorganism affected by biocide action. Terms and categories such as membrane-active biocides and permeabilizers, cell wall inhibitors, cytotoxic agents (affecting targets in cytoplasm and interfering with metabolism and total cell function), and genotoxic agents (affecting DNA biosynthesis and reacting with DNA) have occasionally been used.

The chemical reactivity of biocides provides another, less frequently used, classification. Terms such as oxidizing, non-oxidizing, and electrophilic biocides have been used to separate industrial biocides into smaller groups. Some have used terms such as chlorine-yielding, bromine-yielding, and formaldehyde-releasing compounds to designate specific groups of biocides based on the active moiety/mechanism of action. It is therefore understandable that, depending on the subject, audience, users, and presenters (regulatory, academic, and industry) of information pertaining to industrial biocides, any of these classifications could be used.

## V. EVALUATION

There are numerous methods that have been and can be employed to evaluate biocide efficacy, including a variety of basic microbiological tests, simulation tests in the laboratory, practical tests, and field tests to demonstrate the effectiveness of a biocide. First, it has to be demonstrated that the chemical or preparation being evaluated has antimicrobial activity. In this stage, the spectrum of activity is determined against bacteria (gram-positive, gram-negative, Mycobacteria, etc.), fungi (mold and yeast), and spores (bacterial and fungal) and dose–response relationships are established. The nature of antimicrobial activity, biocidal or biostatic, may also be determined. The second stage includes suspension tests to determine MIC, establishing kill curves by plating, capacity tests (several reinoculations), and carrier tests (effects on organisms on the carrier). These may be followed by practical tests that, although done in the laboratory, demonstrate the efficacy under real-life conditions. Third, and most important, is evaluation in the field and under actual use conditions. For the regulatory agencies and registration purposes the tests should satisfy the label claims for specific applications. There are numerous test methods issued by federal and state governments or government-sanctioned publications, standards societies, and trade organizations as well as test methods developed by biocide manufacturers, users, and testing laboratories to demonstrate efficacy. Among governmental-sanctioned publications are those by the Association of Official Analytical Chemists, the American Public Health Association, and the United States Pharmacopeia. Voluntary consensus standards societies and groups include the American National Standards Institute, the American Society for Testing and Materials, and the International Standards Organization.

## VI. MODE OF ACTION

Considering the heterogeneity of chemicals used as biocides, and the fact that they have been considered general cell poisons for a long time, one can understand the lack of detailed information on mode of action of industrial biocides. For most of the biocides,

### *TABLE IV*
### Selected Industrial Biocides[a]

| Active chemical | Applications |
|---|---|
| 6-Acetoxy-2,4-dimethyl-*m*-dioxane | Metalworking fluids, textile lubricants, polymer emulsions, other aqueous emulsions |
| Acrolein (acrylaldehyde) | Paper and pulp |
| Alkenyl (C12–C18)dimethylethyl ammonium bromide | Paper and pulp, process cooling waters |
| Alkyldimethylbenzyl ammonium chloride | Wood, process cooling waters |
| Arsenic pentoxide | Wood |
| 1-Aza-3,7-dioxa-5-ethylbicyclo-[3.3-0]octane | Metalworking fluids |
| 1,2-Benzisothiazolin-3-one | Adhesive, latex, paper coatings, aqueous emulsions |
| Benzyl bromoacetate | Paint raw materials (cellulose and casein) |
| Benzyl-hemiformals mixture | Adhesives |
| Bis(1,4-bromoacetoxy)-2-butene | Paper and pulp |
| 5,5-Bis(bromoacetoxymethyl)-*m*-dioxane | |
| 2,6-Bis(dimethylaminomethyl) cyclohexanone | |
| 1,2-Bis(monobromoacetoxy) ethane | |
| Bis(tributyltin)oxide | Wood, process cooling water |
| Bis(trichloromethyl)sulphone | Paper and pulp, process cooling water, adhesives, wet state protection concrete additives |
| Boric oxide | Wood |
| Brominated salicylanilides | Water-based latex pains and emulsions, joint cement, PVC plastic, acrylic and PVA water-based paints, polyvinyl acetate latex, adhesives |
|    5,4'-Dibromosalicylanilide | |
|    3,5,6'-Tribromosalicylanilide | |
|    Other brominated salicylanilides | |
| Bromine-yielding chemicals | Process cooling waters |
|    Sodium bromide, NaBr (must be activated by oxidizing agent, e.g., NaOCl, Cl2, and potassium peroxymonosulfate) | |
|    1-Bromo-3-chloro-5,5-dimethylhydantoin | |
| 4-Bromoacetoxymethyl-*m*-dioxolane | Paper and pulp |
| 2-Bromo-4'-hydroxyacetophenone | Pulp and paper mills, paper making chemicals, felt |
| 2-Bromo-2-nitro-1,3-propanediol | Metalworking fluids, textile, Process cooling waters |
| Bromo-nitrostyrene | Pulp and paper mills, water systems, lignosulphonates |
| 1,1'-(2-Butenylene)bis(3,5,7-triaza-1-azoniaadamantane chloride) | Latex paints, resin emulsions, adhesives, dispersed colors |
| Chlorethylene bisthiocyanate | Water systems, emulsions |
| Chlorinated levulinic acids | Paper and pulp |
| Chlorine/chlorine-yielding chemicals: | Process cooling waters |
|    Chlorine (gas), Cl | |
|    NaOCl | |
|    Ca(OCl)$_2$ · 4H$_2$O | |
|    Na dichloro-*s*-triazinetrione/trichloro-*s*-tri azinetrione | |
|    1-Bromo-3-chloro-5,5-dimethylhydantoin | |
|    1-Bromo-3-chloro-5-methyl-5-ethylhydantoin | |
|    1,3-Dichloro-5,5-dimethylhydantoin | |
|    Chlorine dioxide, ClO$_2$ | |

*continues*

*Continued*

| Active chemical | Applications |
| --- | --- |
| 1-(3-Chloroallyl)-3,5,7-triaza-1-azoniaadamantane chloride + sodium bicarbonate | Adhesives, metalworking fluids, latex paints, textile, emulsions, water-based coating formulations |
| Chloromethyl butanethiolsulfonate | Paper and pulp |
| 5-Chloro-2-methyl-4-isothiazolin-3-one + 2-methyl-4-isothiazolin-3-one | Wood veneer, cutting fluids and coolants, paste, slimes, cooling towers, paper, and paperboard |
| *p*-Chlorophenyl diiodomethyl sulfone | Paint |
| Chromic oxide | Wood |
| Coal tar creosote | Wood |
| Copper naphthenate | Wood |
| Copper sulfate | Wood |
| Cupric oxide | Wood |
| Copper-8-quinolinolate | Wood and wood products, glues and adhesives, paper products |
| Cresylic acids | Rubbers (synthetic and natural) |
| Cupric nitrate | Paper and pulp |
| Dialkyl methylbenzyl ammonium chloride | Paper and pulp, wood, process cooling waters |
| 1,2-Dibromo-2,4-dicyanobutane | Metalworking fluids, aqueous paints, latex emulsions, joint cement adhesive |
| 2,2-Dibromo-3-nitrilopropionamide (20, 10, or 5%) in polyethylene glycol | Water cooling towers, pulp and paper mills, metalworking fluids, oil recovery |
| 2,3-Dibromopropionaldehyde | Paper and pulp |
| 2,4 Dichlorobenzyl alcohol | Textile |
| 2,3-Dichloro-1,4-naphthoquinon | Toxic wash of construction material (interior use) |
| Didecyl dimethyl ammonium chloride | Wood |
| (2,2'-Dihydroxy-5,5'-dichloro)-diphenyl methane | Textile, cement additive, toxic wash (exterior use) |
| (2,2'-Dihydroxy-5,5'-dichloro-diphenyl monosulfide | Textile |
| Di-iodomethyl-*p*-tolyl sulfone | Paint |
| Di-isocyanate | Toxic wash construction material (interior use) |
| Ditmethyl aminomethyl phenol | Rubbers (synthetic and natural) |
| Dimethylbenzyl ammonium chloride | Construction toxic wash (exterior and interior use) |
| 4,4-Dimethyloxazoldine + 3,4,4-trimethyloxazolidine | Metalworking fluids, in-can paint |
| 3,5-Dimethyl-tetrahydro-1,3,5,-2*H*-thiadiazine-2-thion | Leather, paint, glue, casein, starch, paper mill |
| Dioctyl dimethyl ammonium chloride and ethanol | Cooling water systems |
| Diquat 1,1-ethylene-2,2-dipyridiylium | Construction toxic wash (exterior and interior use) |
| Disodium cyanodithioimidocarbamate | Paper and pulp, process cooling waters |
| Disodium ethylenebis(dithiocarbamate) | Paper and pulp, process cooling waters |
| Dithio-2,2-bis-benzmethylamide | Adhesives |
| Dithiocarbamates + benzimidazole derivatives | Adhesives, filters, stoppers, groutings, jointing compounds, sealants, putty |
| Dodecylamine salicylate | Construction toxic wash (exterior and interior use) |
| Dodecylguanidine hydrochloride, dodecylguanidine hydrochloride | Paper and pulp, process cooling waters |
| Fatty acids of quaternary compounds | Textile |
| Fluorinated sulfonamide | Filters, stoppers, groutings |
| Formaldehyde | Toxic wash (exterior and interior use) |
| Glutaraldehyde (1,5-pentanedial) | Metalworking fluids, Process cooling waters |

*continues*

*Continued*

| Active chemical | Applications |
| --- | --- |
| 1,2,3,4,5,6-Hexachlorocyclohexane (lindane) | Wood |
| Hexachloro dimethyl sulfone | Industrial emulsions |
| Hexahydro-1,3,5-triethyl-s-triazine | Cutting oils, synthetic rubber latexes, adhesives, latex emulsions |
| Hexahydro-1,3,5-*tris*(2-hydroxyethyl)-*s*-triazine | Cutting oils and diluted coolants |
| Hydrogen peroxide | Process cooling waters |
| p-Hydroxybenzoic acid esters | Adhesives, starch and gum solutions, inks, polishes, latexes, other emulsions |
|   Ethyl p-hydroxybenzoate | |
|   Methyl p-hydroxybenzoate | |
|   Propyl p-hydroxybenzoate | |
|   Butyl p-hydroxybenzoate | |
| 5-Hydroxymethoxymethyl-1-aza-3,7-dioxabicyclo(3.3.0)octane | Latex paints |
| 5-Hydroxymethyl-1-aza-3,7-dioxabicyclo(3.3.0)octane | |
| 5-Hydroxypoly[methyleneoxy (74% C2, 21% C3, 4% C4, 1% C5)]methyl-L-aza-3,7-dioxabicyclo(3.3.0)octane | |
| 2-[(Hydroxymethyl) amino] ethanol | Paints, resin emulsions, in-can paint |
| 2-[(Hydroxymethyl) amino]-2-methylpropanol | Latex paints, resin emulsions |
| 2-(p-Hydroxyphenyl) glyoxylohydroximoyl chloride | Paper and pulp |
| 2-Hydroxypropyl methanethiol sulphonate | Paper and pulp, paint films |
| 3-Iodo-2-propynyl butyl carbamate | Interior and exterior coatings |
| 3-Methyl-4-chlorophenol | Adhesives, filters, stoppers, groutings |
| Methyl-2,3-dibromopropionate | Process cooling waters |
| 2,2'-Methylenebis(4-chlorophenol) | Textiles, rubber products, hoser |
| Methylene bis thiocyanate | Paper slimes, recirculating cooling water systems |
| N-[alpha-(nitroethyl)benzy] ethylenediamine | Paper and pulp |
| N-dimethyl-N'-fluorodichloromethylthio) sulfamide | Construction toxic wash (exterior use) |
| N-(fluordichloromethylthio) phthalmide | Construction toxic wash (exterior and interior use), jointing compounds, sealants, putty, plastic products |
| N-trichloromethylthio-4-cyclohexene-1,2-dicarboximide | Paper and pulp, polyethylene, paint, paste, rubber and rubber-coated products |
| N-(trichloromethylthio) phthalimide | Nonaqueous paints and caulking compounds |
| N-(trimethylthio) phthalimide | Paint film |
| 2-Nitrobutyl bromoacetate | Paper and pulp |
| 4-(2-Nitrobutyl) morpholine + 4.4'-(2-ethyl-2-nitrotrimethylene) dimorpholine | Metalworking fluids, pulp and paper industry, petroleum production, jet fuels |
| 2-n-Octyl-4-isothiazolin-3-one | Latex and oil-based paints, in-can paint preservative, fabrics, wet processing of hides |
| Organic mercurials | Paints |
| Organosulfur compound blends | Cooling towers, air washer systems |
| Organotin, quartemaries and amines | Cooling water systems |
| 10,10'-Oxybisphenoxarsine 5% in a polymeric resin carrier | PVC, polyurethane, other polymeric compositions |
| 10,10'-Oxybisphenoxarsine in various nonvolatile plasticizer carriers | Film and sheeting, extruded plastics, plastisols, molded goods, organosols, fabric coatings, etc. |
| 2,2'-Oxybis-(4.4,6-trimethyl-1,3,2-dioxaborinane)-2,2'-(1-methyltrimethylenedioxy)-bis-(4-methyl-1,3,2-dioxaborinane) | Hydrocarbon fuels, boat and ship fuel and marine storage, home heating fuel |

*continues*

*Continued*

| Active chemical | Applications |
| --- | --- |
| Oxyquinofine | Plastic products |
| Oxyquinoline sulphate | Plastic products |
| Ozone | Process cooling waters |
| Para-chloro-meta-cresol | Metalworking fluids |
| Para-chloro-meta xylenol | Metalworking fluids |
| Pentachlorophenol | Wood preservation, adhesives, cement additive, toxic wash (exterior use), rubbers (synthetic and natural) |
| Pentachlorophenyl laurate | Adhesives, wet state protection concrete additives, plastic products, rubbers (synthetic and natural), textile |
| Phenoxy fatty acid polyester | Bitumen products, jointing compounds, sealants, putty |
| Phenyl mercury acetate | Adhesives |
| Phenyl mercury nonane | Adhesives, wet state protection concrete additives |
| Phenyl mercury oleate | Adhesives, wet state protection concrete additives |
| *o*-Phenylphenol(sodium-*o*-phenylphenate tetrahydrate) | Protein-based paints, metalworking fluids, polishes, adhesives, gums, latexes, textiles |
| Polychlorophenates, alcohol, and amines | Cooling towers and evaporative condensers |
| Polychlorophenates, organosulfurs | Cooling towers |
| Poly[hydroxyethylene (dimethyliminio)-ethylene (dimethyliminio)]methylene dichloride | Industrial water systems, process cooling waters |
| Poly[oxyethylene (dimethyliminio)-ethylene (dimethyliminio)]ethylene dichloride | Cooling water systems, cutting fluids |
| Potassium dichromate | Wood |
| Potassium dimethyl thiocarbamate | Metalworking fluids, process cooling water |
| Potassium *N*-hydroxymethyl-*N*-methyldithiocarbamate | Water-thinned colloids, emulsion reins, emulsion paints, waxes, cutting oils, adhesives |
| Potassium *N*-methyldithiocarbamate | Paper and pulp, process cooling waters |
| Quaternary phosphonium salt + surfactant | Textile |
| Rosin amine D-pentachlorophenate | Paper, textiles, rope, emulsion systems |
| Salicylamide | (Cable insulation) jointing compounds, sealants, putty, plastic products |
| Silver fluoride, silver nitrate | Paper and pulp |
| Sodium dimethyldithiocarbamate | Paper mills, cooling towers, paper and paperboard, cotton fabrics, paste, wood, veneer, cutting oils |
| Sodium fluoride | Wood |
| Sodium 2-mercaptobenzothiazole | Adhesives, wet state protection concrete additives, paper mills, cooling towers, paper and paperboard, cotton fabrics, paste, wood, veneer, cutting oil, water-thinned colloids, emulsion reins, emulsion paints, waxes, adhesives, textiles, rug backings |
| Sodium pentachlorophenate | Paper making, pulp, paper and paper products, leather, hides, drilling muds |
| Sodium 2-pyridinethiol-1-oxide | Aqueous-based metalworking fluid systems, vinyl, latex emulsions for short-term, in-can inhibition of bacterial growth |
| 1,3,6,8-Tetraazatricyclo[6.2.1.1]dodecane | Paper and pulp |
| 2,4,5,6-Tetrachloroisophthalonitrile | Adhesives, jointing compounds, sealants, putty, plastic products, latex paints |

*continues*

Continued

| Active chemical | Applications |
|---|---|
| 2,3,4,6-Tetrachlorophenol | Wood preservation |
| 3.3,4.4-Tetrachlorotetrahydrothiophene-1,1-dioxide | Paper and pulp |
| Tetrahydro-3,5-dimethyl-2H-1,3,5-thiadiazine-2-thione and blends | Slimicide for coatings, clay slurries, adhesives, glues, latex emulsions, casein, titanium slurries, cooling towers |
| 2-(4-Thiazolyl)benzimidazole | Paint |
| 2-(Thiocyanomethylthio)benzothiazole | Wood, paint films |
| Tributyltin acetate | Cement additive, paints |
| Tributyltin fluoride | Wood, antifouling paint |
| Tributyltin maleate | Textile |
| Tributyltin oxide | Construction toxic wash (exterior and interior use), wet state protection concrete additives, antifouling paints, adhesives, wood |
| Tributyltin oxide + nonionic emulsifier | |
| Trifluoromethyl thiophthalmide | Construction toxic wash (exterior and interior use), wet state protection concrete additives |
| 3-(Trimethoxysilyl)-propyl-dimethyloctadecyl ammonium chloride | Construction toxic wash (exterior use) |
| Tris(hydroxymethyl) nitromethane | Oil in water emulsions, pulp and paper industry, water treatment, in-can paint |
| Zinc dimethyldithiocarbamate | Adhesives, cooling water, paper mill, paper and paperboard, textiles |
| Zinc 2-mercaptobenzothiazole | |
| Zinc naphthenate | Textile, wood |
| Zinc 2-pyridinethiol-1-oxide | Aqueous-based metalworking fluids, PVC plastics |

[a] Not necessarily currently registered and some have been discontinued. This list was collected from many sources, including Sharpell (1980), Allsopp and Allsopp (1983), Bravery (1992), Rossmoore (1995a,b), Lutey (1995), Eagon (1995), McCarthy (1995), Downey (1995), and Leightley (1995).

## TABLE V
### Biocides by Chemical Class[a]

| | |
|---|---|
| Phenols | Alcohols |
| Organic and inorganic acids: esters and salts | Perooxygens |
| Aromatic diamidines | Chelating agents |
| Biguanides | Heavy metals and organometallic compounds |
| Surface-active agents: cationic and anionic agents | Anilides |
| Aldehydes: formaldehyde, glutaraldehyde, and others | Formaldehyde adducts |
| Dyes | Isothiazolones |
| Halogen compounds | Organosulfur compounds |
| Quinolines and isoquinoline derivatives | Essential oils |
| | Miscellaneous |

[a] From Hugo and Russell (1992), Rossmoore (1995a), and others.

mode of action seems to be a concentration-dependent phenomenon by which individual effects can be identified and studied. Since biocides will act on organisms in an outside to inside direction, many have classified the target regions based on this directional impact. In other words, the cell wall, cell membrane and membrane-associated components, and the cytoplasmic regions will be sequentially affected by the biocide as it interacts with the intended target organism. Unlike antibiotics that have very specific targets, biocides may have more than one potential target. These could be located at any or all areas of the affected cell. The chemical structure of a biocide determines its affinity to specific targets and is the key to understanding its mode of action. Furthermore, the accumulated effects of sequentially affected regions of the cell may ultimately manifest as antimicrobial activity. Considering the structural and physiological differences of organisms and extrinsic parameters affecting the activity of biocides, the knowledge about mode of action is far from comprehensive. However, it is becoming increasingly evident that biocides indeed have a specific target(s) and cannot be labeled as general cell poisons.

Abnormal morphology of organisms exposed to biocides, studied by light and electron microscopy, has long been considered evidence of damage to the cell wall or its construction process. Lysis of cells due to initiation of autolysis has also been included in this category of mode of action. Early reports classified phenol, formaldehyde, mercurials, alcohols, and some quaternary ammonium compounds in this category. It should be noted that any of these events could also be a consequence of damage(s) exerted on cytoplasmic targets or initiated by transmembrane signaling events. Since the cell wall composition of microorganisms (e.g., gram-positive and gram-negative bacteria, mycobacteria, fungi, and algae) differs significantly, one biocide may cause damage to the cell wall of one organism and may have no effect on the cell wall of another. Interaction with the cytoplasmic membrane, membrane-bound enzymes, electron transport, and substrate transport systems are the next group to be affected by the action of biocides. Among other biocides, chlorhexidine, 2-bromo-2-nitro-1,3-propanediol, and 1,2-benzisothiazolin-3-one have been reported to affect targets in the cytoplasmic membrane. Some membrane-active biocides may cause leakage of the intracellular material, whereas others have been reported to produce an increased permeability to ions acting as uncouplers of oxidative phosphorylation and inhibitors of active transport. Although there are many early reports that describe the mode of action of certain biocides in terms such as coagulation of cytoplasmic proteins and precipitation of cytoplasmic constituents, there are recent reports of more specific actions on selective inhibition of cytoplasmic enzymes and reactions with essential biomolecules. These more specific interactions result in inhibition of selected biosynthetic and energy-producing processes in the affected organisms.

Some recent reports describing more specific aspects of industrial biocides' modes of action include the following examples: 2-Pyridinethiol-1-oxide has been suggested to act on cell membranes to eliminate important ion gradients used to store energy. In fungi, it eliminates the membrane charge gradient and interferes with nutrient transport. The collapse of delta, the pH component of the proton motive force, affects bacterial cells. It has been suggested that 2-pyridinethiol-1-oxide is not accumulated in cells and is not destroyed during action on cells but rather acts catalytically. 2-Hydroxybiphenyl ethers effectively inhibit fatty acid synthesis *in vivo* and the key enzyme of the fatty acid synthase system *in vitro*. This contradicts early reports on mode of action due to direct disruption of cell membranes. 5-Chloro-2-methyl-4-isothiazolin-3-one has been claimed to have multiple modes of action in the inhibition of microorganisms. These include lethal loss of protein thiols by covalent modification of protein molecules through direct electrophilic attack, generation of secondary electrophiles by disulfide exchange and tautomerization to a thioacyl chloride, and intracellular generation of free radicals as a result of the severe metabolic disruption.

Early studies on the mode of action of 2-bromo-2-nitro-1,3-propanediol using *Escherichia coli, Staphylococcus aureus,* and *Pseudomonas aeruginosa* indicated effects on cell membrane integrity and also on aerobic glucose metabolism. The major finding was the inhibition of thiol-containing enzymes such as glyceraldehyde-3-phosphate dehygrogenase. Studies on cysteine and glutathione showed the ability of 2-bromo-2-nitro-1,3-propanediol to oxidize the thiol group to form a disulfide bond and this was postulated as the inhibition mechanism. Later work confirmed this property of 2-bromo-2-nitro-1,3-propanediol, showing that it acted catalytically to oxidize thiol groups under aerobic conditions. In addition, there was evidence that 2-bromo-2-nitro-1,3-propanediol led to the formation of active oxygen species such as superoxide, suggesting interference with the electron transport mechanism within the cell.

There have also been reports which do not directly describe mode of action but rather clarify active moiety(s) involved in mode of action of certain groups of biocides. There are many industrial biocides that are synthesized with formaldehyde as one of the starting materials. The question about the role of formaldehyde in mode of action of formaldehyde–adduct biocides was not always clearly addressed. Studies with bacterial strains resistant to formaldehyde and formaldehyde–adduct biocides derived separately from sensitive wild types and concurrent development of cross-resistance among all resistant strains established formaldehyde as the active moiety in mechanism of action of many formaldehyde–adduct biocides. Subsequently, it was shown that high levels of resistance were coupled to high levels of formaldehyde dehydrogenase in resistant cells. Although this does not resolve the problem of mode of action of formaldehyde, it consolidates the mechanism of action question and clearly demonstrates the involvement of formaldehyde as the active moiety in mode of action of many formaldehyde–adduct biocides. Table VI shows some of these formaldehyde–adduct industrial biocides. There are many other adducts that are not included, although partial formaldehyde involvement in mode of action has been suggested.

## VII. COMBINATION BIOCIDES (MIXTURES AND FORMULATIONS)

Biocides are used in combination for many reasons: (i) to broaden the antimicrobial spectrum, (ii) to minimize physical and chemical incompatibilities, (iii) to minimize toxicity, and (iv) to produce

### TABLE VI
**Formaldehyde–Adduct Biocides with Formaldehyde as Active Moiety in Mode of Action[a]**

Hexahydro-1,3,5-tris(2-hydroxyethyl)-*s*-triazine

Hexahydro-1,3,5-triethyl-*s*-triazine

2-[(Hydroxymethyl) amino]-2-methylpropanol

2-[(Hydroxymethyl) amino] ethanol

4,4-Dimethyloxazolidine + 3,4,4-trimethyloxazolidine

1,3-Dihydroxymethyl)-5,5-dimethylhydantoin

5-Hydroxymethoxymethyl-L-aza-3,7-dioxabicyclo(3.3.0)octane

5-Hydroxymethyl-L-aza-3,7-dioxabicyclo(3.3.0)octane

5-Hydroxypoly[methyleneoxy(74% C2, 21% C3, 4% C4, 1% C5)] methyl-L-aza-3,7-dioxabicyclo(3.3.0)octane

[a] From Rossmoore and Sondossi (1988).

biochemical synergism. In its broadest sense, the subject of interactions among industrial biocides that alter their biological activities would include interactions in the extracellular environment and those within the target organisms. Gathering data on combined modes of action of biocide mixtures is not an easy task. Although many biocide mixtures have been used and are commercially available, a considerable amount of research will be required to define the biochemical nature of these interactions and their physiological effects on microorganisms. A select number of biocide mixtures primarily used in metalworking and hydraulic fluids are listed in Table VII. It should be noted that there are many more mixtures with a variety of applications and different active ingredients.

Traditionally, a toxicological interaction has been described as "a condition in which exposure to two or more chemicals results in a quantitatively or qualitatively altered biological response relative to that predicted from the action of a single chemical. Such multiple-chemical exposures may occur simultaneously or sequentially in time and the altered response may be greater or lesser in magnitude" (Murphy, 1980). It has been common practice to classify the quantitative joint action of chemicals including biocides using three general terms:

- Addition: when the toxic effect produced by two or more biocides in combination is equivalent

**TABLE VII**
**Biocide Mixtures Used in Metalworking and Hydraulic Fluids**[a]

| |
|---|
| Hexahydro-1,3,5-tris(2-hydroxyethyl) triazine + 2-sodium-2-pyridinethiol-1-oxide |
| Sodium dimethyldithiocarbarnate + sodium 2-mercaptobenzothiazole |
| 5-Chloro-2-methyl-4-isothiazolin-3-one + 2-methyl-4-isothiazolin-3-one + $CuSO_4$ |
| 1,3,5-Hexahydro-tris-(2-hydroxyethyl)-triazine + 5-chloro-2-methyl-4-isothiazolin-3-one |
| Bisoxazolidine + 5-chloro-2-methyl-4-isothiazolin-3-one |
| Formols + 5-chloro-2-methyl-4-isothiazolin-3-one |
| Dimethylolurea + formols + 5-chloro-2-methyl-4-isothiazolin-3-one |
| 1,2-Dibromo-2,4-dicyanobutane + 5-chloro-2-methyl-4-isothiazolin-3-one |

[a] From Rossmoore (1995b).

to that expected by simple summation of their individual effects.

- Antagonism: when the effect of a combination is less than the sum of the individual effects.
- Synergism: when the effect of the combination is greater than would be predicted by summation of the individual effects.

For biocides, there must be a quantitatively definable effect for each compound involved. Minimal inhibitory concentrations and other dose–response information could be used to construct a graphic representation (isobologram) to show additive, synergistic, and antagonistic interactions in biocide mixtures. This could easily be applied to combinations of any number of agents. For a combination of more than three agents, no graphic construction is possible; however, the interaction index could be calculated mathematically to describe additivity, antagonism, and synergism.

Because development costs of new biocides are estimated between $10 and $15 million, the introduction of new biocidal compounds to the market is difficult. This cost escalation is due to increasing legislative requirements and concerns regarding environmental impact. Therefore, the use of registered biocides in combinations that yield synergistic activity is an attractive alternative.

There is an extensive range of biocides from which to formulate mixtures, with substantially reduced initial screening costs and possibly an easier registration process if the active ingredients are well-known and individually registered for particular end use(s). However, there are concerns regarding the toxicity and environmental impact of biocide mixtures.

## VIII. RESTRICTIONS ON USE AND REGULATION

The fundamental requirements for industrial biocides suitable for protection of material in the early days of use were effective and aggressive antimicrobial activities, broad spectrum of activity, stability and persistence, and economical feasibility. With the constant expansion of biocide use and number, there has been increasing concern about their impact on human and environmental health. In approximately the past two decades, regulatory agencies have put in place restrictions for the application and selection of industrial biocides. The new requirements include spectrum of activity and effectiveness according to the category of application, stability relevant to application, very low human toxicity according to required toxicological data, very low environmental impact (ecotoxicity), and economical feasibility of use. This has produced a stream of new regulations.

The EPA registers and regulates antimicrobial pesticides including industrial biocides under the Federal Insecticide, Fungicide and Rodenticide Act (FIFRA). To register an industrial biocide, manufacturers of such products must meet EPA requirements to show that (i) the product will not cause unreasonable adverse effects on human health and the environment, and (ii) the product labeling and composition comply with requirements of FIFRA. Since 1996, the antimicrobials division within the Office of Pesticide Programs (OPP) has been responsible for all activities related to regulating antimicrobial pesticides. The OPP reviews submitted detailed and specific information on the chemical composition of the product, efficacy data against specific intended microorganisms, support of directions for use on the label, appropriate labeling for safe and effective use, and extensive toxicological data and hazards associated with the product use.

Title 40 CFR, Part 158, explicitly outlines the data requirements for antimicrobial pesticides. Further amendments are being considered to Part 158. These data requirements are for tiered human health and exposure data requirements for non-food uses, product chemistry, and toxicology. Explicit tiered testing approaches for environmental fate and effects have been developed for antimicrobials, wood preservatives, antifoulants, and algicides. Specifically, data are required for end-use antimicrobial products, including data on end-use formulation, active ingredient, product chemistry information, residue chemistry, efficacy, toxicity, environmental fate, and ecotoxicity. Data are required to assess acute toxicity, chronic and subchronic toxicity, developmental toxicity, reproductive toxicity, mutagenicity, neurotoxicity, metabolic effects, and immunological effects. Toxicology test requirements are set out in tiers based on general requirements and risk assessment. It should be noted that the EPA may require additional data on a case-by-case basis in order to conduct a risk assessment for the product.

## IX. PROBLEMS ASSOCIATED WITH BIOCIDE USE

It should be kept in mind that biocides are all toxic by definition and most are also corrosive. For decades there have been concerns regarding toxicity issues of biocides, even though biocides must be registered for specific use and require a battery of data submissions which include human and environmental toxicological profiles. Recognition for the need to control risks from biocides has come from scientists in academia, regulatory agencies, and industry, and there is a need for comprehensive information and new data especially on the biocide mixtures and biocide-containing formulations. One of the most important problems based on toxicity concerns is the international recognition of the registration of biocides. Acceptance of toxicity data, including ecotoxicity of biocides, by the regulatory bodies in different countries has been of great concern to multinational producers of biocides.

In addition to the regulatory concerns associated with biocide use, there are problems beyond the obvious toxicity of biocides that have to be considered. Like antibiotics, when biocides interact with mixed populations of microorganisms they kill all susceptible organisms and promote the selection of resistant populations. The level of resistance may be intrinsic, developed by mutation, or could even be acquired by gene exchange. It should be very clear from the previous discussion that the ultimate result of biocide use is selection of resistant populations. Although resistance is a relative term, a resistant organism is one that is not affected by biocide concentrations used to control microorganisms regularly found in a system. There are many review articles on the development of resistance to antimicrobial agents (including antibiotics). These reviews and numerous other research articles have classified organisms according to their intrinsic levels of resistance to antimicrobials, mechanism(s) of resistance development, and concepts such as phenotypic and genotypic resistance to antimicrobial agents. Regarding intrinsic resistance to biocides, in general, it can be stated that gram-negative bacteria are more resistant to biocides than are gram-positive bacteria. In addition to this generalization, there are specific examples of intrinsic resistance of microorganisms, such as mycobacterial, peudomonad, and fungal species, to biocides.

Microorganisms may also gain the capacity to resist the biocide by the acquisition of gene function(s). These gene functions are mostly concerned with inactivation or modification of the biocide, efflux systems, specification of a new target, or enzymatic modification of the target. Microorganisms could also simply persist in the presence of the biocide. This phenomenon may result from mutation or temporary resistance due to gene regulatory events or phenotypic changes. It is accepted that the general resistance mechanisms producing biocide resistance in microorganisms are the same mechanisms found in antibiotic resistance. Excessive use of biocides may produce organisms with a non-specific mechanism(s) of cross-resistance to other biocides and, most important, to antibiotics (double resistance to biocides and to antibiotics).

Resistance development to industrial biocides has received much attention, and numerous published research articles and reviews have been devoted to this subject. There should be no doubt that the inappropriate and excessive use of biocides often results in selection of resistant populations. This usually includes unintentional under-dosing and, more important, misunderstanding of the kinetics of biocide effects and the dynamics of the system treated with biocides.

With regard to the resistance categories mentioned previously, there are some points worth noting. When the mechanism of resistance involves inactivation or modification of a biocide and the organism(s) becomes the dominant microbial population in the biocide-treated system, other less susceptible populations may also be protected. There have been reports indicating survival of biocide-sensitive organisms in the presence of resistant populations in metalworking fluids.

The addition of biocides (intermittent slug dosing or continuous addition with pumps) to a system may result in an unintended biocide buildup in which the extremely hostile toxic environment kills virtually all the microbial populations usually found in systems treated with recommended doses of biocide (gramnegative bacteria, especially *Pseudomonas* species). This results in an environment, although hostile, with little or no competition. Microbial populations which could tolerate these conditions will eventually colonize this environment and flourish. There are reports indicating the isolation of unusual organisms in the presence of biocide several times in excess of the recommended dose. The evidence strongly suggests that these organisms have an extremely low permeability to hydrophilic biocides used in the system.

This scenario may be involved in recent outbreaks of hypersensitivity pneumonitis associated with exposure to metalworking fluid aerosols. The evidence suggests that hypersensitivity pneumonitis has occurred where "atypical" flora have predominated in metalworking fluids. Although the microbiological origin of hypersensitivity pneumonitis is strongly suspected, the involvement of biocides and other constituents of the fluids has not been excluded. There have been many reports on allergic contact dermatitis among workers exposed to biocide-treated components of industrial systems and contact sensitization to products containing biocides at the consumer end. These types of reports include most of the frequently used industrial biocides.

## See Also the Following Articles

Biodeterioration • Biopesticides, Microbial • Cosmetic Microbiology • Pulp and Paper

## Bibliography

Allsopp, C., and Allsopp, D. (1983). An updated survey of commercial products used to protect material against biodeterioration. *Int. Biodeterioration Bull.* **19**, 99–145.

Block, S. (Ed.) (1991). "Disinfection, Sterilization, and Preservation," 4th ed. Leo & Feiger, Philadelphia.

Bravery, A. F. (1992). Preservation in construction industry. *In* "Principles and Practice of Disinfection, Preservation and Sterilization" (A. D. Russell, W. B. Hugo, and G. A. J. Ayliffe, Eds.), 2nd ed., pp. 437–458. Blackwell, London.

Denyer, S. P. (1990). Mechanisms of action of biocides. *Int. Biodeterioration* **29**, 89–100. [Special issue]

Downey, A. (1995). The use of biocides in paint preservation. *In* "Handbook of Biocide and Preservative Use" (H. W. Rossmoore, Ed.), pp. 254–266. Chapman & Hall, New York.

Eagon, R. G. (1995). Paper, pulp and food grade paper. *In* "Handbook of Biocide and Preservative Use" (H. W. Rossmoore, Ed.), pp. 83–95. Chapman & Hall, New York.

Hueck, H. J. (1968). The biodeterioration of materials—an appraisal. *In* "Biodeterioration of Materials 6–12." Elsevier, London.

Hugo, W. B. (1992). Historical introduction. *In* "Principles and Practice of Disinfection, Preservation and Sterilization" (A. D. Russell, W. B. Hugo, and G. A. J. Ayliffe, Eds.), 2nd ed., pp. 3–6. Blackwell, London.

Hugo, H. W., and Russell, A. D. (1992). Types of antimicrobial agents. *In* "Principles and Practice of Disinfection, Preservation and Sterilization" (A. D. Russell, W. B. Hugo, and G. A. J. Ayliffe, Eds.), 2nd ed., pp. 7–88. Blackwell, London.

Leightley, L. (1995). Biocide use in wood preservation. *In* "Handbook of Biocide and Preservative Use" (H. W. Rossmoore, Ed.), pp. 283–301. Chapman & Hall, New York.

Lutey, R. W. (1995). Process cooling water. *In* "Handbook of Biocide and Preservative Use" (H. W. Rossmoore, Ed.), pp. 50–76. Chapman & Hall, New York.

McCarthy, B. J. (1995). Biocides for use in the textile industry. *In* "Handbook of Biocide and Preservative Use" (H. W. Rossmoore, Ed.), pp. 238–253. Chapman & Hall, New York.

Murphy, S. D. (1980). Assessment of the potential for toxic

interactions among environmental pollutants. *In* "The Principles and Methods in Modern Toxicology" (C. L. Galli, S. D. Murphy, and R. Paoletti, Eds.), p. 277. Elsevier/North–Holland Biomedical Press.

Rossmoore, H. W. (1995a). Introduction to biocide use. *In* "Handbook of Biocide and Preservative Use" (H. W. Rossmoore, Ed.), pp. 1–17. Chapman & Hall, New York.

Rossmoore, H. W. (1995b). Biocides for metalworking lubricants and hydraulic fluids. *In* "Handbook of Biocide and Preservative Use" (H. W. Rossmoore, Ed.), pp. 133–156. Chapman & Hall, New York.

Rossmoore, H. W., and Sondossi, M. (1988). Application and mode of action of formaldehyde condensate biocides. *Adv. Appl. Microbiol.* **33**, 233–277.

Russell, A. D., Hugo, W. B., and Ayliffe, G. A. J. (Eds.) (1992). "Principles and Practice of Disinfection, Preservation and Sterilization," 2nd ed. Blackwell, London.

Sharpell, F. (1980). Industrial use of biocides in processes and products. *Dev. Ind. Microbiol.* **21**, 133–140.

# Biodegradation

## Wendy B. Bollag, Jerzy Dec, and Jean-Marc Bollag

*The Pennsylvania State University*

I. Agents of Biodegradation
II. Biodegradative Enzymes
III. Mechanisms of Biotransformation and Biodegradation
IV. Biodegradability and Recalcitrance
V. Bioavailability
VI. Applications

## GLOSSARY

**axenic culture** A known species of microorganisms maintained in the laboratory.

**bioavailability** The ability of a compound to be accessed by microorganisms for transformation.

**biotransformation** Alteration of the structure of a compound by an organism.

**cometabolism** Biotransformation of a compound by a microorganism which is incapable of utilizing the compound as a source of energy or growth.

**detoxification** Reduction in the hazardous nature of a compound.

**enrichment** Procedure for isolating microorganisms that are capable of utilizing particular chemicals for their growth.

**mineralization** Complete degradation of a compound to simple inorganic constituents, such as carbon dioxide, water, ammonia, chloride, and sulfate.

**recalcitrance** Resistance of a compound to biodegradation, resulting in its persistence in the environment.

**xenobiotic** A synthetic product not formed by natural biosynthetic processes; a foreign substance.

**BIODEGRADATION** can be defined as the transformation of a substance through the action of biological agents, especially microorganisms. In general, biodegradation is the process of decay initiated by microorganisms. However, in a stricter sense biodegradation has come to signify the complete microbial breakdown, or mineralization, of complex materials into simple inorganic constituents, such as carbon dioxide, water, ammonia, chloride, and sulfate.

This process is important for several reasons: Biodegradation is essential in allowing the recycling of such necessary biological building blocks as carbon, hydrogen, oxygen, nitrogen, and sulfur. Without the activity of microorganisms these atoms might be tied up in the complex nonbiodegradable substances and thus unable to reenter the natural cycles. Furthermore, microbial degradation of dead matter also prevents the accumulation of debris on the earth's surface. Perhaps most important, and the focus of this article, the activity of microorganisms on certain man-made substances can also, in many cases, result in their removal from the environment, in a reduction in their toxicity, or both.

The decomposition of synthetic compounds, or the lack thereof, has generated a great deal of concern in recent years. Almost daily, reports of overflowing landfills and hazardous pollutants in our air, water, and soil are issued. The "biodegradability" of a substance—that is, its susceptibility to decomposition by natural biological processes—has become a criterion by which we evaluate the acceptability of a commercial product. For these reasons, knowledge about the microbial decomposition of anthropogenic chemicals has been actively sought, and as a result our understanding of biodegradation, although far from complete, is continually expanding. In this article an overview of biodegradation, in particular that of man-made compounds, will be presented, and possible applications of the biodegradative potential of microorganisms will be discussed.

## I. AGENTS OF BIODEGRADATION

Although the transformation of organic molecules can be effected by a variety of abiotic catalysts, the most important degradative agents of these chemicals are microorganisms such as bacteria and fungi. In any given ecosystem, many microbial species may be present and capable of degrading a wide variety of structurally unrelated chemical compounds including xenobiotics, which are chemicals derived from human activity. Moreover, as a result of their remarkable powers of adaptation, microorganisms are able to proliferate in the most diverse and inhospitable environments. Thus, microorganisms appear to possess great biodegradative potential; so great, in fact, that the proposal has been made that under the appropriate conditions microorganisms can degrade any organic compound. Although this principle of microbial infallibility has been difficult to prove or disprove, several substances have certainly put this idea to the test (see Section IV).

In general, microorganisms decompose organic substances to generate energy and nutrients for their growth. Thus, a usual consequence of biodegradation of a compound is an increase in the number of the microorganisms degrading that substance. In a process termed enrichment culture, this characteristic has been used to identify microorganisms capable of utilizing a particular chemical for their growth. The enrichment technique involves incubating a source of microorganisms, such as sewage, soil, or water, with the substance of interest as the sole source of carbon and energy. Species which can obtain energy from and subsist on the compound (i.e., microorganisms that degrade the chemical) are able to proliferate under these conditions and can be isolated using the appropriate microbiological methods. In general, this enrichment procedure has proven successful in isolating microbial species that biodegrade naturally occurring compounds. More important, enrichment techniques have also resulted in the isolation of microorganisms that can mineralize various pesticides and other potentially toxic anthropogenic chemicals.

Nevertheless, occasionally the microbial transformation of xenobiotics is observed without the accompanying growth of a degradative microorganism. In some cases, the inability to isolate a microorganism that utilizes the compound as its sole carbon and energy source may be purely a methodological problem: The active species may require for its growth an accessory factor (or factors) that is not present in the incubation medium. Alternatively, although the microorganism may transform the chemical, it may be unable to convert the compound to products that provide energy and a source of carbon for microbial growth. This phenomenon, known as cometabolism, appears to result from a lack of specificity of certain microbial enzymes. These enzymes can modify the compound, which may be chemically related to the natural substrate of the enzyme, but generate products that cannot be further metabolized by the enzymatic machinery of the microorganism. Thus, the consequences of cometabolism are threefold: (i) The microorganisms responsible for the transformation do not proliferate in the presence of the chemical; (ii) as a result of this lack of microbial growth, the rate of transformation of the xenobiotic does not increase over time and is, in fact, generally quite low because of the small starting population of the transforming microorganisms; and (iii) a product or products of the transformation reaction may accumulate in the environment. Because these products may be chemically similar to the parent compound, their presence in the habitat may be equally undesirable.

Nonetheless, in a natural ecosystem microbial species exist not in isolation but in the presence of a wide variety of other types of microorganisms. In some instances, the transformation product generated by the cometabolic reaction of one microorganism may serve as a growth substrate for another. Alternatively, a chemical may be completely biodegraded by a series of sequential cometabolic attacks by various microbial species. Thus, cometabolism may be harmful in that this fortuitous transformation can lead to the production of a compound with increased resistance to further degradation or greater toxicity than the parent compound; on the other hand, cometabolism may initiate the biodegradative reactions of a diverse microbial population in an environment resulting in the ultimate mineralization of the chemical.

The interaction of various microbial populations in an environment is difficult to investigate in a laboratory setting. Often, a microbial species capable of metabolizing a given substance is isolated by enrichment procedures and its degradative capacity studied by the scientist in an axenic culture *in vitro*. Obviously, laboratory conditions may be very different from those encountered by the microorganism in a natural environment. For instance, the mineralizing microbial species may compete poorly with other species for limiting nutrients in the environment; therefore, the microorganism that may in a laboratory culture efficiently degrade a compound, may in the natural habitat grow poorly and thus only minimally metabolize the chemical. On the other hand, the interaction between the various populations may be positive, with the degradative microorganism perhaps deriving necessary growth factors or favorable growth conditions from the activity of other microbial species. Thus, the activity of the heterogeneous community, rather than that of the single species, determines a chemical's biodegradation in the natural environment.

Several other factors influence the biodegradation of a compound in the environment. In order for a microorganism to use a substance for growth, other factors required for growth must also be available at suitable concentrations. These factors include nutrients that provide sources of nitrogen, sulfur, phosphorus, calcium, and magnesium as well as trace metals and an adequate supply of water. In addition, a sufficient supply of a suitable electron acceptor, such as molecular oxygen, nitrate, sulfate, or carbon dioxide, is required. If any one of these factors necessary for microbial growth is scarce or absent, biodegradation of the chemical will be slow. Similarly, other factors that affect microbial proliferation, such as temperature and pH of the environment, will influence a molecule's biodegradation. In addition, as microorganisms "feed" on the chemical in question, so too do other organisms feed on the microorganisms; predation may thus influence microbial numbers and the rate of biodegradation. Moreover, in an environment such as soil, the presence of reactive surfaces and particulate matter may interfere with microbial decomposition of a substance. Diffusional limitations may also inhibit substrate–microorganism interaction, thus slowing the rate of metabolism of a substance. Finally, various inhibitors of microbial growth and metabolism may be present in the habitat and affect mineralization of a compound; indeed, the chemical under investigation may be inhibitory and its presence above certain concentrations may preclude its biodegradation. Thus, the interaction of many factors determines the ultimate fate of a particular compound.

## II. BIODEGRADATIVE ENZYMES

Microbial enzymes are responsible for the degradation of various substances by microorganisms. Because the ultimate result of biodegradation is the production of energy for microbial growth, the enzymes that mediate biodegradative reactions are often those that also initiate essential metabolic pathways. Certain biological transformation mechanisms are unique to microorganisms. For instance, some microbial species are capable of proliferating under both aerobic and anaerobic conditions. Of necessity, this dual capacity requires that these microorganisms possess the enzymatic machinery to use either molecular oxygen or nitrate, $CO_2$, $SO_4^-$, etc. as the final electron acceptor. Alternatively, some species are able to derive the necessary energy for growth by a fermentative process, in which an organic electron acceptor is used. In addition, microorganisms can produce enzymes that are active extracellularly.

The existence of microbial enzymes that exhibit activity outside the organism has contributed to a recurrent problem experienced by scientists investigating biodegradation: the difficulty in distinguishing between enzyme-catalyzed biotransformation reactions and those that occur as a result of purely physical/chemical effects. Thus, transformed products may be generated in many ways, including via: (i) enzyme catalysis occurring in the microorganism, (ii) enzyme catalysis occurring extracellularly in the environment, or (iii) physicochemical catalysis. In addition, transformation may be the result of a combination of these mechanisms: For instance, enzyme-generated products may be further transformed by physicochemical means and vice versa. Further complicating this puzzle is the fact that microorganisms can alter the physicochemical properties of the environment. For instance, microbial activity can affect the pH or redox conditions of the habitat and thus contribute indirectly to physicochemical catalysis of transformation. In addition, sterilization, the method most often used for differentiation of biological and nonbiological processes, may in fact alter not only the microbial properties but also the physicochemical properties of the source of the inoculum under investigation. For example, most techniques employed for sterilizing soil can also cause changes in the physicochemical characteristics of the soil; thus, the inability of sterilized soil to catalyze a transformation reaction may or may not indicate the involvement of microorganisms and their enzymes. Obviously, the investigator is faced with quite a challenge in attempting to determine whether or not a reaction is enzymatically catalyzed.

Nevertheless, it should be noted that although physicochemical processes can result in transformation of a chemical, mineralization is mostly a consequence of microbial activity. More important, many scientists have succeeded in purifying the microbial enzymes involved in various transformation reactions, thereby abolishing all doubt as to the biological nature of the metabolism.

The ability of microorganisms to transform these man-made compounds raises an interesting question: What is the origin of the enzymes capable of degrading such "unnatural" chemicals? It is generally acknowledged that xenobiotics that resemble naturally occurring compounds are most likely to be efficiently degraded by microorganisms. Similarly, synthetic compounds with chemical structures that differ greatly from those of natural substances are often degraded poorly. For these reasons, it is generally assumed that xenobiotic-degrading enzymes have evolved by mutation and natural selection of the genes encoding those constitutive or inducible enzymes responsible for general microbial metabolism. The capacity to use synthetic chemicals might thus be gained as a result of hyperproduction of preexisting enzymes due to gene duplication, mutations that alter regulatory control processes, or mutations that generate novel enzymes with new specific activities. Some of the genes encoding pollutant-degrading enzymes can be found on autonomously replicating plasmids that in certain cases are transmissible among different microbial strains. Plasmid exchange within a population could thus result in the production of novel microbial strains with many degradative activities. In general, it appears that the extreme adaptability of microorganisms gives them the capacity to alter their enzymatic machinery to utilize a wide spectrum of anthropogenic chemicals.

## III. MECHANISMS OF BIOTRANSFORMATION AND BIODEGRADATION

In general, xenobiotics are transformed by the same mechanisms that mediate microbial metabolism of naturally occurring compounds. These processes can be categorized as oxidative, reductive, hydrolytic, or synthetic reactions.

Hydroxylation is a common oxidative reaction and is frequently the initial step in the biodegradation pathway of many substances. For instance, the cleavage of aromatic rings and the degradation of aliphatic side chains resulting in decarboxylation, deamination, or dealkylation are often preceded by hydroxylation. Moreover, the addition of the hydroxyl group often increases the polarity, and thus the water solubility, of the compound, making it more accessible to biological attack. Enzymes that catalyze this reaction include hydroxylases and mixed function oxidases.

Another important oxidative reaction is N-dealkylation which, like hydroxylation, is often a first step in the breakdown of pollutants, in particular alkyl-substituted pesticides. N-Dealkylation can be catalyzed by mixed function oxidases. Other oxidative reactions involved in the biodegradation of xenobiotics include decarboxylation, $\beta$-oxidation (of fatty acid side chains), hydrolysis of ether linkages, epoxidation, sulfoxidation, and cleavage of aromatic and heterocyclic rings.

Reductive transformations of xenobiotics are less well described; however, as studies on the anaerobic biodegradation of these chemicals continue, more such mechanisms will undoubtedly be discovered. Nevertheless, several xenobiotics have been demonstrated to undergo reductive metabolism. Examples of reductive reactions are the conversion of a nitro to an amino group, reductive dehalogenation, saturation of double and triple bonds, reduction of aldehydes, reduction of ketones to secondary alcohols, and conversion of sulfoxide to sulfide.

Hydrolytic reactions, in which cleavage of a molecule is effected by the simultaneous addition of water, often initiate the biodegradation of xenobiotics. These reactions are observed frequently in the microbial metabolism of xenobiotics that possess ether, ester, or amide linkages and are catalyzed by esterase, acrylamidase, phosphatase, hydrolase, and lyase enzymes. The result is the hydrolysis of the ether, ester, phosphoester, or amide bond. Another reaction is hydrolytic dehalogenation in which the halogen atom of a pollutant is replaced by a hydroxyl group generated from water.

Synthetic pathways of xenobiotic transformation involve the modification of pollutants via the addition of some chemical group to form conjugated products (conjugation reactions) or the coupling of pollutants to another molecule or molecules to yield dimeric and polymeric compounds (condensation reactions). Although conjugation processes, such as glycoside formation reactions with amino or sulfur groups, occur frequently in plants and animals, only alkylation (in particular methylation) and acylation (especially formylation and acetylation) are commonly observed in microorganisms. The resulting methylated, acetylated, and formylated products are often less toxic than the parent compound; however, in some instances, the conjugated pollutants may actually prove more toxic to humans and higher organisms, as detailed in Section V.

## IV. BIODEGRADABILITY AND RECALCITRANCE

Through the basic metabolic reactions already described, microorganisms are able to degrade many man-made chemicals. Nevertheless, in some cases microbial degradative capacity can be problematic. The use of pesticides has not only greatly improved the success of modern agriculture but also allowed the control of disease-carrying insects in developing countries. However, the cost of these chemicals can be quite high, and a need for repeated applications may prove prohibitive. For these compounds, then, resistance to microbial decomposition can be a desir-

able characteristic. Similarly, the deterioration of packaging materials and fabrics while still in use would be highly objectionable. Thus, some degree of resistance to biodegradation is a necessary property of various synthetic compounds.

Obviously, resistance to microbial decomposition can also be an undesirable and sometimes hazardous property of various xenobiotics. The persistence of man-made plastic containers and other waste in the environment is not only aesthetically displeasing but also has created a major concern regarding the future disposal of such substances in this age of overfull landfills. Other chemicals used in agriculture and industry have been found to contaminate soil and water, and resistance to biodegradation can lead to accumulation to toxic levels. Often, crops grown in such polluted soil concentrate these compounds in their tissues, creating a greater hazard to humans and animals. In addition, the effects of toxic xenobiotics can frequently be magnified, because of their lack of biodegradability, as these compounds progress through the food chain. A well-known example of this magnification effect is the profound decimation of the bird of prey population observed years ago as a result of the cumulative toxicity of the insecticide DDT. Thus, it is quite clear that a lack of biodegradability can be a dangerous characteristic of some xenobiotics.

What makes a compound resistant to biodegradation? This question has received a great amount of attention from environmental scientists, but the mechanism of recalcitrance, or resistance to biodegradation, is unclear. It should be noted that there are many naturally occurring substances that are quite persistent in the environment. For instance, the organic matter of soil, humus, or a portion at least, appears to be resistant to microbial decomposition under some conditions, and radiocarbon dating has indicated the age of some fossil soils to be between 3,000 and 25,000 years.

Similarly, several man-made chemicals can persist in the environment. For instance, the pesticides chlordane, aldrin, DDT, lindane, and parathion are all present in soil more than 15 years after their last application, indicating that these compounds are resistant to microbial attack. In general, xenobiotics with chemical structures similar to those of naturally occurring compounds are more likely to be degraded by microorganisms. On the other hand, synthetic chemicals with dissimilar structures frequently exhibit the phenomenon of recalcitrance; the more dissimilar the molecule, the more likely the compound is to lack biodegradability. Although the mechanism of recalcitrance is only incompletely resolved, certain features are known to predispose a xenobiotic to persist in the environment. For instance, the presence of halogen (e.g., chlorine) or other substituents, such as nitro, sulfonate, or methyl groups, tends to diminish biodegradability; two or more such substituents are likely to render the compound even more refractory to microbial decomposition. In addition, the position of the substituent(s) can affect the ability of microorganisms to degrade a given xenobiotic. Nevertheless, although some of the characteristics that predispose a substance to resist microbial attack are known, it is not possible to predict with any accuracy which xenobiotics will persist in the environment.

Several factors can contribute to the phenomenon of recalcitrance of a xenobiotic. Clearly, if no microorganism exists that is capable of transforming the compound, the xenobiotic will not be biodegradable and will persist in the environment. Alternatively, a microbial population able to utilize the chemical may exist but may not be present at or may be physically restricted from the site of pollutant contamination. Moreover, even if present, the microbial species may lack an essential nutrient or proper conditions for growth. Thus, environmental factors such as temperature, pH, salinity, osmolarity, predator activity and competition among microbial populations as well as the availability (and identity) of electron acceptors can influence the biodegradability of a xenobiotic. In this regard, it should be noted that some chemicals that are readily degraded with molecular oxygen as the final electron acceptor may under anaerobic conditions be degraded only poorly or not at all and vice versa. Microbial growth, enzymatic activity, or both may also be inhibited by the pollutant, especially if it is present in high concentrations, or by another toxin or enzyme inhibitor present in the environment. In addition, the xenobiotic may be inaccessible to the appropriate degradative enzymes because of binding to high-molecular-weight resistant organic

compounds, lack of water solubility, or failure to gain access to intracellular compartments, or there may be steric hindrance at the site acted on enzymatically. Finally, biodegradation of certain chemicals may require a cooperative interaction among two or more microbial species. Thus, if one population is absent or its growth inhibited by any of the previously mentioned factors, recalcitrance of the compound may result. It is quite obvious, therefore, that there are many possible ways in which a synthetic compound may resist microbial attack, with the result that currently biodegradability or recalcitrance of a xenobiotic are extremely difficult properties to predict.

## V. BIOAVAILABILITY

Binding interactions between xenobiotics and soil contribute significantly to the recalcitrance of biodegradable chemicals in terrestrial environments. All other factors that may suppress biodegradation (see Section IV) are to a degree incidental, whereas the effect of binding is evident at any time after a xenobiotic enters the soil. The ability of soil to retain xenobiotics is attributed to sorption phenomena and chemical reactions occurring on the active surfaces of humus and mineral particles; xenobiotics can also be retained through entrapment within the soil matrix. Whatever their mechanisms, binding interactions seem to create a barrier between microbial populations and xenobiotics. According to the proposed models for biodegradation, soil pollutants must be present in the aqueous phase in order to be available to microorganisms. This bioavailability requirement is constantly challenged in terrestrial systems, in which xenobiotic molecules are continuously removed from the soil solution through immobilization or diffusion to inaccessible locations.

Soil particles can literally form a barrier to biodegradation. If micropores between the particles are smaller than the size of a microbial cell, microorganisms are physically prevented from traversing the porous zone. Xenobiotics, on the other hand, can diffuse across the barrier, thus escaping biodegradation—at least temporarily. Due to the tortuosity associated with the micropores, the diffusion is slow;

therefore, the passage between the particles can be considered a form of entrapment. Before moving out of micropores to a site populated by microorganisms, a considerable portion of migrating xenobiotics are inevitably adsorbed on the surfaces of particulate matter, which causes a further delay in their biodegradation.

Soil particles are also known to have internal micropores, some of which are large enough to be penetrated by xenobiotics but too small for the entry of living cells. Once inside the pores, the molecules are trapped until their concentration in the outside solution decreases to provide a driving force for diffusion. Even if diffusion is possible, however, the entrapped molecules are subject to adsorption on the internal surfaces of micropores, causing an additional setback to biodegradation.

Adsorption phenomena occurring in the inter- and intraparticle micropores do not differ from those that occur on external surfaces. In each case, the retention of xenobiotics can be attributed to the same binding mechanisms, such as H-bonding, van der Waals forces, electrostatic attraction, ligand exchange, or partitioning. One of the most intriguing factors to consider in the diminished rates of biodegradation of externally sorbed xenobiotics is the fact that the separation of microorganisms from the chemicals is not as complete as it is in the case of molecules entrapped in micropore areas. It is true that, through sorption, xenobiotic molecules are removed from the aqueous solution; nevertheless, they continue to be exposed to microorganisms together with the solid surfaces on which they are deposited. In fact, it can be argued that the immobilized chemicals should be more manageable for microorganisms than molecules remaining in solution.

However, such is not the case because of the mechanism of biodegradation. Xenobiotics can be degraded by either intracellular or extracellular enzymes produced by microorganisms. Obviously, xenobiotics adsorbed on solid surfaces are not accessible to the former because immobilized molecules are not free to enter the cells. In this situation, the transformation of the adsorbed chemicals depends entirely on the activity of extracellular enzymes. The efficiency of the latter, however, is considerably diminished because immobilization of xenobiotics may create steric hindrance to the catalytic reaction and because extracellular enzymes are subject to adsorption, which may cause losses in their activity.

Adsorption phenomena may considerably reduce the rate of biodegradation but do not eliminate it entirely. When adsorption is at equilibrium, the concentration of degradable molecules in the soil solution is frequently sufficient to support the growth of microorganisms. As these molecules are consumed, immobilized molecules can be desorbed from the solid phase and become available for biodegradation. The desorption may continue until the concentration of xenobiotics in the liquid phase is insufficient to maintain the microorganisms.

Xenobiotics are, in general, adsorbed faster than they are desorbed—a phenomenon known as hysteresis. According to recent observations, the rates of desorption are subject to reduction with the length of time that the xenobiotics reside in soil or are "aged." With aging, chemicals show increased hysteresis. In addition, considerable amounts of aged pollutants become almost entirely resistant to desorption and are thus unable to be biodegraded.

A considerable part of soil pollution consists of thousands of inert compounds classified as nonionic, nonpolar, or hydrophobic. Like other xenobiotics, inert chemicals show a broad range of susceptibility to biodegradation *in vitro*. The apparent recalcitrance of these chemicals in soil is related to aging and decreased bioavailability rather than to biochemical stability. Aging and recalcitrance of neutral compounds is currently ascribed to immobilization phenomena (sorption and entrapment) occurring within the soil matrix at remote microsites that are totally inaccessible to microorganisms. Inert chemicals reach these sites by diffusion across organic matter. Such a combination of diffusion processes with immobilization is frequently referred to as sequestration or slow sorption because it may require months or even years to reach an equilibrium. Sequestration does not have to be complete in order to prevent biodegradation. In fact, inert chemicals are unavailable to microorganisms at the onset of diffusion. It is noteworthy that sequestered chemicals are not immobilized in soil permanently; on the contrary, they can be recovered, although with difficulty, by vigorous extraction with organic solvents. From the standpoint of biodegradation, however, sequestration is practically irreversible because molecules involved in diffusion and subsequent sorption do not desorb into soil solution as readily as those adsorbed on external surfaces.

A separate category of immobilized chemicals are so-called bound residues. Unlike sequestered compounds, bound residues are formed by covalent binding of xenobiotics to soil organic matter and cannot be recovered by exhaustive extraction with organic solvents. Unextractable residues may also result from physical entrapment of xenobiotic molecules in nanometer-size voids and holes of the molecular net of humic polymers. Bound residues are highly resistant to release by microbial activity or chemical treatment. In a sense, they constitute a dead-end product of microbial activity. In fact, microorganisms may be indispensable in bound residue formation. Experiments using $^{14}$C-labeled compounds demonstrated that only negligible amounts of bound residues are formed in sterile soils. The role of microorganisms in these processes is to condition xenobiotic molecules for covalent binding. Some fungi, for instance, produce extracellular oxidoreductases capable of oxidizing phenolic or aniline contaminants to quinones or free radicals that readily react with humic constituents and result in the formation of covalent linkages. Microorganisms can also partially degrade xenobiotics, thus converting them to more reactive derivatives that may later be involved in covalent binding. As a result of binding, however, these derivatives cannot be further degraded or effectively mineralized on exposure to microbial populations. Nevertheless, research to date suggests that covalently bound molecules have reduced toxicity (see Section VI).

There is little doubt that binding interactions reduce bioavailability and considerably contribute to the recalcitrance of xenobiotics in soil. However, taking into account that a given chemical may undergo binding by several mechanisms simultaneously and that xenobiotic molecules must frequently compete for binding sites with other chemicals present in soil environments, it will never be an easy task to determine the exact effect of bioavailability on xenobiotic recalcitrance in *in vivo* situations.

## VI. APPLICATIONS

Although, as discussed previously, some synthetic chemicals are resistant to biodegradation, microorganisms possess an enormous capacity to transform and/or mineralize a wide range of both natural and man-made compounds. This prowess has been recognized and exploited for many years. For instance, since the turn of the century microorganisms have been used at sewage treatment plants to process wastewater. Recently, it has been proposed that microorganisms (or their enzymes) might be utilized in other systems for bioremediation, the removal of pollutants from a contaminated environment.

Biodegradative microorganisms may prove particularly useful for the cleanup of toxic chemicals in habitats such as soil or groundwater. Conventional decontamination procedures involve physically removing the polluted topsoil; these methods, although effective, are cumbersome and expensive. Furthermore, the pollutant is not degraded but merely moved to a less hazardous site. Obviously, complete decomposition of the chemical would be preferable. Indeed, the microbial conversion of toxic compounds to inorganic natural molecules, such as carbon dioxide, water, methane, nitrate, and sulfate, results ultimately in a detoxification of the pollutant. For those synthetic molecules for which a mineralizing microorganism exists, biodegradation may prove to be an efficient means of detoxifying pollutants in the environment.

Detoxification may also occur without complete mineralization. Often, biotransformation reactions can result in a decrease in the toxicity of the parent compound. Nevertheless, occasionally products of these reactions may in fact be more toxic than the original molecule or may persist and accumulate in the habitat. For example, the microbial metabolism of tetrachloroethylene under anaerobic conditions produces vinyl chloride, which is not only very toxic but also relatively resistant to further biotransformation. Thus, it is clear that the generation of metabolites other than the inorganic products of complete biodegradation should elicit concern until such time as these compounds are proven to be innocuous. However, it should be noted that even pollutants that are eventually mineralized can be converted to intermediates that may transiently accumulate to possibly toxic levels.

In addition to the potential toxicity of microbial metabolites of xenobiotics, there are other limits to the use of microorganisms for decontamination of the environment. First, a microbial species capable of metabolizing the chemical must exist. As discussed in Section IV, some pollutants are recalcitrant under various environmental conditions. Nevertheless, the principle of microbial infallibility (discussed in Section I) is difficult to prove or disprove, and it may be true that any chemical, either naturally occurring or synthetic, can be biodegraded under the appropriate conditions. It remains to be seen whether or not degradative microorganisms can be isolated for all xenobiotics using current methods such as the enrichment technique.

In some cases, isolation of and inoculation with a xenobiotic-degrading microorganism may not be required for biodegradation: At times, microorganisms indigenous to the environment can efficiently degrade the compound if adequate growth conditions are provided. For example, following the oil spill from the Exxon Valdez tanker at Prince William Sound, Alaska, it was determined that nitrogen and phosphorus were limiting to microbial growth. Addition of these elements to the area allowed the indigenous microorganisms to more rapidly degrade the oil constituents. In fact, the added nitrogen and phosphorus accelerated the biodegradation of the oil hydrocarbons such that 60–70% of the oil components were degraded within 16 months. In this instance of successful bioremediation, the indigenous microorganisms were proficient in hydrocarbon biodegradation, but researchers could enhance their activity by adding nutrients.

On the other hand, when indigenous microflora cannot degrade a particular xenobiotic, even identification of a microbial species capable of degrading that compound does not guarantee success because additional factors can influence the effectiveness of bioremediation. In order for biodegradation to occur, the contaminated site must be inoculated with a sufficient microbial biomass. Transport of a large number of microorganisms in an active or inducible state may be difficult. Furthermore, the inoculum may not proliferate in the habitat such that there is no guarantee that biodegradation will proceed rapidly and efficiently. As previously discussed, microorganisms require essential nutrients which must be present in or added to the environment. In addition, appropriate conditions for growth must prevail at the polluted site: Temperature, pH, availability of electron acceptors, salinity, osmolarity, water saturation, predator activity, and competition with native microbial populations for nutrients can all affect proliferation of the inoculated culture. Obviously, the conditions that the inoculum experiences *in situ*—that is, in a natural environment—are more severe than those obtained in a laboratory setting. Also, without expansion of the microbial population, biodegradation will occur only slowly and inefficiently.

Another potential hindrance to a rapid rate of biodegradation is the fact that microbial metabolism of some xenobiotics requires the induction of degradative enzymes, occasionally by a chemical other than that present in the contaminated environment. In addition, microorganisms can be physically restricted from entering certain microenvironments with the result that a xenobiotic remains inaccessible to the microbial metabolic machinery (see Section V). A pollutant may also be inaccessible to intracellular enzymes if the compound is unable to permeate the microorganism due to a lack of uptake by the cell or the adsorption of the chemical to interfering solid substances such as soil or clay. Thus, the use of microorganisms for the detoxification of polluted habitats has some serious potential limitations.

Some of these limitations may be overcome by using isolated enzymes, rather than the entire microorganism, for the decontamination procedure. Technologies have been developed for purifying large quantities of enzymes that function extracellularly to transform xenobiotics. These catalysts have the advantage that they readily interact with pollutants such that accessibility is seldom a problem. In addition, although the initial production of the enzyme might require induction, once introduced into the contaminated environment the enzyme is active immediately since no further protein synthesis is necessary. Moreover, the activity of isolated enzymes is not dependent on cell growth such that these catalysts might be expected to function under quite severe *in situ* conditions.

Nevertheless, the use of enzymes for decontamination purposes presents some unique obstacles. For instance, as discussed previously, complete mineralization is the preferred biotransformation reaction for detoxification of xenobiotics; however, such degradation necessitates the sequential action of many enzymes on various intermediates derived from metabolism of the parent compound. Obviously, the cost of mass producing many enzymes for inoculation into a contaminated site would be prohibitive. Furthermore, in the vast milieu of an *in situ* environment, the diffusion of products formed by one enzyme would decrease the availability of the substrate to the next in the enzymatic series. To combat this problem, investigators have successfully enclosed microbial enzymes catalyzing sequential degradative reactions in a permeable sphere and demonstrated the effectiveness of this apparatus in degrading pollutants. Other researchers have suggested that a series of enzymes might be attached to a solid support (e.g., glass beads or soil) in order to effect complete biodegradation of a compound. Nevertheless, the difficulty of mimicking the metabolic machinery of a complex microorganism using these techniques is obvious.

In addition to the potential difficulty of identifying and isolating large quantities of an appropriate enzyme, other factors that may preclude the use of isolated enzymes for decontamination purposes include their possible inactivation by proteases and extremes of pH and temperature and their requirement, in some cases, for cofactors. Current research is seeking solutions to these potential complications of using microbial enzymes for decontamination of the environment. For instance, researchers have successfully attached enzymes to solid supports and demonstrated that not only do the immobilized enzymes still catalyze transformation reactions but also they are more resistant to proteolytic attack and extremes of temperature and pH. Nevertheless, to date there has been limited application of isolated enzymes to field-scale bioremediation efforts and the feasibility of such methods is unknown.

For some of the difficulties associated with the use of purified enzymes, including the cost of purification and possible inactivation of the enzyme by harsh environmental conditions, the suggestion has been made to utilize crude preparations of "detoxifying" enzymes. This protocol might have the added benefit of providing several biodegradative enzymes to a single site, thus potentially promoting more complete degradation of the xenobiotics. One such proposal involves using horseradish, which contains the enzyme horseradish peroxidase, to biodegrade xenobiotics. Using this procedure, horseradish is ground and mixed, together with the cofactor hydrogen peroxide, with contaminated soil or water, and the horseradish peroxidase is allowed to degrade the xenobiotic. Although results from preliminary tests in the laboratory have been favorable, it is not clear whether this protocol will prove more successful under field conditions than other techniques.

Finally, the incorporation of pollutants into polymers and copolymers has been proposed as a potential means of detoxifying contaminated soils and wastewaters. In wastewater, the polymers formed as a result of microbial activity precipitate from solution and this precipitate can be easily removed by filtration. Furthermore, in soil pollutants can be oxidatively cross-coupled to humic constituents to form copolymers (see Section V). The resulting covalent incorporation of the synthetic compounds into humic material has been shown to reduce the toxicity of the pollutants. Nevertheless, a question remains as to the stability of these humus-bound residues. Clearly, if the compounds are only transiently bound or are subsequently released by the activity of soil microorganisms, they would constitute a future hazard and their binding to soil would present neither a satisfactory nor a permanent solution to the pollution problem. However, all research to date indicates that these covalently bound pollutants are quite stable, with only a very limited release into the environment over time. Furthermore, it appears likely that the small amounts of pollutants that are released can be readily mineralized by soil microorganisms to prevent toxic accumulations. Thus, the information currently available suggests that once incorporated into humus, xenobiotics are unlikely to adversely affect the environment.

It should be obvious from the discussion presented herein that microbial biodegradation is a necessary and important process for preserving a clean environment. Nevertheless, it should also be apparent that, although a significant body of knowledge exists regarding this process, much additional information is needed to fully use the degradative ability of microorganisms. For instance, once the biodegradability of man-made compounds can be predicted with certainty, it should be possible to design and manufacture synthetic materials that are completely biodegradable, thereby helping to solve the problem of overflowing landfills. Furthermore, information concerning the mechanisms and characteristics of biodegradation should enable the efficient and rapid removal of chemical contaminants from our environment. Thus, our expanding knowledge about biodegradation of natural and man-made substances may prove to be a key to a clean and safe future world.

## See Also the Following Articles

Biomonitors of Environmental Contamination • Bioremediation • Pesticide Biodegradation

## Bibliography

Alexander, M. (1999). "Biodegradation and Bioremediation" Second Edition. Academic Press, San Diego.

Alexander, M. (1995). *Environ. Sci. Technol.* 29, 2713–2717.

Bollag, J.-M., and Liu, S.-Y. (1990). Biological transformation processes of pesticides. *In* "Pesticides in the Soil Environment," pp. 169–211. Soil Science Society of America, Madison, WI.

Dec, J., and Bollag, J.-M. (1997). *Soil Sci.* **162**, 858–874.

Huang, W., Schlautman, M. A., and Weber, W. J., Jr. (1996). *Environ. Sci. Technol.* **30**, 2993–3000.

Luthy, R. G., Aiken, G. R., Brusseau, M. L., Cunningham, S. D., Gschwend, P. M., Pignatello, J. J., Reinhard, M., Traina, S. J., Weber, W. J., Jr., and Westall, J. C. (1997). *Environ. Sci. Technol.* **31**, 3341–3347.

Pignatello, J. J., and Xing, B. (1996). *Environ. Sci. Technol.* **30**, 1–11.

Sparks, D. L. (1998). *In* "Structure and Surface Reactions of Soil Particles" (P. M. Huang, N. Senesi, and J. Buffle, Eds.), pp. 413–448. Willey, Chichester, UK.

# Biodeterioration: In Wood, Architecture, Art, and Other Media

**José-Julio Ortega-Calvo**

*Instituto de Recursos Naturales y Agrobiología, Seville, Spain*

## GLOSSARY

**biodeterioration** Any undesirable change in the properties of a material caused by the vital activities of organisms. It is more restrictive than the term biodegradation because the transformation implies the concept of a lowering in quality or value; i.e., it requires an appreciation of the material, in either an aesthetic or a utilitarian sense.

**building materials** Materials that are used for architectural purposes in buildings and other constructions; they include stone, brick, concrete, and mortar.

**fouling** Biodeterioration caused by the presence of living organisms, without significant structural damage to the material; in the case of microorganisms, it usually consists of aesthetic changes that create a generally unacceptable appearance.

**weathering** A process that results from physical, chemical, and biological forces, leading to the destruction of original stone and finally to soil formation.

**THE BIODETERIORATION** of materials comprises a wide variety of processes in which man's materials interact with living organisms, leading to transformations of economic relevance. Material transformation can be structural (i.e., affecting the physical integrity by chemical or mechanical means) or functional, when the growth or the activity of organisms does not cause significant damage in structure but does interfere with the use of the material. Biodeterioration can be caused by a variety of animals, plants, and microorganisms, although only those transformations effected by microbes will be discussed here.

Microbial biodeterioration occurs with many of the diverse materials used by man. Some economically important transformations occur with agricultural products and food materials. Wood, stone, concrete, and paintings are other examples of materials which are subject to deterioration by a wide variety of microorganisms, including bacteria, fungi, and algae. The control measures for such types of biodeterioration usually involve cleaning and disinfection, including the use of biocidal agents to prevent the growth of the microorganisms responsible for the damage.

## I. WOOD

Timbers inside buildings, in exposed window joinery and doors, and archeological wood artifacts can be seriously damaged as a result of microbial biodeterioration. The main agents for such decay are different groups of fungi. Their action starts when moisture content of the wood increases, with mold fungi usually being the first colonizers. These pioneering microorganisms use sugars or simple carbohydrates present in parenchyma cells but are unable to utilize the wood cell wall as a source of nutrients. The biodeterioration caused by mold fungi in wood is mainly functional, causing discoloration, unpleasant smell, and health disadvantages. Genera of *Phycomy-*

*cetes, Ascomycetes,* and *Fungi imperfecti* are included in this group.

Rot fungi use the cellulosic material as nutrient source, causing severe damage to wooden structures. They include the soft rots and the wood-rotting Basidiomycetes. Soft-rot fungi can stand a broader range of environmental conditions and predominate in wood that is too wet or dry for decay by Basidiomycetes. However, the most devastating rot fungi are Basidiomycetes, in which two different classes can be differentiated, namely, the white rots and the brown rots. White rots bleach the wood as decay progresses, whereas the brown rots leave the lignin as a brown residue. Two brown rots cause most cases of wood biodeterioration. The fungus *Serpula lacrymans* causes the so-called "dry rot," whereas *Coniophora puteana* produces an alteration called "wet rot." *Coniophora puteana* causes 90% of the decay within buildings. Dry and wet rots can be differentiated by the moisture required for development, morphology of the fruiting body, and the arrangement of cracks in damaged wood. Dry rot causes more problems than wet rot due to extensive spread of the fungal mycelium from moisture sources to dry wood, and it is more difficult to eradicate.

The main factors for the development of rot damage in wood which is not in contact with the ground are water, temperature, fungus and wood species, and construction design. The biodeterioration risk is highest in the tropical climatic zone with high temperatures, high precipitation, and a great number of causal organisms. Given that fungal attack starts only after an increase in moisture content of the wood, the problems of fungal decay in buildings are primarily caused by moisture damage due to either construction defects or insufficient ventilation.

## II. ARCHITECTURE

### A. Bacteria

Like any natural rock surface exposed to the atmosphere, buildings are colonized by a variety of autotrophic and heterotrophic bacteria. Under appropriate conditions, the building materials, such as stone or concrete, can be chemically attacked by the acids produced by these bacteria. In their redox reactions, chemoautotrophic bacteria produce inorganic acids, which also are present in acid rain. Sulfur-oxidizing bacteria convert reduced forms of sulfur, such as hydrogen sulfide and thiosulfate, to sulfuric acid. The acid may react with calcium carbonate present in limestone and in the calcareous binder of sandstone, leading to the formation of calcium sulfate and the subsequent deterioration of the porous material. The sources of these sulfur compounds in buildings are adjacent soils (from which they are transported by water through capillary forces), dust and soot from the atmosphere, and bird droppings. Several species of the genus *Thiobacillus* (*T. thiooxidans* and *T. thioparus*) have been described as active sulfur-oxidizing bacteria in decayed stones. *Thiobacillus thiooxidans* has been found in numbers up to $1.4 \times 10^6$ cells/g per stone.

Nitrifying bacteria are another important physiological group of chemoautotrophic bacteria responsible for biodeterioration in buildings. These bacteria are significant geochemical agents because they oxidize ammonia to nitrate. Their activity in buildings is supported by the dry and wet deposition of ammonium salts from the atmosphere. The ammonium originates from the decomposition of organic matter by microorganisms and from human activities such as coal combustion or use of fertilizers. The resulting nitric acid initiates the dissolution of stone and formation of nitrate salts, which are readily soluble in water and washed away or crystallized on the stone surface. Nitrification is a two-step process carried out by the combined activities of two different groups of bacteria: the ammonia oxidizers, which convert ammonia to nitrite, and the nitrite oxidizers, which convert nitrite to nitrate. Ammonia-oxidizing bacteria of the genera *Nitrosovibrio, Nitrosospira,* and *Nitrosomonas* can be found in buildings, with *Nitrosovibrio* being the dominant genus. This contrasts with soils, in which the other two genera are the most abundant components of the ammonia-oxidizing populations. The genus *Nitrobacter* is the most common of nitrite-oxidizing bacteria. Nitrifying bacteria may become a significant fraction of the total bacterial population in buildings, reaching numbers of up to $4 \times 10^4$ cells/g stone.

The *in situ* activity of autotrophic organisms, together with the deposition of exogenous organic compounds onto building surfaces, enriches the original substratum, making it colonizable by heterotrophic bacteria. Their metabolic and physiological versatility allows them to use a wide variety of biogenic organic compounds, including carbohydrates, amino acids, fatty acids, and hydrocarbons, and to maintain their activity during nutrient perturbations, even under oligotrophic conditions. In urban areas, air pollutants, such as polycyclic aromatic hydrocarbons and phthalates, contribute significantly to the array of bioavailable organic compounds that are present in building surfaces and which can be transformed through growth-linked reactions. Heterotrophic bacteria may promote the dissolution of minerals by the production of chelating agents and organic acids (such as gluconic acid, 2-oxoglutaric acid, and oxogluconic acid) that form salts or complexes with cations from the minerals. A significant fraction of the heterotrophic bacteria isolated from decayed materials may show, in culture, the ability to acidify the culture medium and produce mineral-dissolution halos in solid media. Total counts of heterotrophic bacteria may reach values of $10^4$–$10^7$ cells/g stone. Of these, gram-positive (*Corynebacterium, Micrococcus,* and *Bacillus*) and gram-negative (*Flavobacterium* and *Pseudomonas*) bacteria can be easily identified.

## B. Fungi

The enrichment in organic matter of building substrates also allows the development of fungi, particularly in places with constant humidity. Fungal hyphae can penetrate deeply into porous materials and cause chemical deterioration through the production of organic acids. Species of *Penicillium, Mucor, Trichoderma,* and *Fusarium* have been isolated from building stones and shown to produce different organic acids, including oxalic, gluconic, malic, and citric acids. These acids form calcium salts or act as chelating agents of mineral cations, favoring the biodeterioration process.

Fungi can also cause aesthetic damage in buildings due to disfigurement and changes in decorative finishes. This effect is increased by the production of dark pigments, such as melanins and melanoidins.

Black fungi from the Dematiaceae group (*Phoma* and *Alternaria*) are capable of extensively staining marble and limestone in exposed parts of buildings, causing black stains which are morphologically similar to soot deposits. Mold fungi can cause aesthetic damage inside the buildings, such as on walls and ceilings subject to water condensation. The source of moisture need not be particularly great—often the presence of air pockets which are not renewed by ventilation, such as those found behind pictures hung on walls, is sufficient. Cold-storage rooms may present significant problems of contamination by mold fungi after periods of increased temperature—for example, due to cleaning or an accident. The damp conditions, together with organic matter accumulated from the stored material (usually foodstuffs), may cause appreciable fungal growth on walls of these storage facilities. Cleaning can be extremely difficult if molds have developed in cavities between the wall and insulating panels in these storage rooms.

## C. Cyanobacteria and Algae

The presence of these phototrophic microorganisms on buildings is often associated with high humidity and water retention. Cyanobacterial and algal epilithic growths are easily visible and may contribute a considerable amount of biomass on the surface of the material. Chlorophyll *a* content, usually taken as a biomass indicator for these communities, is typically within the range of 32–364 mg chlorophyll *a* m$^{-2}$. The coloration produced by the growth of phototrophic microorganisms is especially unsightly on walls, marbles, and frescoes present in historic buildings. Extreme cases of colonization have been described in Venice (Italy), where algal growth is extensive in most of the historic buildings, and in the tropics, where buildings and natural rock surfaces usually have a blackish covering of cyanobacteria.

Taxonomic studies have been performed on the populations of cyanobacteria and algae present in stone monuments throughout the world. These studies have shown a wide diversity of species. In general, the species are not characteristic of the stone environment but grow on the stone surface when conditions are appropriate for colonization and development. Most of the forms present are generally recognized as "soil algae," but they may also be present in the air. The most common species belong to genera of filamentous cyanobacteria (*Phormidium* and *Microcoleus*) and chlorophytes or green algae (*Klebsormidium* and *Trentepohlia*), although unicellular forms (e.g., the cyanobacteria *Gloeocapsa* and *Chroococcus* and the chlorophytes *Chlorella* and *Chloroccocum*) can be readily observed. Genera of *Bacillariophyta* (diatoms) and *Chrysophyta* (brown algae) have also been found on buildings. For example, up to 17 different species of diatoms have been reported from marbles of the Parthenon (Athens, Greece).

In addition to water availability, a combination of other ecological factors, such as temperature, light, or pH, may also influence the distribution of such organisms in the buildings due to their adaptation to the prevailing conditions. In buildings there are microclimatic differences even between very close places. This may lead to species segregation and/or different biomass content between adjacent materials, such as mortar and the bricks or stones in contact with it.

The aggressive action of cyanobacteria and algae in relation to the substrates on which they develop is based on chemical and mechanical mechanisms. The development of these communities on and in the materials initiates a different microclimate, in which photosynthesis and respiration affect the partial pressure of $CO_2$, which has an immediate effect on the carbonate-dissolution equilibrium. This is the most commonly accepted mechanism explaining the dissolution processes associated with algal and cyanobacterial growths. Weathering is also favored by the water-retention capacity of the communities formed by these terrestrial microorganisms. Their survival strategies include the production of hygroscopic, extracellular polymeric substances, which act a reservoir of water to ensure biological activity. The water accumulated in their biomass can change volume when subjected to freezing and thawing at appropriate temperatures, thus causing mechanical disruption of the building material. In addition, the sealing action of the biofilm may affect water flow through the stone, contributing to water-driven processes such as dissolution and recrystallization. Algal biofilms can also cause mechanical deterioration of the substrate, by loosening stone grains, due to their large changes in volume during repeated cycles of drying and rewetting.

Electron microscopy has shown that these communities are often composed of entangled masses of filaments in intimate contact with the material. Heterotrophic microorganisms are also very common. This is not surprising because the organic matter produced by photosynthesis may be used and metabolized by heterotrophic microorganisms that synthesize their own organic compounds, which may include organic acids, leading finally to salt formation. The heterotrophic microorganisms can live at the expense of either the extracellular organic matter synthesized by living algae (such as mucilages and cell-wall polysaccharides) or their intracellular products after algal cell death and lysis. The association of high counts of bacteria and fungi with algal growths in buildings has led to their being described as "photosynthesis-based microbial communities." Such association has also been described for rocks. In addition, environmental particles (dust, pollen, spores, and oil- and coal-fired particles), material from the substrate (quartz, calcium carbonate, and silicates), and detritus (dead cells, microbial by-products, etc.) may be entrapped within the entangled microbial mass at the material surface, giving rise to complex crusts and patinas which are difficult to eliminate.

## D. Significance

The presence of microorganisms, even in great numbers, on weathered materials in buildings does not necessarily imply that these organisms have caused the damage observed. Despite great scientific effort in recent years to prove the presence of the structural biodeterioration processes already described, their exact contribution to the weathering of building materials is still not fully understood. The coexistence of several types of deterioration processes operating in tandem makes it difficult to assign the decay to only one cause. On the contrary, biological deterioration acts synergistically with chemical and physical deterioration. The biological processes are perhaps the least understood of the processes that damage building materials, and continued research is needed to assess their exact significance.

## III. PAINTINGS AND SCULPTURES

The main factor causing microbial biodeterioration of paintings, sculptures, and other works of art is increased humidity. In many cases, the biodeterioration agents are the same as those described in the previous sections simply because they are growing on the same materials—wood, stone, plaster, etc.—which form the object, at least partially. Obviously, aesthetic biodeterioration is of crucial importance with art objects.

In addition to humidity, the development of microorganisms on painted surfaces is affected by the nature of the materials comprising the support and the paint layers. For example, paint coats on wooden supports become covered with fungal growth faster than coats applied on other materials. Different paint media also show dissimilar susceptibilities to attack by microbes, especially depending on whether or not they provide nutrients for heterotrophic growth. The most susceptible to attack are paint media rich in organic matter, such as casein, egg distemper, emulsion distemper, or linseed oil, whereas paints containing ions of heavy metals, such as lead white, are generally resistant.

Fungi are the microorganisms most commonly found on paintings and painted sculptures. Wooden supports can be attacked by species of soft-rot fungi, such as *Coniophora cerebella* and *Poria vaporaria*. The growth of these fungi often causes physical and aesthetic damage because the destruction of the support is followed by irreversible detachment of paint layers. Growth of species of the genera *Chaetomium*, *Penicillium*, and *Aspergillus* can also cause surface damage of the wooden support. Biodeterioration of paintings on canvas is usually caused by fungi of the genera *Penicillium*, *Aspergillus*, *Cladosporium*, and *Mucor*. Their colonizing usually starts on the reverse side of the paintings and is favored by contact with cold walls. In advanced stages, their hyphae may totally penetrate the paint and outer varnish layers, and the fungi may colonize significant portions of the painted surface. Wall paintings can also be colonized by the same fungal genera when conditions are appropriate for their development, such as high humidity and the presence in the plaster of organic compounds derived from dust or by infiltration of ground-water or by their presence in paint binders. The fungi produce variously colored surface stains which may seriously affect the aesthetic appearance of the paintings. Once formed, these stains are difficult to remove, causing problems to the conservators.

## IV. CULTURAL HERITAGE IN HYPOGEAL SITES

Damage by rot fungi can be important in archeological wood. The form of biodeterioration found in wooden archeological artifacts is strongly dependent on the conditions of preservation in excavated sites. Soft-rot and brown-rot types of degradation have been described for wooden archeological remains present in ancient tombs. Extreme conditions inside tombs, such as dryness, high pH due to surrounding limestone, and restricted oxygen exchange, may favor soft-rot attack rather than the aggressive wood-rotting Basidiomycetes. Under less extreme conditions, the brown-rot type of degradation may develop, leading to extremely fragile objects. Wooden cultural properties from Egyptian tombs dating from 2500 BC have been found to be affected considerably by deterioration due to brown rot.

Cyanobacteria and algae may also colonize the cultural heritage preserved in caves and rock-carved tombs, especially the walls receiving a low irradiance and having a relatively high humidity. Such conditions may lead to the formation of characteristic calcified communities of cyanobacteria composed of filamentous forms, such as *Scytonema*, *Geitleria*, and *Loriella*. Such communities represent a serious threat to mural paintings and fine architectural carvings due to calcite deposition on external zones, forming characteristic white-green coatings on the stone.

Environmental disturbances, such as artificial light sources or pollution created by large numbers of visitors, may also cause the development of algal communities in such hypogeal niches. For example, the invasion of algae in Lascaux caves (France), a unique monument with 15,000-year-old rock paintings and drawings, occurred after their opening to the public, which resulted in the caves being visited by approximately 500–600 persons per day. The invasion of rock drawings by the chlorophyte *Bracteacoccus minor* was controlled quickly using a chemical treatment. Afterwards, the cave had to be closed to the public.

## See Also the Following Articles

BIOCIDES • CONSERVATION OF CULTURAL HERITAGE • TIMBER AND FOREST PRODUCTS

## Bibliography

Allsopp, D., and Seal, K. J. (1986). "Introduction to Biodeterioration." Edward Arnold, London.

Eggins, H. O. W., and Allsopp, D. (1975). Biodeterioration and biodegradation by fungi. *In* "The Filamentous Fungi. Vol. 1: Industrial Mycology" (J. E. Smith and D. R. Berry, Eds.), pp. 301–319. Edward Arnold, London.

Griffin, P. S., Indictor, N., and Koestler, R. J. (1991). The biodeterioration of stone: A review of deterioration mechanisms, conservation case histories, and treatment. *Int. Biodeterioration* **28**, 187–207.

Rose, A. H. (1981). "Microbial Biodeterioration," Economic Microbiology Series, Vol. 6. Academic Press, London.

# *Biofilms and Biofouling*

### Karen T. Elvers[1] and Hilary M. Lappin-Scott

*University of Exeter*

## GLOSSARY

**biofilm**  Complex association or matrix of microorganisms and microbial products attached to a surface.

**biofouling**  Damage caused to a surface by microorganisms attached to a surface.

**consortia**  Spatial grouping of bacterial cells within a biofilm in which different species are physiologically coordinated with each other, often to produce phenomenally efficient chemical transformations.

**planktonic**  Free-floating bacteria living in the aqueous phase and not associated with a biofilm.

**sessile**  Bacteria living within a biofilm.

**BIOFILMS**  are generally described as consisting of the cells of microorganisms immobilized at a substratum, attached to a surface, and frequently embedded in an extracellular polymer matrix of microbial origin. In this context, studies have concentrated on bacterial cells rather than on other microorganisms. Bacteria attach firmly to almost any surface submerged in an aquatic environment or bulk liquid. Immobilized

bacterial cells within a biofilm are called sessile, whereas those free floating in the aquatic environment are called planktonic. The immobilized cells grow and reproduce, with the newly formed cells attaching to each other as well as to the surface. They also produce extracellular polymers, which extend from the cells to form a matrix of fibers. This matrix entraps debris, nutrients, and other micro organisms establishing a biofilm that has a very heterogeneous structure and composition. Although bacteria may attach to surfaces in minutes, biofilms can take hours or days to develop. Biofouling refers to the damage caused by biofilms to surfaces. The combination of growth processes, the production of metabolites, and the physical presence of the biofilm can damage the surface and reduce its efficiency or effectiveness.

Early studies on the significance of bacterial adhesion to surfaces emerged from the work of Claude ZoBell in the 1930s. Since this initial research, it is now known that bacterial adhesion is widespread in the environment and the subject of biofilms constitutes an extensive field within microbiology. In addition, modern biofilm studies have shown that biofouling affects a surprisingly wide range of materials. This article contains examples of biofilms in medical and industrial situations and describes how particular biofilms cause damage and resist treatment.

## I. BIOFILM FORMATION AND DETACHMENT

Many physical, chemical, and biological processes determine biofilm formation. A general description of biofilm formation on a surface begins with the

---

1. Present address: University of Wales Institute.

transportation of molecules and small particles to the surface by molecular diffusion to form a conditioning film. This occurs very rapidly or almost instantaneously on exposure of a surface to an aqueous environment. Its effect is to cause changes in the surface properties, including the acquisition of a small negative surface charge and a decrease in hydrophobicity. The composition of the conditioning film varies depending on the surface type but apparently it contains polysaccharides, glycoproteins, and proteins. It is generally uniform in composition and coverage and is an important influence on the subsequent adsorption of bacteria. The growth phase follows the initial phase of biofilm formation.

Fluid dynamics within the aquatic environment play an important role in determining the transport of bacteria to the surface during the growth phase. Under quiescent flow conditions, bacterial transport is affected by gravitational forces, Brownian motion, or motility. Under laminar flow conditions, bacteria are transported to the surface by diffusion with a significant increase in transport rate if the cells are motile. Under turbulent flow conditions, bacteria are transported to the surface by fluid dynamic forces (inertia, lift, drag, drainage, and downsweeps) which can be enhanced by further increasing turbulence and surface roughness. Furthermore, eddies that develop in turbulent flow are able to propel bacteria to the surface. The Reynolds number, which describes the relative magnitude of inertia to viscous forces, can be used to describe whether a system is laminar or turbulent.

Bacteria approaching the surface are subjected to repulsion forces which must be overcome if they are to adsorb to the surface. The outcome of the forces is described by the Derjaguin and Landau: Verwey and Overbeek theory of colloidal stability. The theory postulates two separation distances from the surface where adhesion can occur. Two- and three-step mechanisms have been proposed for the adhesion process, which results in irreversible adsorption usually by the production of exopolysaccharide (EPS). Development of the biofilm includes further attachment, cell growth, cell division, and EPS production resulting in the formation of distinct microcolonies. Mature biofilms then develop by the attraction of more planktonic bacteria and entrapment of inor-

ganic and organic molecules and microbial products, developing a complex consortia within which there is physiological cooperation between different species. This results in increased heterogeneity and the development of chemical microgradients within the biofilm.

With time, portions of the biofilm detach and biofilm development reaches a plateau or steady state of development with accumulation equaling loss by detachment. Detachment is defined as the loss of components (biomass) from the biofilm matrix to the bulk liquid and is a means of interaction and cell turnover between the planktonic organisms in the liquid phase and the sessile organisms within the biofilm. This interaction can affect the overall species distribution. Detachment occurs by erosion, sloughing, and abrasion. It can be caused by several factors: the action of polymerases from the biofilm organisms, the result of grazing or predator harvesting by protozoa, the effects of substratum texture and surface chemistry, the production of unattached daughter cells through attached cell replication, and the availability of nutrients. Fluid dynamics is also thought to significantly influence detachment, in which an increase in fluid velocity causes an increase in detachment. There are also artificial methods of detachment which aim to control biofilm growth and biofouling, including chemical treatment (chelants, surfactants, and oxidants) and physical treatments (increased fluid velocity, ultrasound, and scrubbing).

## II. EPS AND THE GLYCOCALYX

EPS and glycocalyx are terms used to describe the polysaccharide produced by bacterial cells. EPS refers to one of the major components of biofilms, and glycocalyx refers to the polysaccharide matrix surrounding individual cells. EPS has an important role in biofilm structure and function and has a complex physical and chemical nature. Its functions are mostly protective in nature and this is one of the benefits for bacteria in the sessile state. Because the glycocalyx is the outermost component of bacterial cells, this layer mediates virtually all bacterial associations with surfaces and other cells: It dictates location, juxtaposition, and the eventual success in the ecosystem.

EPS production may be a direct response to selective pressures in the environment and may protect against desiccation (by binding water molecules) and predation by feeding protozoa. It also provides protection against antimicrobial agents, including antibiotics, biocides, and host defense mechanisms. This defense may occur by means of a physical barrier or through aiding the bacteria to evade phagocytosis. Other advantages for bacteria of EPS derive from its polyanionic nature, which confers on the biofilm some ion-exchange properties which assist entrapment and the concentration of nutrients, the removal of toxins, and the exchange of metabolites within the consortia. Finally, the close proximity of cells within the biofilm allows plasmid transfer and an alteration in phenotypical characteristics as a response to changes in the environment.

## III. BIOFILM STRUCTURE

Biofilm structure has been studied using many techniques, including transmission electron microscopy, scanning electron microscopy (SEM), and confocal scanning laser microscopy (CSLM). SEM has been used extensively to study the surface architecture of biofilms. The resulting images reveal an uneven outer surface topography, with the high resolution achieved by this method allowing individual cells to be clearly distinguished among a condensed matrix. Although this technique provides valuable information regarding the nature of biofilms, it is not entirely useful because it is well-known that the dehydration stages of sample preparation for SEM can destroy the EPS matrix. CSLM allows nondestructive *in situ* analysis of hydrated biofilms in combination with a wide range of fluorescent compounds. This technique can be used to form 3-D computer reconstructions of biofilms. These show a variable distribution of biomass with bacteria aggregating at different horizontal and vertical sites, with the highest cell densities at the biofilm base or at the top of the biofilm, forming "mushroom," "cone," or "stacks" shapes. Where biofilms have developed under turbulent conditions, they form additional struc-

tures termed "streamers." CSLM has also shown that biofilms are highly hydrated and that the total biofilm volume is made up of cell clusters, horizontal and vertical interstitial voids, and conduits beneath the clusters. These clusters and channels produce biofilms of varying depth and structure. Species composition has been shown to be an important determining factor in biofilm structure.

Recently, it was suggested that the structural complexity of biofilms is determined by the organisms through signaling molecules. It has been established that a family of diffusible chemical signals (*N*-acyl homoserine lactones) can regulate the production of virulence determinants and secondary metabolites, in suspended cultures, in a cell density-dependent manner. Also known as quorum sensing, it is thought that this may be important for the formation of biofilms which also contain densely packed cells. Evidence based on a pure culture *Pseudomonas aeruginosa* biofilm growing in laminar flow by Davies and coworkers (1998) supports this theory. They reported that *N*-(3-oxododecanoyl)-L-homoserine lactone (OdDHL) was required for the biofilm to develop a complex structure by comparing wild-type biofilms with a Lasl defective mutant (Lasl directs the synthesis of OdDHL). This work illustrates the interest in this field, which has a huge potential for biofilm control. However, since quorum sensing is a concentration-dependent phenomenon, it will be strongly influenced by mass transfer processes. It may be expected that quorum sensing will have a greater significance in diffusion-dominated regions such as those found in large cell clusters or channels when bulk liquid flow is very low.

## IV. MIXED-SPECIES BIOFILMS

Much of the understanding of biofilm development, activity, and physiology is derived from studying single cultures of bacteria, with relatively few studies having been done on mixed cultures. There has been little discussion of the significance of other species within biofilms (e.g., bacterial and algal interactions and fungi), despite the fact that they are excellent colonizers of surfaces. Fungi are able to respond by growth at a surface and fungal hyphal slimes may have many of the functions attributed to bacterial EPS. These functions include the anchorage of mycelium to the substrate, retardation of desiccation, and service as a source of support and nutrition. Biofilms of filamentous fungi have been involved in industrial processes, such as the degradation of aromatic pollutants, biofouling of cooling tower timbers, voice prostheses, and photoprocessors.

## V. TECHNIQUES FOR BIOFILM ANALYSIS

Techniques available to cultivate and study biofilms can be broadly categorized as disruptive and non-disruptive to the biofilm. These include fermentors and sampling devices such as the modified Robbins device (MRD). The MRD contains replaceable surfaces that can be examined (viewed by epifluorescence microscopy and SEM) for viable counts, total carbohydrate, total protein, and metabolic activity. The MRD is versatile in that colonization of different surfaces can be investigated, surface roughness can be controlled, and biocides and antibiotics can be tested.

Chemostats are widely used for studying microorganisms under constant environmental conditions over long periods of time. They can be used to cultivate well-defined two- or three-member mixed cultures or those with even more members. Other reports demonstrate the use of a two-stage chemostat system, with the inoculum grown in the first vessel before being passed to the second. This second or test vessel allows parameters to be changed, e.g., addition of biocide and insertion of coupons of differing materials on which the biofilm develops. Chemostats have also been used in combination with the MRD.

Other biofilm fermentors include the constant depth film fermentor, which allows the biofilm to accumulate to a pre-set depth which can be maintained, and the continuous perfused biofilm fermentor, which allows establishment of a biofilm on the underside of a cellulose membrane perfused with sterile fresh medium.

Microscopic techniques include light, epifluorescence and electron microscopy, CSLM and computer-enhanced microscopy with image analysis, and Nomarski differential contrast microscopy. Epifluorescence is particularly useful when cells are stained with fluorescent dyes such as acridine orange and propidium iodide, which mark nucleic acids, or those that determine metabolic activity, such as rhodamine and 5-cyano-2,3-ditolyl tetrazolium chloride. CSLM can be used in combination with microelectrodes which, depending on their construction, can measure oxygen, pH, and sulfide gradients within cell clusters, voids, and fluorescent latex beads.

Other techniques include the use of continuous-flow cell cultures with image analysis, Fourier transform infrared spectroscopy, nuclear magnetic resonance, atomic force microscopy, and cryosectioning. The data generated from all these techniques have greatly altered the understanding of biofilms in both pure and mixed cultures. They have shown biofilms as being spatially and temporally heterogeneous systems with microscale variations in architecture, chemistry, microgradients, and reactions to antimicrobial agents.

## VI. BIOFILMS AND BIOFOULING IN DIFFERENT ENVIRONMENTS: THEIR CONTROL AND RESISTANCE

The phenotypic plasticity of bacteria allows colonization in a wide variety of environments. Adhering bacterial species are inherently different from their planktonic equivalents. In particular, biofilm bacteria are more resistant to medical and industrial control strategies than their planktonic counterparts. Biofilms may be either beneficial or detrimental for their host systems. The following sections discuss the variety and importance of biofilms and biofouling in the context of medical and industrial systems.

### A. Biofilms in Medical Systems

Biofilms affecting human health can be divided into the following categories:

1. Biofilms formed on human tissue: These biofilms occur in the healthy body, for example, on

teeth, in the digestive tract, and in the female genital tract. They may have a role in prevention of certain infections but can be overgrown by pathogenic microorganisms.

2. Biofilms formed on medical implants within the body.

3. Biofilms formed on surfaces outside the body that may harbor harmful pathogens. Examples of these surfaces include those in water systems that may harbor potentially pathogenic bacteria such as *Legionella* sp. and that consequently may be protected from chlorination. Biofilms have also been found on contact lenses and contact lens storage cases, for which bacteria induce severe eye irritation and inflammation and may play a role in persistence of the organisms.

In all cases, once established, the biofilm's resistance to phagocytosis and antibiotics allows the organism within it to continue living after planktonic organisms in the same environment have been killed by treatment.

Artificial implants are used for the replacement of diseased or damage body parts, e.g., joint or vascular prostheses. Many temporary devices, (e.g., urinary catheters, intravascular catheters, and endotracheal tubes) are inserted into patients for various lengths of time. Many inert materials are used for such devices, including vitallium, titanium, stainless steel, polyethylene, polymethyl methacrylate, silicone rubber polytertrafluorethylene (Teflon), and polyvinyl chloride. All of these can serve as substrata for bacterial biofilms.

A variety of bacteria are involved in the colonization of implants. These include gram-negative organisms (e.g., *Pseudomonas aeruginosa* and *Escherichia coli*) and gram-positive bacteria (e.g., *Staphylococcus aureus* and *S. epidermidis*). The latter, which are normally found on the skin, possess a high degree of adhesiveness to the prosthetic device surface. In the biofilm these species are protected from the effects of antibiotics and they can act as the disseminating center for infection. In addition, biofilm formation can also lead to malfunction of the device and destruction of adjacent tissue. Biofilms have been the cause of significant problems for patients receiving artificial hearts (Jarvik hearts).

In cystic fibrosis, patients' lungs become chronically infected by EPS-producing strains of *P. aeruginosa*. This bacterium has also been found frequently in catheterized patients. The production of large amounts of EPS and copious quantities of mucous by *P. aeruginosa* allows it to cause persistent infections. Isolation of mucoid strains and subsequent subculture results in reversion to non-mucoid colonies. This suggests that the host defense mechanisms must have a selective effect in favor of the mucoid strains. Treatment with antibiotics further selects for the mucoid strains. The mucous and EPS protects *P. aeruginosa* from attack by antibiotics, surfactants, and macrophages. It has been shown that EPS is a large anionic hydrated matrix that can partition charged molecules, preventing them from reaching the bacterial cell.

Silicone is a material that is widely used for tubing, catheters, mammary and testicular implants, and voice prostheses. Voice prostheses become colonized rapidly by mixed biofilms of bacteria and yeasts and these devices must be removed and replaced frequently before infection can be eradicated. It has been shown by SEM that voice prostheses become damaged by the yeast cells, which grow under the silicone surface. Treatment of infections for short-term devices, such as urinary and intravenous catheters, consists of their immediate removal followed by administration of antibiotics to the patient.

Urinary tract infections are most commonly caused by *E. coli*, *Proteus mirabilis*, *Enterococcus*, and *Streptococcus* spp., found in the gastrointestinal tract, and by pathogens directly transmitted through sexual activity. These infections include acute and chronic cystitis, struvite urolithiasis, chronic prostatitis, and catheter-associated infections. Once the microorganisms are established, they adopt the biofilm mode of growth. The bladder resists infection by the periodic passing of urine, which washes out unattached pathogens, and by sloughing of colonized uroepithelial cells on the glycosaminoglycan (GAG) mucous layer. The GAG layer is a very thin cover on the cell epithelium of the bladder that physically shields the bladder from surface pathogens. Catheter-associated infections increase by approximately 10% each day the catheter is in place. The organisms initially colonize the external surfaces, form a biofilm, and ascend into the bladder where the biofilm can act as a source of infection for the bladder and kidneys. Mineralization can also occur, which can reduce the diameter or block the catheter. Frequent replacement of catheters would reduce infections but is not always practical. Methods to control biofilm growth on catheters are being investigated and include the development of materials that block or kill adherent organisms. These methods include altering the hydrophobicity of polymers and the incorporation of disinfectants and antibiotics in the design of the implant.

Surfaces within the mouth become readily colonized with bacterial deposits, forming a biofilm, usually called dental plaque. By attaching to the teeth or dental implants, the biofilm helps to prevent colonization of the mouth by pathogenic bacteria. Although dental plaque forms naturally without good oral hygiene, it can be a source of dental caries or periodontal disease. The attached organisms obtain nutrients from the ingested food, saliva, and gingival crevice fluid found between the teeth and gums: It is thought that most of the nutrients are derived from the host rather than the from the host's diet.

Environmental factors that contribute to plaque formation are an optimum temperature of 35 or 36°C and a neutral pH. The pH can become more acidic when carbohydrates are metabolized or more alkaline during an inflammatory host response. These local changes in pH can lead to shifts in the colonized species. The resident microflora of dental plaque is extremely diverse and consists of gram-positive and -negative bacteria. Few are truly aerobic; most are facultatively or obligately anaerobic. These include *Streptococcus, Neisseria, Actinomyces, Lactobacillus, Corynebacterium,* and *Fusobacterium* species, but there are many others and not all are culturable in the laboratory. Sometimes, a particular species will colonize a preferred habitat in the oral cavity, e.g., *Streptococcus mutans* colonizes the occlusal fissures.

Formation of dental plaque begins by the adsorption of a proteinaceous conditioning film or acquired pellicle which is composed of albumin, lysozyme, glycoproteins, and lipids from saliva and gingival cervicular fluid. The first colonizers are streptococci and actinomycetes, which rapidly divide to form microcolonies that quickly change into a confluent film of varying thickness. Species diversity increases with the attachment of rods and filaments and layering that is attributable to bacterial succession. Unusual combinations of bacteria such as "corn-cobs" (gram-positive filaments covered by cocci), "rosettes" (cocci covered by small rods), or "bristle brushes" (large filaments surrounded by rods) are seen under SEM.

If plaque formation continues undisturbed for weeks, its composition will vary with location on the teeth. Different environmental conditions exist on and between the teeth, resulting in different chemical gradients and shear forces. The bacterial communities are thought to form as a result of short-range specific molecular interactions between the bacterial cell adhesions of primary colonizers and host receptors in the conditioning film, the attachment of secondary colonizers to primary colonizers (coaggregation) and EPS synthesis and growth. Coaggregation has a major role in forming the distinct patterns in plaque.

Dental caries are formed as a result of the localized dissolution of the tooth enamel by acids produced by metabolism of carbohydrates, lowering the pH and favoring the growth of mutans streptococci and lactobacilli. Periodontal diseases occur when the supporting tissues of the teeth are attacked by obligately anaerobic gram-negative rods, filaments, or spiral-shaped bacteria. Prevention of dental plaque is by efficient oral hygiene (brushing and flossing can almost completely prevent plaque-mediated diseases), fluoridization of drinking water, and the addition of antiplaque or antimicrobial agents to toothpastes and mouthwashes.

Biofilms are central to the survival of bacteria when they are attacked by the normal host immune system or antibiotics. Gram-positive and -negative bacteria activate the complement system, with the major components causing this reaction being peptidoglycan and lipopolysaccharide, respectively. Activation of complement would eradicate the serum-sensitive bacteria but may also react to live or dead bacteria or bacterial fragments. Continual production of complement may destroy the tissues. Studies on the immune response to biofilms have concentrated on *P. aeruginosa* and infection in cystic fibrosis patients. It was shown that biofilm-grown *P. aeruginosa* was able to resist complement action. The biofilm bacteria activated the complement system to a lesser extent than did the planktonic bacteria. However, some fragments of the activated complement were deposited on the biofilm contributing to chronic inflammation.

## B. Biofilms in Industrial Systems

Biofilm formation in industries involves the ability of the biofilm to act as a reservoir for potential pathogens and in instances in which the biofilm causes surface damage. The degree of contamination in a system is often measured by planktonic counts that fail to detect the presence of sessile bacteria and this leads to incorrect conclusions regarding the level of pathogens in the system. In the water industry, biofilms form on the pipe surfaces which connect the consumer to the supply. The level of biofilm formation is difficult to monitor in these situations, and levels of coliforms, pseudomonads, and *Flavobacterium* sp., detaching from biofilms, have been reported as being higher than permitted the levels. Treatment with chlorine does not control the problem because the biofilm bacteria are protected from the disinfectant. There is also evidence of accelerated material deterioration (corrosion) due to biofilm accumulation in water distribution pipes.

Excessive biofilm accumulation in porous media, on heat exchanger surfaces, and in storage tanks is responsible for reduced efficiency of heat transfer and reduction of flow rates. Transfer of heat is reduced because the thick surface growth physically prevents an efficient heat exchange between the liquid phase and the cooling surface.

Biofilms on ship hulls consist of diatoms, single-celled algae, and bacteria. This biofilm growth reduces speed in the water and increases fuel consumption. As the biofilm develops, the hull must be physically cleaned, which results in further expense. In an attempt to control this growth, antifouling paints have been used. These are not always effective; although good at preventing colonization of small animals, they do not stop bacterial growth.

Corrosion in marine environments on structures such as oil rigs is a result of biofilms that contain sulfate-reducing or acid-producing bacteria. These micro-organisms create anodes and cathodes on metal surfaces. This unequal distribution of ions causes electrical currents, resulting in metal loss. Ideal anaerobic conditions for the biofouling action of sulfate-reducing bacteria are found around oil rig legs.

Biofilms in the food processing industry may form on food contact and non-contact surfaces. These biofilms may contain food spoilage and pathogenic micro-organisms which affect the quality and safety of the food product by reducing shelf life and increasing the probability of food poisoning. Stainless steel is commonly used as a food contact surface because it is chemically and physiologically stable at a variety of processing temperatures, easy to clean, and has a high resistance to corrosion. Food processing environments provide a variety of conditions that favor the formation of biofilms, e.g., flowing water, suitable attachment surfaces, ample nutrients (although possibly sporadic); and the raw materials or the natural flora providing the inocula, however, these conditions may be extremely varied. Time available for biofilm development is relatively short; for example, the production line may run for a few hours before cleaning. Various preventative and control strategies, such as hygienic plant lay-out and design of equipment, choice of materials, correct use and selection of detergents and disinfectants, coupled with physical methods, can be applied for controlling biofilm formation on food contact surfaces.

Biofilms have been shown to occur in many food environments. In the dairy industry, pasteurization ensures the destruction of pathogens and most vegetative organisms within raw milk. However, heat-resistant organisms and spores survive and may form biofilms that could result in post-pasteurization contamination. Biofilms have been found on gaskets and "O" rings from the pipes within the dairy industry. Pathogens, *Listeria* and *Bacillus* sp., have also been isolated from food contact and environmental surfaces in the dairy industry. Biofilms have been found in pipes of breweries, on rubber seals, conveyor belts, and in waste-water pipes, and in flour mills and malt houses. There is also evidence of microbial adherence to environmental surfaces during poultry processing. This could result in cross-contamination during the slaughter process, which may play and important role in product contamination with *Listeria, Campylobacter,* and *aureus.*

## See Also the Following Articles

ADHESION, BACTERIAL • ORAL MICROBIOLOGY • *PSEUDOMONAS*

## Bibliography

American Society for Microbiology, Biofilm image collection: *http://www.asmusa.org/edusrc/biofilms/index.html.*

Costerton, J. W., Lewandowski, Z., Caldwell, D. E., Korber, D., and Lappin-Scott, H. M. (1995). Microbial biofilms. *Annu. Rev. Microbiol.* **49**, 711–745.

Davies, D., Parsek, M. R., Pearson, J. P., Iglewski, B. H., Costerton, J. W., and Greenburg, E. P. (1998). The involvement of cell-to-cell signals in the development of a bacterial biofilm. *Science* **280**, 295–298.

Lappin-Scott, H. M., and Costerton, J. W. (Eds.) (1995). "Microbial Biofilms." Cambridge Univ. Press, Cambridge, UK.

# Biological Control of Weeds

## Knud Mortensen
*Agriculture and Agri-Food Canada*

I. Classical Biocontrol
II. Inundative Biocontrol

## GLOSSARY

**biocontrol agent** An organism (e.g., insect, nematode, fungus, bacterium, or virus) which has detrimental effects on another pest organism.

**biocontrol of weeds** The deliberate use of biocontrol agents to control unwanted vegetation (weeds).

**classic biocontrol (or inoculative biocontrol)** Introduction and release of an exotic biocontrol agent into an area where it is allowed to establish and become part of the environment. Insects and fungi have been used in this manner for control of introduced weeds.

**inundative biocontrol (or bioherbicides)** Biocontrol agents are increased artificially and applied periodically to a target weed in a similar manner as chemical herbicides. Mainly indigenous fungi (mycoherbicides) have been used in this manner for control of weeds in crops.

**rhizobacteria** Root-colonizing bacteria.

**WEEDS** have caused serious problems in crops since agriculture was introduced and continue to be one of the most yield-reducing factors in agriculture worldwide. Introduced aggressive weed species have invaded and outcompeted native grass vegetation and considerably reduced the grazing value of rangeland in many areas. Competing vegetation has caused serious problems in establishing forest trees, and unwanted vegetation in waterways has caused problems in irrigation systems as well as in recreational areas. Chemical herbicides have been used extensively in agricultural crops and in other situations with success. Recently, the use of chemical herbicides has come under public criticism. Therefore, alternative weed control measures are being sought and biological control is an area in which much attention has been directed in the past three or four decades.

Biocontrol of weeds has been attempted using various approaches and organisms, depending on the situations in which the unwanted vegetation occurs. Two main approaches have been used: classical biocontrol (or inoculative biocontrol) and inundative biocontrol (or bioherbicides). Classical biocontrol is based on the concept that introduced weeds have escaped their natural enemies and, therefore, such weeds have a competitive edge against other vegetation in their new habitat. By collecting natural enemies from the origin of the weed and releasing them into its new area, stress is exerted on the weed, rendering it less competitive and consequently decreasing its population to an acceptable level. Using this approach, weeds have been successfully and cost-effectively controlled with insects in uncultivated rangeland areas as well as in waterways.

Inundative biocontrol is the process in which biocontrol agents are increased artificially and applied periodically to a target weed in a similar manner as chemical herbicides. Mainly indigenous fungal weed pathogens have been used in this approach. In contrast to classical biological control, which has mainly been funded by the public sector, bioherbicides offer an incentive for private industry to become involved because they require mass production of pathogen propagules and special storage and application techniques. Consequently, inundative biocontrol is a more expensive approach and therefore is mostly directed towards control of weeds in intensive cropping situations. In the following sections, an overview of biological control of weeds with microorganisms will be given along with discussion of the constraints and future of weed biocontrol.

## I. CLASSICAL BIOCONTROL

All plant pathogens that cause diseases on weeds, including viruses, bacteria, fungi, and nematodes, can be used in classical biocontrol. Generally, rusts and other fungi capable of self-dissemination by airborne spores, which cause epidemics after initial release, have received the most attention. In a recent review (Watson, 1991) it was reported that 8 exotic plant pathogens have intentionally been released and that 23 have been or are under investigation. A dramatic example of a successful introduction of an exotic plant pathogen is the rust *Puccinia chondrillina* Bub. and Syd. introduced into Australia for control of skeleton weed (*Chondrilla juncea* L.). Skeleton weed was effectively controlled in wheat by up to 79%, resulting in a benefit of approximately $16 million (Australian) annually. This rust was later introduced to the western United States—California, Oregon, Washington, and Idaho—where it has significantly reduced the population of rush skeleton weed. Two other rusts, *Phragmidium violaceum* (Schultz) Winter, introduced into Chile in 1973 and into Australia in 1984 for control of blackberries (*Rubus* spp.), and *Uromycladium tepperianum* (Sacc.) McAlp., a native gall rust on *Acacia saligna* (Labill.) Wendl introduced into South Africa for control of the Port Jackson willow, have proven to be effective. Another fungus, *Entyloma ageratinae* Barretto and Evans (Ustilaginales), was introduced to Hawaii from Jamaica in 1975. In areas favorable to the disease, it reduced populations of hamakua pamakana or mistflower [*Ageratina riparia* (Regel) K & K & R] on the islands Oaha and Maui by 80% within 9 months. This fungus was released on *A. riparia* in South Africa in 1989. By April 1990, the pathogen had spread throughout the weed infestation surrounding the inoculated plants and the plants were severely defoliated.

Several criteria have been proposed for selecting effective and safe biological control agents. The ideal classical biocontrol agent causes severe damage only to the target weed, and will not be a risk to other plant species in the area of introduction. To evaluate their safety to non target native plant species, host range testing has to be conducted.

Because classical biocontrol involves introduction of exotic agents, regulations have to be followed before an organism can be released into a new environment. These regulations vary from country to country. In most countries introduction of biocontrol agents is regulated under "quarantine acts." In addition, Australia also has a "biological control act" designed to deal with conflicts of interest in biocontrol issues. In Canada, introduction of biocontrol agents is regulated under the Plant Protection Act of 1990 and in the United States under the Federal Plants Pest Act of 1957. The United Nations Food and Agricultural Organization developed an "international code" for the import and release of exotic biocontrol agents, which was approved by member states in 1995. Clarified procedures and responsibilities set out in this code have proven helpful in certain developing countries, where biocontrol has not previously been done.

## II. INUNDATIVE BIOCONTROL

Inundative biocontrol involves application of propagules of a microorganism in the same manner as chemical herbicides. The term "bioherbicide" implies that the target weed is killed and thus the causal organisms are plant pathogens. Recent research has shown that microbials in the soil can have a detrimental effect on seed germination and root growth without infecting and causing disease symptoms on the target weeds. Therefore, inundative biocontrol of weeds in this article is separated into two groups: biocontrol with foliar and stem pathogens and biocontrol with soil microbials.

### A. Biocontrol with Foliar and Stem Pathogens

High inoculum concentrations of a plant pathogen sprayed onto its host plant can compensate for the constraints on its epidemic development in nature.

The canopy of plants in a young field crop often creates an excellent microclimate for disease development. A bioherbicide applied at this stage can kill or severely suppress nearly all plants of a target weed. Host specificity is a more important issue for introduced classical biocontrol agents than it is for bioherbicide agents. However, pathogens considered for use as bioherbicides must be sufficiently specific so the crops in which the weed is to be controlled will not be harmed. Bioherbicide agents should not spread beyond the area of application to avoid risk of infection of beneficial plant species, and they do not need to survive the winter to cause epidemics the following year. If these criteria are met, they can be used on weeds that are problematic only in localized areas and have value in other situations (e.g., volunteer crop plants). Several review papers have recently been published on the status of bioherbicides. A comprehensive list of mycoherbicide projects prepared by Charudattan in 1989 showed that 67 different weeds have been or are being investigated using 107 fungal taxa as potential mycoherbicide agents. Charudattan compared this to a similar list by Templeton in 1982 in which 35 weeds were listed under investigation using 67 fungal taxa. This is nearly a doubling in mycoherbicidal activity in only 7 years, and more have been reported since then. To date, four bioherbicides have been registered in North America. *Phytophthora palmivora* (Butler) Butler (Oomycetes), isolated from milkweed vine (*Morrenia odorata* Lindl.), was registered as a bioherbicide (DeVine) in 1981 for control of this weed in citrus groves in Florida and is marketed by Abbott Laboratories (North Chicago, IL). The product, consisting of a liquid suspension of chlamydospores, effectively controls seedling and adult milkweed vine for up to 2 years when applied as a postemergent spray. The market for DeVine is quite small and concentrated in the citrus-growing area of Florida. *Colletotrichum gloeosporioides* (Penz.) Penz. and Sacc. f. sp. *aeschynomene* (Coelomycetes) produced as a dry formulation by The Upjohn Company (Kalamazoo, MI) was sold commercially under the trade name Collego for control of northern jointvetch (*Aeschynomene verginica* (L.) B.S.P. in soybean and rice crops in the United States from 1982 to 1992. Collego was reregistered and sold commercially by Encore Technologies

(Minnetonka, MN) in 1997 and 1998. *Colletotrichum gloeosporioides* f. sp. *malvae* was registered in 1992 under the trade name BioMal by Philom Bios (Saskatoon, Saskatchewan, Canada) for control of round-leaved mallow (*Malva pusilla* Sm.) in field crops in Canada. Due to low market prospects and high production costs, this product has not been sold commercially. Agriculture and Agri-Food Canada has signed an agreement with Encore Technologies for re-registration and commercialization of this fungus. The fourth registered bioherbicide is an endemic rust *Puccinia canaliculata* (Schw.) Lagerh. developed for control of yellow nutsedge (*Cyperus esculentus* L.) using the inundative approach. In 1996, the product was marketed by CCT Corporation (Carlsbad, CA). Between 160 and 200 ha, mostly in Texas and New Mexico, were treated in 1996.

Outside North America, a few bioherbicides have been registered or used on a larger scale. A granular mixture form of *C. gloeosporioides*, isolated from dodder (*Cuscuta* spp.), was developed in China in 1963; it was used as a mycoherbicide under the trade name Lubao No. 1 for control of dodder in China. A formulation of wheat bran colonized with a strain of *C. gloeosporioides* isolated from silky hakea (*Hakea sericea* Schrad.), an invasive shrub in South Africa, had a provisional registration and was used successfully on large-scale field trials in the southwestern Cape Province. However, a limited market resulted in withdrawal of the company involved, and the Plant Protection Research Institute is currently supplying small quantities of the product annually to landowners for the control of silky hakea. Recently, a white-rot basidiomycete fungus, *Cylindrobasidium laeve,* was developed and registered in South Africa to prevent regrowth of stumps of *Acacia* spp. This product, known as "Stumpout," may be used in wattle clearing programs. A bacterium, *Xanthomonas campestris,* was registered as a bioherbicide in Japan in 1997 for control of annual bluegrass (*Poa annua* L.).

## B. Biocontrol with Soil Microbials

Soil bacteria and their influence on weed growth and development have basically been ignored until recently. The soil immediately around the roots (the rhizosphere) frequently has more bacteria and other microorganisms than soil even a few millimeters away from the root. The rhizosphere microbial populations can affect plant nutrition and plant health and have been researched quite intensively in connection with crop development in the past 20 years. Rhizobacteria produce metabolites which have various effects on root and plant development. Some rhizobacteria have been shown to enhance growth and increase yield of plants, and these are referred to as plant growth-promoting rhizobacteria; others negatively affect plant growth and are termed deleterious rhizobacteria (DRB). The DRB are being explored for biocontrol of weeds. DRB have been shown to be host specific in that they show a deleterious effect on one or a few species and no effect, or in some cases an enhancing growth effect, on other plant species. In contrast to bioherbicides using foliar and stem pathogens, which mainly have been directed toward dicotyledonous weeds, by far the greatest efforts with rhizobacteria have been directed toward grassy weeds in cereal crops. Kremer and Kennedy (1996) listed 18 weed species as targets for control with DRB. Nearly all projects have identified *Pseudomonas* spp. as the major group with potential for biocontrol. The most advanced project has used *Pseudomonas fluorescens* for control of downy brome (*Bromus tectorum* L.) in winter wheat; 3 or more years of large-scale field trials have been conducted in this project. A significant reduction in downy brome shoot biomass and seed production, as well as increased winter wheat yield, was shown in field trials in Washington State. Extensive screening of rhizobacteria from western Canadian soils has revealed several isolates that have shown good potential as biocontrol agents for downy brome, green foxtail (*Setaria viridis* L.), and wild oats (*Avena fatua* L.) with little or no effect on cultivated cereals. These examples and others indicate that rhizobacteria have potential in weed control. However, application techniques and delivery systems are critical in attaining a high level of efficacy. Survival and root colonization by bacteria may be affected by many soil factors, including soil water and temperature. Early seed colonization is critical to subsequent root colonization and plant growth inhibition. The microfauna and microflora of the rhizosphere are very rich and dynamic and can be influenced by cultural practices and crop rotations. Thus, it is very important that all these factors be studied so that the biology and ecology of the rhizosphere is better understood in order to increase the efficacy of these biocontrol agents.

## C. Constraints in Inundative Biocontrol

Despite the considerable research on bioherbicides, there are currently only three bioherbicides commercially available in North America and three bioherbicides available in other parts of the world (see Section II.A). Obviously, there are several constraints in the development of commercial bioherbicides which need to be overcome. Bioherbicides need to be fast-acting, predictable, easy to use, and provide a level of weed control comparable to that of chemical herbicides before they will have general acceptance from industry and users. Unfortunately, only few naturally occurring pathogens fulfill these requirements. A detailed paper by Auld and Morin (1995) categorized constraints to the development of commercial herbicides into four areas: biological constraints, environmental constraints, technological constraints, and commercial constraints.

Biological constraints involve host specificity of the agents and variation in resistance to the agent in a plant population. Host specificity is an advantage when a weed is closely related to the crop in which it is to be controlled; however, when many weeds occur in a crop situation, host specificity is a disadvantage and other means of control are necessary. Host specificity may be overcome by mixing different agents to extend the host range of a bioherbicide. The problem of inadequate pathogenicity of an agent may be solved by applying a synergistic chemical herbicide at sublethal dose or perhaps by slightly wounding plants. It might also be possible to increase pathogenicity through genetic engineering or protoplast fusion. The interaction of bioherbicide agents with microorganisms inhabiting the phyllosphere of weeds or leachates from plants might result in competition for nutrients and space or direct antagonism, which could reduce the efficacy of foliar bioherbicides. This area needs more attention in biocontrol.

Environmental factors such as moisture and dew period durations are reported to be the main limiting factors to disease initiation and development. Appropriate timing of inoculum application to take advantage of humidity, dew period, and irrigation in the field can address these limitations. Also, formulations of foliar bioherbicide agents in water-retaining materials are considered a promising approach to make plant pathogens less dependent on available water for initial infection.

Technological challenges involve mass production of viable, infective, and genetically stable propagules (e.g., spores, mycelium fragments, and sclerotia) of a plant pathogen. Spores of three of the four bioherbicides registered in North America are produced in submerged fermentation. This system has been traditionally chosen over solid-substrate fermentation systems because it is cost-effective and is a readily available technology in industrialized countries. Nevertheless, alternative large-scale production methods are required for fungi that do not produce spores well in liquid media. Formulation of a bioherbicide agent is one of the most challenging technological constraints to the development of reliable and efficacious bioherbicides. One of the goals in formulating bioherbicides is to keep the propagules viable and infective for a reasonable length of time, preferably 1 or 2 years. In addition, a formulation should ensure effectiveness and consistent activity of a biocontrol agent. Adjuvants can be added to improve the adhesion and distribution of propagules on the host surface and to enhance spore germination, germ-tube growth, and appressorium formation. Bioherbicides should be formulated for easy delivery into agricultural systems and ideally should be fully compatible with conventional application methods such as a boom sprayer or granular applicator.

Commercial considerations involve market size, production, and registration costs of a bioherbicide agent. The market for a bioherbicide that targets only one weed is quite restricted unless the product is active on an economically important weed that escapes control with traditional methods. The small niche markets of most potential bioherbicides to date have deterred industry from getting involved due to limited opportunities to recover the cost of registration and large-scale production. Powell and Jutsum (1993) estimated that the market for commercial bioherbicides is less than $1 million in the United States and predicted that significant penetration of bioherbicides on the agricultural market will only be achieved if political forces become involved. If the reliability, efficacy, and cost to the users become comparable to those of chemical herbicides in the future, it is predicted that bioherbicides will be favored in the marketplace since they generally have no mammalian toxicity and less impact on the environment. The use of plant pathogens as biocontrol agents is not without risks, and these need to be seriously and thoroughly assessed. Their safety, persistent survival, and potential for genetic change are major concerns to scientists and regulatory bodies. Since bioherbicide products are applied in a similar manner as chemical herbicides, they must be treated as pesticides and thus subject to government regulations. In Canada, microbial pest control agents are regulated under the Canadian Environmental Protection Act. The Pest Management Regulatory Agency under Health Canada deals with registration of microbial pest control agents. In the United States, registration of pesticides including microbial agents is regulated under the U.S. Environmental Protection Agency. Guidelines for registration of naturally occurring microbial pest control agents in Canada and the United States are currently being combined as part of the North American Free Trade Agreement.

Based on the research reported here, biocontrol of weeds with microorganisms has good potential in the future; however, there are challenges that need to be overcome. It is necessary that cross-disciplinary team work be established between plant pathologists, microbiologists, molecular biologists, formulation experts, weed ecologists, and application technologists and agronomists to overcome the challenges of weed biocontrol. Biocontrol should be part of an integrated weed management approach, in which all aspects of crop protection are taken into consideration. We need to know much more about the interaction of microorganisms and plant development before we can fully utilize microbials in agriculture. There is enormous potentials for increasing environmentally sustainable crop production if more is known about utilizing and manipulating what is already present in nature.

## See Also the Following Articles

BIOCIDES • RHIZOSPHERE • RUST FUNGI

## Bibliography

Auld, B. A., and Morin, L. (1995). Constraints in the development of bioherbicides. *Weed Technol.* 9, 638–652.

Boyetchko, S. M. (1996). Impact of soil microorganisms on weed biology and ecology. *Phytoprotection* 77, 41–56.

Bruckart, W. L., Supkoff, D. M., and Yang, S. M. (1996). Indigenous plant pathogens in evaluations of foreign biological control candidates in the United States of America. *In* "Proceedings of the IX International Symposium Biological Control of Weeds, 1996" (V. V. Moran and J. H. Hoffmann, Eds.), pp. 71–77. Cape Town University, South Africa.

Charudattan, R. (1991). The mycoherbicide approach with plant pathogens. *In* "Microbial Control of Weeds" (D. O. TeBeest, Ed.), pp. 24–57. Chapman & Hall, New York.

Green, S., Stewart-Wade, S. M., Boland, G. J., Teshler, M. P., and Liu, S. H. (1998). Formulating microorganisms for biological control of weeds. *In* "Plant–Microbe Interactions and Biological Control" (G. J. Boland and L. D. Kuykendall, Eds.), pp. 249–281. Dekker, New York.

Harris, P. (1991). Invitation paper (C. P. Alexander Fund): Classical biocontrol of weeds: Its definition, selection of effective agents, and administrative–political problems. *Can. Entomol.* 123, 827–849.

Kremer, R. J., and Kennedy, A. C. (1996). Rhizobacteria as biocontrol agents of weeds. *Weed Technol.* 10, 601–609.

McFadyen, R. E. C. (1998). Biological control of weeds. *Annu. Rev. Entomol.* 43, 369–393.

Mortensen, K. (1998). Biological control of weeds using microorganisms. *In* "Plant–Microbe Interactions and Biological Control" (G. J. Boland and L. D. Kuykendall, Eds.), pp. 223–248. Dekker, New York.

Powell, K. E., and Jutsum, A. R. (1993). Technical and commercial aspects of biocontrol products. *Pesticide Sci.* 37, 315–321.

Skipper, H. D., Ogg, A. G., Jr., and Kennedy, A. C. (1996). Root biology of grasses and ecology of rhizobacteria. *Weed Technol.* 10, 610–620.

TeBeest, D. O. (1996). Biological control of weeds with plant pathogens and microbial pesticides. *Adv. Agric.* 56, 115–137.

Templeton, G. E. (1992). Use of *Colletotrichum* strains as mycoherbicides. *In* "*Colletotrichum*: Biology, Pathology and Control" (J. A. Bailey and M. J. Jeger, Eds.), pp. 358–380. CAB International, Wallingford, UK.

Watson, A. K. (1991). The classical approach with plant pathogens. *In* "Microbial Control of Weeds" (D. O. TeBeest, Ed.), pp. 3–23. Chapman & Hall, New York.

# Biological Nitrogen Fixation

### Donald A. Phillips
*University of California, Davis*

### Esperanza Martínez-Romero
*Universidad Nacional Autónoma de México*

## GLOSSARY

**cyanobacteria** Photosynthetic prokaryotes, some species of which can fix nitrogen as both free-living and symbiotic cells; found symbiotically with lower plant taxa.

***Frankia*** Symbiotic, nitrogen-fixing actinomycetes that form root nodules on shrubs and trees which are not legumes.

**nif genes** Bacterial genes required for nitrogen fixation which encode nitrogenase proteins, regulate synthesis of nitrogenase, or are involved in processing nitrogenase.

**nitrogenase** An enzyme complex that catalyzes the conversion of dinitrogen to ammonia; all known nitrogenases contain multiple subunits and metal cofactors. Some bacteria can make alternative nitrogenases when certain metal elements are unavailable.

**Nod factors** Symbiotic signal molecules synthesized in rhizobia by proteins encoded by nodulation genes; all share a similar lipo-chitin structure and have additional chemical substituents that allow the molecule to regulate root nodule formation in particular host legumes at low concentrations.

**nod genes** Rhizobial genes that play a role in root nodule formation; some *nod* genes encode proteins required for synthesizing Nod factors, whereas, others have regulatory functions. Many rhizobia carry *nod* genes on plasmids; the large number of nodulation genes has led to the use of the abbreviations *nol* and *noe* for recently discovered genes.

**rhizobia** A diverse group of nitrogen-fixing bacteria that form symbiotic relationships with certain legume plants; development of the symbiosis requires a series of molecular signals between the plant and bacteria, which results in formation of a plant nodule occupied by the bacteria.

**BIOLOGICAL NITROGEN FIXATION (BNF)** is the enzymatic process by which certain eubacteria and archaebacteria reduce elemental $N_2$ to ammonia. The ammonia is incorporated by other enzymes into cellular protoplasm. BNF is found only in certain prokaryotes, but some of these microorganisms have evolved complex symbiotic associations with particular plants which benefit from the reduced nitrogen.

## I. SIGNIFICANCE OF BIOLOGICAL NITROGEN FIXATION

Nitrogen is required in all biological systems to synthesize proteins, nucleic acids, and other important molecules. Neither plants nor animals can use the vast reservoir of elemental nitrogen (dinitrogen or $N_2$), a gas that comprises nearly 80% of the atmosphere above the earth, but certain taxa of eubacteria and archaebacteria can reduce $N_2$ to ammonia in the biological nitrogen fixation (BNF) process. In ecological terms, the BNF conversion of $N_2$ to ammonia is important for balancing denitrification events in the nitrogen cycle.

Estimates of microbial BNF range from 175 to 335 Tg N/year with more or less equal amounts possibly occurring in oceanic and terrestrial ecosystems (Table I). Terrestrial BNF in the absence of agriculture is approximately 100 Tg N/year, but the estimates of oceanic fixation are less certain. Agricultural uses of rhizobial BNF in legumes contribute 45 Tg N/year, whereas the Haber–Bosch chemical reduction of $N_2$ produces 80 Tg N/year for N fertilizer. Lightening "fixes" $N_2$ to nitrate by oxidation, but this process involves only approximately 3 Tg N/year. Humans also fix 21 Tg N/year by oxidizing $N_2$ to

*TABLE I*
**Estimated Microbial BNF in Various Ecosystems**

| *Ecosystem* | *Tg $N_2$ fixed/year* |
|---|---|
| Agricultural legumes | 45 |
| Nonlegumes | 10 |
| Permanent grassland | 40 |
| Forest and woodland | 40 |
| Total terrestrial | 135 |
| Oceans | 40–200 |
| Total land and sea | 175–335 |

NO during the combustion of coal, petroleum, and natural gas. Thus, total microbial BNF at 175–335 Tg N/year is a dominant component in the nitrogen cycle, compared with the 104 Tg N/year supplied by all forms of non-microbial $N_2$ fixation.

Many genetically diverse eubacteria are capable of BNF. These prokaryotes have diverse life-styles and morphologies, including aerobic, anaerobic, photosynthetic, autotrophic, heterotrophic, single-celled, filamentous, free-living, and symbiotic. In addition to the 54 genera of eubacteria capable of BNF listed in Table II, BNF has been demonstrated with physiological and/or biochemical measurements in several archaebacteria genera. Many other archaebacteria genera contain genes normally associated with BNF and may show the trait under certain conditions. At least 30 genera in 10 families of cyanobacteria also exhibit BNF (Table III). The amounts of nitrogen fixed by these bacteria depends on the environmental conditions encountered by the organisms and can range from trace amounts for free-living soil bacteria to more than 300 kg/ha/year for the rhizobia in some legumes.

*TABLE II*
**Families and Genera of Nitrogen-Fixing Eubacteria, Excluding Cyanobacteria**

| *Family/genus* | *Family/genus* |
|---|---|
| Acetobacteriaceae | Rhizobiaceae |
| *Acetobacter* | *Allorhizobium* |
| Azotobacteraceae | *Azorhizobium* |
| *Azomonas* | *Bradyrhizobium* |
| *Azotobacter* | *Mesorhizobium* |
| *Beijerinckia* | *Rhizobium* |
| *Derxia* | *Sinorhizobium* |
| Bacillaceae | Rhodospirillaceae |
| *Bacillus* | *Rhodobacter* |
| *Clostridium* | *Rhodocyclus* |
| *Desulfotomaculum* | *Rhodopila* |
| Beggiatoaceae | *Rhodomicrobium* |
| *Beggiatoa* | *Rhodopseudomonas* |
| Chlorobiaceae | *Rhodospirillum* |
| *Chlorobium* | Spirillaceae |
| *Chloroherpeton* | *Azospirillum* |
| *Pelodictyon* | *Campylobacter* |
| *Prosthecochloris* | *Herbaspirillum* |
| Chromatiaceae | Streptomycetaceae |
| *Amoebobacter* | *Frankia* |
| *Chromatium* | Thiobacteriaceae |
| *Lamprobacter* | *Thiobacillus* |
| *Thiocapsa* | Vibrionaceae |
| *Thiocystis* | *Vibrio* |
| Ectothiorhodospiraceae | Uncertain families |
| *Ectothiorhodospira* | *Alcaligenes* |
| Enterobacteriaceae | *Ancylobacter* |
| *Citrobacter* | *Azoarcus* |
| *Enterobacter* | *Burkholderia* |
| *Erwinia* | *Desulfobacter* |
| *Klebsiella* | *Desulfovibrio* |
| Methylococcaceae | *Heliobacterium* |
| *Methylococcus* | *Mycoplana* |
| *Methylomonas* | *Propionospira* |
| Pseudomonadaceae | *Xanthobacter* |
| *Pseudomonas* | |

## II. THE BIOLOGICAL NITROGEN FIXATION PROCESS

Dinitrogen, a triple-bonded molecule, has a high activation energy for the reduction reaction involved in converting $N_2$ to ammonia: $3H_2 + N_2 \rightarrow 2NH_3$. To overcome this stability, metal catalysts are used both in the commercial Haber–Bosch process and in the nitrogenase enzyme complex. The high temperatures and pressures used in the Haber–Bosch process are replaced in biological systems with nitrogenase which facilitates dissociation of $N_2$ and transfers reductant to the substrate. The nitrogenase complex uses large amounts of adenosine triphosphate (ATP) as an energy source to drive the reaction at biological

### TABLE III
### Orders and Genera of Cultured Cyanobacteria with Nitrogen-Fixing Species

| Order/genus | Order/genus |
| --- | --- |
| Chroococales | Nostocales |
| *Chroococcus* | *Anabaena* |
| *Cyanothece* | *Anabaenopsis* |
| *Gloeothece* | *Aphanizomenon* |
| *Synechococcus* | *Aulosira* |
| Pleurocapsales | *Calothrix* |
| *Chroococcidiopis* | *Cylindrospermum* |
| *Pleurocapsa* | *Nodularia* |
| *Stanieria* | *Nostoc* |
| *Xenococcus* | *Richelia* |
| Oscillatoriales | *Scytonema* |
| *Lyngbya* | *Tolypothrix* |
| *Microcoleus* | Stigonematales |
| *Oscillatoria* | *Chlorogloeopsis* |
| *Phormidium* | *Fischerella* |
| *Plectonema* | *Mastigocladus* |
| *Pseudanabaena* | |
| *Trichodesmium* | |

temperatures. Nitrogenase is extremely sensitive to elemental oxygen. Both components of the protein are irreversibly inactivated by $O_2$. Nitrogenase in many anaerobic and facultative microorganisms functions without danger of encountering $O_2$, but $N_2$-fixing aerobes generally use $O_2$ to supply ATP from oxidative phosphorylation. For this reason, many specialized mechanisms, which are indicated in connection with specific organisms, have evolved to protect nitrogenase from $O_2$. Thus, the overall success of BNF in a prokaryote depends on the following: (i) a metal-containing nitrogenase enzyme complex, (ii) a source of ATP, (iii) a strong reductant, and (iv) a mechanism for protecting nitrogenase from oxygen.

Studies with nitrogenases purified from heterogeneous eubacteria grown in the presence of molybdenum identified "classical" nitrogenase which was quite similar in all cases studied from 1960 to 1980. In the early 1980s, two alternative (i.e., additional) nitrogenases were found in *Azotobacter vinelandii* cells grown without molybdenum. Evidence sup-

ports the concept that a iron–molybdenum cofactor in the classical nitrogenase is the catalytic site of reduction for $N_2$. The iron–molybdenum cluster is a cofactor in the sense that it can be removed from acid-denatured nitrogenase and used to regenerate an active enzyme in protein isolated from mutant bacteria incapable of synthesizing the iron–molybdenum cluster. The protein containing the iron–molybdenum cofactor is designated as component I and has four subunits with a total molecular weight between 200,000 and 240,000, depending on the species. The second nitrogenase protein, component II, has two identical subunits with a total molecular weight of approximately 60,000, and it contains a different type of iron cluster. Two genes, *nif*D and *nif*K, encode the two heterologous subunits of the component I protein, whereas *nif*H codes for the two subunits of the component II protein. *Azotobacter vinelandii* cells grown without molybdenum use vanadium to make a vanadium–iron cluster in the component I protein, and the two subunits of that protein are encoded by the genes *vnf*D and *vnf*K. A third gene, *vnf*H, codes for an iron-containing protein which serves as an alternative to component II under molybdenum-free conditions. In the absence of both molybdenum and vanadium, *A. vinelandii* cells use a third set of genes, the *anf* genes, to produce a less efficient and less well understood nitrogenase complex containing only iron without either molybdenum or vanadium. One interpretation of these facts suggests that the evolution of three distinct sets of BNF genes in this organism emphasizes the importance of the BNF process. The extent to which other microorganisms make alternative nitrogenases is poorly understood. Although *Azotobacter* has evolved several metal catalysts for reducing nitrogen, more than 30 years of attempts by inorganic chemists have failed to develop new metallic catalysts which decrease the high pressure and temperature requirements in the Haber–Bosch chemical process for producing nitrogen fertilizer.

An interesting characteristic of nitrogenase is that it simultaneously reduces both $N_2$ to form ammonia and protons ($H^+$) to form elemental hydrogen gas ($H_2$). Production of $H_2$ requires ATP and uses at least 25% of the total reductant consumed by the enzyme complex. Hydrogen evolution is viewed as an inefficiency in the system, but no species or mutants that allocate 100% of the electrons flowing through nitrogenase to $N_2$ have been isolated. Thus, many scientists believe that $H_2$ evolution is a necessary function of nitrogenase. Some BNF microorganisms contain a separate enzyme system that recovers a portion of the energy in $H_2$ by oxidizing it to water. Such uptake hydrogenase systems may increase the efficiency of BNF.

Various strategies are used to exclude oxygen from nitrogenase in aerobic bacteria. Facultative organisms fix nitrogen only under anaerobic conditions. Aerobic organisms have a variety of other mechanisms for protecting the enzyme complex from oxygen. Many grow under microaerophilic conditions accomplished by scavenging free oxygen for metabolism or sharing the ecosystem with other organisms that consume excess $O_2$. Evidence indicates that some free-living aerobes such as *Azotobacter* can change the conformation of nitrogenase protein to a less oxygen-sensitive configuration. Photosynthetic aerobes, such as cyanobacteria, often form special thick-walled cells called heterocysts, in which nitrogenase is active and the $O_2$-evolving mechanism in photosynthesis is absent. In other cases cyanobacteria fix $N_2$ without forming heterocysts, and thus they must have other means for protecting nitrogenase from $O_2$. One frequently studied protective mechanism is found in the symbiotic association involving rhizobia and legumes. In the bacteria-filled nodules, which form from plant cells, the plant protein leghemoglobin maintains a suitably low concentration of free oxygen and thus protects rhizobial nitrogenase while permitting oxidative phosphorylation needed to supply ATP in the bacterial cells. Genetic and/or biochemical mechanisms that may restrict oxygen availability in nitrogen-fixing cells of other organisms (e.g., *Frankia* and non-heterocystous cyanobacteria) remain to be proven.

In addition to the limitations to BNF caused by free oxygen, the presence of combined nitrogen, as either ammonia or nitrate, generally inhibits $N_2$ fixation. Genetic mechanisms by which both $O_2$ and combined nitrogen operate have been clarified in several systems. Although the mechanisms for regulation differ in various bacteria, in general terms $O_2$ and combined nitrogen decrease transcription of *nif* genes by affecting either *nif*A expression or the activity of the NifA protein. Despite our understanding of these mechanisms, it currently is impractical to combine BNF with fertilizer nitrogen for crop production.

BNF studies were greatly stimulated by the development of two important techniques for measuring nitrogenase activity. The first production of $^{15}N$ in the 1930s offered scientists a method for proving that organisms were actually reducing $^{15}N_2$. Although this technique required a special mass spectrometer, it was approximately 1000 times more sensitive than the Kjeldahl method used to quantify nitrogen. This advance eliminated erroneous conclusions drawn in some cases when microorganisms grew well in "N-free" media by scavenging trace amounts of nitrogenous contaminants. Thirty years later, the discovery that classical nitrogenase reduces acetylene to ethylene led to the development of an inexpensive and rapid assay which is 1000 times more sensitive than $^{15}N_2$ techniques. Despite several disadvantages associated with the fact that acetylene is a physiologically less natural compound than $^{15}N_2$, ecologists and agronomists have used the acetylene reduction assay to measure BNF under many different conditions.

## III. FREE-LIVING, NITROGEN-FIXING BACTERIA

Most of the 54 different genera of eubacteria (excluding the cyanobacteria) that are listed in Table II, as well as nearly all 29 genera of cyanobacteria listed in Table III, fix nitrogen in a free-living rather than symbiotic state. However, BNF was first discovered in symbiotic rhizobia because the presence or absence of rhizobia caused relatively massive changes in plant growth which were easily correlated to nitrogen availability using the analytical chemistry methods in the 1880s. Winogradsky demonstrated BNF by free-living *Clostridium pasteurianum* in 1893, and in 1901 Beijerinck detected BNF in *Azotobacter*. Discovery of other free-living, nitrogen-fixing bacteria lagged until $^{15}N$ isotope techniques and the acetylene-reduction assay became common. Thus, many of the free-living, nitrogen-fixing bacteria listed in *Bergey's*

*Manual of Systematic Bacteriology* have been described in the past 35 years using these techniques. Free-living nitrogen fixers are not necessarily photoautotrophic, and thus in some cases it is difficult to separate them from "associative" nitrogen fixers discussed in Section IV. In general, they can be separated by the concept that, although many free-living nitrogen fixers often occur on plant roots in which associative nitrogen fixers are also found, their overall requirements are less restrictive than those of the associative nitrogen fixers because they are also found in many other environments in which carbon substrates are available.

The quantity of nitrogen fixed by free-living nitrogen fixers is probably quite small. Russian workers estimated that *Clostridium* or *Azotobacter* cells may fix 0.3 kg N/ha/year, which is 1000 times less than the amount fixed in a good rhizobia–legume association. Associative organisms such as *Azospirillum* have been estimated to fix from trace amounts (i.e., 0.3 kg N/ha) to 36 kg N/ha. In most cases, the ecologically relevant limitation on BNF is probably the amount of carbon substrate available. For example, although *Clostridium* requires an anaerobic environment for BNF, this requirement is much easier to meet than the availability of sufficient carbon substrates. If carbon substrates are available, *Clostridium* probably can depend on other microorganisms to deplete oxygen concentrations in certain microsites to a level at which clostridia can use the carbon source to fix nitrogen and grow.

Cyanobacteria listed in Table III use their photosynthetic capability to overcome the need for a carbon source faced by most other nitrogen fixers. Estimates of annual BNF in free-living cyanobacteria range from approximately 5 to 80 kg N/ha/year. The highest values are from tropical aqueous environments, such as rice paddies, in which decay of these organisms can supply agronomically significant amounts of N for the rice plants. BNF by cyanobacteria has been a major contributor to eutrophication of lakes in many regions of the world, but the causative factor is usually an excess of phosphate supplied by human activities. Many cyanobacteria occur as both free-living and symbiotic organisms. In many cases, the identity of cyanobacteria in a symbiosis has been disputed because attempts to isolate and reinfect with the microorganism have failed. For this reason, only those genera of cyanobacteria claimed to show BNF in pure culture have been listed in Table III.

Specialized cells known as heterocysts are the site of BNF in cyanobacteria. The heterocysts contain nitrogenase and have a greatly modified photosynthetic apparatus which cannot fix $CO_2$ or evolve $O_2$ but still generates ATP by photophosphorylation. This modification, coupled with the thickened walls in heterocysts which decrease $O_2$ diffusion into the cell, makes heterocysts much better suited for fixing $N_2$ than the adjacent vegetative cells. As a result, photosynthesis and nitrogen fixation occur in different cells, and thus nitrogenase is protected from excess oxygen.

## IV. ASSOCIATIVE NITROGEN-FIXING BACTERIA

Some BNF bacteria found frequently on the roots of certain plants are termed "associative" nitrogen-fixing bacteria. This type of plant–microbe interaction has been documented most often on the roots of grasses such as wheat, corn, sorghum, and sugarcane, which have been selected for their high rates of photosynthesis and growth. Generally, such plants exude large amounts of carbon substrates from the roots, and the associative bacteria use these as a source of energy for growth and BNF. The major associative $N_2$-fixing systems documented in the literature are summarized in Table IV. *In vitro* studies show that many of these bacteria can achieve high rates of $N_2$ fixation under optimum conditions. However, estimates of *in vivo* BNF are extremely variable and give rise to a recurring question as to whether or not energy substrates in the rhizosphere are sufficient to support growth and high levels of BNF by these associative bacteria. Nitrogenase is repressed by fixed nitrogen; therefore, in the presence of nitrogen fertilizer BNF by free-living or associative bacteria generally is diminished. Thus, a mixed BNF–nitrogen fertilizer system would work best under field conditions if the organisms were genetically altered to allow nitrogenase expression when fixed nitrogen is present.

### TABLE IV
#### The Major Associative Nitrogen-Fixing Bacteria

| Plant species | Known associates |
|---|---|
| Rice (*Oryza sativa*) | *Achromobacteri, Azospirillum, Burkholderia* |
| Sugarcane (*Saccharum* spp.) | *Acetobacter, Azospirillum, Azotobacter, Bacillus, Beijerinckia, Burkholderia, Derxia, Herbaspirillum, Klebsiella* |
| Pearl millet and sorghum (*Pennisetum purpureum*) | *Azospirillum, Bacillus, Klebsiella, Azotobacter, Derxia, Pantoea, Herbaspirillum* |
| Maize (*Zea mays*) | *Azospirillum lipoferum, Azotobacter vinelandii* |
| Coffee (*Coffea arabica*) | *Acetobacter* |
| *Paspalum notatum* var. *batatais* | *Azotobacter paspali* |
| *Panicum maximum* | *Azospirillum lipoferum* |
| *Cynodon dactylon* | *Azospirillum lipoferum* |
| *Digitaria decumbens* | *Azospirillum lipoferum* |
| *Pennisetum purpureum* | *Azospirillum lipoferum* |
| *Spartina alterniflora* Loisel | *Campylobacter* |
| Kallar grass (*Leptochloa fusca*) | *Azoarcus, Enterobacter, Klebsiella, Beijerinckia, Azospirillum* |
| Wheat (*Triticum* spp.) | *Bacillus polymyxa, Rhizobium leguminosarum* bv. *trifolii* |

Some type of special relationship undoubtedly facilitates root colonization by associative BNF bacteria, but little is known about this process. For example, a specific host plant may stimulate a positive chemotaxis, trigger some specialized adhesion, or induce a particularly strong growth response in the associative bacteria with unidentified regulatory molecules. The documented result of these poorly understood events is that a large proportion of the bacteria colonizing the root can belong to one species and thus be viewed as "associated" with that host plant. The ultimate evolutionary product of such associations may be symbioses such as those formed by rhizobia and *Frankia*. As a result of increased interest in endophytic bacteria, additional cases in which microorganisms containing *nif* genes establish special associative relationships internally in plants have been found. Some of these bacteria may occupy space between plant cells. Others have been isolated from within the xylem cells, which conduct water in plants. How such bacteria infect the xylem is unknown.

It is often difficult to prove unequivocally that associative BNF bacteria contribute fixed nitrogen to the host plant. The best documentation for such cases requires use of the mass isotope $^{15}$N and control bacteria which have been mutated in the *nif* genes to eliminate any BNF. The problem with drawing a conclusion that particular bacteria benefit a host plant through nitrogen supplied through BNF is the fact that many root-associated bacteria, and also possibly endophytes, promote plant growth by other mechanisms. If bacteria stimulate root growth in a plant, more soil nitrogen will be available to the plant, and the end result is the same as if the bacteria had supplied the nitrogen through BNF. This phenomenon probably has been studied more in *Azospirillum* than in any other associative nitrogen-fixing bacteria. Although *Azospirillum* cells definitely can fix nitrogen, they also can induce dense growths of root hairs which increase the surface area for absorption of soil nitrogen. Thus, grasses associated with *Azospirillum* often grow better than sterile controls, but the striking effect is not necessarily a result of BNF. Estimates of BNF in associative symbioses grown under field conditions have been calculated with several methods, and they support claims that *Azospirillum* in association with various grasses (*Pennisetum americanum, Panicum maximum,* and *Digitaria decumbens*) and unknown associates with sugarcane fix approximately 40 and 150–170 kg N/ha/year, respectively.

## V. SYMBIOTIC NITROGEN-FIXING BACTERIA

Three groups of nitrogen-fixing eubacteria establish symbiotic associations with plants: (i) heterocystous cyanobacteria that occupy tissues in many diverse plant hosts ranging from liverworts (*Anthoceros*) to ferns (*Azolla*), cycads, and a dicot (*Gunnera*); (ii) filamentous *Frankia* actinomycetes, which form root nodules with many woody non-legume plants, including alder (*Alnus*) trees and antelope bush (*Purshia*); and (iii) rhizobia which form nodules on many legumes and one non-legume (*Parasponia*).

## A. Cyanobacteria

Cyanobacteria form symbioses with more diverse hosts than any other $N_2$-fixing microorganisms. Although rhizobia and *Frankia* associate with highly evolved plants, cyanobacteria favor more primitive plants. Cyanobacteria also join with fungi to form lichens, associations in which the fungal tissues protect the cyanobacteria from drying while the bacterial cells photosynthesize and, in some cases, fix $N_2$. At least one cyanobacterium, *Nostoc,* forms symbioses with many different plant taxa.

Symbiotic cyanobacteria often fix much larger amounts of nitrogen than free-living cells. One of the most productive cyanobacterial symbioses is that involving *Anabaena* and the small water fern *Azolla. Anabaena* is found in most *Azolla* plants as an endophyte in special leaf cavities wherever the fern grows, from the tropics to subtropics and even temperate regions of the world. Whereas free-living cyanobacteria probably never fix more than 80 kg N/ha annually, the *Anabaena*–*Azolla* symbiosis can reduce three times that amount if three sequential crops are grown during the same year in tropical rice production systems. Under such conditions, however, the water fern is the only crop that can be grown on the site. Thus, in Southeast Asia, where this practice developed, it is more common to alternate rice and *Azolla* or to grow *Azolla* on one site and incorporate it into the soil as a green manure on another site.

*Anabaena* cells fixing $N_2$ in the *Azolla* leaf cavity show several traits that are quite different from those displayed by free-living cyanobacteria. First, there is a much higher frequency of the $N_2$-fixing heterocysts in the cyanobacteria under symbiotic conditions. Second, *Anabaena* cells release the fixed N as ammonia within the *Azolla* leaf cavity, whereas free-living *Anabaena* cells use newly fixed N for their own growth. Finally, BNF in symbiotic *Anabaena* cells is less susceptible to inhibition by nitrogen fertilizer than in free-living cells. These facts have led to considerable interest in growing the *Anabaena*–*Azolla* symbiosis as a companion crop with rice in many

parts of the world. This practice is used successfully to reduce nitrogen fertilizer inputs for those areas where rice yields are not maximized, but the higher-producing U.S. growers who optimize all other crop inputs have not been able to supply enough N from *Anabaena*–*Azolla* using this method to support maximum rice yields.

Much less is known about cyanobacterial symbioses with plants other than *Azolla.* In general, these associations involve cyanobacteria that occupy normal morphological structures in the host plant, such as leaf cavities, rather than modified structures such as nodules produced by rhizobia or *Frankia.* Only in the case of cycad roots is infection followed by notable morphological changes.

## B. Frankia

The actinomycete *Frankia* forms $N_2$-fixing root nodules on the 23 genera of dicotyledonous plants listed in Table V. These genera contain 277 species in eight families. Older taxonomic analyses distinguished no pattern among these largely temperate, woody host plants, but molecular analyses of the small subunit of ribulose bisphosphate carboxylase show strong similarities and a possible relationship to legumes. *Purshia* species are harvested for firewood and serve as an important rangeland forage crop in several parts of the world. *Casuarina* is an important timber species in the Far East. On the basis of molecular analyses, some individual *Alnus* plants are claimed to be among the largest organisms in the world because many shoots are connected to the same root system. *Frankia* supplies the reduced nitrogen that allows these plants to grow vigorously in N-depleted soil.

*Frankia* symbionts differ from other BNF prokaryotes in that they are multicellular and differentiated. In pure culture, *Frankia* isolates grow very slowly as microaerophilic, mesophilic, heterotrophic organisms, usually with septate hyphae that develop sporangia. Isolates vary morphologically and nutritionally. Most strains can fix dinitrogen in pure culture, and *nif* genes are highly conserved. Protein studies show that *Frankia* nitrogenase closely resembles that of other nitrogen-fixing bacteria, but specialized cells termed "vesicles" are the site of $N_2$ fixa-

### TABLE V
### Distribution of *Frankia* BNF Symbioses among Host Plant Families and Genera

| Plant family | Genus | No. nodulated species |
|---|---|---|
| Betulaceae | *Alnus* | 42 |
| Casuarinaceae | *Allocasuarina* | 58 |
| | *Casuarina* | 18 |
| | *Gymnostoma* | 18 |
| Coriariaceae | *Coriaria* | 16 |
| Datiscaceae | *Datisca* | 2 |
| Elaeagnaceae | *Elaeagnus* | 35 |
| | *Hippophaë* | 2 |
| | *Shepherdia* | 2 |
| Myricaceae | *Comptonia* | 1 |
| | *Myrica* | 28 |
| Rhamnaceae | *Ceanothus* | 31 |
| | *Colletia* | 3 |
| | *Discaria* | 5 |
| | *Kentrothamnus* | 1 |
| | *Retanilla* | 1 |
| | *Talguenea* | 1 |
| | *Trevoa* | 2 |
| Rosaceae | *Cercocarpus* | 4 |
| | *Chamaebatia* | 1 |
| | *Cowania* | 1 |
| | *Dryas* | 3 |
| | *Purshia* | 2 |

tion. *Frankia* cells are gram-positive, but unlike other gram-positive bacteria *Frankia* has a discontinuous membranous layer.

The first reproducible demonstration that *Frankia* cells could be isolated, grown in pure culture, and reinoculated to form root nodules was reported in 1978. Various groups have used these techniques to isolate *Frankia* from many of the plants indicated in Table V. Molecular methods for taxonomy such as DNA/DNA homology have demonstrated considerable genetic diversity among these isolates, but no species designations are widely accepted in *Frankia*. In those cases in which infection of the host plant has been studied, two general pathways have been observed: through root hairs and via intercellular penetration. These modes of entry are analogous to infections in rhizobial symbioses with legumes, but no nucleotide sequences similar to rhizobial nodula-

tion genes have been found in hybridization studies. *Frankia* isolates routinely show infective specificities for particular host plant species, but there is no evidence for molecules analogous to the Nod factors identified from rhizobia (see below). Nodules have been found only on roots, and each nodule lobe has an internal anatomy similar to that of a lateral root. There are fewer studies of biochemical and genetic traits in *Frankia* than those of rhizobia for several reasons, including the fact that Koch's postulates were fulfilled 90 years later in *Frankia*. Even today, conditions required for culturing some *Frankia* strains outside root nodules have still not been defined.

Actinorhizal plants nodulated by *Frankia* often are found on soils very low in N. In fact, *Dryas drummondii* is a classic pioneer plant on soils forming where glaciers have recently exposed rock surfaces. Individual *Frankia* symbioses probably fix as much $N_2$ as those reported for comparable rhizobial symbioses with woody legumes, but few data are available for BNF by large populations of actinorhizal plants.

### C. The *Rhizobium*–Legume Symbiosis

Legumes traditionally have been classified as one family of flowering plants with three subfamilies: Mimosoideae, Caesalpinoideae, and Papilionoideae. Rhizobia form symbioses with most species in the Mimosoideae and Papilionoideae, but only approximately 30% of the species in the Caesalpinoideae establish BNF associations with rhizobia. In the past, rhizobia were known to form symbioses only in root nodules. During the past decade, however, it has become apparent that a few legumes, primarily those growing in very moist condition have stem nodules. Only one nonlegume is known to form a nitrogen-fixing association with rhizobia. The existence of nitrogen-fixing root nodules on the tropical plant genus *Parasponia* in the Ulmaceae (elm) family proves that plant genes required for BNF symbioses are not restricted to legumes and offers hope for the eventual establishment or discovery of other nonlegume rhizobial symbioses. It is conceivable, and perhaps probable, that rhizobial symbioses will be identified in additional nonlegumes as scientists search

### TABLE VI
### Typical Amounts of BNF in Grain Legumes

| Plant | BNF (kg N/ha/year) |
|---|---|
| Cool-season crops | |
| Faba bean (*Vicia faba*) | 50–140 |
| Lupin (*Lupinus* spp.) | 50–250 |
| Pea (*Pisum sativum*) | 120–185 |
| Warm-season crops | |
| Green gram (*Phaseolus aureus*) | 100–200 |
| Soybean (*Glycine max*) | 100–250 |

more extensively for these beneficial associations in the future.

Nitrogen fertilizers produce dramatic increases in plant growth under agricultural conditions, but they are expensive and often pollute groundwater or surface streams with nitrate. These problems with traditional nitrogen fertilization practices have stimulated numerous measurements of BNF in legumes. Under agronomic conditions, legumes can obtain large total amounts, and proportions, of their nitrogen requirements from rhizobial BNF. BNF values measured in various grain and forage legumes are shown in Tables VI and VII. These amounts are reduced dramatically if significant nitrogen is supplied by microbial nitri-

### TABLE VII
### Typical Amounts of BNF in Forage Legumes

| Plant | BNF (kg N/ha/year) |
|---|---|
| Temperate forages | |
| Alfalfa (*Medicago sativa*) | 100–300 |
| Subclover (*Trifolium subterraneum*) | 40–200 |
| Vetch (*Vicia sativa*) | 100 |
| White clover (*Trifolium repens*) | 54–200 |
| Tropical forages | |
| *Centrosema* spp. | 70–250 |
| *Desmodium* spp. | 50–300 |
| Leucaena (*Leucaena leucocephala*)— browse tree | 100–200 |
| Kudzu (*Pueraria* spp.) | 100 |
| Stylo (*Stylosanthes* spp.) | 80–160 |

fication of organic material in soils. Fertilizer nitrogen also suppresses BNF, and for many years knowledgeable agronomists throughout the world have recommended that the proper rhizobia, rather than fertilizer nitrogen, should be used with legumes. This form of sustainable agriculture is not a modern invention. Romans were aware that legumes could improve soil quality, but the importance of bacteria for this process was first demonstrated in 1888 by the German plant physiologists Hellriegal and Wilfarth.

One misconception about rhizobial BNF in legumes deserves attention. Legumes have learned a mechanism that forces rhizobial cells to excrete ammonia formed from $N_2$ reduction. The legumes use this ammonia from bacteria to synthesize amino acids. Although root exudates contain traces of amino acids, healthy legumes do not normally excrete significant amounts of the fixed nitrogen into the soil. The concept that legumes "improve" soil, which is often attributed to Roman agriculturalists, is based on the fact that legumes eventually decompose and thus release proteins and amino acids which form substrates for microbial nitrification. Thus, nitrogen from BNF is eventually released from legumes if growers do not harvest and remove it for their own purposes.

"Root nodule bacteria," as the rhizobia are often called, originally were characterized by the host plant from which they were isolated. Although many rhizobia form root nodules on only a few genera of legumes, others nodulate a wide range of different genera. Today, we know this trait of host specificity is controlled to a large extent by molecular signals called Nod factors, and the custom of creating taxonomic classifications of rhizobia according to their normal host legume has been discontinued. The most recent taxonomic groupings of rhizobia are shown in Table VIII. This extensive list of new organisms is rapidly being modified as a result of two factors. First, during the past decade microbiologists have found new rhizobial symbionts by examining host legumes not previously analyzed. These scientists used the classical technique of isolating bacteria from plant nodules together with modern methods of detecting $N_2$ fixation, such as acetylene reduction. Second, as the bacteria in these nodules were characterized with modern molecular techniques, it became

***TABLE VIII***
**Current Taxonomic Classification of the Rhizobia**

| Recognized genus | Recognized species | Representative plant host |
| --- | --- | --- |
| Allorhizobium | A. undicola | Neptunia natans |
| Azorhizobium | A. caulinodans | Sesbania rostrata |
| Bradyrhizobium | B. elkanii | Soybean |
| | B. Liaoningense | Soybean |
| | B. japonicum | Soybean |
| Mesorhizobium | M. amorphae | Amorpha fruticosa |
| | M. ciceri | Cicer arietinum |
| | M. huakuii | Astragalus |
| | M. loti | Lotus |
| | M. mediterraneum | Cicer arietinum |
| | M. plurifarium | Acacia, Leucaena |
| | M. tianshanense | Glycyrrhiza, Sophora, Glycine |
| Rhizobium | R. etli | Phaseolus vulgaris |
| | R. galegae | Galega |
| | R. gallicum | Phaseolus vulgaris |
| | R. giardinii[a] | Phaseolus vulgaris |
| | R. hainanense | Stylosanthes, Centrosema, Desmodium, Tephrosia |
| | R. huautlense | Sesbania herbacea |
| | R. leguminosarum | Vicia, Trifolium, Phaseolus vulgaris |
| | R. mongolense | Medicago ruthenica, Phaseolus vulgaris |
| | R. tropici | Phaseolus vulgaris, Leucaena |
| (Sino)rhizobium | S. fredii | Soybean |
| | S. meliloti | Medicago santiva |
| | S. saheli | Sesbania |
| | S. terangae | Sesbania, Acacia |
| | S. medicae | Medicago spp. |

[a] This branch is the least related to *Rhizobium* and may become a new genus.

obvious that older classifications did not reflect the genetic relationships among the known rhizobia. Some physiological and genetic characteristics of various rhizobial genera are listed in Table IX.

In the 1980s, it was discovered that many tropical plants in the genera *Aeschynomene, Sesbania, Neptunia,* and *Discolobium* form stem nodules which are occupied by $N_2$-fixing rhizobia. The stem nodules are actually associated closely with dormant meristematic tissues that can form adventitious lateral roots; thus, the phenomenon is not as bizarre as it first seems. Plants forming stem nodules are aquatic legumes that normally grow in areas where water levels fluctuate to different heights on the stem and possibly induce the formation of adventitious roots. Stem nodules on some herbaceous *Aeschynomene* plants appear green, and tests have shown that rhizobia forming such nodules synthesize bacteriochlorophyll a. Recently, these rhizobia, conditionally classified as *Bradyrhizobium*, have been shown to contain 16S rRNA genes that are closely related to *Blastobacter denitrificans, Afipia felis,* and *Rhodopseudomonas palustris*.

The discovery of so many new rhizobial symbioses has stimulated debate on their evolution. The monophyletic origin of legumes contrasts with the polyphyletic origin of their symbiotic rhizobia. The polyphyletic origin of rhizobia means that not a single bacterial group but rather separate groups of bacteria, probably with different origins, evolved the capacity to establish symbioses. Although many molecular genetic markers differ among rhizobia, the similarity of nitrogen fixation and nodulation genes among these groups of bacteria suggests that a lateral transfer of these genes occurred. The most likely mechanism for such a lateral movement of genes would involve the transfer of a plasmid carrying them. Large pieces of DNA, including symbiotic genes, move naturally among *Mesorhizobium loti* cells in soils, and such events may reflect how symbioses evolved in rhizobia.

One of the more remarkable stories in both microbiology and plant biology was the discovery during the past decade of powerful signals that facilitate molecular communication between legumes and rhizobia. The compounds are involved in root colonization, infection, and root nodule formation. Conclusions from these experiments are based on a broad intellectual foundation that includes the use of defined bacterial mutants, modern analytical chemistry, and studies of biological diversity in both bacteria and plants. These findings are relevant for BNF because rhizobia express and use *nif* genes most actively in legume nodules.

**TABLE IX**
**Characteristics of Rhizobia**

| Trait | Rhizobium and Sinorhizobium | Mesorhizobium | Bradyrhizobium |
|---|---|---|---|
| Generation time | <6 hr | 5–15 hr | >6 hr |
| Carbohydrate substrate | Pentoses, hexoses, mono-, di-, trisaccharides | Mono-, disaccharides | Pentoses and hexoses only |
| Flagella type | Peritrichous | Polar or subpolar and peritrichous | Subpolar |
| Symbiotic gene location | Plasmid | Plasmids or chromosome | Chromosome only |
| Nitrogen-fixing gene organization | *nif*H, -D, and -K in same operon | ND[a] | *nif*D, -K, and -H in separate operons |
| Intrinsic antibiotic resistance | Low | ND | High |

[a] ND, not determined.

## 1. Rhizobial Nitrogen Fixation

Proteins encoded by the *nif*HDK genes in rhizobia are similar to those found in other bacteria. However, these genes show quite different patterns of localization in various rhizobia. At one extreme, in *Rhizobium* and *Sinorhizobium*, *nif*HDK occurs as a single operon, whereas at the other extreme, in *Bradyrhizobium*, *nif*H, *nif*D, and *nif*K are located in separate operons. As in other nitrogen-fixing bacteria, transcription of the *nif*HDK genes in rhizobia is regulated by both oxygen and combined nitrogen in the form of ammonia and nitrate. Rhizobia, however, clearly differ from other nitrogen-fixing bacteria in the sense that under symbiotic conditions they do not use the reduced nitrogen for growth but rather excrete it directly as ammonia or, in one case, as alanine. The precise genetic controls of these events remain to be defined, and they may show somewhat more complexity than in other bacteria because the plant is a controlling factor through its synthesis of the leghemoglobin protein for transporting oxygen and its incorporation of ammonia excreted by rhizobia in root nodules. Although many rhizobia express *nif* genes under microaerophilic conditions in the laboratory, it is generally believed that relatively little BNF can be attributed to rhizobia existing outside the plant because the availability of carbon substrates usually limits growth of rhizobia in soil.

Synthesis of the leghemoglobin protein offers an intriguing example of how completely two symbiotic organisms can integrate their functions. Leghemoglobin, a legume nodule protein involved in transferring oxygen to the nitrogen-fixing rhizobia, is located outside the rhizobial cells. It is composed of apoprotein subunits and a hemoprotein prosthetic group. Genetic and biochemical evidence indicates that legumes, as well as many nonlegumes, contain genes encoding the apoproteins, whereas rhizobia synthesize the heme cofactor.

Rhizobia require a continuing supply of carbon substrates from the host plant cell. A major portion, possibly all, of the carbon is transferred into rhizobial cells as dicarboxylic acids. This conclusion is based on the fact that rhizobia mutated in *d*icarboxylic acid *t*ransport (*dct*) genes are unable to take up and thus utilize succinate, fumarate, and malate in pure culture and fail to fix nitrogen in root nodules. The operon responsible for dicarboxylic acid transport contains three genes—*dct*A, *dct*B, and *dct*D. The DctA protein is the structural transporter, whereas DctB senses the presence of dicarboxylic acids and DctD functions as a regulator in a typical two-component system that responds to environmental stimuli.

Based on the fundamental understanding of genes important for nitrogen fixation, genetically altered rhizobia that show increased BNF have been constructed. For example, supplying extra copies of the *dct*ABD operon and the regulatory *nif*A gene to *S.*

*meliloti* produced a strain that increased alfalfa yield significantly (3.8%) in field tests. Although this seems like a small improvement, it is typical of the increase in forage which is used to justify the release of a new alfalfa variety, and these bacteria are currently being sold in commercial inoculants.

## 2. Nodule Formation by Rhizobia

Root nodule formation by rhizobia depends on the presence of nodulation genes. Nodulation genes are defined as being rhizobial genes that play a role in nodulation or which are coordinately regulated with such genes. These genetic loci are often referred to as *nod* genes; however, with the discovery of increasingly more genes, the list of names in this series has been extended in chronological order of discovery from *nod* to *nol* and finally to *noe* genes using subsequent letters in the word *nodule*. Homologous nodulation genes in different rhizobia have the same name. Nodulation genes show quite different patterns of localization in various rhizobia. At one extreme, in *Rhizobium* and *Sinorhizobium*, all *nod* genes are localized on plasmids; at the other extreme, in *Bradyrhizobium*, symbiotic genes are found only on the chromosome. An intermediate pattern is found in *Mesorhizobium* in which *nod* genes occur either on plasmids or in the chromosome in various species. Early work established that some nodulation genes are conserved in all rhizobia, whereas others are found in only a few species or strains. These groups were characterized as common or host-specific nodulation genes, respectively. Some nodulation genes play a regulatory role, and many nodulation genes contain a conserved promoter sequence called the *nod* box, which permits coordinate regulation. The *syr*M gene, a *nod*D homolog, was identified as a symbiotic regulator, which influences both exopolysaccharide synthesis and nodulation gene regulation.

The regulation and function of nodulation genes offers a fascinating example of how fundamental microbiology studies can address important questions being asked for other organisms. These investigations were prompted by the simple observation that not all rhizobia formed nodules on all legumes. Initially, it was expected that this example of specificity would be explained by a single factor, but as data accumu-

lated it became apparent that at least two levels of regulation are involved in determining interactions between rhizobia and legumes.

One level of regulation involves plant signal molecules that control transcription of rhizobial nodulation genes. Examples of alfalfa signals that function as transcriptional regulators in *S. meliloti* are shown in Fig. 1. Legumes release many flavonoid inducers of nodulation genes in root exudates. Alfalfa releases other flavonoid inducers and additional signal molecules, such as stachydrine and trigonelline, from seeds during germination when the root, the seed, and rhizobia are all in very close proximity. The most powerful of these molecules, the methoxychalcone released by alfalfa roots, induces nodulation genes to a half-maximum transcription rate at concentrations as low as 1 n*M*. Rhizobia have evolved regulatory circuits, generally involving NodD proteins, whose sensitivities are inversely related to the amount of the molecule released from the legume. Thus, in *S. meliloti* the NodD1 protein is quite sensitive to methoxychalcone, which is released at very low levels by roots, but the NodD2 protein requires much higher concentrations of the betaines which are present in large amounts on alfalfa seeds. Some black bean seeds release large amounts of anthocyanins, which induce nodulation genes in *Rhizobium etli*. Another class of inducer molecules, the C-4 aldonic acids, which includes erythronic and tetronic acids, are released from *Lupinus* seeds and induce nodulation genes in several rhizobia. The NodD reg-

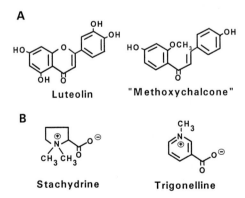

***Fig. 1.*** Representative plant molecules inducing rhizobial *nod* genes. Both flavonoids (A) and non-flavonoids (B) from alfalfa induce *nod* genes in *Sinorhizobium meliloti*.

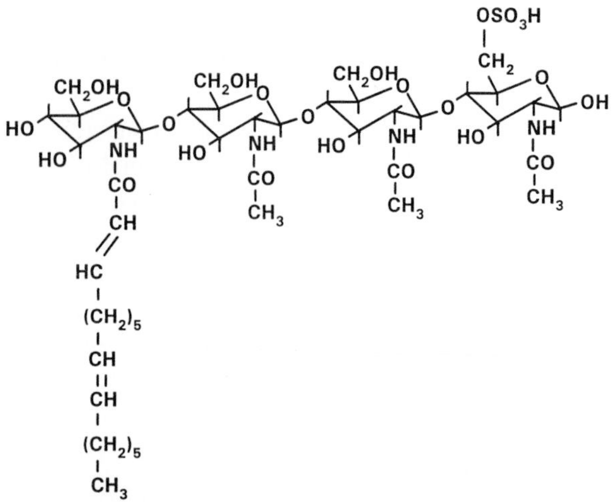

**Fig. 2.** A Nod factor produced by *Sinorhizobium meliloti* which allows the bacteria to infect alfalfa. *Rhizobium leguminosarum* bv. *viciae* produces an identical molecule lacking the sulfate group which allows it to infect vetch plants but not alfalfa.

ulatory proteins in rhizobia interact in a poorly defined manner with inducer molecules from an appropriate host plant and induce transcription of the nodulation genes required to synthesize a host-specific Nod factor. Although a certain amount of host specificity results from this interaction, many legumes nodulated by different rhizobia release some of the same nodulation gene inducers, and many NodD proteins are activated by inducers released from non-host plants. Thus, the induction of transcription in nodulation genes is not the only mechanism controlling rhizobial specificity.

A second level of signals affecting *Rhizobium–legume* interactions involves the Nod factors synthesized by rhizobia. One Nod factor synthesized by *S. meliloti* is shown in Fig. 2. All known Nod factors have a chitin-like backbone attached to a fatty acid. However, legumes do not respond with equal sensitivity to all Nod factors. A preferred legume will usually respond to lower concentrations of Nod factors produced by rhizobia that normally form root nodules on that plant species. Some of this specificity is determined by the position and number of double bonds in the fatty acid portion of the Nod factor, but small moieties or "decorations" on the carbohydrate part of the molecule also play an important

role. Thus, if the sulfate group on the Nod factor in Fig. 1 is removed, the Nod factor is converted from one specific for alfalfa to one that affects vetch and pea plants.

The effects of Nod factors on legumes are surprisingly varied, and they are induced by concentrations in the pico- to nanomolar range. The plant response that was used to isolate and identify Nod factors is the root hair curling response which occurs during normal rhizobial infection. Later it was shown that Nod factors can affect many fundamental genetic and biochemical events in the normal host legume. These responses include induction of cortical cell divisions in the root, reorientation of the cell cytoskeletons required for root nodule formation, and induction of plants genes involved in synthesizing flavonoids. Some of these responses are involved in root nodule formation, but others may reflect primitive responses more typically found in plant–pathogen interactions. Some workers suggest that rhizobia evolved Nod factors because these molecules interact with the most fundamental regulatory systems in plant cells. For this reason, many scientists are using Nod factors as reagents in experiments designed to determine how plants regulate growth and development of root nodules and possibly other organs.

In summary, because of interest in the *Rhizobium–legume* symbiosis during the past 20 years there is a remarkable collection of new organismic and molecular facts that have important effects throughout microbiology and related fields. For example, most of the plasmid vectors used for transferring genes among gram-negative bacteria were derived from work on *nif* and *nod* genes in rhizobia. Also, as noted previously, Nod factors are being used to define plant growth and development. Finally, the maturation of rhizobial genetics has produced, in the case of *S. meliloti,* an organism that serves as a credible model for many other important but less well understood soil microorganisms.

## See Also the Following Articles

## Bibliography

Dilworth, M. J., and Glenn, A. R. (Eds.) (1991). "Biology

and Biochemistry of Nitrogen Fixation." Elsevier, Amsterdam.

Elmerich, C., Kondorosi, A., and Newton, W. E. (Eds.) (1998). "Nitrogen Fixation for the 21st Century." Kluwer, Dordrecht.

Legocki, A., Bothe, H., and Pühler, A. (Eds.) (1997). "Biological Fixation of Nitrogen for Ecology and Sustainable Agriculture." Springer, Berlin.

Spaink, H. P., Kondorosi, A., and Hooykaas, P. J. J. (Eds.) (1998). "Rhizobiaceae." Kluwer, Dordrecht.

Stacey, G., Burris, R., and Evans, H. J. (Eds.) (1992). "Biological Nitrogen Fixation." Chapman & Hall, New York.

# Biological Warfare

## James A. Poupard and Linda A. Miller

*SmithKline Beecham Pharmaceuticals*

## GLOSSARY

**biological warfare** Use of microorganisms, such as bacteria, fungi, viruses, and rickettsiae, to produce death or disease in humans, animals, or plants. The use of toxins to produce death or disease is often included under the heading of BWR (U.S. Army definition, included in U.S. Army report to the Senate Committee on Human Resources, 1977).

**biological weapons** Living organisms, whatever their nature, which are intended to cause disease or death in man, animals, or plants and which depend for their effects on their ability to multiply in the person, animal, or plant attacked [United Nations definition, included in the report of the secretary general titled "Chemical and Bacteriological (Biological) Weapons and the Effects of Their Possible Use," 1969].

**genetic engineering** Methods by which the genomes of plants, animals, and microorganisms are manipulated: includes but is not limited to recombinant DNA technology.

**recombinant DNA technology** Techniques in which different pieces of DNA are spliced together and inserted into vectors such as bacteria or yeast.

**toxin weapon(s)** Any poisonous substance, whatever its origin or method of production, which can be produced by a living organism, or any poisonous isomer, homolog, or derivative of such a substance (U.S. Arms Control and Disarmament Agency definition, proposed on August 20, 1980).

**THE MOST GENERAL CONCEPT OF BIOLOGICAL WARFARE** involves the use of any biological agent as a weapon directed against humans, animals, or crops with the intent to kill, injure, or create a sense of havoc against a target population. This agent could be in the form of a viable organism or a metabolic product of that organism, such as a toxin. This article will focus on the use of viable biological agents because many of the concepts relating to the use of toxins are associated more with chemical warfare. The use of viable organisms or viruses involves complex issues that relate to containment. Once such agents are released, even in relatively small numbers, the focus of release has the potential to enlarge to a wider population due to the ability of the viable agent to proliferate while spreading from one susceptible host to another.

## I. INTRODUCTION

As the twentieth century draws to a close three events mark significant alterations in the concept of biological warfare (BW): the end of the Cold War, the open threat of using BW agents in the Gulf War, and the realization that the developed world is quite susceptible to attack by radical terrorists employing BW agents. These events mark major changes in the concept of BW and transform the subject from one which was once limited to the realm of political and military policy makers to one that must be considered by a wide range of urban disaster planners, public health officials, and the general public. BW is a complex subject that is difficult to understand without a basic knowledge of a long and convoluted history.

BW can be traced to ancient times and has evolved into more sophisticated forms with the maturation of the science of bacteriology and microbiology. It is important to understand the history of the subject because often there are preconceived notions of BW that are not based on facts or involve concepts related more to chemical rather than biological warfare. Many of the contemporary issues relating to BW deal with Third World conflicts, terrorist groups, or nonconventional warfare. An understanding of these issues is important because many of the long-standing international treaties and conventions on BW were formulated either in an atmosphere of international conflict or during the Cold War period of international relations. Many of the classic issues have undergone significant alteration by recent events. The issue of BW is intimately bound to such concepts as offensive versus defensive research or the need for secrecy and national security. It is obvious that BW will continue to demand the attention of contemporary students of microbiology and a wide range of specialists during the twenty-first century.

## II. HISTORICAL REVIEW

### A. 300 BC to 1925

Many early civilizations employed a crude method of warfare that could be considered BW as early as 300 BC when the Greeks polluted the wells and drinking water supplies of their enemies with the corpses of animals. Later, the Romans and Persians used these same tactics. All armies and centers of civilization need palatable water to function, and it is clear that well pollution was an effective and calculated method for gaining advantage in warfare. In 1155 at a battle in Tortona, Italy, Barbarossa broadened the scope of BW by using the bodies of dead soldiers as well as animals to pollute wells. Evidence indicates that well poisoning was a common tactic throughout the classical, medieval, and Renaissance periods. In modern times, this method has been employed as late as 1863 during the Civil War by General Johnson, who used the bodies of sheep and pigs to pollute drinking water at Vicksburg.

Catapults and siege machines in medieval warfare were a new technology for delivering biological entities. In 1422 at the siege of Carolstein, catapults were used to project diseased bodies over walled fortifications, creating fear and confusion among the people under siege. The use of catapults as weapons was well established by the medieval period, and projecting diseased bodies over walls was an effective strategy employed by besieging armies. The siege of a well-fortified position could last for months or years, and it was necessary for those outside the walls to use whatever means available to cause disease and chaos within the fortification. This technique became commonplace, and numerous classical tapestries and works of art depict diseased bodies or the heads of captured soldiers being catapulted over fortified structures.

In 1763, BW took a significant turn from the crude use of diseased corpses to the introduction of a specific disease, smallpox, as a weapon in the North American Indian wars. It was common knowledge at the time that the Native American population was particularly susceptible to smallpox, and the disease may have beeen used as a weapon in earlier conflicts between European settlers and Native Americans. In the spring of 1763, Sir Jeffrey Amherst, the British commander-in-chief in North America, believed the western frontier, which ran from Pennsylvania to Detroit, was secure, but the situation deteriorated rapidly during the next several months. The Indians in western Pennsylvania were becoming particularly aggressive in the area near Fort Pitt (Pittsburgh). It became apparent that unless the situation was resolved, western Pennsylvania would be deserted and Fort Pitt isolated. On June 23, 1763, Colonel Henry Bouquet, the ranking officer for the Pennsylvania frontier, wrote to Amherst, describing the difficulties Captain Ecuyer was having holding the besieged Fort Pitt. These difficulties included an outbreak of smallpox among Ecuyer's troops. In his reply to Bouquet, Amherst suggested that smallpox be sent among the Indians to reduce their numbers. This well-documented suggestion is significant because it clearly implies the intentional use of smallpox as a weapon. Bouquet responded to Amherst's suggestion by stating that he would use blankets to spread the disease.

Evidence indicates that Amherst and Bouquet were

not alone in their plan to use BW against the Indians. While they were developing a plan of action, Captain Ecuyer reported in his journal that he had given two blankets and handkerchiefs from the garrison smallpox hospital to hostile chiefs with the hope that the disease would spread. It appears that Ecuyer was acting on his own and did not need persuasion to use whatever means necessary to preserve the Pennsylvania frontier. Evidence also shows that the French used smallpox as a weapon in their conflicts with the native population.

Smallpox also played a role in the American Revolutionary War, but the tactics were defensive rather than offensive: British troops were vaccinated against smallpox, but the rebelling American colonists were not. This protection from disease gave the British an advantage for several years, until Washington ordered vaccination of all American troops.

It is clear that by the eighteenth century BW had become disease oriented, even though the causative agents and mechanisms for preventing the spread of diseases were largely unknown. The development of the science of bacteriology in the nineteenth and early twentieth centuries considerably expanded the scope of potential BW agents. In 1915, Germany was accused of using cholera in Italy and plague in St. Petersburg. Evidence shows that Germany used glanders and anthrax to infect horses and cattle, respectively, in Bucharest in 1916 and employed similar tactics to infect 4500 mules in Mesopotamia the next year. Germany issued official denials of these accusations. Although there apparently was no large-scale battlefield use of BW in World War I, numerous allegations of German use of BW were made in the years following the war. Britain accused Germany of dropping plague bombs, and the French claimed the Germans had dropped disease-laden toys and candy in Romania. Germany denied the accusations.

Although chemical warfare was far more important than BW in World War I, the general awareness of the potential of biological weapons led the delegates to the Geneva Convention to include BW agents in the 1925 Protocol for the Prohibition of the Use in War of Asphyxiating, Poisonous or Other Gases, and of Bacteriological Methods of Warfare. The significance of the treaty will be discussed in Section III.

## B. 1925–1990

The tense political atmosphere of the period following the 1925 Geneva Protocol and the lack of provisions to deter biological weapons research had the effect of undermining the treaty. The Soviet Union opened a BW research facility north of the Caspian Sea in 1929; the United Kingdom and Japan initiated BW research programs in 1934. The Japanese program was particularly ambitious and included experiments on human subjects prior to and during World War II.

Two factors were significant in mobilizing governments to initiate BW research programs: (i) continuing accusations regarding BW and (ii) the commitment of resources for BW research by several national adversaries, thus creating insecurity among governments. The presence of BW research laboratories in nations that were traditional or potential adversaries reinforced this insecurity. Thus, despite the Geneva Protocol, it was politically unwise for governments to ignore the threat of BW, and the result was increasingly sophisticated biological weapons.

In 1941, the United States and Canada joined other nations and formed national programs of BW research and development. Camp Detrick (now Fort Detrick) became operational as the center for U.S. BW research in 1943, and in 1947 President Truman withdrew the Geneva Protocol from Senate consideration, citing current issues such as the lack of verification mechanisms that invalidated the underlying principles of the treaty. However, there was no widespread use of BW in a battlefield setting during World War II. BW research, however, continued at an intense pace during and after the war. By the end of the decade, the United States, the United Kingdom, and Canada were conducting collaborative experiments involving the release of microorganisms from ships in the Caribbean. In 1950, the U.S. Navy conducted open-air experiments in Norfolk, Virginia, and the U.S. Army conducted a series of airborne microbial dispersals over San Francisco using *Bacillus globigii*, *Serratia marcescens*, and inert particles.

Not surprisingly, the intense pace of BW research led to new accusations of BW use, most notably by China and North Korea against the United States during the Korean War. In 1956, the United States changed its policy of "defensive use only" to include possible deployment of biological weapons in situations other than retaliation. During the 1960s, all branches of the U.S. military had active BW programs, and additional open-air dissemination experiments with stimulants were conducted in the New York City subway system. By 1969, however, the U.S. military concluded that BW had little tactical value in battlefield situations, and since it was believed that nuclear weapons dominated the strategic equation the United States would be unlikely to need or use BW. Thus, President Nixon announced that the United States would unilaterally renounce BW and eliminate stockpiles of biological weapons. This decision marked a turning point in the history of BW: Once the U.S. government made it clear it did not consider biological weapons a critical weapon system, the door was opened for negotiation of a strong international treaty against BW.

Once military strategists had discounted the value of BW, an attitude of openness and compromise on BW issues took hold, leading to the 1972 Convention on the Prohibition of the Development, Production and Stockpiling of Bacteriological (Biological) and Toxin Weapons and on Their Destruction (see Section III). The parties to the 1972 convention agreed to destroy or convert to peaceful use all organisms, toxins, equipment, and delivery systems. Following the signing of the 1972 treaty, the U.S. government generated much publicity about its compliance activities, inviting journalists to witness destruction of biological weapons stockpiles.

The problem of treaty verification beleaguered the 1972 convention. Press reports accusing the Soviet Union of violating the treaty appeared as early as 1975. When an outbreak of anthrax was reported in Sverdlovsk, Soviet Union, in 1979, the United States claimed it was caused by an incident at a nearby Soviet biological defense laboratory that had released anthrax spores into the surrounding community. The Soviet government denied this allegation, claiming the outbreak was caused by contaminated black market meat.

BW continued to be discussed in the public media throughout the 1980s. In 1981, reports describing the American "cover-up" of Japanese BW experiments on prisoners of war began to surface in the public and scientific literature. In 1982, *The Wall Street Journal* published a series of articles on Soviet genetic engineering programs that raised many questions about the scope of Soviet BW activities. The environmental effects of testing biological agents at Dugway Proving Grounds in Utah received considerable press attention in 1988, leading to a debate over the need for such a facility.

The 1980s also were characterized by debate over larger issues relating to BW. A public debate in 1986 considered the possible role of biological weapons in terrorism. Scientific and professional societies, which had avoided discussing BW for many years, began considering both specific issues, such as Department of Defense support for biological research, and more general issues, such as adopting ethical codes or guidelines for their members.

## C. 1990 and Contemporary Developments

The last decade of the twentieth century witnessed three significant events that will have long-term effects on developing policies relating to BW. The first event was the demise of the Soviet Union. Most U.S. defensive research was directed to counter potential use by the Soviet Union. As the wall of Soviet secrecy eroded during the 1990s the extent of the Soviet BW program became apparent. There is international concern that many unemployed BW researchers will find work as advisors for developing countries that view BW as a rational defense strategy, especially those countries without nuclear capability or those without restrictive laws against radical terrorist groups. This is an ongoing issue without readily apparent solutions.

The second major event was the Gulf War. The open threat by the Iraqi military to use BW agents raised serious concerns and changed attitudes about BW. The plans for Operation Desert Storm included provisions for protective equipment and prophylactic administration of antibiotics or vaccines to protect against potential biological weapons. Many of the critics of the U.S. Biological Defense Research Program (BDRP) were now asking why the country was not better prepared to protect its troops against biological attack. Fortunately, BW was not used during the Gulf War, but the threat of its use provided several significant lessons. Although there was considerable concern that genetic engineering would produce new, specialized biological weapons, most experts predicted that "classical" BW agents, such as anthrax and botulism, would pose the most serious threats to combat troops in Operation Desert Storm. Efforts by the United Nations after the war to initiate inspection programs demonstrated the difficulty of verifying the presence of production facilities for BW agents; these difficulties highlight the need for verification protocols for the BW convention. Verification and treaty compliance are major contemporary BW issues. Following the Gulf War the extent of the intense Iraq BW research programs demonstrated the inadequacy of all estimates and post war verification procedures of Iraq BW capacity.

The third significant contemporary development is the realization that urban centers and public facilities are vulnerable to attack by terrorists employing BW agents. Local and national governments are now realizing the extent of this vulnerability and are taking early measures to formulate policies to address these issues. Much work remains to be accomplished in this area.

## III. INTERNATIONAL TREATIES

### A. The 1925 Geneva Protocol

The 1925 Geneva Protocol was the first international treaty to place restrictions on BW. The Geneva Protocol followed a series of international agreements that were designed to prohibit the use in war of weapons that inflict or prolong unnecessary suffering of combatants or civilians. The St. Petersburg Declaration of 1868 and the International Declarations Concerning the Laws and Customs of War, which was signed in Brussels in 1874, condemned the use of weapons that caused useless suffering. Two major international conferences were held at the Hague in 1899 and 1907. These conferences resulted in declarations regarding the humanitarian conduct of war. The conference regulations forbid nations from using poison, treacherously wounding enemies, or using munitions that would cause unnecessary suffering. The so-called Hague Conventions

also prohibited the use of projectiles to diffuse asphyxiating or deleterious gases. The Hague Conventions still provide much of the definitive law of war as it exists today.

The Hague Conventions did not specifically mention BW, due in part to the lack of scientific understanding of the cause of infectious diseases at that time. The conventions have, however, been cited as an initial source of the customary international laws that prohibit unnecessary suffering of combatants and civilians in war. Although biological weapons have been defended as humanitarian weapons on the grounds that many biological weapons are incapacitating but not lethal, there are also biological weapons that cause a slow and painful death. It can be argued, therefore, that the Hague Conventions helped to set the tone of international agreements on laws of war that led to the 1925 Geneva Protocol.

The 1925 Geneva Protocol, formally called the Prohibition of the Use in War of Asphyxiating, Poisonous or Other Gases, and of Bacteriological Methods of Warfare, was opened for signature on June 17, 1925 in Geneva. More than 100 nations signed and ratified the protocol, including all members of the Warsaw Pact and North Atlantic Treaty Organization (NATO). The 1925 Geneva Protocol was initially designed to prevent the use in war of chemical weapons; however, the protocol was extended to include a prohibition on the use of bacteriological methods of warfare. The Geneva Protocol distinguishes between parties and nonparties by explicitly stating that the terms of the treaty apply only to confrontations in which all combatants are parties and when a given situation constitutes a "war." In addition, many nations ratified the Geneva Protocol with the reservation that they would use biological weapons in retaliation against a biological weapons attack. This resulted in the recognition of the Geneva Protocol as a "no first-use" treaty.

### B. The 1972 Biological Warfare Convention

International agreements governing BW have been strengthened by the 1972 BW convention, which is officially called the 1972 Convention on the Prohibition of the Development, Production and Stockpiling of Bacteriological (Biological) and Toxin Weapons and on Their Destruction. The convention was signed simultaneously in 1972 in Washington, London, and Moscow and entered into force in 1975. The preamble to the 1972 BW convention states the determination of the parties to the treaty to progress toward general and complete disarmament, including the prohibition and elimination of all types of weapons of mass destruction. This statement places the convention in the wider setting of international goals of complete disarmament. The 1972 BW convention is also seen as a first step toward chemical weapons disarmament.

The 1972 BW convention explicitly builds on the Geneva Protocol by reaffirming the prohibition of the use of BW in war. The preamble, although not legally binding, asserts that the goal of the convention is to completely exclude the possibility of biological agents and toxins being used as weapons and states that such use would be repugnant to the conscience of humankind. The authors of the 1972 convention, therefore, invoked societal attitudes as justification for the existence of the treaty.

The 1972 BW convention evolved, in part, from a process of constant reevaluation of the Geneva Protocol. From 1954 to the present, the United Nations has periodically considered the prohibition of chemical and biological weapons. The Eighteen-Nation Conference of the Committee on Disarmament, which in 1978 became the Forty-Nation Committee on Disarmament, began talks in 1968 to ban chemical weapons. At that time, chemical, toxin, and biological weapons were being considered together in an attempt to develop a comprehensive disarmament agreement. However, difficulties in reaching agreements on chemical warfare led to a series of separate negotiations that covered only BW and toxin weapons. The negotiations resulted in the drafting of the 1972 BW convention.

The 1972 BW convention consists of a preamble followed by 15 articles. Article I forms the basic treaty obligation. Parties agree never in any circumstance to develop, produce, stockpile, or otherwise acquire or retain the following:

1. Microbial or other biological agents, or toxins whatever their origin or method of production, of types and in quantities that have no justification for prophylactic, protective, or other peaceful purposes.

2. Weapons, equipment, or means of delivery designed to use such agents or toxins for hostile purposes or in armed conflict.

Article II requires each party to destroy, or divert to peaceful purposes, all agents, toxins, equipment, and delivery systems that are prohibited in Article I and are under the jurisdiction or control of the party. It also forbids nations from transferring, directly or indirectly, materials specified in Article I and prohibits nations from encouraging, assisting, or inducing any state, group of states, or international organizations from manufacturing or acquiring the material listed in Article I. There is no specific mention of subnational groups, such as terrorist organizations, in the treaty.

Articles IV requires each party to the convention to take any measures to ensure compliance with the terms of the treaty. Article IV has been interpreted by some states as the formulation of civil legislation or regulations to ensure adherence to the convention. This civil legislation could regulate activities by individuals, government agencies, universities, or corporate groups.

Articles V–VII specify procedures for pursuing allegations of noncompliance with the 1972 BW convention. The United Nations plays an integral part in all the procedures for investigating allegations of noncompliance. According to Article VI, parties may lodge a complaint with the Security Council of the United Nations if a breach of the treaty is suspected. All parties must cooperate with investigations that may be initiated by the Security Council. Article VII requires all parties to provide assistance or support to any party that the Security Council determines has been exposed to danger as a result of violation of the convention. Articles VII–IX are general statements for obligations of the parties signing the protocol. Article X gives the parties the right to participate in the fullest possible exchange of equipment, materials, and scientific or technological information of the use of bacteriological (biological) agents and toxins for peaceful purposes. Article XI allows parties to propose amendments to the convention. The amendments only apply to those states that accept them and enter into force after a majority of the states' parties to the convention have agreed to accept and be governed by the amendment.

Article XII requires that a conference be held 5 years after the entry into force of the BW convention. Article XIV states that the 1972 BW convention is of unlimited duration. A state party to the treaty is given the right to withdraw from the treaty if it decides that extraordinary events, related to the subject matter of the convention, have jeopardized the supreme interests of the country. This article also opens the convention to all nations for signature. Nations that did not sign the convention before its entry into force may accede to it at any time.

## C. Review Conferences

The 1972 convention contained a stipulation that a conference be held in Geneva 5 years after the terms of the convention entered into force. The purpose of the conference was to review the operation of the convention and to ensure that the purposes of the convention were being realized. The review was to take into account any new scientific and technological developments that were relevant to the convention. The first review conference was held in Geneva in 1980. Several points contained in the original convention were clarified at this conference. The second review conference was held in 1986, and a third was held in 1991. There is general agreement that these conferences and the one that followed serve a definite function in solving contemporary problems that need clarification based on changing events and have made significant contributions in keeping the 1972 convention relevant to the needs of a changing world situation.

## D. Additional U.S. Laws and Acts

The following U.S. laws have been enacted since 1989 that impact on BW:

- Biological Weapons and Anti-Terrorist Act (1989): established as a federal crime the development, manufacture, transfer, or possession of any biological agent, toxin, or delivery system for use as a weapon.

- Chemical and Biological Weapons Control Act (1991): places sanctions on companies that knowingly export goods or technologies relating to biological weapons to designated prohibited nations.
- The Defense Against Weapons of Mass Destruction Act (1996): designed to enhance federal, state and local emergency response capabilities to deal with terrorist incidents.
- Antiterrorism and Effective Death Penalty Act (1996): established as a criminal act any threat or attempt to develop BW or DNA technology to create new pathogens or make more virulent forms of existing organisms.
- Centers for Disease Control (CDC) Hazardous Biological Agent Regulation (1997): identification of infective agents that pose a significant risk to public health. Some of the organisms regulated by the CDC are listed in Table I.

## IV. CURRENT RESEARCH PROGRAMS

Biological weapons research in the United States is under the direction of the BDRP, headquartered at Fort Detrick, Maryland. In accordance with official U.S. policy, the BDRP is solely defensive in nature, with the goal of providing methods of detection for, and protective measures against, biological agents that could be used as weapons against U.S. forces by hostile states or individuals.

Current U.S. policy stems from the 1969 declaration made by President Nixon that confined the U.S. BW program to research on biological defense such as immunization and measures of controlling and preventing the spread of disease. Henry Kissinger further clarified the U.S. BW policy in 1970 by stating that the United States biological program will be confined to research and development for defensive purposes only. This did not preclude research into those offensive aspects of biological agents necessary to determine what defensive measures are required.

The BDRP expanded significantly in the 1980s in an apparent response to alleged treaty violations and perceived offensive BW capabilities of the Soviet Union. These perceptions were espoused primarily by representatives of the Reagan administration and

***TABLE I***
**Representative Organisms Regulated by the CDC**

| Bacteria | Viruses |
|---|---|
| *Bacillus anthracis* | Crimean–Congo hemorrhagic fever virus |
| *Brucella abortus, melitensis, suis* | Eastern equine encephalitis virus |
| *Burkholderia mallei, pseudomallei* | Ebola virus |
| *Clostridium botulinum* | Equine morbillivirus |
| *Francisella tularensis* | Lassa fever virus |
| *Yersinia pestis* | Marburg virus |
| | Rift Valley fever virus |
| | South American hemorrhagic fever viruses |
| Rickettsiae | Tick-borne encephalitis complex virus |
| *Coxiella burnetii* | Variola (smallpox) major virus |
| *Rickettsia prowazekii* | Venezuelan equine encephalitis virus |
| *Rickettsia rickettsii* | Hantavirus |
| | Yellow fever virus |

the Department of State. At congressional hearings in May 1988, the U.S. government reported that at least 10 nations, including the Soviet Union, Libya, Iran, Cuba, Southern Yemen, Syria, and North Korea, were developing biological weapons. Critics of the U.S. program refuted the need for program expansion.

The BDRP is administered through two separate government organizations—the army and the CIA. Details of the program are described in the April 1989 Environmental Impact Statement published by the Department of the Army, U.S. Army Medical Research and Development Command.

The BDRP is located at three sites: the U.S. Army Medical Research Institute of Infectious Diseases (USAMRIID) at Fort Detrick, Maryland; the Aberdeen Proving Ground in Maryland; and the Dugway Proving Ground in Utah. USAMRIID is designated as the lead laboratory in medical defense against BW threats. Research conducted at the USAMRIID focuses on medical defense such as the development of vaccines and treatments for both natural diseases and potential BW agents. Work on the rapid detection of microorganisms and the diagnosis of infectious diseases is also conducted. The primary mission at the Aberdeen Proving Ground is nonmedical defense against BW threats including detection research, such as the development of sensors and che-

miluminescent instruments to detect and identify bacteria and viruses, and development of methods for material and equipment decontamination. The U.S. Army Dugway Proving Ground is a Department of Defense major range and test facility responsible for development, testing, evaluation, and operation of chemical warfare equipment, obscurants and smoke munitions, and biological defense equipment. Its principle mission with respect to the BDRP is to perform developmental and operational testing for biological defense material, including the development and testing of sensors, equipment, and clothing needed for defense against a BW attack.

One hundred secondary sites have received contracts for biological defense research. Secondary sites include the Swiftwater Lab, operated by the Salk Institute in Swiftwater, Pennsylvania; the Naval Medical Research Institute in California; medical centers; universities; and private biotechnology firms in the United States, Scotland, and Israel.

The CIA also participates in the administration of the BDRP. In 1982, Thomas Dashiell of the office of the secretary of defense reported on a classified technology watch program related to BW that was operated by the intelligence community. The program was designed to monitor worldwide developments related to BW that could affect the vulnerability of U.S. and NATO forces to biological attack.

BDRP research focuses on five main areas:

1. Development of vaccines
2. Development of protective clothing and decontamination methods
3. Analysis of the mode of action of toxins and the development of antidotes
4. Development of broad-spectrum antiviral drugs for detecting and diagnosing BW agents and toxins
5. Utilization of genetic engineering methods to study and prepare defenses against BW and toxins

The BDRP has often been a center of controversy in the United States. One BDRP facility, the Dugway Proving Ground, was the target of a lawsuit that resulted in the preparation of the environmental impact statement for the facility. A proposal for a high-level containment laboratory (designated P-4) was ultimately changed to a plan for a lower-level (P-3) facility.

The use of genetic engineering techniques in BDRP facilities has also been a focus of controversy. The BDRP takes the position that genetic engineering will be utilized if deemed necessary. The Department of Defense stated that testing of aerosols of pathogens derived from recombinant DNA methodology is not precluded if a need should arise in the interest of national defense.

One specific program requires special note. The Defense Advanced Research Project Agency is a Pentagon program that invests significantly in pathogen research through grants to qualified institutions. This project initially focused on engineering and electronics (computer) projects; however, starting in 1995 biology became a key focus, and several BW defensive research grants are now in operation at several academic and private institutions.

Very little is written in the unclassified literature on BW research conducted in countries other than the United States. Great Britain has maintained the Microbiological Research Establishment at Porton Down; however, military research is highly classified in Great Britain and details regarding the research conducted at Porton are unavailable.

During the 1970s and 1980s, much of the U.S. BW policy was based on the assumption of Soviet offensive BW capabilities. Most U.S. accounts of Soviet BW activities were unconfirmed accusations or claims about treaty violations. The Soviet Union was a party to both the 1925 Geneva Protocol and the 1972 BW convention. According to Pentagon sources, the Soviet Union operated at least seven top-security BW centers. These centers were reported to be under strict military control. Although the former Soviet Union proclaimed that their BW program was purely defensive, the United States consistently asserted that the Soviet Union was conducting offensive BW research.

## V. CONTEMPORARY ISSUES

### A. Genetic Engineering

There has been considerable controversy regarding the potential for genetically engineered organisms to serve as effective BW agents. Recombinant DNA technology has been cited as a method for creating novel, pathogenic microorganisms. Theoretically, organisms could be developed that would possess predictable characteristics, including antibiotic resistance, altered modes of transmission, and altered pathogenic and immunogenic capabilities. This potential for genetic engineering to significantly affect the military usefulness of BW has been contested. It has been suggested that because many genes must work together to endow an organism with pathogenic characteristics, the alteration of a few genes with recombinant DNA technology is unlikely to yield a novel pathogen that is significantly more effective or usable than conventional BW agents.

The question of predictability of the behavior of genetically engineered organisms was addressed at an American Society for Microbiology symposium held in June 1985. Some symposium participants believed that the use of recombinant DNA increases predictability because the genetic change can be precisely characterized. Other participants, however, believed that the use of recombinant DNA decreases predictability because it widens the potential range of DNA sources. Other evidence supports the view that genetically engineered organisms do not offer substantial military advantage over conventional

BW. Some studies have shown that in general, genetically engineered organisms do not survive well in the environment. This fact has been cited as evidence that these organisms would not make effective BW agents.

Despite the contentions that genetic engineering does not enhance the military usefulness of BW, a significant number of arguments support the contrary view. At the 1986 review conference of the BW convention, it was noted that genetic engineering advances since the convention entered into force may have made biological weapons a more attractive military option.

Several authors have contended that the question of the potential of genetic engineering to enhance the military usefulness of BW is rhetorical because the 1972 BW convention prohibits development of such organisms despite their origin or method of production. Nations participating in both the 1980 and 1986 review conferences of the BW convention accepted the view that the treaty prohibitions apply to genetically engineered BW agents. An amendment to the treaty, specifically mentioning genetically engineered organisms, was deemed to be unnecessary. In addition, the United States, Great Britain, and the Soviet Union concluded in a 1980 briefing paper that the 1972 BW convention fully covered all BW agents that could result from genetic manipulation.

Although the utility of genetic engineering for enhancing the military usefulness of BW agents has been questioned, the role of genetic engineering for strengthening defensive measures against BW has been clear. Genetic engineering has the potential to improve defenses against BW in two ways: (i) vaccine production and (ii) sensitive identification and detection systems. The issues of the new technologies in defensive research have been evident in the U.S. BW program. Since 1982, U.S. Army scientists have used genetic engineering to study and prepare defenses against BW agents. Military research utilizing recombinant DNA and hybridoma technology includes the development of vaccines against a variety of bacteria and viruses, methods of rapid detection and identification of BW agents, and basic research on protein structure and gene control. By improving defenses against BW, it is possible that genetic engineering may potentially reduce the risk of using BW.

The primary effect of BW on government regulations on genetic engineering is the tendency toward more stringent control of the technologies. The fear of genetically engineered BW agents has prompted proposals for government regulation of BW research utilizing genetic engineering research. The Department of Defense released a statement indicating that all government research was in compliance with the 1972 BW convention. The government has also prepared an environmental impact statement of research conducted at Fort Detrick.

Government regulations on genetic engineering also affect BW research through limitations on exports of biotechnology information, research products, and equipment. In addition to controls of exports due to competitive concerns of biotechnology companies, a substantial amount of information and equipment related to genetic engineering are prohibited from being exported from the United States. The Commerce Department maintains a "militarily critical technology" list, which serves as an overall guide to restricted exports. Included on the list are containment and decontamination equipment for large production facilities, high-capacity biological reactors, separators, extractors, dryers, and nozzles capable of disseminating biological agents in a fine mist.

Genetic engineering has altered the concept of BW. A current, comprehensive discussion of BW would include both naturally occurring and potential genetically engineered agents. Many current defenses against BW are developed with genetic engineering techniques. Government regulations on biotechnology have limited BW research, while fears of virulent genetically engineered BW agents have strengthened public support for stronger regulations. Future policies related to BW will need to be addressed in light of its altered status.

## B. Mathematical Epidemiology Models

Although genetic engineering may potentially alter characteristics of BW agents, mathematical models of epidemiology may provide military planners with techniques for predicting the spread of a released BW agent. One of the hindrances that has prevented BW from being utilized or even seriously considered by military leaders has been the inability to predict the spread of a BW agent once it has been released into the environment. Without the capability to predict the spread of the released organisms, military planners would risk the accidental exposure of their own troops and civilians to their own weapons. The development of advanced epidemiology models may provide the necessary mechanisms for predicting the spread of organisms that would substantially decrease the deterrent factor of unpredictability.

## C. Low-Level Conflict

Another important factor that has affected the current status of BW is the increase in low-level conflict or the spectrum of violent action below the level of small-scale conventional war, including terrorism and guerrilla warfare. In the 1980s, the low-intensity conflict doctrine, which was espoused by the Reagan administration, was a plan for U.S. aid to anti-Communist forces throughout the world as a way of confronting the Soviet Union without using U.S. combat troops. Despite the significant changes in the world since the inception of the low-intensity conflict doctrine, the probability of increasing numbers of small conflicts still exists. Although no evidence indicates that the United States would consider violating the 1972 BW convention and support biological warfare, the overall increase in low-level conflicts in the future may help create an environment conducive to the use of BW.

Although BW may not be assessed as an effective weapon in a full-scale conventional war, limited use of BW agents may be perceived as advantageous in a small-scale conflict. Although strong deterrents exist for nuclear weapons, including unavailability and, most formidably, the threat of uncontrolled worldwide "nuclear winter," BW may be perceived as less dangerous. In addition, the participants of low-level conflicts may not possess the finances for nuclear or conventional weapons. BW agents, like chemical weapons, are relatively inexpensive compared to other weapon systems and may be seen as an attractive alternative to the participants and leaders of low-level conflicts. Low-level conflict, therefore, increases the potential number of forums for the use of BW.

## D. Terrorism

A final factor that could significantly affect BW is the worldwide increase in terrorism or the violent activities of subnational groups. Although there has not been an incident to date of the successful use of BW by a terrorist group, the possibility of such an event has increased in many forums.

The relationship of terrorism and BW can be divided into two possible events. The first is terrorist acts against laboratories conducting BW-related research. The level of security at Fort Detrick is high, the possibility of a terrorist attack has been anticipated, and contingency plans have been made. Complicating the problem of providing security against terrorist attack in the United States is the fact that although most BW research projects are conducted with the BW research program of the Army, an increasing number of projects are supported by the government that are conducted outside of the military establishment. These outside laboratories could be potential targets.

The second type of terrorist event related to BW is the potential use of BW by terrorists against urban areas or major public facilities. Biological weapons are relatively inexpensive and easy to develop and produce compared to conventional, nuclear, or chemical weapons. BW agents can be concealed and easily transported across borders or within countries. In addition, terrorists are not hampered by a fear of an uncontrolled spread of the BW agent into innocent civilian populations. On the contrary, innocent civilians are often the intended targets of terrorist activity and the greater chance for spread of the BW agent may be considered to be a positive characteristic (see Section II.C).

## E. Offensive versus Defensive Biological Warfare Research

The distinctions between "offensive" and "defensive" BW research have been an issue since 1969, when the United States unilaterally pledged to conduct only defensive research. The stated purpose of the U.S. BDRP is to maintain and promote national defense from BW threats. Although neither the Geneva Convention nor the 1972 convention prohibits any type of research, the only research that nations have admitted to conducting is defensive. The problem is whether or not the two types of research can be differentiated by any observable elements.

Although production of large quantities of a virulent organism and testing of delivery systems have been cited as distinguishing characteristics of an offensive program, a substantial amount of research leading up to these activities, including isolating an organism and then using animal models to determine pathogenicity, could be conducted in the name of defense.

Vaccine research is usually considered defensive, whereas increasing the virulence of a pathogen and producing large quantities are deemed offensive. However, a critical component of a strategic plan to use biological weapons would be the production of vaccines to protect the antagonist's own personnel (unless self-annihilation was also a goal). This means that the intent of a vaccine program could be offensive BW use. Furthermore, research that increases the virulence of an organism is not necessarily part of an offensive strategy because one can argue that virulence needs to be studied in order to develop adequate defense.

The key element distinguishing offensive from defensive research is intent. If the intent of the researcher or the goals of the research program are the capability to develop and produce BW, then the research is offensive BW research. If the intent is to have the capability to develop and produce defenses against BW use, then the research is defensive BW research. Although it is true that nations may have policies of open disclosures (i.e., no secret research), "intent" is not observable.

Although the terms offensive BW research and defensive BW research may have some use in describing intent, it is more a philosophical than a practical distinction—one that is based on trust rather than fact.

## F. Secrecy in Biological Warfare-Related Research

Neither the Geneva Protocol nor the 1972 BW convention prohibits any type of research, secret or nonsecret. Although the BDRP does not conduct secret or classified research, it is possible that secret BW research is being conducted in the United States outside of the structure of the BDRP. The classified nature of the resource material for this work makes it impossible to effectively determine if secret research is being conducted in the United States or any other nation.

It is not, however, unreasonable to assume that other nations conduct significant secret BW research. Therefore, regardless of the facts, one cannot deny the perception that such research exists in a variety of countries and that this perception will exist for the foreseeable future.

Secrecy has been cited as a cause of decreased quality of BW research. If secret research, whether offensive or defensive, is being conducted in the United States or other nations, it is unclear if the process of secrecy affects the quality of the research. If the secret research process consists of a core of highly trained, creative, and motivated individuals sharing information, the quality of the research may not suffer significantly. It must be stated, however that secrecy by its very nature will limit input from a variety of diverse observers.

Secrecy may increase the potential for violations of the 1972 BW convention; however, violations would probably occur regardless of the secrecy of the research. Secrecy in research can certainly lead to infractions against arbitrary rules established by individuals outside of the research group. The secret nature of the research may lure a researcher into forbidden areas. In addition, those outside of the research group, such as policy-makers, may push for prohibited activities if the sense of secrecy prevails. Secrecy also tends to bind those within the secret arena together and tends to enhance their perception of themselves as being above the law and knowing what is "right." As in the case of Oliver North and the Iran-Contra Affair, those within the group may believe fervently that the rules must be broken for a justified purpose and a mechanism of secrecy allows violations to occur without penalty.

The distrust between nations exacerbates the perceived need for secret research. The animosity between the United States and the Soviet Union during the 1980s fueled the beliefs that secret research leading to violations of the 1972 BW convention was being conducted in the Soviet Union. As the belligerence of the 1980s faded into the new world order of the 1990s, the questions focus less on the Soviet Union and more on the Middle East and Third-World countries. There are factions in the United States that believe strongly that other countries are conducting secret research that will lead to violations of the convention. There is also a tendency to believe that the secrecy in one's own country will not lead to treaty violations, whereas the same secret measures in an enemy nation will result in activities forbidden by international law.

The importance of the concept of secrecy in BW research is related to the perception of secrecy and arms control agreements. Regardless of the degree of secrecy in research, if an enemy believes that a nation is pursuing secret research, arms control measures are jeopardized. The reduction of secrecy has been suggested as a tool to decrease the potential for BW treaty violations. A trend toward reducing secrecy in BW research was exemplified by the 1986 review conference of the 1972 BW convention, which resulted in agreements to exchange more information and to publish more of the results of BW research. Whether or not these measures have any effect on strengthening the 1972 BW convention remains to be seen.

Organizations and individuals have urged a renunciation by scientists of all secret research and all security controls over microbiological, toxicological, and pharmacological research. This action has been suggested as a means of strengthening the 1972 BW convention. The belief that microbiologists should avoid secret research is based on the assumption that (i) secret research is of poor quality due to lack of peer review and (ii) secrecy perpetuates treaty violations.

Although it may be reasonable to expect microbiologists to avoid secret research, it is not realistic. Secrecy is practiced in almost every type of research including academic, military, and especially industrial. Furthermore, there will always be those within the military and intelligence structures who believe that at least some degree of secrecy is required for national security.

Secrecy in BW research is a complex issue. The degree to which it exists is unclear. Individuals are generally opposed to secrecy in BW research although other examples of secrecy in different types of research exist. The effect of secrecy on the quality of research, the need for the secrecy, and the choice of microbiologists to participate in secret BW research remain unanswered questions.

## G. Problems Relating to Verification

One of the major weaknesses of the 1972 BW convention has been the lack of verification protocols. Problems with effectively monitoring compliance include the ease of developing BW agents in laboratories designed for other purposes and the futility of inspecting all technical facilities of all nations. Measures that have been implemented with the goal of monitoring compliance included (i) open-inspections, (ii) intelligence gathering, (iii) monitor-research, (iv) use of sampling stations to detect the presence of biological agents, and (v) international cooperation. The progress achieved with the Chemical Weapons Convention has renewed interest in strengthening mechanisms for verification of compliance with the 1972 BW convention. Although this renewed interest in verification along with the emergence of the Commonwealth of Independent States from the old Soviet Union has brought an optimism to the verification issue, the reticence of countries such as Iraq to cooperate with United Nations inspection teams is a reminder of the complexities of international agreements.

The examples discussed in this article are typical of the many issues attached to the concept of BW.

## See Also the Following Articles

INTERNATIONAL LAW AND INFECTIOUS DISEASE • RICKETTSIAE • SMALLPOX

## Bibliography

Atlas, R. M. (1998). Biological weapons pose challenge for microbiology community. *ASM News* **64**, 383–389.
Buckingham, W. A., Jr. (Ed.) (1984). "Defense Planning for the 1990s." National Defense Univ. Press, Washington, DC.
Cole, L. (1996, December). The specter of biological weapons. *Sci. Am.* 60–65.
Frisna, M. E. (1990). The offensive–defensive distinction in military biological research. *Hastings Cent. Rep.* **20**(3), 19–22.

Gravett, C. (1990). "Medieval Siege Warfare." Osprey, London.

Harris, R., and Paxman, J. (1982). "A Higher Form of Killing." Hill & Wang, New York.

Livingstone, N. C. (1984). Fighting terrorism and "dirty little wars." *In* "Defense Planning for the 1990s" (W. A. Buckingham, Jr., Ed.), pp. 165–196. National Defense Univ. Press, Washington, DC.

Livingstone, N. C., and Douglass, J., Jr. (1984). "CBW: The Poor Man's Atomic Bomb." Tufts University, Institute of Foreign Policy Analysis, Medford, MA.

Meselson, M., Guillemin, J., Hugh-Jones, M., Langmuir, A., Popova, I., Shelokov, A., and Yampolskaya, O. (1994). The Sverdlovsk anthrax outbreak of 1979. *Science* **266**, 1202–1208.

Milewski, E. (1985). Discussion on a proposal to form a RAC working group on biological weapons. *Recombinant DNA Technol. Bull.* 8(4), 173–175.

Miller, L. A. (1987). The use of philosophical analysis and Delphi survey to clarify subject matter for a future curriculum for microbiologists on the topic of biological weapons. Unpublished thesis, University of Pennsylvania, Philadelphia. (University Micro-films International, Ann Arbor, MI. 8714902).

Murphy, S., Hay, A., and Rose, S. (1984). "No Fire, No Thunder." Monthly Review Press, New York.

Poupard, J. A., Miller, L. A., and Granshaw, L. (1989). The use of smallpox as a biological weapon in the French and Indian War of 1763. *ASM News* **55**, 122–124.

Smith, R. J. (1984). The dark side of biotechnology. *Science* **224**, 1215–1216.

Stockholm International Peace Research Institute (1973). "The Problem of Chemical and Biological Warfare," Vol. 2. Humanities Press, New York.

Taubes, G. (1995). The defense initiative of the 1990s. *Science* **267**, 1096–1100.

Wright, S. (1985). The military and the new biology. *Bull. Atomic Sci.* **42**(5), 73.

Wright, S., and Sinsheimer, R. L. (1983). Recombinant DNA and biological warfare. *Bull. Atomic Sci.* **39**(9), 20–26.

Zilinskas, R., (Ed.), (1992). "The Microbiologist and Biological Defense Research: Ethics, Politics and Intermediate Security." New York Academy of Sciences, New York.

# Bioluminescence, Microbial

## J. Woodland Hastings

*Harvard University*

I. Bacteria
II. Dinoflagellates
III. Fungi

## GLOSSARY

*autoinducer* A homoserine lactone produced by bacteria which, after accumulating in the medium to a critical concentration, initiates transcription of specific genes by a mechanism referred to as autoinduction, recently dubbed **quorum sensing.**

*bioluminescence* Emission of light by living organisms that is visible to other organisms. It derives from an enzyme-catalyzed chemiluminescence, a highly exergonic reaction in which chemical energy is transformed into light energy.

*bioluminescent, quantum yield* The number of photons produced per luciferin (substrate) molecule oxidized in a bioluminescent reaction.

*blue and yellow fluorescent proteins* Accessory proteins in the bioluminescence system in some bacteria, carrying lumazine and flavin chromophores, respectively, and serving as secondary emitters under some conditions.

*luciferase* The generic name for enzymes that catalyze bioluminescent reactions. Luciferases from different major groups of organisms are not homologous (e.g., firefly and jellyfish luciferases are unrelated to bacterial luciferase) so the organism must be specified in referring to a specific luciferase.

*luciferin* (light bearing) The generic name for a substrate that is oxidized to give light in a bioluminescent reaction; identified as a **flavin** in bacteria and a **tetrapyrrole** in dinoflagellates.

*scintillons* Bioluminescent organelles unique to dinoflagellates which emit brief bright flashes of light following stimulation.

**BIOLUMINESCENCE** is defined as an enzyme-catalyzed chemiluminescence, a chemical reaction in which the energy released is used to produce an intermediate or product in an electronically excited state, which then emits a photon. It does not come from or depend on light absorbed, as in fluorescence or phosphorescence. However, the excited state produced in such a chemical reaction is indistinguishable from that produced in fluorescence after the absorption of a photon by the ground state of the molecule concerned.

All bioluminescent reactions involve the oxidation by molecular oxygen of a substrate by an enzyme, generically referred to as luciferin and luciferase, respectively, with the production of an electronically excited state, typically luciferase bound (Fig. 1a). The energy released from the oxidation of a luciferin in such reactions is about 10 times greater than that obtained from the hydrolysis of ATP.

There are numerous (20–30) extant bioluminescent systems, which mostly bear no evolutionary relationships with one another. The many different luciferases are thus considered to have arisen *de novo* and evolved independently, and the luciferins are likewise different. Thus, genes coding for luciferases from fireflies and jellyfish, for example, have no sequence similarities to bacterial or dinoflagellate luciferase, which themselves are unrelated. Thus, the luciferases discussed in this article should be called bacterial luciferase and dinoflagellate luciferase.

## I. BACTERIA

### A. Occurrence, Habitats, Species, and Functions

In the ocean luminous bacteria occur ubiquitously and can be isolated from most seawater samples from

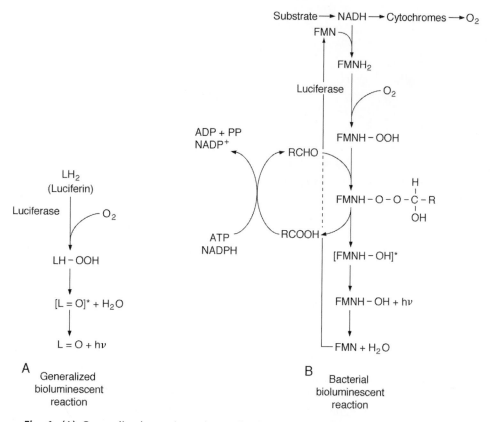

**Fig. 1.** (A) Generalized reaction scheme for bioluminescent reactions. (B) The luciferase reaction showing the components involved in the bacterial system. Reduced flavin derived from the electron transport pathway reacts with luciferase and molecular oxygen to form an intermediate peroxide. In a mixed function oxidation with long-chain aldehyde (RCHO), hydroxy-FMN is formed in its excited state (*), from which emission occurs. The FMN and long-chain acid products are recycled.

the surface to depths of ~1000 m, and they appear as bright colonies on plates (Fig. 2). They are very often found in some kind of symbiotic association with higher organisms (e.g., fish or squid), in which the light emission is evidently of functional importance to the host. In parasitic or saprophytic associations the advantage of light emission accrues more to the bacteria: The light attracts animals to feed, enhancing the dispersal of the bacteria. The maximum light emission of a bacterial cell is about $10^4$ q s$^{-1}$, meaning that to be seen, the cell density must be high—about $10^9$ to $10^{10}$ cells ml$^{-1}$.

Most luminous bacteria are classed under three major genera—*Vibrio, Photobacterium,* and *Photo-*

*rhabdus,* the first two of which are almost exclusively marine, whereas the last is terrestrial. All are characterized as enteric bacteria and are notable for the symbioses in which they participate, most commonly in light organs in which the light is used by the host for some purpose. The flashlight fish, *Photoblepharon* (Fig. 3), maintains cultures of such bacteria in special organs located beneath the eyes. For all luminous bacterial species the primary habitat can be assumed to be in some association, either as a light organ or gut symbiont, or in a parasitic or saprophytic association.

If such associations are viewed as primary habitats, planktonic or "free-living" bacteria in the ocean may

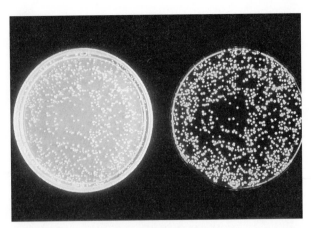

**Fig. 2.** Colonies of luminous bacteria photographed by their own light (right) and in room light (left). Light is emitted continuously but is controlled by a quorum-sensing mechanism (autoinducer) and is thus not proportional to growth or cell density. See color insert.

be considered secondary or reservoir habitats, produced as overflows or escapees into an environment in which luminescence may not be advantageous and thus not selected for. Thus, the failure, for whatever reason, of the luminescence system to be expressed under these conditions may be advantageous for the survival of the bacteria possessing the genes for luminescence and thus for their ability to compete favorably with heterotrophs not carrying the genes.

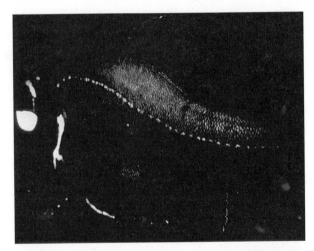

**Fig. 3.** The flashlight fish (Photoblepharon) showing the exposed light organ, which harbors luminous bacteria and is located just below the eye. A special lid allows the fish to turn the light on and off (photograph by Dr. James Morin). See color insert.

Different species occupy different specific habitats. *Vibrio harveyi* is the most cosmopolitan species and is not known to be involved in a light organ symbiosis. It occurs as a gut symbiont in many marine animals, and it is known to parasitize and/or infest saprophytically crustaceans and other species. Fish or squid having specific associations with *Vibrio fischeri*, *Photobacterium phosphoreum*, and *Photobacterium leigonathi* as symbionts have been identified, and all of these species have more restricted requirements for growth. Still other symbionts have not been cultured successfully, but affinities and relationships are known from their luciferase DNA sequences.

*Photorhabdus luminescens* is symbiotic with nematodes, which parasitize caterpillars, where they release the bacteria as an inoculum into the body cavity along with their own fertilized eggs. The bacteria grow, providing nutrient for the developing nematode larvae. The caterpillar does not survive but becomes brightly luminous, possibly to attract animals to feed on it and thereby disperse both nematodes and bacteria. Each young nematode then carries a fresh inoculum, estimated to be about 50–100 bacteria.

## B. Biochemistry

### 1. Light-Emitting Reaction

Biochemically, light emission results from the luciferase-catalyzed mixed function oxidation of reduced flavin mononucleotide and long-chain aldehyde by molecular oxygen, populating the excited state of a luciferase–hydroxyflavin intermediate, which emits a blue-green light ($\lambda_{max} \sim 490$ nm).

Bacterial luciferase is an $\alpha$–$\beta$ heterodimer lacking metals, prosthetic groups, and non-amino acid residues. To date, no sequences in data bases exhibit any similarities to it, so the origin of the gene for the enzyme remains unknown. Although the two subunits are homologous, the active site and the detailed kinetics features of the reaction are properties of the $\alpha$ subunit.

The reaction represents a biochemical shunt of the respiratory electron transport system, carrying electrons from the level of reduced flavin ($FMNH_2$) directly to oxygen (Fig. 1B). $FMNH_2$ reacts first with oxygen to form a linear hydroperoxide, which then reacts with long-chain fatty aldehyde to give the postulated peroxyhemiacetal intermediate. This breaks down to give long-chain acid and the intermediate hydroxyflavin in a high-energy electronically excited state. Although aldehydes with chain lengths from 7 to 18 carbon atoms give light in the reaction with isolated luciferase, tetradecanal (14C) has been identified as the naturally occurring molecule in the species studied. While its oxidation provides energy, the aldehyde is not the emitter and is thus not a luciferin, which means "light-bearing." The flavin is the luciferin in the bacterial system.

One photon is produced for about every four molecules of $FMNH_2$ oxidized; thus, the bioluminescence quantum yield is 25%. However, since the fluorescence quantum yield of FMN is about 30%, and the excited state produced as in Fig. 1B is equivalent to that which would be produced from light absorption by the hydroxyflavin, it may be concluded that the luciferase reaction is highly efficient.

In the living cell light is produced continuously; the oxidized FMN formed in the reaction is reduced again as indicated in Fig. 1B by pyridine nucleotide. Similarly, the myristic acid product is converted back to the corresponding aldehyde by enzymes of a specific fatty acid reductase complex with ATP and NADPH as cofactors.

## 2. Luciferase Structure

The tertiary structure of luciferase (Fig. 4) was correctly predicted based on the x-ray crystal structure of a related and homologous protein expressed from *lux F*. The structures of the $\alpha$ and $\beta$ subunits are similar, differing in a region in which substrate is presumed to bind to the $\alpha$, although the structure of the site is not known because a determination of the structure with flavin bound has not been made. Both subunits exhibit the so-called $[\beta/\alpha]_8$ barrel form ($\beta/\alpha$ do not refer to subunits), in which stretches of beta sheet alternate with alpha-helical strands, all of which are parallel to one another, together forming a closed barrel with the eight $\alpha$ helices on the outside. The region of the $\alpha$ subunit where substrate is likely to bind was not seen in the electron density map, including a region known to be highly sensitive to protease attack that is absent in the $\beta$ subunit.

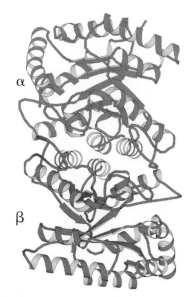

**Fig. 4.** Ribbon representation of the structure of bacterial luciferase showing the $\alpha$ and $\beta$ subunits and how they may associate (from Fisher *et al.*, 1995).

## 3. Antenna Proteins: Blue and Yellow Fluorescent Proteins as Emitters

The basic structure of the luciferase and the biochemistry of the reaction are the same in all luminous bacteria, which typically emit light peaking at about 490 nm. However, in some bacterial strains, the color of the light emitted by the living cell is blue or red shifted, even though its isolated luciferase still peaks at ~490 nm. In a strain of *P. phosphoreum*, the emission is blue shifted, peaking at about 480 nm, whereas in a strain of *V. fischeri* the light is yellow in color ($\lambda_{max}$ ~540 nm). In both cases a second ("antenna") protein with its own chromophore is responsible (lumazine and flavin, respectively for the two cases). The mechanisms involved in these cases have not been fully resolved, but they may be mechanistically similar because the proteins are homologous. Nonradiative energy transfer has been suggested, but evidence indicates that this alone cannot be responsible since the antenna protein appears to actually enter into the light-emitting reaction in the case of the yellow-emitting system. The functional importance for such spectral shifts has not been elucidated, although strains with a blue-shifted emission occur at depths of ~600 m in the ocean.

## 4. *Molecular Biology: Genes of the Lux Operon*

*Lux* genes cloned from several different species exhibit sequence similarities indicative of evolutionary relatedness and conservation. In *V. fischeri*, the species most extensively studied, the *lux* operon has five structural and two regulatory genes with established functions. As shown in Fig. 5, these include two that code for the $\alpha$ and $\beta$ subunits of luciferase and three that code for the reductase, transferase, and synthetase components of the fatty acid reductase complex responsible for aldehyde synthesis and reduction and recycling of the acid product. Upstream, in the same operon, is the regulatory gene *lux I*, and immediately adjacent but transcribed in the opposite direction is *lux R*, whose product in responsible for the transcriptional activation of *lux A–E* and others. The latter include *lux F* and *G*, found in some species and located in the same region; these code for proteins whose functions are not well established. However, genes coding for the antenna proteins responsible for color shifting are located elsewhere on the genome but still subject to regulation by the autoinduction mechanism. In luminous Vibrios the regulatory genes (*lux I* and *R* or their counterparts) are also located remotely from the *lux A–E* operon.

## 5. *Physiology: Regulation of Light Emission*
### a. *Autoinduction and Quorum Sensing*

Quorum sensing, which was first discovered and referred to as autoinduction in luminous bacteria, refers to a mechanism causing the *lux* genes to be transcribed only at higher cell densities. It is mediated by a homoserine lactone molecule produced by the cells that has been dubbed the autoinducer. In luminous bacteria in a confined environment, such as a light organ, autoinducer can accumulate and act, whereas in free-living bacteria, in which the light could not be seen at the low cell densities, luciferase is of no value and is not produced.

Autoinduction was discovered in the early 1970s and was proposed is as an explanation for the fact that luciferase and other components of the light-emitting system are not produced in cells growing at low cell densities but are produced, and rapidly so, above a critical cell concentration (Fig. 6). In laboratory cultures subjected to continuous (or repetitive) dilution (maintaining densities lower than $\sim 10^7$ cells ml$^{-1}$), such that autoinducer accumulation is not possible, no synthesis of luciferase or its messenger RNA occurs. The same is true of planktonic populations in the ocean, which are typically at densities of no greater than $\sim 10^2$ cells ml$^{-1}$.

The autoinducer in *P. fischeri* is the product of the *lux I* gene and acts as a positive regulator of the *lux* operon in the presence of a functional *lux R* gene. In the early 1990s it was found that a similar mechanism, also utilizing specific homoserine lactones, occurs in many other diverse groups of bacteria in which expression of certain specific genes is functionally important only at higher cell densities. The

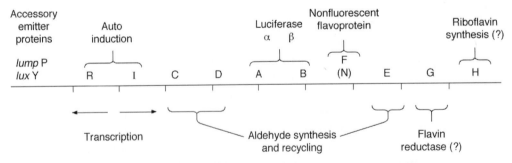

**Fig. 5.** Organization of the *lux* genes in *Vibrio fischeri*. The operon on the right, transcribed from the 5′ to the 3′ end, carries genes for synthesis of autoinducer (*lux* I), for luciferase $\alpha$ and $\beta$ subunits (*lux A* and *B*), and for aldehyde synthesis (*lux C–E*). The operon on the left carries the *lux R* gene, which encodes for a receptor molecule that binds autoinducer; the complex controls the transcription of the right operon. Other genes, *lux F* (*N*). *G*, and *H* (right), are associated with the operon but with uncertain functions; genes for accessory emitter proteins also occur (left).

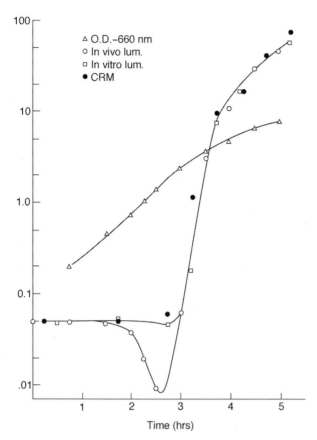

**Fig. 6.** An experiment demonstrating autoinduction in luminous bacteria. Growth of the cells (measured by optical density at 660 nm) is exponential for the first few hours, during which time there is no change in the bioluminescence or the luciferase content of the culture (arbitrary units). After about 3 hr, at a cell density of 2 or greater, the *lux* genes are rapidly transcribed and luciferase and other related proteins are synthesized, determined also by reaction with antiluciferase (CRM).

phenomenon was then appropriately dubbed "quorum sensing."

### b. Glucose, Iron, and Oxygen

In both *V. harveyi* and *V. fischeri* luminescence is repressed by glucose, reversible by cyclic AMP. All species except *Photorhabdus luminescens* exhibit induction of luminescence by the addition of iron after growth under conditions of iron limitation, suggesting that eukaryotic hosts might use iron limitation to limit growth while maximizing luminescence of bacterial symbionts.

As a reactant in the luciferase reaction, oxygen can control light emission directly but only at extremely low oxygen concentrations (lower than ~0.1%), above which the luminescence is independent of oxygen. Growth, however, is reduced at concentrations lower than that of air (21%), so growth could be strongly inhibited without affecting the luciferase reaction. Indeed, in some species and strains, transcription of the *lux* operon is greatly favored over growth under microaerophilic conditions, where bright light emission may occur at low cell densities. Regulation by control of oxygen has thus been proposed as a mechanism whereby eukaryotic hosts might control growth of bacterial symbionts in light organs while maximizing luminescence.

In *P. luminescens* grown in pure (100%) oxygen, which is lethal for many bacteria including other luminous species, both luciferase synthesis and luminescence are enhanced in relation to cell mass. It has been proposed that in this case the luciferase system serves to detoxify damaging oxygen radicals.

### c. Dark Variants

In culture collections it has often been reported that bacteria may lose their luminosity over time in cases in which subculturing care has not been taken to reisolate single bright colonies each time. This can be attributed to the spontaneous occurrence and overgrowth of dark (e.g., very dim) variants, which is some ways appear to be similar to phase variants reported in other groups of bacteria. These dark variants do not produce luciferase or other luminescence components and are pleiotropic, being altered in several other properties such as cell morphology and phase sensitivity.

Dark variants could presumably provide a genetic mechanism whereby cells could respond to environmental conditions that select for or against the property of luminescence. Although such conditions have not been established, this would allow cells to compete better with other heterotrophic bacteria under conditions where luminescence is of no use and thereby become more widely dispersed but prepared to populate a niche where luminescence is functionally important.

## II. DINOFLAGELLATES

### A. Occurrence, Habitats, Species, and Functions

Ocean "phosphorescence," commonly seen at night (especially in summer) when the water is disturbed, is due in large part to the bioluminescence of dinoflagellates. The organisms occur ubiquitously in the oceans as planktonic forms and respond to mechanical stimulation when the water is disturbed, such as by waves or fish swimming, by emitting brief (~0.1 s) bright flashes (~$10^9$ photons each). The wake of a large ship may be evident from such light emission for approximately 20 miles. Luminescent dinoflagellates occur primarily in surface waters and many species are photosynthetic. Only approximately 20–30% of marine species are bioluminescent.

The so-called red tides are transient blooms (usually for weeks) of individual dinoflagellate species. Cells typically migrate vertically during the night to deeper water where available nutrients are taken up, returning to the surface to photosynthesize during the day. Phosphorescent bays (e.g., in Puerto Rico and Jamaica) are persistent blooms of this type; in Puerto Rico the dominant species is *Pyrodinium bahamense*.

As a group, dinoflagellates are important as symbionts, notably for contributing photosynthesis and carbon fixation in certain animals. Unlike bacteria, however, luminous dinoflagellates are not known to be harbored as symbionts on the basis of their light emission.

Since dinoflagellates are stimulated to emit light when predators (e.g., crustaceans) are active, predators might thereby be alerted to feed on crustaceans, resulting in a reduced predation on dinoflagellates generally. Predation on dinoflagellates may also be impeded more directly and help individual cells. The flash could startle or divert a predator, allowing that cell to escape predation. The response time to stimulation (milliseconds) is certainly fast enough to have this effect. This latter explanation, though supported by experiment, does not easily account for the fact that not all species are bioluminescent.

### B. Cell Biology

Luminescence in dinoflagellates is emitted from many small (~0.5 $\mu$m) cortical locations (Fig. 7). The structures have been identified as a new type of organelle termed scintillons (flashing units). They occur as outpocketings of the cytoplasm into the cell vacuole, like a balloon, with the neck remaining connected. Scintillons contain only dinoflagellate luciferase and luciferin and a protein that binds luciferin and keeps it from reacting with luciferase in between flashes. Other cytoplasmic components are somehow excluded from scintillons, which can be identified ultrastructurally by immunolabeling with antibodies raised against the luminescence proteins. They can also be visualized using image intensification by their bioluminescent flashing following stimulation as well as by the fluorescence of luciferin, which is present nowhere else in the cell.

### C. Biochemistry

Dinoflagellate luciferin is a highly reduced novel tetrapyrrole related to chlorophyll (Fig. 8) and in extracts remains tightly bound to a ~75-kDa specialized protein at cytoplasmic pH (~8). The luciferase

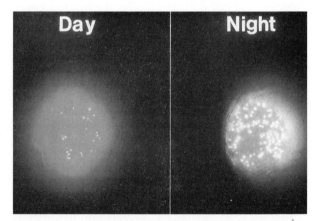

**Fig. 7.** *Gonyaulax* cells viewed by fluorescence microscopy showing scintillons (bioluminescent organelles) visualized by the fluorescence of dinoflagellate luciferin ($\lambda_{max}$ of emission, 475 nm), with chlorophyll fluorescence as the dark background. Scintillons are structurally formed and destroyed on a daily basis, controlled by the circadian clock. (Left) Night phase cell with many scintillons; (right) day phase cell with few scintillons.

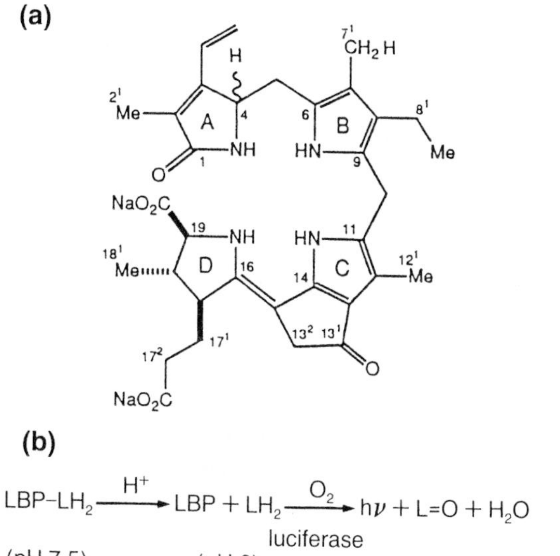

**(a)**

**(b)**

$$\text{LBP-LH}_2 \xrightarrow[\text{(pH 7.5)}]{\text{H}^+} \text{LBP} + \text{LH}_2 \xrightarrow[\substack{\text{luciferase}\\\text{(pH 6)}}]{\text{O}_2} h\nu + \text{L=O} + \text{H}_2\text{O}$$

**Fig. 8.** (a) Dinoflagellate luciferin, a tetrapyrrole, showing the location ($13^2$) of the oxygen addition and (b) the steps in the bioluminescent reaction.

is also inactive at pH 8; it is a large single polypeptide chain of about 136 kDa with three contiguous and intramolecularly homologous domains, each having luciferase activity.

Activity can be obtained in soluble extracts made at pH 8 simply by shifting the pH to 6; the luciferin is released from its binding protein and the luciferase assumes an active conformation. The p$K$ for both proteins is at pH 6.7. A similar activity can be found in the particulate (scintillon) fractions. Together, these results suggest that during extraction some scintillons are lysed with the proteins released into the soluble fraction, whereas others seal off at the neck and form closed vesicles. With the scintillon fraction, the *in vitro* activity is also triggered by a pH change and occurs as a flash (~100 ms), very close to that of the living cell, and the kinetics are independent of the dilution of the suspension. For the soluble fraction, the kinetics are dependent on dilution, as in an enzyme reaction.

## D. Cellular Flashing

The flashing of dinoflagellates *in vivo* is typically initiated by mechanical shear or cell stimulation, which has been shown to result in the generation of

a conducted action potential in the vacuolar membrane. It is postulated that as this action potential traverses the vacuolar membrane it sweeps over the scintillons, opening voltage-gated ion channels, thus allowing protons from the acidic vacuole to enter, causing a transient pH change in the scintillons and thus a flash. Spontaneous flashes also occur (Fig. 9A).

## E. Circadian Clock Control of Dinoflagellate Luminescence

Unlike bacteria, cell density and growth conditions have no effect on the development and expression of bioluminescence in dinoflagellates. However, in *G. polyedra* and some other dinoflagellates, luminescence is regulated by day–night light–dark cycles and an internal circadian biological clock mechanism. Spontaneous flashing (and also flashing in response to mechanical stimulation) is far greater during the night than during the day (and therefore flashes are more frequent), and a steady low-level emission (glow) exhibits a peak toward the end of the night phase. The regulation is attributed to an endogenous mechanism; cultures maintained under constant conditions (light and temperature) continue to exhibit rhythmicity (Fig. 9B), but with a period that is not exactly 24 hr—it is only about (*circa*) 1 day (*diem*) (thus the origin of the term).

Genes coding for molecular components of the circadian clock have been indentified and studied in several systems, and a mechanism involving negative feedback on the transcription of a gene by its protein product is postulated to be responsible for the rhythm. How such a mechanism might exert physiological control is not understood. In humans and other higher animals, in which it regulates the sleep–wake cycle and many other physiological processes, the mechanism involves the nervous system. However, it also occurs in plants and unicellular organisms, such as *G. polyedra,* in which daily changes in the cellular concentrations of luciferase, luciferin, and its binding protein occur. The two proteins are synthesized and destroyed each day, as are the scintillons in which they are located. Hence, the biological clock exerts control at a very basic level by controlling gene expression. This might explain the greater amount of lumines-

A

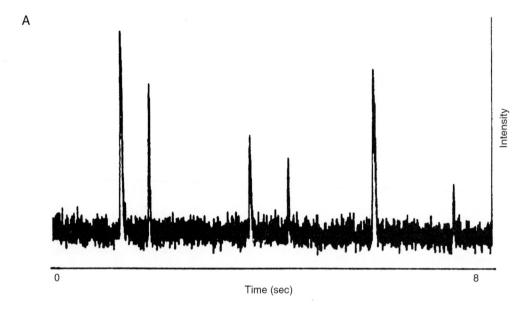

Time (sec)

B

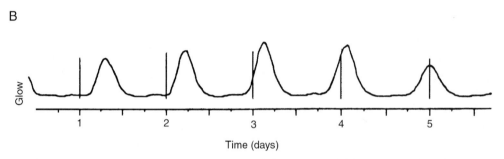

Time (days)

**Fig. 9.** Bioluminescent flashes and glow of *Gonyaulax*. (A) Oscilloscope trace (ordinate, light intensity; abscissa, time, 8 s) recording from a vial with 32,000 cells. Six flashes having durations of about 100 ms are superimposed on a background glow. (B) Recording for 5 days from a similar vial kept in constant conditions showing the circadian rhythm of the background glow. The frequency of flashing also exhibits a circadian rhythm (not shown).

cence at night, but a biochemical basis for the increased sensitivity to mechanical stimulation is not evident.

### III. FUNGI

### A. Occurrence, Habitats, Species, and Functions

Light emission now known to be due to fungi has been observed since ancient times and was noted by both Aristotle and Pliny. Robert Boyle placed "shining wood" in his vacuum apparatus and showed that light emission was reversibly extinguished by the removal of air, anticipating the requirement for molecular oxygen by all bioluminescent systems. Definitive knowledge of the fungal origin of luminous wood emerged during the nineteenth century from extensive studies of timbers used for support in mines, and by the mid-twentieth century about 80 luminous species had been inventoried. As in bacteria, the emission is continuous and not affected by mechanical stimulation, but it is really quite dim.

There is no indication that luminescence is regulated in relation to cell growth or density, but there is some evidence that nutrition may play a role. There have been reports that the luminescence is circadian regulated, as in dinoflagellates, but such results have not been confirmed or extended.

With one possible exception, all luminous fungi are basidiomycetes, and most are in the mushroom family; both the mycelium and fruiting body are luminous (Fig. 10). Such fungi occur in the many diverse habitats in which fungi occur, with the luminescence being visible most readily in dark forests—both tropical and temperate. The most striking reports describe luminescence from the interior or an infested tree split open by lightning.

The function of bioluminescence in fungi is not well understood. It has been suggested that the light serves as an attractant, which is consistent with the generalization that a continuous light emission acts in this way. If so, insects or other invertebrates might be attracted and enhance spore dispersal. However, this leaves the function of emission in the mycelium unexplained. The system might have evolved biochemically without constraints regarding its localization, and since it is probably not an energy-intensive function its value in any part of the life cycle could be adequate to justify its retention.

## B. Biochemistry

The spectrum of the light emitted has been determined from several species, all of which peak at about 525 nm, consistent with a flavin emitter. However, no biochemical evidence indicates this, and indeed no satisfactory understanding of the chemical basis for light emission has been obtained. Many years ago a luciferin–luciferase-type system was reported with a link to reduced pyridine nucleotide, comparable to the bacterial system. However, this has not been confirmed in more recent studies, which suggest that the reaction may be a nonenzymatic chemiluminescence.

### *See Also the Following Articles*

DINOFLAGELLATES • QUORUM SENSING IN GRAM-NEGATIVE BACTERIA

### *Bibliography*

Fisher, A. J., Raushel, F. M., Baldwin, T. O., and Rayment, I. (1995). Three dimensional structure of bacterial luciferase from *Vibrio harveyi* at 2.4 Å resolution. *Biochemistry* **34**, 6581–6586.

Hastings, J. W. (1994). The bacterial luciferase reaction: Model or maverick in flavin biochemistry? *In* "Flavins and Flavoproteins" (K. Yagi, Ed.), pp. 813–822. De Gruyter, Amsterdam.

Hastings, J. W. (1996). Chemistries and colors of bioluminescent reactions—A review. *Gene* **173**, 5–11.

Hastings, J. W. (1998) Bioluminescence. *In* "Cell Physiology" (N. Sperelakis, Ed.), 2nd ed., pp. 984–1000. Academic Press, New York.

Hastings, J. W., Kricka, L. J., and Stanley, P. E. (Eds.) (1997). "Bioluminescence and Chemiluminescence: Molecular Reporting with Photons." Wiley, Chichester, UK.

Roda, A., Kricka, L. J., and Stanley, P. E. (Eds.) (1999). "Bioluminescence and Chemiluminescence: Perspectives for the 21st Century." Wiley, Chichester, UK.

Taylor, F. J. R. (Ed.) (1987). "The Biology of Dinoflagellates. Blackwell, Oxford.

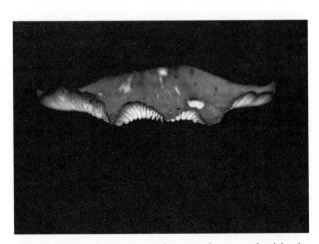

**Fig. 10.** Bioluminescent mushroom photographed by its own light (photograph by Dr. Dan Perlman). See color insert.

# Biomonitors of Environmental Contamination by Microorganisms

Marylynn V. Yates

*University of California, Riverside*

## GLOSSARY

**bacteriophages** Viruses that infect bacterial host cells; they usually consist of a nucleic acid molecule enclosed by a protein coat.

**coliform** A member of a group of bacteria that has traditionally been used as an indicator of the presence of pathogenic microorganisms in water.

**coliphages** Viruses that infect *Escherichia coli* bacteria.

**enteric microorganism** A microorganism that replicates in the intestinal tract of warm-blooded animals and is shed in fecal material.

**gastroenteritis** A clinical syndrome characterized by one or more of the following symptoms: nausea, vomiting, diarrhea, fever, and general malaise.

**BIOMONITORS, OR MICROBIAL INDICATORS,** are used to indicate the microbiological quality of air, water, and soil. Because it is impossible to test these media for all possible pathogenic microorganisms, it is desirable to find one microorganism (or group of microorganisms) that can be used to indicate whether or not pathogens are present. Although there is no perfect indicator organism, research is ongoing to find a microorganism that is a better indicator of the presence and behavior of some of the newly identified etiologic agents of waterborne disease than traditional indicators.

## I. SIGNIFICANCE OF MICROBIOLOGICAL CONTAMINATION OF THE ENVIRONMENT

### A. Waterborne Disease Outbreaks

Between 1920 and 1994, 1715 waterborne disease outbreaks involving more than 850,000 people and resulting in 1214 deaths were reported in the United States. These data are summarized in 10-year increments in Fig. 1. The numbers of reported outbreaks and the numbers of associated cases of illness have increased dramatically since 1971 compared with the period from 1951 to 1970. The increase in reported numbers of outbreaks may be due to an improved system for reporting implemented in 1971; however, it is still believed that only a fraction of the total number of outbreaks is reported. The trend in reported deaths from waterborne disease outbreaks is also noteworthy. There was a dramatic decrease in the number of deaths between the 1920s and the 1950s, and the number remained low through the 1980s. However, between 1991 and 1994, there were more than 100 reported deaths due to consumption of contaminated water. The majority of these deaths were associated with two outbreaks caused by *Cryptosporidium*, a protozoan parasite that causes gastroenteritis. The majority of the deaths occurred in indi-

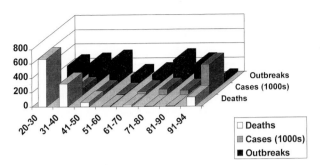

**Fig. 1.** Reported waterborne disease in the United States, 1920–1994.

viduals with weakened immune systems (e.g., people with AIDS or on cancer chemotherapy or immuno-suppressive drugs after organ transplants). There are concerns that, as the number of people with weakened immune systems increases as the population ages and more people are treated with immunosuppressive drugs, the number of people who may be at increased risk for serious health problems as a result of exposure to microbially-contaminated water will also increase.

Groundwater supplies more than 100 million Americans with their drinking water; in rural areas, there is an even greater reliance on groundwater because it comprises up to 95% of the water used. It has been assumed traditionally that groundwater is safe for consumption without treatment because the soil acts as a filter to remove contaminants. As a result, private wells generally do not receive treatment, nor do many public water supply systems. The United States Environmental Protection Agency (EPA) estimates that there are 158,000 public groundwater systems in the United States, only 30% of which disinfect their water prior to distribution for consumption. However, the use of contaminated, untreated, or inadequately treated groundwater has been a major cause of waterborne disease outbreaks in the United States since 1920. In the 1990s, the use of untreated or inadequately treated groundwater was responsible for 72% of the outbreaks that were reported in the United States (Fig. 2).

Causative agents of illness were identified in approximately one-half of the disease outbreaks during the period from 1971 to 1994 (Table I). The most commonly identified causative agents were *Giardia*, chemicals, and *Shigella*. In one-half of the outbreaks,

no causative agent could be identified, and the illness was listed as gastroenteritis of unknown etiology. However, recent results suggest that the majority of these outbreaks were caused by enteric viruses and parasites.

## B. Characteristics of Enteric Microorganisms

Microorganisms that infect the gastrointestinal tract of animals are termed enteric microorganisms. They are shed in feces and thus are present in domestic sewage. Enteric pathogens can be transmitted by exposure to domestic waste, whether through swimming in contaminated waters, ingesting contaminated water, or eating food derived from crops that have been irrigated with contaminated water or grown in contaminated soil. Many enteric pathogens can infect an individual without resulting in clinical illness. Thus, although the individual shows no signs of disease, he or she is excreting the organism in his or her fecal material. Others who contact the fecal material can become infected with the pathogen, through secondary infection.

Bacteria are microscopic organisms ranging from approximately 0.2 to 10 $\mu$m in length. They are distributed ubiquitously in nature and have a wide variety of nutritional requirements. Many types of harmless bacteria colonize the human intestinal tract and are routinely shed in the feces. One group of intestinal bacteria, the coliform bacteria, has historically been used as an indication that an environment has been contaminated by human sewage. In addition, pathogenic bacteria, such as *Salmonella* and *Shigella,* are present in the feces of infected individuals. Thus, a wide variety of bacteria are present in domestic wastewater.

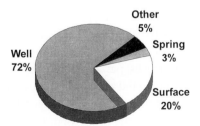

**Fig. 2.** Water source in disease outbreaks in the United States, 1991–1994.

***TABLE I***
**Causative Agents of Waterborne Disease in the United States, 1971–1994[a]**

| Causative agent | Outbreaks | | Illnesses | |
|---|---|---|---|---|
| | No. | % of total | No. | % of total |
| Gastroenteritis, unknown cause | 321 | 49.1 | 81229 | 14.4 |
| *Giardia* | 119 | 18.2 | 27039 | 4.8 |
| Chemical poisoning | 65 | 9.9 | 4233 | 0.7 |
| *Shigella* | 43 | 6.6 | 9219 | 1.6 |
| Viral gastroenteritis | 27 | 4.1 | 12699 | 2.2 |
| Hepatitis A virus | 26 | 4.0 | 772 | 0.1 |
| *Campylobacter* | 15 | 2.3 | 5456 | 1.0 |
| *Salmonella typhimurium* | 13 | 2.0 | 2995 | 0.5 |
| *Cryptosporidium* | 10 | 1.5 | 419939 | 74.3 |
| *Salmonella typhi* | 5 | 0.8 | 282 | <0.1 |
| *Yersinia* | 2 | 0.3 | 103 | <0.1 |
| Toxigenic *E. coli* | 2 | 0.3 | 1243 | 0.2 |
| *Vibrio cholera* | 2 | 0.3 | 28 | <0.1 |
| Chronic gastroenteritis | 1 | 0.2 | 72 | <0.1 |
| Dermatitis | 1 | 0.2 | 31 | <0.1 |
| Amebiasis | 1 | 0.2 | 4 | <0.1 |
| *Cyclospora* | 1 | 0.2 | 21 | <0.1 |
| Total | 654 | 100.0 | 565365 | 100.0 |

[a] From Yates and Gerba (1998). Used by permission of the publisher. Technoic Publishing Company, Lancaster, PA.

Viruses are obligate intracellular parasites; that is, they are incapable of replication outside of a host organism. They are very small, ranging in size from approximately 20 to 200 nm. Viruses that replicate in the intestinal tract of man are referred to as human enteric viruses. These viruses are shed in the fecal material of individuals who are infected either purposely (i.e., by vaccination) or inadvertently by consumption of contaminated food or water, swimming in contaminated water, or person to person contact with an infected individual. More than 100 different enteric viruses may be excreted in human fecal material; as many as $10^6$ plaque-forming units of enteroviruses (a subgroup of the enteric viruses) per gram and $10^{10}$ rotaviruses per gram may be present in the feces of an infected individual. Thus, viruses are present in domestic sewage and, depending on the type of treatment process(es) used, between 50 and 99.999% of the viruses are inactivated during sewage treatment.

A third group of microorganisms of concern in domestic sewage is the parasites. In general, parasite cysts (the resting stage of the organism which is found in sewage) are larger than bacteria, although they can range in size from 2 to more than 60 $\mu$m. Parasites are present in the feces of infected persons; however, they may also be excreted by healthy carriers. Cysts are similar to viruses in that they do not reproduce in the environment but are capable of surviving in the soil for months or even years, depending on environmental conditions.

Concentrations of several pathogenic and indicator microorganisms in untreated domestic wastewater are shown in Table II. Diseases that may be caused by ingestion of enteric microorganisms are shown in Table III.

## C. Sources of Microbial Contamination of the Environment

Microorganisms may be introduced into the environment in a variety of ways. In general, any practice

**TABLE II**

**Representative Concentrations of Pathogenic and Indicator Microorganisms in Untreated Domestic Wastewater**

| Microbial group | No. per liter |
| --- | --- |
| Total coliform bacteria | 100 million–1 billion |
| Fecal coliform bacteria | 10 million–100 million |
| *Salmonella* | 1 million–10 million |
| *Shigella* | 10–10,000 |
| Enteroviruses | 10,000–100,000 |
| Rotaviruses | 100–100,000 |
| *Giardia* | 100–100,000 |
| *Cryptosporidium* | 100–10,000 |
| Ascaris | 10–10,000 |

**TABLE III**

**Diseases Caused by Selected Enteric Pathogens**

| Pathogen | Disease |
| --- | --- |
| Bacteria | |
| *Campylobacter jejuni* | Gastroenteritis |
| Enteropathogenic *E. coli* | Gastroenteritis |
| *Legionella pneumophila* | Acute respiratory illness |
| *Salmonella* | Typhoid, paratyphoid, salmonellosis |
| *Shigella* | Bacillary dysentery |
| *Vibrio cholerae* | Cholera |
| *Yersinia enterocolitica* | Gastroenteritis |
| Protozoa | |
| *Cryptosporidium* | Diarrhea |
| *Entamoeba histolytica* | Amebic dysentery |
| *Giardia lamblia* | Diarrhea |
| *Naegleria fowleri* | Meningoencephalitis |
| Enteroviruses | |
| Adenovirus | Respiratory illness, eye infection, gastroenteritis |
| Astrovirus | Gastroenteritis |
| Calicivirus | Gastroenteritis |
| Coxsackievirus A | Meningitis, respiratory illness |
| Coxsackievirus B | Myocarditis, meningitis, respiratory illness |
| Echovirus | Meningitis, diarrhea, fever, respiratory illness |
| Hepatitis A virus | Infectious hepatitis |
| Norwalk virus | Diarrhea, vomiting, fever |
| Poliovirus | Meningitis, paralysis |
| Rotavirus | Diarrhea, vomiting |

that involves the application of domestic wastewater to the land has the potential to cause microbiological contamination of water because the treatment processes to which the wastewater is subjected do not effect complete removal or inactivation of the disease-causing microorganisms present. For example, expected removals of pathogenic microorganisms after various levels of wastewater treatment are shown in Table IV.

Viruses, enteric bacteria, and parasites may be introduced into the subsurface environment in a variety of ways. Viruses have been isolated from the groundwater beneath cropland being irrigated with sewage effluent. Viruses have also been detected in the groundwater at several sites practicing land treatment of wastewater. The burial of disposable diapers in sanitary landfills is a means by which pathogenic microorganisms in untreated human waste may be introduced into the subsurface. Viruses have been detected as far as 408 m downgradient of a landfill site in New York. Land application of treated sewage effluent for the purpose of groundwater recharge has also resulted in the introduction of viruses to the underlying groundwater.

Septic tank effluent may be the most significant source of pathogenic bacteria and viruses in the subsurface environment. Septic tanks are the source of approximately 1 trillion gallons of waste disposed to the subsurface every year and are frequently reported as sources of groundwater contamination.

Another source of microorganisms to the subsurface is municipal sludge. Land application of municipal sludge is becoming a more common practice as alternatives are sought for the disposal of the ever-increasing amounts of sludge produced in the United States. The sludge that is produced during the process of treating domestic sewage contains high levels of nitrogen and other nutrients that are required by plants. However, it may also contain pathogenic microorganisms at concentrations sufficient to cause disease if individuals are exposed to a sufficient quantity of the contaminated material (Tables V and VI).

## D. Risks Associated with Microorganisms in Water

As discussed previously, microorganisms (not chemicals) are the major cause of illness associated

***TABLE IV***
**Pathogen Removal during Sewage Treatment[a]**

|  | Enteric viruses | Salmonella | Giardia | Cryptosporidium |
|---|---|---|---|---|
| Concentration in raw sewage (no. l⁻¹) | 100,000–1,000,000 | 5,000–80,000 | 9,000–200,000 | 1–3960 |
| Removal during |  |  |  |  |
| Primary treatment[b] |  |  |  |  |
| % removal | 50–98.3 | 95.5–99.8 | 27–64 | 0.7 |
| No. remaining per liter | 1,700–500,000 | 160–3,360 | 72,000–146,000 |  |
| Secondary treatment[c] |  |  |  |  |
| % removal | 53–99.92 | 98.65–99.996 | 45–96.7 |  |
| No. remaining per liter | 80–470,000 | 3–1,075 | 6,480–109,500 |  |
| Tertiary treatment[d] |  |  |  |  |
| % removal | 99.983–99.9999998 | 99.99–999999995 | 98.5–99.99995 | 2–7[e] |
| No. remaining per liter | 0.007–170 | 0.000004–7 | 0.099–2,951 |  |

[a] From Yates and Gerba (1998). Used by permission of the publisher. Technoic Publishing Company, Lancaster, PA.
[b] Primary sedimentation and disinfection.
[c] Primary sedimentation, trickling filter/activated sludge, and disinfection.
[d] Primary sedimentation, trickling filter/activated sludge, disinfection, coagulation, filtration, and disinfection.
[e] Filtration only.

with the consumption of contaminated food and water. On a worldwide basis, in 1980 approximately 25,000 people died each day from consumption of contaminated water, and it has been estimated that 80% of all diseases in the world may be related to contaminated water. Food and waterborne diseases are one of the major causes of diarrhea, resulting in an estimated 1 billion cases every year in children younger than 5 years. In underdeveloped or developing countries, acute gastroenteritis is the leading cause of death of children younger than 4 years. The importance of waterborne disease in the United States is much less than that in developing countries. However, waterborne disease continues to occur, re-

sulting in millions of dollars of lost productivity in the workplace.

Based on recently reported waterborne outbreak data, the risk of acquiring an illness from contaminated water in the United States has been estimated to be approximately $4 \times 10^{-5}$ per year or $2.8 \times 10^{-3}$ during a lifetime. This risk estimate is probably low due to the fact that many waterborne outbreaks are not reported. There are several reasons for this including the fact that many waterborne pathogens cause gastroenteritis, which is generally not severe

***TABLE V***
**Summary of Microbial Reductions Attained during Sludge Treatment**

| Treatment | Reduction (%) | | |
|---|---|---|---|
|  | Bacteria | Viruses | Parasites |
| Anaerobic digestion | 99–99.9 | 99 | <10 |
| Aerobic digestion | 99–99.9 | 99 | <10 |
| Composting | 99.9–99.99 | 99.9–99.99 | 99.9–99.99 |
| Air-drying | 99.9–99.99 | 99–99.99 | 99–99.99 |
| Lime stabilization | 99.9–99.99 | 99.99 | <10 |

***TABLE VI***
**Microorganisms in Anaerobically Digested Sludge**

| Organism | No. per gram dry weight |
|---|---|
| Total coliform bacteria | 100–1 million |
| Fecal coliform bacteria | 100–1 million |
| Salmonella | 3–1,000 |
| Shigella | 20 |
| Enteroviruses | 0.2–210 |
| Rotaviruses | 14–485 |
| Giardia | 100–1,000 |
| Cryptosporidium | 1,250–38,700 |
| Ascaris | 0.5–9.6 |

**TABLE VII**
**Probability of Infection from Ingestion of One Organism[a]**

| Microorganism | Probability |
|---|---|
| Hepatitis A virus | 42/100 |
| Coxsackie B virus | 0.78/100 |
| Rotavirus | 27/100 |
| *Shigella* | 6.1/100 |
| *Campylobacter* | 1.8/100 |
| *Cryptosporidium* | 0.47/100 |
| *Giardia* | 1.96/100 |

[a] Adapted from Rose and Yates (1998).

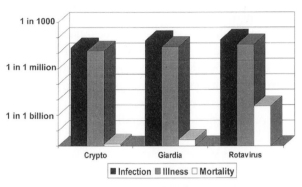

**Fig. 4.** Daily risk from exposure to 100 ml of treated wastewater (data from Rose and Carnahan, 1992).

enough to require medical attention. Therefore, unless many people are involved, the outbreak is unrecognized. Another reason is that reporting of waterborne disease outbreaks is not required in the United States. In addition, it is difficult to assess the number of cases of illness associated with waterborne pathogens because of secondary infection to individuals who were not directly exposed to the contaminated water.

The impacts of very low levels of pathogens in drinking water are very difficult to document. However, the fact that only one or two virus or parasite particles may be required to cause infection necessitates an attempt to quantitate this risk. The probability of infection resulting from the ingestion of one organism has been estimated for several different pathogens using data from dose–response curves derived from human feeding studies (Table VII). It is

important to remember that infection will not necessarily result in illness in all cases. The health risks from exposure to 100 ml of treated wastewater from a storage tank was estimated using the data from a wastewater treatment plant in Florida (Fig. 3). The risks of infection, illness, and mortality from ingesting three different microorganisms—*Giardia, Cryptosporidium,* and rotavirus—are shown in Fig. 4. It can be seen that although the risks of infection and illness are comparable among the three microorganisms, the risk of mortality from rotavirus is approximately 100-fold higher than that for the two parasites.

## II. INDICATORS OF MICROBIAL CONTAMINATION OF THE ENVIRONMENT

There are more than 100 different pathogens that may be excreted in the fecal material of an infected individual. Obviously, it would not be technically or economically feasible to test all drinking water or wastewater for the presence of all pathogens that could potentially be present. Therefore, in 1914 the United States Public Health Service adopted the coliform group of bacteria to serve as an indicator of the fecal contamination of drinking water. Since that time, all public water supplies have been routinely tested for the presence of coliform bacteria. The detection of coliform bacteria in drinking water is used as an indication that the water has been contaminated by fecal material and therefore may contain patho-

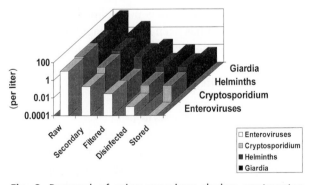

**Fig. 3.** Removal of microorganisms during wastewater treatment in St. Petersburg, Florida (data from Rose and Carnahan, 1992).

genic microorganisms. Drinking water that is found to contain coliform bacteria must be treated to inactivate any pathogens that may be present in the water and its distribution must be discontinued until the source of the problem has been ascertained and remedied. The absence of coliform organisms in water has been interpreted to mean that there has been no fecal contamination of the water supply and that pathogenic microorganisms are not present. The low rates of waterborne disease outbreaks (relative to those of other countries) that occur in the United States are due primarily to the implementation of the total coliform standard to assess the sanitary quality of water. However, as discussed previously, many waterborne disease outbreaks continues to occur every year in the United States.

## A. Concepts of an Indicator Organism

The lack of a consistent correlation between the presence of the traditional indicators of water quality (i.e., free chlorine residuals, coliform bacteria, and turbidity) and waterborne pathogens (especially viruses and parasites) has spurred efforts to identify a new indicator (or group of indicators) that would better reflect the virological and parasitological quality of water. Criteria for an ideal indicator microorganism have been discussed by many researchers during the past several years. The following is a compilation of the most important of these criteria:

An ideal indicator microorganism should:

1. Always be present when pathogens are present and always be absent when pathogens are absent
2. Be present at a density that has some constant, direct relationship to the density of the pathogen
3. Be present and detectable in all types of contaminated media
4. Be unable to reproduce in contaminated media
5. Be nonpathogenic to humans and easily identifiable
6. Survive in the environment at least as long as the pathogens survive
7. Be detectable by simple, rapid, and economical methods

Obviously, there is no one microorganism that can meet all these criteria. The microorganism used as an indicator should also be chosen on the basis of the particular application of the information.

Potential applications of an indicator include being an indicator of

1. Fecal contamination
2. The presence of domestic sewage
3. The presence of pathogens
4. The efficiency of a particular water or waste treatment process
5. The environmental fate of a pathogen of interest
6. The movement of particles suspended in water during subsurface transport

## B. Traditional Indicators

### 1. Total Coliform Bacteria

The total coliform group of bacteria is defined as all aerobic and facultative anaerobic, gram-negative, non-spore-forming, rod-shaped bacteria that ferment lactose with the production of gas within 48 hr at 35°C. The total coliform group consists of members of the genera *Citrobacter*, *Klebsiella*, and *Enterobacter*, and the species *Escherichia coli*. Coliform bacteria are shed in the feces of all humans at an average concentration of approximately $10^7$ to $10^8$ organisms per gram or $10^9$ to $10^{10}$ per day. Thus, total coliform bacteria can be, and are, used as indicators of the presence of fecal contamination. However, some members of the total coliform group are not specific to fecal material and may be found in uncontaminated soil or on vegetation. Therefore, the presence of total coliform bacteria is not definitive proof that the environment has been contaminated by fecal material. Another negative aspect of using total coliform bacteria as indicators is that some of them are capable of multiplying in environmental waters.

### 2. Fecal Coliform Bacteria or Thermotolerant Coliform Bacteria

The fecal coliform bacteria, sometimes called thermotolerant coliform bacteria, are a subgroup of the total coliform bacteria that are capable of fermenting lactose at 44.5°C. The majority of the coliform bacteria present in human fecal material are members of the fecal coliform subgroup which consists primarily of the bacterium *E. coli.* Bacteria in this group have been found to have a high correlation with the presence of fecal contamination from warm-blooded animals. Because fecal coliform bacteria are almost exclusively found in the waste of warm-blooded animals, this group more accurately reflects the presence of fecal contamination from animal waste in water than does the total coliform group. However, some bacteria that meet the definition of fecal coliform bacteria are members of the genus *Klebsiella,* which have been isolated from environmental samples not contaminated by fecal material.

### 3. Fecal Streptococci and Enterococci

Fecal streptococci and enterococci have also been used as indicators of fecal contamination, especially in bathing waters. *Streptococcus faecalis* is found in the feces of warm-blooded animals, including humans, whereas other streptococci, such as *S. bovis* and *S. equinus,* are specific indicators of nonhuman fecal contamination. *Streptococcus bovis* and *S. equinus* die off very rapidly in the environment; therefore, their presence is indicative of very recent fecal contamination by cattle and horses, respectively.

The ratio of the fecal coliform : fecal streptococci (FC : FS) concentrations in a sample has been used to indicate whether contamination is derived from a human or animal source. A FC : FS ratio of <0.7 is indicative of animal sources, whereas a FC : FS ratio of >4.0 is indicative of human sources. This relationship is only valid for very recent contamination (24 h) because fecal coliform bacteria may not survive as well as fecal streptococci, depending on the environmental conditions.

### 4. Heterotrophic Plate Count Bacteria

Heterotrophic plate count (HPC) bacteria (formerly called standard plate count bacteria) are all aerobic bacteria capable of growing on a defined organic carbon-containing medium such as plate count agar. Enumeration of the HPC bacteria in a sample does not indicate the level of public health risk that might be posed by the microorganisms in the sample because pathogenic bacteria are not differentiated from nonpathogenic bacteria. However, the HPC bacteria are used as an indicator of the overall

microbiological status of an environment. For example, the EPA has stated that the concentration of HPC bacteria in water from a well-operated water treatment plant and well-maintained drinking water distribution system should be well below 500 cfu/ml.

### 5. Anaerobic Bacteria

Many genera of anaerobic bacteria, including *Clostridium, Bacteroides,* and *Lactobacillus,* are present in human and animal fecal material. *Clostridium perfringens* is a spore-forming bacterium and, as such, persists for a relatively long time in the environment (compared to the coliform bacteria). This organism has been suggested for use as an indicator of past pollution because of its persistence in the environment. For the same reason, *Clostridium* spores have also been suggested as tracers of pathogen movement in the subsurface. However, the extreme resistance of bacterial spores to environmental stresses may render them inappropriate as indicators of the presence of pathogens, which are less resistant. Few data are available on the relative densities of *Clostridium* spp. and other indicators and pathogens in environmental samples.

Other potential indicators of fecal contamination are several species of *Bacteroides.* These anaerobic bacteria are present in fecal material at higher ccentrations than the coliform bacteria or fecal streptococci, and their potential for regrowth in the environment is lower than that of these indicators. However, the need to maintain strictly anaerobic conditions during the isolation and identification of these bacteria has resulted in little interest in their widespread use as indicators.

## C. New Indicators

An increasing amount of evidence collected during the past 20–25 years suggests that the coliform group may not be an adequate indicator of the presence of pathogenic viruses and protozoan parasites in water. In many waterborne disease outbreaks, coliform bacteria are not detected in the water, but pathogens are detected. In the large waterborne outbreak of cryptosporidiosis that occurred in Milwaukee, Wisconsin in 1993, for example, *Cryptosporidium* oocysts were isolated from the water, but coliform bacteria were not detected.

One group of microorganisms that has been proposed as an indicator of the presence of pathogenic viruses is the bacteriophages, which are viruses that infect bacteria. Bacteriophages have many of the same characteristics as human enteric viruses but are less expensive and much easier and less time-consuming to detect in environmental samples.

The use of bacteriophages, specifically coliphages (viruses that infect *E. coli*), as indicators of the efficiency of water and wastewater treatment processes in inactivating pathogens has received some study. As shown in Table VIII, viruses are generally more resistant to inactivation by disinfectants than are indicator bacteria. Parasites in general are more resistant to inactivation than either viruses or bacteria. Studies performed using MS2 coliphages have shown that it is usually one of the most resistant of the organisms tested, which has generated interest in its potential for use as an indicator for pathogenic viruses.

There is very little information on the effectiveness of various treatment processes against Norwalk virus and many of the other viral agents of waterborne gastroenteritis. More research is necessary to determine the resistance of these pathogens to various disinfection processes. The organism chosen as an indicator must be at least as resistant to treatment as the etiologic agents of the majority of the waterborne disease outbreaks.

Bacteriophages have also been used as models for pathogens in studies on the fate and transport of microorganisms through soil and groundwater systems. Chemicals, which are generally used as tracers of water and contaminant movement, are inappropriate tracers of microbial transport for several reasons. An important reason is size: microorganisms are so much larger than chemical molecules that they are transported only through large pores. Bacteriophages are the same size and possess many of the same adsorptive properties as pathogenic viruses, and thus they are attractive as models or surrogates. Comparative studies have shown that some bacteriophages are transported at least as far and survive for at least as long as hepatitis A virus and other enteric viruses, suggesting that bacteriophage may be acceptable model organisms. However, until data on the transport and fate behavior of Norwalk virus and other pathogenic human viruses are obtained, it is impossible to determine what organism is the best model to use for this purpose.

## III. REGULATIONS PERTAINING TO MICROBIAL CONTAMINATION OF THE ENVIRONMENT

Standards for allowable concentrations of indicator bacteria in water have been established by many organizations. Some of theses standards for drinking water and recreational fresh water are shown in Table IX.

The fact that microorganisms are responsible for numerous waterborne disease outbreaks led the EPA to propose maximum contaminant level goals

*TABLE VIII*
**Summary of C · t (mg/liter × min) for 99% Inactivation of Enteric Microorganisms by Disinfectants at 5°C[a]**

| Microorganism | Chlorine[b] | Chloramine[c] | Chlorine dioxide | Ozone |
| --- | --- | --- | --- | --- |
| *E. coli* | 0.04 | 95–130 | 0.48 | 0.02 |
| Poliovirus | 1.7 | 1420 | 0.2–6.7 | 0.1–0.2 |
| *G. lamblia* | 50–250 | 430–580 | — | 0.5–0.6 |
| *G. muris* | 250 | 1400 | 10.7–15.5 | 1.8–2.0 |
| *Cryptosporidium* | 7200 | — | — | 3 |

[a] From Yates and Gerba (1998). Used by permission of the publisher. Technoic Publishing Company, Lancaster, PA. C · t, concentration × time.
[b] pH 6.0.
[c] Preformed.

***TABLE IX***
**Drinking Water and Recreational Freshwater Standards for Indicator Microorganisms**

| Standards established by | Total coliform bacteria (per 100 ml) | | Fecal (thermotolerant) coliform bacteria (per 100 ml) | | Enterococci (per 100 ml) |
|---|---|---|---|---|---|
| | Drinking | Recreational[a] | Drinking | Recreational[a] | Recreational[a] |
| World Health Organization | 1–10 | | 0 | | |
| Canada | <10 | | 0 | 200 | 35 |
| European Economic Community | 0 | <10,000 | | <2000 | |
| United States | 0 | 2,002 | | | |

[a] Primary contact (swimming waters).

[b] This is a criterion rather than an enforceable standard.

(MCLGs) for viruses and *Giardia*, a protozoan parasite, in 1985. These standards are in addition to the standard for the indicator microorganism, total coliform bacteria. Rather than require public water systems to monitor the water for the presence of these pathogenic microorganisms, the EPA proposed treatment technique regulations to ensure that the levels of these pathogens would be reduced to nonharmful numbers in treated drinking water. In 1989, requirements for surface water treatment that require a minimum of 99.9% removal of *Giardia* and 99.99% removal of viruses were finalized. In 1994, the EPA proposed the Enhanced Surface Water Treatment Rule. In this rule, they proposed an MCLG of zero for *Cryptosporidium*. They also proposed several alternatives for required pathogen removal by treatment. These alternatives would require different levels of pathogen removal based on the quality of the source water.

Treatment requirements to protect the public from pathogens in groundwater used for public drinking water supplies have not been finalized. It is likely that a multiple-barrier approach will be taken, that includes elements such as source water protection, sanitary survey, monitoring, and possible disinfection in the distribution system.

The EPA also regulates the use and disposal of sewage sludge. In the regulations, sludge is classified based on requirements for pathogen and indicator organism reduction and/or specified maximum concentrations of pathogens and indicator organisms (fecal coliform bacteria and fecal streptococci). The crops that can be grown on the land and limitations of human and animal access to sludge-applied land are dependent on the class of sludge applied, with the strictest controls on land receiving the least treated sludge.

In addition to federal standards, several states have laws and regulations designed to minimize the potential for pathogen contamination of drinking water. For example, most states have prescribed minimum setback distances between septic tanks and drinking water wells. Setback distances range from 7.6 m in South Carolina to 122 m in Rhode Island and Massachusetts.

Another practice regulated by many states is the reuse of treated domestic wastewater. As stated previously, even tertiary treated sewage effluent may contain concentrations of pathogens high enough to pose a threat to human health. The state of California is revising its regulations pertaining to the use of reclaimed water for irrigation and other purposes. In a manner similar to the EPA's sludge standards, the California State Department of Health Services proposed different classifications for reclaimed water. These classifications include secondary reclaimed water, disinfected secondary reclaimed water (two classifications based on total coliform bacteria concentrations), and disinfected tertiary (secondary treatment plus coagulation, filtration, and disinfection) reclaimed water. The disinfected tertiary wastewater has been treated using processes that have been shown to reduce levels of viruses, parasites, and helminths to acceptable levels. This wastewater has relatively fewer restrictions on its use compared to the next class. The lowest classes are treated using processes that may not reduce the concentrations of pathogenic microorganisms to low enough levels to be safe for human contact. Therefore, the secondary reclaimed water can only be used for purposes such as irrigation of fiber crops.

## See Also the Following Articles

Bacteriophages • Enteropathogenic Bacteria • Enteroviruses • Wastewater Treatment, Municipal • Water, Drinking

## Bibliography

Bitton, G. (1994). "Wastewater Microbiology." Wiley, New York.

Gerba, C. P. (1996). Pathogens in the environment. *In* "Pollution Science" (I. L. Pepper, C. P. Gerba, and M. L. Brusseau, Eds.). Academic Press, San Diego.

Gerba, C. P. (1996). Municipal waste and drinking water treatment. *In* "Pollution Science" (I. L. Pepper, C. P. Gerba, and M. L. Brusseau, Eds.). Academic Press, San Diego.

Hurst, C. J. (Editor-in-Chief) (1997). "Manual of Environmental Microbiology." American Society for Microbiology Press, Washington, DC.

IAWPRC Study Group on Health Related Water Microbiology (1991). Bacteriophages as model viruses in water quality control. *Water Res.* **25**, 529–545.

Rose, J. B., and Carnahan, R. P. (1992). Pathogen removal by full-scale wastewater treatment. Report to Florida Department of Environmental Regulation, Tampa, FL.

Rose, J. B., and Yates, M. V. (1998). Microbial risk assessment applications for groundwater. *In* "Microbial Pathogens within Aquifers" (S. Pillai, Ed.). Springer-Verlag, New York.

Yates, M. V., and Gerba, C. P. (1998). Microbial considerations in wastewater reclamation and reuse. *In* "Wastewater Reclamation and Reuse" (T. Asano, Ed.). Technomic, Lancaster, PA.

# Biopesticides, Microbial

## Mark Alan Jackson

*United States Department of Agriculture, Agricultural Research Service*

## GLOSSARY

**biopesticide** A living microbial pathogen which selectively infects and kills its insect or weed host or which is a microbial antagonist of a plant pathogen. Infective propagules of the microbial biocontrol agent are mass produced and applied in an inundative fashion to control the target pest. Weed control (bioherbicide); insect control (bioinsecticide).

**classical biocontrol** The use of co-evolved, native predators or pathogens to control plants or insects which have become pests in a foreign environment. Control of the pest in the new environment is achieved through the introduction of native predators or pathogens. The goal of this control method is the establishment of an ongoing host–pathogen relationship which significantly reduces pest populations.

**endemic pathogen** A microbial pathogen of an insect or weed which is native to the environment in which its host occurs.

**glass state** A highly viscous liquid which appears to be solid. Biopesticides dried in the presence of various carbohydrates can be stabilized when encapsulated in the glass state formed by the carbohydrate.

**integrated pest management** The management of insect pests, weedy plants, and plant pathogens in agronomic crops using a combination of chemical pesticides, biopesticides, and cultivation practices.

**inundative biocontrol** The application of massive quantities of selective, aggressive microbial pathogens to control weeds, insects, and plant pathogens; also termed the biopesticide approach.

**THE IDEA OF USING MICROBIAL PATHO-GENS** of agronomic pests as a method of biological control dates back to the nineteenth century. Two approaches to biological control have been employed: the classical and the inundative or biopesticide approach. The classical approach to biocontrol is generally practiced on public or low-value lands where introduced weedy plants or insects have become pest problems due to the lack of natural pathogens and predators. Co-evolved, natural pathogens of the pest are introduced into the pest population with the hope that a host–pathogen relationship develops which keeps the pest in check. The inundative or biopesticide approach mimics chemical control practices in that massive quantities of specific, aggressive pathogens or antagonists of the pest are applied, as needed, for the control of targeted agronomic pests.

The loss of chemical control measures and public concerns regarding the wide-spread use of chemical pesticides have piqued commercial interest in the development of the biopesticide approach to pest control. Bacteria, fungi, and viruses are all used to control insects, weeds, and plant diseases. The use of bacterial biocontrol agents for the control of insects, plant pathogens, and weeds is based, principally, on the ability of selected bacterial strains to produce specific antimicrobial, insecticidal, or herbicidal compounds. Unlike bacterial biocontrol agents, most fungal biopesticides do not produce toxins to kill their pest host. Fungi possess the unique ability to actively infect, colonize, and kill their host. The selection of the appropriate biocontrol agent for a given pest is dependent on the biology of the pest–pathogen interaction. Bacterial biocontrol agents work well on insect pests that actively feed on plant tissues or as antagonists for suppression of plant diseases. Fungal biocontrol agents work well as contact bioinsecticides and bioherbicides, and for the control of various soil-borne plant diseases. The commercial use of all biopesticides is dependent on low-cost production methods, stable products with a shelf life of 6–18 months, and consistent pest control under field conditions. Commercial methods of production for biopesticidal propagules include the use of a living host, liquid culture fermentation, and solid substrate fermentation. All production methods must be optimized to yield high concentrations of stable, effective biopesticidal propagules. Desiccation is the principale method used to stabilize biopesticidal propagules. Prior to drying, the biopesticidal propagules are mixed with various formulations which can include glass-forming polysaccharides, desiccants, cryoprotectants, or antioxidants. Production, formulation, and application technology all play important roles in ensuring consistent pest control under field conditions. The development of living microbial biopesticides has augmented current chemical pest control measures by providing farmers with an additional pest control tool. The use of biopesticides in an integrated approach to pest management promises to further our pursuit of sustainable agricultural systems.

## I. MICROBIAL BIOCONTROL STRATEGIES

### A. Living Microbes

For more than 100 years, man has contemplated the use of microbial pathogens to control agronomic pests. In the late nineteenth century, renowned European scientists such as Le Caunte, Metchnikoff, and Pasteur were interested in the possibility of using fungal pathogens to control insect pests. Metchnikoff was the first to describe *Metarhizium anisopliae* "green muscardine" infections on the cereal cockchafer and suggested the use of the microorganism as a biological control agent. Subsequent studies showed

that an application of *M. anisopliae* spores could kill the cereal cockchafer and the sugar beet weevil via direct infection. Initial production methods focused on the use of the host insect or artificial media as a growth vehicle for the pathogen. The challenge then, and today, was and is the development of economic methods for the production of infective microbial propagules. Before economic methods for the mass-production of these early biopesticides were realized, interest in using these control measures waned with the discovery of cheap, effective chemical pesticides. Since the 1940's, chemical pesticides have been the method of choice for control of agronomic pests. Renewed interest in the use of biologically-based pest control measures has been brought about by the development of pest resistance to many chemical pesticides coupled with public concerns about the adverse impact of widespread chemical use on human health, food safety, and the environment. The control of weed and insect pests with living microbial agents is practiced using two approaches: classical biocontrol and inundative biocontrol.

The classical approach to biological control is based on the fact that many weedy plants and insect pests are organisms which have been transplanted from one part of the world to another (Fig. 1). Once established in their new environment, the plant or insect rapidly proliferates, due to the lack of predators or pathogens. Control of the pest is achieved by discovering natural enemies of the pest which co-evolved in their native environment. These predators or pathogens are then introduced into the new environment in which the weedy plant or insect pest presents problems. The goal of this approach is the establishment of an ecological balance in which the pest population is held in check by its natural enemies. Obviously, caution in releasing selective or benign predators or pathogens is an absolute requirement using this strategy. Since the classical approach to biocontrol is generally practiced by the use of a limited number of inoculations with the microbial control agent, there is little commercial interest in developing this approach. Classical biocontrol is generally a state-subsidized activity which is used in situations in which a noxious weed or insect pest occurs on public or low-value land. Using the classical biocontrol approach, rush skeletonweed has been effectively controlled in California and Australia with

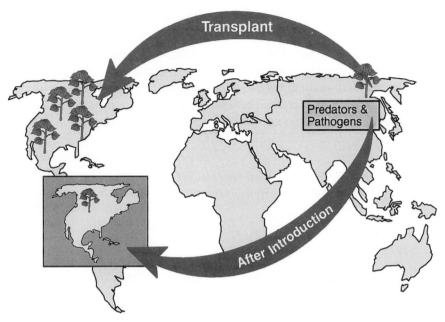

**Fig. 1.** The classical approach to biological control. Native predators and pathogens of an introduced weed or insect pest are introduced into the new ecosystem. Control occurs when the native enemies of the pest reduce the pest population to manageable levels. See color insert.

an insect predator and a fungal pathogen obtained from the weed's European homeland.

The inundative (biopesticide) approach to pest management with microbial pathogens has gained popularity in recent years for use in agronomic situations (Fig. 2). In this approach, an endemic microbial

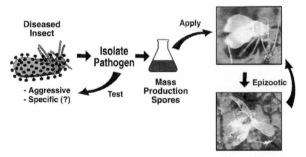

**Fig. 2.** The inundative (biopesticide) approach to biological control. This commercially attractive control measure uses aggressive, specific pathogens of the weed, insect, or plant disease to control these pests. The living microbial pathogen is mass produced and applied in an inundative fashion when pest control is required. After contact, the biopesticidal propagules infect and kill the pest host. Under appropriate conditions, the biopesticide may cause epizootics (insects) or epidemics (weeds) in the pest population. See color insert.

pathogens of an insect or weed pest is identified which is capable of rapidly infecting and killing the pest when applied in an inundative fashion. In the case of crop diseases, microbial antagonists are sought which inhibit the colonization by or growth of the disease-causing microorganism. Initial studies focus on finding aggressive antagonists or pathogens of the target pest. Pathogen specificity is examined by conducting host-range studies to ensure that the potential microbial control does not harm the agronomic or native plants in the growing region in which the agent will be used. The availability of a cost-effective method for mass-producing stable, infective propagules of the biopesticide must also be considered when selecting microbial biocontrol agents for commercial development. Once produced, the biopesticide is used in a manner similar to chemical pesticides. Weed or insect infestations are treated with an inundative application of the biopesticidal agent. Since the agent is specific for the target pest, only propagules which contact the host survive by germinating, penetrating, and growing in the weed or insect host. The inundative application of the infective biopesticidal propagules produces multiple infections in the weed or insect pest host which result in the death of the target pest. In a similar fashion, microbial antagonists are inundatively applied to seeds, seedlings, or stored fruits and vegetables at a time when infection by disease-causing organisms is probable. Microbial antagonists exclude disease-causing organisms by utilizing nutrients required by the pathogen or by producing antimicrobial secondary metabolites. The inundative approach to biocontrol does not produce a long-lasting control of the pest. Annual applications of the biopesticide provides the commercial incentive for developing these products.

## B. Insecticidal Toxins

Although the focus of this article is on the production of living microbial biopesticides, a brief discussion of the production and use of *Bacillus* toxins for control of insect pests is presented. Natural insecticidal toxins are produced by various *Bacilli* and have been commercially exploited for the control of insect pests. In 1901, the Japanese scientist Ishiwata identified *Bacillus sotto* (*thuringiensis*) as a pathogen on silkworm larvae. Since that time, numerous *B. thuringiensis* (*Bt*) isolates have been discovered which produce toxins against many important insect pests, including the Colorado potato beetle, diamondback moth, European corn borer, black-files, and mosquitos. These insecticidal toxins are widely used for the control of numerous insect pests. The toxins produced by *Bt* are crystalline proteins that are formed when the bacterium differentiates to form an endospore. Four types of crystalline protein toxins are produced by various *B* isolates based on the insecticidal spectrum of the toxin: CryI toxins, Lepidoptera specific; CryII, Lepidoptera and Diptera specific; CryIII, Coleoptera specific; and CryIV, Diptera specific. The crystalline proteins are protoxins which become active after ingestion by the insect. In the insect gut, protoxins are solubilized by the alkaline digestive juices and then hydrolyzed by proteolytic enzymes to form toxic fragments. The toxic protein fragments insert into the brush border membrane of the midgut of susceptible insects, disrupting the permeability barrier. Water and ions flow into the intestinal cells causing them to swell and burst. Insect feeding immediately ceases and death occurs within 2 or 3 days. In addition to the commercialization of insecticidal toxins produced by strains of *B. thuringiensis*, toxin-producing strains of *B. sphaericus* and *B. popillae* have been commercially developed for the control of mosquitos and Japanese beetle grubs, respectively.

Since the use of *Bt* toxins as a biologically based pesticide is not dependent on the production of a living microbe, various strategies have been used to obtain the toxic protein. Deep-tank fermentations under conditions which induce *Bt* sporulation and protoxin formation are routinely used to obtain the crystalline protein. Since *Bt* toxins are proteins, advances in molecular biology have expanded the possibilities for the production and delivery of this natural chemical pesticide. For example, to decrease fermentation times and avoid the need to induce *Bt* sporulation for protoxin production, the genes which encode for the synthesis of various *Bt* toxins have been cloned into fast-growing bacteria such as Pseudomonads. An even more interesting approach involves cloning *Bt* toxin genes into agronomic crops such as cotton and soybean. The *Bt* protoxin is produced in the plant biomass and delivered to the susceptible insect pest when it begins to feed on the crop. Although *Bt*-transformed crop plants ensure protection from insect pests without the need for pesticide application, there are fears that continued exposure of insect populations to a specific *Bt* toxin may lead to the development of resistance. To reduce the likelihood of resistance development, crop plants are being transformed with a variety of *Bt* toxins to reduce insect exposure to the same toxin year after year.

## II. BIOCONTROL MICROORGANISMS

### A. Bacteria

Bacteria are currently used to control weeds, insects, and plant pathogens. The control of insects with toxins of various *Bacillus* species was discussed (in Section I.B). Numerous living bacterial products for the control of weeds and plant pathogens are commercially available or in development (Table I). Bacteria are ideal biocontrol microbes for use in the control of plant diseases and postharvest diseases of fruits and vegetables. Seed coatings and seedling root

***TABLE I***
**Survey of Microbial Pathogens Commercially Produced or in Development for Use as Biopesticides**

|  | *Organism* | *Target pest* | *Method of production*[a] |
|---|---|---|---|
| Fungi | *Beauveria bassiana* | Insects | SS |
|  | *Metarhizium* spp. | Insects | SS |
|  | *Paecilomyces fumosoroseus* | Insects | LC |
|  | *Verticillium* spp. | Insects, plant diseases | ? |
|  | *Fusarium* spp. | Weeds, plant diseases | LC, SS |
|  | *Colletotrichum* spp. | Weeds | LC |
|  | *Phytophthora palmivora* | Weeds | LC |
|  | *Alternaria* spp. | Weeds | SS |
|  | *Trichoderma* spp. | Plant diseases | SS, LC |
|  | *Ampelomyces quisqualis* | Plant diseases | LC |
|  | *Candida oleophila* | Plant diseases | LC |
|  | *Coniothyrium minitans* | Plant diseases | LC |
|  | *Gliocladium virens* | Plant diseases | LC |
| Bacteria | *Bacillus* spp. | Insects, plant diseases | LC |
|  | *Pseudomonas* spp. | Weeds, plant diseases | LC |
|  | *Xanthomonas* spp. | Weeds | LC |
|  | *Burkholderia cepacia* | Plant diseases | LC |
|  | *Agrobacterium radiobacter* | Plant diseases | LC |
|  | *Streptomyces griseoviridis* | Plant diseases | LC |
| Viruses | Baculoviridae | Insects | IH |
|  | Bacteriophage | Plant diseases | IH |

[a] SS, solid substrate fermentation; LC, liquid culture fermentation; IH, in host.

dips with bacterial biocontrol agents effectively suppress fungal root diseases by rapidly colonizing root tissues and by producing antimicrobial compounds. Similarly, the application of bacterial biocontrol agents on fruits and vegetables prior to storage leads to the competitive exclusion of fungal and bacterial postharvest diseases. Most of the bacterial pathogens of weeds are incapable of directly infecting their host. The weedy plant must be compromised so that high concentrations of the bacterium can gain entry. For example, *Poa annua* (annual bluegrass) is a weed problem on golf courses. To infect *P. annua* with the bioherbicidal bacterium *Xanthomonas campestris,* the grass is mowed followed by the spray application of cells of *X. campestris*. The mowing exposes the vascular tissues of the grass and allows the bacterium to specifically colonize and kill the annual bluegrass.

Other bacterial biocontrol agents overcome host barriers to infection when sprayed in combination with wetting agents. The use of a surfactant allows the aqueous bacterial suspension to penetrate the waxy barrier which protects the stomatal tissue of the plant.

A major advantage to the use of bacterial biopesticides is ease of production. Since most bacteria are small, unicellular organisms, deep-tank liquid fermentation is used to rapidly produce high concentrations of infective agents. The spore-forming bacteria, such as *Bacillus subtillus,* are easily stabilized as dry preparations or seed coatings. Obtaining adequate shelf-life for many of the gram-negative bacteria which show promise as biopesticidal propagules is more difficult and currently the subject of considerable research effort.

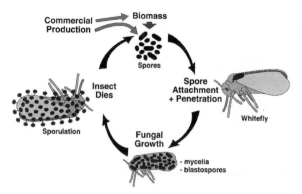

**Fig. 3.** The fungal infection cycle for *Paecilomyces fumosoroseus* In whiteflies. Spores attach to and penetrate through the insect cuticle. The fungus grows in a yeast-like fashion in the insect hemolymph consuming nutrients and, ultimately, killing the whitefly. Spores are produced on the insect cadaver leading to infections in other whiteflies.

## B. Fungi

Hundreds of fungal pathogens of weeds and insects have been identified which show promise as biopesticides. These potential biopesticides are aggressive pathogens which selectively infect and kill the pest host. The ability of fungal spores to directly infect and kill weeds, insects, and fungal plant pathogens is a key factor which has led to their widespread use as commercial biopesticides (Table I). Although fungal spores do not require that the host defenses be compromised for infection to occur, free moisture must be available during the time from spore germination to germ tube penetration into the host. Once in the host, the fungal pathogen spreads throughout the tissue consuming nutrients (Fig. 3). When the insect or weed host dies, the fungus erupts from the host tissue and sporulates on its surface, providing infective propagules for neighboring insect or weed pests. Under optimal conditions, epidemics or epizootics may occur in target weed or insect populations, respectively. Due to the hot, dry environments in which pest control products are often used in agriculture, the lack of free moisture is a major constraint to fungal infection by biopesticides. To overcome this constraint, spore production and formulation methods are sought which reduce the time required for spore germination and penetration into the host

(Fig. 4). The nutritional environment present during the growth and sporulation of fungal biopesticides has been shown to impact endogenous reserves within the spore which ultimately affect spore qualities such as desiccation tolerance, rate of germination, and biocontrol efficacy. Similarly, formulation can be used to provide a physical matrix around the spore which maintains a moist environment for the germinating spore and supplies external nutrients to augment spore germ tube penetration into the host.

A commercial constraint to the use of fungal biopesticides is the cost of production. Fungi grow more slowly than bacteria and often sporulate poorly or not at all in submerged culture. For commercial use, most fungal biopesticides must be capable of rapidly producing high concentrations of spores on either liquid or solid media.

## C. Viruses

Currently, the commercial use of viral biopesticides is limited to the control of insect pests. More than 1000 species of insects and mites are known to be susceptible to viral infections. Sixty percent of the viruses which infect insects belong to the family Baculoviridae (Baculoviruses). Baculoviruses are good candidates for use as biocontrol agents for insect pests since most baculoviruses will not infect plants or vertebrates and are pathogenic to insects which are important agronomic pests. To be infective, baculoviruses must be ingested by the insect. The digestive juices in the gut of the insect disaggregate virions or occlusion bodies, protective structure which contain viral particles, to release the infective virus. Through a series of complex replicative events, the viral particles infect cells throughout the insect, produce virions and occlusion bodies, and ultimately kill the insect. Massive numbers of infective viral particles are produced within the insect. Ingestion of viral-infected insect cadavers by other susceptible insects spreads the disease. A constraint to the commercial use of viral biopesticides is the time between infection and death of the insect host. Typically, viral infections take 4–6 days to kill the insect, during which time the insect continues to feed. Other constraints to the commercial use of viral biocontrol agents include cost of production and inactivation

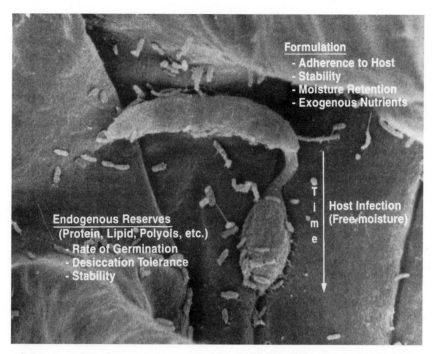

**Fig. 4.** Scanning electron micrograph of a *Colletrotrichum truncatum* conidium germinating and forming an appressorium (penetration structure) on the root of the weed hemp sesbania. The free moisture requirement for spore germination and host penetration is a major constraint to host infection which can be enhanced by optimizing nutrition and formulation (electron micrograph courtesy D. A. Schisler).

of viral particles by ultraviolet rays after spray application.

## III. SELECTION OF BIOPESTICIDES

A critical consideration in the development of a commercial biopesticide is the identification of the target pest and the agronomic crop in which it is a pest. In general, biopesticides are more expensive than chemical control measures. Therefore, to support the additional costs associated with the use of a biological control, the target pest should have a significant economic impact on a higher value crop. Likewise, the lack of chemical control measures and the propensity of the pest to become resistant to chemical pesticides are important positive selection factors for biopesticides. The environment in which the pest is a problem can also weigh heavily on potential commercial success. For example, biologi-

cal control of postharvest diseases of fruits and vegetables with microbial antagonists is strengthened by the fact that the temperature and humidity of the storage environment are controlled. Microbial biocontrol agents for postharvest use can be selected which flourish under the storage conditions in which they will operate. Likewise, greenhouses and irrigated crops, such as turf and vegetables, offer high-value crops which are grown under conditions in which temperature and moisture levels can be regulated. Controlled growth conditions enhance the likelihood that the biopesticide will provide consistent pest control under field conditions. Conversely, developing biopesticides for use in major row crops is more challenging. Consistent control of insect or weed pests with biopesticides in field crops such as cotton, corn, or soybean can be difficult due to the lack of environmental control. In addition, the size of the pest control market in these crops increases competition for low-cost effective control measures from the chemical pesticide producers.

Once a pest has been targeted, a bacterial, fungal, or viral pathogen must be discovered and developed. Insect and plant pathologists isolate pathogens of weed and insect pests by surveying the pest populations in the area where the agent is to be used for sick or dying individuals. The discovery and development of an endemic rather than foreign pathogen for use as a biopesticide reduces registration costs and increases chances for successful registration. Once the disease-causing agent is isolated, it must be evaluated in terms of pathogenicity. Many pathogens are capable of infecting the host but do not cause death. Some researchers have suggested that weaker pathogens can be effectively used as a biopesticide if they can reduce crop losses by lessening the competitiveness of the weed or stopping the feeding activity of the insect pest. Although there is validity to this approach, weak pathogens are not generally developed commercially as biopesticides. Aggressive microbes that cause rapid death of the pest when applied in an inundative fashion are favored candidates for biopesticide development. Once an aggressive pathogen is isolated, host-range studies must be conducted. The pathogen must selectively infect the target pest. Crop and native plants, beneficial insects, and native fauna in the environment in which the biopesticide is to be used must be unaffected by the agent.

After identifying a specific, aggressive pathogen of the target pest, the selection process focuses on the commercial potential of the organism. For commercial consideration, low-cost methods must exist or be developed for the rapid production of high concentrations of effective, stable biopesticidal propagules. In general, fungal pathogens which produce large, multicellular spores, sporulate slowly or poorly in liquid or solid media or that require a living host to produce infective propagules are poor candidates for commercial development. Most bacteria can be rapidly produced to high concentrations using deep-tank fermentation. As previously noted, viral pathogens must be produced *in vivo* on the pest and are therefore more expensive to produce than fungi or bacteria. Higher cost viral pathogens are generally targeted for the control of serious insect pests in high-value crops.

## IV. PRODUCTION METHODS FOR BIOPESTICIDES

### A. Living Host

The life or disease cycle for a plant and insect pathogen involves infection of the host, growth of the pathogen within in the host, and the production of infective structures. Fungal pathogens produce spore masses or sclerotial structures within or on the host, bacterial pathogens of insects, such as various *Bacillus* species, produce bacterial spores in the insect cadaver and viruses produce massive quantities of viral particles within the insect host. Since many pathogens are obligate parasites, production of the pathogen in the host is often the only method available. Examples of biopesticidal agents which must be produced in a living host are the insect viruses, the rust fungi, and some spore-forming bacteria. The production of a biopesticide in a living host has been employed for regional or small-scale usage or for the classical approach to biocontrol. For use as an inundative biocontrol agent, inexpensive methods for producing large quantities of infective propagules of the biopesticide are required. In general, production of a biopesticide in a living host is cost prohibitive. Technical challenges in scale-up of the production process include maintenance of a healthy, aseptic host population and harvesting of the living biopesticidal propagule without contamination by unwanted organisms. Quality assurance is a critical requirement for biopesticide usage since the inundative application of the microbe is conducted under conditions conducive to pathogen infectivity. If deleterious microorganisms are harvested along with the biopesticide, diseases may be transmitted to the crop or farm worker. Currently, only a few viral biopesticides for insect control and *B. popillae,* a spore-forming bacterial biopesticide for control of the Japanese beetle grub, are being produced using living hosts. The majority of biopesticidal products are produced using liquid culture and solid substrate production methods (Fig. 5).

### B. Liquid Culture Fermentation

Since the development of the pharmaceutical industry in the 1940s, the use of liquid culture fermen-

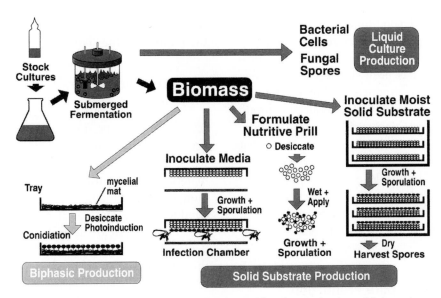

**Fig. 5.** Outline of the production methods used for the production of living microbial biopesticides. Liquid culture fermentation, solid substrate fermentation, and biphasic production are the most widely used commercial production methods.

tation has been the method of choice for the industrial production of various microbial products. Biopesticide production is no exception. For biopesticides such as bacteria or fungi, which sporulate in liquid culture, deep-tank fermentation provides a rapid, simple method of production (Fig. 5). All commercial biopesticide production methods, other than the use of a living host, share common beginnings which include the use of liquid culture fermentation. Briefly, the production process for biopesticides begins with the development of stable stock cultures. Typical storage methods for stock cultures include air-drying, freeze-drying, freezing at ultralow temperatures, submersion in oil or sterile water, and maintenance in host material. Stock cultures of the biopesticide are used to inoculate shake flask starter cultures. Liquid cultures of the fungal or bacterial biopesticide are then serially transferred to increasingly larger vessels, depending on the scale at which production will be conducted. An obvious requirement for this scale-up process is a stable culture which consistently produces high propagule yields and efficacious biopesticidal propagules after repeated growth cycles. In the case of liquid culture production for fungal spores or bacterial cells, this scale-up process is repeated until a sufficiently large

volume of product is produced. For solid substrate or biphasic production methods for fungal biopesticides, the biomass obtained from the liquid culture scale-up process is used as inoculum for the solid substrate growth phase or as spore-forming mycelium (Fig. 5).

There are numerous advantages to the use of liquid culture fermentation methods for biopesticide production. Liquid culture fermentations are relatively low-cost, automated processes that can be scaled up to very large volumes. The technology needed to carry out deep-tank fermentation processes has been perfected from years of use in the pharmaceutical and beverage industries. Temperature, pH, dissolved oxygen, and nutritional components, factors which can dramatically impact biopesticide yield and fitness, can be controlled in modern fermentation equipment. Recent studies have shown that the nutritional environment in which biopesticides are produced has a significant impact on the quantity and quality of microbial biocontrol agents. The ability of fungal spores to germinate rapidly, form infection structures frequently, and survive drying and storage has been linked to the nutritional environment in which they are produced. Since cultures grown in deep-tank fermentations are in a homogenous environment, nutritional conditions can be optimally controlled for the production of effective biopesticidal propagules. In addition, downstream processing equipment has been developed to harvest and dry biopesticidal products. Although virtually all bacterial biocontrol agents are produced in liquid culture, most fungal biopesticides are not. Many fungi do not sporulate in liquid culture. Those that do sporulate in liquid culture often produce spores that are short-lived or unable to survive drying. Until the technical constraints which limit the shelf life of liquid culture-produced fungal spores are resolved, alternative production methods for these biopesticides must be used.

## C. Biphasic Spore Production

The biphasic spore production method can be used to produce conidia for some fungal biopesticides which cannot be induced to sporulate in liquid culture. This method begins with the liquid culture production of fungal biomass of the biopesticidal agent. The liquid medium provides the culture with an appropriate diet so that nutrients necessary for spore production are sequestered in the fungal mycelium. To induce sporulation, the mycelial biomass is dewatered into thin mycelial mats which are then slowly air-dried, often in the presence of periodic light (Fig. 5). As the biomass dries, sporulation occurs on the surface of the mycelial mat. High concentrations of spores of the fungus *Altermaria cassiae,* a biocontrol for the weed sicklepod, have been produced using this technique. An advantage of this method is that fungi which do not sporulate in submerged culture can be induced to sporulate after one growth cycle in liquid culture. Fungal spore production on solid substrates requires an additional growth cycle on the solid substrate. Scale-up is a disadvantage to the use of the biphasic production method. The production of commercial quantities of biopesticidal spores using this method requires immense, sterile rooms in which the mycelium can be dried and sporulated. Water removal, gas exchange, temperature control, and aseptic conditions are all technical hurdles which are not easily remedied as the scale of production increases. Additional costs are incurred during the spore harvest process.

Again, aseptic conditions must be maintained during the removal of the spores from the mycelial mat.

## D. Solid Substrate Fermentation

The use of solid substrate fermentation is generally restricted to the production of fungal biopesticidal agents. This technique involves inoculating a nutritive solid substrate, usually moistened grains or inert material soaked with liquid nutrients, with fungal biomass. The fungus is provided an environment conducive to growth as it consumes the nutrients present in the solid substrate. After the fungus has depleted these nutrients, aerial spores are formed on the solid surface of the medium. A major advantage to the use of the solid substrate production methods is the fact that most fungi identified as potential biopesticides are imperfect fungi (deuteromycetes) which are amenable to aerial spore formation when grown on solid substrates. Due to the relative simplicity of the process, this method is widely practiced on a commercial scale, particularly in underdeveloped countries in which inexpensive labor is readily available. The use of solid substrate sporulation for the production of biopesticides can be practiced in various ways (Fig. 5). Trapping devices, granular products, and sprayable spore preparations can all be obtained using solid substrate production methods. The production method of choice is dictated by the target pest, available application methodology, and labor costs. For instance, if the biopesticide is to be used as a contact biopesticide for control of weeds or sessile insects, spore preparations must be produced which can be applied as a spray. In the underdeveloped countries of Africa, Latin and South America, Asia, and Eastern Europe, a common solid substrate production method employs the use of small bags of moistened, autoclaved grains. The bags are slit open, inoculated with liquid cultures of the fungal biopesticide, and resealed. After the growing fungal culture consumes the nutrients in the grain, the bags are opened and the contents allowed to dry. The drying process induces sporulation. By using small bags, temperature and gas exchange can be moderately controlled. The spores are collected from the moldy grains by rinsing, vacuuming, or grinding the sporulated solid substrate. This method is used for the production of spores of the fungal bioinsecticides *Beauveria bassiana*, *Metarhizium anisopliae*, and *M. flavoviride*. In developed countries such as the United States, labor costs and quality assurance issues prohibit the use of this solid substrate production method.

More advanced solid substrate fermentation methods, similar to those used in producing fermented foods in Asia, are employed in developed countries such as the United States. Moistened grains or inert solid substrates soaked with liquid nutrients are inoculated with fungal biomass obtained from deep-tank fermentations. The inoculated solid substrates are then either spread thinly onto trays which are placed in the solid substrate fermentor or placed in bulk in fermentors with mixing capabilities. The moisture, temperature and gaseous environment must be controlled during the growth and sporulation processes. Because these environmental conditions can be difficult to control in solid substrate fermentors, moderate volume fermentors are generally employed. Scale-up involves increasing the number of moderately sized fermentors. After the nutrients in the grain have been consumed by the growing fungal culture, air flow in the fermentor is increased to dry the biomass and to induce sporulation. Sporulation occurs on the surface of the solid substrate. Optimizing particle size and surface-to-volume ratios increases spore yields. After sporulation is completed and the whole culture is dried, either spores are separated from the biomass or the entire dried product is ground to a fine powder to allow for spray application. Conidia powders of biopesticidal fungi such as *B. bassiana*, *M. anisopliae* and *Trichoderma harizium* are produced in the United States and Europe using these methods. If the product is to be used as a granular application, such as soil amendments of various *Trichoderma* strains for control of seedling damping-off disease, sprayable spore powders are not required.

Another solid substrate production method involves the inoculation of nutritive prills with liquid culture-produced fungal biomass. These inoculated prills are immediately dried to stabilize the inoculum within them. Nutritive prills are produced for use as granular inoculum for the control of plant diseases and mobile Insects. The rewetting of the prill allows the fungal biopesticide to grow, consume the nutrients present in the prill and, subsequently, sporulate on the surface of the prill. In this case, the spores of the biopesticide are produced *in situ*. Mobile insects become infected by the biopesticide after contact with the sporulated prill. For plant disease control, the nutritive prills are applied in the rhizosphere in proximity to the growing plant. Spores produced on the prill inundate the root system, colonize, and competitively exclude disease-causing microbes. A disadvantage of the prill production method is the requirement for *in situ* conditions which are conducive to the growth and sporulation of the biopesticide and passive contact of the pest by the infective propagule.

Bait stations are another interesting approach to the *in situ* solid substrate production of fungal spores. The control of insect pests such as termites and roaches with spray-applied biopesticides is impractical due to the secretive nature of these pests. Bait stations containing media inoculated with the fungus *M. anisopliae* were designed to control these pests. The trap is activated by initiating fungal growth and sporulation on the nutritive medium. Roaches or termites entering the trap become inoculated with spores of the fungus and carry the infection back to their nests. Continued exposure of the pest population to the fungal pathogen leads to the development of an epizootic within the termite or roach colony. The trap design enhances spore viability by the production of fresh spores at the point of use and by protecting spores in the trap from adverse environmental conditions, such as ultraviolet radiation. Biopesticide bait stations for termites and insects are excellent examples of how understanding the behavior of the insect pest can be used to design effective biological control strategies.

Although solid substrate production methods for fungal biopesticides are widely used, there are disadvantages. This method of production is generally more expensive than biopesticide production using deep-tank liquid fermentation. Solid substrate fermentations require two growth phases since the inoculum for the solid substrate is produced in liquid culture (Fig. 5). The technical constraints associated with scale-up, such as mass transfer of oxygen, removal of carbon dioxide, temperature control, and reactor size, all translate into increased production costs. Quality assurance is also an issue in underdeveloped countries where more primitive solid substrate production methods are employed.

## V. BIOPESTICIDE STABILIZATION

### A. Drying Microbes

Biopesticides are living microbial products. The commercial use of these products requires that they be stable and have a shelf life of 6–18 months. Stabilization in terms of commercial use as a living biopesticide is much different than stabilization of microbes for maintenance in a culture collection. Although losses of 99.99% are acceptable in preserved cultures, microbial biopesticides must maintain more than 50% and ideally > 75% survival after storage. Losses in viability translate directly into increased product usage and product cost. Drying is a preferred method for stabilizing microbes. Compared to wet microbial preparations, dried preparations are more temperature stable, less susceptible to microbial contamination, less expensive to transport, and in general easier to use. The removal of water from a living cell drastically reduces metabolic activity. Many microbial propagules are designed to survive the desiccation process. The goal of the industrial microbiologist is to optimize production, drying, and storage conditions so that the desiccation tolerance of the biopesticidal propagule is maximized. Drying living microbial products involves two important processes: dehydration and rehydration. During the dehydration process, the cell loses water and the osmotic pressure within the cell increases due to the increasing solute concentration. Both these processes can cause cell death. The removal of water can disrupt cell membrane integrity and denature proteins. Likewise, osmotic stress can disrupt cellular functions leading to cell death. Once dried, basal metabolic activity continues within the cell. Drying cells to an appropriate moisture level which minimizes metabolic activity without destroying cellular activity is necessary for cell stabilization. The gaseous environment present during storage of the desiccated cell

can also impact storage stability. The removal of oxygen from the storage environment has been shown to improve cell survival. An equally important event in determining cell survival after desiccation is the rehydration of the cell. The rapid influx of water can physically damage the cell membrane and inhibit cell components from obtaining their biologically active conformation. A gradual rehydration of the desiccated cell often will improve cell survival. Two methods commonly used to gradually rehydrate desiccated cells are exposure of the desiccated cells to an atmosphere of high relative humidity and initial rehydration in an aqueous solution of high osmotic strength. Both methods allow dehydrated cells to slowly imbibe water. On a commercial scale, three basic methods of drying are used: spray-drying, air-drying, and freeze-drying. The spray-drying process involves delivering a fine mist of the product into a large chamber through which hot air is passed. The fine particle size of the product coupled with the elevated temperatures leads to rapid drying of the product. The higher temperatures and the rapid removal of water are physical conditions which are detrimental to cell survival. Because of these features, spray-drying is used infrequently for the drying of biopesticides. The greatest success in maintaining cell viability after drying has occurred with the use of air-drying and freeze-drying. The term "air-drying" is used in this context to describe cell drying techniques which incorporate ambient drying temperatures. In this process, cells are generally mixed with a filter aid, dewatered, and slowly dried with ambient temperature air. Diatomaceous earth is often used as a filter aid and provides the additional benefit of enhancing the friability of the dried product. Once the biopesticidal product has been mixed with the filter aid and dewatered to a wet cake of approximately 65% moisture, the drying process begins. The air-drying process requires 6–20 hr and can be performed in various commercial dryers, such as tumbler dryers, rotating blade dryers, turbo dryers, and fluidized bed dryers. The slow removal of water inherent in air-drying systems allows the cells time to adjust to the desiccated environment and osmotic stress associated with drying. The final moisture content in the dried microbial product is determined by the drying time and by the relative humidity of the drying air. A final moisture content of 1–4% has been shown to enhance cell survival. Air dryers are relatively inexpensive to operate and require lower capital costs compared to those for spray-drying or freeze-drying. Of all the drying methods, freeze-drying is the gentlest and the most expensive. In freeze-drying, the cell preparation is dewatered by filtration or centrifugation, frozen, and placed under a vacuum. The water is slowly removed by sublimation. Freezing helps maintain cell integrity as the water is removed. During the primary drying phase, free water present in the cell is removed. The product moisture content after primary drying is generally between 4 and 8% depending on the medium in which the cells are suspended. In secondary drying, heat energy is applied to the product and water which is bound to the cellular components is removed. In general, higher cell viability is observed when only part of the bound water is removed. Maximal cell survival and shelf life are often obtained when cells are dried to a final moisture content of 1–3%. Although higher moisture content can increase initial cell survival, a positive correlation between lower water content in the cell and cell survival during storage suggests that a higher moisture content is not necessarily desirable. Cell survival rates of 70–90% are often obtained with freeze-drying. Good storability has also been noted with freeze-dried living microbial preparations stored at refrigerated temperatures. Although freeze-drying is an excellent method for stabilizing living microbial products, its higher cost has limited its use for the production of many biopesticides. With all drying methods for biopesticides, the ultimate goal is long-term stability under a range of storage conditions. Various formulations have been employed to aid in cell survival after drying. Many polysaccharides will form a glass state during the desiccation process. The glass state is believed to stabilize cellular components in the dried cell and reduce the basal metabolic rate of the cell. By mixing biopesticidal cells in aqueous suspensions of glass-forming polysaccharides, stable formulations of the cell can be produced. Cell survival is also enhanced by formulations which contain desiccants and antioxidants. Reductions in free water and oxygen help lessen the basal metabolic activity of the dried cells.

## B. Freezing

Another commonly used method of storing cells is freezing. In the presence of cryoprotectants which inhibit ice crystal formation in the cells during freezing, many microbial cells can survive the freezing process and remain viable for an indefinite period of time. Bacterial cells or fungal spores are often easily preserved in this manner. The freezing process is relatively inexpensive, and produces cell suspensions with high survival rates and good storage stability. The commercial use of frozen biopesticides is impeded by shipping and handling problems. Most pesticide distributors and farmers do not have adequate frozen storage facilities to handle the biopesticidal material required to treat hundreds of acres of farmland. The shipping cost associated with frozen products is also problematic. This approach has been used with a high-value bacterial biopesticide *X. campestris,* which is the only effective control measure for a weedy grass of golf courses. The high value of this biopesticide allows the product to support the additional costs associated with shipping and handling a frozen product.

## C. Storage Environment

The storage environment can have a dramatic impact on the stabilization of microbial biopesticides. As a general rule, storing microbial preparations at lower temperatures increases long-term survival. Again, the relationship between elevated temperature and increased basal metabolic activity is likely responsible for increased cell survival at lower temperatures. From a commercial standpoint, there is a trade-off between the expense of storage at lowered temperatures and increased product stability. The use of living microbial agents as biopesticides will likely require cold storage for these agents. The storage atmosphere can also dramatically affect cell stability. The removal of oxygen and maintenance of stable moisture levels within the stored product are essential for long-term cell survival. Purging the cell preparation with nitrogen, vacuum packing, and the addition of antioxidants can all be used to remove oxygen from the storage environment. The relative humidity of the storage environment can be regulated by adequate drying and the addition of desiccants to the dried cell preparation.

## VI. COMMERCIALIZATION OF BIOPESTICIDES

The commercial development of a microbial biopesticide comprises a complex series of developmental steps which requires researchers to draw from numerous scientific disciplines (Fig. 6). Commercial interest in controlling troublesome weeds, insects, and plant pathogens guides insect and plant pathologists to discover specific, aggressive pathogens of these pests. If these potential biopesticides meet the requirements for host-range specificity and biocontrol efficacy under field conditions, microbiologists and fermentation engineers determine if low-cost production methods can be developed. Commercial use of these agents will require low-cost methods for producing high concentrations of stable, infective propagules. Formulation chemists work with the fermentation scientists to maximize propagule stability and efficacy. In the case of fungal biocontrol agents, both the nutritional environment during spore production and the exogenous nutrients provided by the formulation can impact stability and efficacy (Fig. 4). After the production and formulation of the biopesticide are optimized, agricultural engineers must determine a suitable application technology for the biopesticide. Registration of the product with the appropriate regulatory agency must also

be pursued. Registration of a biopesticide involves evaluating the environmental impact of applying large quantities of the biopesticidal organism in the environment along with the human and animal health risks associated with the use of the biopesticide. After overcoming these developmental hurdles, the biopesticide must then be packaged, marketed, and distributed to the end user. Current biopesticides usage represents <1% of the pest control market. The recent registration of numerous microbial biocontrol products and the expected entry of other products in the near future suggest that this percentage will increase. Public concerns regarding human safety and the environmental consequences of widespread chemical use for pest control have provided the impetus for the development of safer chemical pesticides and alternative methods of pest control. The use of natural pathogens of pests as biological controls is a promising alternative to less environmentally friendly control measures. It is envisioned that biopesticides will not replace chemical control measures but rather will be used with chemicals in an integrated approach to pest management. By rotating chemical and biopesticide usage for the control of various pests, resistance to the chemical pesticide is impeded and chemical pesticide usage is reduced. The integrated pest management approach provides a sustainable methodology for pest control. Sustainable agricultural systems are an absolute necessity if we are to continue to enjoy a safe, plentiful food supply.

### See Also the Following Articles

BIOLOGICAL CONTROL OF WEEDS • INSECTICIDES, MICROBIAL • PLANT PATHOGENS

### Bibliography

Burges, H. D. (1986). Production and use of pathogens to control insect pests. *J. Appl. Bacteriol. Symp. Suppl.* 127–137.

Campbell, R. (1989). "Biological Control of Microbial Plant Pathogens." Cambridge Univ. Press, Cambridge, UK.

Chamley, A. K. (1991). Microbial pathogens and insect pest control. *Lett. Appl. Microbiol.* **12**, 149–157.

Churchill, B. W. (1982). Mass production of microorganisms for biological control. *In* "Biological Control of Weeds with Plant Pathogens" (R. Charudattan and H. L. Walker, Eds.), pp. 139–156. Wiley, New York.

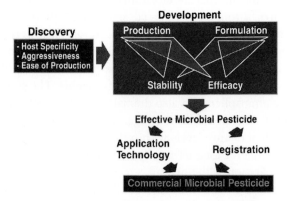

**Fig. 6.** The developmental sequence for the commercialization of microbial biopesticides.

Glazer, A. N., and Nikaido, H. (1995). Microbial insecticides. *In* "Microbial Biotechnology," pp. 209–240. Freeman, New York.

Jackson, M. A. (1997). Optimizing nutritional conditions for the liquid culture production of effective fungal biological control agents. *J. Ind. Microbiol. Biotechnol.* **19**, 180–187.

Stowell, L. J. (1991). Submerged fermentation of biological herbicides. *In* "Microbiological Control of Weeds" (D. O. TeBeest, Ed.), pp. 225–261. Chapman & Hall, New York.

Templeton, G. E., and TeBeest, D. O. (1979). Biological weed control with mycoherbicides. *Annu. Rev. Phytopathol.* **17**, 301–310.

Zorner, P. S., Evans, S. L., and Savage, S. D. (1993). Perspectives on providing a realistic technical foundation for the commercialization of bioherbicides. *In* "Pest Control with Enhanced Environmental Safety" (S. O. Duke, J. J. Menn, and J. R. Plimmer, Eds.), pp. 79–86. American Chemical Society, Washington, DC.

# Biopolymers, Production and Uses of

## William R. Finnerty

*Finnerty Enterprises, Incorporated*

**BIOPOLYMERS** are natural substances derived from a variety of plant and microbial sources. Most biopolymers are high-molecular-weight polysaccharides that yield solution properties of broad commercial relevance.

Biopolymers are either hydrophobic or hydrophilic with physical properties that impart either gelling or highly viscous solutions in water at a low dry weight concentration of biopolymer. The term "gum," as adopted by industry, refers to all plant or microbial polysaccharides that are dispersible in cold or hot water, producing viscous mixtures or solutions. Historically, the sources of gums are wide and varied, including plant exudate gums, seaweed gums, seed gums, starch, cellulose, and microbial gums. In recent years, unique microbial biopolymers have emerged that reflect the polymerization of β hydroxy acids of various carbon chain lengths. Other biopolymers that are chemically and structurally different from polysaccharide gums are DNA, RNA, and protein, all of which are not discussed in this article.

Properties of gums that are important to performance in the food and nonfood industries are primarily physical. The physical effects of gelling and viscosity increases the interactions of polysaccharide molecules between themselves and with the constituents of an array of commercial products. The most important property of polysaccharides as performance chemical additives is their ability to continuously interact with water molecules. Gums occur as either linear or branched chains of glycosyl monomeric units and consist of hundreds to thousands of such units. These polysaccharide chains can consist of either single glycosyl units termed homoglycans or two or more different glycosyl units termed het-

## GLOSSARY

**gums**  High-molecular-weight polymers, usually with colloidal properties, that in appropriate solvents or swelling agents produce gels or highly viscous solutions at low dry weight polymer concentrations.

**hysteresis**  The ability of viscous solutions to recover instantaneously to initial viscosity values after removal of shear stress forces.

**pseudoplasticity**  Changes that occur in viscous solutions as a result of increases in stress forces. The polymer molecules tend to orient in the direction of solution flow as the force (shear stress) is increased. The resistance to flow (viscosity) is thereby decreased. When lesser forces are applied, the solution viscosity remains high due to random orientation of nonaligned molecules effecting increased resistance to flow.

**shear rate**  A measure of the speed at which the intermediate fluid layers move with respect to each other. The unit of measure is the reciprocal second.

**shear stress**  A measure of the force per unit area required to produce shearing action. The unit of measure is dynes/cm$^2$.

**viscosity**  A measure of the internal friction of a fluid in motion. The greater the friction, the greater the force required to cause this motion. The forced motion is termed shear. Shearing occurs whenever the viscous solution is physically placed in motion by pouring, mixing, spreading, or pumping. Mathematically, viscosity is the ratio of shear stress to shear rate expressed as poises or Pascal-seconds. One Pascal-second equals 10 poises.

eroglycans. Linear polysaccharides are the most abundant in the world due to the enormous quantities of cellulose, whereas branched polysaccharides are the most numerous, occurring in a large variety of non-cellulosic plants. Linear glycans generally yield more viscous solutions than branched glycans, whereas branched glycans serve as better bulking agents.

Polysaccharide chains in aqueous solution collide to form associations over several glycosyl units termed "junction zones." Junction zones occur primarily through hydrogen bonding associative interactions between polysaccharide chains, with the strength dependent on the degree and extent of intermolecular hydrogen bonding at the junction zones. If the bonding is weak, then the gel structure is easily disrupted by shaking or stirring and the gel is termed thixotropic. However, when junction zones are of greater strength as a result of increased associative hydrogen bonding, an identifiable gel results that is disrupted only through physical or chemical means. The interchain hydrogen bonding forms a three-dimensional network structure with an accompanying decrease in water-filled spaces between molecules. Accordingly, water is excluded from the gel producing syneresis.

Chemical modifications of polysaccharides are employed to impart new and useful chemical and physical properties, providing new product applications and opportunities. Occasionally, chemical modification of low-cost gums introduces physical properties that allow for their substitution for more expensive gums. Properties of neutral gums are altered significantly by insertion of neutral or ionic constituents to yield a product with entirely new physical properties. Charged polysaccharides, however, are marginally affected by chemical modifications. The following are types of chemical modifications employed for neutral polysaccharides: introduction of basic or acidic groups, grafting of linear or branched polymers, thermal dextrinization, partial hydrolysis, and mild oxidations. The ultimate goal is to modify low-cost polysaccharides to address new market needs and applications.

The diversity, sources, and uses of plant and microbial gums are summarized in Table I. This discussion addresses only gums and polyalkanoic acids pro-duced by microorganisms. Extensive literature documents the physiology, biochemistry, physical properties, and commercial uses of these microbial biopolymers, many of which have established major roles in food, nonfood, medical, pharmaceutical, agricultural, cosmetic, and personal care products.

## I. XANTHAN, GELLAN, WELAN, AND RHAMSAN

### A. Xanthan

The polysaccharide backbone consists of repeating pentasaccharide units involving two D-glucosylpyranosyl units, two D-mannosylpyranosyl units, and one D-glucopyranosyluronic acid unit. The linkage units within the backbone are (1 → 4)-linked β D-glucopyranosyl units that are identical to cellulose. Alternate D-glucosyl units at the O-3 position have positioned a trisaccharide unit consisting of a D-glucoronosyl unit located between two D-mannosyl units. The terminal β D-mannosyl unit is linked glycosidically to the O-4 position of the β D-glucopyranosyluronic acid, which is in turn linked to the O-2 position on the α-D-mannopyranosyl unit. Approximately one-half of the terminal D-mannosyl units contain pyruvic acid as a cyclic 4,6-cyclic acetal, and the nonterminal D-mannosyl unit is stoichiometrically substituted at O-6 with an acetyl group. Molecular weight estimates range from 15 to 50 × 10⁶ daltons. Recent studies report the molecular weight of the native molecule to be 3–7.5 × 10⁶ daltons. The wide range of molecular weight estimates indicates that xanthan is an aggregate of several individual chains present as either single or dimeric helices. Many chemically modified xanthan derivatives have been prepared, including deacetylated xanthan, carboxymethyl ether derivative, the propylene glycol ester, cationic derivatives, and graft co-polymers: these derivatives are not commercially viable.

Xanthan dissolves in either cold or hot water, yielding highly viscous solutions at low polymer concentrations. A high degree of pseudoplasticity is characteristic of xanthan solutions, i.e., viscosity decreases rapidly as shear rate increases. No hysteresis is detectable and shear thinning and recovery are

***TABLE I***
**Summary of Plant and Microbial Gums**

| Gum | Source | Uses |
| --- | --- | --- |
| Agar | *Rhodophyceae* | Microbiology, food, medical, pharmaceutical |
| Algin | *Phaeophyceae* | Food, packaging, medical, pharmaceutical |
| Carrageenan | *Phaeophyceae* | Food and nonfood products |
| Guar | *Cyanopsis* | Food, petroleum, paper, textiles, cosmetics |
| Locust bean | *Ceretonia* | Food, industrial |
| Tara | *Caesalpina* | Food |
| Aloe | *Aloe barbadensis* | Pharmaceuticals, cosmetics |
| Psyllium | *Plantago* | Medical |
| Quince | *Cyclonia* | Personal care products |
| Pectin | Citrus peels | Food |
| Hemicellulose | Plants | Food, pharmaceuticals, cosmetics |
| Gum arabic | *Acacia* | Food, pharmaceuticals, cosmetics, adhesives |
| Gum karaya | *Sterculia* | Food, pharmaceutical, textiles |
| Gum ghatti | *Anogeissus* | Food, pharmaceutical, petroleum |
| Gum tragacanth | *Astragalus* | Food, pharmaceutical |
| Methyl cellulose | Woody plants | Agriculture, food, paper, coatings, pharmaceuticals, ceramics, textiles, adhesives, cosmetics, toiletries, suspension polymerization |
| Hydroxyalkyl and ethyl ether cellulose | Woody plants | Paint, cements, cosmetics, paper, pharmaceuticals, petroleum, slurries, toiletries |
| Carboxymethyl cellulose | Woody plants | Paper, textiles, detergents, food, drilling fluids, coatings, cosmetics, pharmaceuticals |
| Starch gums | Plants | Paper, textiles, absorbents, foods, adhesives, coatings, dyes, ore refining, pharmaceuticals |
| Chitin | Invertebrate shells | Agriculture, dyes, cements, paper, textiles, coatings |
| Xanthan | *Xanthomonas campestris* | Food, pharmaceuticals, cosmetics, agriculture, industrial |
| Gellan | *Pseudomonas elodea* | Microbiology, food |
| Welan | *Alcaligenes* species | Petroleum |
| Rhamsan | *Alcaligenes* species | Agriculture, coatings |
| Dextran | *Leuconostoc mesenteroides* | Chromatography, medical |
| Curdlan | *Alcaligenes faecalis* | Food, agriculture |
| Pullulan | *Aureobasidium pullulans* | Food, adhesives, pharmaceuticals, coatings, binders, cosmetics |
| Scleroglucan | *Sclerotium rolfii* | Petroleum, food, agriculture, cosmetics, pharmaceuticals |

instantaneous. A remarkable feature of xanthan solutions is their well-defined yield value, i.e., the shear stress required to initiate flow. For example, moderate concentrations of xanthan (1%) are essentially gel-like at rest but show low resistance to mixing or pumping. The viscosity of xanthan solutions is essentially constant at pH values between 1 and 13. The effect of electrolytes such as NaCl on solution viscosity is dependent on the xanthan concentration. At gum concentrations <0.15%, viscosity is reduced slightly, whereas higher gum concentrations increase in viscosity in the presence of electrolytes. Maximum xanthan viscosities are normally achieved at 0.02–0.07% NaCl concentrations. Higher salt concentrations have little or no effect on solution viscosity or stability. Xanthan solution viscosities are essentially independent of temperatures ranging from −4 to 95°C. Xanthan solutions are refractory to hydrolytic enzymes such as protease, cellulase, hemicellulase, pectinase, and amylase. However, xanthan is biodegradable due to the enzyme xanthanase, which is produced by certain microorganisms. The compatibility of polyvalent cations on xanthan solution viscosity is largely pH dependent. Gellation or precipitation occurs over broad pH ranges in the presence of chromium, lead, mercury, ferrous iron, and aluminum. Neither magnesium nor calcium affect solution viscosities except at high pH values. Xanthan dissolves in acidic solutions such as 5% sulfuric acid, 5% nitric acid, 5% acetic acid, 10% hydrochloric acid, and 25% phosphoric acid, remaining relatively stable for several months at 25°C. Basic xanthan solutions are produced with sodium hydroxide. These highly alkaline, very viscous solutions exhibit excellent stability at ambient temperatures. Xanthan solutions are also compatible with ethanol, methanol, isopropanol, and acetone in concentrations of up to 50–60% in which gelation or precipitation occurs. Xanthan is insoluble in most organic solvents but is soluble in formamide at 25°C and glycerol and ethylene glycol at 65°C. Xanthan Interactions with galactomannans yield synergistic increases in solution viscosity.

The production of the extracellular polysaccharide xanthan has been reported for many *Xanthanomonas* species since 1946. Type species reported as efficient producers of xanthan are *X. campestris, X. phaseoli, X. malvacearum, X. carotae, X. oryzae,* and *X. juglandis. Xanthanomonas campestris* NRRL B-1459 has probably received the most attention as the microorganism of choice for xanthan production. The Kelco Company, a division of Merck and Company, initiated pilot plant feasibility studies in 1960 and semi-commercial production of Kelzan (xanthan gum) in 1961 and full-scale commercial production in 1962. Detailed studies on the physiological and nutritional requirements for optimal exopolysaccharide production established conditions for large-scale production of xanthan by *X. campestris.* Typical growth conditions for xanthan production were aerated and stirred-tank fermentors containing 2.5–3.0% glucose, 0.4% dried distillers solubles, 0.5% dipotassium hydrogen phosphate, and 0.01% magnesium sulfate heptahydrate, adjusted to pH 7.0. The following are operational parameters of the fermentor: 1.0 mmol oxygen per liter per minute, 28°C, and pH control maintained at 7.0. Maximum polysaccharide production occurs in approximately 96 h with the fermenta-

tion broth becoming extremely viscous. The final fermentation culture broth is diluted with water to reduce viscosity and centrifuged to remove biomass, and the spent culture broth is treated with either methanol or isopropanol containing 2% KCl to a final concentration of 50% (wt/wt) to quantitatively precipitate xanthan. The recovered xanthan is dried, milled, tested for quality assurance, blended to specifications, and packaged. Process economics dictates that essentially complete recovery of the alcohol for recycling is required to manufacture a product that is cost competitive. Physiological and nutritional studies demonstrated that pyruvate, $\alpha$ ketoglutarate, and succinate increased xanthan yields. The pyruvate content of xanthan was increased by a minimum concentration of diammonium hydrogen phosphate and a total phosphate concentration of 0.25%. Performance properties of xanthan are influenced by total pyruvate content of the final product. It is established that the molecular composition and the metal profile, rheological properties, and immunological reactions of manufactured xanthan are indistinguishable from those of naturally occurring xanthan. Xanthan is one of the most extensively studied polysaccharides with respect to safety for human and animal consumption. The U.S. Food and Drug Administration (FDA) approved xanthan in 1969, allowing its use in food products without any specific quantity limitations. It has also received FDA approval for paper products used to package foods and the Environmental Protection Agency has approved its use as an inert ingredient in pesticide formulations.

The commercial uses and applications of xanthan gum are many and diverse, impacting market sectors such as food, agricultural, pharmaceutical, cosmetics, and personal care products. Applications in the industrial sector include petroleum production for bore-hole cleaning; oil well drilling fluids; workover and completion fluids for maintaining well productivity; hydraulic fracturing to effect deep penetrating reservoir fractures to improve well productivity; pipeline cleaning; enhanced oil recovery functioning as a "viscous pusher slug" to move an oil bank; textile printing and dyeing to control the rheological properties of the paste and to achieve sharp patterns; ceramic glazes; acid and alkaline surface cleaning preparations; stabilization of slurry explosives; ink, paper, and wallpaper adhesives; suspension polymerization; flowable pesticides; coal/water slurries; foundry coatings; pigment suspensions; and industrial emulsions.

Xanthan gums have become an important performance-additive to foods due to their (i) solubility in cold or hot water, (ii) high viscosity at low polymer concentrations, (iii) lack of significant viscosity changes due to temperature, (iv) excellent solubility and stability in acid systems, (v) rheological properties that impart high viscosity under low shear and low viscosity under high shear, (vi) excellent suspension properties due to high yield values, (vii) compatibility with a wide range of electrolytes, (viii) outstanding thermal stability, and (ix) good freeze–thaw stability. Food applications for xanthan include salad dressings; dry mixes such as desserts, gravies, sauces, and beverages; syrups, toppings, relishes, and sauces; bulking agents for beverages; stabilizers for cottage cheese and cheese spreads; ice cream and ice milk; baked goods, in which the property of pseudoplasticity imparts improved flow properties.

Agricultural applications include: animal feed, in which 1 or 2 lbs per ton of feed minimizes stratification and separation of ingredients, and agricultural chemicals to improve the efficiency of flowable fungicides, herbicides, and insecticides.

Pharmaceutical and cosmetic uses include stabilization of emulsified cream formulations; suspension of barium sulfate as a radiographic opacifier, denture cleaning formulations; tooth-paste; and personal care products such as shampoos, creams, lotions, and makeup. Xanthan provides creams and lotions with the property of good skin feel during and following use.

## B. Gellan

Native high acyl gellan consists of a linear tetrasaccharide sequence containing two D-glucopyranosyl units, one D-glucoronopyranosyl unit, and one L-rhamnopyranosyl unit plus the acyl groups acetyl and L-glyceryl units attached to O-6 and O-2, respectively, of one of the two D-glucopyranosyl units. The molecular weight of gellan is estimated to be 1 or $2 \times 10^6$ daltons for both deacylated and acylated gellan. The polysaccharide is characterized as a parallel, half-staggered, double helix in which each polymer chain is in a left-handed, three-fold helical conformation and in which two such duplexes are packed antiparallel to each other in the unit cell. Monovalent cations (Na and K) and interchain hydrogen bonding plus interactions with water serve to stabilize the structure responsible for gel formation.

Physical properties of gellan can be modified by deacylation to produce firm, brittle gels or, by varying the degree of acylation, to provide a range of gel textures. Gellan solutions exhibit thermo-reversible viscosity changes. Gellan solutions prepared in ion-free water can be heated and cooled without gelation. Gellan has good thermal stability and resists loss of viscosity by autoclaving. Gellan requires the presence of either monovalent or divalent cations for gelation. Gel texture and strength can be modified by changing the concentration and types of cations.

Gellan is an extracellular polysaccharide produced by *Pseudomonas elodea* in an aerobic, submerged fermentation. The growth medium consists of D-glucose, ammonium nitrate, and soy protein hydrolysate as a nitrogen source, potassium phosphate, and trace minerals. The viscosity of the fermentation broth reaches 5000–6000 centipoises (cP). The high viscosity and gel-like texture of the fermentation broth reduces mixing efficiency effecting a drastic decrease in mass transfer coefficients during the aerobic fermentation. Gellan is recovered from the fermentation broth by isopropanol precipitation, and then dried, milled, and packaged.

The main application of gellan (Gelrite) has been as a replacement for agar in the preparation of solid microbiological media. Due to increasing agar prices, shortage, and product variability, other substitutes have been sought. Gellan has proved to be an excellent replacement for agar in the culturing of most microorganisms. Gellan is used in plant tissue culture in which the concentration needed is one-fourth that of agar. To date, Gellan has no applications in the food industry. Other uses for gellan are antigen–antibody diffusion techniques and as a matrix for enzyme and cell immobilization.

## C. Welan

Welan gum is commercially available under the registered trademark Biozan. Its chemical composition is similar to that of gellan, having a single glycosyl side-chain substituent. The side-chain unit can be either $\alpha$ L-rhamnopyranosyl or $\alpha$ 1-mannopyranosyl linked $(1 \rightarrow 3)$ to the 4-O-substituted $\beta$ D-glucopyranosyl backbone unit. Approximately two-thirds of the side chain is composed of L-rhamnosyl units and one-half of the repeating units contain an O-acyl group. However, the location and identity of the acyl group are unknown. The L-mannose in welan is unusual, having never been reported as a constituent of other microbial polysaccharides.

The physical properties of welan solutions are unique, exhibiting exceptional thermo-stability (it withstands 150°C for 1 hr). Welan imparts high solution viscosity at low solute concentrations (8000 cP at 2% concentration) and remains unchanged in viscosity for pH ranges of 2–12. Welan solutions are pseudoplastic, compatible with high salt concentration including salt-water and brine, unaffected by extreme pH values, and exhibit good yield values.

Welan is produced by an *Alcaligenes* species (ATCC-31555) in an aerobic, submerged fermentation. The growth medium consists of D-glucose, phosphate buffer, ammonium nitrate, soy peptone, and trace minerals. The extracellular polysaccharide is recovered by isopropanol precipitation and then dried, milled, and packaged.

Oil-field applications are the major use of welan solutions due primarily to its thermal stability. Deep-bore holes in which temperatures exceed 120°C are suited to welan solutions. Based on its physical properties, welan has been shown to be suitable as a drilling fluid additive and in workover and completion systems for wells with high temperatures. Other potential applications, considering its insensitivity to high salt concentrations, are hydraulic fracturing and as a mobility control agent in enhanced oil recovery. Rheological properties of welan solutions appear to offer many benefits to many oil field problems, including (i) superior suspension properties of particles, (ii) increased penetration rates into well formations, (iii) reduced formation damage, (iv) effective cleaning of severely washedout holes without increasing pump rate or viscosifier concentration, (v) less sloughing, (vi) reduced fluid loss, and (vii) friction pressure reduction.

## D. Rhamsan

Rhamsan has the same repeating backbone as gellan but with a disaccharide side chain on O-6 of the 3-O-substituted $\beta$ D-glucopyranosyl unit. The side chain is a $\beta$ D-glucopyranosyl-$(1 \rightarrow 6)$-$\alpha$ D-glucopyranosyl unit. The location and identity of acyl substituents are unknown.

Rhamsan possesses unusually good stability to shear, excellent compatibility with high salt concentration, and excellent suspending ability. A 0.25% rhamsan solution in tap water exhibits a viscosity value of 2000 cP at very low shear rates. Temperature and pH have little effect on solution viscosities. The pseudoplastic rhamsan is compatible with high concentrations of salts including phosphates. Most commercial polysaccharide gums tend to precipitate in the presence of phosphate.

Potential applications of rhamsan appear to be focused on the agriculture and coating industries. Agricultural uses as a suspending agent in fluid fertilizers and flowable pesticide formulations are well-suited to rhamsan physical performance properties. Rhamsan as a high-performance additive offers good spraying, rolling, and brushing characteristics as well as control of "sagging" in high-build and texture paints.

## II. DEXTRAN

Dextran produced by *Leuconostoc mesenteroides* NRRL B-512(F) is a $(1 \rightarrow 6)$-linked $\alpha$ D-glucan with side chains attached to O-3 of the polymer backbone. Sequential degradation of dextran established that 40% of side chains are one unit long, 45% are two units long, and 15% contain more than two units with an overall 5% degree of branching. The average molecular weights of native dextran ranges from $9 \times 10^6$ to $500 \times 10^6$ daltons. The $(1 \rightarrow 6)$-linked polysaccharides are very flexible, extended polymer chains that behave in solution as an expandable coil.

Production of native dextran is dependent on the rapid growth of *L. mesenteroides* and optimal synthesis of the enzyme dextransucrase for efficient dextran production. Extensive physiological and nutritional studies document 2% sucrose as the only carbon and energy source that induces dextransucrase. Vitamins, cofactors, and amino acid supplements are supplied as yeast extract; com steep liquor, acid-hydrolyzed casein, or malt extract plus peptone and tryptone broth are supplied as a nitrogen source; and phosphate concentrations are between 0.1 and 0.5%. Initial pH values for the fermentation medium are between 6.7 and 7.2, with maximum dextransucrase synthesis occurring at pH 6.7 within 6–8 hr. Optimum temperature for the fermentation is 25°C, with recovery of dextran from the spent fermentation culture broth after 24–48 hr. Dextran is recovered by ethanol or methanol precipitation, dried, and analyzed for quality assurance prior to molecular size fractionation.

Medical applications of dextran comprise the major uses for this polysaccharide. The conversion of native dextran involves partial acid-hydrolysis to products containing appropriate molecular weight sizes which are recovered by fractional precipitation with either ethanol or methanol. Molecular weight fractions most commonly used in medical applications have molecular weight distributions of 70 and 40 kDa.

Dextran 70 (average molecular weight distribution of 70 kDa) is marketed as a 6% solution in normal saline. This product is the plasma volume extender of choice worldwide. It is recommended for treatment of shock, reducing risk of thrombosis, and postoperative pulmonary emboli.

Dextran 40 (average molecular weight distribution of 40 kDa) appeared on the market in 1961 for reduction of blood viscosity and inhibition of erythrocyte aggregation. The antithrombotic effect of both Dextran 40 and Dextran 70 provides a prophylactic treatment regimen for deep venous thrombosis and postoperative pulmonary emboli.

Dextran 1 was developed in response to dextran-induced anaphylactic shock reactions in sensitive individuals following treatment with either Dextran 40 or Dextran 70. Administration of a monovalent haptene dextran fraction (molecular weighth of 1 kDa) prior to Dextran 70 or Dextran 40 infusions reduces the incidence of anaphylactic reactions. Many chemically-modified dextran derivatives have been tested, such as iron–dextran, dextran sulfate, DEAE–dextran, and epichlorohydrin cross-linked dextran. Various medical uses of these derivatives

are reported, but they have yet to be widely accepted in clinical medicine.

Other nonmedical uses include the introduction of cross-linked dextran beads (Sephadex) in 1959 for the chromatographic separation of biochemical molecules. Many anion- and cation-exchange resins based on Sephadex are available commercially with sulfonyloxypropyl and quaternized DEAE derivatives for the separation of charged molecules at extreme pH values. DEAE- and carboxymethyl-Sephadex resins are used for the separation of charged molecules in intermediate pH ranges. Hydroxypropyl derivatives of Sephadex were developed for the separation of hydrophobic molecules such as complex lipids, hormones, and fatty acids.

## III. CURDLAN, PULLULAN, AND SCLEROGLUCAN

### A. Curdlan

Curdlan, a $\beta$ $(1 \rightarrow 3)$-linked D-glucan discovered in 1996, is a thermogelable polysaccharide. Takeda Chemical Ind. Ltd. became interested in curdlan production for food and industrial applications. In 1971 and 1972, Wako Pure Chemicals Ind. Ltd. studied pilot plant production of curdlan and initiated investigations into its toxicology and overall safety. Curdlan was found to be nontoxic and nutritionally inert. Takeda Chemicals began commercial production of curdlan at about 200–300 tons per year for food use, and Wako Pure Chemicals currently manufacturers curdlan as a chemical reagent for industrial applications.

More than 99% of the linkages in curdlan are $(1 \rightarrow 3)$-$\beta$ D-glucosidic with an average degree of polymerization of 450. Curdlan is insoluble in acidic or neutral water but soluble at basic pH values. Other solvents that dissolve curdlan are formic acid, dimethyl sulfoxide, saturated solutions of urea or thiourea, and 25% potassium iodide. Suspensions of curdlan become clear solutions when heated to 55°C, forming "low-set" gels when cooled. Curdlan suspensions heated at higher temperatures form firm, resilient, "high-set" gels that melt at 140–160°C. Curdlan gels are stable over wide pH ranges and stable to freeze–thaw.

*Alcalignenes faecalis* var. *myxogenes* 10C3K produces large amounts of curdlan in a medium consisting of 4% glucose, 0.1% citrate, succinate, or fumarate, 0.15% diammonium hydrogen phosphate, and mineral salts.

Curdlan is useful for improving the texture of various foods such as tofu, yokan, boiled fish paste, noodles, sausage, jellies, and jams. Curdan at concentrations between 0.05 and 3.0% improves texture, palatability, stability, and water binding and holding; prevents scorching and adhesion; masks odors; preserves aromas; and improves body and gloss to foods. Nonfood uses are as a binder in animals feeds, as a support carrier of immobilized enzymes, and as a substitute soil for rice plants.

## B. Pullulan

Pullulan is an extacellular glycan produced by *Aureobasidium* species. Pullulan was first commercially produced in 1976 by Hayashibara Chemical Company. Pullulan is found among many strains of the genus *Aureoblasidium*. Structurally, pullulan is a linear glucan consisting of repeating units of maltotriose linked by $\alpha$ D-$(1 \rightarrow 6)$ bonds. Molecular weight estimates of native pullulan are approximately $2 \times 10^5$ daltons.

Pullulan dissolves in water forming stable, viscous solutions that do not gel. Pullulan solution viscosity is relatively unaffected by extreme pH values and is essentially heat stable with solution viscosities compatible with most electroyltes. Barium and titanium ions effect dramatic increases in pullulan solution viscosities. A significant feature of pullulan is its high stability to sodium chloride, in which heating at 100°C for 6 hr causes no solution viscosity changes. Pullulan is highly biodegradable and soluble in water. These properties can be chemically modified by esterification, etherification, or cross-linking.

Pullulan production by *Aureobasidium pullulans* IFO 4464 employs 15% acid-hydrolyzed starch syrup, 0.2% dipotassium hydrogen phosphate, 0.2% sodium chloride, 0.2% peptone, 0.04% magnesium sulfate heptahydrate, and 0.001% ferrous sulfate. The fermentation broth has an initial pH value of 6.5 and a temperature of 30°C, and the contents are vigorously aerated in a stirred tank fementor. Pullu-

lan molecular weight is dependent on culture broth pH and phosphate concentration. The molecular weight of pullulan declines as the phosphate concentration increases, whereas a high-molecular-weight pullulan is produced when pH values are less than 6.8. Fermentations run 100–125 hr with pullulan synthesis becoming maximum at approximately 100 hr with a polymer molecular weight of $3 \times 10^6$ daltons and a culture broth viscosity >300 cP.

Pullulan is recovered from the spent culture broth by diluting the viscous solution to approximately 30 cP and then filtered, decolorized with activated carbon, and precipitated with isopropanol. This product is dissolved in water and processed through ion exchange columns and ultrafiltration to remove salts, protein, and oligosaccharides. The pure solution is concentrated, drum dried, and milled to a fine powder.

Pullulan has niche markets in the food, pharmaceutical, and various industrial sectors. Pullulan shows no abnormalities in animal feeding tests and no apparent reactions in acute, subacute, chronic toxicity, and mutagenic testing regimes. Accordingly, pullulan is considered a safe, nontoxic product.

Food uses include its substitution as a low-calorie additive to wheat flour or starch in bakery products and dietary foods. Its viscosity properties extend its application to a thickener in beverages, creams, frostings, fillings, and sauces. Its strong adhesive properties allows pullulan to be used in food pastes and binders for the preparation of snack foods. Pullulan thin films are oil resistant, antistatic, transparent, readily soluble in water, and have low oxygen permeability. Therefore, it represents a novel and versatile packaging material for sauces, soups, and freeze-dried vegetable and meats. The contents can be cooked and prepared without opening the package since the biopolymer is water soluble. Such an edible coating can be applied to fresh vegetables, fits, fish, and meats to retain freshness and prevent oxidation over long time periods.

Medical applications of pullulan include use in tablet coatings, contact lenses, plasma expanders, and toxin–pullulan conjugates. Currently, formalin-treated toxins or aluminum adjuvants are used as prophylactic inoculations for many diseases. Their use, however, is know to effect production of IgG,

IgM, and IgE antibodies, immune factors known to cause allergic and anaphylactic reactions in humans. Comparison of conjugated pullulan toxoids with conventional toxoids showed quite favorable results, inducing much less IgE while stimulating IgG and IgM antibody responses.

Industrial uses of pullulan are as coatings for lithographic printing and plate protection, as binders in the preparation of tobacco sheets, and as a foundry sand binder.

## C. Scleroglucan

Scleroglucan is a general term designating a class of homoglucans produced by fungi, particularly *Sclerotium*. This gum exhibits superior rheological properties and resistance to hydrolysis, temperature, and electrolytes. *Sclerotium rolfii* is a septate mycelial fungus that parasitizes various plant species. The fungus produces many hydrolytic enzymes and characteristically produces oxalic acid.

Scleroglucan is a branched homopolysaccharide that yields only d-glucose on hydrolysis. The polymer is composed of a main chain of $(1 \rightarrow 3)$-linked $\beta$-D-glucopyranosyl units, with every third unit bearing a single $\beta$-D-glucopyranosyl unit linked $(1 \rightarrow 6)$. The molecular weight of scleroglucan is between 5 and $6 \times 10^6$ daltons, forming a triple-helical backbone conformation similar to that of curdlan. Scleroglucan powders disperse in water at all temperatures and over wide pH ranges. Viscous solutions are prepared by either vigorous stirring or heating to 90°C. Scleroglucan solutions are quite viscous, exhibit shear-thinning properties and high yield values, offering favorable suspending properties. At 0.075% concentrations, the solution viscosity is 35–60 cP, whereas a 1% solution has a viscosity of 2500 cP. Dilute solutions of scleroglucan are pseudoplastic, becoming more Newtonian at low shear rates. Scleroglucan solutions of 0.1 or 0.2% stabilize 5–10% suspensions of fine powders. Solution viscosity remains constant over temperature ranges of 15 to 90°C and can be sterilized by heating at 121°C for 20 hr without change in viscosity. When electrolyte concentrations are very high, solutions may gel and flocculate. Scleroglucan is compatible without synergism with most other thickening agents, such as guar gum, locust bean gum, alginates, gelatin, polyacrylamides, xanthan, carrageenans, and cellulose derivatives.

There are two main grades of scleroglucan commercially available. Native scleroglucan contains the mycelium and purified scleroglucan lacks mycelia. Native scleroglucan is harvested by isopropanol precipitation of the sterilized culture broth. Purified scleroglucan is recovered by filtration of the fermentation culture broth to remove mycelia and scleroglucan precipitated with isopropanol. Both products are dried, milled, and marketed as colorless, odorless powders approximately 100 $\mu$m in size. Toxicological studies of scleroglucan in rats, dogs, guinea pigs, rabbits, and humans indicate no adverse reactions or sensitizations.

Scleroglucan is produced by aerobic submerged culture of *Sclerotium rolfii* by batch fermentation. The growth medium contains 5% glucose, com-steep liquor, nitrate, and mineral salts. Fermentation occurs over 60 hr at 28 to 30°C. The initial pH value of 4.6 decreases rapidly to pH 2 due to oxalic acid production. This acid production can be suppressed by the use of ammonium salts rather than corn-steep liquor as a nitrogen source. Mycelial growth and scleroglucan production occur simultaneously, yielding 10–20 grams of scleroglucan per liter.

Applications of scleroglucan are primarily for enhanced oil recovery initiatives. Scleroglucan's high viscosity at low polymer concentrations, compatibility with electroyltes, good heat and shear stability, and good filterability makes it well-suited for use in oil fields with high salinities and temperatures. Rheological properties and stability of scleroglucan solutions make them suitable for mobility control, for thickening drilling muds, as a fluid additive for formation loss control, as a fracturing fluid additive, and for pipeline cleaning.

## IV. POLY-$\beta$-HYDROXYALKANOATES

Polyhydroxyalkanoates (PHAs) have emerged as viable commercial entities that impact many market sectors, including medical, agriculture, food, textiles, coatings, and films. Accordingly, a new Industry exists that specializes in the production and marketing of "bioplastics." The most widely developed PHAs are poly β-hydroxybutyrate (PHB), poly β-hydroxyvalerate, and polylactic acid (PLA). These PHAs are linear, homochiral, thermoplastic polyesters produced either by fermentation with selected microorganisms or through synthetic chemical polymerization of the subunits. In microorganisms, these unique biopolymers accumulate as intracellular inclusions in response to nutrient limitations. Other PHAs reported are poly-hydroxypentanoate and poly-hydroxyoctanoate, which form homo- and heteropolymers. A diverse range of microorganisms produce PHAs, including *Pseudomonas* species, *Rhodobacter* species, *Alcaligenes eutrophus,* and *Syntrophomonas wolfei*. The genetics and biochemistry of PHB are best delineated in *A. eutrophus*. PHAs are highly biodegradable—a property of considerable importance in medical applications, food, and other nonfood uses—compared to many synthetic polymers which have low biodegradability and toxicity profiles impacting safety in specific applications. PHB has physical properties similar to those of polyethylene and polyethyleneterephthalate, including molecular weight, melting point, cyrstallinity, tensile strength, odor barrier properties, resistance to ultraviolet light, good water resistance, and heat resistance to 130°C.

Recent innovations in PHB applications include the use of transgenic plants for PHB production rather than microorganisms grown in large-scale, stirred-tank reactors. Genes from *A. eutrophus* encoding acetoacetyl-CoA reductase (*phb*B) and PHB synthase (*phb*C) were transferred into *Arabidospis thaliana* through Ti plasmid-mediated transformation. The coding sequences of *phb*B and *phb*C were individually cloned into the binary Ti plasmid pBl121 with the PHB genes under the transcription control of the constitutive cauliflower mosaic virus 35S promoter. Transgenic plant lines that contained the PHB genes accumulated PHB granules as electron-transparent granules in the cytoplasm, nucleus, and vacuoles. The size and appearance as well as chemical structure were similar to those of PHB granules that accumulate in *A. eutrophus*.

Additional innovations concern the development of transgenic cotton plants using *A. eutrophus* genes *phb*B and *phb*C in combination with fiber-specific promoters, producing novel cotton fiber with normal texture. This technical advance was successful as a result of the identification of two genes from cotton fibers that are developmentally regulated and tissue-specific in expression. The fiber-specific promoters were linked to *phb*B and *phb*C placed under control of a constitutive CaMV35S promoter. The cotton fibers produced by the transgenic plants appeared normal in texture, with PHB granules present in clusters in the cotton fibers. The new transgenic cotton fibers showed 12% higher heat uptake than control cotton fibers and lower thermal conductivity.

PLA polymers have become valuable products, particularly for medical applications. Their synthesis is part biological and part chemical. Starch is converted to glucose and the glucose is fermented to lactic acid. Water is then removed from the lactic acid to form a lactide, which is converted to PLA resins using a solvent-free polymerization reaction.

PLA polymers offer a broad spectrum of functional performance properties and are expected to compete with hydrocarbon-based thermoplastics. Properties associated with PLA are good tensile strength, oil and grease resistance, flavor and odor barriers, heat sealability at lower temperatures, and complete biodegradability. The polmers can be processed by most melt fabrication techniques, including thermoforming, sheet and fiber extrusion, flown film processing, fiber spinning, and injection molding. Cargil Dow Plastics, Inc., estimated that the production capacity would reach 20–25 million lbs by the year 2000.

Biodegradable polymers have become established products for many medical applications. Most of these polymers are synthesized from biomolecules as the monomeric subunit followed by ring-opening chain polymerization. Examples are polylactide, polyglypcolic acid, and poly-ε-caprolactone homopolymers and heteropolymerse. Properties associated with such biodegradable polymers are mechanical strength, the absence of inflammatory or toxic responses in human tissue, rapid metabolism in the body, acceptable shelf life, and easy sterilization. Uses of these biodegradable polymers include wound closure (sutures and staples), orthopedic fixation (pins, rods, screws, tacks, and ligaments) dental applications, cardiovascular applications (stents and grafts), and intestinal uses (anastomosis rings).

One of the new and exciting areas of biodegradable polymer research is tissue engineering. The use of these materials as a matrix for living cells confers properties supporting cell in-growth and proliferation, surfaces that balance hydrophilicity and hydrophobicity for cell recognition and binding, mechanical strength compatible with target tissue, and degradation rate and by-products. Recent successful applications involve *in situ* bone regeneration.

## See Also the Following Articles

BIODEGRADATION • *XANTHOMONAS*

## Bibliography

Anderson, A. J., and Dawes, E. A. (1990). Occurrence, metabolism, metabolic role, and industrial uses of bacterial polyhdroxy acids. *Microbiol. Rev.* **54**, 450–472.

Chin-Chang, C., Greisler, H. P., and Von Fraunhofer, J. A. (1996). "Wound Closure Biomaterial and Devices." CRC Press, Boca Raton, FL.

John, M. E., and Keller, G. (1996). Metabolic engineering in cotton: Biosynthesis of polyhydroxybutyrate in fiber cells. *Proc. Natl. Acad. Sci. USA* **93**, 12768–12773.

Whistler, R. L., and BeMiller, J. N. (Eds.) (1993). Industrial Gums: Polysaccharides and Their Derivatives." 3rd ed., pp. 341–474. Academic Press, New York.

# Bioreactor Monitoring and Control

Roland Ulber, Bernd Hitzmann,
and Thomas Scheper

*Institut für Technische Chemie*

Kenneth F. Reardon

*Colorado State University*

## GLOSSARY

**analysis system** A combination of the sensor system and hardware systems (including liquid handling units) which provides the opportunity to run a fully automated analysis of specific properties.

**chemical/physical sensor** A device that provides information about the chemical or physical nature of a microenvironment. Normally a transducer and a selective recognition part are combined.

**control** If a process is controlled, the controller compares the actual value (measured value) of the control variable with its desired value (set point) and adjusts the manipulated variable so that the difference of the measured value and the desired value is minimal. A typical goal of process control is to maintain process-dependent changes of the process variable within optimal limits around the set point. Another goal is for the control variable to follow a predefined trajectory.

**expert system** A computer program which uses the heuristics of operators to carry out a task in a restricted domain.

**model** A mathematical representation of the physical and chemical phenomena of a system.

**sensor system** The combination of sensor element, electrics, data collection, and data-handling units. It is fully working to monitor a specific property.

**software sensor** A sensor that uses data from measured variables as well as a mathematical model (e.g., a state space model) to predict other, mostly difficult to measure, variables.

**transducer** A device that provides an electronic signal generated by changes in a specific property in its microenvironment (e.g., for temperature, piezo-electric effects, and light density effect).

**BIOREACTORS** are closed systems in which cells or microorganisms can be cultivated under defined, controllable conditions that can be optimized with regard to viability, reproducibility, and product-oriented productivity.

## I. INTRODUCTION

In the bioreactor, the cells constitute a biological system that is surrounded by physical and chemical environments (Fig. 1). The interaction between these three compartments of the bioreactor is complex, especially when the multiphase aspects of the system are considered. To drive the biochemical reaction network of the biological system through the desired reaction optimally, the complex interactions of the overall system must be understood and controlled. This requires detailed, fast, and reliable monitoring. In addition, appropriate models and control systems must be set up for direct control of the biological system so that its metabolic potential can best be harnessed.

Research on bioreactor monitoring, modeling, and control strategies must be tightly integrated since sensors and actuators interact through the process

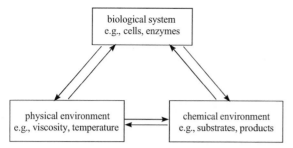

**Fig. 1.** Interactions between the three different environments of a bioprocess.

models. All changes in the temperature, pH, and oxygen profiles, the feed or perfusion rates, and the gene induction steps are performed to meet the optimal process needs calculated by the models. Models can be used to predict the optimal profiles of the process variables a priori, to adapt them to the actual process condition on the basis of a given scheme, or to optimize the entire process in real time with regard to a given goal (e.g., productivity). A reliable analytical system is always necessary to check if the changes to the process conditions do in fact drive the process in the desired direction.

Currently, no general bioanalytical system has been developed. Since modern bioprocesses are extremely complex and differ from process to process (e.g., antibiotic production vs mammalian cell cultivation), appropriate analytical systems must be set up from different basic modules, designed to meet the special demands of each particular process.

A large variety of analytical systems have been produced for different applications in the life sciences. However, more research and development efforts are required to meet the special demands of modern and future bioprocessing. Advances will likely proceed in two directions: adaptation of existing systems and evolution of new procedures or devices. Both are necessary to achieve efficient monitoring and to enable the necessary degree of control.

Here, we describe the principle elements of bioprocess monitoring. First, the trade-offs between different analytical strategies will be reviewed, including *in situ* vs *ex situ* analysis and invasive vs noninvasive analysis. Then different sampling devices, which are a critical component of any *ex situ* analytical system, are discussed. Two methods of introduc-

ing a sample to a detection system, flow and sequential injection, are then reviewed. Different detection methods for parameters of the biological system and the physical and chemical environments will be presented, ranging from conventional methods such as electrodes and gas chromatography to biosensors and optical sensors. We conclude with an overview of the mathematical methods used to process the monitoring data and to control the bioprocess.

## II. ANALYTICAL STRATEGIES

### A. *In Situ* and *Ex Situ* Analysis

An important consideration of bioreactor monitoring is whether an *in situ* or an *ex situ* analytical system will be used. There are advantages and disadvantages for both types. The principles of *in situ* and *ex situ* analysis are shown in Fig. 2.

In general, an *in situ* system offers the possibility to obtain data with a short response time (typically that of the sensor). In most cases, measurement is continuous. Typical *in situ* devices are the well-known pH, oxygen, and carbon dioxide electrodes and sensors for the measurement of temperature, optical density, and foam.

However, difficulties occur when sensors are used *in situ*. Biofilms may grow on the surface of the sensing device, and sensor membranes may become fouled in cultivation media with a high protein content. The application of biosensors for *in situ* analysis presents special problems, the most important of which is biosensor sterilization since these devices include a labile biological component. Because of these issues, only a few applications using biosensors as *in situ* systems have been described.

These problems can be avoided using *ex situ* sensor

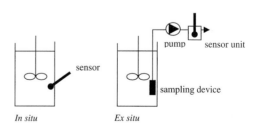

**Fig. 2.** Principles of *in situ* analytical devices.

systems, in which the analytical device is external to the bioreactor. Thus, the sample must be transferred from the reactor to this device; sampling systems for this purpose are described. With this approach, the quality of the analysis is influenced by the characteristics of the sampling devices. Potential problems of *ex situ* systems are longer response times and blockage of the flow due to fouling. With the appropriate sampling device, most established analytical systems (gas chromatography, high-performance liquid chromatography, etc.) can be used as *ex situ* sensors for on-line bioreactor monitoring.

## B. Invasive and Noninvasive Analysis

Both *in situ* and *ex situ* analytical systems are invasive and can have impacts on the biological system. The following are potential interferences: Cells are subjected to mechanical shear within sampling devices, the composition of the fermentation medium changes with each sample, cell-free sampling changes the cell density, and the insertion of a probe provides additional surfaces for growth and increases the risk of contamination. Thus, a noninvasive detection method offers advantages for bioreactor monitoring such as no consumption of substrates and no change in cell density. Noninvasive methods are described later.

Attempts to improve the performance of bioprocess modeling and control have revealed the need for development of alternative methods for accessing information from biological systems that are better suited to the nature of organisms. Some novel noninvasive approaches have been reported, including the use of so-called software sensors that provide data that cannot be monitored directly. Such sensors are based on mathematical models and easy-to-use sensors.

## C. In-Time Analysis

An important factor in bioprocess monitoring is the response time of the entire analytical system. The analysis time must be at least as short as the important biological time constants (e.g., the doubling time). With this consideration, it is less important whether the analysis is done on- or off-line. Instead,

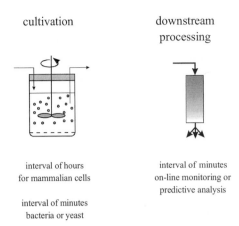

**Fig. 3.** Required time scale for analysis in different biological processes.

the critical issue is whether the data are produced and evaluated as soon as they are needed for an efficient process control. This time constraint varies from process to process as shown in Fig. 3. Thus, a sensor system with a low analysis frequency ($<3$ analyses h$^{-1}$) might be useful for the control of a mammalian cell cultivation but not for growth of bacteria or yeast. If a system oscillates with a given time constant, it is usually sufficient to analyze one cycle and then to predict the next cycle using the proceeding data. To verify the prediction, the next cycle is then analyzed and these data are then used for the prediction of the next cycle, and so on. In this way, control responses to changes within the process can be performed quickly.

## III. SAMPLING AND SAMPLE INJECTION

### A. Sampling

To interface analytical systems to bioprocesses, one needs sampling devices that transport a representative sample (with or without cells) from the bioprocess to the measurement device. The performance of this interface can be critical to the achievement of fast, reliable bioprocess monitoring. All sampling devices should work continuously without disturbing the bioprocess.

The withdrawal of cell-containing samples provides the possibility to monitor all analytes (intra- or extracellular) of interest (Olsson *et al.*, 1998).

Sampling from a continuous process (e.g., chemostat and perfusion culture system) is relatively simple, since the effluent can be monitored directly. However, the time constant of sampling must be short enough to guarantee that the sample being analyzed is representative of the actual bioprocess state. If this is not possible, then the metabolic activity of the cells must be stopped by adding special reagents. Coaxial catheter probes are used to withdraw samples by pulling the medium into a stream containing reagents that stop metabolism immediately. However, problems occur when the flow of the system is blocked, since these reagents might be pumped directly into the bioreactor.

For noncontinuous bioprocesses, samples must be taken directly from the bioreactor. This can be accomplished with automated systems that withdraw a cell-containing sample at a given time interval and transfer it to the appropriate analytical unit. This discrete sample withdrawal requires complex mechanical systems, and sterility problems occur frequently. Since the sample will continue to react during the entire sampling time, complicated metabolism-halting procedures are necessary if the sampling is not sufficiently rapid.

After removal of a sample that contains cells, separation steps (e.g., microcentrifugation and extended bed chromatography) must be performed. Automated robotic systems have been described for a high-frequency sampling (as short as 0.1-s intervals) to study the dynamic behavior of bioprocesses.

The use of filtration sampling devices allows one to withdraw cell-free samples from the bioprocess. An advantage of this approach is that the composition of the sample stream will not change due to biological activity (however, abiotic reactions may still occur). These filtration devices can be used in a bypass (e.g., cross-flow membrane systems) or *in situ* (e.g., tubular membrane probes). Different devices, based on micro- or ultrafiltration, dialysis, or even pervaporation, are commercially available. One potential problem with filtration samplers is an unacceptably long response time caused by large dead volumes in the device. Although the response time can be decreased by increasing the sample flow rate, the resulting high sampling flow rates may cause problems. This is particularly true for smaller reactor volumes, when the continuous analysis must be performed within a few minutes. Another problem that plagues filtration samplers is fouling of the filter surface by the accumulation of layers of biomolecules and cell debris. When sampling for low-molecular-weight components (sugars and amino acids), this does not normally cause problems with regard to the representativeness of the sample. However, sampling for high-molecular-weight components (e.g., proteins) is highly susceptible to interference by fouling.

## B. Sequential Injection Analysis and Flow Injection Analysis

*Ex situ* analytical systems can be interfaced to a bioreactor via flow injection analysis (FIA) or sequential injection analysis (SIA). Many applications, mostly in combination with biosensor systems, have been reported. The development of new tools for FIA and SIA in process control is a research priority both in industry and in universities. This effort is motivated by the recognition that continuous monitoring of bioprocesses results in products of better quality with less waste.

Flow injection analysis was investigated extensively by Ruzicka and Hansen (1989). The principle of a FIA system is shown in Fig. 4. The system features several pumps and valves to control sample and buffer flow. Using an injector valve, a sample of defined volume can be injected in the buffer flow and is then transported to the analytical device. A selector valve is used to choose between sample (for measurement) and standards (for calibration). The FIA system is coupled to different analytical devices, such as spectrophotometers, conductivity sensors, thermistors, electrochemical sensors, and biosensors.

A sequential injection analysis system is less complicated. SIA was especially developed for industrial applications since this system provides the robustness and ease of use required for those environments. A typical SIA system, as described by Ruzicka

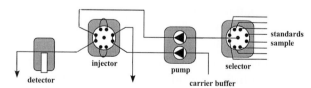

*Fig. 4.* Experimental setup for flow injection analysis systems.

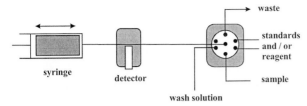

**Fig. 5.** Experimental set-up for sequential injection analysis systems.

and Marshall (1990), is shown in Fig. 5. The system consists of a reversing syringe pump, a selector valve, and the detector of choice (e.g., biosensors).

An assay cycle based on the principle of SIA consists of four steps. Each measurement starts by aspirating a wash solution during the backward movement of the syringe pump. This is followed by the injection of sample and any required reagent; the appropriate solutions are chosen simply by switching to the different positions of the SIA valve. During the next backward movement of the syringe pump piston, the measurement is performed. In this way, well-defined zones of fluid are injected sequentially into the reaction loop (e.g., an enzyme reactor) and the detector system (e.g., a spectrophotometer). The measurement cycle is terminated when the flow is reversed and the different injection zones are propelled back to the valve and directed into the waste stream.

By using FIA or SIA any analytical procedure can be automated for on-line bioprocess monitoring. SIA as well as FIA systems yield information from discrete analyses at a relatively high frequency. Many FIA and SIA applications have been published; this body of work demonstrates that these principles can be used to monitor many high- and low-molecular-weight components including carbohydrates, amino acids, antibiotics, metabolites, ammonium, phosphate, magnesium, calcium, and intra- or extracellular proteins.

## IV. DETECTION METHODS

### A. Sensors for the Physical Environment

The most widely used sensors in biotechnology are those quantifying the physical environment of a bioreactor (Scheper and Reardon, 1991). Temperature, pressure, liquid level, foam, power input, and impeller speed are monitored in most bioreactors. Less common, but often important, are sensors of viscosity, liquid velocity, and entrained gas quantities.

Temperature sensors (platinum resistance, thermocouples, and thermistors) are the most common probes in biotechnology. They are the most accurate and often the cheapest sensors, and they provide reliable data. Since cells are extremely sensitive to temperature changes, these sensors are an important part of a bioreactor's control system.

Gas phase pressure measurements are necessary to monitor the partial pressures of gaseous components, and to obtain information about the dissolved gas concentrations. Membrane-type pressure sensors are most commonly used since they are compatible with the sterility requirements of biotechnological processes.

Liquid volume/level measurement is important for bioprocess control since the liquid phase must be managed within the bioreactor. These sensors are necessary to run the process at a given volume. Membrane pressure devices, strain gauges, capacity sensors, conductivity probes, and floating sensors are commonly used. A related parameter, liquid feed rate, can be determined by placing either the bioreactor or the vessel containing the feed on a load cell system, which continuously monitors the mass of the contents. The changes in the mass are used to determine the actual feed rate.

Sensors for foam are similar to level sensors. Foam often causes problems in biotechnological processes since protein-rich media aerated at high volume rates produce large volumes of foam. The amount of foam can be measured with conductivity, conductance, or light scattering probes.

To control the power input in a bioprocess and obtain information about the degree of mixing (used to evaluate mass transfer rates), the impeller speed, shaft power input, and fluid velocity must be monitored. Impeller speed is normally monitored via electronic or mechanical tachometers, whereas the shaft power input is monitored via a torsion dynamometer or a strain gauge balance. Fluid velocity is monitored via different approaches, such as heat pulse monitoring and Doppler anemometer systems.

Viscosity is also an interesting parameter for the physical environment of cells, since power input and mass transfer are extremely affected by changes in viscosity. The viscosity can be affected by the microorganisms (e.g., formation of mycelia) or by the excretion of products such as xanthan. Monitoring viscosity on-line is difficult. Rotational viscosimeters and other devices for this purpose have been described mainly for research purposes.

Another interesting parameter is entrained gas volume, which gives information about the rate of interphase mass transfer. The amount and size of gas bubbles can be determined by ultrasonic devices.

## B. Sensors for the Chemical Environment

During the operation of a bioreactor, substrates are consumed, products and metabolites are formed, and the pH (proton concentration) may change (Scheper and Reardon, 1991). During batch or fed-batch processes, the levels of these chemicals change substantially, and they are maintained within a narrow range in chemostats. These different concentration ranges, and a variety of other factors, place strict requirements on the chemical environment analytical system. When one considers that the chemical environment has a major impact on the biocatalyst, and that the success of a process usually relies on product formation, the importance of chemical sensors becomes even clearer.

Devices for these measurements are diverse, and include electrodes, optical (absorbance and fluorescence) sensors, chromatographs, and biosensors. Depending on the device, they are applied *in situ* or *ex situ* (interfaced to a bioprocess by using automated robotic systems as described previously).

The monitoring of pH and $pO_2$ is common in biotechnology. Sterilizable potentiometric pH electrodes or amperometric $pO_2$ electrodes are used *in situ*. Intrac systems can be used to withdraw the sensor for cleaning and recalibration during longer bioprocesses and to return the sensor after sterilization. Of less importance are redox electrodes, which supply information about the global redox potential in the cultivation process, and ion-selective electrodes, which as used to monitor different anions and cations.

The most commonly used sensors for the analysis of the gas phase composition are magnetic devices for oxygen and infrared analyzers for carbon dioxide. However, on-line mass spectroscopy and gas chromatography are gaining importance and provide the possibility of monitoring other gaseous compounds (e.g., ethanol and volatile fatty acids). Recently, "electronic nose" systems based on different detection principles (polymer sensors or semiconducting sensors) have been reported; these are likely to increase in importance for the monitoring of volatile components in the bioreactor. Special sampling devices with membranes permeable to the volatile components are used to interface gas-phase analytical devices with the bioreactor.

High-performance liquid chromatography and gas chromatography are common methods for manually analyzing the chemical environment of a bioreactor. In the past decade, many applications have been reported in which these instruments were interfaced to bioprocess using FIA or SIA for automated, on-line use. The range of target analytes is very broad and includes high-molecular-weight components. These techniques offer the possibility to simultaneously analyze different components in complex cultivation media and to provide information about the microheterogenity of proteins produced in a bioprocess. Similar efforts to interface other analytical devices, such as capillary electrophoresis, electrospray mass spectrometry, or flow cytometry, to bioreactors for on-line monitoring are under way.

Of all the available sensor systems for analysis of the chemical environment in a bioreactor, biosensors and optical sensors are of particular interest because of the potential advantages they present to detailed bioprocess monitoring. We describe these in more detail in the following sections.

### 1. Biosensors

Increasingly more biosensor systems are used in university research and in the development of monitoring and control systems for chemical, biochemical, and biotechnological processes. However, biosensors have not been implemented in industrial processes, mainly because of problems with poor stability and inaccuracy. Biosensors have applications in medicine, mainly for the control of blood components such as glucose or lactate.

A typical biosensor is shown schematically in Fig. 6. It consists of a biological component, a transducer, an amplifier, and a data-processing unit. The biological component of the sensor (enzymes, antibodies, cells, cell compartments, or DNA) interacts through reaction or binding with the analyte of interest at a high degree of specificity. The inherent specificity of biocomponents provides biosensors with low cross-sensitivities to other media components, which is an important advantage over other sensor types. The analyte–biocomponent interaction causes a change in a physical or chemical parameter such as pH, fluorescence, or mass. The transducer monitors this change with high sensitivity and produces a signal that is amplified and passed to a data processing unit that allows the biosensor data to be used for bioprocess control.

Thousands of applications of biosensors have been described in the literature for the monitoring of substrates and products in bioreactor processes (Canh, 1993). Recently, research on biosensors has focused on the simultaneous monitoring of multiple parameters during a cultivation by coupling FIA (with microdialysis sampling) and two or more biosensors. A principal benefit of the combination of biosensors and FIA or SIA techniques is a very flexible experimental setup.

As mentioned earlier, biosensors require continued development to make them more useful in industry. The most important need is to increase their long-term stability. New immobilization techniques for enzymes and antibodies offer the possibility to

obtain biosensors with both a long lifetime and stabilization against deactivation caused by cultivation components. Another interesting development is the use of reversible immobilization techniques based on affinity ligands. These allow one to immobilize or re-immobilize enzymes on a biosensor, even during a bioprocess.

### 2. Optical Sensors

During the past few years, optical sensors have become increasingly important for bioprocess monitoring. They offer the possibility to perform different spectroscopic analyses in a bioreactor, including noninvasive measurements. Complex optical detector systems can be interfaced to the bioreactor via appropriate fiber optics. In this linkage, light is guided through the optical fibers to the sensor tip, where the spectroscopic assay is performed. The results of these assays (e.g., changes in absorbance or fluorescence) are transported back as light signals and are evaluated in the optical detector system. Since a wide range of powerful spectroscopic analyses have been developed, the potential of linking them to bioprocesses as optical sensors is clear.

In general, optical sensors can be described as either selective chemosensors or integral spectroscopic sensors. An optical chemosensor is designed with a selective chemistry fixed on the fiber tip (Wolfbeis, 1991). Within this sensing element, a special dye that reversibly binds to the analyte is immobilized. The binding reaction can be monitored by changes in optical transmission (or absorbance), by luminescent effects (such as fluorescence changes), or by other properties. In particular, fluorescence-based chemosensors have demonstrated many advantages for biotechnology. In these sensors (Fig. 7), a selective fluorophore is immobilized on the fiber tip. The binding of the analyte (e.g., protons and oxygen) to the fluorophore causes a change in fluorescence intensity or decay time. When the fiber tip and the sensing element are illuminated with light of the appropriate wavelength, the changes in fluorescence can be detected. Since fluorescence is undirected, a part of the fluorescence is transmitted back to the detector via the fiber. Optical sensors (optodes) for oxygen and pH monitoring are the most advanced. Because of their small size, ability to perform

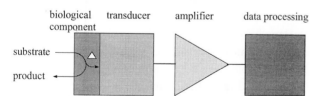

**Fig. 6.** Schematic of a biosensor system. Δ denotes the detectable change caused by the biocomponent–analyte interaction, which may be heat, electrons, protons, light, ions (e.g., $NH_4^+$), gases (e.g., $O_2$), fluorescence, or mass changes.

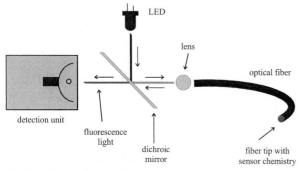

**Fig. 7.** Schematic of a fiber optical chemosensor ($\lambda_1$, excitation light; $\lambda_2$, emission light). The dichroic mirror reflects $\lambda_1$ but transmits $\lambda_2$.

multipoint measurements, insensitivity to electromagnetic fields, high sensitivity even under extreme reaction conditions (e.g., high pressure), and lack of electrical contact with the sample, these optical chemosensors have advantages over conventional electrochemical sensors.

Integral spectroscopic sensors do not use a selective sensing element. Instead, a spectral analysis is performed through a defined slit in the sensing fibers (transmission measurements) or via reflected, scattered, or backward fluorescence light. Transmission measurements have been used to monitor samples non-invasively in the ultraviolet visible or near-infrared (NIR) region. Also, by combining these devices with selective membrane materials (e.g., for gaseous compounds), a new near-infrared carbon dioxide sensors has been developed. Depending on the degree of interfering spectroscopic signal from other substances, a substantial effort in data evaluation may be necessary to obtain good quality information about the analyte. In particular, complex Fourier transformation analysis on the background signal is necessary to derive analyte profiles from NIR measurements. These data processing steps can be automated, and they do not detract from the main benefits of this technique: noninvasive, simultaneous monitoring of different substances. These sensor types will certainly gain in importance in the future.

Another type of nonselective optical sensor is the turbidity sensor. In this sensor, a decrease of transmission or an increase of reflected light caused by turbidity changes in the sample are monitored. When turbidity changes are mainly caused by cell growth,

these sensors give on-line information about the biomass concentration and the bioprocess.

A third type of nonselective optical sensors not only provides information about the medium composition but also yields insights into the metabolic state of the cells. In these devices, generally referred to as fluorosensors, excitation light of a special wavelength is guided into the bioreactor (and cells) via fiber optics. Within the cell-containing cultivation medium, the incoming light causes certain fluorophores to fluoresce; the backward fluorescence light is collected and transmitted to the detection unit via the same fiber optic. Using a single-wavelength monitoring system (defined excitation light and defined emission light), one can monitor the concentration of all fluorophores sensitive to these wavelengths. It is even possible to monitor fluorescent intermediates [e.g., NAD(P)H] in the metabolic network of the cultivated cells as a function of the process conditions. More sophisticated fluorosensors provide the option of scanning through excitation and emission wavelengths simultaneously. Thus, information about the concentration of all fluorophores present in the medium can be obtained using this two-dimensional spectrofluorometric system. Both intracellular components (representing the metabolic state of the cells) and extracellular components can be monitored simultaneously.

## C. Sensors for the Biological System

Measurements of the biological system in a bioreactor are of great interest since this is the catalyst of the process. Two main parameters can be quantified: biomass concentration and the metabolic state.

Biomass concentration estimation can be performed by sensors based on optical (turbidity, fluorometric, or spectrofluorometric), calorimetric, filtration, viscosity, electrochemical, acoustic, and electrochemical principles. Optical scattering/turbidity sensors have been more commonly used than the others due to their lower cost and the ease of application. However, impedimetric and other optical sensors are gaining importance. Potentiometric, amperometric, or impedimetric methods can be used to distinguish between the concentrations of viable and nonviable cells.

To monitor the metabolic state of the cell—energy

levels, key metabolites, or enzymes—both invasive and non-invasive methods have been developed. As described previously, fluorometers can provide information about the metabolic state of microorganisms during the bioprocess by monitoring intracellular fluorophores such as NAD(P)H. Nuclear magnetic resonance spectroscopy (NMR) provides the ability to monitor several intracellular components directly. However, the use of this method has been limited by its extremely restrictive analysis conditions (small bioreactors, high cell density, and a complicated analytical procedure). Invasive methods are simpler to use and therefore have been more broadly applied. In this case, cell-containing samples are withdrawn from the bioreactor and transferred to an automated robotic analysis system, in which their metabolic activity is stopped with a reagent such as perchloric acid and the metabolites are extracted. Simple systems have been described to monitor intracellular enzyme concentrations, and more sophisticated systems can be used to perform the analyses at high frequencies (e.g., at 100-ms intervals on separately withdrawn samples). However, the analysis time can be long (in the range of 30 min for each assay), and thus data are available only with a relatively long time lag even though the samples are withdrawn at short time intervals.

Sensors for the analysis of biomass concentration and metabolic state are rarely used, despite years of research and development. *In situ* sensors suffer from interferences due to solid particles, gas bubbles, or certain chemicals (e.g., fluorescent metabolic products). In other cases, the analytical devices have been developed for research purposes rather than industrial application. New advances can be made if compromises are sought among the goals of metabolic research, industrial application, and real-time monitoring.

## V. MODELS, DATA PROCESSING, AND BIOPROCESS CONTROL

### A. Models

For the analysis, optimization, performance, and especially the automation of bioprocesses, models are a fundamental requirement. The first bioprocesses (wine and vinegar fermentation, and leavening of bread) were carried out long before detailed knowledge about microorganism was available, and verbally formulated models were used to perform these processes. In succeeding years, more knowledge about these processes was gathered and a mathematical formalism was developed to enable us to express this knowledge through mathematical equations (i.e., models). However, the variety and the complexity of the different models are as large as the variety and complexity of bioprocesses. Structured and unstructured, segregated and unsegregated, cybernetic and stochastic models are all utilized in biotechnology to express knowledge, to elucidate unknown behavior and new strategies, to generate a consistent world of ideas, and to optimize and automate technical bioprocesses (Bailey, 1998).

Both mechanistic and black box models are used to predict the hypothetical course of a bioprocess, especially product formation. Machanistic models use detailed knowledge about the process (based on principles such as the conservation of mass and energy). In contrast, black box models present correlations (mathematical relationships with no direct relation to or knowledge about the process) which allow the calculation of process behavior or a bioprocess variable from other process values. Although mechanistic models, with their underlying knowledge, can in principle be transferred from one application to another (the quality of extrapolation), the functioning of black box models must be demonstrated for each specific application and cannot typically be extrapolated. However, due to the fact that microorganisms are very complex systems (e.g., each bacterial cell contains more than 1,500,000 protein molecules, the dynamic behavior of which is only partly understood and is highly nonlinear), almost all mechanistic models use only the essential rate-limiting steps rather than all involved reaction and transport processes. Of course, these steps will vary from application to application, restricting even the applicability of mechanistic models. However, the rapid increase in available computing power will soon allow modelers to deal with very complex mechanistic models that include all known processes affecting the growth of cells (as well as product formation) in a nonideal bioreactor. Even though important parameters are not available for these models—and will not be available in the near future—the models will yield detailed information about what might occur in the cells and which steps in the reaction network (including regulation) and transport systems are important.

## B. Software Sensors

Since many important bioprocess variables are difficult or impossible to measure, software sensors are used for elucidation of the bioprocess state and behavior. One type of software sensor is state observer. With an observer, nonmeasurable (or difficult to measure) variables of a process can be predicted using a mathematical model (state space model) as well as data from measured variables. Integrating the general state observer equation, the values of the missing variables are calculated online. Through the application of different optimization criteria during calculation of the variables, different observers, such as the (extended) Luenberger or Kalman observers, have been utilized successfully.

Another type of software sensor is based more on black box models such as artificial neural networks or principal component regression. Here, the model structure and equation are not based on inherent knowledge about the process. The values of measured process variables and sometimes their history form patterns that are used by these models to determine the model structure as well as their parameter values. However, these data-driven methods require large amounts of measurement data from different process runs to build the model reliably. The predictive ability of these models can be lost if the process conditions are changed. If the measured values are highly correlated, as is the case for 2-D fluorescence measurements, then principal component analysis is applied for data transformation and reduction. The data transformation is based on variance analysis and creates so-called latent variables, which are orthogonal. The latent variables, whose significance must be determined by special criteria, are then used as an input pattern for artificial neural networks or for a multilinear regression model to predict the non-measurable variables. Using this approach, glucose concentrations have been predicted

with an error of approximately 5% using 2-D fluorescence measurements and principal component regression.

These two different types of software sensors are also used together as a hybrid or "gray box" model. In this case, the process knowledge is used to develop a mechanistic model whose unknown relations, such as the dependence of a reaction rate on specific variables, are modeled by a black box model. This new type of model has increased in importance and application, and will continue to do so.

## C. Control

The control and supervision of bioprocesses have become increasingly vital because of increasing competition and therefore increasing efforts to increase product quality, yield, and security and to decrease process expenditures, including energy, raw materials, and staff. The operation of a typical production process is based on at least three different phases: upstream processing (filling, mixing, and sterilization), cultivation (growing and producing), and downstream processing (harvesting and product recovery). In each phase, a high degree of automation is demanded. With respect to the control problem, the cultivation phase requires the most attention. However, examples of control applications are rare in industry, although there are many examples of control application in academia.

The control of bioprocesses is difficult because the cultivation process includes a large network of complex biochemical reactions as well as multilayered transport processes. Furthermore, the bioprocesses are nonlinear and time variant. The microorganisms have their own inherent control system, which bioprocess operators can influence only indirectly by changing the cells' environment. Key variables may be impossible or at least very difficult to measure, and any measurement data obtained will entail time delays and discontinuities. Because most bioprocesses are carried out as batch or fed-batch operations, the control task is almost exclusively performed with the goal of providing an optimal environment for the cells. Common goals of control systems are to

Compensate for disturbances

Minimize the use of energy and raw materials

Maximize yield and product quality

Ensure safe operation

Prevent substrate, catabolite, and product inhibition

Induce or repress enzyme activity

Avoid shear stress

Some of these goals have been achieved for years using standard control technique. Control loops for volume, temperature, pH, DO, antifoam, and stirrer speed are very basic features of a bioreactor. These loops are most often on–off controllers or proportional–integral–derivative (PID) controllers.

In general, the control loop consists of a measurement system, a computer, and an actuator (a valve or a pump). The measurement system, which provides the controlled variable data, is connected to the bioreactor and sends the data to the computer, in which they are treated with the control algorithm. The output of the algorithm is used by the actuator, which is also connected to the bioreactor so that a closed loop is created. During the cultivation process, the control algorithm calculates the control action in real time on the basis of the measurement data, with the result that these parameters will follow desired values or will remain at the set point to fulfill a certain performance criterion (such as a maximum yield).

In contrast to the on–off controller, which merely switches its value if the controlled variable moves higher or lower than a certain threshold, the PID controller utilizes the magnitude and time course of the control error (the difference of the data of the desired set point and the control variable). Using these controllers, almost no bioprocess knowledge is applied. However, significant improvement of bioprocess performance can be achieved if—based on the knowledge of the specific bioprocess—variables such as substrate, biomass, or synthesis rates are controlled. However, more advanced controllers then have to be applied, such as adaptive controllers (Bastin and Dochain, 1990). In this case, a software sensor is used in real time. That is, a parameter identification is performed to adapt the parameters of the underlying process model to the measurement data by considering the time-variant characteristics of the bioprocess. Based on these parameters, the best control action is determined and then performed by the actuator. Corresponding to the diversity of models developed for bioprocesses, various degrees of process knowledge can be implemented in these controllers. Although the adaptive controllers compensate to a certain degree for the shortcoming or inadequacy of their models, their robustness cannot always be guaranteed. Various applications of controllers have demonstrated their enormous potential for process optimization; a good example is high cell density cultivation.

A drawback of all controllers is their sensitivity to the measurement data. To improve the robustness of the measurement systems as well as that of the controller, knowledge-based systems, such as expert systems, have been developed. These supervise and validate both complex process analyzers and the process. Knowledge-based systems use a description of the entire process in terms of submodels, which are only valid during certain phases, and heuristic rules. Specific process phases are identified just as would be done by a human operator. Consistency checks are utilized to identify defects and faults in the technical, analytical, and biological system. Even operator actions are supervised by such systems. In this manner, the reliability of the analyzer system as well as that of the bioprocess can be significantly enhanced. The processes operating under knowledge-based systems require reduced supervision, and the operator is freed of repetitive work. The drawbacks to the use of knowledge-based systems are the time and cost of development, but these can be justified by the improved performance of the bioprocess.

## See Also the Following Articles

Biosensors • Industrial Biotechnology

## Bibliography

Bailey, J. E. (1998). Mathematical modeling and analysis in biochemical engineering: Past accomplishments and future opportunities. *Biotechnol. Prog.* **14,** 8–20.

Bastin, G., and Dochain, D. (1990). "On-Line Estimation

and Adaptive Control of Bioreactors." Elsevier, Amsterdam.

Canh, T. M. (1993). "Biosensors." Chapman & Hall, New York.

Olsson, L., Schulze, U., and Nielsen, J. (1998). On-line bioprocess monitoring—An academic discipline or an industrial tool? *Trends Anal. Chem.* 17(2), 88–95.

Ruzicka, J., and Hansen, E. H. (1989). "Flow Injection Analysis," 2nd ed. Wiley, New York.

Ruzicka, J., and Marshall, G. D. (1990). Sequential injection: A new concept for chemical sensors, process analysis and laboratory assays. *Anal. Chim. Acta* 237, 329.

Scheper, T., and, Reardon, K. F. (1991). Sensors in biotechnology. *In* "Sensors," (W. G. Göpel, J. H Hesse. and J. N. Memel, Eds.), Vol. 2, pp. 1024–1046. VCH, Weinheim.

Wolfbeis, O. S. (1991). "Fiber Optic Chemical Sensors and Biosensors." Vols. 1 and 2. CRC Press, Boca Raton, FL.

# *Bioreactors*

## Larry E. Erickson

*Kansas State University*

## GLOSSARY

***airlift reactor*** Column with defined volumes for upflow and downflow of the culture broth; vertical circulation occurs because air is bubbled into the upflow volume.

***batch bioreactor*** Culture broth is fed into the reactor at the start of the process; air may flow continuously.

***bubble reactor*** Aerated column without mechanical agitation.

***fed batch*** Liquid media is fed to the reactor continuously; the broth accumulates in the reactor because there is no outflow of liquid.

***heterotrophs*** Microorganisms growing on an organic compound that provides carbon and energy.

***insect cell culture*** Cultivation of insect cells in a bioreactor to produce a protein or other product.

***photoautotrophs*** Microorganisms that use light for energy and carbon dioxide for their carbon source.

***plant cell culture*** Production of plant cells in a bioreactor to produce useful products.

***protein engineering*** The design, development, and production of new protein products with properties of commercial value.

***tissue engineering*** The design, development, and production of tissue cells (biomaterials) for use on or in humans.

**BIOREACTORS** are vessels or tanks in which whole cells or cell-free enzymes transform raw materials into biochemical products and/or less undesirable by-products. The microbial cell is a miniature bioreactor; other examples include shake flasks, petri dishes, and industrial fermentors. Diagnostic products based on enzymatic reactions, farm silos for silage fermentations, bread pans with fermenting yeast, and the soil in a Kansas wheat field may also be viewed as bioreactors. Although the bioreactor may be simple or highly instrumented, the important consideration is the ability to produce the desired product or result. The bioreactor is designed and operated to provide the environment for product formation selected by the scientist, baker, or winemaker. It is the heart of many biotechnological systems that are used for agricultural, environmental, industrial, and medical applications.

## I. INTRODUCTION

The importance of the bioreactor is recorded in early history. The Babylonians apparently made beer before 5000 BC. Wine was produced in wineskins, which were carefully selected for their ability to produce a beverage that met the approval of the king and other members of his sensory analysis taste panel. Food and beverage product quality depended on art and craftsmanship rather than on science and engineering during the early years of bioreactor selection and utilization. Early recorded history shows that some understood the importance of the reactants and the environmental or operating conditions of the reactor. This allowed leavened bread and cheese to be produced in Egypt more than 3000 years ago.

The process of cooking food to render it microbiologically safe for human consumption and to improve its sensory qualities is also an ancient tradition. The process of thermal inactivation of microorganisms through the canning of food to allow safe storage was an important early achievement in bioreactor design and operation.

As humans learned to live in cities, waste management including wastewater treatment became a necessity for control of disease. One of the first process engineering achievements was the biological treatment of wastes in bioreactors designed and built by humans for that purpose. Because a significant fraction of the population of a city could die from disease spread by unsanitary conditions, these early bioreactors represented important advancements.

After microorganisms were discovered, microbiologists and engineers increased their understanding of the biochemical transformations in bioreactors. Simple anaerobic fermentations for the production of ethyl alcohol, acetone, and butanol were developed. Aerobic and anaerobic treatment of waste-water became widely used. Sanitary engineering became a part of civil engineering education.

In the 1940s, the field of biochemical engineering emerged because of developments in the pharmaceutical industry that required large-scale bioreactors for the production of streptomycin and penicillin. Progress in bioreactor design and control resulted from research on oxygen transfer, air and media sterilization, and pH control. The central concern of the early biochemical engineers was the development of bioreactors that could achieve and maintain the chemical and physical environment for the organism that the biochemist/microbiologist recommended. The ability to scale-up from laboratory bioreactors to large fermentors required the development of instrumentation such as the sterilizable oxygen electrode. Early courses in biochemical engineering were concerned with the analysis, design, operation, and control of bioreactors. Although the field of biochemical engineering is less than 60 years old and some of the pioneers are still available to provide a first-person account of those exciting days, great progress has been made in bioreactor engineering. Some of the significant developments in bioreactor technology and their approximate dates are listed in Table I.

## II. CLASSIFICATIONS OF BIOREACTORS

Several methods have been used to classify bioreactors, including the feeding of media and gases and the withdrawal of products; the mode of operation may be batch, fed batch, or continuous. The classification may be based on the electron acceptor; the design may be for aerobic, anaerobic, or microaerobic conditions. In aerobic processes, the methods of providing oxygen have resulted in mechanically agitated bioreactors, airlift columns, bubble columns, and membrane reactors. The sterility requirements of pure culture processes with developed strains differ from those of environmental mixed-culture processes, which are based on natural selection. In some bioreactors the vessel is made by humans and there are also natural bioreactors, such as the microbial cell, the flowing river, and the field of native grass. In this article, the classification of bioreactors is based on the physical form of the reactants and products.

### A. Gas Phase Reactants or Products

Oxygen and carbon dioxide are the most common gas phase reactants and products; others include hydrogen, hydrogen sulfide, carbon monoxide, and methane. Oxygen is a reactant in aerobic heterotrophic growth processes, whereas it is a product in photoautotrophic growth. Generally, the concentration of the reactants and products in the liquid phase in the microenvironment of the cell influences the kinetics of the cellular reaction. Mass transfer to and from the gas phase affects bioreactor performance in most processes with gas phase reactants or products. The anaerobic reactor is designed to exclude oxygen. In some cases, inert gases are bubbled into the anaerobic reactor to provide a gas–liquid interfacial area to remove the product gases.

Because the solubility of oxygen in water is very low, the dissolved oxygen in the broth is rapidly depleted if oxygen transfer from the gas to the liquid phase is disrupted in aerobic processes. The distribution of dissolved oxygen throughout the reactor volume and the transient variation affect reactor performance. When mold pellets or biofilms are present, the diffusion of oxygen into the interior should be considered. A significant portion of the bioreactor

*TABLE I*
**Significant Developments in Bioreactor Technology**

| Development | Year[a] |
|---|---|
| Fermented beverages | 5000 BC |
| Pasteur's discovery of yeast | 1857 |
| First medium designed for culturing bacteria | 1860 |
| Trickling filter for wastewater | 1868 |
| Anaerobic digester | 1881 |
| Production of citric acid using mold | 1923 |
| Production of penicillin in a petri dish | 1928 |
| Production of penicillin in small flasks | 1942 |
| Hixon and Gaden paper on oxygen transfer | 1950 |
| Air sterilization in fermentors | 1950 |
| Continuous media sterilization | 1952 |
| Aiba, Humphrey, and Millis biochemical engineering textbook on bioreactor design | 1965 |
| Continuous airlift reactor for production of yeast | 1969 |
| Advances in instrumentation and computer control | 1970 |
| Progress in airlift bioreactor design | 1973 |
| Recombinant DNA technology | 1973 |
| Insect cells grown in suspension culture | 1975 |
| Large-scale cell culture to produce interferon | 1980 |
| Insulin produced using bacteria | 1982 |
| Bioreactors for fragile cell cultures | 1988 |
| Textbook on plant cell biotechnology | 1994 |
| Textbook on protein engineering | 1996 |
| Textbook on tissue engineering | 1997 |

[a] The dates are approximate and are indicative of periods of time when advances were progressing from initial studies to published works or commercial use.

literature is devoted to oxygen transfer and the methods recommended for the design and operation of aerobic bioreactors. The phase equilibrium relationship is based on thermodynamic data, whereas the rate of oxygen transfer depends on the gas–liquid interfacial area and the concentration driving force. Mechanical agitation increases the gas–liquid interfacial area. Aeration provides the supply of oxygen, and it affects the gas–liquid interfacial area.

Oxygen has been supplied by permeation through membranes in cultures in which bubbles may damage shear-sensitive cells. The membrane area and concentration driving force determine the oxygen transfer rate in these bioreactors.

Most large-scale bioreactors have either oxygen or carbon dioxide among the reactants or products. In many anaerobic fermentations the formation of carbon dioxide results in bubbling, and often no additional mixing is required for either mass transfer or suspension of the microbial cells. Methane is produced through anaerobic digestion of waste products. It is also a product of microbial action in landfills, bogs, and the stomach of the cow.

Packed-bed bioreactors are used to biodegrade volatile organic compounds in air pollution control applications. The rhizosphere provides a natural environment in which many volatile compounds in soil are transformed by microbial and plant enzymes.

## B. Liquid Phase Reactants or Products

Many bioreactors have liquid phase reactants and products. Ethanol, acetone, butanol, and lactic acid are liquid products that can be produced by fermentation. The kinetics of biochemical reactions depends on the liquid phase concentrations of the reactants and, in some cases, the products. The Monod kinetic model and the Michaelis–Menten kinetic model show that many biochemical reactions have first-order dependence on reactant (substrate) concentration at low concentrations and zero-order dependence at higher concentrations. Rates are directly proportional to concentrations lower than 10 mg/liter for many reactants under natural environmental conditions. At very high concentrations, inhibition may be observed.

Hydrocarbons that are relatively insoluble in the water phase, such as hexadecane, may also be reactants or substrates for biochemical reactions. Microbial growth on hydrocarbons has been observed to occur at the liquid–liquid interface and in the water phase. The oxygen requirements are greater when hydrocarbon substrates are used in place of carbohydrates. In the past, there was great interest in the production of microbial protein from petroleum hydrocarbons. The commercialization of the technology was most extensive in the former Soviet Union. The airlift bioreactor is uniquely suited for this four-phase process because of the tendency of the hydrocarbon phase to migrate to the top of the fermentor. The hydrocarbons are found suspended as drops in the water phase, adsorbed to cells, and at the gas–liquid interface. The cells are found adsorbed to hydrocarbon drops, suspended in the water phase, and at the gas–liquid interface. In the airlift fermentor, the vertical circulation mixes the hydrocarbons and cells that have migrated to the top of the fermentor with the broth that enters the downflow side of the column.

One of the oldest and most widely practiced fermentations is the microbial production of ethanol and alcoholic beverages such as beer and wine. Because ethanol inhibits fermentation at high concentrations, the process of inhibition has been extensively studied for this fermentation. Ethanol affects the cell membrane and the activities of enzymes. This inhibition limits the concentration of ethanol that can be obtained in a fermentor. Because ethanol is also produced for use as a motor fuel, there is still considerable research on ethanol production. Because the cost of the substrate is a major expense, inexpensive raw materials such as wastes containing cellulose have been investigated.

## C. Solid Phase Reactants or Products

There are many examples of bioreactors with solid phase reactants. The cow may be viewed as a mobile bioreactor system that converts solid substrates to methane, carbon dioxide, milk, and body protein. Although the cow is a commercial success, many efforts to transform low-cost cellulosic solid waste to commercial products in human-made bioreactors have not achieved the same level of success.

Solid substrates such as soybean meal are commonly fed into commercial fermentations. Through the action of enzymes in the fermentation broth, the biopolymers are hydrolyzed and more soluble reactants are obtained.

Many food fermentations involve the preservation of solid or semisolid foods such as in the conversion of cabbage to sauerkraut and meats to sausage products. Cereals, legumes, vegetables, tubers, fruits, meats, and fish products have been fermented. Some fermented milk processes result in solid products such as cheeses and yogurts.

Other examples include the composting of yard wastes, leaching of metals from ores, silage production, biodegradation of crop residues in soil, microbial action in landfills, and the remediation of contaminated soil.

In many of these fermentations, mixing is difficult or expensive. Transport of essential reactants may depend on diffusion; the concentrations of reactants and products vary with position. Rates may be limited by the transport of essential reactants to the microorganisms.

Most compounds that are present as solids in bioreactors are somewhat soluble in the water phase. For reactants that are relatively insoluble, biochemical reaction rates may be directly proportional to the available interfacial area. The surface of the solid may be the location of the biochemical transformation. An example of microorganisms growing on the surface of a solid substrate is mold on bread. To design bioreactors for solid substrates and solid products, the solubility and the transport processes should be considered as well as the kinetics of the process.

Recently, there has been considerable progress in tissue engineering. The rational design of living tissues and the production of these tissues by living cells in bioreactors are advancing rapidly because of progress in systems design and control for both *in vitro* flow reactors and *in vivo* maintenance of cell mass.

## D. Microorganisms in Bioreactors

The rate of reaction in bioreactors is often directly proportional to the concentration of microbial biomass. In biological waste treatment, the influent concentration of the organic substrate (waste) is relatively low, and the quantity of microbial biomass that can be produced from the waste is limited. The economy of the operation and the rate of biodegradation are enhanced by retaining the biomass in the bioreactor. In the activated sludge process, this is done by allowing the biomass to flocculate and settle; it is then recycled. The trickling filter retains biomass by allowing growth on the surfaces of the packing within the bioreactor.

A variety of immobilized cell reactors and immobilized enzyme reactors have been designed and operated because of the economy associated with reuse of cells and enzymes. In the anaerobic production of ethanol, lactic acid, and the other fermentation products, the product yield is greatest when the organisms are not growing and all the substrate is being converted to products. Continuous processes can be designed in which most of the cells are retained and the limiting maximum product yield is approached. Ultra-filtration membrane bioreactors have been used to retain cells, enzymes, and insoluble substrates.

In nature, cells are retained when biofilms form along flow pathways. The biofilms allow microorganisms to grow and survive in environments in which washout would be expected. The excellent quality of groundwater is the result of microbial biodegradation and purification under conditions in which microbial survival is enhanced by biofilm formation and cell retention on soil and rock surfaces. The ability of microorganisms to survive even after their food supply appears to be depleted is well established; this is the reason that there are microorganisms almost everywhere in nature. When spills occur, organic substances will often be degraded by microorganisms, if the nutritional environment is balanced. Nitrogen, phosphorous, and other inorganic nutrients often must be added.

The concentration of cells adsorbed to the surface and the concentration in the water phase depends on an adsorption phase equilibrium relationship and the operating conditions. In many environmental applications, most of the cells are adsorbed to surfaces. However, in large-scale fermentors with high cell concentrations and rich media feeds, only a small fraction of the cells are found on surfaces.

## E. Photobioreactors

Light is the energy source that drives photoautotrophic growth processes. Because light is absorbed by the growing culture, the intensity decreases rapidly as the distance from the surface increases. Photobioreactors are designed to produce the quantity of product that is desired. Heat transfer is an important design aspect because any absorbed light energy that is not converted to chemical energy must be dissipated as heat.

## III. PRINCIPLES OF BIOREACTOR ANALYSIS AND DESIGN

The basic principles of bioreactor analysis and design are similar to those for chemical reactors; however, many biochemical processes have very complex biochemistry. The chemical balance equations or stoichiometry of the process must be known or investigated. The yield of microbial biomass and products depends on the genetics of the strain and the operating conditions. The consistency of data from experimental measurements can be evaluated using mass balances such as the carbon balance and the available electron balance.

Microorganisms obey the laws of chemical thermodynamics; some heat is produced in heterotrophic growth processes. The free energy change is negative for the complete system of biochemical reactions associated with heterotrophic growth and product formation. Thus, the chemical energy available for growth and product formation decreases as a result of microbial assimilation of the reactants.

The rate of growth and product formation depends

on the number of microorganisms and the concentrations of the nutrients. The kinetics of growth and product formation is often written in terms of the concentration of one rate-limiting substrate; however, in some cases, more than one nutrient may be rate limiting. The kinetics must be known for rational design of the bioreactor.

Heat is evolved in microbial bioreactors. For aerobic processes, the quantity of heat generated (heat of fermentation) is directly proportional to the oxygen utilized. Thus, the heat transfer and oxygen transfer requirements are linked by the energy regularity of approximately 450 kJ of heat evolved per mole of oxygen utilized by the microorganisms.

Transport phenomena is widely applied in bioreactor analysis and design. Many fermentation processes are designed to be transport limited. For example, the oxygen transfer rate may limit the rate of an aerobic process. Bioreactor design depends on the type of organism and the nutritional and environmental requirements. For example, in very viscous mycelial fermentations, mechanical agitation is often selected to provide the interfacial area for oxygen transfer. Likewise, animal cells that grow only on surfaces must be cultured in special bioreactors, which provide the necessary surface area and nutritional environment. In other cases, animals are used as the bioreactors because the desired biochemical transformations can best be achieved by competitively utilizing animals; cost and quality control are both important when food and pharmaceutical products are produced.

## IV. SENSORS, INSTRUMENTATION, AND CONTROL

The ability to measure the physical and chemical environment in the fermentor is essential for control of the process. In the past 50 years, there has been significant progress in the development of sensors and computer control. Physical variables that can be measured include temperature, pressure, power input to mechanical agitators, rheological properties of the broth, gas and liquid flow rates, and interfacial tension. The chemical environment is characterized by means of electrodes for hydrogen ion concentra-

tion (pH), redox potential, carbon dioxide partial pressure, and oxygen partial pressure. Gas phase concentrations are measured with the mass spectrometer. Broth concentrations are measured with gas and liquid chromatography; mass spectrometers can be used as detectors with either gas or liquid chromatography. Enzyme thermistors have been developed to measure the concentrations of a variety of biochemicals. Microbial mass is commonly measured with the spectrophotometer (optical density) and cell numbers through plate counts and direct microscopic observation. Instruments are available to measure components of cells such as reduced pyridine nucleotides and cell nitrogen. On-line biomass measurements can be made using a flow cell and a laser by making multi-angle light scattering measurements. Multivariate calibration methods and neural network technology allow the data to be processed rapidly and continuously such that a predicted biomass concentration can be obtained every few seconds.

The basic objective of bioreactor design is to create and maintain the environment that is needed to enable the cells to make the desired biochemical transformations. Advances in instrumentation and control allow this to be done reliably.

## V. METABOLIC AND PROTEIN ENGINEERING

Genetic modification has allowed many products to be produced economically. With the use of recombinant DNA technology and metabolic engineering, improved cellular activities may be obtained through manipulation of enzymatic, regulatory, and transport functions of the microorganism. The cellular modifications of metabolic engineering are carried out in bioreactors. Successful manipulation requires an understanding of the genetics, biochemistry, and physiology of the cell. Knowledge of the biochemical pathways involved, their regulation, and their kinetics is essential.

Living systems are bioreactors. Through metabolic engineering, man can modify these living bioreactors and alter their performance. Metabolic engineering is a field of reaction engineering that utilizes the concepts that provide the foundation for reactor design, including kinetics, thermodynamics, physical chemistry, process control, stability, catalysis, and transport phenomena. These concepts must be combined with an understanding of the biochemistry of the living system. Through metabolic engineering, improved versions of living bioreactors are designed and synthesized.

Although many products are produced in microbial cells, other cell lines, including insect cells, mammalian cells, and plant cells, are utilized for selected applications. The science to support these various living bioreactors is growing rapidly and the number of different applications is increasing steadily. The choice of which organism to select for a specific product must be made carefully, with consideration of biochemistry, biochemical engineering, safety, reliability, and cost. Both production and separation processes affect the cost of the product; however, the costs of product development, testing, regulatory approval, and marketing are also substantial.

Proteins with specific functional properties are being designed, developed, and produced through applications of protein engineering. Through molecular modeling and computer simulation, proteins with specific properties are designed. Protein production may involve applications of recombinant DNA technology in host cell expression bioreactors. An alternative is the production of a protein with the desired amino acid sequence through direct chemical synthesis.

## VI. STABILITY AND STERILIZATION

Although beneficial genetic modification has led to many successful industrial products, contamination and genetic mutations during production operations have resulted in many batches of useless broth. Batch processes are common in bioreactors because of the need to maintain the desired genetic properties of a strain during storage and propagation. Continuous operation is selected for mixed-culture processes such as wastewater treatment, in which there is natural selection of effective organisms.

Bioreactors that are to operate with pure cultures or mixed cultures from selected strains must be free of contamination; i.e., the reactor and associated in-

strumentation must be sterilizable. The vessels that are to be used for propagation of the inoculum for the large-scale vessel must also be sterilizable. Methods to sterilize large vessels, instrumentation, and connecting pipes are well developed; however, there is a continuous need to implement a wide variety of good manufacturing practice principles to avoid contamination problems.

Steam sterilization has been widely applied to reduce the number of viable microorganisms in food and in fermentation media. As temperature increases, the rates of biochemical reactions increase exponentially until the temperature affects the stability of the enzyme or the viability of the cell. The Arrhenius activation energies, which have been reported for enzymatic reactions and rates of cell growth, are usually in the range of 20–80 kJ/g/mol, whereas activation energies for the thermal inactivation of microorganisms range from 200 to 400 kJ/g/mol. Many of the preceding principles also apply to the thermal inactivation of microorganisms in bioreactors. When solids are present in foods or fermentation media, heat transfer to the interior of the solids occurs by conduction. This must be considered in the design of the process because of the increase in the required sterilization time.

## VII. CONCLUSIONS

Bioreactors are used for a variety of purposes. The knowledge base for their application has increased significantly because of the advances in chemical, biochemical, and environmental engineering during the past 60 years.

### See Also the Following Articles

BIODEGRADATION • BIOFILMS AND BIOFOULING • BIOREACTOR MONITORING AND CONTROL

### Bibliography

Asenjo, J. A., and Merchuk, J. C. (Eds.) (1995). "Bioreactor System Design." Dekker, New York.

Bailey, J. E., and Ollis, D. F. (1986). "Biochemical Engineering Fundamentals," 2nd ed. McGraw-Hill, New York.

Barford, J. P., Harbour, C., Phillips, P. J., Marquis, C. P., Mahler, S., and Malik, R. (1995). "Fundamental and Applied Aspects of Animal Cell Cultivation." Singapore Univ. Press, Singapore.

Blanch, H. W., and Clark, D. S. (1996). "Biochemical Engineering." Dekker, New York.

Carberry, J. J., and Varma, A. (Eds.) (1987). "Chemical Reaction and Reactor Engineering." Dekker, New York.

Characklis, W. G., and Marshall, K. C. (Eds.) (1990). "Biofilms." Wiley–Interscience, New York.

Christi, M. Y. (1989). "Airlift Bioreactors." Elsevier, New York.

Cleland, J. L., and Craik, C. S. (Eds.) (1996). "Protein Engineering: Principles and Practice." Wiley, New York.

Cookson, J. T. (1995). "Bioremediation Engineering." McGraw-Hill, New York.

Endress, R. (1994). "Plant Cell Biotechnology." Springer-Verlag, Berlin.

Erickson, L. E., and Fung, D. Y. (Eds.) (1988). "Handbook on Anaerobic Fermentations." Dekker, New York.

Fan, L. T., Gharpuray, M. M., and Lee, Y. H. (1987). "Cellulose Hydrolysis." Springer-Verlag, Heidelberg.

Goosen, M. F. A., Daugulis, A. J., and Faulkner, P. (Eds.) (1993). "Insect Cell Culture Engineering." Dekker, New York.

Lanza, R. P., Langer, R. S., and Chick, W. L. (Eds.) (1997). "Principles of Tissue Engineering." Academic Press, San Diego.

Lubiniecki, A. S. (Ed.) (1990). "Large-Scale Mammalian Cell Culture Technology." Dekker, New York.

Moo-Young, M. (Ed.) (1988). "Bioreactor Immobilized Enzymes and Cells: Fundamentals and Applications." Elsevier, New York.

Nielsen, J. H., and Villadsen, J. (1994). "Bioreaction Engineering Principles." Plenum, New York.

Shuler, M. L., and Kargi, F. (1992). "Bioprocess Engineering." Prentice Hall, Englewood Cliffs, NJ.

Sikdar, S. K., and Irvine, R. L. (Eds.) (1998). "Bioremediation: Principles and Practice." Technomic, Lancaster, PA.

Twork, J. V., and Yacynych, A. M. (Eds.) (1990). "Sensors in Bioprocess Control." Dekker, New York.

Van't Riet, K., and Tramper, J. (1991). "Basic Bioreactor Design." Dekker, New York.

# Bioremediation

## Joseph B. Hughes, C. Nelson Neale, and C. H. Ward

*Rice University*

## GLOSSARY

**bioattenuation** The nonengineered, natural decomposition of organic contaminants in soil and groundwater systems.

**biochemical markers** Easily monitored (e.g., substrate-specific microbial population) or chemical (e.g., metabolic intermediates and end products) indicators of biodegradation or biotransformation.

**biodegradation** Metabolism of a substance by microorganisms that yields mineralized end products.

**bioslurry treatment** Accelerated biodegradation of contaminants by the suspension of contaminated soil or sediment in water through mixing energy.

**biotransformation** Microbially mediated process in which the original compound is converted to secondary or intermediate products.

**bioventing** Accelerated biodegradation of contaminants in contaminated subsurface materials by forcing and/or drawing air through the unsaturated zone.

**cometabolism** Fortuitous metabolism of a compound by a microorganism that neither yields energy directly nor produces a metabolic product that can subsequently be involved in energy metabolism.

**composting** Accelerated biodegradation of contaminants at high temperatures by aerating and adding bulking agents and possibly nutrients to waste in a compost pile.

**ex situ bioremediation** Biological treatment of excavated or removed contaminated media.

**immobilization** Chemical and/or physical processes by which contaminants become strongly associated or sorbed with a soil matrix or sludge and desorption is limited.

**in situ bioremediation** Treatment without physical disruption or removal of contaminated media.

**land treatment** Accelerated biodegradation of contaminated media through application to surface soils to enhance aeration and, in some cases, to allow for nutrient amendment.

**microcosm** Highly controlled laboratory-scale apparatus used to model or simulate the fate or transport of compounds under the biological, chemical, and physical conditions found in the natural environment.

**plume** Dissolved contaminants emanating from a source region due to groundwater transport processes.

**unsaturated zone** Region which spans the area located just beneath the surface and directly above the water table.

**BIOREMEDIATION** is defined in this article as the process by which microorganisms are stimulated to rapidly degrade hazardous organic contaminants to environmentally safe levels in soils, sediments, subsurface materials, and groundwater. Biological remediation processes have also recently been devised to either precipitate or effectively immobilize inorganic contaminants such as heavy metals; however, treatment of inorganics will not be included in this definition of bioremediation. Stimulation is achieved by the addition of growth substrates, nutrients, terminal electron acceptor, electron donors, or some combination therein, resulting in an increase in contaminant biodegradation and biotransformation. The microbes involved in bioremediation processes may obtain both energy and carbon through the metabolism of organic contaminants. In some cases, metabolism occurs via a co-metabolic process or by a terminal electron-accepting process. Independent of the metabolic pathways, bioremediation systems are designed to degrade hazardous organic contaminants sorbed to soils and sediments or dissolved in water. Bioremediation of contaminants may occur *in situ* or within the contaminated soil, sediments, or groundwater. Alternatively, the contaminated media may be removed and treated using *ex situ* techniques.

## I. INTRODUCTION

With the advent of petroleum refining and manufacture of synthetic chemicals, many potentially hazardous organic compounds have been introduced into the air, water, and soil. One method for removing these undesirable compounds from the environment is bioremediation, an extension of carbon cycling. Given the appropriate organism(s), time, and growth conditions, a variety of organic compounds, such as oil and petroleum products, creosote wastes, and a variety of synthetic organic chemicals can be metabolized to innocuous materials, usually carbon dioxide ($CO_2$), water, inorganic salts, and biomass (mass of bacterial cells); however, metabolic by-products, some of which are undesirable, may accumulate when biodegradation of compounds is incomplete. Bioremediation is normally achieved by stimulating the indigenous microflora (naturally occurring microorganisms) present in or associated with the material to be treated. In instances in which the indigenous microflora fails to degrade the target compounds or has been inhibited by the presence of toxicants, microorganisms with specialized metabolic capabilities may be added.

The technical basis for modern bioremediation technology has a very long history (e.g., composting of organic wastes into mulch and soil conditioners). Bioremediation technology has grown to include the biological treatment of sewage and wastewater, food processing wastes, agricultural wastes, and, recently, contaminants in soils and groundwater. In this article, bioremediation is defined and limited to the biological treatment of organic contaminants. First, we present important background information on the metabolic processes that drive bioremediation, the requirements for the stimulation of specific metabolic processes, and the influence of contaminant behavior and distribution on contaminant availability for microbial uptake. This discussion is followed by sections outlining favorable growth conditions for microorganisms that are capable of degrading common classes of organic contaminants found in soil, sediments, and groundwater. Engineered systems used for the treatment of contaminated media are then presented.

## II. BACKGROUND SCIENCES

The following two sections describe the fundamental metabolic processes that govern bioremediation as well as biodegradation and biotransformation characteristics of selected classes of organic contaminants. A more thorough treatment of the subject matter may be found in many texts and monographs, and the reader is encouraged to consult these materials for further information. Some of the more notable and recent references include *Microbial Transformation and Degradation of Toxic Organic Chemicals* (Young and Cerniglia, 1994), *Biological Degradation and Bioremediation of Toxic Chemicals* (Chaudry, 1994), *Biodegradation and Bioremediation* (Alexander, 1994), *Biology of Microorganisms* (Madigan *et al.*, 1997), and *Biodegradation of Nitroaromatic Compounds* (Spain, 1995).

### A. Metabolic Processes

The metabolism of organic contaminants can be broadly differentiated by the ability of the organisms to gain energy for cell growth from the process. If the metabolism of a compound provides energy for cell maintenance and division, the contaminant is referred to as a primary substrate. In some cases, a compound is metabolized and provides the cell with energy but does not support growth. Contaminants of this type are referred to as secondary substrates. If a compound is transformed without benefit of the cell (no energy or carbon provided for use by the organism) while the cell is obtaining energy from another transformable compound, the biotransformation is referred to as cometabolic. Finally, an additional classification has been recently identified in which some contaminants are capable of serving as the terminal electron acceptor in the respiratory chain of certain anaerobic (without oxygen) bacteria. In this case, energy is not obtained from the contaminant itself, but its transformation is a component of metabolic processes that provide energy to the cell for growth.

## B. Growth Requirements

An essential element of bioremediation processes is the ability to sustain enhanced levels of metabolic activity for extended periods of time. To accomplish this objective, an assessment of conditions at contaminated sites is conducted to determine limiting factors that will be manipulated in an engineered process. A comprehensive list of considerations in this assessment is provided in Table I. For naturally occurring organic compounds (i.e., petroleum hydrocarbons), the availability of oxygen as an electron acceptor is often the primary limiting factor. This can be demonstrated through an evaluation of the stoichiometry of hydrocarbon mineralization, as is shown here for benzene or $C_6H_6$ (a common contaminant of concern at sites at which gasoline has been spilled):

$$C_6H_6 + 7.5O_2 \rightarrow 6CO_2 + 3H_2O$$

For the complete mineralization of 1 mol of $C_6H_6$, 7.5 mol of oxygen will be consumed. Water, in equilibrium with the atmosphere, contains approximately 8 mg/liter dissolved oxygen, which can support the oxidation of 2.6 mg/liter $C_6H_6$. Since the solubility of $C_6H_6$ in water is approximately 1800 mg/liter, the availability of oxygen limits the extent to which hydrocarbons may be biodegraded.

## C. Bioaugmentation

For contaminant metabolism to occur in a bioremediation system, organisms with the genetic capacity to transform compounds of interest must be present. Experience has demonstrated that this is often the case in media in which contamination has been present for even short time periods. In certain cases, the addition of organisms acclimated to specific contaminants, or bioaugmentation, may decrease the duration of lag phases. The ability to effectively bioaugment bioremediation systems is a function of the process used. Bioaugmentation is best suited for processes in which contaminated soil or sediments have been excavated and can be mixed or tilled. The bioaugmentation of *in situ* processes is more difficult because of difficulties in uniformly distributing cells throughout a porous medium. Few cases exist in which bioaugmentation of contaminated groundwater aquifers has proven beneficial.

## III. ENHANCEMENT OF CONTAMINANT METABOLISM

The method by which the rate or extent of contaminant metabolism can be increased in a bioremediation system is governed largely by the substrate-specific metabolic processes that result in its transformation. An understanding of contaminant metabolism is essential. In the following sections, an overview of specific metabolic pathways for common contaminant classes is presented.

## A. Monoaromatic Hydrocarbons

As constituents of gasoline, diesel, and jet fuels, monoaromatic hydrocarbons enter the subsurface environment due to accidental spills and leaking underground storage tanks (UST). These contaminants are commonly found in the environment in the form of free product entrapped or sorbed to porous media or dissolved in water. Monoaromatics are typically referred to as light nonaqueous phase liquids because their specific gravity is less than that of water. Of particular interest in this class of pollutants are benzene, toluene, ethylbenzene, and xylene isomers (BTEX). The biodegradation of these compounds has been and continues to be studied extensively. Under aerobic (containing oxygen) conditions, all the constituents are rapidly biodegraded as primary substrates. Oxygen is important in this process in two ways. First, it is a substrate in the initial attack of the aromatic ring catalyzed by oxygenase enzymes. Second, oxygen serves as the terminal electron ac-

***TABLE I***
**Requirements for Microbial Growth in Bioremediation Processes**

| *Requirement* | *Description* |
|---|---|
| Carbon source | Carbon contained in many organic contaminants may serve as a carbon source for cell growth. If the organism involved is an autotroph, $CO_2$ or $HCO_3^-$ in solution is required. In some cases, contaminant levels may be too low to supply adequate levels of cell carbon, or the contaminant is metabolized via cometabolism. In these cases the addition of carbon sources may be required. |
| Energy source | In the case of primary metabolism, the organic contaminant supplies energy required for growth. This is not the case when the contaminant is metabolized via secondary metabolism or cometabolism or as a terminal electron acceptor. If the contaminant does not serve as a source of energy, the addition of a primary substrate(s) is required. |
| Electron acceptor | All respiring bacteria require a terminal electron acceptor. In some cases, the organic contaminant may serve in this capacity. Dissolved oxygen is a common electron acceptor in aerobic bioremediation processes. Under anaerobic conditions, $NO_3^-$, $SO_4^{2-}$, $Fe^{3+}$, and $CO_2$ may serve as terminal electron acceptors. Certain cometabolic transformations are carried out by fermentative and other anaerobic organisms, in which terminal electron acceptors are not required. |
| Nutrients | Nitrogen (ammonia, nitrate, or organic nitrogen) and phosphorus (*ortho*-phosphate or organic phosphorus) are generally the limiting nutrients. In certain anaerobic systems, the availability of trace metals (e.g., Fe, Ni, Co, Mo, and Zn) can be of concern. |
| Temperature | Rates of growth and metabolic activity are strongly influenced by temperature. Surface soils are particularly prone to wide fluctuations in temperature. Mesophilic conditions are generally best suited for most applications (with composting being a notable exception). |
| pH | A pH ranging between 6.5 and 7.5 is generally considered optimal. The pH of most groundwater (8.0–8.5) is not considered inhibitory. |
| Absence of toxic materials | Many contaminated sites contain a mixture of chemicals, organic and inorganic, which may be inhibitory or toxic to microorganisms. Heavy metals and phenolics are particular concerns. |
| Adequate contact between microorganisms and substrates | For a contaminant to be available for microbial uptake it must be present in the aqueous phase. Thus, contaminants that exist as nonaqueous phase liquids or are sequestered within a solid phase may not be readily metabolized. |
| Time | This is an important factor in the start-up of bioremediation systems. Even when the first eight considerations in this table are met, lag phases are often observed prior to the onset of activity. In some cases, the dramatic bacterial population shifts that are required for bioremediation will lengthen periods of slow activity. |

ceptor for respiratory chains. Figure 1 illustrates the dual functionality of oxygen in the metabolism of benzene.

The biodegradation of BTEX compounds is not as well characterized under anaerobic conditions as it is under aerobic conditions. Certainly, the biodegradation of all BTEX compounds has been observed under a range of anaerobic electron acceptor conditions, but it does not occur in all cases. In particular, benzene can be recalcitrant under anaerobic condi-

tions. In some cases, however, the metabolism of benzene has been observed in the absence of oxygen. Little is known about the pathways of these processes or the enzymes that may be involved in these reactions.

In any case, the anaerobic degradation of BTEX compounds is generally slower than aerobic processes. Thus, bioremediation systems targeted for BTEX remediation are typically operated under aerobic conditions. The basis of most BTEX bioremedia-

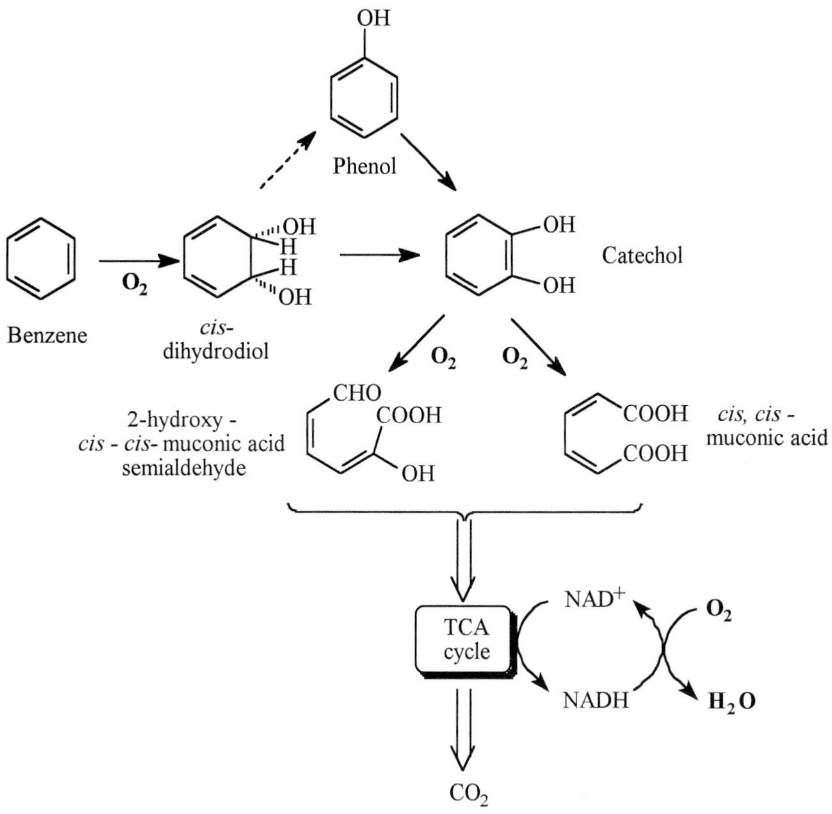

**Fig. 1.** The metabolic pathways of benzene biodegradation under aerobic conditions.

tion systems is the enhancement of the rate of aerobic metabolism by increasing the availabililty of oxygen in contaminated areas. Several methods for doing so are presented later.

## B. Polynuclear Aromatic Hydrocabons

Polynuclear aromatic hydrocarbons (PAHs) typically result from activities including combustion of fossil fuels and coal gasification processes, and they may also be found in creosote wastes used in wood preservation. PAHs are generally found sorbed to soils and sediments in the natural environment. This class of chemicals contains many compounds with varying biodegradation and physicochemical characteristics. In general, PAH biodegradation is limited to aerobic metabolism and is initiated by oxygenase attack (similar to that depicted in Fig. 1). PAHs of three or fewer rings, including naphthalene, fluorene, and phenanthrene, are known to be primary sub-

strates for bacterial growth. Larger PAHs (i.e., four rings and larger) tend to behave as secondary substrates in the presence of the smaller, more water-soluble PAHs.

## C. Phenolic Compounds

Phenol and chlorinated phenols have historically been used in the treatment or preservation of wood products and have served as bacterial disinfectants. These compounds are biodegraded as primary substrates under aerobic and anaerobic conditions. These compounds are often recalcitrant in the environment due to their toxicity and the low water solubility of certain chlorinated forms (e.g., pentachlorophenol). When present at concentrations lower than toxic thresholds, phenols can be rapidly mineralized by a wide range of microorganisms. As the degree of chlorine substituents increases, the rate of degradation often decreases, especially under aerobic conditions.

## D. Chlorinated Hydrocarbons

Chlorinated methanes, ethanes, and ethenes comprise a group of compounds commonly referred to as chlorinated hydrocarbons (also referred to as chlorinated solvents). These compounds have been used extensively as degreasers, dry cleaning agents, and paint removers, and they are widely present and persistent in the environment. They are common contaminants of subsurface soils and groundwater and contamination has resulted from leaking storage facilities or improper disposal practices. Due to their high specific gravity and density, chlorinated hydrocarbon compounds may often be referred to as dense nonaqueous phase liquids (DNAPLs). DNAPLs will typically be found near the lower confining unit of an acquifer since their densities are greater than the density of water. Common chlorinated hydrocarbon contaminant compounds include trichloroethane, perchloroethene (PCE), trichloroethene (TCE), dichloroethene (DCE), carbon tetrachloride, chloroform, and vinyl chloride.

The metabolism of chlorinated hydrocarbons is perhaps more diverse than that of any other group of environmental contaminants. Depending on the compound of interest, the electron acceptor condition, and the presence of inducing substrates, the metabolism of chlorinated hydrocarbons may occur through primary metabolism, secondary metabolism, cometabolism, or terminal electron acceptor processes. Table II lists common chlorinated hydrocarbon contaminants and the processes by which individual compounds are known to be transformed.

## E. Nitroaromatic Compounds

Nitroaromatics are common pollutants of water and soils as a result of their use in plastics, dyes, and explosives. Typical nitroaromatic contaminants used in explosives manufacture include trinitrotoluene (TNT), hexahydro-1,3,5-trinitro-1,3,5-triazine (RDX), and octahydro-1,3,5,7-tetranitro-1,3,5,7,-tetrazoncine (HMX) (Spain, 1995). The nitro group has a strong electron withdrawing functionality, which previously was thought to reduce the potential for oxygenase attack toward the aromatic ring. Recent studies have demonstrated that certain organisms are capable of oxidizing selected nitroaromatic compounds to obtain energy for growth (i.e., primary metabolism). The activity is generally limited to nitroaromatics containing two or fewer nitro groups.

Under anaerobic conditions, nitroaromatic transformation generally yields reduced aromatic prod-

*TABLE II*
**Summary of the Biotransformation Processes of Chlorinated Hydrocarbons**

| Compound | 1° Substrate | 2° Substrate | Cometabolic substrate | Terminal electron acceptor |
|---|---|---|---|---|
| Dichloromethane | Yes | Yes | Yes | No |
| Chloroform | No | No | Yes | No |
| Carbon tetrachloride | No | No | Yes | No |
| Perchloroethene | No | No | Yes | Yes |
| Trichloroethene | No | No | Yes | Yes |
| Dichloroethenes[a] | No[b] | No | Yes | Yes[c] |
| Vinyl chloride | Yes | Possible | Yes | Yes[c] |
| Hexachloroethane | No | No | Yes | No |
| 1,1,1-Trichloroethane | No | No | Yes | No |

[a] Three isomers of dichloroethenes exist: 1,1-dichloroethene, *cis*-dichloroethene, and *trans*-dichloroethene.

[b] Recent studies have identified oxidative pathways for *cis*-dichloroethene that may yield energy for growth.

[c] Vinyl chloride and *cis*-dichloroethene are intermediates during the respiration of perchloroethene and trichloroethene to ethene.

ucts. For example, the product of the complete reduction of nitrobenzene is aniline (aminobenzene). The formation of an aryl amine from an aryl nitro group requires that two intermediate forms be produced; the first is any aryl nitroso intermediate followed by the second intermediate, an aryl hydroxylamine. Recent work has demonstrated the importance of the aryl hydroxylamine intermediate in the ultimate fate of nitroaromatics under anaerobic conditions. The hydroxylamine can be reduced to the amine or undergo more complex reactions that can result in binding with natural organic matter or the formation of an aminophenol through rearrangement reactions.

## IV. APPLICATION OF CONTAMINANT METABOLISM IN ENGINEERED SYSTEMS

The process of transforming an individual contaminant molecule into a nontoxic form occurs at the enzymatic level. Potential remediation sites contain kilograms to tons of contaminants distributed over large areas. Reconciling the difference in scale between molecular processes and the cleanup of tremendous volumes of contaminated media is a significant engineering challenge. Fundamentally, the application of microscale phenomena to the field-scale bioremediation of large, complex contaminated sites begins with a thorough analysis of site conditions. Key steps in site characterization may include (i) determination of the contaminants present and their concentration and distribution, (ii) delineation of the volume of material undergoing treatment, (iii) evaluation of the physical and chemical state of contaminants, (iv) analysis of the redox conditions at the site, and (v) establishment of site hydrogeologic conditions. Upon completion of this phase of the investigation, an analysis would be conducted to determine whether *in situ* or *ex situ* treatment or some other technology would be most appropriate given the site conditions. Regardless of the selected mode of treatment, systems would be designed to create the appropriate ecological conditions to select for organisms that possess the ability to degrade target contaminants. Furthermore, considerations outlined

in Table I would be evaluated to identify potential limiting factors to bioremediation so that modifications or additions to the treatment scheme could be made to enhance the rates of contaminant biodegradation and biotransformation.

Specific bioremediation technologies are discussed in detail later. In all cases, these technologies are predicated on the stimulation of specific metabolic activities. The selection of a bioremediation process begins with the understanding of how specific contaminants may be metabolized. In some cases, metabolism may already be occurring, and application of a bioremediation system to those sites would focus on accelerating the rate of the naturally occurring processes. In other cases, contaminant metabolism may be negligible and conditions may require significant alteration through an engineered process. In all cases, bioremediation technologies intended to distribute metabolic activity throughout a region of contamination that is vastly larger than that of a bacterial cell. Thus, the coupling of microscale metabolic processes with macroscale mass transfer processes is one of the most significant challenges in the development of efficient bioremediation technologies. It should be noted that more detailed information on these technologies may be found in many texts as well as in various collections of monographs. Some of the more pertinent references include *In Situ Bioremediation: When Does It Work?* (Rittman *et al.,* 1993), *Handbook of Bioremediation* (Norris *et al.,* 1994), *Bioremediation: Field Experience* (Flathman *et al.,* 1994), *Innovative Site Remediation Technology: Bioremediation* (Ward *et al.,* 1995), *Bioremediation Engineering: Design and Application* (Cookson, 1995), *Innovations in Ground Water and Soil Cleanup* (Rao *et al.,* 1997), *Soil Bioventing: Principles and Practice* (Leeson and Hinchee, 1997), *Subsurface Restoration* (Ward *et al.,* 1997), and *Innovative Site Remediation Technology Design & Application: Bioremediation* (Dupont *et al.,* 1998).

## V. NATURAL BIOATTENUATION

### A. Overview

Natural bioattenuation, sometimes termed intrinsic bioremediation or natural bioremediation, refers

**TABLE III**
**Application of Bioremediation Treatment Options to Various Classes of Contaminants[a]**

| | | Contaminant class | | | | |
|---|---|---|---|---|---|---|
| | | Monoaromatic hydrocarbons | Chlorinated solvents | Nitroaromatics | Phenols | PAHs |
| *In situ* | Natural bioattenuation | Yes | Yes | ?[b] | ? | ? |
| | Biostimulation | Yes | Yes | ? | Yes | ? |
| | Electron donor delivery | No | Yes | ? | ? | No |
| | Bioventing | Yes | No | No | No | Yes |
| | Permeable reactive barriers | Yes | Yes | ? | ? | ? |
| *Ex situ* | Land treatment | Yes | No | Yes | Yes | Yes |
| | Composting | Yes | No | Yes | Yes | Yes |
| | Bioslurry processes | Yes | Yes | Yes | Yes | Yes |

[a] Adapted in part from Rao *et al.* (1997)
[b] ?, Undetermined or in developmental stages.

to the biodegradation or biotransformation of both subsurface soil and groundwater contaminants through microbially mediated processes. This mechanism for contaminant mass reduction represents a key component of the broader remediation process of natural attenuation which focuses on the reduction of contaminant concentration, mass, mobility, and/or toxicity through natural processes, including dilution, dispersion, volatilization, adsorption to solid surfaces, and chemical and biological transformation reactions. Bioattenuation is a nonintrusive process (i.e., does not require a mechanical or engineered system for remediation) and is generally more cost-effective than other *in situ* and *ex situ* cleanup strategies. This remediation process has been successfully demonstrated in the mitigation of BTEX contamination resulting from leaking underground storage tanks and may also be applicable to the remediation of other compounds, including chlorinated solvents. The applicability of this treatment scheme has not been determined for PAHs, PCBs, explosives, and pesticides (as shown in Table III; Rao *et al.*, 1997). For many UST sites (47%), natural attenuation is the chief mechanism for groundwater remediation, whereas nearly 67% of U.S. states recognize and implement natural attenuation as a viable alternative for soil and groundwater cleanup (USEPA, 1997). Table IV compares the use of natural attenuation with other remediation technologies (some of which are described later) for both soil and ground-

water cleanup. It is important to recognize that natural bioattenuation may not necessarily replace active remediation processes, but it does offer an attractive option to complement techniques that may be very costly to implement. For example, at UST sites, large pools of nonaqueous phase liquids may serve as a

**TABLE IV**
**Use of Remediation Technologies at UST Sites[a]**

| Remediation technology | Use at UST sites (% of sites) |
|---|---|
| Soil remediation | |
| Soil washing | 0.2 |
| Bioventing | 0.8 |
| Incineration | 2 |
| Thermal desorption | 3 |
| Landfarming | 7 |
| Soil vapor extraction | 9 |
| Biopiles | 16 |
| Natural attenuation | 28 |
| Landfilling | 34 |
| Groundwater remediation | |
| Biosparging | 2 |
| Dual-phase extraction | 5 |
| *In situ* bioremediation | 5 |
| Air sparging | 13 |
| Pump and treat | 29 |
| Natural attenuation | 47 |

[a] Source: USEPA (1997).

continual source for groundwater contamination. Typically, a more intensive strategy is required to remove most of the free-phase contaminant before natural bioattenuation is implemented as a cleanup method. Natural bioremediation should also not be characterized as a "no action" approach to cleanup; rather, it requires both long-term monitoring of the parent contaminant compound and secondary metabolites and monitoring of other chemical and biological markers that are indicative of the attenuation process (Ward *et al.,* 1997). However, the efficacy of natural attenuation for meeting remedial objectives and managing risk of groundwater contamination is controversial in research and regulatory communities. Its role in soil and groundwater cleanup continues to develop as we learn more about quantifying the processes involved.

The rate and extent of contaminant biodegradation are governed by many environmental factors, including contaminant and cell biomass concentration, temperature, pH, supply of nutrients, adequacy of carbon and energy sources, the presence of toxins such as heavy metals, availability of contaminants to microorganisms (i.e., contact, contaminant solubility and hydrophobicity, and desorption from solids), time for acclimation, and availability of electron acceptors (Table I). The supply and availability of electron acceptors is often cited as the controlling or limiting factor in the bioattenuation process. Aerobic biodegradation occurs in the presence of oxygen, whereas alternate electron acceptors, including nitrate, sulfate, trivalent iron ($Fe^{3+}$), and carbon dioxide, are utilized under anaerobic conditions. For relatively soluble petroleum hydrocarbons such as BTEX, the rate and extent of biological transformation of contaminants is typically much greater under aerobic conditions than under oxygen-limited conditions. For highly chlorinated solvents (e.g., PCE and TCE), the rate and extent of biological transformation, through reductive dechlorination, is greater under anaerobic conditions than under aerobic conditions, whereas less halogenated compounds (e.g., vinyl chloride) may be more amenable to aerobic biodegradation.

The oxygen demand exerted by the microorganisms during petroleum hydrocarbon biodegradation generally exceeds the rate of oxygen replenishment, especially in areas of high contaminant concentration (i.e., near the source zone). In fact, the limiting dissolved oxygen concentration for aerobic biodegradation is approximately 2 mg/liter (Rao *et al.,* 1997), although a study by J. Salanitro and coworkers published in *Ground Water Monitoring and Review* in 1997 suggests that this concentration may be as low as 0.2 mg/liter. The characteristic shape of a groundwater contaminant plume may be partially explained by the presence or absence of oxygen as a terminal electron acceptor. Zones of aerobic biodegradation generally occur on the outermost and leading edges of the plume where contaminated groundwater meets with uncontaminated, well-oxygenated groundwater. Mixing of the two waters via dispersion provides an adequate supply of oxygen for the aerobic biodegradation process. However, contaminant biodegradation in the central region of the plume is generally governed by contaminant-specific anaerobic processes due to the rapid depletion of oxygen in these areas of high metabolic activity. The diffusion rate of oxygen through water is four orders of magnitude less than the diffusion rate in air; thus, the rate of oxygen consumption easily exceeds its rate of transport in water, which results in anaerobic conditions (Norris *et al.,* 1994; Rao *et al.,* 1997). Figure 2 presents a typical UST spill and indicates the areas or zones of aerobic and anaerobic biodegradation.

The previous discussion illustrates the importance of oxygen as a driving force in the natural aerobic bioattenuation of subsurface contaminants. Oxygen may be naturally delivered to the contaminant plume either through mixing with uncontaminated groundwater or through reaeration from the overlying unsaturated zone. Reaeration may serve as a significant source of oxygen and is governed by many factors, including soil hydrogeologic properties, soil moisture, precipitation, and respiration rate of soil microorganisms. Macroporous sand materials can easily and rapidly contribute to the oxygen supply of a contaminant plume, whereas the diffusion of oxygen through clay materials is generally impeded, especially in the presence of moisture. Moisture may cause swelling of certain clay soils and reduces the number of air-filled pore spaces in the soil through which oxygen may easily diffuse. The respiration rate of soils may also serve as a significant oxygen sink

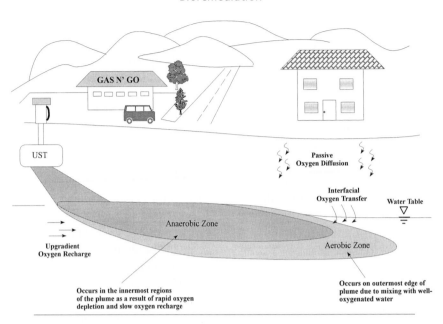

*Fig. 2.* The role of oxygen flux in the bioattenuation of hydrocarbon contaminants (adapted in part from Norris *et al.,* 1994).

and will restrict delivery of the gas to a contaminant plume.

## B. Demonstration

Several demonstrations have been completed to determine the efficacy of natural bioattenuation of contaminants in groundwater. A study by C. Y. Chiang and coworkers, published in *Ground Water* in 1989, investigated the aerobic bioattenuation of a petroleum hydrocarbon plume at a gas manufacturing plant in Michigan using a large network of monitoring wells. The contaminated aquifer was located 10–25 ft below the surface and was overlain by coarse sand. The initial mass of benzene at the site was approximately 10 kg; after a period of 21 months, the mass had been reduced to approximately 1.3 kg of benzene. A first-order bioattenuation rate of 0.0095/day was determined for the site. Analysis of groundwater samples throughout the study period revealed an inverse relationship between dissolved oxygen and benzene concentration in the plume. Samples from locations in which the BTX concentration was high were coupled with low dissolved oxy-

gen concentrations as a result of increased microbial activity or biodegradation. Likewise, samples with low BTX concentrations contained higher dissolved oxygen concentrations due to the reduction in oxygen demand. Other natural attenuation processes were found to have very little effect on the reduction of benzene contaminant mass. Only 5% of benzene contaminant loss was attributed to volatilization from the groundwater, and sorption was thought to have little impact on the attenuation process based on the low organic carbon content of the aquifer material. Subsequent modeling and microcosm studies confirmed that natural aerobic bioattenuation was a dominant mechanism in the reduction of contaminant mass at this particular site.

Bioattenuation of chlorinated solvents has also been demonstrated in field studies. In 1995, L. Semprini and coworkers investigated the biotransformation of chlorinated solvents in groundwater at a site in Michigan. A series of multilevel samplers bounding the width and length of the contaminant plume were used to determine the concentrations of TCE, isomers of DCE, vinyl chloride, and ethene with depth in the sandy aquifer. The results of the study indicated that the reductive dechlorination of TCE had occurred over time in the plume based on the presence of less chlorinated compounds as well as the presence or absence of biochemical markers, including methane (methanogenesis) and sulfate (sulfate reduction).

The transformation of TCE to isomers of DCE (predominantly *cis*-DCE) was associated with sulfate reducing conditions, whereas further transformation of *cis*-DCE to vinyl chloride and ethene was coupled with areas high in methanogenic activity. Although the mass of original TCE contaminant could not be established, Semprini and coworkers suggested that, on the basis of calculated flux rates for each of the contaminant compounds, TCE reduction to ethene was on the order of 20%.

## VI. ENHANCED *IN SITU* BIOREMEDIATION/BIOATTENUATION

Many *in situ* bioremediation processes have been designed or engineered to maintain or accelerate the biodegradation of organic contaminants in soil and groundwater by supplying those materials which may limit the breakdown of the contaminant compound. For example, in petroleum hydrocarbon-contaminated environments which are nutrient limited, nitrogen, phosphorus, and other minerals may be added to the environmental system (either through soil tilling or through injection into groundwater) to stimulate growth of the contaminant-degrading microbial population. In many cases, the natural supply of oxygen is rapidly extinguished in areas of high metabolic activity and therefore limits the rate and extent of biodegradation. Oxygen replenishment may also be achieved by soil tilling or by the introduction of air, pure oxygen, hydrogen peroxide ($H_2O_2$), or other oxygen-releasing materials into soil and groundwater systems. Microorganisms that have been previously acclimated to the contaminant of interest may also be mixed into soil or groundwater environments to stimulate the rate of contaminant decomposition. A recent approach to enhancing *in situ* treatment of chlorinated solvents is the introduction of electron donors such as hydrogen, lactic acid,

etc. Installation of reactive barrier walls into groundwater aquifers may also improve the bioremediation of a variety of organic contaminants.

### A. Biostimulation

#### 1. Overview

The earliest system of enhanced or engineered *in situ* bioremediation of groundwater was designed by R. L. Raymond and co-workers with Sun Research and Development Company in Philadelphia and described in a 1978 American Petroleum Institute report titled "Field Application of Subsurface Biodegradation of Gasoline in a Sand Formation." The "Raymond process" was a patented system [U.S. Patent No. 3,846,290 (1974)] in which biodegradation of petroleum hydrocarbons (namely, gasoline constituents) in groundwater by indigenous subsurface microorganisms was stimulated through the injection of nutrients and oxygen. Although subsurface microorganisms require many minerals, the two most common nutrient amendments are nitrogen (as ammonium or nitrate) and phosphorus (as phosphate). The necessary mass of each nutrient may be determined stoichiometrically, and the ratio between carbon, nitrogen, and phosphorus is typically $100:10:1$ ($C:N:P$) (Norris *et al.*, 1994). Many compounds have been used to increase the dissolved oxygen concentration of contaminated groundwater aquifers. Initial attempts to increase dissolved oxygen concentration in groundwater aquifers relied on air sparging of water before injection into the subsurface or sparging air into wells; however, the low solubility of oxygen in water (8–12 mg/liter) precluded maximum contaminant biodegradation. Subsequent methods for oxygen delivery resulted in greater solubility of the gas. Dissolved oxygen concentrations increase to approximately 40–50 mg/liter when sparging with pure oxygen, whereas injection of $H_2O_2$ can easily result in dissolved oxygen concentrations in the range of 250–500 mg/liter and higher, although $H_2O_2$ may be toxic to the microorganisms at higher concentrations (Rao *et al.*, 1997).

Oxygen-releasing compounds (e.g., ORC, marketed by Regenesis, Inc.) are a more recent innovation for meeting the oxygen demand of microorganisms in subsurface environments. These formulations promote the slow release of oxygen which is produced when magnesium peroxide (the typical active ingredient in these compounds) reacts with water. Oxygen-releasing compounds may be added as a slurry injection or may be placed in a series of wells in the aquifer to form a barrier through which the contaminated groundwater flows. Oxygen is therefore introduced into the central regions of the plume (usually anaerobic) to promote aerobic biodegradation of the contaminant compound (Du-Pont *et al.*, 1998).

Bioaugmentation, or the introduction of contaminant-acclimated or genetically engineered microorganisms, is another method for enhancing biodegradation of contaminants. Although bioaugmentation has been successfully implemented in a variety of laboratory-scale and larger *ex situ* reactor systems, the success of bioaugmentation in soils and groundwater is limited (Alexander, 1994). Some of the problems associated with adding an inoculum to soils or groundwater aquifers are the presence of environmental toxins and bacterial predators, adequate conditions for growth (i.e., nutrients, pH, temperature, etc.; see Table I), contact with target contaminant, and cell movement or distribution (Alexander, 1994). The movement or distribution of the inoculum throughout the contaminated region of interest may be inhibited by sorption to solid surfaces, bacterial mobility, and the structure of the porous media. Microorganisms may be able to move freely through large macropores in the soil; however, their movement may be restricted through soil micropores in which larger pools of the contaminant may often reside (Alexander, 1994).

A schematic of a typical biostimulation *in situ* remediation system is presented in Fig. 3. Groundwater is initially drawn from a series of recovery wells downgradient from the source of contamination. The groundwater is then pumped to an aboveground treatment facility at which both nutrient amendments and oxygen (through either sparging or $H_2O_2$ injection) are added after the water is initially passed through a contaminant treatment scheme. After addition of chemicals, the groundwater is returned to the aquifer either through an injection well or through an infiltration gallery above the zone of contamination.

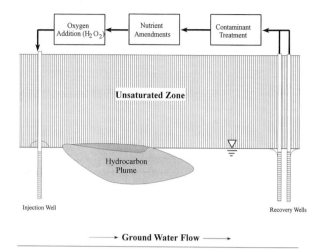

**Fig. 3.** Simplified schematic of an *in situ* biostimulation remediation system (Raymond process).

This process continues until the contaminant concentration is reduced to the target level (DuPont *et al.*, 1998).

### 2. Demonstration

J. T. Wilson, J. M. Armstrong, and H. S. Rifai reported the bioremediation of an aviation gasoline spill at a Coast Guard air station in Traverse City, Michigan, using nutrient and $H_2O_2$ amendments (Flathman *et al.*, 1994). The shallow sandy aquifer underlying the site was contaminated by approximately 25,000 gallons of aviation fuel emanating from an UST. Analysis of soil cores taken from the site identified a vertical zone of petroleum hydrocarbon contamination, and the remediation process was aimed at reducing the concentration of BTEX dissolved in the groundwater and bound in the aquifer material. A series of six monitoring wells were placed downgradient of the infiltration wells to quantify BTEX loss due to biodegradation.

Nutrients introduced into the contaminated region included ammonium chloride, disodium phosphate, and potassium phosphate, whereas $H_2O_2$ was incrementally injected into the subsurface to allow for microbial acclimation (to a maximum of approximately 400 mg/liter oxygen). A high degree of BTEX removal was observed in each of the six monitoring wells. For example, BTEX was reduced from 1200 to 380 mg/liter at a monitoring well 83 ft from the infiltration wells. Benzene was most amenable to bio-degradation in the groundwater, whereas the isomers of xylene were most resistant to biodegradation. Re-mediation of the aquifer material was also investi-gated by taking soil cores after completion of the experiment. The results indicated that the process generally led to a reduction in BTEX concentrations in the aquifer materials; however, concentrations of total petroleum hydrocarbons at each of the monitor-ing points remained fairly high. In areas in which oxygen concentration was low, nitrate was deter-mined to be the terminal electron acceptor support-ing most of the BTEX biodegradation.

## B. Electron Donor Delivery

### 1. Overview

The delivery of electron donors to groundwater systems is another *in situ* biostimulation approach to promote or accelerate the biotransformation of chlorinated solvent compounds. Unlike many of the petroleum hydrocarbon contaminants that may be directly utilized by microorganisms to obtain cell energy and promote cell growth, chlorinated solvents are not often used as primary substrates. However, chlorinated solvents may be biodegraded or bio-transformed under either aerobic or anaerobic condi-tions. Under aerobic conditions, biodegradation can be achieved through cometabolic processes in which enzymes capable of breaking down the target con-taminant are fortuitously expressed during the bio-degradation of other primary substrates. More fre-quently, chlorinated compounds are biotransformed to less chlorinated products under anaerobic condi-tions through the process of reductive dechlorina-tion. Microorganisms require a sufficient supply of electron donors in order to carry out the reductive dechlorination process. A variety of potential elec-tron donors have been evaluated both in field and in laboratory studies and include acetate, methane, hydrogen, ammonia, benzoate, lactate, and metha-nol. Cocontaminants such as petroleum hydrocar-bons may also serve as electron donors in subsurface environments.

Many of the same difficulties experienced with the introduction of nutrients, microorganisms, and other materials into subsurface environments also occur with electron donor delivery (Norris *et al.,* 1994). Excessive microbial growth may result near the point of injection due to the high electron donor concentra-tion and availability. This problem may be further exacerbated by the simultaneous introduction of other materials that are essential for bacterial growth (i.e., oxygen and nutrients).

### 2. Demonstration

In 1997, in a paper titled "Scale-up Issues for *in situ* Anaerobic Tetrachloroethene Bioremediation" M. D. Lee and co-workers reported laboratory and field experiments relating to electron donor selection and delivery to enhance anaerobic PCE biotransforma-tion. Microcosm studies were used to determine the most efficient substrates to effect PCE dechlorina-tion. The substrates included yeast extract [38% car-bon (C)], wastewater (4.5% C), cheese whey perme-ate (26% C), molasses (29% C), corn steep liquor (17% C), manure tea (3% C), sodium benzoate (58% C), and acetate (29% C). The field site under investigation was a landfill associated with a chemical plant in Texas. The saturated zone of the aquifer underlying this site consisted primarily of sand. A series of injection, withdrawal, and monitoring wells were used in the field experiments which were designed to determine an optimal electron donor delivery system.

The initial microcosm study investigated dechlori-nation of chlorinated ethenes (23 $\mu$M PCE, 0.6 $\mu$M TCE, and 3.3 $\mu$M 1,2-DCE) using yeast extract, wastewater, molasses, corn steep liquor, and manure tea at varying initial carbon loadings. A high degree of carbon utilization was achieved in each microcosm (>60% TOC removal), and PCE was transformed to vinyl chloride at carbon concentrations >60 mg/ liter. Cell counting experiments indicated a positive relationship between the amount of carbon in the microcosm and the number of microorganisms pres-ent. A second microcosm experiment, using sodium benzoate, sodium acetate, corn steep liquor, and mo-lasses, studied the effect of very high organic loadings on both PCE dechlorination and microorganism con-centration. In contrast to the results from the first study, higher organic loadings inhibited TOC re-moval and resulted in either no transformation or only partial transformation of PCE.

The field tracer experiments compared the injection and distribution of the substrate and nutrient amendments under three conditions: tracer (bromide) injection at the rate of groundwater flux, tracer (iodide) injection at a rate of 60 times groundwater flux, and cross-gradient injection [bromide, substrate, and nutrients (N, P)] at a rate of 3.8 liters/min for the withdrawal wells (two) and the injection well. Distribution or dispersion was enhanced when the injection rate was increased to 60 times the natural groundwater gradient. The third condition, employing the cross-gradient injection scheme, further increased dispersion of the bromide tracer. Measurements of TOC also indicated that sodium benzoate was successfully transported downgradient from the injection well. However, transport of both the injected nutrients and electron acceptor (sulfate) was retarded either by sorption to the aquifer solids or by biodegradation processes.

## C. Bioventing

### 1. Overview

Bioventing is another *in situ* technique designed to stimulate aerobic biodegradation of contaminants by replenishing oxygen levels in oxygen-depleted, unsaturated zone environments. The process was first described by J. T. Wilson and C. H. Ward in an article published in 1986 in the *Journal of Industrial Microbiology*. R. E. Hinchee, R. R. DuPont, R. N. Miller, and others were responsible for developing and testing the process (Hinchee and Leeson, 1997). Bioventing has been successfully applied at several petroleum hydrocarbon-contaminated sites and may also be implemented to remediate sites contaminated with chlorinated solvents, although it typically requires the addition of substrates to promote cometabolism of the chlorinated hydrocarbons (Norris *et al.*, 1994). A recent report suggests that bioventing is being used at less than 1% of UST contaminated soil sites. However, this percentage translates into the application of bioventing at more than 800 UST sites (USEPA, 1997). Bioventing is designed to emphasize biodegradation over contaminant volatilization; however, the relationship between the two mechanisms may be determined by both the properties of the contaminant of interest (e.g., molecular weight

and vapor pressure) and site conditions (Norris *et al.*, 1994; Leeson and Hinchee, 1997). Hydrocarbon contaminants with higher vapor pressures will tend to volatilize with injection of air and may not be suitable for bioventing, whereas biodegradation of heavy hydrocarbons with lower vapor pressures may be achieved using this treatment technology (Cookson, 1995).

In addition to contaminant characteristics, soil properties play a major role in the success of bioventing applications. These properties include physical characteristics, such as hydraulic conductivity, gas permeability, and moisture content, as well as properties that will affect the growth of microorganisms (in addition to oxygen supply), such as temperature, pH, and nutrient supply. Bioventing applications are best suited for soils with high gas permeabilities so that the injected air readily moves through the contaminated soil matrix (Leeson and Hinchee, 1997; Ward *et al.*, 1997). The flow of air may be severely restricted in low-permeability soils and will subsequently impact the extent of contaminant biodegradation. Gravel and sand may be considered highly gas-permeable materials, whereas silts and clays represent soils with lower gas permeabilities. Although moisture is required by soil microbes for contaminant metabolism, high percentages of water in the soil will negatively impact the flow of oxygen in the soil pores. The majority of pore spaces in high moisture content soils are filled with water, and the diffusion of oxygen through water is much slower than through air.

As with other treatment technologies, microbial growth factors (temperature, pH, and nutrients) may also impact the rate and extent of biodegradation in bioventing applications. Higher temperatures are generally associated with higher rates of contaminant biodegradation. However, Leeson and Hinchee (1997) pointed out that psychrophilic microorganisms at a field test site in Alaska were able to significantly biodegrade petroleum hydrocarbons in the subsurface. Nutrient amendment also may need to be considered in deficient subsurface soils. Delivery or transport of nutrients to the target zone may be difficult and will also depend on the soil physical properties. Soils generally contain sufficient nutrients to support the biodegradation of hydrocarbon

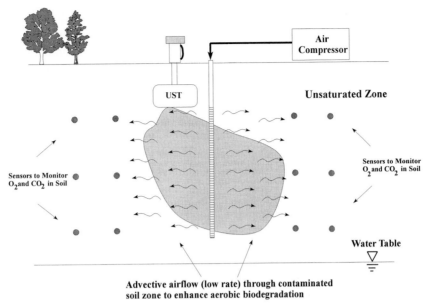

*Fig. 4.* Schematic of a bioventing system (adapted from Leeson and Hinchee, 1997).

contaminants, and the advantage of adding nutrients to subsurface soils has not been firmly established (Leeson and Hinchee, 1997).

Figure 4 presents a schematic of a bioventing system (Leeson and Hinchee, 1997). Bioventing is accomplished by advective flow of air through a series of vent wells into areas that have exhausted their supply of oxygen in the soil gas. Monitoring points are distributed throughout the zone of contamination to determine both the decrease in oxygen concentration and the increase in the carbon dioxide concentration (primary product of biodegradation). Low airflow rates are usually incorporated into the system design to favor contaminant biodegradation over volatilization. In theory, contaminant biodegradation should be much greater than volatilization; therefore, management of gases that are transported to the soil surface is usually not required. If volatilization is high, a separate extraction and treatment system will have to be installed to handle the vapors being generated by the bioventing system. Bioventing is frequently applied in cooperation with and usually following soil vapor extraction (SVE) for vadose zone remediation.

## 2. Demonstration

One of the earliest and best known bioventing remediation systems was implemented at a site at Hill Air Force Base in Utah where 27,000 gallons of jet fuel were spilled (Leeson and Hinchee, 1997). Fuel contamination migrated to a depth of approximately 65 ft in the unsaturated zone, which consisted primarily of sand and gravel constituents. The average contaminant concentration in the soils was approximately 400 mg/kg. A series of vent wells were installed over the length of the contamination to evaluate the potential of bioventing. Enhanced bioventing using both moisture and nutrient addition was also investigated. The system was initially constructed to investigate contaminant volatilization and capture at higher air flow rates (SVE); however, after several months of testing, lower airflow rates were employed to favor biodegradation over volatilization.

A series of soil samples were taken with depth before and after implementation of the SVE and bioventing remediation system at the site. After application of SVE and bioventing, nearly all of the posttreatment hydrocarbon concentrations in the soils were <5 mg/kg, indicating successful cleanup of the site.

It was estimated that approximately 1500 lbs of hydrocarbon fuel was removed through volatilization, whereas 93,000 lbs of fuel was removed through biodegradation. Much of the biodegradation of the fuel was attributed to the bioventing phase of cleanup. Enhanced bioventing by adding moisture and nutrients yielded mixed results. The addition of moisture resulted in a significant increase in contaminant biodegradation, whereas addition of nutrients (N and P) did not enhance removal of the petroleum hydrocarbons.

## D. Permeable Reactive Barriers

### 1. Overview

The use of *in situ* permeable reactive barriers is another method that introduces reactants which may stimulate the biotic or abiotic transformation of environmental contaminants. As opposed to other *in situ* remediation methods that rely on injection of reactants (i.e., oxygen and nutrients) and their transport with groundwater flow through the contaminated aquifer, stationary barrier walls containing the reactive porous media are placed into the subsurface using a variety of methods. The contaminated groundwater is directed to and passes through the reactive barrier, thus enabling reaction between the porous media and the contaminant of interest. Permeable reactive barriers are typically used to treat target contaminants, including petroleum hydrocarbons and chlorinated solvents (Table III).

A schematic of an *in situ* permeable reactive barrier is presented in Fig. 5. The barrier may span the width of the zone of contamination or a series of sheet pilings may be inserted into the subsurface which direct the contaminated water through the reactive barrier. This "funnel and gate" system was devised R. C. Starr, J. A. Cherry, and other researchers at the University of Waterloo and published in 1994 in *Ground Water*. In cases in which the reactants in the barrier may be rapidly extinguished due to biochemical reactions, these materials may be replenished by designing replacement cassettes that may be easily exchanged in the barrier. Cassettes can also be placed in series to target the biodegradation or biotransformation of a particular contaminant or to remediate groundwater with many contaminants, each of which has specific requirements for degradation. Permeable reactive barrier technologies may also incorporate a series of smaller reactive walls if the size of the plume

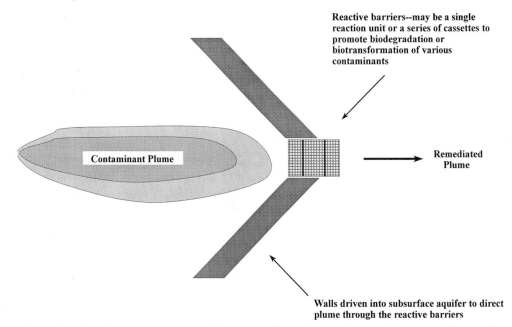

**Fig. 5.** Funnel and gate system to remediate contaminated groundwater using permeable reactive barriers (adapted in part from Starr and Cherry, 1994).

is large, thus facilitating easier removal and replacement when compared to a single large wall.

Starr, Cherry, and others pointed out that the most important considerations for the design and application of this type of system include (i) time required to effect desired biochemical reaction (combination of groundwater flow rate, reaction rate, influent contaminant concentration, and target effluent contaminant concentration), (ii) the potential formation of hazardous products resulting from reactions within the reactive barrier, and (iii) costs associated with installation and media regeneration. Examples of reactants or amendments used in permeable reactive barrier technologies to enhance contaminant biodegradation and transformation include nutrient amendments (N and P), oxygen addition using oxygen-releasing compounds or biosparging (introduction of air), and introduction of zero valent iron to achieve abiotic reduction of chlorinated compounds.

### 2. Demonstration

J. F. Barker, J. F. Devlin, and co-workers demonstrated the use of permeable reactive barrier remediation technologies at the Canadian Forces Base Borden site in Ontario, Canada. The work was documented in a 1998 report sponsored by the Department of Defence Advanced Applied Technology Demonstration Facility (AATDF) at Rice University. Contaminants within the groundwater plume targeted for remediation using this *in situ* technology included carbon tetrachloride, PCE, and toluene. Remediation of the highly chlorinated aliphatics (i.e., carbon tetrachloride and PCE) was accomplished through both biotic and abiotic reduction processes, whereas biodegradation of the less chlorinated aliphatics and toluene was achieved in an aerobic treatment zone. Three test gates containing different sequences of reactive cassette barriers were installed at the site. Gate 1 consisted of two granular iron cassettes (to effect abiotic reductive dechlorination of chlorinated hydrocarbons) followed by a cassette containing oxygen-releasing compounds. Gate 2 did not contain reactive media and served as a control and/or natural attenuation gate. Gate 3 contained a benzoate injection well (to serve as substrate for microorganisms and to achieve anaerobic conditions for microbially mediated reductive dechlorination) followed by a

biosparging wall. Initial spiked contaminant concentrations in the groundwater were approximately 1 or 2 mg/liter for carbon tetrachloride and PCE and 10 mg/liter for toluene.

Results from Gate 1 indicated that PCE was completely transformed to ethane and ethene (half-life = 0.5 days). Carbon tetrachloride was transformed to chloroform prior to reaching the gate and was rapidly dechlorinated in the iron barrier to dichloromethane. High pH next to the granular iron cassette required emplacement of the ORC downgradient at lower pH to stimulate oxygen release and toluene biodegradation. Gate 2 (natural biodegradation and biotransformation) results also indicated biotransformation of carbon tetrachloride and chloroform (each having a half-life of approximately 11 days). In Gate 3, PCE was successfully transformed to *cis*-DCE. Subsequent passage of the contaminated groundwater in Gate 3 through the biosparging wall (aerobic zone) resulted in biodegradation of toluene as well as the less chlorinated end products of reductive dechlorination produced in the anaerobic zone (e.g., *cis*-DCE).

## VII. ENHANCED *EX SITU* BIOREMEDIATION

Like *in situ* processes, enhanced *ex situ* bioremediation processes are engineered to accelerate the biodegradation or biotransformation of organic contaminants in soils and solids. In many cases, *ex situ* technologies generally offer better control of the parameters that govern biodegradation than do *in situ* techniques. *Ex situ* bioremediation technologies include land farming, composting, and slurry reactors. Land treatment employs nutrient addition and aeration (by tilling) to stimulate biodegradation of land-applied wastes. Composting of contaminated soils and sludges is a high-temperature, exothermic process in which bulking agents (e.g., wood chips and mulch) and, in some cases, nutrients are added to encourage biodegradation. Finally, *ex situ* bioslurry reactors may be used to treat either contaminated liquids or solids through nutrient addition, aeration, and bioaugmentation.

## A. Land Treatment

### 1. Overview

Land treatment or land farming refers to the accelerated aerobic biodegradation of organic wastes in either near-surface or excavated soils through the addition of nutrients, lime (pH control), and moisture and through increased aeration by tilling or other mechanical mixing (Loehr and Malina, 1986). Biodegradation is generally carried out by indigenous soil microorganisms, although some form of bioaugmentation may enhance the rate of degradation. Typically, land farming is an *ex situ* process whereby the contaminated soils are excavated from a site and sent to an engineered treatment unit (also termed a prepared bed system or reactor); however, *in situ* methods (nutrient addition and tilling) may be adequate to enhance biodegradation of the soil contaminants near the surface of excavated wastes that are mixed or tilled into the top soil layer (to a depth of approximately 1 ft). A wide variety of organic contaminants have been successfully treated in land farming applications, including petroleum hydrocarbons, pesticides, PCPs, PCBs, and PAHs (Cookson, 1995).

Land farming typically requires the addition of nutrient amendments (namely, N and P) to the soils to enhance biodegradation of contaminants. The minerals may be introduced into the soil either as a solid or mixed with water and applied through a spraying system (Cookson, 1995). The spraying system may also provide needed moisture to soils and enhance contaminant biodegradation. Plowing, tilling, or other methods of mechanical mixing of the soils stimulates biodegradation through (i) mixing and distribution of soil amendments (nutrients, lime), (ii) distribution of contaminants (by breaking up soils) and increased contact between contaminants and microorganisms, and (iii) increased aeration of soils (increased oxygen supply) (DuPont *et al.*, 1998; Ward *et al.*, 1995; Cookson, 1995).

Figure 6 presents an engineered land treatment system. Much like conventional municipal solid waste treatment units or landfills, controls or collection systems may be placed in the land treatment unit. To prevent groundwater contamination, the base of a typical land treatment unit is covered with a highly impermeable clay or geosynthetic (plastic)

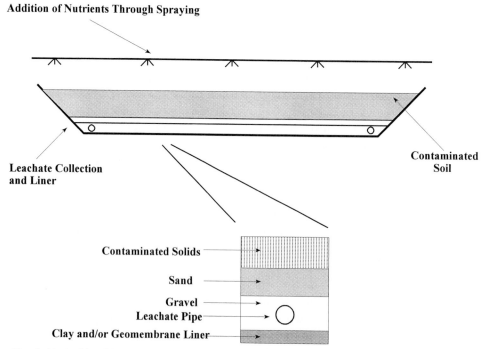

**Fig. 6.** Typical land treatment unit (inset depicts liner configuration) [adapted in part from Cookson (1995) and Alexander (1994)].

liner. A series of leachate recovery pipes are then placed near the base of the system to collect wastes that may percolate through the soil. A thick layer of sand covers the collection system, and the contaminated soil is then placed on the sand layer. Collected leachate may be recycled or sent to another treatment system. A cover or enclosure may be added to the land treatment unit to eliminate rainfall percolation and off-site migration of contaminant vapors (Cookson, 1995; Alexander, 1994).

### 2. Demonstration

In 1979, J. T. Dibble and R. Bartha published work (*Soil Science*) on the land treatment of hydrocarbon-contaminated soil resulting from a pipeline leak in New Jersey in which approximately 1.9 million liters of kerosene was spilled onto 1.5 hectares (ha) of an agricultural plot. After removal of approximately 200 m$^3$ of heavily contaminated soil, both lime and nutrients (N, P, and potassium) were applied to the field soil (to a depth of 117 cm) to enhance biodegradation. Aerobic biodegradation of the kerosene contaminant was further stimulated by periodic tilling or mixing of the soil to promote distribution of oxygen. The applied nutrient concentrations were 200 kg nitrogen/ha, 20 kg phosphorus/ha, and 17 kg potassium/ha and were added at two different times after an initial loading of 6350 kg/ha of lime. The contaminated soil was characterized as a well-drained, sandy loam soil. Kerosene biodegradation was monitored during a 24-month period to determine the efficiency of the treatment system.

Over the course of the experiment, kerosene concentrations in the soil decreased from 8700 mg/kg to very low levels in the upper 30 cm of the soil. Likewise, kerosene concentration in the lower portion of the soil (30- to 45-cm depth) also decreased over the 24-month period to <3000 mg/kg. Biodegradation was determined to be the primary mechanism for removal (compared to volatilization) based on the disappearance patterns of compounds of varying molecular weight. The rate of biodegradation in the upper portion of the soil was initially greater than the rate of biodegradation in the lower portion. However, more rapid kerosene biodegradation was observed in the lower portion of the soil after 6 months of system operation and evaluation. Temper-

ature also played a major role in the biodegradation of the kerosene contaminants. The greatest decreases in kerosene concentration due to biodegradation occurred during time periods when temperatures were at or higher than 20°C; contaminant removal was diminished at lower temperatures.

## B. Composting

### 1. Overview

Composting is another *ex situ* process in which organic compounds are biodegraded, biotransformed, or otherwise stabilized by mesophilic and thermophilic bacteria. Addition of other readily biodegradable materials, bulking agents, moisture, and possibly nutrients to contaminated soils enhances or stimulates the composting process (Ro *et al.*, 1998). Nitroaromatics, petroleum hydrocarbons, PAHs, chlorinated phenols, and pesticides are classes of contaminants that are amendable to biodegradation using a composting system (Table III).

Composting at high temperatures typically accelerates the biodegradation or biotransformation process and has historically been required to kill pathogenic organisms remaining in wastewater treatment sludges; however, high-temperature composting of contaminated soils and other solids may not be required due to the absence of pathogens in these materials (Cookson, 1995). As a result, composting of contaminated soils may occur either under mesophilic (15–45°C) conditions or under thermophilic (50–70°C) conditions. The most suitable temperatures for composting range from 55 to 60°C, whereas temperatures higher than 70°C severely inhibit the ability of the microorganisms to metabolize or transform the contaminants (Ro *et al.*, 1998). Bulking agents are used to increase the pore space or porosity of contaminated soil which results in greater air movement through the compost pile and higher rates of aerobic biodegradation. Typical bulking agents used in composting include wood chips, straw, tree bark, and plant matter (Alexander, 1994). Moisture content may also be a controlling parameter in the composting of contaminated soils. Excess moisture will impede the diffusion of oxygen through the compost pile and therefore restrict aerobic biodegradation. Optimal percentage moisture contents in compost piles range from 50 to 65% (Ro *et al.*, 1998). Cookson (1995) reports that hydrocarbon biodegradation in a composting system is optimized at a moisture content of 60%, whereas slightly lower moisture contents are suitable for other hazardous constituents.

The three most common types of composting systems are the windrow, static pile, and in-vessel systems. In windrow composting systems, the composting materials (mixture of organic material, contaminated soil, and bulking agents) are placed in long rows and are turned or mixed using a mechanical device to provide aeration or oxygen replenishment. Static pile systems are similarly arranged in long rows of composting material, but oxygen is supplied through a series of pipes that are placed at the base of the piles. Finally, in-vessel systems are typically enclosed units in which composting materials are transported on a conveyor system through a reaction vessel that is responsible for mixing, forced aeration, and temperature control (Cookson, 1995). In-vessel systems allow for greater engineering control (i.e., capture of volatile compounds and temperature and aeration regulation) and may greatly accelerate the biodegradation process when compared to the other two types of composting systems.

## 2. Demonstration

In 1992, R. T. Williams, P. S. Ziegenfuss, and W. E. Sisk published work in the *Journal of Industrial Microbiology* on the static pile composting of explosives-contaminated sediments from two U.S. Army facilities—Louisiana Army Ammunition Plant (LAAP) and Badger Army Ammunition Plant (BAAP). Target contaminants to be biodegraded using this remediation scheme included TNT, RDX, HMX, tetryl, and nitrocellulose (NC). Additives to the contaminated soils included alfalfa, straw, manure, wood chips, and horse feed in varying combinations along with nitrogen, phosphorus, potassium, and water. The initial concentration of contaminants in the LAAP soil included 56,800 mg/kg TNT, 17,900 mg/kg RDX, 2390 mg/kg HMX, and 650 mg/kg tetryl, whereas the initial concentration of NC in the BAAP soil was 18,800 mg/kg. Compost pile temperatures of the various configurations (two LAAP piles and four BAAP piles) were set at 35 and 55°C to investigate composting of explosives under both mesophilic and thermophilic conditions.

The results indicated successful remediation of the contaminants using various combinations of bulking agents and temperatures. For the LAAP soil static piles, the combined concentration of explosives decreased from 17,870 to 74 mg/kg in the thermophilic pile, whereas mesophilic conditions effected a concentration decrease from 16,560 to 326 mg/kg during the 153-day test cycle. Half-lives for TNT, RDX, and HMX under thermophilic conditions were 12, 17, and 23 days, respectively. Half-lives of the contaminants under mesophilic conditions were nearly double those calculated under thermophilic conditions. Very low levels of amino transformation products (e.g., 2-amino-4,6-dinitrotoluene, 4-amino-2,6-dinitrotoluene) were detected at the end of the test cycle. Nitrocellulose concentrations were dramatically reduced in the BAAP soil static piles. Under thermophilic conditions, NC concentration in two of the test piles was reduced from an average of approximately 13,090 mg/kg to approximately 20 mg/kg.

R. Valo and M. Slkinoja-Salonen (1986) investigated windrow composting of chlorophenol-contaminated soils from a sawmill in Finland. Two 50-m³ compost piles were constructed and contained contaminated soil along with bark and ash. Nitrogen, phosphorus, and potassium were also added to the compost pile in the aqueous phase to ensure adequate nutrient levels throughout the system. The initial concentration of chlorophenols in the soil ranged from 400 to 500 mg/kg soil, whereas the initial concentration in the compost ranged from 200 to 300 mg/kg. The composting unit was monitored over the course of 17 months with the majority of sampling and analysis being conducted during the first 5 months of operation (summer months, presumably when microbial activity was greatest).

The results of the study indicated a significant decrease in the concentration of chlorophenols in the composting unit. Most of the contaminant loss or destruction occurred during the first few months of operation. The concentration of chlorophenol decreased rapidly to approximately 30 mg/kg after a few months of operation, and the concentration decreased to approximately 15 mg/kg by the end of the test period. Bacterial identification and counts also indicated that the compost material contained a greater number of pentachlorophenol-degrading microorganisms when compared to an agricultural clay soil that was not previously contaminated by chlorophenols. Subsequent jar tests on the compost material with radiolabeled pentachlorophenol confirmed that biodegradation was a major removal mechanism because approximately 30% of the radiolabeled carbon evolved as $^{14}CO_2$ during a 40-day test period.

## C. Bioslurry Processes

### 1. Overview

Slurry reaction systems are another type of *ex situ* bioremediation process in which biodegradation of contaminants is effected either in a highly controlled bioslurry reactor or in a waste lagoon. Typically, contaminated soils, sediments, or other solids are added to the system and mixed with a host of amendments, including water, nutrients, oxygen (if an aerobic environment is desired), surfactants to enhance contaminant mobilization, and/or microorganisms that may specifically biodegrade or biotransform the contaminant of interest. Bioslurry systems, especially enclosed bioreactors, offer a high degree of engineering control. Most of the major parameters that impact contaminant biodegradation (e.g., temperature, pH, and nutrient addition) may be monitored and adjusted using this remediation approach. Many contaminant compound classes are amenable to biodegradation using bioslurry processes and include phenols, chlorinated phenols, PAHs, pesticides, chlorinated hydrocarbons, and petroleum hydrocarbons (Cookson, 1995; Alexander, 1994). Highly viscous contaminants such as tars and certain oils may not be appropriate for bioslurry treatment.

Treatment of the contaminated material may occur either in a bioslurry reactor or in a lagoon. The bioreactor system may consist of a single reactor or a series of reactors, and these reactors are typically closed to the atmosphere to prevent escape of volatile compounds and to maintain system control. Both the size and the volume of the bioslurry reactors can be highly variable. The percentage solids concentration in these reactors ranges from 5 to 50% and depends on both the physical properties of the soil and the characteristics of the treatment system. Reactors in series offer a potential method of creating both aerobic and anaerobic environments in sequence, and this type of system may be very efficient in coupling the reductive dechlorination of highly chlorinated solvents (anaerobic conditions) with the subsequent metabolism of less chlorinated compounds (aerobic conditions). Typically, engineered waste lagoons vary in size and may be equipped with a variety of mixers and aerators to provide oxygen to the system. As in land treatment applications, a highly impermeable layer of clay soil or synthetic liner should be situated at the base of waste lagoons to prevent contaminant percolation into groundwater.

The continuously mixed bioreactors or waste lagoons have significant engineering advantages compared to other *ex situ* technologies such as composting and land farming, although bioreactor systems may be costly to operate (Cookson, 1995). The mixing of the solids within the reactor enhances the distribution of both the solid materials containing the contaminants and the amendments that are added to the reactor system. Increased aeration and mass transfer of oxygen throughout the bioreactor as a result of mixing or sparging encourages aerobic biodegradation of the contaminants. If the bioslurry system contains volatile compounds, the rate of volatilization may be increased due to agitation and mixing. Both the accessibility of the contaminant to the microorganisms (contact) and the fraction of bioavailable contaminant are increased in this type of reactor system.

Bioslurry processes promote the breakup of aggregated soil particles that may sequester or contain high concentrations of the target contaminant. This breakup of larger particles into smaller ones leads to a greater soil surface area to volume ratio and thus may increase contaminant desorption by maximizing surface contact with the aqueous phase. Contaminated clay soils may be especially amenable to bioslurry treatment processes due to their decreased permeability and difficulty in treating *in situ*. Organic contaminants adsorb strongly to adhesive clay materials and may be easily entrapped in the intra- and inter particle pore spaces, and subsequent transport of materials (i.e., nutrients, oxygen or other electron acceptor, and microorganisms) through clay soils is very difficult.

## 2. Demonstration

In 1991, G. C. Compeau and coworkers reported results from laboratory-scale experiments used in the design and implementation of a full-scale bioslurry reactor treatment system. The full-scale system was designed to treat 3400 cubic yards of PCP-contaminated soil from a spill. PCP concentrations in the soil were variable, with a maximum of 9000 mg/kg. Initial testing of the contaminated soil indicated that the indigenous microflora were not capable of breaking down the PCP contaminant; therefore, subsequent bench and full-scale treatment systems incorporated specialized PCP-degrading microorganisms to augment the existing soil organisms and stimulate biodegradation of the contaminant.

The laboratory-scale bioslurry treatability studies indicated that for a variety of solids with concentrations ranging from 5 to 40%, PCP could be successfully biodegraded when the reactor was inoculated with the PCP-degrading culture. For example, in the 40% solids concentration bioslurry test with an initial concentration of approximately 275 mg/liter, very little of the PCP was removed from the system during the initial 13-day test period. After inoculation, nearly all the PCP in the reactor was biodegraded during a 10-day period. The laboratory studies also revealed that the majority of the PCP contaminant resided within the more coarse particles that may not be easily suspended in a bioslurry reactor system. As a result, design of the full-scale treatment system was amended to include a washing step to desorb the PCP from the coarse particles. The wash solution containing PCP along with the finer unwashed soil particles represented the major influents to the bioslurry reactors.

A pair of 25,000-gallon bioslurry reactors were used in the full-scale cleanup operation. Nitrogen and phosphorus were added to the reactors to meet microbial growth requirements. Results from the full-scale experiment supported the laboratory findings that inoculation was necessary to stimulate PCP biodegradation. A testing period of 2 weeks was required to decrease PCP soil concentrations from 370 to <0.5 mg/kg in one of the inoculated reactors.

This degree of treatment was also reached in the second reactor, but only after addition of the inoculum following a 7-day test period in which biodegradation did not occur. It is generally believed that bioaugmentation decreases the lag time in biodegradation studies but that, given time, selection processes will result in microbial populations capable of degrading target contaminants.

## VIII. SUMMARY

Bioremediation refers to the transformation of organic wastes by microorganisms into biomass, carbon dioxide, water, and inorganic salts, depending on the structure of the compounds in the waste. These organic waste materials may also be biotransformed to less toxic compounds or compounds that may be more amenable to complete mineralization. Many *in situ* and *ex situ* technologies are currently available to address organic waste contamination in both soils and groundwater.

Natural bioattenuation is an *in situ* method for remediating contaminated subsurface soils and groundwater. It is a nonintrusive method that takes advantage of the abilities of natural microflora in subsurface environments to biodegrade organic contaminants. Although natural bioattenuation does not require complex engineered systems, monitoring for contaminant concentration and biochemical markers is necessary to validate the efficiency of this type of treatment option. Enhanced *in situ* bioremediation technologies include the Raymond process (biostimulation), electron donor delivery, bioventing, and permeable reactive barriers. Biostimulation technology involves the addition of nutrients (namely, N and P), oxygen, and perhaps microorganisms to groundwater aquifers to enhance biodegradation of organic contaminants. Oxygen may be added to the groundwater by injection of air, pure oxygen, hydrogen peroxide, or oxygen releasing compounds. Injection of microorganisms into the subsurface, or bioaugmentation, also may be an option for biodegradation enhancement; however, to date there has been little success in field-scale experiments.

*In situ* biodegradation and biotransformation of chlorinated organic compounds may be accelerated by the injection of electron donors, such as lactate, methanol, and hydrogen, to the contaminant region of interest in groundwater. In a cometabolic process, breakdown of the primary substrate (e.g., methane) leads to the fortuitous expression of enzymes that are capable of oxidizing highly chlorinated organics such as TCE. Biotransformation through reductive dechlorination also requires an adequate supply of electron donors to serve as a primary substrate for the microorganisms that mediate this process.

Bioventing of contaminated subsurface unsaturated zone soils focuses on delivering oxygen to areas in which oxygen has been previously depleted due to microbiological reactions in the soil. This treatment technology is typically applied to soils that have high permeabilities and thus a greater ability to transfer oxygen to the contaminant region. The treatment technology is designed to favor contaminant biodegradation over volatilization, but site hydrogeology and contaminant physical properties may also have an impact on the effectiveness of the two mechanisms. Permeable reactive barriers provide another *in situ* method in which groundwater is routed through a wall or barrier containing materials that will enhance either the biodegradation or biotransformation of organic contaminants. Materials contained in the reaction zone may include both nutrients and oxygen releasing compounds to enhance aerobic biodegradation of contaminants or other reactive agents such as zero-valent iron which lead to the abiotic reductive dechlorination of chlorinated solvents.

Land treatment or land farming is an *ex situ* method to treat contaminated soils and sludges. Excavated materials are placed either in an engineered treatment unit or on top of the natural soil surface. Biodegradation in these systems is enhanced through tilling and mixing to promote aeration, nutrient amendment, and possibly the addition of contaminant-degrading microorganisms. *Ex situ* composting of contaminated soils is achieved by addition of bulking agents such as wood chips to promote aeration, nutrients, and readily biodegradable materials to the contaminated soils. These mixtures are then placed in windrow, static pile, or in-vessel composting systems in which higher temperature, thermophilic conditions are initiated to accelerate the biodegradation process. Finally, bioslurry processes promote treatment of contaminated soils, solids, and sludges by placement in bioslurry reactors and mixing with water, nutrients, oxygen, microorganisms, or other materials that might enhance the biodegradation or biotransformation of the contaminant. Bioslurry processes offer a high degree of control over the parameters that influence biodegradation, including temperature, pH, and nutrient concentration, but they can be expensive when compared to land treatment and composting.

Bioremediation processes for the treatment of contaminated environmental media such as soils and the saturated (aquifer) and unsaturated (vadose) zones of the subsurface may prove to be the most cost-effective treatment options depending on site-specific remedial objectives. In common with most other remediation technologies, bioremediation processes are usually applied as part of a system or treatment in conjunction with other complementing processes to obtain optimal results.

### See Also the Following Articles

BIODEGRADATION • BIOTRANSFORMATIONS • SOIL MICROBIOLOGY

### Bibliography

Alexander, M. (1994). "Biodegradation and Bioremediation." Academic Press, San Diego.

Chaudry, G. R. (Ed.) (1994). "Biological Degradation and Bioremediation of Toxic Chemicals." Dioscorides Press, Portland, OR.

Cookson, J. T. (1995). "Bioremediation Engineering: Design and Application." McGraw-Hill, New York.

DuPont, R. R., Bruell, C. J., Downey, D. C., Huling, S. G., Marley, M. C., Norris, R. D., and Pivetz, B. (1998). "Innovative Site Remediation Technology Design & Application: Bioremediation" (W. C. Anderson, Ed.). American Academy of Environmental Engineers, Annapolis, MD.

Flathman, P. E., Jerger, D. E., and Exner, J. H. (Eds.) (1994). "Bioremediation: Field Experience." Lewis, Boca Raton, FL.

Leeson, A., and Hinchee, R. E. (1997). "Soil Bioventing: Principles and Practice." Lewis, Boca Raton, FL.

Loehr, R. C., and Malina, J. F. (Eds.) (1986). "Land Treatment—A Hazardous Waste Management Alternative." Center for Research in Water Resources, University of Texas at Austin/Van Nostrand Reinhold, Austin/New York.

Madigan, M. T., Martinko, J. M., and Parker, J. (1997). "Biology of Microorganisms," 8th ed. Prentice-Hall, Upper Saddle River, NJ.

Norris, R. D., Hinchee, R. E., Brown, R., McCarty, P. L., Semprini, L., Wilson, J. T., Kampbell, D. H., Reinhard, M., Bouwer, E. J., Borden, R. C., Vogel, T. M., Thomas, J. M., and Ward, C. H. (1994). "Handbook of Bioremediation." Lewis, Boca Raton, FL.

Rao, P. S., Brown, R. A., Allen-King, R. M., Cooper, W. J., Gardner, W. R., Gollin, M. A., Hellman, T. M., Heminway, D. F., Luthy, R. G., Olsen, R. L., Palmer, P. A., Pohland, F. G., Rappaport, A. B., Sara, M. N., Syrrist, D. M., and Wagner, B. J. (1997). "Innovations in Ground Water and Soil Cleanup: From Concept to Commercialization." National Academy Press, Washington, DC.

Rittman, B. E., Alvarez-Cohen, L., Bedient, P. B., Brown, R. A., Chappelle, F. H., Kitanidis, P. K., Mahaffey, W. R., Norris, R. D., Salanitro, J. P., Shauver, J. M., Tiedje, J. M., Wilson, J. T., and Wolfe, R. S. (1993). "*In Situ* Bioremediation: When Does It Work?" National Academy Press, Washington, DC.

Ro, K. S., Preston, K. T., Seiden, S., and Bergs, M. A. (1998).

Remediation composting process principles: Focus on soils contaminated with explosive compounds. *Crit. Rev. Environ. Sci. Technol.* **28**(3), 253–282.

Spain, J. C. (Ed.) (1995). "Biodegradation of Nitroaromatic Compounds." Plenum, New York.

U.S. Environmental Protection Agency (USEPA) (1997). Cleaning up the nation's waste sites: Markets and technology trends, EPA 542-R-96-005. USEPA, Washington, DC.

Ward, C. H., Loehr, R. L., Norris, R., Nyer, E., Piotrowski, M., Spain, J., and Wilson, J. (1995). "Innovative Site Remediation Technology: Bioremediation" (W. C. Anderson, Ed.). American Academy of Environmental Engineers, Annapolis, MD.

Ward, C. H., Cherry, J. A., and Scalf, M. R. (Eds.) (1997). "Subsurface Restoration." Ann Arbor Press, Chelsea, MI.

Young, L. Y., and Cerniglia, C. E. (Eds.) (1994). "Microbial Transformation and Degradation of Toxic Organic Chemicals." Wiley–Liss, New York.

# *Biosensors*

## Yoko Nomura and Isao Karube

*University of Tokyo*

I. Principle of Biosensors
II. Applications of Biosensors
III. Current Topics in Biosensors

*transducer*   An electronic signal-transducing element that can convert a change in the concentration of a product of a biological reaction into an electronic signal. Examples are electrodes and optical apparatus.

## GLOSSARY

*biochemical oxygen demand* (*BOD*)   The amount of dissolved oxygen (DO) needed to biologically degrade the organic compounds in an aquatic environment. BOD measurements are conventionally carried out according to the BOD 5-day method which measures the DO by titration (modified Winkler method) before and after a 5-day sample incubation period during which biodegradation occurs.

*biological sensing element*   A biomolecule or a biomaterial used in a biosensor for analyte recognition; sometimes referred to as a biological recognition element. It undergoes a specific biological reaction with the analyte so that the analyte can be selectively detected by the biosensor. Examples include enzymes, antibodies, DNA oligomers, and microorganisms.

*flow injection analysis* (*FIA*)   A technique sometimes used in flow-type biosensors; developed in the 1970s. The sample is injected directly into carrier solution running through fine tubes of manifolds which include an electrical detection apparatus. Reactions such as those resulting in fluorescence or chemiluminescence occur *in situ* and are detected as electronic signals. FIA systems afford precise control of the mixing ratio of injected samples and carrier solutions, which results in highly reproducible measurements. Because the detection by FIA is simple, rapid, precise, and continuous, it is used for various measurements, such as in medical diagnosis, food quality control, and environmental monitoring.

*glucose oxidase*   An enzyme which catalyzes glucose oxidation. It is usually suitable for industrial use because of its high stability. It is one of the typical biological sensing elements and was used in the first biosensor.

**A BIOSENSOR**   is broadly defined as a sensing system which uses biological reactions such as enzymatic or immunological reactions. Most biosensors are composed of a biological sensing element and a transducer.

Many biosensors (Cass, 1990; Suzuki, 1990; Buerk, 1993) have been constructed since the first report describing the development of the first enzyme sensor for glucose measurement by Clark in 1962 (Buerk, 1993). This biosensor measured the product of an enzyme reaction using an electrode, which was a remarkable achievement even though the enzyme was not immobilized on the electrode.

Today's basic biosensors originated from the investigation by Updike and Hicks in 1967 (Buerk, 1993). Their sensor combined membrane-immobilized glucose oxidase with an oxygen electrode, and oxygen measurements were carried out before and after the enzyme reaction. Many other biological elements and transducers have been examined since this first glucose biosensor was developed. For example, in 1977 Karube reported the first microbial sensor which used the whole cell as a biological sensing element. Many immuno-sensors using antibodies were fabricated in 1980s and recently DNA, RNA, and even artificial recognition elements have been employed. Transducers have also been improved, and novel transducing elements such as optical detectors, including surface plasmon resonance (SPR) detectors, are widely used in modern biosensors.

## I. PRINCIPLE OF BIOSENSORS

A biosensor is a detection system composed of biological sensing elements, such as enzymes, antibodies, microorganisms, and DNA, and an electronic signal-transducing element (Fig. 1) (Buerk, 1993). A transducer can convert a change in the concentration of a product of a biological reaction into an electronic signal. For example, an oxygen electrode converts a change in the oxygen concentration of a sample caused by enzymes or biodegradation into a change in electric current. The transducers used in biosensors include electrodes, piezo-electric quartz crystals, and optics. Many biosensors can be applied to important fields such as diagnosis and environmental monitoring.

The principle of a simple glucose sensor using glucose oxidase (GOD) is shown in Fig. 2. The target analyte, glucose, is a substrate of GOD. Glucose diffuses into the membrane and a biological reaction occurs within the membrane. When GOD catalyzes the glucose oxidation, dissolved oxygen in the sample is consumed and gluconic lactone and hydrogen peroxide are produced. The oxygen electrode detects a change in dissolved oxygen concentration of the sample as a change in electric currrent. Since the change in dissolved oxygen concentration is a result of the glucose oxidation, the glucose concentration of the sample can be measured. The biosensor does not directly detect the target analyte (glucose). Instead, it measures the change in the concentration of a co-reactant (oxygen) or a co-product (hydrogen peroxide) of the reaction catalyzed by the immobilized biological-sensing material (i.e., GOD).

Biosensor configurations are categorized into two types; batch type (a) and flow type (b) as depicted in Fig. 3 (Buerk, 1993). In flow-type sensors, a bioreactor, a column stuffed with biomaterial-immobilized beads, can be incorporated separately from a transducer. Flow-type biosensors are very useful for continuous monitoring of target analytes. Immobilization of biomaterials is usually required for biosensor fabrication. Typical immobilization carriers are glass, alginate and artificial resin beads, and membranes.

Disposable biosensors such as amperometric glucose sensors for medical diagnosis are examples of a batch-type sensor. Flow injection analysis (FIA) is a technique sometimes used in flow-type biosensors. Because biosensors using FIA yield very rapid and accurate measurements, these have been applied to various fields, such as environmental monitoring and food quality control.

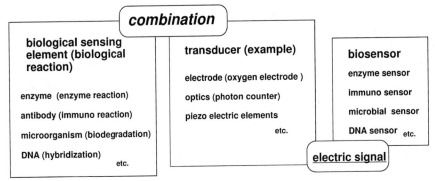

**Fig. 1.** Biological elements are combined with transducers when biosensors are fabricated. Electrodes and optical devices are widely used as transducers in biosensors. A piezo-electric device such as a quartz crystal detects a weight change before and after the biological reaction as applied to immuno- and DNA sensors. Transducers convert a change in the concentration of the compound into an electronic signal.

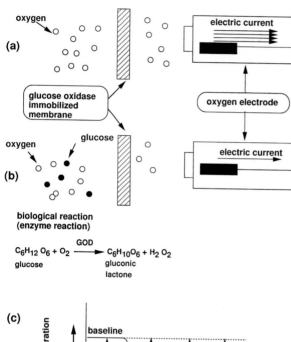

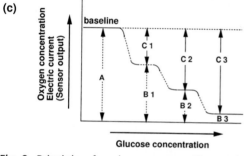

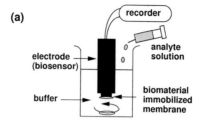

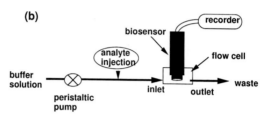

**Fig. 2.** Principle of a glucose sensor. The analyte is glucose, and the biological-sensing element of the biosensors is glucose oxidase (GOD). The membrane-immobilized GOD is combined with an oxygen electrode as a transducer. An oxygen electrode generates electric current depending on the dissolved oxygen concentration. Glucose and oxygen permeate into the membrane-immobilized GOD. (a) Dissolved oxygen is not consumed when a sample which does not contain glucose such as pure buffer solution is measured by the glucose sensor. The sample is air-saturated and the oxygen electrode produces stable high current. This value is defined as the baseline current of the sensor. (b) A sample containing glucose is measured by the glucose sensor. GOD catalyzes the glucose oxidation using oxygen and dissolved oxygen is consumed. The oxygen concentration is lower than that in (a) and the electric current decreases from the baseline current. (c) Typical reaction curve of the sensor is illustrated. A, the baseline current: B1–B3, the electric currents obtained from samples containing glucose. The differences between A and B1–B3 are the sensor responses (C1–C3). As glucose concentration increases, the sensor response will also increase.

**Fig. 3.** Two types of biosensor measurements. The illustrated biosensor is a combination of an electrode and a membrane-immobilized biomaterial. For example, adsorption or entrapment methods may be used to immobilize biomaterials. The membrane with immobilized biomaterial such as cellulose acetate membrane (0.45 $\mu$m) is attached to the electrode by an O-ring. (a) Batch-type measurement. The biosensor is immersed in the buffer solution and the analyte solution is directly injected into the buffer solution. (b) Flow-type measurement. The biosensor is attached to a flow cell and a flow-type biosensor is fabricated. The buffer solution is propelled by a peristaltic pump and the analyte solution is injected into the flow line. The buffer solution mixed with the analyte is introduced to the flow cell and is measured by the biosensor.

In a typical biosensor study, parameters such as the amount of immobilized biological-sensing elements (e.g., enzymes), pH, and temperature of the buffer are optimized, and then a calibration curve is generated using standard solutions containing known concentrations of the analyte. Figure 4 shows a typical calibration curve of a biosensor. Calibration curves are normally obtained by one of two methods: from reaction curves of the biological co-reaction measurement (Fig. 4a) or the biological co-product measurement (Fig. 4b). In both cases the sensor responses

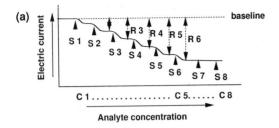

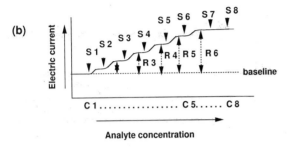

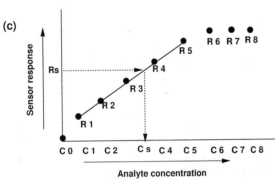

**Fig. 4.** Typical calibration curve of a biosensor. The sample injections were carried out eight times (S*n*). (a) A reaction curve of a biosensor based on the measurement of co-reactants. Co-reactant is consumed during the measurement and the sensor output such as the electric current in the figure decreases as the analyte concentration increases. The baseline current is higher than that of the sample containing the analyte. The sensor response (R*n*) is calculated by subtracting the measurement value (e.g., the electric current) of the sample containing the analyte from the baseline value. (b) A reaction curve of a biosensor based on the measurement of co-products. Co-product or sensor output increases as the analyte concentration increases. The baseline value is less than that of the sample containing the analyte. The sensor response (R*n*) is obtained by subtracting the baseline value from the measurement value of the sample containing the analyte. (c) A calibration curve. The dynamic range of a biosensor is the linear correlation from the detection limit C1 to C5. The sensitivity of the biosensor, for example, is calculated as

are calculated from the difference between the values of pure buffer and the sample containing the analyte.

The sensitivity of a biosensor is defined as the slope of the linear range of the calibration curve. The linear range is between the lower detection limit (C1) and the nonlinear profile at higher concentration (C6, −7, and −8). The biosensor response (biosensor output signal Rs) obtained from the sample measurement is substituted into the calibration curve in Fig. 4 and the analyte concentration of the sample can be calculated (Cx).

Reproducibility and the life-time of a biosensor are usually examined, and selectivity must also be evaluated in some cases.

Biosensors have replaced conventional methods, which are often complicated, time-consuming, expensive, and require pretreatment or clean-up of real samples prior to analysis. Biosensors generally have the following advantages compared to other analytical methods:

1. Rapid and convenient detection
2. Direct measurement of real samples
3. Very specific detection

On the other hand, stability and reproducibility have been problematic for biosensors due to the inherent instability of biomaterials used as sensing elements. Although biosensors have disadvantages, numerous investigations on biosensors to date have helped to overcome at least some of these difficulties, allowing practical application of many biosensors in the real world.

## II. APPLICATIONS OF BIOSENSORS

Biosensors have been applied in many important fields, such as food quality control, environmental

---

(R4 − R2)/(C4 − C2). Rs is obtained when an unknown concentration sample is measured by the biosensor and it is substituted into the linear correlation, and the sample concentration Cs is obtained.

monitoring, and medical diagnosis. Recently, some groups reported biosensors for detecting chemical or toxic agents for use in military settings (Buerk, 1993). A few examples of biosensors in practical use in major fields are described in the following sections.

## A. Food Analysis

Many biosensors such as enzyme sensors have been developed for food analysis and food quality control. Enzyme sensors are used for the measurement of sugars, such as glucose, sucrose, and fructose. Vitamin C (ascorbic acid) and glutamate in food are also measured by biosensors. Some of these sensors are also being used in the medical field and for monitoring waste-water. Many of these sensors operate on the same principle as described previously for the glucose sensor shown in Fig. 2. The freshness of fish meat can also be measured by enzyme sensors. The freshness sensor that detects the degradation products of adenosine triphosphate (ATP) in fish meat, as well as many other enzyme sensors, achieves very high sensitivity by combining an FIA system coupled with chemiluminescence detection.

Microbial sensors are also applied to food quality analysis for measuring free fatty acids in milk (Schmidt *et al.*, 1996), alcohol, or acetic acid (Suzuki, 1990). The free fatty acid sensor uses *Arthrobacter nicotianase*, and both the alcohol and the acetic acid sensors use same bacterium, *Tricosposporon blassicae*.

## B. Medical Diagnosis

Enzyme sensors and microbial sensors for antibiotics and vitamins have been fabricated since the 1970s. Diabetes has been a particularly important target for many biosensors intended for medical use. Glucose sensors have been applied to diagnosis and monitoring of diabetes patients and to food quality analysis. Insulin biosensors have also been developed for use in diabetes treatment.

Since the first glucose sensor using an oxygen electrode was reported, numerous glucose sensors have been developed using techniques aimed at practical use. For example, screen-printing (Nagata *et al.*, 1995) and micromachining techniques (Hiratsuka *et al.*, 1998) have been applied to glucose sensors.

Disposable biosensors have very promising applications in medical diagnosis, such as monitoring blood glucose concentrations in diabetes patients. Matsushita Company (Osaka, Japan) has commercialized a circular-type glucose sensor which utilizes semiconductor technology.

## C. Environmental Monitoring

Biosensors can rapidly detect and measure eutoriphicants, toxicants, and biochemical oxygen demand (BOD) in the environment. Enzyme immuno and microbial sensors have been mainly developed to detect pollutants in the environment. Biosensors for environmental monitoring have been reviewed (Karube *et al.*, 1995).

The phosphate sensor is a typical example of an enzyme sensor for environmental monitoring. In the past few years, dramatic improvements have been made in phosphate detection systems using enzyme sensors (Nakamura *et. al.*, 1997), and it is expected that some of these sensors will be used in the field in the near future.

Many biosensors have been developed to detect toxicants in the environment such as pesticides and cyanide. Jeanty and Marty (1998) reported organophosphates detection systems based on acetylcholine esterase inhibition. Immuno-sensors, in place of conventional enzyme-linked immuno sorbent assays are also frequently used to detect pesticides. Carl *et al.* (1997) fabricated an immuno-sensor which detects chemical endocrine disrupters (PCB) using a screen-printing technique, and recently Seifert and Hock (1998) investigated a novel sensor which uses a human estrogen receptor and an SPR-detection system. Microbial sensors have been constructed which detect cyanide and detergents. Karube *et al.* (1995) reviewed developments in microbial sensors for environmental monitoring.

The BOD sensor, which uses an omnivorous yeast *Trichosporon cutaneum*, is a well-known example of a microbial biosensor applied to environmental monitoring (Cass, 1990). The microbial BOD sensor measures the oxygen uptake by the respiratory system of the microorganism which changes as a result of the biodegradation of organic compounds in the sample. (Fig. 5). The microbial BOD sensor systems have been commercialized and marketed since 1983 by several companies (DKK, Nisshin Denki, and Central Kagaku Co., Tokyo).

## III. CURRENT TOPICS IN BIOSENSORS

Enzyme-, immuno-, and microbial sensors have become very popular. Sensors that take advantage of new transducing techniques such as SPR and a charge-coupled device have increasingly been reported (Buerk, 1993). Novel molecular recognition elements, such as DNA oligomers having specific affinity to various target molecules, have also been tested for use in biosensors.

Stability of a biosensor is very important, especially when the sensors must be used continuously in the field. Microorganisms and few stable enzymes are suitable for this purpose. However, many enzymes and antibodies used in biosensors are not stable enough for long-term practical use. Molecularly im-

printed polymers (MIPs) have been employed in place of antibodies to construct biosensors with enhanced stability (Kriz *et al.,* 1995). These polymers are prepared by polymerization of various monomers in the presence of the target compound which acts as a template. After the polymer is removed from the template compound, the polymer retains the memory of the template and can selectively rebind the template compound. The use of MIPs to replace biomolecules in biosensors has advantages such as enhanced stability and inexpensive cost, which may expand the scope and applicability of the biosensors of tomorrow.

### Acknowledgment

We thank Yohei Yokobayashi at The Scripps Research Institute for his help and advice in preparing the manuscript.

### Bibliography

Buerk, D. G. (1993). "Biosensors." Technomic, Lancaster, Pennsylvania.

Carl, M. D., Iionti, I., Taccini, M., Cagnini, A., and Mascini, M. (1997). Disposable screen-printed electrode for the immunochemical detection of polychlorinated biphenyls. *Anal. Chim. Acta* **324,** 189–197.

Cass, A. E. G. (1990). "Biosensor." IRL/Oxford Univ. Press, New York.

Hiratsuka, A., Sasaki, S., and Karube, I. (1998). A self-contained glucose sensor chip with arrayed capillaries. *Electroanalysis* **10,** 231–235.

Jeanty, G., and Marty, J. L. (1998). Detection of paraoxon by continuous flow system based enzyme sensor. *Biosensor Bioelectronics* **13,** 213–218.

Karube, I., Nomura, Y., and Arikawa, Y. (1995). Biosensors for environmental control. *Trends Anal. Chem.* **14,** 295–299.

Kriz, D., Ramstrom, O., Svensson, A., and Mosbach, K. (1995). Introducing biomimetic sensors based on molecularly imprinted polymers as recognition elements. *Anal. Chem.* **67,** 2142–2144.

Nagata, R., Yokoyama, K., Clark, S. A., and Karube, I. (1995). A glucose sensor fabricated by the screen printing technique. *Biosensor Bioelectronics* **10,** 261–267.

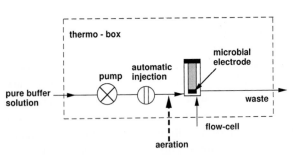

**Fig. 5.** A schematic of a basic microbial BOD sensor. A microbial electrode consists of a membrane-immobilized *T. cutaneum* and an oxygen electrode. BOD measurement is performed aerobically using phosphate buffer at 30°C. Glucose–glutamic acid solution is used as the standard solution for preparation of a calibration curve. After the standard solution measurement is obtained, real samples are examined and the BOD value is estimated. This system has been commercialized and the measurements are carried out automatically and continuously.

Nakamura, H., Ikebukuro, I., McNiven, S., Karube, I., Yamamoto, H., Hayashi, K., Suzuki, M., and Kubo, I. (1997). A chemiluminescent FIA biosensor for phosphate ion monitoring using pyruvate oxidase. *Biosensor Bioelectronics* **12**, 959–966.

Schmidt, A., Gabisch, C. S., and Bilitewski, U. (1996). Microbial biosensor for free fatty acids using an oxygen electrode based on thick film technology. *Biosensor Bioelectronics* **11**, 1139–1145.

Seifert, M., and Hock, B. (1998). Analytics of estrogens and xenoestrogens in the environmental using a SPR-Biosensor, *Proc. Biosensor* **98**, 47.

Suzuki, S. (1990). "Biosensor," 5th ed. Kohdan-sha, Tokyo. (In Japanese)

# Biosurfactants

## Fazilet Vardar-Sukan
*Ege University*

## Naim Kosaric
*University of Western Ontario*

## GLOSSARY

**biosurfactants** Biodegradable surfactants produced by microorganisms or enzymes.

**enzyme-synthesized surfactants** Surfactants produced by the enzymes.

**growth-associated production** Production during the growth phase of an organism.

**growth-limited production** Production at the stationary phase of an organism.

**immobilized biocatalysts** Microorganisms or enzymes that are attached to various surfaces by physical and/or chemical bonds.

**microbial biosurfactants** Biosurfactants produced by microorganisms.

**resting cells** Nongrowing cells.

**MICROBIAL SURFACE-ACTIVE AGENTS (BIO-SURFACTANTS)** are important products which have many applications in many industries. Their properties of interest regard changing surface-active phenomena such as a lowering of surface and interfacial tensions, wetting and penetrating actions, spreading, hydrophilicity and hydrophobicity, emulsification and deemulsification, detergency, gelling, foaming, flocculating actions, microbial growth enhancement, metal sequestration, and anti-microbial action. They can be classified under different headings according to their production methods and areas of application.

## I. INTRODUCTION

Most applications today involve the use of chemically synthesized surfactants. The total sales volume of specialty surfactants in the United States in 1992 was estimated to be $7 billion and was expected to increase at a rate of 3–5% annually.

There are many advantages of biosurfactants compared to their chemically synthesized counterparts, including the following:

Biodegradability

Generally low toxicity

Biocompatibility and digestivity, which allows their application in cosmetics, pharmaceuticals, and as functional food additives

Availability of raw materials: Biosurfactants can be produced from cheap raw materials which are available in large quantities. The carbon source may come from hydrocarbons, carbohydrates, and/or lipids, which may be used separately or in combination with each other.

Acceptable production economics: Depending the application, biosurfactants can also be produced from industrial wastes and by-products and this is of particular interest for bulk production (e.g., for use with petroleum-related technologies).

Use in environmental control: Biosurfactants can be effectively used in handling industrial emulsions, control of oil spills, biodegradation and detoxification of industrial effluents, and in bioremediation of contaminated soil.

Specificity: Biosurfactants, because they are complex organic molecules with specific functional groups, are often specific in their action. This is

*Encyclopedia of Microbiology, Volume 1*
SECOND EDITION

**618**

of particular interest in detoxification of specific pollutants, de-emulsification of industrial emulsions, and specific cosmetic, pharmaceutical, and food applications.
Effectiveness at extreme temperatures, pH, and salinity.

Most biosurfactants are high-molecular-weight lipid complexes which are normally produced under highly aerobic conditions. This is achieved in their *ex situ* production in aerated bioreactors. When their large-scale application in petroleum and soil is needed, their *in situ* production (and action) would be advantageous. Low oxygen availability under these conditions requires maintenance of anaerobic microoganisms and their anaerobic syntheses of biosurfactants, whereby other conditions for microbial growth are also most unfavorable (e.g., mixing, availability of substrate, mass transfer, and availability of trace nutrients). Screening for anaerobic biosurfac-

tant producers is of greatest importance for these conditions.

## II. CLASSIFICATION OF BIOSURFACTANTS

In general, biosurfactants can be classified as shown in Fig. 1.

### A. Classification According to the Structure of the Bioproduct

Biosurfactants include the following chemical structures.

1. Glycolipids
2. Hydroxylated and cross-linked fatty acids (mycolic acids)
3. Polysaccharide–lipid complexes

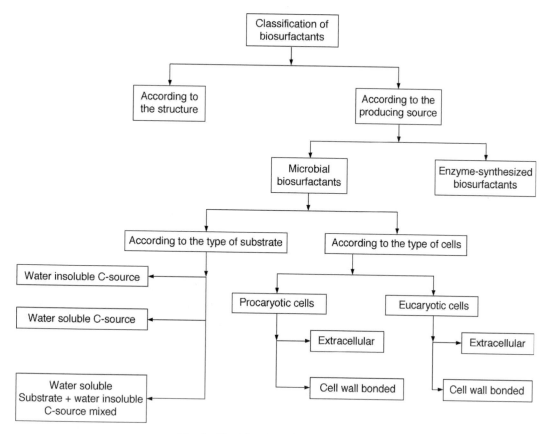

***Fig. 1.*** Classification of biosurfactants.

4. Lipoprotein–lipopeptides
5. Phospholipids
6. The complete cell surface

The microorganisms that produce biosurfactants and their structures are listed in Table I.

As can be seen from Table I, a considerable number of bacteria and yeasts are able to produce biosurfactants. These microorganisms prefer a wide range of environments, such as soil, water (lakes, oceans, and seas), and alkanes (oil reservoirs), and they can easily be adapted to these environments to produce biosurfactants under aerobic and/or anaerobic conditions.

A Many researchers have investigating novel strains with capabilities for producing microbial surface active substances. A strain of *Pseudomonas aeruginosa* isolated from crude oil-associated injection water in Venezuelan oil fields was found to adopt to the conditions prevalent in this oil reservoir. *Ochrobactrum anthropii* was isolated from contaminated fuels. In another study, 31 microbial strains were selected and tested for the biodegradation of diesel oil. The biodegradation of oily sludge was facilitated by *P. aeruginose* USB-CSI.

Rhamnolipids, produced by *P. aeruginosa*, were not inactivated by pH, temperature, salinity, calcium, or magnesium at concentrations in excess of those found in many oil reservoirs in Venezuela. Samples from oil-producing wells, contaminated soils, and oil-producing fluids in northern Germany were screened for heterothrophic bacteria producing biosurfactants and growing at high salinities and temperatures. *Bacillus* strain SPO18 was found to tolerate anaerobic conditions up to 50°C. The halo-tolerant *Bacillus licheniformis* strain JF-2 was also isolated from oil field injection water and found to produce biosurfactants under both aerobic and anaerobic conditions. Six heterotrophic bacterial strains were isolated from enriched mixed cultures obtained from sea water/sediment samples collected near the Isle of Borkum (North Sea) using Mihagol-S (C14, 15-*n*-alkanes) as the principal carbon source. *Pseudomonas aeruginosa* have been isolated from oceanic oil.

Volatile fatty acids (mostly HOAc and propionic acid) have been generated in an anaerobically digested sewage sludge and then converted to a biosurfactant for use in dispersing oil spills. Subsequently,

*Pseudomonas putida* BH has been used to produce a biosurfactant from HOAc-based sludge.

Other microorganisms have been isolated from hydrocarbon-contaminated soils, such as *Rhodococcus*, *Bacillus pumilus*, and *Arthrobacter* sp. strain MIS38. Two strains of *Bacillus subtilis* (MTCC 2423 and MTCC 1427) produced a biosurfactant using molasses, an agro-industrial by-product, at 45°C. *Pseudomonas aeruginosa* and *Pseudomonas fluorescens*, biotype C, which are able to emulsify heavy crude petroleum, have been isolated from enriched cultures with soil samples from Maracabio Lake.

## B. Classification of Biosurfactants According to the Producing Source

### 1. Microbial Biosurfactants
#### a. Classfication by Type of Substrate Used
Biosurfactant-producing microbes can be divided into three categories depending on the carbon source they use:

1. Those producing biosurfactants with alkanes as carbon sources (*Corynebacterium* sp. and *Arthrobacterium* sp.)
2. Those producing biosurfactants with water-soluble substrates as carbon sources (*Bacillus* sp.)
3. Those producing biosurfactants with alkanes and water-soluble substrates as carbon sources (*Pseudomonas* sp.)

These carbon sources are used separately or in combination with each other and are subsequently converted to glycolipids by the possible biosynthetic routes shown in Fig. 2.

#### b. Classification by the Type of Cell
*(1) Biosurfactants Produced by Procaryotic Cells*
RHAMNOSE LIPIDS.    Many bacteria have been identified as glycolipid producers. The glycolipids may contain various sugar moieties, such as rhamnose, trehalose, sucrose, and glucose.

The rhamnolipids may contain one or two rhamnose units and in general $\beta$-hydroxydecanoic acid residues. Rhamnolipid (RL2) contains one molecule of rhamnose and two molecules of fatty acid. Rham-

**TABLE I**
**Various Biosurfactants Produced by Microorganisms**

| Organism | Type of surfactant | Reference |
|---|---|---|
| *Acinetobacter calcoaceticus* RAG-1 | Lipoheteropolysaccharide (Emulsan) | Kaplan and Rosenberg, 1982; Zuckerberg *et al.*, 1979; Gutnick and Shabtai, 1987 |
| *Acinetobacter caloceticus* 2CAC | Whole cell (lipopeptide) | Kosaric, 1996 |
| *Acinetobacter* sp. HOI-N | Fatty acids, mono- and diglycerides | Kosaric, 1996 |
| *Alcanivorax borkumensis* | Glycolipid | Abrahams, 1998; Yakimov *et al.*, 1998a,b |
| *Arthrobacter* MTS38 | Lipopeptide | Morikawa *et al.*, 1993 |
| *Arthrobacter* RAG-1 | Heteropolysaccharides | Rosenberg *et al.*, 1979 |
| *Arthrobacter paraffineus* | Sucrose and fructose glycolipids | Suzuki *et al.*, 1974 |
| *Arthrobacter* sp. EK1 | Glycolipids (trehalose lipids) | Schulz *et al.*, 1991; Wagner and Lang, 1996 |
| *Bacillus licheniformis* | Lipoprotein, lipopeptide (lichenysin A) | Lin *et al.*, 1998; Horowitz *et al.*, 1990; Jenneman *et al.*, 1983; Javaheri *et al.*, 1985; McInerney *et al.*, 1990; Lin *et al.*, 1990 |
| *Bacillus pumilis* A1, *Bacillus subtilis* | Surfactin | Kakinuma *et al.*, 1969; Morikawa *et al.*, 1992; Arima *et al.*, 1968; Makkar *et al.*, 1997; Makkar and Cameotra, 1998; Kim *et al.*, 1997 |
| *Bacillus* sp. AB-2 | Rhamnose lipids | Banat, 1993 |
| *Bacillus* sp. C-14 | Hydrocarbon–protein complex | Eliseev *et al.*, 1991 |
| *Candida antarctica* WSH 112 | Glycolipids, mannosylerythriol lipids | Hua *et al.*, 1998; Kitamolo *et al.*, 1990a,b, 1992, 1993 |
| *Candida bombicola, Candida apicola, Candida lipolytica* Y-917, *Candida gropengiesseri* | Glycolipid (sophorose lipids) | Cooper and Paddock, 1984; Hommel *et al.*, 1987; Gobbert *et al.*, 1984; Asmer, 1988; Stuwer *et al.*, 1987; Weber *et al.*, 1990; Brakemeier *et al.*, 1995; Lesik *et al.*, 1989; Lee ve Kim, 1993; Klekner *et al.*, 1991; Zhou *et al.*, 1992; Davila *et al.*, 1992, 1997; Daniel *et al.*, 1998a,b |
| *Candida lipolytica* | "Liposan" (mostly carbohydrate) | Kosaric, 1996 |
| *Candida petrophilum* | Peptidolipid | Kosaric, 1996 |
| *Candida tropicalis* | Polysaccharide–fatty acid complex, Mannan–fatty acid | Kappell and Fiechter, 1976 |
| *Clostridium pasteurianum* | Neutral lipids | Copper *et al.*, 1980 |
| *Corynebacterium diphteriae* | Acyl glucoses | Brennan *et al.*, 1970 |
| *Corynebacterium hydrocarboclastus* | Polysaccharide–protein complex, protein–lipid–carboxy, sucrose ester | Zajic *et al.*, 1977; Zhao and Wang, 1996 |
| *Corynebacterium insidiosum* | Phospholipids | Akit *et al.*, 1981 |
| *Corynebacterium lepus* | Corynomycolic acids, fatty acids | Cooper *et al.*, 1979; Kosaric, 1996 |
| *Corynebacterium salvonicum* SFC | Neutral lipid | Kosaric, 1996 |
| *Nocardia corynebacteroides* | Glycolipid (pentasaccharide lipids) | Powalla *et al.*, 1989; Kim *et al.*, 1990 |
| *Nocardia erythropolis* | Neutral lipids, fatty acid + neutral lipids | Park *et al.*, 1998; MacDonald *et al.*, 1981 |
| *Nocardia* sp. | Whole cell deemulsifier | Raap *et al.*, 1979; Powella *et al.*, 1989; Kim *et al.*, 1998 |
| *Pseudomonas* sp. | Rhamnose lipids | Amin and Radwan, 1997 |
| *Pseudomonas aeroginosa* | Glycolipid (rhamnose lipid) | Patel and Desai, 1997; Guerra *et al.*, 1986; Reiling *et al.*, 1986; Robert *et al.*, 1989; Sim *et al.*, 1997; Parra *et al.*, 1989; Linhardt *et al.*, 1989; Manresa *et al.*, 1991; Ochsner *et al.*, 1996 |
| *Pseudomonas cepacia* | Glycolipids | Fiebig *et al.*, 1997 |
| *Pseudomonas fluorescens* | Rhamnose lipid, viscosin | Neu *et al.*, 1990; Kosaric, 1996 |
| *Pseudomona srubescens, Thiobacillus thiooxidans* | Ornithin | Wilkson, 1972; Knoche, 1972 |
| *Pseudomonas* sp. DSM 2847 | Glycolipids (rhamnose lipid) | Kosaric, 1996 |
| *Rhodococcus aurantiacus, Rhodococcus* ST-5, *Rhodococcus* H13-A | Glycolipid | Ramsav *et al.*, 1988; Abu-Ruwaida *et al.*, 1991a; Singer and Finnerty, 1990 |
| *Rhodococcus erythropolis* | Trehalose dimycolates, trehalose dicorynomycolate, PE amines | Rapp *et al.*, 1979; Wagner and Lang, 1996; Schultz, *et al.*, 1991 |
| *Rhodococcus erythropolis* SD-74 | Glycolipids (trehalose lipids) | Shulga *et al.*, 1990 |
| *Rhodococcus* sp. 33 | Polysaccharide | Neu *et al.*, 1992 |
| *Serratia marcescens* | Serrawettin | Matsuyama *et al.*, 1985, 1986 |
| *Serratia rubidae* | Rubiwettins | Matsuyama *et al.*, 1990; Nakagawa and Matsuyama, 1993; Passeri *et al.*, 1992; Ishigami *et al.*, 1994 |
| Strain MM1 | Glucose, lipid and hydroxydecanoic acids | Passeri, 1992 |
| *Streptococcus thermophilus* B | Glycolipid | Busscher *et al.*, 1997 |
| *Streptomyces tandae* | Peptides (streptofactin) | Richter *et al.*, 1998 |
| *Torulopsis petrophilum* | Glycolipid and/or protein | Kosaric, 1996 |

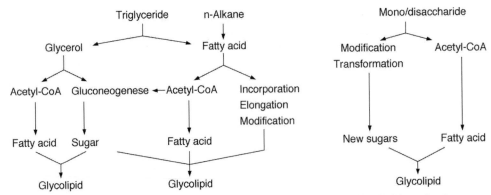

**Fig. 2.** General scheme of possible routes for the microbial glycolipid synthesis.

nolipids containing one or two rhamnose units are presented in Fig. 3.

These surfactants can be produced by carbon sources such as glycerol, ethanol, fructose, glucose, n-alkanes, and vegetable oils. Wastes such as molasses, pollutants such as phenanthrene, or waste vehicle oil can also be used as carbon sources. Recently, the production of rhamnolipids using ethanol with a conversion rate of 58% was reported.

The lowest interfacial tension that has been obtained with the molecule containing two rhamnose units is 0.2 mN/m (against kerosene). Rhamnolipids are very good emulsifiers. They can be used for the removal of copper and zinc from contaminated soils.

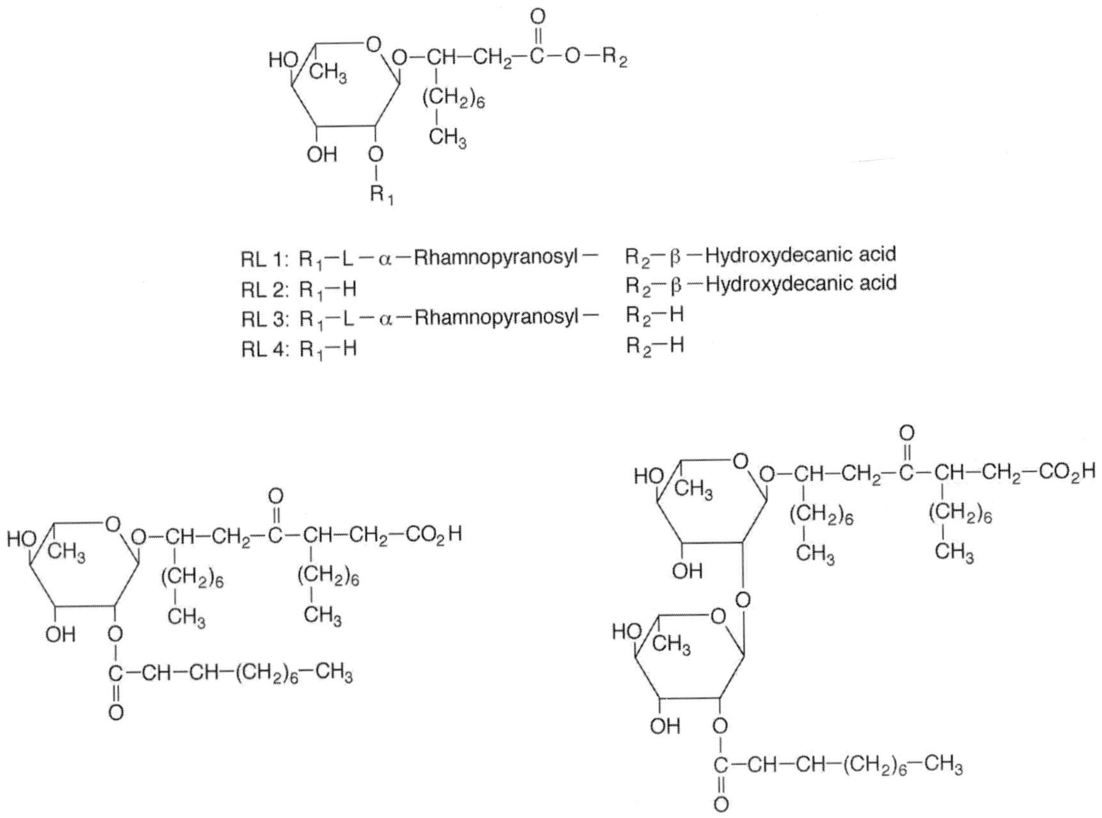

RL 1: $R_1$–L–α–Rhamnopyranosyl–   $R_2$–β–Hydroxydecanic acid
RL 2: $R_1$–H                      $R_2$–β–Hydroxydecanic acid
RL 3: $R_1$–L–α–Rhamnopyranosyl–   $R_2$–H
RL 4: $R_1$–H                      $R_2$–H

**Fig. 3.** Rhamnolipids from *Pseudomonas* sp.

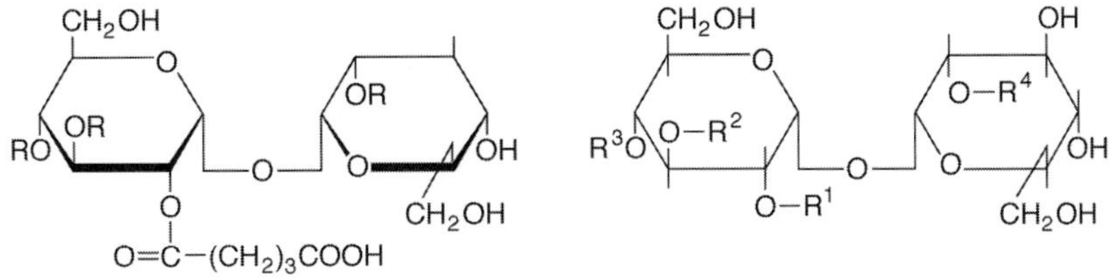

R = OC(CH)$_m$CH$_3$ m = 6 - 12

STL·1: R$^1$ ~ R$^2$ = 2 x succinoyl + 2 x alkanoyl.

STL·1: R$^1$ ~ R$^1$ = 1 x succinoyl + 2 x alkanoyl. R$^4$ = H

***Fig. 4.*** Trehalose lipids from *Rhodococcus erythropolis* (right) and *Arthrobacter* sp. (left).

Also, rhamnose is a very valuable sugar for the food industry.

TREHALOSE LIPIDS. Trehalose lipids are, in most cases, cell-wall associated. The $\alpha$-branched $\beta$-shydroxy fatty acids are usually esterified with the 6- and 6′-hydroxyl groups of the trehalose unit (Fig. 4). *Rhodococcus,* when cultivated on waste lubricant oil medium, yields 2,2′,3,4-trehalose tetraester, and *Anthrobacter* sp produces a trehalose lipid containing succinoyl residues.

Treholose tetra esters reduce the surface tension of water to 26 mN/m and interfacial tension (against *n*-hexadecane) from 40 to <5 mN/m at a concentration of 15 mg/liter.

GLUCOSE LIPIDS. These glycolipids contain 3-hydroxy fatty acids (Fig. 5). The one produced by the marine bacterial strain MM1 and Rubiwettin RG1 produced by *Serratia rubidaea* are the two important glucose lipids found in the literature.

Rubiwettin RG1 lowers the surface tension of saline to 26 mN/m. Glucose lipid from strain MM1 has the same value but also has an excellent emulsifying action. The marine bacterial strain MM1 produces anionic glucose lipid. *Alcanivorax borkumensis* produces ionic glucose lipid with tetrameric oxyacyl from side chain.

SUCROSE LIPIDS. When grown on sucorse, *Arthrobacter paraffineus* produces sucrose lipids. Acyl glucoses are formed when *Corynebacterium diphteriae* is grown on glucose as a carbon source. Figure 6 show this glycolipid.

ORNITHIN-CONTAINING LIPIDS. Ornithin-containing lipids are produced by *Pseudomonas rubescens*

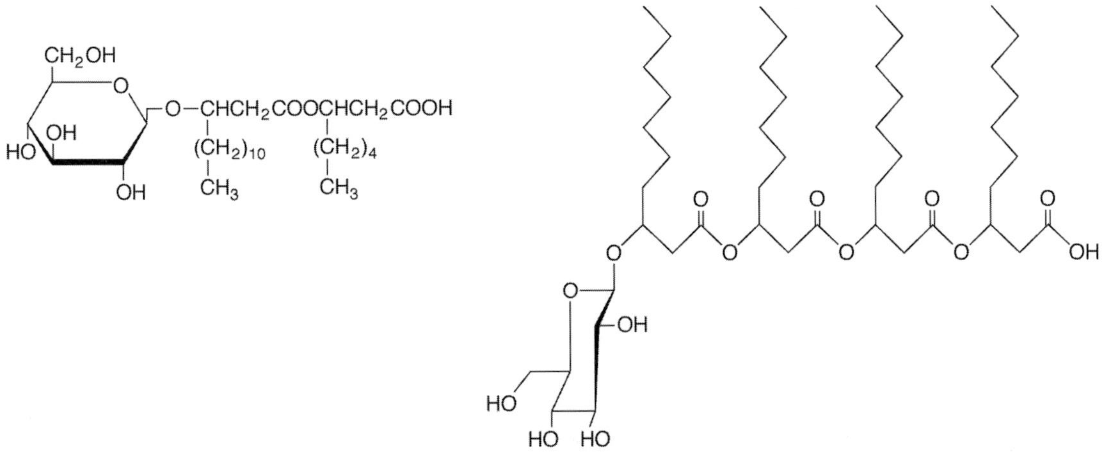

***Fig. 5.*** Glucose lipids of *Serratia rabidae* (left) and marine bacterial strain MM1 (right).

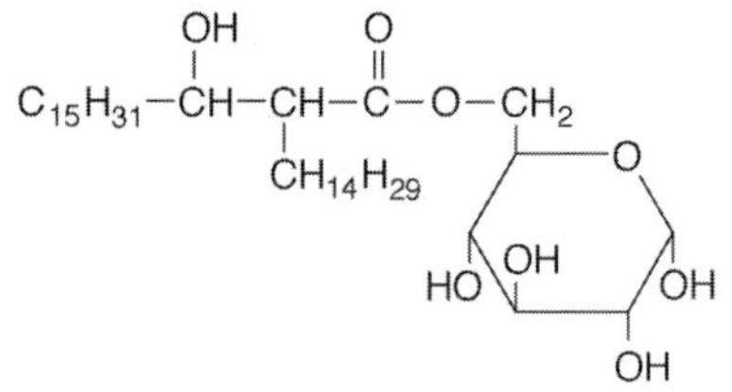

$$C_{15}H_{31}-\overset{\underset{\displaystyle OH}{|}}{CH}-\overset{\underset{\displaystyle CH_{14}H_{29}}{|}}{CH}-\overset{\overset{\displaystyle O}{\|}}{C}-O-CH_2$$

**Fig. 6.** Glucose-6-monocorynomycolate from *Corynebacterium diphteriae.*

and *Thiobacillus thiooxidans*. Structures are shown in Fig. 7.

SURFACTIN. This is a lipid produced by *B. subtilis*. The structure is given in Fig. 8.

PENTASACCHARIDE LIPIDS. The pentasaccharide lipid produced by *Nocardia corynebacteroides* SM1 is shown in Fig. 9. It is obtained by cultivation on *n*-alkanes. The surface tension of water is lowered to 26 mN/m and the interfacial tension (vs *n*-C16) to <1 mN/m at a CMC value of 30 mg/liter with this biosurfactant.

EXOPOLYSACCARIDE BIOEMULSIFIERS. Microbial exocellular polysaccharides as high-molecular-weight polymers show useful physical and mechanical properties, such as high viscosity, tensile strength, and resistance to shear. They are widely used in industry as gums, rheology modifiers, thickening agents, high-

viscosity stabilizers, gelling agents, etc. These materials are also believed to play an important role in the adaptation of microorganisms to specific echological challenges, such as in attachment and adsorption from surfaces, interface with cell surface receptors, and in the utilization of specific carbon and energy sources.

The major characteristic of these bioemulsifiers appears to be their high affinity for oil–water interfaces, thus making them excellent emulsion stabilizers by forming a stable film around the oil droplet and preventing coalescence.

One of the best studied of such bioemulsifiers is Emulsan, produced by the soil-degrading bacterium *Acinetobacter calcoaceticus* RAG-1. Emulsan is a polyanionic heteropolysaccharide bioemulsifier with a high molecular weight of $9.8 \times 10^5$. The polymer is also characterized by a reduced viscosity of more than 500 cm$^3$/g which depends on the ionic strength, pH, and temperature, Emulsan can also be produced using soybean oil. Emulsan does not appreciably reduce interfacial tension (10 dyn/cm) but binds tightly to the newly created interface and protects the oil droplets form coalescence.

OTHER BIOSURFACTANTS. There are less common glycolipids such as (3)2-dipalmitoyl-3(1)-(glucopyronsoyl-(6-decanoyl)-α-D(1,4)-glucopyranosoyl-α-D)-glucerol from *Thermotoga maritima*, bis-sulfated glycolipids from *Archaebacterium* strain 122, and unique cholesteryl glucosides from *Helicobacter pylori*, all

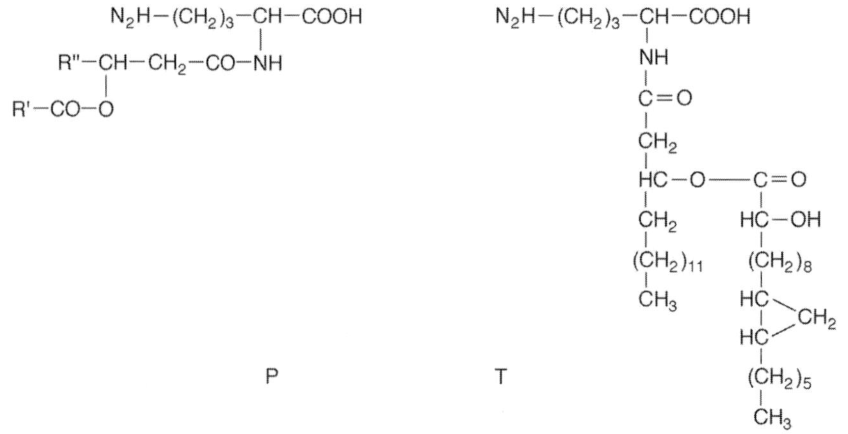

P

T

**Fig. 7.** Ornithin-containing lipids from *Pseudomonas rubescens* (P) and *Thiobacillus thiooxidants* (T).

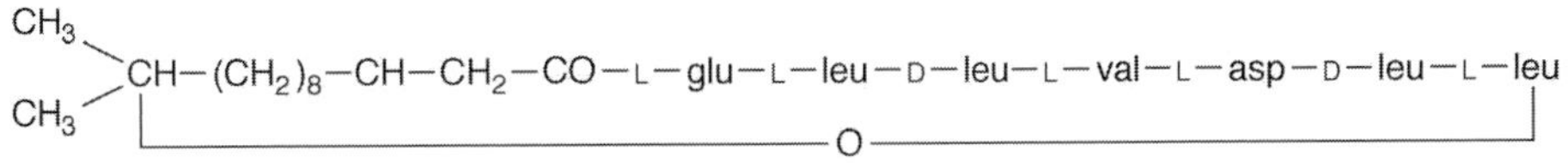

$$CH_3 \diagdown CH—(CH_2)_8—CH—CH_2—CO—L—glu—L—leu—D—leu—L—val—L—asp—D—leu—L—leu$$
CH3 ⟍ ... O

**Fig. 8.** Surfactant from *Bacillus subtilis*.

reported by different workers. In addition, a sucrose ester can be produced by *Corynebacterium hydrocarboclastus* in a medium containing sucrose.

### c. Biosurfactants Produced by Eukaryotic Cells

(1) *Yeast Biosurfactants* Yeast biosurfactants are of particular interest for applications in food and cosmetics.

SOPHOROSE LIPIDS. Sophorose lipids can be synthesized by the yeasts *Candida bombicola, Candida gropengiesseri*, and *Candida apicola*. Their hydrophillic moiety is the disaccharide sophorose (2-O-$\beta$-D-glucopyranosyl-$\beta$-D-glucopyranose) to which a hydroxy fatty acid unit is ether-linked at the 1′position. The sophorose moiety is mostly linked by lactonic bonds to the saturated or unsaturated fatty acid. Figure 10 shows the major component, the classical lactonic structure, including a 17-hydroxy C18 (un)-saturated fatty acid.

Sophorose lipids are used as high value skin moisturizers and they are also used in the petroleum industry and cosmetics and food areas. Consequently, approaches to improve the production of sophorose lipids have been numerous. For overproduction, 1:1 blends of glucose and lipophilic compounds are used as carbon sources under growth-limited conditions. Examples of successfully used lipophilic carbon sources are palm oil, safflower oil, soybean oil, ethylesters of rapeseed oil, linseed oil fatty acids, animal fats, and canola oil. Different production methods can be used, such as batch, fed-batch, resting cells, and two-stage fed batch. The maximum volumetric yields reached were higher than 340 g/liter.

With *n*-hexane as a cosubstrate, concentrations of 0.46 g/liter can be obtained when *C.* (*Torulopsis*) *apicola* IMET 4347 is used instead of *C. bombicola* ATCC 22214. This sophorolipid contains a 16-hydroxy hexadecanoic acid as the major fatty acid. Metabolic pathways for the biosynthesis of key enzymes for glycolipid production as well as metabolic regulation have been studied by many workers.

When C-10–C-14 alkanes, fatty acids/esters, and *n*-primary fatty alcohols were used to obtain sophorose lipids with a fatty acid chain shorter than 16-C atoms, none of them could be incorporated to the glycolipid. They were degraded and used for *de novo* synthesis of the C-16/C-18 fatty acids. However, theoretically 2-alkanols could be incorporated directly by a glycosidic linkage between the sophorose and the 2-hydroxyfunction of the hydrophobic moiety.

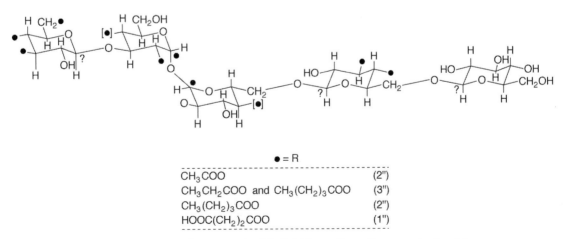

● = R

| | |
|---|---|
| CH₃COO | (2″) |
| CH₃CH₂COO and CH₃(CH₂)₃COO | (3″) |
| CH₃(CH₂)₃COO | (2″) |
| HOOC(CH₂)₂COO | (1″) |

**Fig. 9.** Structure of pentasaccharide lipid from *Nocardia corynebacteroides*.

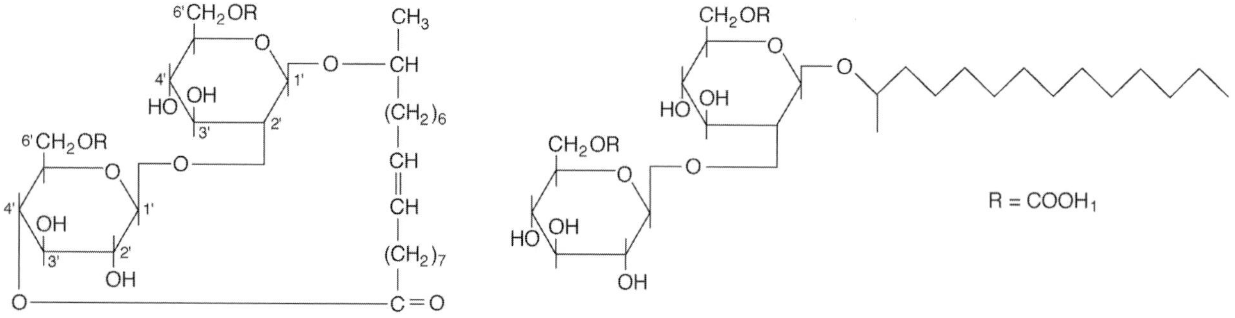

**Fig. 10.** Classical-type (left) and novel-type (right) sophorose lipid from *Candida bombicola* ATCC 22214 (Davila *et al.,* 1992; Brakemeier *et al.,* 1995).

Thus, the $(\omega\text{-}1)$-OH alkanoic acid is formed by the terminal oxidation of the non-functionalized end.

When glucose and 2-alkanols are used as carbon sources for the cultivation of *C. bombicola,* novel types of sophorose lipids are obtained as major products. Additional monooxygenation of the alcohol can also occur, yielding glucolipids containing up to four glucose units (Fig. 11). Novel sophorose lipids can be obtained from *C. bombicola* using dodecanols. The structure of microbial alkyl-sophorosides based on 1-dodecanol or 2-, 3-, or 4-dodecanones is given in Fig. 12.

MANNOSYLERYTHROTOL LIPIDS. Mannosylerythriol lipids are produced by *Candida* sp B-7 and *Candida antarctica* T-34, which are extracellularly accumulated compounds. Their structures are shown in Fig. 13. In an experiment in which the yeast were cultivated on 8% soybean oil (v/v), the total lipids reached 40 g/liter (including 80% MELs) after 8 days, whereas resting cells (similar biomass weight) led to a higher yield—47 g/liter after 6 days. The mannosylerythriol lipids reduce the surface tension and the interfacial tension against *n*-tetradecane to 28 and 2 mN/m, respectively (Table II).

## C. Enzyme-Synthesized Biosurfactants

Many isolated enzymes that catalyze hydrolysis, alcoholysis, condensation, acylation, or esterification reactions have been used for the production of various surfactants, including monoglycerides, phospholipids, glycolipids, and amino acid-based surfactants, from relatively inexpensive raw materials such as fats and plant oils. Compared with the conventional chemical synthesis, these enzymatic methods have the advantages of low energy requirement, minimal thermal degradation, high biodegradability, and high regioselectivity. Immobilized microbial lipases, such as Lipozyme from *Rhizomucor (Mucor) miehei* or lipase SP 435 from *C. antarctica* (Novo, Begsvaerd, DK), are the most frequently used enzymes. Using this technology, glycolipids such as fructose oleate, monocapryloyl-1$\alpha$-D-fructofuranose, $\beta$-1-fructopyranose-oleate, 1-fructofuranose-oleate, a mixture of C-1 and C-6 monopalmitoyl fructose, 6-octanoylglucose, and various primary monoesters of sugar alcohols such as sorbitol, mannitol, and xylibol have been produced in milligram and gram scales. Aliphatic alcohol glycosides, phenol glycosides, vitamin glycosides, glyceroglycolipids and glycolipid biosurfactants, fructose monoolates, monooleoyl glycerol, and uncommon hydroxy compounds such as 2-hydroxyethyl-trimethyl silane, which is attached to C1 glucose, are among the recently synthesized enzymatic surfactants.

Different chemical routes have been reported for the enzymatic synthesis of glycolipids. These can be grouped under several main headings:

Glycolipid synthesis without protection of group chemistry

Gycolipid synthesis via sugar acetals

Glycolipid synthesis via alkyl glycosides

Glycolipid synthesis via phenyboronic acid complexation

Akyl glycosides from glycosidase catalysis

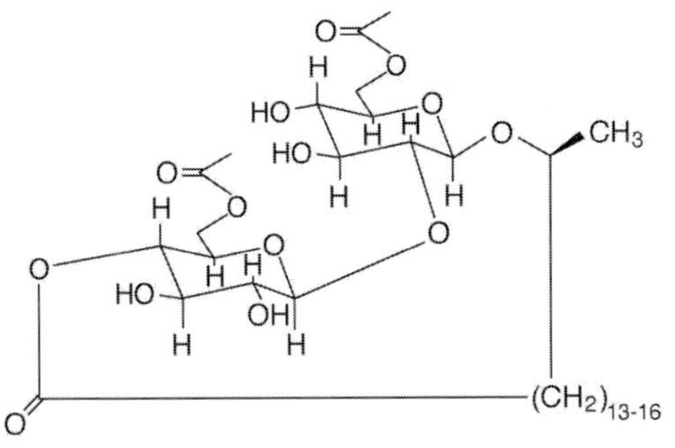

SL-Lactone

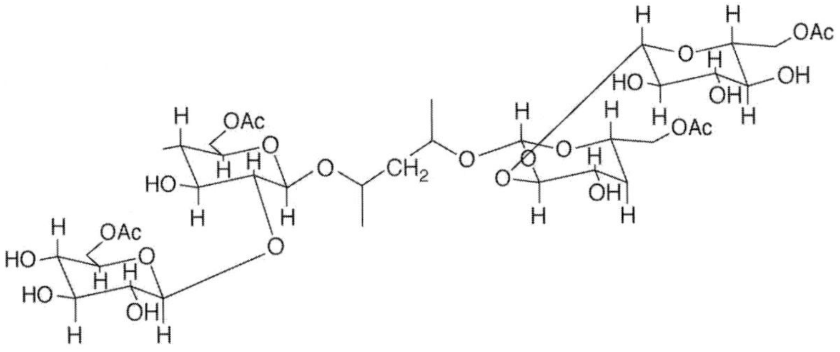

SL-A

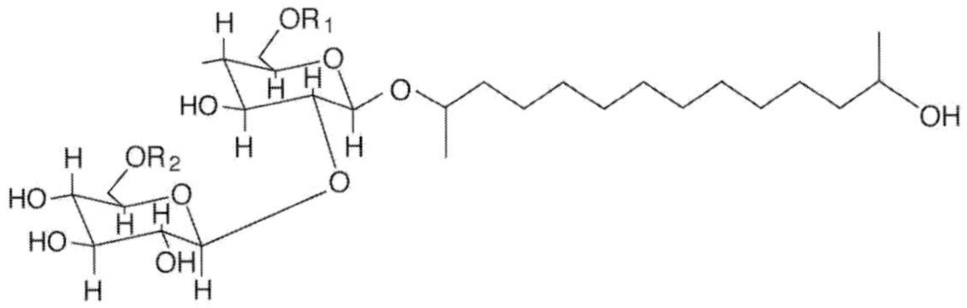

SL-B: $R_1 = COCH_3$: $R_2 = H$
SL-C: $R_1 = R_2 = COCH_3$

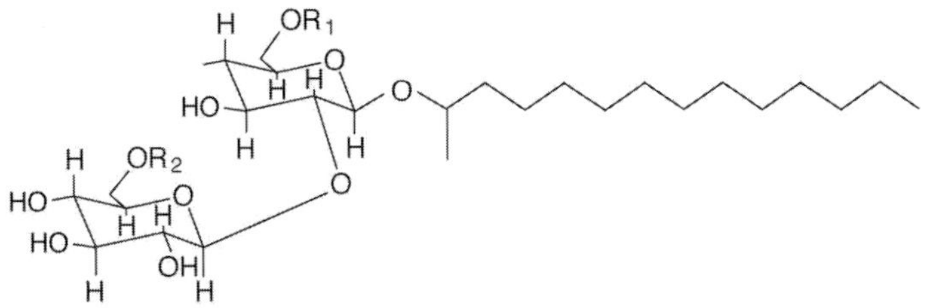

SL-D: $R_1 = R_2 = H$
SL-E: $R_1 = COCH_3$: $R_2 = H$
SL-F: $R_1 = R_2 = COCH_3$

**Fig. 11.** Molecular structure of the known sophorose lipid–lactone and the new compounds SL-A–SL-F.

Various primary monoesters of sugar alcohols such as sorbitol, mannitol, and xylibol have been produced using lipase from *Aspergillus terreus*. Glycolipids have also been synthesized by *Candida antarctica* lipase from alkyl glycosides. Sugar acetals have been successfully used to synthesize glycolipids by lipase-catalyzed reactions in good yields.

Alkyl glucides have been obtained from glycosidase catalysis. $\beta$-Xylosidase from *Aspergillus niger* has been used for the preparation of various alkyl $\beta$-xylosides from xylose and primary alcohols. Recently, uncommon hydroxy compounds such as 2-hydroxy-ethyl-trimethyl silane have been attached to C1 glucose.

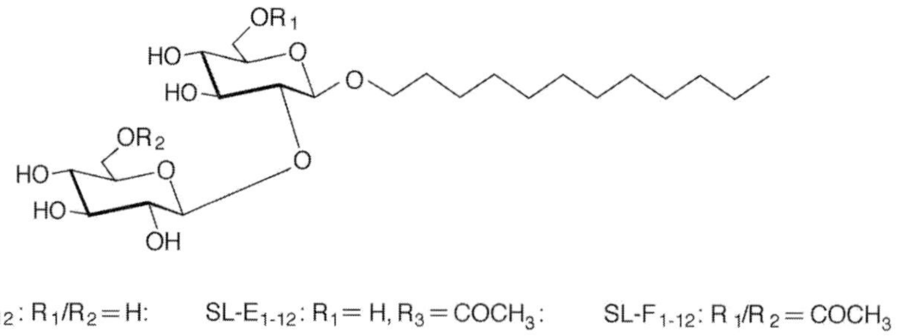
OR1
HO
O
HO
O
OR2
HO
O
O
HO
OH
SL-D1-12: R1/R2=H:
SL-E1-12: R1= H, R3=COCH3:
SL-F1-12: R1/R2=COCH3

*Fig. 12.* Structure of the novel sophorose lipids (major components) after cultivation on glucose-1-dodecanol.

Table III compares the major features of microbial- and enzyme-synthesized surfactants.

Microbial biosurfactants have low production costs, whereas enzymatic processes have lower recovery costs. However, many potential applications of microbial biosurfactants (e.g., as *in situ* bioremediation) do not require high-purity products. Therefore, the potential applications of the enzyme-synthesized surfactants are at the more expensive end of the market, such as pharmaceutical or cosmetics. Major disadvantages of enzymatic processes are high enzyme costs and the difficulty in solubilizing both hydrophilic and hydrophobic substrates in the reaction media. Developments in enzyme technology together with non-aqueous phase kinetics will immensely contribute toward the elucidation of these issues.

Similarly, the main disadvantage of high recovery costs and large liquid waste volumes are likely to be eliminated as a result of future research in strain development, metabolic engineering, and fermentation technology (i.e., recycling and whole cell immobilization).

## III. BIOSURFACTANT PRODUCTION

Biosurfactants can be produced under growth-associated and growth-limiting conditions as well as by resting cells and by addition of precursors. The different production methods of microbial biosurfactants are presented in Table IV.

### A. Media Formulation

Carbon, nitrogen, and phosphate sources, metal ions, and other additives used in media formulation may play a critical role in the production and yield of biosurfactants.

Carbon source is quite important. For example, *Pseudomonas* species show the best biosurfactant production when *n*-alkanes are present in the medium for rhamnolipid production. On the other hand, a *Pseudomonas* sp. showes significantly higher production rates when grown on vegetable oils in comparison to liquid hydrocarbon, hexane. Also, *P. aeruginosa* UW-1 produces rhamnolipid in vegetable oil-containing media. *Nocardia erythropolis* (ATCC

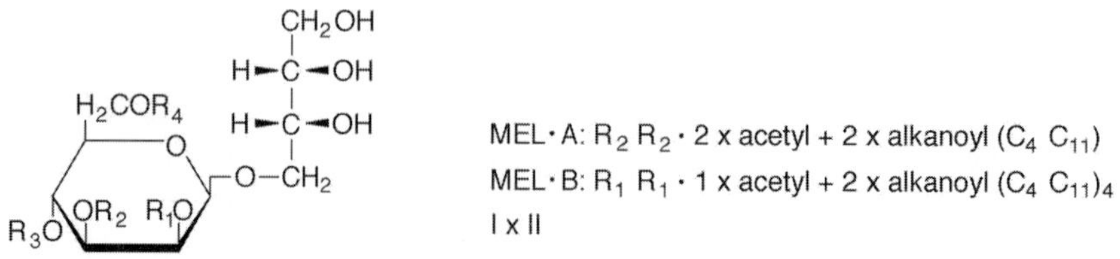
CH2OH
H-C-OH
H2COR4
H-C-OH
O
O-CH2
R3O
OR2 R1O
MEL·A: R2 R2 · 2 x acetyl + 2 x alkanoyl (C4 C11)
MEL·B: R1 R1 · 1 x acetyl + 2 x alkanoyl (C4 C11)4
I x II

*Fig. 13.* Mannosylerythriol lipids from *Candida antarctica* T-34 (Kitamoto *et al.*, 1990a,b).

| Biosurfactant | Microorganism | Carbon source | Surface tension (Nm/m) | Interfacial tension (Nm/m) | Reference |
|---|---|---|---|---|---|
| Glycolipids | *Rhodococcus aurantiacus* | n-Alkanes | 26 | 0.35 | Ramsav *et al.*, 1988 |
| Glycolipids | *Rhodococcus* sp. strain H13A | Hexadecane | na | 0.02[b] | Finnerty and Singer, 1984 |
| Glycolipids | *Torulopsis apicola* | Alkane/carbohydrate | 30 | <0.9[b] | Hommel *et al.*, 1987 |
| Pentasaccharide lipid | *Nocardia* | n-Alkane | 26 | <1[c] | Powalla *et al.*, 1989 |
| Rhamnolipid | *Pseudomonos aeruginosa* | Glucose | 29 | 0.25 | Guerra *et al.*, 1986; Reiling *et al.*, 1986; Robert *et al.*, 1989 |
| Rubiwettins | *Serratia rubidoea* | Glycerol | 25 | na | Matsuyama *et al.*, 1990 |
| Sophorose lipids | *Candida bombicola* | Glucose/oleic acid | 33 | 1.8 | Cooper and Paddock, 1984; Gobbert *et al.*, 1984; Asmer, 1988 |
| Trehalose mono- and di-corynomycolates | *Nocardia Corynebacteroides Rhodococcus erythropolis* | n-Alkanes | 32–36 | 14–17 | Raap *et al.*, 1979; Powalla *et al.*, 1989 |
| Lipopeptides | *Bacillus licheniformis* JF2 | Glucose | 27 | 0.016[b] | Jenneman *et al.*, 1983; Javaheri *et al.*, 1985; Lin *et al.*, 1990 |
| Lipopeptides | *Bacillus licheniformis* 86 | Glucose | 27 | 0.36[a] | Horowitz *et al.*, 1990 |
| Viscosin | *Pseudomonas fluresencens* | Glycerol | 26.5 | na | Neu *et al.*, 1990 |
| Serrawettin | *Serratia marcescens* | Glycerol | 28.8–33.9 | na | Matsuyama *et al.*, 1985, 1986 |
| Surfactin | *Bacillus subtilis* | Glucose | 27–32 | 1[c] | Arima *et al.*, 1968; Cooper *et al.*, 1981; Sheppard and Mulligan, 1987; Sandrin *et al.*, 1990 |
| Fatty acids | *Corynebacterium lepus* | Kerosene/alkanes | <30 | 2[d] | Cooper *et al.*, 1979; Gerson and Zajic, 1978 |
| Fatty acid + neutral lipids | *Nocardia erythropolis* | Hexadecane | 32 | <3 | MacDonald *et al.*, 1981 |
| Protein–carbohydrate complex | *Pseudomonas fluorescens* 378 | n-Alkanes | 27 | na | Persson *et al.*, 1988 |
| Phosphatidylethanol amines | *Rhodococcus erythropolis* | n-Alkanes | 30 | <1 | Kretschmer *et al.*, 1982 |
| na | *Corynebacterium insidiosum* | Hexadecane | 28.5 | 0.55[c] | Akit *et al.*, 1981 |

[a] From Georgiou *et al.* (1992). na, not available.
[b] Interfacial tension measured against decane.
[c] Interfacial tension measured against hexadecane.
[d] Interfacial tension measured against kerosene.

4277) can be grown on *n*-hexadecane as the sole C source to yield a biosurfactant. Sometimes the hydrogen chain length also has an effect. *Corynebacterium hydrocarboclastus* gives the best yields when linear alkanes of chain length C12, C13, and C14, are present.

In the production of sophorose lipids from yeasts such as *C. bombicola*, *C. gropengiesseri*, and *C. apicola*, blends of carbohydrates and hydrocarbons have been observed to give the highest yields. The specific productivity increased using mixtures of glucose or sucrose with vegetable oils from soybean, sunflower, safflower, and ethylesters of rapeseed oil and linseed oil fatty acids. On the other hand, *C. bombicola* also gave a very high yield on whey concentrate and rapeseed oil without consuming lactose. Moreover, it was

**TABLE III**
**Major Characteristics of Microbial Biosurfactants and Enzyme-Synthesized Surfactants**[a]

| Feature | Microbial biosurfactants | Enzyme-synthesized surfactants |
|---|---|---|
| Advantages | Biodegradability | Biodegradibility |
| | Diversity | Ease of structural modification |
| | Low production costs | Low recovery costs |
| | *In situ* applications | Ease of purification |
| Disadvantages | High recovery costs | High enzyme costs |
| | High waste volume | Low solubility of substrates |
| Key points for further developments | Strain improvement | Enzyme immobilization |
| | Whole cell immobilization | Enhanced enzyme stability and activity |
| | Improved fermentation technology | Multiple-phase systems |
| | Metabolic engineering | Supercritical fluid technology |

[a] From Lin (1996).

observed that the glycolipid production with the same culture increased considerably when the vegetable oils were added in the later exponential growth phase.

The nitrogen source is also important. The nature and the concentration of the N source affect biosurfactant production by *A. paraffineus* ATCC 19558. Rhamnolipid production increases when nitrogen is exhausted in the medium. Nitrogen limitation is also important in the production of sophorose lipids. The ability of *B. subtilis* strain to grow and produce biosurfactants on different carbon and nitrogen sources has been studied under thermophilic conditions. Production of biosurfactants by *Pseudomonas* sp., *Acineobacter* sp., and *Torulopsis* sp. can be regulated by the ratio of nitrogen to carbon source or the concentra-

**TABLE IV**
**Methods for Production of Biosurfactants by Microorganisms**

Cell growth-associated production of biosurfactants
   Induction of production by lipophilic substrates
   Increase in production by optimization of medium composition
   Increase in production by optimization of environmental factors such as pH, temperature, aeration, and
      agitation speed
   Increase in production by addition of reagents such as penicillin, ethambutol, and EDTA which cause a
      change in cell wall permeability
   Increase in production by addition of reagents such as alkanes, kerosene, and EDTA which cause a
      detachment of cell wall-bounded biosurfactants into the medium
Biosurfactant production by growing cells under growth-limiting conditions
   Production under N limitation
   Production under limitation of multivalent cations
   Increase in production under growth-limiting conditions by a change of environmental conditions such
      as pH or temperature
Biosurfactant production by resting cells
   Production by resting-free cells
   Production by resting-immobilized cells
   Production by resting-immobilized cells with simultaneous product removal
Biosurfactant production by growing, resting-free, and resting-immobilized cells in the presence of
   precursors

tion of yeast extract which contains nitrogen, phosphate, and all oligoelements required for yeast growth and production of sophorose lipids. When inorganic salts are used as a nitrogen source, the microorganisms prefer ammonium rather than nitrate forms of nitrogen. Urea can be utilized both as a sole source of nitrogen and in combination with an inorganic nitrogen salt, yielding relatively high surfactant concentration in the broth.

Amino acids such as aspartic acid, asparagine, glycine, and glutamic acid in mineral salts medium, as well as yeast extract, peptone, bactotryptone, and nutrient broth, can be used. The structure of surfactin has been shown to be influenced by amino acid concentration in the media to produce a Va-7 or Leu-7 surfactin. *Rhodococcus* sp. shows maximum growth and biosurfactant production on medium containing 2% (v/v) *n*-paraffin and nitrate as the N source and its product is a primary metabolite that can be produced in continuous culture.

The production of biosurfactants is also affected by the phosphate source. The production of lipopeptide biosurfactant by *Bacillus licheniformis* JF-2 was increased from 35 to 110 mg day m$^{-3}$ by reducing the phosphate concentration from 100 to 50 mmol day m$^{-3}$.

The addition of iron or manganese salts increases the yield of surfactin by *B. subtilis*. The yield of biosurfactant production is either enhanced or inhibited by the addition of antibiotics, such as penicillin or chloramphenicol. 2-Bromooctanoic acid drastically inhibits the lipid synthesis under growing and resting cell conditions of *C. antarctica*.

Culture conditions such as pH, temperature, dissolved oxygen, and ionic strength also influence biosurfactant production. The temperature is especially important in the case of *A. parraineus* ATTCC 19558, *R. erithropolis*, and *Pseudomonas* sp. *Bacillus subtilis* C9 had been observed to produce a three fold higher yield of a lipopeptide under oxygen-limited conditions compared to that under oxygen-sufficient conditions.

In order to reduce production costs, inexpensive and commercially available substrates such as rice hull hydrolysate, starch waste liquors, domestic waste, potato processing wastes, and why can be used in biosurfactant production. Olive oil mill effluent, whey, and peat pressate have been used for biosurfactant production. *Pseudomonas aeruginosa* GS3 produces rhamnolipid biosurfactants during growth on molasses and com-steep liquor as the primary carbon and nitrogen sources, respectively.

## B. Fermentation

Similar to other bioprocesses, the goals in the production of biosurfactants are to maximize the productivity (i.e., grams/liter/hour), to increase the yield of biosurfactants from the carbon source, and to achieve high final concentrations. Furthermore, it is important to reduce the production and/or accumulation of other metabolic products that may interfere with the physical properties or the recovery of the surface-active agent.

Since biosurfactants are a diverse group of compounds produced by a variety of microbial species, it is difficult to develop general guidelines for process development. Production must be optimized for individual cases. Although most biosurfactants are released into the culture medium throughout the exponential phase, some can also be produced by resting cells or by immobilized biocatalysts.

In some cases, the biosurfactants produced during a part of the growth cycle are subsequently either inactivated or incorporated into other metabolites. For example, *Corynebacterium lepus* produces two distinct surface-active compounds during the course of the fermentation. Surface-active corynomycolic acids produced at the early stage of growth are rapidly incorporated into lipopeptides, the major surfactants in the latter phase of the fermentation.

*Bacillus licheniformis* JF-2 grown in minimal media exhibits an interesting pattern of biosurfactant production. A change in the interfacial tension of the fermentation broth is observed due to the accumulation of the active agent reaching a maximum in the mid-exponential phase and subsequently decreasing rapidly. Initially, the reason was thought to be its conversion into a metabolite with no surface activity. However, this was later shown to be the result of biosurfactant uptake by the stationary phase cells.

The production of biosurfactants can be carried out using batch or continuous fermentation (at low dilution rates). The production of biosurfactants that

**TABLE V**
**Application of Biosurfactants**

| Area | Use | Effect | Reference |
|---|---|---|---|
| Metals | Concentration of ores, cutting and forming, casting, rust and scale removal, plating | Wetting, foaming, emulsifying, lubrication, corrosion inhibition in rolling oils, cutting oils, mold release additives in pickling and electric cleaning, electrolytic plating | Kosaric, 1996 |
| Paper | Pulp treatment, paper machine, calendar | Deresinification, washing, defoaming, color leveling and dispersing, wetting and levering, coating and coloring | Kosaric, 1996 |
| Paint and protective coating | Pigment preparation, latex paints, waxes and polishes | Dispersion and wetting of pigment during grinding, emulsification, stabilize latex, retard sedimentation and pigment separation, stabilize emulsions, antistat | Kosaric, 1996 |
| Petroleum products and production | Drilling fluids, workover of producing wells, producing wells, second recovery, refined products | Emulsify oil, disperse solids, modify rheological properties of drilling fluids for oil and gas wells, emulsify and disperse sludge and sediment in cleanout of wells, demulsifying crude petroleum, inhibit corrosion of equipment in flooding operations, preferential wetting detergent sludge dispersant and corrosive inhibitor in fuel oils crank case oils and turbine oils | Yarbrough and Coty, 1983; Tanner *et al.*, 1991; Hitzman, 1983; Wagner, 1991; Nelson and Launt, 1991; Bayrant *et al.*, 1993; Zhang and Zhang, 1993; Sheehy, 1990; Shennan and Levi, 1987; Bubela, 1985; Singer and Finnerty, 1984 |
| Textiles | Preparation of fibers, dyeing and printing, finishing of textiles | Detergent and emulsifier in raw wool scoaring, dispersant in viscouse rayon spin bath, lubricant and antistat in spinning of hydrophobic filaments, wetting penetration, solubilization emulsification, dye leveling, detergency, finishing formulations, softening, antistatic additive to finishes | Masuoka *et al.*, 1998 |
| Building and construction | Paving, concrete, ceramic | Improve bond of asphalt to gravel and sand, promote air entrainment | Kosaric, 1996 |
| Agriculture | Phosphate fertilizers, spray application | Prevent caking during storage, wetting, dispersing, suspending of powdered pesticides and emulsification of pesticides solutions | Kosaric, 1996 |
| Elastomers and plastics | Emulsion polymerization, foam polymers, latex adhesive, plastic articles, plastic coating and laminating | Wetting, solubilization, emulsification of monomers, introduction of air, control of cell size, improve bond strength, antistatic agents | Kosaric, 1996 |

*continues*

*Continued*

| Area | Use | Effect | Reference |
|---|---|---|---|
| Food and beverages | Food processing plants, fruits and vegetables, bakery and ice cream, crystallization of sugar, cooking fat and oils | For cleaning and sanitizing, improve removal of pesticides and wax coating, solubilization flower oils, control consistency, regard stalling, improve washing, reduce processing time, prevent spattering due to superheat and water | Kachholz and Schlingman, 1987; Velikonja and Kosaric, 1993; Li et al., 1998; Pierce and Heilman, 1997 |
| Industrial cleaning | Janitorial supplies, descaling, soft goods | Detergents and sanitizers, wetting agents and corrosion inhibitors in acid cleaning of boiler tubes and heat exchangers | Kosaric, 1996 |
| Cosmetics and pharmaceuticals | Insect repellent, antacid, bath products, acne pads, antidandruff products, contact lense solution, hair color and care products, deodorant, nail care, body massage accessories, lipstick, lipmaker, eye shadow, mascara, soap, toothpaste and polish, denture cleaner, adhesives, antiperspirant, lubricated condoms, baby products, food care, mousse, antiseptics, shampoo, conditioner, shave and depilatory products, moisturizer, health and beauty products | Emulsifier, foaming agent, solubilizer, wetting agent, cleanser, antimicrobial agent, mediator of enzyme action | Klekner and Kosaric, 1993; Abe et al., 1980; Tsutsumi et al., 1980; Yamane, 1987 |
| Pollution control | Soil bioremediation, oil storage tank cleanup, removal of oil spills | Emulsifiers, deemulsifiers | Lo et al., 1997; Ban et al., 1998; Hong et al., 1998; Bregnard et al., 1998; Bai et al., 1998; Ike et al., 1998; Torrens et al., 1998; Mulligan et al., 1997; Carvalho et al., 1997; Takasima et al., 1997; Noordman et al., 1998; Ryoo et al., 1997; Rojas et al., 1996; Rocha and Infante, 1997; Zhang et al., 1997; Banat et al., 1991; Lillienberg et al., 1992 |

can be produced by resting cells, such as the glycolipids by *Torulopsis bombicola,* can be carried out by immobilized biocatalyst. It is possible to further enhance the yield through on-line removal using an adsorption column or by foam fractionation. Other fermentation techniques used to enhance production of biosurfactants include applications of an airlift fermentor and aqueous two-phase fermentation.

In addition to the traditional submerged fermentation technology, other fermentation methods have been employed for the production of secondary metabolites. For example, the production of surfactin in solid-state fermentation on soybean curd residue using a recombinant *B. subtilis* has been reported in which the yield was at least four times higher than that in submerged fermentation. The specific production rate of teracycline by *Streptomyces aurefaciens* using self-cycling fermentation was shown to be higher than that using traditional batch fermentation. Self-cycling fermentation is a semi-continuous, computer-controlled fermentation operation, with the level of dissolved oxygen as the control parameter.

In order to reduce production costs, a multiorganism strategy for biosurfactant production is proposed. Using this strategy, microbial single-cell oil is obtained from *Lipomyces* and/or *Chlorella*. The single-cell oil obtained is used as a substrate for the production of glycolipid by *C. bombicola*. Recently, it was reported that sophorose lipids can also be produced from deproteinized whey and rapeseed oil in a two-stage fed-batch process using *C. bombicola* ATCC 22214 and *Cryptococcus curvatus* ATCC 20509.

## IV. PRODUCT RECOVERY

The separation and concentration of biosurfactants from the production medium can account for a large fraction of the total production costs. Often, the low concentration and amphiphilic character of these compounds present serious drawbacks to efficient separation. Fortunately, for most applications the final degree of product purity is not very important as long as the final preparation exhibits the desired properties. As a result, the separation of biosurfactants for preparative purposes typically involves only a few steps, such as precipitation, organic extraction, and adsorption chromatography.

The optimum methodology for biosurfactant isolation is a function of the physicochemical properties of the desired biosurfactants as well as the process parameters. When water-insoluble hydrocarbons are used as the carbon sources, it may be necessary to remove the unused hydrocarbons before the isolation of biosurfactants is attempted. In one study, refrigeration at 40°C was shown to be effective in solidifying the unassimilated hexadecane and affecting yeast set-

tling for isolation of bioemulsfier from *Candida lipolytica.*

The isolation of water-soluble extracellular biosurfactants generally involves various concentration steps, whereas the isolation of membrane-associated or water-insoluble extracellular biosurfactants is relatively easy. For example, membrane-associated biosurfactants, such as the phospholipids from *Micrococcus cerificans,* can be easily isolated from the cell mass by organic extraction. Water-insoluble biosurfactants, such as the glycolipids produced by *C. bombicola,* can be separated from the broth as heavy oils following centrifugation.

Specific examples are available in the literature for the different methods employed. Biosurfactants from *Nocardia amerae,* for example, have been isolated by methanol precipitation, whereas rhamnolipids from *P. aeruginosa* have been isolated by acidification of culture media followed by extraction with a chloroform/methanol solvent. Recovery of biosurfactants produced by *Rhodococcus* sp. H13A is accomplished using XM 50 diafiltration and isopropanol precipitation. The advantage of this technique is that it separates the glycolipid from co-isolated proteins.

In other studies, bioprocess modifications have been attempted. An aqueous two-phase fermentation system has been developed which separates surfactants on the basis of their charge. In this two-phase system, cationic surfactants are separated to the bottom phase and anionic surfactants to the top phase with polyethylene glycol and dextran. *Bacillus subtilis* cells move into the bottom phase, whereas the biosurfactants (surfactin) partitiones into the top phase. Charged biosurfactants, such as surfactin by *B. subtilis,* can be isolated by adjusting the supernatant pH to isoelectric points of desired biosurfactants. Ice-cold acetone and ethanol, and other salts such as ammonium sulfate, can also be used to precipitate biosurfactants from the fermentation medium. Organic extraction is also used as an alternative or in addition to precipitation. A high partition coefficient in the extracting phase can be obtained by the appropriate selection of organic solvent and adjustment of the ionic strength and pH of the aqueous solution.

Ultrafiltration can be used successfully to recover biosurfactants from the fermentation broth. The molecular weight cut-off of the ultrafiltration membranes, which is two orders of magnitude larger than the biosurfactant molecular weight, has been used for biosurfactant concentration without significant loss of biosurfactant because of the formation of supramolecular structures such as micelles at biosurfactant concentrations higher than their CMC.

For large-scale or continuous isolation of biosurfactants from the fermentation supernatant, adsorption chromatography on ion-exchange resins, activated carbon, or hydrophobic adsorbents such as Amberlite XAD-2 are effective. To further purify the biosurfactants, partition liquid chromatography with silica gel, gel filtration with lipophilic resins such as Sephadex LH 20, and preparative TLC can also be used. Moreover, homogeneous biosurfactant preparations can be obtained by preparative reverse-phase chromatography.

Foam fractionation is an effective recovery method for the removal of Lichenysin $\beta$ produced by *B. licheniformis* JF-2. Surfactin produced by *B. subtilis* can be recovered from fermentation broth by ultrafiltration with a 30-kDa MWCO membrane.

# V. APPLICATIONS OF BIOSURFACTANTS

Biosurfactants reported to be used for many different purposes and new application areas appear continuously in the literature. Recent developments in the microbial overproduction of glycolipids with uncommon structures, together with the rapid progress in enzymatic catalysis yielding glycolipids in nonconventional media, have focused intensive attention to the surfactant industry.

Depending on their molecular structures, some of these hydrophilic biosurfactants are suitable for o/w emulsification purposes, whereas the more lipophilic compounds seem to be suitable for wetting or coating. Table V summarizes the different applications with respect to industrial sectors.

The recent developments in the field of production and recovery of biosurfactants indicate that biosurfactants will be providing promising substitutes to chemically synthesized surfactants in the new millennium. However, development of novel approaches which are industrially applicable and economically acceptable requires comprehensive studies, especially in the area of bioprocess engineering.

## See Also the Following Articles

Industrial Fermentation Processes • Lipids, Microbially Produced

## Bibliography

Banat, I. M. (1995). Biosurfactants production and possible uses in microbial enhanced oil recovery and oil pollution remediation: A review. *Biosource Technol,* **51,** 1–12.

Brakemeier, A., Lang, S., Wullbrant, D., Merschel, L., Benninghoven, A., Buschmann, N., and Wagner, F. (1995). Novel sophorose lipids from microbial conversion of 2-alkanols. *Biotechnol. Lett.* **17,** 1183–1188.

Brakemeier, A., Lang, S., Wullbrant, D., and Lang, S. (1998). Microbial alkyl-sophorosides based on 1-dodecanol or 2-, 3-, or 4-dodecanones. *Biotech. Lett.* **20**(3), 215–218.

Cairns, W. L., and Gray, N. C. (1987). "Biosurfactants and Biotechnology" (N. Kosaric, Ed.) Dekker, New York.

Georgiou, G., Lin, S.-C., and Sharma, M. M. (1992). Surface active compounds from microorganisms. *Biotechnology* **10,** 60–65.

Kosaric, N. (Ed.) (1993). "Biosurfactants." Dekker, New York.

Kosaric, N. (1996). "Biosurfactants in Biotechnology, Volume 6" (M. Roehr, Ed.), pp. 659–671. VCH, Weinheim.

Lin, S. C. (1996). "Biosurfactants: Recent advantages". *J. Chem. Tech. Biotechnol.* **66,** 109–120.

Passeri, A., Schmidt, M., Haffner, T., Wray, V., Lang, S., and Wagner, F. (1992). "Marine biosurfaktants, IV. Production, characterization and biosynthesis of an anionic glucose lipid from the marine bacterial strain MM1". *Appl. Microbiol. Biotechnol.* **37,** 281–286.

Wagner, F., and Lang, S. (1996). Microbial and enzymatic synthesis of interfacial active glycolipids. Paper presented at the 4th World Surfactants Congress, Barcelona, pp. 3–7.

# Biotransformations

## Herbert L. Holland

*Brock University*

## GLOSSARY

**abzyme** A catalytic antibody raised in response to an antigen that is designed as a model of the transition state for the reaction to be catalyzed.

**diastereoselectivity** The ability of a catalyst or reagent to distinguish between stereoisomers other than enantiomers.

**enantiomeric excess** The difference in the percentage composition of a mixture of two enantiomers.

**enantioselectivity** The ability of a catalyst or reagent to distinguish between two mirror-image isomers.

**immobilization** The entrapment of a biocatalyst in an inert three-dimensional matrix, or the attachment of a biocatalyst onto a solid surface, by chemical or physical means.

**meso selectivity** The ability of a catalyst or reagent to distinguish between two chemically identical but stereochemically different parts of a single molecule that contains chiral centers and a symmetry plane.

**prochiral selectivity** The ability of a catalyst or reagent to distinguish between two chemically identical but stereochemically different parts of a single molecule that does not contain a chiral center.

**(R)- and (S)-configuration** The definition of the three-dimensional arrangement of four different groups on a central atom as defined by the Cahn–Ingold–Prelog rules.

**regioselectivity** The ability of a catalyst or reagent to direct reactivity towards a particular portion or region of a molecule.

**replacement culture** The resuspension of a microorganism in a medium other than its growth medium.

**transition state analog** A small molecule designed as a close model for the transition state of a reaction and used as an antigen to raise catalytic antibodies.

**BIOTRANSFORMATION,** or biocatalysis, is the use of biological agents to effect specific chemical changes on compounds that are not part of their normal biochemistry. These conversions of xenobiotic compounds can be carried out by intact microbial cells, plant cells, isolated enzymes, or catalytic antibodies, and they result in the formation of novel or useful products that are often difficult or impossible to obtain by conventional chemical means. This definition differentiates biotransformation from biosynthesis or metabolic chemistry, both of which are concerned with reactions carried out by biological systems on components of their natural biochemistry, and from biodegradation, which is concerned with metabolic breakdown and the elimination of xenobiotic materials from a biological system. The distinguishing feature of biotransformation is its use for the preparation of products of defined chemical structure that are related to the substrate or starting material for the reaction by only a small number of chemical changes and in many cases by changes brought about by the action of only a single enzyme.

## I. HISTORY AND DEVELOPMENT

### A. The Evolution of Whole Cell-Catalyzed Biotransformation

Biotransformation reactions were reported in the chemical literature of the nineteenth century but were not fully utilized for preparative purposes until the 1930s when the conversions of D-sorbitol to L-sorbose by *Acetobacter suboxydans* and benzaldehyde into (R)-phenylacetyl carbinol by yeast (Fig. 1) were developed as part of the synthetic routes for

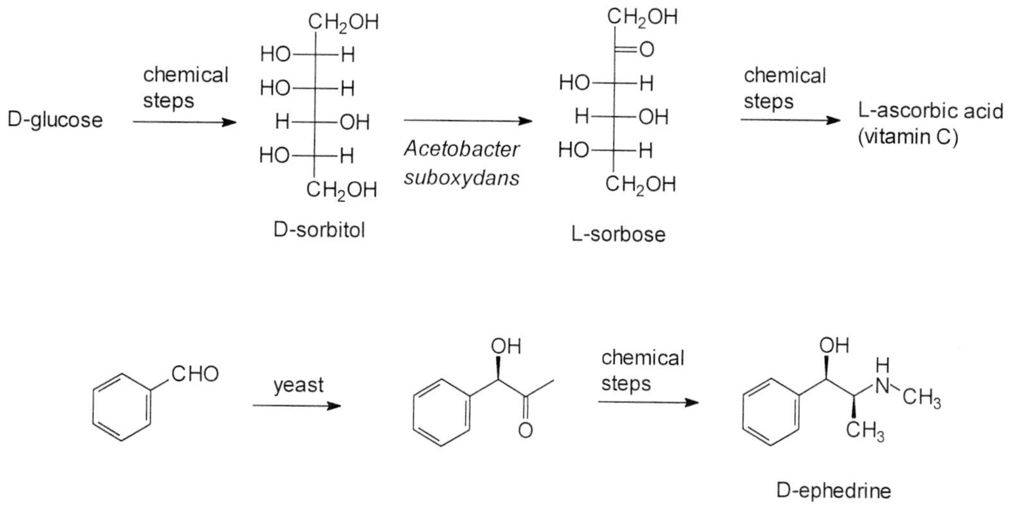

**Fig. 1.** Early applications of biotransformations.

the production of L-ascorbic acid (vitamin C) and D-ephedrine, respectively.

A major impetus in the development of biotransformation as a tool for synthetic chemistry was provided by the report in 1952 of the conversion of the steroid hormone progesterone to its 11α-hydroxy derivative by the fungus *Rhizopus arrhizus* (Fig. 2). The product of this biotransformation served as a key intermediate in the manufacture of corticosteroids. Its production using *R. arrhizus* and *R. stolonifer* triggered intensive activity focussed on the hydroxylation of a large variety of steroid and other molecules by a wide range of biological catalysts that continues to this day and represents a type of reaction that remains impossible to duplicate by chemical means.

Parallel with the growth of steroid hydroxylation during the 1950s and 1960s was the discovery and development of other whole cell-catalyzed biotransformation reactions, notably the side-chain degradation of sterols, the Baeyer–Villiger oxidation of ketones to esters, redox reactions resulting in the

interconversion of alcohol and carbonyl groups, dehydrogenation reactions, and hydrolytic reactions of esters and amides, particularly those applicable to the production of the β-lactam antibiotics. These common biotransformation processes are illustrated in Fig. 3.

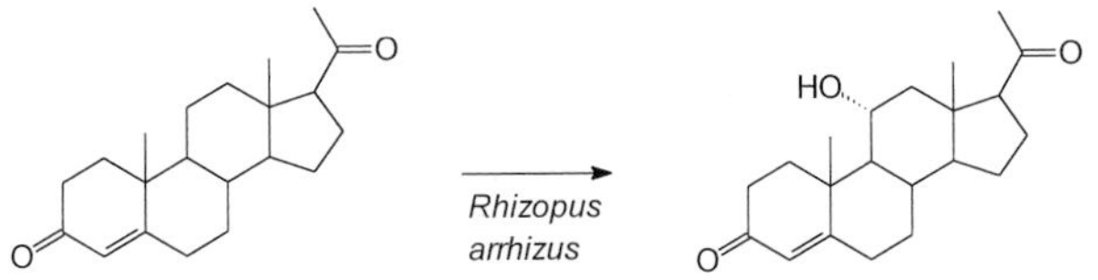

## B. Biotransformations Using Isolated Enzymes

With advances in fermentation technology came the advent of cheaper enzymes, and the majority of biotransformations using isolated enzymes date from the post-1970 era. The range of reactions currently known to be catalyzed by isolated enzymes is vast and apparently limited only by the ease of isolation and the stability, and hence cost, of these biocatalysts. The influence of genetic engineering and recombinant DNA techniques in this field holds the potential to facilitate production of heretofore expensive enzymes and perhaps to partially or completely remove many of the current limitations on the application of isolated enzymes for biotransformations.

## C. Biotransformation in the Modern Era

The rapid growth in the field of biotransformations since 1970 is illustrated by the analysis shown in

**Fig. 2.** Hydroxylation of progesterone by *Rhizopus arrhizus.*

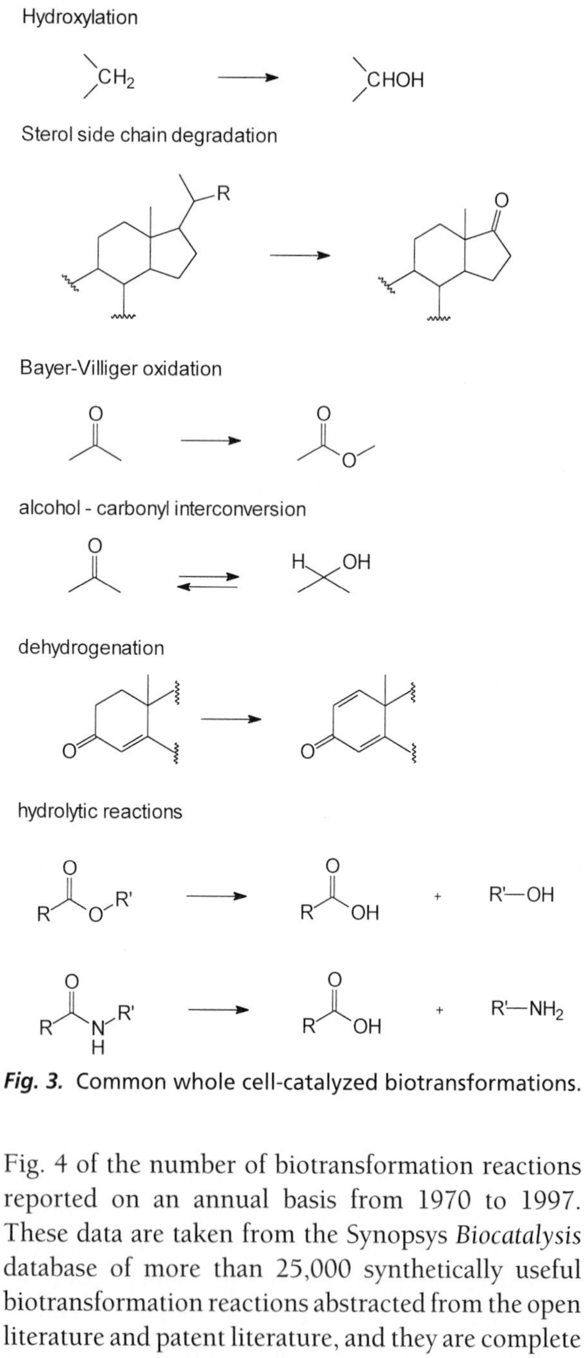

Hydroxylation

$$\diagdown CH_2 \longrightarrow \diagdown CHOH$$

Sterol side chain degradation

Bayer-Villiger oxidation

alcohol - carbonyl interconversion

dehydrogenation

hydrolytic reactions

**Fig. 3.** Common whole cell-catalyzed biotransformations.

Fig. 4 of the number of biotransformation reactions reported on an annual basis from 1970 to 1997. These data are taken from the Synopsys *Biocatalysis* database of more than 25,000 synthetically useful biotransformation reactions abstracted from the open literature and patent literature, and they are complete for the period up to 1996. Data for 1997 are only partially complete. Particularly striking is the almost exponential growth during the period from 1982 to 1992, and there is no apparent diminution in the increase in biotransformations reported since that time.

Figure 5, which is based on data from the same source as that used for Fig. 4, illustrates the interna-

tional nature of this area by analysis of the country of origin of the literature citations for 4800 whole cell-catalyzed biotransformations for the period since 1980. Not surprisingly, the field is dominated by the United States and Japan, but there has been substantial contributions from European and other sources.

## II. SCOPE AND UTILITY

### A. Types of Biocatalysts

The range of biocatalysts for biotransformation reactions is illustrated in Table I, which presents a summary of the number of different biocatalytic agents that have been reported to carry out 10 or more biotransformation reactions.

### B. Biotransformation by Isolated Enzymes

As noted in Table I, biotransformations catalyzed by isolated enzymes are dominated by the use of various lipases for the hydrolysis or formation of esters. This is also evident from the data presented in Table II, which lists the 10-most commonly used enzymes in order of their frequency of application expressed as the percentage use of each enzyme with respect to the total usage of isolated enzymes.

With the exception of the commonly used hydrolytic enzymes chymotryosin and subtilisin, the data presented in Table II refer to classes of enzymes. The predominance of lipase applications is consistent with the overall view that hydrolytic enzymes constitute the most frequently used biocatalysts of this

*TABLE I*
**Types of Biocatalysts for Biotransformation Reactions**

| Biocatalyst | Number |
|---|---|
| Isolated enzymes | 189[a] |
| Microorganisms | 161 |
| Plant cells | 3 |
| Catalytic antibodies | 2 |

[a] This total includes 43 different types of lipase enzymes.

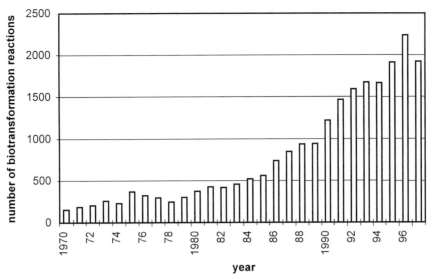

**Fig. 4.** Biotransformation reactions, 1970–1997.

type: Of 12,500 synthetically useful biotransformations reported since 1965 and that involve the use of isolated enzyme catalysts, 4217 employed hydrolytic enzymes.

## C. Biotransformations by Microorganisms

The 10 most frequently used whole cell biocatalysts are listed in Table III. The importance of baker's

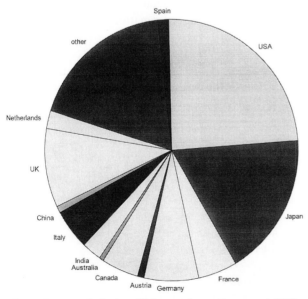

**Fig. 5.** Source of whole cell biotransformations, post-1980.

yeast is attributable to its ease of availability and use, with the commercial dried preparation often being used without any other processing. It is remarkable that only three microorganisms (baker's yeast, *Pseudomonas putida*, and *Aspergillus niger*) account for 50% of the usage of whole cell biocatalysts. Also noteworthy from Table III is the predominance of fungal biocatalysts, one of which (*Beauveria bassiana*, also known as *B. sulfurescens* and *Sporotrichum sulfurescens*) is probably the most versatile of the known biocatalysts in terms of the number of different chemical reactions that it can perform. More than 100 reports in the literature deal with the use of this

*TABLE II*
**The 10 Most Frequently Used Isolated Enzymes for Biotransformation**

| Enzyme | Percentage of total usage |
| --- | --- |
| Lipases (all types) | 21 |
| Chymotrypsin | 3 |
| Acylases | 2.7 |
| Transferases | 2.5 |
| Esterases | 2.5 |
| Subtilsin | 2.1 |
| Aldolases | 2.1 |
| Alcohol dehydrogenases | 1.4 |
| Hydrolases | 1.1 |
| Glycosidases | 1.0 |

**TABLE III**
**The 10 Most Frequently Used Microbial Biocatalysts**

| Biocatalyst | Percentage of total usage |
|---|---|
| Baker's yeast | 30 |
| *Pseudomonas putida* | 11 |
| *Aspergillus niger* | 8 |
| *Beauveria bassiana, Beauveria sulfurescens, Sporotrichum sulfurescens* | 6 |
| *Cunninghamella elegans* | 5 |
| *Rhizopus nigricans, Rhizopus stolonifer* | 5 |
| *Curvularia lunata* | 4 |
| *Rhizopus arrhizus, Rhizopus oryzae* | 4 |
| *Cunninghamella echinulata* | 3.5 |
| *Mortierella isabellina* | 3 |

fungus for the biotransformation of more than 300 different substrates, involving a wide range of reactions such as hydroxylations of saturated and aromatic carbon, keto-alcohol redox reactions, alkene reduction and oxidation, sulfide oxidation, Baeyer–Villiger oxidations, conjugation reactions, epoxide hydrolysis, and the hydrolysis of esters, amides, and other functional groups.

## D. Biotransformations by Other Biocatalysts

The general use of plant cells for biotransformation is not common. This area has focussed on the use of those cells which are most easily grown [e.g., *Datura carota* (carrot), *Nicotinia tabacum*, and *Catharanthus roseus*] for the transformation of simple substrates, being otherwise restricted to a small number of relatively specialized applications involving reactions that are often closely related to the biosynthetic processes of the parent plants.

The use for biotransformation of catalytic antibodies (abzymes), raised in response to a small-molecule transition state analog such as antigen, has received considerable attention in the past decade. Although considerable progress has been made in the understanding of this process, its application for prepara-

tive biotransformation is still in the early stages of development.

## E. Applications of Biotransformation

### 1. Range of Biotransformation

In contrast to the wide range of reactions catalyzed by isolated enzymes referred to previously, the range of biotransformations carried out by whole cell biocatalysts is relatively small. Almost 50% of such biotransformations reported since 1980 are concerned with only two reactions—hydroxylation at saturated carbon and the reduction of carbonyl groups. This is illustrated in Table IV, which presents the frequency of literature citation for the 10 most commonly reported whole cell biotransformations, taken from an analysis of the 4800 papers on this topic which have appeared after 1980.

### 2. Stereochemical Features

Biotransformations are used for a variety of chemical purposes, many of which rely on the regioselectivity, diastereoselectivity, or enantioselectivity inherent in enzyme-catalyzed reactions for the formation of a product with defined stereochemistry. The biotransformation illustrated in Fig. 2 is a classic example of regio- and diastereoselectivity, whereas most of the common biotransformations listed in Fig. 3 are generally enantioselective in terms of substrate consumption, product formation, or both. The ma-

**TABLE IV**
**The 10 Most Frequently Reported Whole Cell Biotransformations**

| Type of reaction | Percentage |
|---|---|
| Hydroxylation at saturated carbon | 23.4 |
| Carbonyl reduction | 14.8 |
| Alkene oxidation | 3.7 |
| Alkene reduction | 3.7 |
| Hydroxylation at aryl carbon | 3.4 |
| Arene dioxygenation | 3.3 |
| Ester hydrolysis | 3.2 |
| Baeyer–Villiger oxidation | 2.3 |
| Sulfide oxidation | 2.0 |
| Heteroatom dealkylation | 1.6 |

jority of biotransformations involve some aspect of stereochemical selectivity. This may be expressed as meso selectivity (Fig. 6a), prochiral selectivity (Fig. 6b) enantioselectivity in either substrate utilization (Fig. 6c) or product formation (Fig. 6d), diastereoselectivity in either substrate utilization (Fig. 6e) or product formation (Fig. 6f), or as a combination of several of the previously mentioned features.

## 3. Green Chemistry

Not all useful biotransformations rely on stereochemical properties: The conversion of acrylonitrile to acrylamide by *Rhodococcus rhodrochrous*, the hydroxylation of nicotinic acid and related compounds at C-6 by *Pseudomonas* and other bacteria, and the conversion of indole to indigo by *Escherichia coli* expressing the naphthalene dioxygenase gene, illustrated in Fig. 7, are important examples of valuable biotransformations with regiochemical but no explicit stereochemical features. Such biotransformations represent "green" alternatives to conventional chemical procedures involving extreme conditions of temperature of pressure or harsh reagents, and as such they exemplify the current emphasis placed

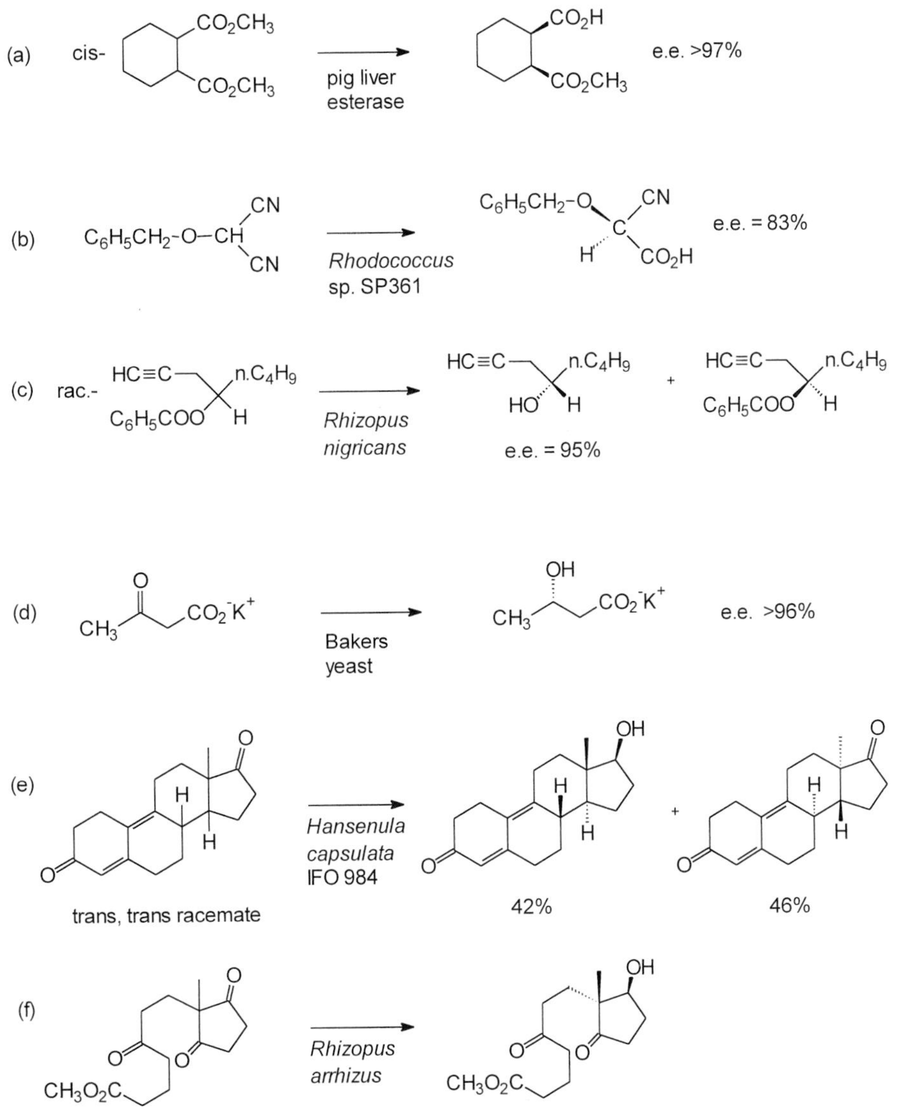

**Fig. 6.** Stereochemical selection in biotransformations. e.e., enantiomeric excess.

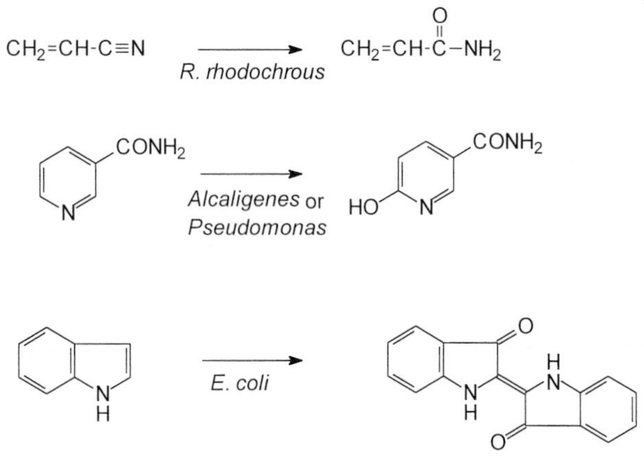

**Fig. 7.** Commercially important biotransformations without stereochemical features.

on the development of environmentally responsible industrial processes.

## 4. Unique Reagents

Biocatalysts are frequently used to perform reactions for which no analogous chemical method is available. This use of biotransformation is exemplified by the hydroxylation reaction shown in Fig. 2 and is often applied to the production of single enantiomers or diastereomers of products (Fig. 6) or for the formation of specific target molecules such as drug metabolites. Figure 8 illustrates some appli-

cations of *Cunninghamella elegans* for biotransformation in the latter area, in which the metabolic activity of microorganisms, particularly fungi, may duplicate some of the metabolic processes of mammalian metabolism.

Biotransformations are also used for the production of intermediates in the environmental biodegradation or mammalian metabolism of other xenobiotic compounds. Figure 9 illustrates the use of fungal biotransformations for the production of oxidized intermediates present in the biodegradation pathways of some polycyclic aromatic hydrocarbons.

## 5. Large-Scale Applications

Large-scale applications for enzymatic processes, summarized in Table V, are restricted to the use of inexpensive enzymes with high activity for the desired conversion, almost invariably hydrolytic enzymes with no cofactor requirements.

Research-scale applications do not share these restrictions, and it is in these applications that the wider range of enzyme activities is manifested.

Large-scale applications for whole cell-catalyzed biotransformations are summarized in Table VI.

These include the long-established processes shown in Figs. 1 and 2 and two of the reactions presented in Fig. 1. Many of these processes use

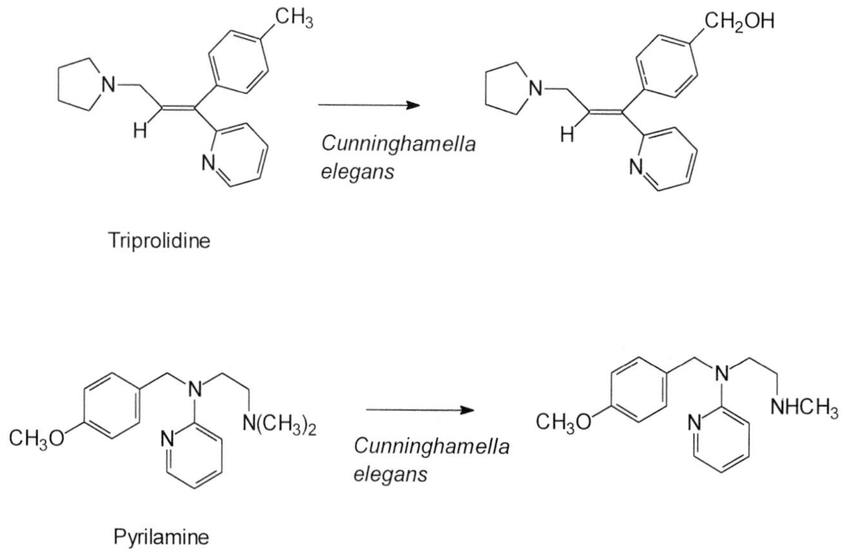

**Fig. 8.** Formation of drug metabolites by biotransformation.

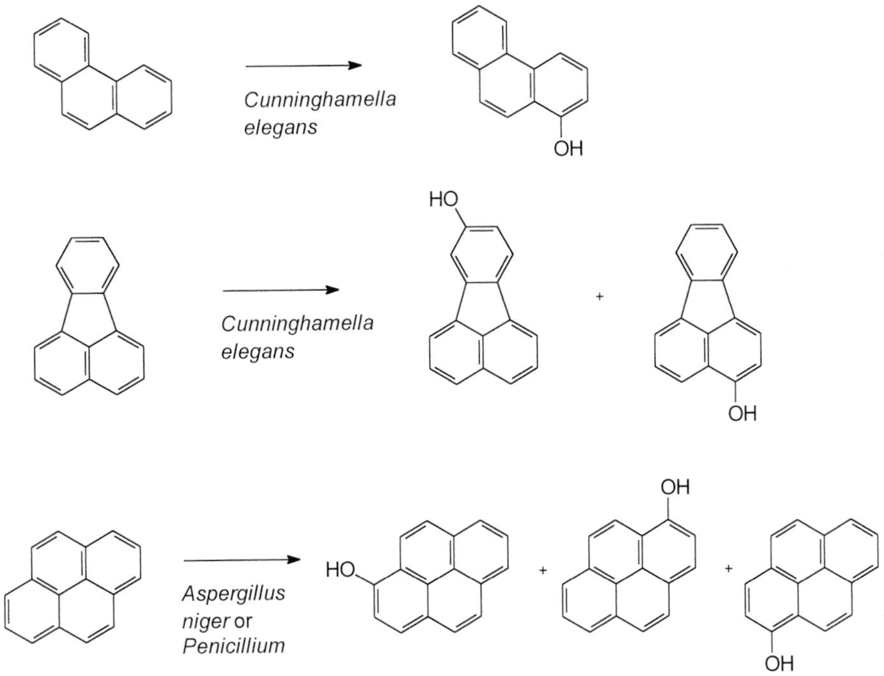

**Fig. 9.** Formation of oxidized biodegradation intermediates by biotransformation.

immobilized cell preparations (discussed in Section III.C).

## III. METHODOLOGY

### A. Isolated Enzymes

The use of isolated enzymes for biotransformations is limited by the availability of an enzyme for the desired transformation, and subject to optimization of parameters such as temperature, pH, solvent, and substrate-protecting groups (if appropriate). Such reactions, carried out mostly by the enzymes listed in Table II, are most conveniently performed on milligram to gram scales. Although some are readily amenable to scale-up to process tens or even hundreds of grams of substrate, many of the more esoteric biotransformations catalyzed by isolated enzymes are seriously limited in scale by the availability of the enzymes, and such reactions are typically carried out on only milligram quantities of material.

Procedures for using isolated enzymes are dictated by the nature of the enzymes, the biotransformation

**TABLE V**
**Large-Scale Biotransformations by Isolated Enzymes**

| Enzyme | Conversion | Approximate scale (tons p.a. of product) |
|---|---|---|
| Aminoacylases | Resolution of amino acids | ca. 1000 |
| Penicillin acylases | Hydrolysis of penicillin-G or penicillin-V | 5000 |
| Thermolysin | Synthesis of aspartame | 2000 |
| Trypsin | Conversion of porcine to human insulin | <1 |
| Various lipases | Preparations of chiral esters (e.g., glycidyl butyrate and isopropyl myristate) | ca. 2000 |

***TABLE VI***
**Large-Scale Biotransformations by Microbial Cells**

| Microorganism | Process | Approximate scale (tons p.a. of product) |
|---|---|---|
| *Acetobacter suboxydans* | Sorbitol oxidation | 50,000 |
| *Achromobacter, Pseudomonas,* or *Alcaligenes* | Hydroxylation of nicotinic acid | 1,000 |
| *Agrobacterium radiobacter* or *Bacillus brevis* | Hydantoin hydrolysis in amino acid production | 1,000 |
| *Arthrobacter* | Steroid dehydrogenation | 50 |
| *Aspergillus sclerotiorum* | Hydroxylation in oxamniquine production | <1 |
| *Curvularia lunata* or *Rhizopus stolonifer* | Steroid hydroxylation | 50 |
| *Escherichia coli* | Conversion of fumaric to L-aspartic acid | 400 |
| *Mycobacteria* or *Nocardia* | Steroid side-chain degradation | 50 |
| *Pseudomonas putida* | Dehalogenation in (S)-2-chloropropionate production | 2,000 |
| *Rhizopus arrhizus* | Carbonyl reduction in steroid synthesis | 1,000 |
| *Rhodococcus* | Nitrile hydrolysis in acrylamide production | 8,000 |
| Yeast | L-Phenylacetyl carbinol production | 300 |
| Various | Conversion of fumaric to L-malic acid | 50 |
| Various | Hydration of crotonobetaine to L-carnitine | 150 |

reaction to be catalyzed, and the requirement (if any) for cofactors or cofactor recycling. For preparative uses, an immobilized form of the enzyme is often desirable to facilitate catalyst recovery and product isolation, whereas the use of an organic solvent or co-solvent for the reaction may be indicated when dealing with substrates or products of low water solubility and is necessary in the application of hydrolytic enzymes for ester or amide formation. These factors are considered in more detail in later.

## B. Microbial Biocatalysts

Microbial biocatalysts provide access to a range of biotransformations for which no isolated enzymes are available. These reactions are typified by the hydroxylation at saturated and aryl carbons and arene dioxygenation, referred to in Table IV. Whole cell-catalyzed biotransformations may be carried out using growing cultures, resting cells in replacement culture or minimal media, or immobilized cell preparations. Biotransformations carried out by enzymes with extensive cofactor requirements, such as the hydroxylation and oxygenation reactions discussed previously, may necessitate the use of cells in a medium sufficient to maintain the primary metabolism necessary for cofactor recycling. Biotransformations catalyzed by baker's yeast most often involve the use of lyophilized cells which may be suspended in an aqueous medium containing a carbon source, such as sucrose or glucose, to permit cofactor recycling to occur via primary metabolism or in an organic solvent. In the latter instance, cell viability may be compromised but sufficient enzyme activity will be maintained for biotransformation purposes.

## C. Immobilization Techniques

The immobilization of an isolated enzyme or whole cell leads to increased ease of biocatalyst recovery and thus facilitates reuse and often results in greater stability, leading to an increase in the usable lifetime of the catalyst. In some instances, however, immobilization can result in a catalyst of lower activity, but this is often an acceptable trade-off for the more desirable consequences of immobilization.

Immobilization of isolated enzymes is appropriate for all the applications listed in Table V. Many methods are available for enzyme immobilization, from a simple adsorption onto an inert surface to covalent binding of the enzyme into an insoluble polymer matrix. Gel entrapment or encapsulation of an enzyme provides a simple means for immobilization that is also applicable to whole cell biocatalysts, for which immobilization in a calcium alginate matrix is the method most commonly used.

Immobilization allows for the possibility of locating two or more enzymes or microbial cells on the same carrier, making it possible for sequential biotransformations to be carried out using a single immobilized preparation. However, the increased complexities of the kinetics of substrate conversion under immobilized catalyst conditions (which must include terms for substrate and product diffusion within an immobilized environment) means that such applications are not common.

## D. Solvent Selection

The application of enzyme catalysis under nonaqueous or low-water conditions includes the use of enzymes operating in water-miscible solvents (e.g., methanol/water mixtures), water-immiscible solvents (e.g., hexane), and reverse micelle environments. The stability of an enzyme in such environments depends on the hydrophobicity of the solvent and the state of the enzyme (free or immobilized). In general, water-miscible solvents are used only as a means to increase substrate solubility, whereas water-immiscible solvents can also be used to alter an enzyme's reactivity, converting, for example, hydrolytic enzymes such as lipases into catalysts for the formation of esters. The most useful non-aqueous media are water-immiscible solvents such as octane that do not displace the enzyme's solvation shell of water molecules. In the appropriate solvent enzyme-catalyzed dehydrations, transesterifications, and alcohol-carbonyl oxidoreductions have been observed.

Whole cell biocatalysts can also be used in nonaqueous media, water/solvent two-phase systems, and reverse micelles. Such methods are particularly useful when dealing with the biotransformation of water-immiscible substrates that can act as the second phase (e.g., toluene), biotransformations for which extensive cofactor recycling and thus cell viability is not a requirement, and for biotransforma-

tions involving microorganisms (such as *Rhodococcus*) that maintain high viability in the presence of organic solvents. In some instances, such as in cases in which competing enzymes may have different activities in many solvents, the nature of the solvent may also control the regio- or stereoselectivity of the biotransformation of a single substrate by whole cells.

## See Also the Following Articles

BIOCATALYSIS FOR SYNTHESIS OF CHIRAL PHARMACEUTICAL INTERMEDIATES • LIPASES, INDUSTRIAL USES • YEASTS

## Bibliography

Cabral, J. M. S., Best, D., Boross, L., and Tramper, J. (1994). "Applied Biocatalysis." Harwood Academic, Chur, Switzerland.

Davies, H. G., Green, R. H., Kelly, D. R., and Roberts, S. M. (1989). "Biotransformations in Preparative Organic Chemistry." Academic Press, London.

Drauz, K., and Waldmann, H. (Eds.) (1995). "Enzyme Catalysis in Organic Synthesis." VCH, Weinheim.

Faber, K. (1997). "Biotransformations in Organic Chemistry," 3rd ed. Springer-Verlag, Berlin.

Hanson, J. R. (1995). "An Introduction to Biotransformations in Organic Chemistry." Freeman, Oxford.

Holland, H. L. (1992). "Organic Synthesis with Oxidative Enzymes." VCH, New York.

Kelly, D. R. (1998). Biotransformations. *In* "Biotechnology" (H. J. Rehm, and G. Reed, Eds.), Vol. 8a. Wiley–VCH, Weinheim.

Roberts, S. M. (Ed.) (1993–1997). "Preparative Biotransformations." Wiley, Chichester, UK.

Roberts, S. M., Turner, N. J., Willetts, A. J., and Turner, M. K. (1995). "Introduction to Biocatalysis Using Enzymes and Microorganisms." Cambridge Univ. Press, Cambridge UK.

Servi, S. (Ed.) (1992). "Microbial Reagents in Organic Synthesis." Kluwer, Dordrecht.

Synopsys Scientific Ltd. (1998). "Biocatalysis" database; URL. http://www.synopsys.co.uk.

Wong, C.-H., and Whitesides, G. M. (1994). "Enzymes in Synthetic Organic Chemistry." Pergamon/Elsevier, Oxford.

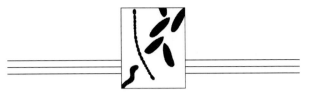

# Carbohydrate Synthesis and Metabolism

**Robert T. Vinopal and Antonio H. Romano**

*University of Connecticut*

## GLOSSARY

**capsular polysaccharide (*extracellular polysaccharide, EPS*)** Extracellular carbohydrate polymer, usually containing sugar acids, that give the cell surface a negative charge.

**carbohydrate** A sugar (polyhydroxy aldehyde or ketone) or a derivative thereof.

**central metabolic pathways** Pathways used by an organism for the production of energy and biosynthetic precursors regardless of the source of carbon and energy being used; for the majority of known microorganisms, central metabolism consists of the Embden–Meyerhof–Parnas glycolytic pathway, the hexose monophosphate pathway, and the tricarboxylic acid cycle.

**derived sugars** Sugars in which the aldehyde group is oxidized or reduced, or a hydroxyl group is substituted or derivatized.

**electron transport phosphorylation** ATP production energized by an ion gradient across a membrane, resulting from the passage of electrons along a membrane-associated transport chain to a terminal electron acceptor; the primary source of ATP in respiration.

**fermentation** Biological oxidation resulting in ATP production in which organic substances serve as both primary electron donor and final electron acceptor.

**glycogenesis (*gluconeogenesis*)** Synthesis of central metabolic six-carbon sugars for biosynthetic precursors during growth on carbon sources other than these sugars.

**glycolysis** The process of sugar catabolism; commonly used as a synonym for the most widely known glycolytic pathway, the Embden–Meyerhof–Parnas path; used here to refer to glycolytic pathways generally.

**glycolytic pathways** General central pathways for the metabolism of sugars for production of energy and precursors for biosynthesis.

**lipopolysaccharide (*LPS*)** A molecule making up the outer leaflet of the gram-negative outer membrane, consisting of a hydrophobic membrane-associated base (glucosamine and fatty acids), a hydrophilic core (six-, seven-, and eight-carbon sugars), and an o-polysaccharide (linked four- or five-sugar repeating units, containing derived six-carbon sugars).

**substrate-level phosphorylation** ATP production in which an organic phosphate intermediate compound with a high-energy bond is formed, which then drives the phosphorylation of ADP to ATP.

**teichoic and teichuronic acids** Cell wall-associated polymers in gram-positive bacteria; they consist of sugar alcohols connected by phosphodiester bonds, and polysaccharides incorporating sugar acids, respectively.

**CARBOHYDRATES** are the most abundant and most widely distributed organic substances on Earth, and the recycling of the carbon in these compounds is an indispensable role of microorganisms, in the biosphere. Thus, carbohydrates are a principal nutrient of microorganisms and their catabolism provides a major source of energy and carbon for microbial growth. Although microorganisms are extremely diverse in the details of their carbohydrate metabolic pathways, a core set of central pathways provide, in addition to energy, a pool of carbon compounds that are the starting point for the biosynthesis of all microbial cell constituents, including carbohydrates.

## I. CARBOHYDRATES: NATURE, ORIGIN AND OCCURRENCE

Carbohydrates derive their name from their general empirical formula of $C_nH_{2n}O_n$, often denoted as $(CH_2O)_n$. Early workers considered them to be hydrates of carbon. The modern definition is that a carbohydrate is a polyhydroxyl aldehyde or ketone, or a compound derived therefrom. Derived carbohydrates include: (a) sugar acids, derived from sugars by oxidation of an aldehyde, ketone, or carbinol group to a carboxyl group; (b) sugar alcohols, derived from sugars by reduction of an aldehyde or ketone group; (c) amino sugars, sugars with a hydroxyl group replaced by an amino group, most commonly in the 2 position, with the nitrogen often the site of attachment of an acetyl group; (d) deoxy sugars, sugars with a hydroxyl group replaced by a hydrogen atom, most commonly at the 2 or 6 position, although 3,6-dideoxy hexoses are also common; (e) sugar phosphates, sugars with one or more phosphate groups attached by ester linkages; and (f) polymerized sugars, oligo- and polysaccharides, composed of sugar moieties connected by dehydration (glycosidic) bonds between hydroxyl groups.

Carbohydrates are the most abundant and most widely distributed organic substances on Earth. The greatest mass of carbohydrates in nature is accounted for by polysaccharides that are structural components or storage nutrients of plants, animals, and microbes. The concentration of mono-, di-, and oligosaccharides in natural environments is kept low by their rapid use by microorganisms inhabiting soils, water basins, and oceans. The most abundant structural polysaccharides are cellulose, a $\beta$-1,4 linked homopolymer of glucose that makes up the rigid cell wall of plants; chitin, a homopolymer of $\beta$-1,4-linked *N*-acetylglucosamine that is a major component of fungal cell walls and arthropod exoskeletons; murein, the rigid cell wall of bacteria, based on a backbone of a $\beta$-1,4-linked heteropolymer containing *N*-acetylglucosamine and *N*-acetylmuramic acid; laminarin and paramylon, $\beta$-1,4-linked glucose homopolymers found in cell walls of algae; and hemicelloses, a diverse group of heteropolymers made up of hexose or pentose units (glucans, mannans, galactans, and xylans) and hexuronic acids that occur in woody plants as a complex with cellulose and lignin. Storage polysaccharides include starch, found in plants, and glycogen, found in animals and microorganisms. These are homopolymers of glucose with $\alpha$-1,4 linkages in the main chains and differing degrees of $\alpha$-1,6 branching. Glucose and its derivatives are the most abundant sugar moieties in nature. It has been estimated that D-glucose constitutes 99.95% of the carbohydrates on Earth, either in combined or derivatized form (Robyt, 1998).

The global primary production of carbohydrates comes about by the fixation of carbon dioxide in photosynthesis. The preponderance of the carbon that is fixed is found in the land plants of forests and grasslands, though significant amounts are fixed by aquatic and marine microflora. Recently, ecosystems dependent on chemosynthetic rather than photosynthetic primary $CO_2$ fixation have been discovered near deep ocean hydrothermal vents that are beyond the limits of sunlight penetration. Products of $CO_2$ fixation are assimilated by plants, animals, and microorganisms in the global carbon cycle, but are eventually degraded to $CO_2$ to complete the cycle. This degradation of organic compounds in nature comes about largely through the activities of microorganisms; the degradation of the most chemically resistant and most abundant organic substances in nature, such as cellulose, chitin, lignin, and keratin, is carried out almost exclusively by microorganisms. Thus, the microbes are the purifiers of Earth.

## II. DEGRADATION OF POLYSACCHARIDES

The most abundantly available carbohydrates are polysaccharides, notably plant cell-wall components (cellulose, hemicelluloses, mannans, xylans), plant carbon and energy reserve materials (the various starches), fungal cell wall components (chitin and various glycans), the exoskeleton of arthropods (based on chitin), and murein (bacterial cell walls).

All of these are more or less insoluble (for cellulose or chitin, chains of more than six or seven monomers are highly insoluble), so microbes must use extracellular enzymes to use them (Warren, 1996). Degradative enzymes, depolymerases, are secreted to hydrolyze their glycosidic bonds, breaking them down into fragments that are soluble and small enough to be transported. Microbes often secrete multiple enzymes when attacking a specific polymer, composing a specialized system for efficient hydrolysis, for example, of cellulose. The individual enzymes are often complex, with multiple domains, one or more for catalysis and often one for binding to the polymer substrate. Some are specialists in internal attack (endodepolymerases), others in attack at polymer ends (exodepolymerases) or in debranching, all acting together to produce pieces small enough for transport. Degradation to oligosaccharides, followed by transport and final breakdown to monomers in the cell may be more advantageous than complete breakdown to free sugars outside the cell, both because of energetically cheaper transport per residue in oligosaccharides and the potential for conservation of glycosidic bond energy by phosphorolysis in the cell, and because of reduced loss of solubilized products to competing microbes by diffusion. The secreted starch-degrading enzymes of *Bacillus amyloliquefaciens* produce maltotriose, maltohexaose, and maltoheptaose, which are not further degraded until taken up by the cell. *Pseudomonas stutzeri* and *Enterobacter aerogenes* attack starch with secreted exoamylases, releasing exclusively maltotetraose and maltohexaose, respectively. A few bacteria, mostly gram-positive but including *Klebsiella oxytoca,* secrete cyclodextrin glycosyltransferases, which act on starch to release cyclodextrins, closed rings of $\alpha$-1,4 glucose with six, seven, or eight sugars. These are not metabolizable by most other microbes, but are transported by specific uptake systems and used by the organisms producing them. Cyclodextrins form stable inclusion complexes with organic molecules and have many uses in chemistry and biotechnology.

While depolymerization of dead material for use as a carbon and energy source is the function of many microbial polysaccharide breakdown systems, other such systems are specialized to accomplish the infection of living plants or animals, although the sugars released can also be catabolized. Phytopathogens often secrete pectinases, polygalacturonidases, and cellulases, as well as depolymerases for noncarbohydrate plant surface components, such as cutin and proteins. Insect pathogens, especially fungi, commonly secrete chitinases. Streptococci grown on glycoproteins secrete mannosidases, and these enzymes might be invasive agents, targeting mammalian cell-surface glycoproteins.

## III. DEGRADATION OF OLIGOSACCHARIDES AND MONOSACCHARIDES

Exogenous carbohydrates are favored sources of carbon and energy for many or most microorganisms. Any carbohydrate made by living cells can be degraded and used by microorganisms as sources of carbon and energy. For degradative pathways generally, the rule is that favored carbon and energy sources, in general those supporting the most rapid growth of the microbe in question, are used first, repressing catabolism of others until the favored sources are exhausted. Because glucose is overwhelmingly the most abundant carbohydrate on Earth, it is the favored carbon and energy source for many microbes, both bacteria and fungi, and glucose catabolite repression of the use of other sources is correspondingly widespread. Organisms having glucose as the favored carbon and energy source typically have the Embden–Meyerhof–Parnas glycolytic pathway (see following discussion). Some bacteria, usually having an alternative glycolytic pathway, for example the Entner–Doudoroff pathway in pseudomonads, may have other favored carbon and energy sources. For pseudomonads, organic acids and tricarboxylic acid (TCA) cycle intermediates are favored sources and inhibit the catabolism of glucose when both are present.

When sugars and small oligosaccharides are available in the medium they are taken up into the cell, either by energy-dependent active transport, or by energy-independent facilitated diffusion in the unusual cases of organisms that live in environments with high sugar concentrations (e.g., the yeast *Saccharomyces cerevisiae* and the bacterium *Zymomonas mobilis*) or, in many bacteria, by group translocation, concomitant with phosphorylation. Free sugars in the cell, including those released by hydrolysis from oligosaccharides, are phosphorylated, sometimes after preliminary conversion reactions, activating them for subsequent metabolism and assuring cell retention. Derived sugars are then catabolized by what amounts to a reversal of the process for their synthesis, although the steps are catalyzed by different enzymes, regulated for their catabolic role. Sugar alcohols are oxidized, sugar phosphates are either taken up directly or acted upon first by a secreted phosphatase, sugar acids are reduced, and deoxy sugars are hydrated and oxidized (Fig. 1); amino sugars are deaminated, and any acetyl groups are removed (Fig. 2). Exogenous nucleosides can be used as sole sources of carbon and energy by some bacteria, transport being followed by phosphorolysis and catabolism of the released sugar phosphates.

## IV. CENTRAL METABOLISM

Catabolic pathways act to convert sugars into a group of metabolic intermediates consisting of sugar phosphates, organic acids, and phosphate esters of organic acids that are interconverted by a set of central pathways referred to as central metabolism. These pathways generate the biological energy necessary for growth and also a pool of intermediates that are the precursors for the synthesis of building blocks, such as amino acids, nucleotides, long-chain fatty acids, and sugar phosphates, which are polymerized to form cell macromolecules. Central metabolism in most organisms includes the Embden–Meyerhof–Parnas (EMP) pathway, the hexose monophosphate pathway, and the tricarboxylic acid (citric acid) cycle. Provided there is a means for transport into the cell, any intermediate of these pathways can serve as a source of all others.

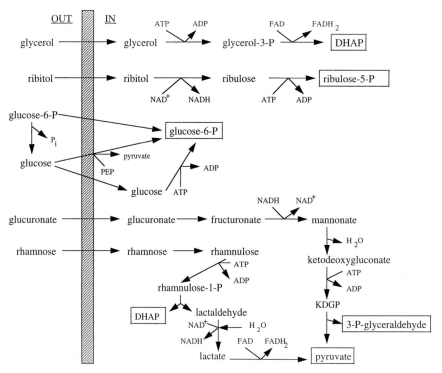

***Fig. 1.*** Typical degradative pathways for derived sugars (sugar alcohols: glycerol, ribitol; sugar phosphate: glucose-6-phosphate; sugar acid: glucuronate; deoxy sugar: rhamnose). Intermediates of central metabolic pathways are shown in boxes. Abbreviations: DHAP, dihydroxyacetone phosphate; KDGP, 2-keto-3-deoxy-6-phosphogluconate; PEP, phosphoenolpyruvate.

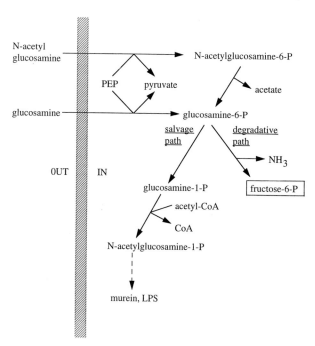

**Fig. 2.** Degradative and salvage pathways for the amino sugars glucosamine and *N*-acetyl glucosamine in *E. coli*. Abbreviations: CoA, coenzyme A; LPS, lipopolysaccharide; PEP, phosphoenolpyruvate.

## V. GLYCOLYTIC PATHWAYS

Biochemists usually define glycolysis as a specific set of metabolic reactions in which glucose is oxidized to pyruvate; this is the EMP pathway. This set of reactions is essentially ubiquitous in eukaryotes and is the principal means of hexose dissimilation in many prokaryotes. However, there is considerable metabolic diversity among bacteria and archaea with respect to pathways of glucose dissimilation. Thus, a more inclusive definition of glycolysis is adopted here that will encompass other modes of metabolic conversion of glucose to pyruvate: Glycolysis is defined here as sugar dissimilation.

The principal glycolytic pathways that occur in yeasts, fungi, protozoa, and bacteria are shown in Fig. 3. These include, in addition to the EMP pathway, the Entner–Doudoroff (ED) pathway, the pentose phosphoketolase (PPK) pathway, and the hexose monophosphate (HMP) pathway (shunt), also known as the pentose phosphate pathway (shunt) or the Warburg–Dickens pathway. Interesting varia-

tions of some of these pathways found recently in archaea are mentioned later. These pathways are shown with glucose as the substrate, but other sugars gain entry to glycolytic pathways after their phosphorylation, and in many cases the subsequent action of isomerases or epimerases. Examples of means of entry used by derived sugars are shown in Figs. 1 and 2.

Pyruvate is considered to be the end product of glycolytic pathways, but it should be realized that the reaction sequence glucose → pyruvate is not balanced electrically; electrons are transferred to pyridine nucleotide coenzymes (nicotinamide adenine dinucleotide, $NAD^+$; and nicotinamide adenine dinucleotide phosphate, $NADP^+$) to form NADH and NADPH, respectively, and these are also products of glycolytic pathways. Thus, pyruvate is a dynamic metabolic intermediate rather than an end-product, occupying a central position in central metabolism. The fates of pyruvate, NADH, and NADPH are discussed in later sections.

### A. Characteristics of the Modes of Glycolysis

In comparing the four modes of glycolysis shown in Fig. 3, note the following points.

1. The series of reactions in which glyceraldehyde 3-phosphate is metabolized to pyruvate is common to all the glycolytic pathways. This common trunk of glycolysis is among the most highly conserved sets of reactions in biology.
2. Each of the modes of glycolysis has reactions catalyzed by enzymes that are characteristic or unique to that pathway. These are shown in Table I.
3. The common trunk of glycolysis contains the two substrate-level phosphorylation reactions that are common to all the modes of glycolysis and are the sole sources of ATP in the EMP, HMP, and ED pathways. These are the reactions catalyzed by the glyceraldehyde-3-phosphate dehydrogenase and 2-phosphoglycerate enolase systems, which result in the production of 1,3 bisphosphoglycerate and phosphoenolpyruvate (PEP), respectively, both molecules with high-energy phosphate groups that are transferred to ADP to form ATP. (The PPK pathway has

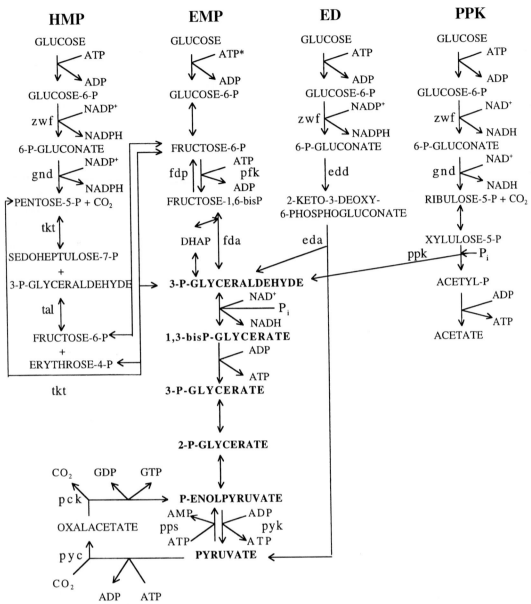

**Fig. 3.** Pathways of glycolysis and glycogenesis. Abbreviations: DHAP, dihydroxyacetone phosphate; ED, Entner-Doudoroff pathway; EMP, Embden-Meyerhof-Parnas pathway; HMP, hexose monophosphate pathway; PPK, pentose phosphoketolase pathway. Reactions common to all four pathways are indicated in boldface type. Key enzymes of each pathway are indicated by their genetic abbreviations: eda, 2-keto-3-deoxy-6-phosphogluconate aldolase; edd, 6-phosphogluconate dehydratase; fda, fructose -1,6-bisphosphate aldolase; fdp, fructose diphosphatase; gnd, 6-phosphogluconate dehydrogenase; pck, PEP carboxy kinase; pfk, phosphofructokinase; ppk, xylose-5-phosphate phosphoketolase; pps, PEP synthase; pyc, pyruvate carboxylase; tal, transaldolase; tkt, transketolase; zwf, glucose-6-phosphate dehydrogenase. *PEP is the phosphoryl donor in bacteria transporting sugars by a PEP–sugar phosphotransferase system.

*TABLE I*
**Key Enzymes of Glycolytic Pathways**[a]

| Enzyme[b] | EMP | ED | PPK | HMP |
|-----------|-----|----|----|----|
| PFK | + | − | − | − |
| FDA | + | − | − | − |
| ZWF | − | + | + | + |
| GND | − | − | + | + |
| EDD | − | + | − | − |
| EDA | − | + | − | − |
| PPK | − | − | + | − |
| TAL | − | − | − | + |
| TKT | − | − | − | + |

[a] Pathway abbreviations: ED, Entner–Doudoroff; EMP, Embden–Meyerhof–Parnas; HMP, hexose monophosphate; PPK, pentose phosphoketolase. Enzymes that are unique to a pathway are indicated by a boldface plus sign.

[b] Enzyme abbreviations: EDA, 2-keto-3-deoxy-6-phosphogluconate aldolase; EDD, 6-phosphogluconate dehydratase; FDA, fructose-1-6-bisphosphate aldolase; GND, 6-phosphogluconate dehydrogenase; PFK, phosphofructokinase; PPK, xylulose-5-phosphate phosphoketokase; TAL, transaldolase; TKT, transketolase.

xylulose 5-phosphate phosphoketolase, which generates acetyl phosphate, a high-energy phosphate compound and potentially a source of ATP. However, except in the presence of an auxiliary electron acceptor, acetyl phosphate is converted to acetyl coenzyme A and reduced to ethanol to reoxidize NADH).

4. The EMP pathway is the only mode of glycolysis in which all of the glucose carbon is metabolized through the ATP-generating common trunk of glycolysis. Thus, the EMP pathway is twice as efficient in terms of ATP produced per glucose catabolized as the ED or HMP pathways, and more efficient than the PPK pathway to whatever extent acetyl phosphate is reduced to ethanol in different organisms. The net ATP yields per mole glucose for each of the pathways are EMP, 2; HMP, 1; ED, 1; and PPK 1–2.

5. Sugars must be phosphorylated before they can be metabolized. The phosphoryl donor is usually ATP, but in a large number of bacteria with the EMP pathway, PEP generated during glycolysis can be recycled to act as the phosphoryl donor, concomitant with the transport of the sugar into the cell by a PEP–sugar phosphotransferase system (PTS). This phosphorylation during transport (group translocation) is an efficient arrangement because it does not require additional expenditure of energy to concentrate free sugar in the cell before phosphorylation.

6. All of the reactions of the EMP pathway between glucose-6-phosphate and pyruvate are reversible, except those catalyzed by phosphofructokinase and pyruvate kinase. However, in these two cases separate enzymes or combinations of enzymes catalyze the reverse reactions (see Fig. 3). These are the key enzymes of glycogenesis (see later sections); they are even more widely distributed than the enzymes of the EMP pathway because they allow the synthesis of sugars from smaller compounds. Thus, they are nearly ubiquitous, occurring in autotrophs as well as heterotrophs.

## B. Distribution of the Modes of Glycolysis

### 1. The Embden–Meyerhof–Parnas and Hexose Monophosphate Pathways

The EMP, ED, and PPK pathways represent primary modes of glycolysis because each of these is known to function as the core catabolic pathway in the central metabolism of a significant group of organisms, generating ATP via substrate-level phosphorylation. In contrast, the HMP pathway occurs predominantly as an ancillary pathway, in combination with the EMP or ED pathway, where its principal function is to provide pentose, heptose, and tetrose phosphates, and reduced nicotinamide adenine dinucleotide phosphate (NADPH), all of which are required for biosynthesis. The combination of EMP and HMP pathways is the most frequent in the known living world, representing the core of the central metabolism of higher animals and plants, protozoa, yeasts and filamentous fungi, and of many aerobic, anaerobic, and facultative bacteria, including those that are best known (e.g., *Escherichia coli,* species of *Salmonella* and other Enterobacteriaceae, *Bacillus,* and *Clostridium*). Enzymes of the EMP and HMP pathways in these organisms are typically constitutive. The bulk of the carbon flux is through the EMP pathway; the HMP pathway rarely accounts for more than 20% of the carbon metabolized. However, *E.*

*coli* mutants lacking phosphofructokinase, the key enzyme of the EMP pathway, can grow on glucose-6-phosphate, showing that the HMP pathway can function as a primary energetic pathway (Fraenkel and Vinopal, 1973), and there are some bacteria that have only the HMP (e.g., *Acetobacter suboxydans*). These appear to be rare.

In addition to the widespread occurrence of the EMP pathway in conjunction with the HMP pathway, there exists a distinct physiological group of obligately fermentative bacteria in which the EMP pathway is the sole mode of glycolysis. These are the homofermentative lactic acid bacteria, organisms that characteristically lack cytochromes and hence are dependent on substrate-level phosphorylation for energy. These bacteria metabolize glucose to a single product, lactic acid, which is produced by the reduction of the pyruvate generated by the EMP pathway (see Section V.D), with a stoichiometry of 2 moles lactic acid/mole glucose used. Homofermenters include all species of *Streptococcus, Enterococcus, Lactococcus,* and *Pediococcus,* and some species of *Lactobacillus* (e.g., *L. casei* and *L. plantarum*). The consequence of the absence of an ancillary pathway like the HMP in these organisms is extremely limited biosynthetic capacity and very complex nutritional requirements. Media for their culture must contain a full range of nucleotides, amino acids, and vitamins.

## 2. Pentose Phosphoketolase Pathway

Heterofermentative lactic acid bacteria resemble homofermenters with respect to morphology and growth characteristics (both groups are obligately fermentative, aerotolerant, gram-positive spheres or rods with complex nutritional requirements), but heterofermenters produce $CO_2$ and acetic acid or ethanol in addition to lactic acid from sugar degradation. This difference was once considered to be due to differences in the metabolic fate of pyruvate at the end of the EMP pathway, but studies with isotopically labeled glucose, allowing the determination of the fate of individual glucose carbon atoms, show that heterolactic fermenters have a fundamentally different glycolytic pathway. A pentose phosphoketolase that catalyzes the phosphorylytic cleavage of

xylulose-5-phosphate to produce acetyl phosphate, $CO_2$, and glyceraldehyde-3-phosphate accounts for the equimolar amounts of acetate or ethanol, $CO_2$, and lactic acid found in the metabolic products (Fig. 3). Thus, this mode of glycolysis was named after the signature enzyme of the pathway, pentose phosphoketolase. This PPK pathway is the distinguishing characteristic of the heterofermentative lactic acid bacteria, which include all species of *Leuconostoc* and some species of *Lactobacillus* (e.g., *L. brevis* and *L. mesenteroides*).

## 3. The Entner–Doudoroff (ED) Pathway

The ED pathway is the most prevalent primary mode of glycolysis among strictly aerobic gram-negative bacteria, such as species of *Pseudomonas, Xanthomonas, Azotobacter, Rhizobium, Agrobacterium, Arthrobacter,* and *Neisseria*. The lower energy yield of the ED pathway from substrate-level phosphorylation is of no significant consequence to these highly oxidative bacteria because their principal source of energy is electron-transport phosphorylation. Though the ED pathway represents the core of central carbohydrate metabolism in bacteria, it is usually inducible rather than constitutive because sugars are not the preferred carbon sources in these organisms—citric acid cycle organic acids are preferred. The ED pathway is rare among gram-positive bacteria.

The ED pathway is accompanied by the HMP pathway in many of these organisms, but appears to be the sole glycolytic path in others. For example, among the pseudomonads, *Ps. cepacia* has 6-phosphogluconate dehydrogenase, a key enzyme of the HMP, but *Ps. aeruginosa* does not. Instead, *Ps. aeruginosa* can generate NADPH with a glyceraldehyde-3-phosphate dehydrogenase that is coupled to the operation of the signature ED enzymes 6-phosphogluconate dehydratase (edd) and 2-keto-3-deoxy-6-phosphogluconate aldolase (eda) (Fig. 3; Table I). A cyclic mode of operation of the ED pathway has also been identified, whereby glyceraldehyde-3 phosphate can be recycled to 6-phosphogluconate (Lessie and Phibbs, 1984). This allows for synthesis of tetrose, pentose, and heptose phosphates by the successive action of transketolase and transaldolase, starting from glyceraldehyde-3-phosphate and fructose-6-phosphate, which are intermediate in the cyclic ED pathway. These capabilities allow *Ps. aeruginosa* to grow on minimal glucose media without a complete HMP pathway.

Inducible ED pathways also occur in other physiological types of bacteria. For example, ED pathway enzymes are induced in the purple photosynthetic bacteria *Rhodopseudomonas capsulata* and *R. sphaeroides* when grown heterotrophically with glucose. Also, although *E. coli* has constitutive EMP and HMP pathways as stated above, growth on gluconate induces a gluconate permease and enzymes of the ED pathway, and metabolism of gluconate takes place exclusively by this pathway. *E. coli* also uses a part of the inducible ED pathway in the metabolism of glucuronate, important in its intestinal habitat, where it uses glucuronate released from glucuronides that are secreted into the intestine through the bile duct as a product of liver detoxification reactions.

*Zymomonas mobilis* represents a unique case of the ED pathway operating anaerobically as the sole energy-yielding set of reactions. The ED is the only means of sugar metabolism in this aerotolerant but obligately fermentative organism, with necessary metabolic precursors for biosynthesis being provided by the transketolase–transaldolase system and an incomplete citric acid cycle. Pyruvate produced from glycolysis is converted to ethanol and $CO_2$, just as it is in yeast alcoholic fermentation, but *Z. mobilis* is the only ethanol producer known to use the ED pathway.

The low energy yield of the ED pathway renders *Z. mobilis* one of the most inefficient bacteria known in terms of growth yield on glucose. In order to support a significant growth rate, high rates of sugar uptake and metabolism must be maintained. This is accomplished by a high-velocity facilitated diffusion glucose uptake system and very high levels of ED and alcohologenic enzymes—together, they account for 50% of the soluble cell protein (Conway, 1992). *Z. mobilis* is found in sugar-rich plant saps in warm climates, and is involved in alcoholic fermentations of such materials as sugar cane juice, agave, honey, and palm sap. The high rate of metabolism and favorable alcohol yield make *Z. mobilis* an attractive candidate organism for industrial alcohol production.

## C. Variations in Glycolytic Pathways

### 1. The Methylglyoxal Bypass

A variant pathway in the metabolism of glyceraldehyde-3-phosphate to pyruvate is found in *E. coli* and other members of the Enterobacteriaceae (EMP pathway), and in *Pseudomonas saccharophila* (ED pathway), whereby the common trunk of glycolysis is bypassed. Glyceraldehyde-3-phosphate is metabolized successively, through dihydroxyacetone phosphate, methylglyoxal, and lactate, to pyruvate (Cooper, 1984). The energy-yielding steps of glycolysis are thus bypassed. The physiological role of this pathway is to allow the conversion of glyceraldehyde-3-phosphate to pyruvate under conditions of low phosphate concentrations, where activity of glyceraldehyde-3-phosphate dehydrogenase would be limited (Gottschalk, 1979). Bacteria using the methylglyoxal pathway would gain no energy from glycolysis, only from the subsequent metabolism of pyruvate.

### 2. Modified Modes of Glycolysis in Archaea

Studies of the modes of glycolysis in saccharolytic archaea are interesting because they allow insights into the nature of sugar metabolism in the phylogenetically deepest-rooted and slowest-evolving organisms known. None of the classical pathways of glycolysis described here has yet been found, complete in all its details, in any archaeon. Rather, interesting modifications of the ED and EMP pathways have been described (Danson, 1993; Kengen, *et al.*, 1996; Selig, *et al.*, 1997). The aerobic halophile *Halobacterium saccharovorum* has a "partially phosphorylated" ED pathway in which there is no initial phosphorylation of glucose; instead, successive actions of a glucose dehydrogenase and a gluconate dehydratase lead to formation of 2-keto-3-deoxygluconate (KDG), which is phosphorylated by ATP to form 2-keto-3-deoxy-6-phosphogluconate (KDGP). Further metabolism to pyruvate is the same as in the conventional ED pathway, with a net yield of one ATP per molecule of glucose metabolized. A further modification, called the nonphosphorylated ED pathway, occurs among the more deeply rooted hyperthermophilic archaea, for example in the aerobe *Sulfolobus acidocaldarius*. In this pathway, an aldol cleavage of KDG by a KDG aldolase yields pyruvate and glyceraldehyde, which is oxidized to glycerate. ATP-dependent phosphorylation of glycerate yields 2-phosphoglycerate, which is metabolized to pyruvate through PEP. Because there is only one substrate-level phosphorylation reaction associated with the transfer of a high-energy phosphate group from PEP to ADP in the pyruvate kinase reaction, there is no net synthesis of ATP by this pathway; ATP generation results from the subsequent metabolism of pyruvate (see later sections).

Modifications of the EMP pathway found in archaea involve the sugar and sugar phosphate kinases and the enzyme systems involved in the oxidation of glyceraldehyde-3-phosphate. *Pyrococcus furiosus* and *Thermococcus celer* have ADP-dependent instead of ATP-dependent hexokinase (HK) and phosphofructokinase (PFK), while *Thermoproteus tenax* has pyrophosphate-dependent HK and PFK. *Desulfurococcus amylolyticus* is the only sugar-using archaeon in which conventional ATP-dependent HK and PFK have been found so far. *Pyrococcus furiosus*, *Thermococcus celer*, and *Desulfurococcus amylolyticus* oxidize glyceraldehyde-3-phosphate via a novel tungsten-containing glyceraldehyde-3-phosphate–ferredoxin oxidoreductase (GAP–FdOR), while *Thermoproteus tenax* has a conventional phosphate-dependent $NAD^+$-linked GAP dehydrogenase. These modifications in the EMP pathway in the various hyperthermophilic archaea are shown in Fig. 4, where they are compared with the conventional EMP pathway that is found in the hyperthermophilic bacterium *Thermotoga maritima*. As with the nonphosphorylated ED pathway previously described, the net yield of ATP from these modified EMP pathways that metabolize glyceraldehyde-3-phosphate via the GAP–FdOR system (*Pyrococcus*, *Thermococcus*, and *Desulfurococcus*) is zero because ATP gained from the PEP kinase system must be spent to regenerate ATP or ADP used in the HK and PFK reactions. The ATP yield in *Thermoproteus tenax*, which has phosphate-dependent $NAD^+$-GAP-DH, would be 2,

the same as for the bacterium *Thermotoga maritima*.

Determinations of flux of $^{13}C$-glucose through these modified ED and EMP pathways have shown that *Sulfolobus* uses the ED-type pathway exclusively, while the EMP-type pathway is predominant in the anaerobic archaea. *Thermococcus*, *Desulfurococcus*, and probably *Pyrococcus* use the modified EMP exclusively, while *Thermoproteus* uses both EMP (85%) and ED (15%). Although the number of archaea studied so far is small, the emerging picture is that archaea parallel bacteria with respect to the occurrence of nonphosphorylated ED versus modified EMP pathways: The ED pathway is generally characteristic of strict aerobes, while the EMP pathway is most frequent in anaerobes and facultative anaerobes.

## D. The Fates of Pyruvate, NADH, and NADPH Produced in Glycolysis

Recall that pyruvate produced by glycolytic pathways occupies a central position in metabolism. Pyruvate can be converted to anabolic products, such as amino acids, or it can be catabolized via a number of pathways by different organisms, under differing environmental conditions. NADH and NADPH are reoxidized in these reactions. In general, NADPH participates in reductive biosynthesis (e.g., the reductive amination of α-ketoglutarate to produce glutamate) while NADH transfers electrons to a number of different electron acceptors, either directly or through a system of electron carriers, in a variety of processes involved in energy metabolism (e.g., to free oxygen in respiration, or to an inorganic substance other than $O_2$, such as nitrate, in anaerobic respiration; or to an organic compound in fermentation). The principal modes of pyruvate metabolism and NADH → $NAD^+$ recycling are discussed here.

### 1. Aerobic Bacteria or Facultative Bacteria under Oxidative Conditions

Pyruvate is converted to acetyl-CoA + $CO_2$ by pyruvate dehydrogenase, an enzyme complex found in most aerobic organisms but not in anaerobes. The overall reaction is

$$\text{pyruvate} + \text{CoA} + NAD^+ \rightarrow \text{acetyl-CoA} + CO_2 + NADH + H^+$$

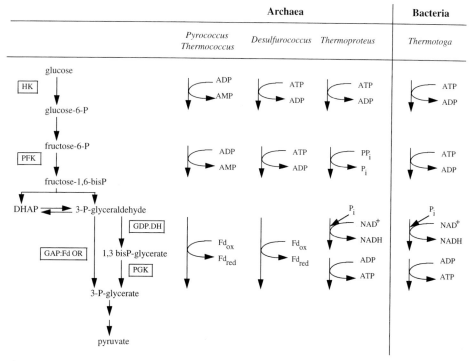

**Fig. 4.** Comparison of proposed EMP-type glycolytic pathways in hyperthermophilic archaea and the bacterium *Thermotoga*. The phosphoryl-donor specificities (ATP, ADP, PP$_i$) of hexokinase (HK) and 6-phosphofructokinases (PFK), and the enzymes proposed for glyceraldehyde-3-phosphate oxidation are indicated (GAP–FdOR, glyceraldehyde-3-phosphate–ferredoxin oxidoreductase; GAP-DH, glyceraldehyde-3-phosphate dehydrogenase; PGK, phosphoglycerate kinase). Abbreviations: DHAP, dihydroxyacetone phosphate; PP$_i$, inorganic pyrophosphate; Fd$_{ox}$, oxidized ferredoxin; Fd$_{red}$, reduced ferredoxin. [Reproduced, with permission, from Selig, M., Xavier, K. B., Santos, H., and Schönheit, P. (1997). Comparative analysis of Embden–Meyerhof and Entner–Doudoroff glycolytic pathways in hyperthermophilic archaea and the bacterium *Thermotoga*. *Arch. Microbiol.* **167**, 217–232, copyright Springer-Verlag.]

Acetyl-CoA is then oxidized to $CO_2$ and $H_2O$ via the tricarboxylic acid (citric acid) cycle (Fig. 5). After the condensation of acetyl-CoA with oxalacetate to form citrate, there are four dehydrogenase reactions in each turn of the cycle, which generate two molecules of $CO_2$, three NADH, and the reduced prosthetic group of succinic dehydrogenase, flavine adenine dinucleotide ($FADH_2$). The NADH and $FADH_2$ generated here, as well as the NADH formed in glycolysis and the pyruvate dehydrogenase reaction, are reoxidized by the electron-transport system, whereby electrons are carried to the ultimate electron acceptor, oxygen, with the concomitant synthesis of ATP by electron transport phosphorylation.

A number of aerobic or facultative bacteria, such as pseudomonads or enterobacteria, respectively, can use an alternate electron acceptor such as nitrate in the electron-transport chain. This process, a case of anaerobic respiration known as dissimilatory nitrate reduction, is repressed by oxygen and operates only in its absence.

## 2. Facultative Bacteria under Anaerobic Conditions

In the absence of oxygen or other suitable electron-transport-terminal electron acceptor, facultative bacteria use organic substances, often intermediates in metabolic pathways, as ultimate electron acceptors. This process, called fermentation, results in the accumulation of reduced products that are of economic

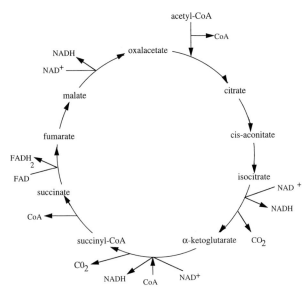

**Fig. 5.** The tricarboxylic acid cycle.

value in many cases (e.g., lactic acid, ethanol, butanol, and acetone).

In the simplest case of a fermentation, pyruvate serves as the electron acceptor, with the formation of lactate and the regeneration of $NAD^+$ in the reaction catalyzed by lactate dehydrogenase:

$$\text{pyruvate} + NADH + H^+ \rightarrow \text{lactate} + NAD^+$$

Lactate production by this means, through glycolysis, represents the only means the homofermentative lactic acid bacteria have for gaining energy from sugar metabolism.

Ethanol is produced by *Saccharomyces cereviseae* (brewers' yeast) and *Zymomonas mobilis* via the decarboxylation of pyruvate (pyruvate decarboxylase) followed by the reduction of acetaldehyde (alcohol dehydrogenase) by NADH, as follows:

$$\text{pyruvate} \rightarrow \text{acetaldehyde} + CO_2$$

$$\text{acetaldehyde} + NADH + H^+ \rightarrow \text{ethanol} + NAD^+$$

Most fermentations yield a mixture of products. For example, *E. coli* and other enterobacteria carry out a mixed-acid fermentation. In addition to lactate production, pyruvate is converted to acetyl-CoA by pyruvate–formate lyase, an oxygen-sensitive enzyme that is distinct from the pyruvate dehydrogenase system that operates under aerobic conditions. The reaction is

$$\text{pyruvate} + \text{CoA} \rightarrow \text{acetyl-CoA} + \text{formate}$$

Acetyl-CoA can be converted to acetyl phosphate, and then to acetate and ATP (a substrate-level phosphorylation). Alternatively, acetyl-CoA can serve as electron acceptor to regenerate 2 $NAD^+$, being reduced first to acetaldehyde and then to ethanol in the process. This flexibility in electron acceptors allows organisms with the mixed-acid fermentation to ferment sugars at oxidation states higher or lower than glucose (sugar acids or sugar alcohols). *E. coli* also has formate-hydrogenlyase, which catalyzes the cleavage of formate to $H_2$ and $CO_2$, an identifying characteristic of the *E. coli* fermentation of sugars. Enterobacteria such as *Shigella*, which lack formate-hydrogenlyase, accumulate formate and do not produce gas.

### 3. Anaerobic Bacteria

Strict anaerobes convert pyruvate to acetyl-CoA by a third mechanism, the pyruvate–ferredoxin oxidoreductase system (Pyr–FdOR), whereby electrons are not transferred to $NAD^+$, as in the pyruvate dehydrogenase system, but to ferredoxin (Fd), an iron-containing low-redox-potential protein ($E_0' = -0.41$ V), as follows:

$$\text{pyruvate} + \text{Fd(ox)} + \text{CoA} \rightarrow \text{acetyl-CoA} + CO_2 + \text{Fd(red)}$$

Hydrogenase then catalyzes the reoxidation of ferredoxin and evolution of hydrogen,

$$\text{Fd(red)} + 2\, H^+ \rightarrow \text{Fd(ox)} + H_2$$

Phosphotransacetylase in turn converts acetyl-CoA to acetyl phosphate, a high-energy compound that can generate ATP by action of acetate kinase:

$$\text{acetyl-CoA} + \text{Pi} \rightarrow \text{acetyl phosphate} + \text{CoA}$$

$$\text{acetyl phosphate} + \text{ADP} \rightarrow \text{acetate} + \text{ATP}$$

This conversion of pyruvate and inorganic phosphate to acetyl phosphate, $CO_2$, and $H_2$, called the phosphoroclastic reaction, is widespread and very important to anaerobes. It provides a means for ATP generation in addition to the ATP harvested in glycolysis, if an organism has a means to reoxidize NADH without using pyruvate or its derivatives as electron acceptor. A number of anaerobes have a hydrogenase that can transfer electrons from NADH ($E_0' = -0.32$ V) to $2H^+$ to form $H_2$ ($E_0' = -0.42$ V), but this reaction is not thermodynamically favorable in the direction of $H_2$ formation. Thus, many anaerobes couple the phosphoroclastic reaction with a variety of fermentation reactions to maximize energy yield while providing for $NAD^+$ regeneration (Gottschalk, 1979; Gottschalk and Andreeson, 1979). The butyric acid fermentation, carried out by species of *Clostridium*, *Butyrovibrio*, *Eubacterium*, and *Fusobacterium*, is an example. Here, two acetyl-CoA (produced from two pyruvate in the EMP pathway) are condensed by acetyl-CoA-acetyltransferase to form acetoacetyl-CoA, which is reduced by NADH to butyryl-CoA, which is in turn converted to butyrate and ATP. The total yield is three ATP per glucose metabolized, which is 50% greater than the ATP yields from the lactic acid or ethanol fermentations of lactic-acid bacteria and yeast, respectively.

The oxidation of NADH by the hydrogenase reaction becomes thermodynamically feasible in environments where $H_2$ is kept at a very low concentration. Such environments exist in the presence of $CO_2$ and methanogenic bacteria, which are very efficient in trapping $H_2$ in the formation of methane. These interactions between hydrogen-producing and hydrogen-using species, called interspecies hydrogen transfer, allow an increase in the ATP yield of saccharolytic anaerobes. Clearly, such interactions are important in anaerobic habitats.

### 4. Archaea

As stated previously, ATP yields from the nonphosphorylated ED pathway carried out by the aerobic hyperthermophile *Sulfolobus* and from the modified versions of the EMP pathway carried out by the anaerobic hyperthermophilic anaerobes *Thermococcus*, *Pyrococcus*, and *Desulfurococcus* are zero. Thus, all energy must come from the metabolism of pyruvate derived from these modified glycolytic pathways.

All these hyperthermophilic archaea produce acetyl-CoA and $CO_2$ from pyruvate and CoA via a pyruvate–ferredoxin oxidoreductase (FdOR) reaction that is analogous to that described for anaerobic bacteria. Acetyl-CoA is oxidized to two $CO_2$ via the TCA cycle by the aerobe *Sulfolobus*. The anaerobes *Pyrococcus*, *Thermococcus*, and *Desulfurococcus* convert acetyl-CoA to acetate and ATP in the presence of ADP as follows:

$$\text{acetyl-CoA} + \text{ADP} + \text{P}_i \rightarrow \text{acetate} + \text{CoA} + \text{ATP}$$

The enzyme catalyzing this reaction, named for the reverse reaction as acetyl-CoA synthase (ADP forming), is a novel prokaryotic enzyme, specific for the domain Archaea. Because two pyruvates are formed per glucose molecule metabolized by these anaerobic archaea, two ATP are harvested in the overall conversion of one glucose to two acetate plus two $CO_2$.

## VI. GLYCOGENESIS (GLUCONEOGENESIS)

Many microorganisms can grow on $C_4$ TCA-cycle intermediates. $C_3$ compounds, such as lactate or pyruvate, or $C_2$ compounds, such as acetate as sole sources of carbon, and autotrophic organisms can synthesize all their carbon constituents from a single carbon compound, $CO_2$. In all these cases, a net synthesis of glucose or fructose phosphates is required for cellular polysaccharide synthesis (see the following). This synthesis of sugars from smaller compounds is called glycogenesis or gluconeogenesis. The pathway of glycogenesis typically includes the same compounds found in the EMP pathway in reverse order. The enzymes of EMP glycolysis catalyze reversible reactions, except two that are strongly exergonic because they involve hydrolysis of high-energy phosphate compounds (i.e., the hydrolysis of ATP by phosphofructokinase and PEP by pyruvate kinase; see Fig. 3). The reverse reactions are catalyzed by distinctly different enzymes. Hydrolysis of fructose-1,6,bisphosphate is catalyzed by a specific phosphatase. The synthesis of PEP from pyruvate represents a significant energy barrier, requiring expenditure of two energy-rich phosphate bonds. Thus, the synthesis of PEP is the key step in glycogenesis.

*E. coli* and other enterobacteria have a PEP synthase that catalyzes a one-step synthesis of PEP from pyruvate as follows:

$$\text{pyruvate} + \text{ATP} + \text{H}_2\text{O} \rightarrow \text{PEP} + \text{AMP} + \text{P}_i$$

Higher animals and plants, fungi, and certain bacteria (e.g., *Pseudomonas*) use a two-step process. The first, catalyzed by pyruvate carboxylase, is an ATP-dependent carboxylation of pyruvate to form oxalacetate,

$$\text{pyruvate} + CO_2 + \text{ATP} \rightarrow \text{oxalacetate} + \text{ADP} + P_i$$

The second is a GTP- (ITP- in some organisms) dependent formation of PEP by PEP carboxykinase,

$$\text{oxalacetate} + \text{GTP} \rightarrow \text{PEP} + CO_2 + \text{GDP}$$

This latter reaction is also used in the synthesis of PEP for glycogenesis from oxalacetate generated from other citric acid cycle intermediates and the glyoxylate bypass (cycle).

## VII. BIOSYNTHESIS OF DERIVED SUGARS, OLIGOSACCHARIDES, AND POLYSACCHARIDES

### A. Derived Sugars

Cell growth and the production of extracellular polymers require the biosynthesis of many sugars and sugar derivatives. Free sugars are rare in the cell; derived sugars are much more common. Sugar acids are important in conferring a negative charge to polymers, especially extracellular polysaccharides, and in making sugar conjugates soluble (e.g., glucuronic, mannuronic acids, and glucuronides). Sugar alcohols, polyhydroxyl compounds having many sites with alcohol reactivity, play important roles in lipids and polymers (e.g., glycerol, ribitol, and mannitol). Amino and N-acetyl-amino sugars are important in glycoconjugates and cell walls (e.g., glucosamine and N-acetylglucosamine). Deoxy sugars, which are generally more stable than the parent sugar, are often used in structural roles, especially in extracellular polysaccharides, where they modify surface properties and interactions with the surroundings, and act as antigenic determinants [e.g., 2-deoxyribose, rhamnose (6-deoxymannose), and abequose (3,6-dideoxy-D-galactose)]. Sugar phosphates are important in central metabolic pathways, in which the anionic phosphate group assures cell retention (e.g., glucose-6-phosphate, fructose-1,6-bisphosphate). Polymerized sugars represent the vast majority of cell and cell-associated sugars. These polymers have remarkable diversity, due to the wide variety of monosaccharides, including derived types, and the many different glycosidic bonds possible between them. Most play a structural role [e.g., chitin (poly $\beta$-1,4-N-acetylglucosamine); the closely related sugar backbone of peptidoglycan (poly $\beta$-1,4 N-acetylmuramyl N-acetylglucosamine); and cellulose (poly $\beta$-1,4-glucose)].

### B. Carbohydrates as Cell Constituents

Carbohydrates are quantitatively much more important as cell constituents than is commonly realized. The microbial cell comprises mostly macromolecules and membranes, which form about 96% of the total on a dry-weight basis. Cell carbohydrate content is commonly reported as the percent dry weight of polysaccharides, lumping cell-wall sugar backbones (murein in bacteria and chitin in fungi) with storage polysaccharides (e.g., glycogen), giving a content of about 5%. This is far below that of protein, about 55% of dry weight, or nucleic acids, close to 25%. But if the sugar components of RNA, DNA, and membranes are considered, the total cell carbohydrate is much higher. Using the reported cell composition of *E. coli* (Neidhardt et al., 1990), and summing the sugar, deoxy sugar, sugar alcohol (glycerol in phospholipids), and amino sugar content of cell components, the cell is more than 17% dry weight carbohydrate, and this is for a strain lacking o-polysaccharide on the lipopolysaccharide (LPS). Adding 20 five-sugar repeats of a typical o-antigen to the LPS (repeats may go as high as 40) increases the cell carbohydrate content to over 28%. Including in addition the exopolysaccharides (EPS) typically found in nature as part of cell-surface structure raises the figure to more than 33%. By comparison, protein then makes up less than 45% dry weight.

On a dry-weight basis, cells consist mostly of macromolecules and membranes, and cell carbohydrate content follows this generalization. Some important cell components have a major sugar content but no sugar–sugar bonds—RNA, DNA, and glycerol-based lipid membranes—but the structural and functional characteristics of polysaccharides depend on glycosidic bonds. Perhaps the most important polysaccharides in microbes are those forming the cell walls, providing strength for cell integrity and osmotic stability in dilute environments. In fungi chitin, poly $\beta$-1,4-N-acetylglucosamine provides the main wall component, with associated $\beta$-glucans adding to the complex whole. In bacteria murein (peptidoglycan) plays this role, with the wall strength based on a sugar backbone very similar to chitin, alternating $\beta$-1,4-linked N-acetylglucosamine and N-acetylmuramic acid (an N-acetylglucosamine derivative), cross-linked with short peptides. The very thick murein layer of gram-positive bacteria is associated with anionic polymers, typically either teichuronic acid, a repeating polysaccharide with glucuronic acid and N-acetylgalactosamine, made under low phosphate conditions, or teichoic acids, polyglycerol-P or polyribitol-P, with a phosphodiester backbone like that of nucleic acids, made under conditions of phosphate excess. Archaea lack peptidoglycan, but their walls are also based on sugar polymers, some very similar to those of peptidoglycan; in pseudopeptidoglycan, N-acetyltalosaminuronic acid replaces N-acetylmuramic acid in alternating with N-acetylglucosamine, in a $\beta$-1,3-linked backbone. Inside the cell, polymers of $\alpha$-1,4-linked glucose serve as storage forms of sugar for energy and raw materials in fungi and most bacteria. With varying degrees of $\alpha$-1,6 branching to provide multiple ends for rapid retrieval, these make up a continuum called starch (unbranched), pectin, or glycogen (highly branched). A form of glycogen called granulose is accumulated in species of *Clostridium,* providing material and energy for endospore formation. Under conditions favoring its formation, glycogen can make up as much as 70% of the dry weight of some bacteria.

The surface of the microbial cell is typically dominated by carbohydrates, which, along with protein cell appendages, are important in determining surface binding and attachment specificity. In gram-positive bacteria there may be a glycolipid layer closely associated with the wall, as in the mycobacteria. The surface of gram-negative bacteria is defined by the protective outer membrane, a lipid bilayer in which the outer leaflet is composed of LPS, with a hydrophobic membrane component consisting of two glucosamines linked to fatty acids, and an elaborate polysaccharide assemblage extending outward

from the surface, with a large variety of sugars, including seven- and eight-carbon sugars, and as many as 200 or more total sugar residues per LPS molecule in some strains. The o-polysaccharide, commonly called o-antigen, is a highly polymorphic structure, rich in deoxy sugars.

Associated with the wall of gram-positive bacteria or the outer membrane of gram-negative bacteria are a variety of other polysaccharides, which can be lumped under the term exopolysaccharides (EPS), characterized by a negative charge, due to their content of glucuronate and other sugar acids (Roberts, 1996; Whitfield and Valvano, 1993). If the EPS is fairly closely associated with the cell surface, it is referred to as a capsule; if loosely associated, it is a slime layer. The EPS has a variety of functions. Highly hydrated (~95% water), it provides protection against desiccation and against viruses, may function in binding nutrients, provides a matrix for surface attachment and the formation of biofilms, and is often an important virulence factor in animal pathogens, interfering with phagocytosis. The EPS is extremely diverse, even within a single species. More than 80 capsular (K) antigens are known for *E. coli.* Some EPS, for example xanthan gum from *Xanthomonas* species, have valuable practical applications. Alginic acid, a polymer of mannuronic acid, is a commercial product of seaweeds. Similar alginic acids are produced as capsular polysaccharides by *Pseudomonas aeruginosa,* in which they constitute an important virulence factor in lung infections in cystic fibrosis patients, and by *Azotobacter vinelandii,* in which the viscous capsule helps protect nitrogenase from oxygen during nitrogen fixation.

Bacteria have a cell surface dominated by oligo- or polysaccharides attached to lipids and elongated glycan chains; with few exceptions they lack glycoproteins, which are essential in determining the surface properties of eukaryotic cells. Glycoproteins are also important in the Archaea, where surface proteins decorated with oligosaccharides are major determinants of surface properties (Lechner and Wieland, 1989).

Sialic acids, variously substituted oligomers of the nine-carbon sugar N-acetyl-D-neuraminic acid, are essential constituents of mammalian cell surface glycoproteins, for example in nerve tissues, but are unusual in prokaryotes. However, several pathogenic bacteria causing meningitis in humans have capsular polysaccharides based on poly N-acetyl-D-neuraminic acid (*Neisseria meningitidis* and *E. coli* K1), and it has been suggested that this polysaccharide may permit infection by specific cell recognition.

Although most cell carbohydrate content is in macromolecules and membranes, carbohydrates are well represented in the approximately 3% dry weight of cells making up the soluble organic pool. Some are, of course, destined for polymerization, but others function in low-molecular-weight compounds. Ribose is present in the oxidation–reduction cofactor nucleotides (FAD, NAD, and NADP) and in cyclic AMP and other modified nucleotides with roles as cell-regulatory signals. The flavins (FAD and FMN) contain ribitol, as part of riboflavin. Carbohydrates often act as osmoregulatory agents, including sugar alcohols and the nonreducing glucose disaccharide trehalose, which are accumulated in the cytoplasm of many bacteria, fungi, and algae in concentrated environments. Cyclic or linear membrane-derived oligosaccharides, based on glucose residues linked with $\beta$-1,2 glycosidic bonds, are accumulated in the gram-negative periplasm in dilute environments, keeping the periplasm nearly isosmotic with the cytoplasm and preventing high turgor pressure on the

cytoplasmic membrane. In addition, many secondary metabolites have carbohydrates as precursors and components, for example, the aminoglycoside antibiotics (e.g., streptomycin).

## C. Biosynthesis of Carbohydrate Cell Constituent

Biosynthetic pathways for carbohydrates usually start from central metabolism, although there are salvage pathways for use of carbohydrates released from cell components by turnover, and some sugars or derived sugars present in the medium may be transported and used directly. Unlike other precursors of cell macromolecules (purines, pyrimidines, and amino acids) sugars are only rarely required nutrients, even for nutritionally fastidious microbes. A number of bacteria require riboflavin, which includes ribitol, and some fungi require inositol (cyclohexitol). However, many strictly fermentative bacteria (i.e., unable to respire) require a fermentable sugar as a source of energy.

Figures 6, 7, and 8 show some typical biosynthetic pathways for derived sugars of various types and for several kinds of polysaccharides, leading outward from central metabolism. In Figs. 6 and 7, lipopolysaccharide is taken to have o-polysaccharide with

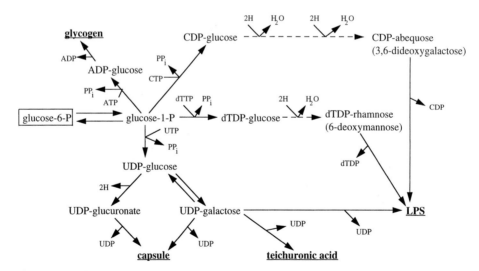

**Fig. 6.** Typical biosynthetic pathways for some carbohydrate-containing cell components, leading from the central metabolic intermediate glucose-6-phosphate. Abbreviations: LPS, lipopolysaccharide; PP$_i$, inorganic pyrophosphate; 2H incorporation, NADH + H$^+$ → NAD$^+$; 2H release, NAD$^+$ → NADH + H$^+$. (See also Figs. 7–8.)

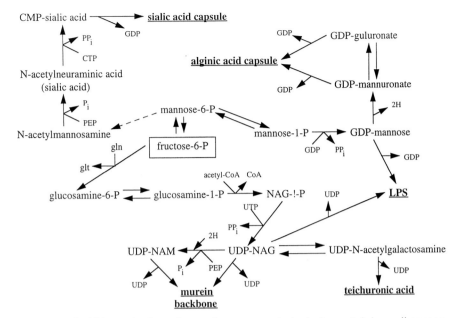

**Fig. 7.** Typical biosynthetic pathways for some carbohydrate-containing cell components, leading from the central metabolic intermediate fructose-6-phosphate. Abbreviations (see also legend for Fig. 6): CoA, coenzyme A; gln, glutamine; glt, glutamic acid; NAG, *N*-acetyl glucosamine; NAM, *N*-acetyl muramic acid; PEP, phosphoenolpyruvate. (See also Figs. 6, 8).

the composition of *Salmonella typhimurium* LT2, containing galactose, mannose, the deoxy sugar rhamnose, and the dideoxy sugar abequose. Sugars with three, four, five, six, and seven carbons are produced in the EMP pathway and the hexose monophosphate shunt, and these serve as precursors for derived sugars with the same number of carbons. Sugars with eight or nine carbons are made by addition of a three-carbon pyruvic acid group (from PEP) at the one-carbon of a five- or six-carbon ketose (examples: PEP + the pentose arabinose → KDO, ketodeoxyoctulosonic acid, the eight-carbon component of LPS; PEP + *N*-acetylmannosamine → *N*-acetylneuraminic acid, the nine-carbon monomer of sialic acids).

A common theme in polysaccharide biosynthesis is the formation of activated subunits, in the form of nucleotide sugars. The energy in the bonds between sugars and nucleotides is then used to link the sugars into polymers. For synthesis of extracellular polysaccharides, a mechanism for transfer across the cell membrane is needed. The glycan component of glycoconjugates may be exported attached to the lipid or protein component. Other polysaccharides are exported as shorter oligomeric repeating units, either linked to a membrane-associated polyisoprenoid (e.g., the C55 carrier lipid, undecaprenol phosphate, for the export of repeating units of murein and o-polysaccharide) or via an ABC membrane protein transporter (ATP-binding casette family of transporters, e.g., for export of the poly *N*-acetylneuraminic acid capsule of *Neisseria meningitidis*), and then linked for elongation outside. Both ATP and a membrane proton-motive force are required for translocation and assembly of cell-surface polysaccharides.

## D. Pathways for Cellular Carbohydrate Turnover

These degradative pathways are routes for recovery of cell storage polysaccharides and for salvage of carbohydrate components of other cell constituents when they are turned over or no longer needed. With respect to the recovery of cell products, the rule is that biosynthetic and degradative pathways do not

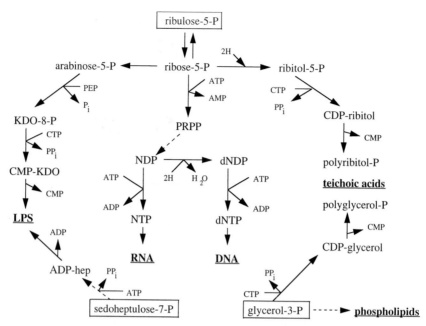

**Fig. 8.** Typical biosynthetic pathways for some carbohydrate-containing cell components, leading from the central-metabolic intermediates glycerol-3-phosphate, ribulose-5-phosphate, and sedoheptulose-7-phosphate. Abbreviations (see also legends for Figs. 6–7): hep, L-glycero-D-manno-heptose; KDO, 3-deoxy-manno-octulosonic acid; NDP and dNDP, nucleoside- and deoxynucleoside diphosphates; NTP and dNTP, nucleoside- and deoxynucleoside triphosphates; PRPP, phosphoribosyl pyrophosphate.

act at the same time in the same cell compartment; they differ in the enzymes involved and often in the chemical intermediates, preventing futile cycles of synthesis and recovery. An example is provided by glycogen, a stored source of carbon and energy, used especially for energy for surviving starvation, but sometimes also for carbon for adaptive synthesis, including endospore production. Flow through the biosynthetic pathway is controlled by allosteric regulation of glycogen synthetase (Fig. 9). A combination of high carbon and energy source availability and limitation for some other requirement for cell growth results in activation of this enzyme, triggering glycogen synthesis and accumulation. Under conditions of energy starvation, the synthetase is inhibited, and an allosteric phosphorylase, which is inhibited under conditions of glycogen accumulation, is activated and releases glucose units as glucose-1-P, thus conserving the energy in the glycosidic bonds (Fig. 9).

A parallel example is provided by the synthesis and recovery of the disaccharide trehalose, an osmolyte made by a variety of bacteria and fungi under hyperosmotic stress, including conditions of desiccation, and then degraded when no longer needed. As with glycogen, regulation of production and recovery prevents futile cycling. *E. coli* provides an example. Under conditions of low osmolarity, exogenous trehalose can be used as a source of carbon and energy by PTS transport and phosphorylation to trehalose-6-phosphate, followed by cleavage by trehalose-6-phosphatase, producing glucose and glucose-6-phosphate. Under conditions of high osmolality, trehalose is synthesized in the cytoplasm by induced enzymes:

$$\text{glucose-6-P} + \text{UDP-glucose} \rightarrow \text{trehalose-6-P} + \text{UDP}$$

$$\text{trehalose-6-P} + H_2O \rightarrow \text{trehalose} + P_i$$

During biosynthesis, trehalose-6-phosphate is protected by osmotic repression of the cytoplasmic trehalose-6-phosphatase. However, *E. coli* can use tre-

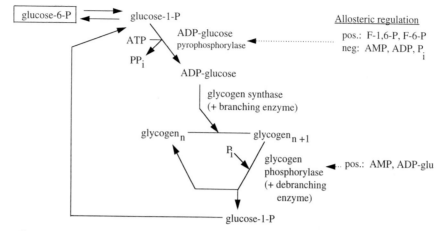

**Fig. 9.** Pathways and typical allosteric control of biosynthesis and recovery of glycogen. Abbreviations: F-1,6-P, fructose-1,6-bisphosphate; F-6-P, fructose-6-phosphate; glu, glucose; neg., allosteric inhibition; pos., allosteric activation; $P_i$ and $PP_i$, inorganic phosphate and pyrophosphate.

halose from the medium for carbon and energy at the same time as producing it in the cytoplasm for osmoregulation, by using a different degradative pathway. Under these conditions, exogenous trehalose is hydrolyzed to glucose by a periplasmic trehalase induced by high osmolality, and the glucose is taken into the cell. As a consequence of this system, trehalose cannot be taken up from the medium for use as an osmoprotectant, unlike other osmolytes used by *E. coli* (e.g., betaine). When no longer needed as an osmolyte, cytoplasmic trehalose may be degraded by a cytoplasmic trehalase or perhaps leaked into the periplasm for action of the trehalase there. Cytoplasmic trehalose phosphorylases have been reported from some bacteria. Trehalose is found at high levels in spores of streptomycetes, where it serves as an energy reserve in addition to its presumed role in stabilization of macromolecules against damage by desiccation.

During cell growth, cell components containing carbohydrates may be damaged or released by turnover, and derived sugars may be recycled by truncated degradative pathways, being fed into biosynthetic pathways instead of being returned all the way to central metabolism. An example is provided by the routes for re-use by bacteria of *N*-acetylglucosamine and glucosamine released from murein and EPS outside the cell membrane; Fig. 2 shows the

pathways for *E. coli*. Recycling of derived sugars is limited, however, because many of them are synthesized on nucleotides (Figs. 6–8) as activated subunits for polymerization and, when released from polymers, cannot be reactivated. Nucleoside salvage pathways function to extract ribose or deoxyribose for carbon and energy sources, not to recycle them as carbohydrates, although the degradative path for extracted ribose goes through ribose-5-P, which could be used for resynthesis of nucleosides and deoxynucleotides.

## VIII. GENOMICS

Increasingly from the 1950s, genes for the enzymes of biosynthetic and degradative pathways and of central metabolism have been painstakingly characterized by mutant analysis in a few genetic strains of microorganisms, especially *E. coli* and related gramnegative bacteria, *Bacillus subtilis*, and the yeast *Saccharomyces cerevisiae*, and then cloned and sequenced as the technology became available. Now that entire microbial genomes are routinely being sequenced, genes in organisms that have never been studied biochemically or genetically can be identified by homology with genes of known function in intensively studied organisms, and metabolic pathways can be inferred. This is especially applicable to central pathways because the reactions of central metabolism and the enzymes catalyzing them are of ancient evolutionary origin, and are highly conserved. Reports on newly sequenced genomes always include comments on any central metabolic pathways revealed, including transport systems for initiating the degradation of sugars, if present. Pathways for carbohydrate biosynthesis and degradation are less often commented upon, but the gene homologs found are listed, grouped by function.

The first complete genome sequence of a free-living organism reported was that of the bacterium *Haemophilus influenzae*, in 1995. Genes for all of the enzymes of the EMP pathway of glycolysis were identified, as well as genes for formation of fermentation products and for electron transport phosphorylation. No genes were found for three enzymes of the TCA cycle—citrate synthase, isocitrate dehydrogenase, and aconitase—explaining the observed requirement of this bacterium for large amounts of glutamate, which can be metabolized to provide $\alpha$-ketoglutarate.

The first archael genome sequence completed was for *Methanococcus jannaschii*, a thermophilic methanogen. Genes for the Ljungdahl–Wood path for autotrophic $CO_2$ fixation were identified, but, as expected, genes for glycolytic pathways (e.g., for enzymes of the ED path and for phosphofructokinase, the key indicator of the EMP path) were absent. No pathway for glycogenesis could be found, although a path of some sort must be present in this free-living organism. The component enzymes may not have known homologs. The genome sequence for another archaeon, *Archaeoglobus fulgidus*, has been reported. This hyperthermophilic sulfate-reducer has been reported to use glucose as a carbon source, but no transporter or catabolic pathway could be identified, consistent with the failure of enzymatic studies to find any of the classic pathways of glycolysis in archaea.

Genome sequences of three parasitic bacteria revealed similar simplified metabolic strategies. The genome of the smallest known self-replicating organism, *Mycoplasma genitalium*, shows a minimum gene complement, with almost no biosynthetic genes. Genes for a PTS transporter for glucose, for all of the enzymes of the EMP path, and for lactate and acetate production were identified, but no cytochromes were found, confirming fermentation of sugar as the source of energy. All TCA-cycle enzymes are missing, the biosynthetic products of the cycle being available from the host, but reducing power, needed for at least one enzyme of fatty-acid biosynthesis, may be available from a partial hexose monophosphate pathway. The genome of the spirochete *Borrelia burgdorferi*, agent of Lyme disease, shows a similar fermentative energy metabolism, with a PTS sugar transporter, enzymes for the entire EMP path and for conversion of pyruvate to lactate, but no genes for components of the TCA cycle or electron transport phosphorylation are present. Sequencing the genome of a second parasitic spirochete, *Treponema pallidum*, the agent of syphilis, was an important demonstration of the power of genomics because this organism cannot be cultured continuously *in vitro* and is thus very difficult to study. DNA for sequencing was obtained by harvesting tissue from infected rabbits and extracting the bacteria. The genome sequence revealed an energy metabolism like that of *M. genitalium* and *B. burgdorferi*. There is no electron transport phosphorylation or TCA cycle (contrary to earlier reports, which may have resulted from contaminating rabbit tissue), but genes are present for a complete EMP path. Instead of genes for the PTS uptake of sugars, homologs of known active transporters for sugars were found, as well as a hexokinase homolog for phosphorylation after transport. *T. pallidum* is microaerophilic; thus, although genes for conversion of pyruvate to lactate and acetate are present, reoxidation of NADH by NADH oxidase, the only identified enzyme using $O_2$, may be needed for redox balance. A parasitic lifestyle is reflected in the limited array of biosynthetic genes, but a careful analysis of the predicted biosynthetic capabilities and deficiencies of *T. pallidum* might suggest a medium for its culture *in vitro*.

The genome of *Rickettsia prowazekii*, an obligate intracellular parasite and the agent of louse-borne typhus, shows a similar reduction in the number of biosynthetic genes, but an energy metabolism very different from that of the other parasites. This bacterium lacks genes for the fermentation of sugars for energy and has instead a complete TCA cycle and all components needed for electron transport phosphorylation, in addition to membrane-bound ATP–ADP translocases for uptake of ATP from the host cell cytoplasm, when available. These properties are like those of mitochondria, and *R. prowazekii* gene sequences are in fact the most similar to mitochondrial genes yet known, narrowing the field for endosymbiotic evolutionary precursors of mitochondria.

Amino acids, purines, and pyrimidines are universal cell constituents and thus are potentially available to parasites from their hosts. Derived sugars are less universal, and their biosynthesis often occurs at the level of nucleotide sugars, only rarely transportable by bacteria. Thus, it is not surprising that the residual biosynthetic repertoires of all of these bacteria except *M. genitalium*, which lacks a cell wall, include complete sets of genes for peptidoglycan biosynthesis. *R. prowazekii* is gram-negative and has genes for biosynthesis of LPS, including o-polysaccharide, as well as genes for capsular polysaccharides, including a polysialic acid. Several genes for capsule synthesis are homologs of genes implicated in the virulence of *Staphylococcus* and may participate in formation of a microcapsular layer involved in virulence.

Doolittle (1998) and Gray (1998) provide an entry into the literature on microbial genome sequences and provide addresses for relevant Web sites (e.g., *www.tigr.org/*). Once the genome sequence for a microorganism is known, gene chips with immobilized gene sequences can be constructed and used to detect and quantify mRNA from cells, allowing physiological studies based on differential transcriptional activity (DeSaizieu *et al.,* 1998). Thus, the methods for elucidation of metabolic pathways in the twenty-first century promise to be very different from the biochemical methods used in the twentieth century.

## See Also the Following Articles

AUTOTROPHIC $CO_2$ METABOLISM • ENERGY TRANSDUCTION PROCESSES • GLYOXYLATE BYPASS IN *ESCHERICHIA COLI* • PEP: CARBOHYDRATE PHOSPHOTRANSFERASE SYSTEMS

## Bibliography

Conway, T. (1992). The Entner-Doudoroff Pathway: History, physiology and molecular biology. *FEMS Microbiol. Rev.* **103**, 1–28.

Cooper, R. A. (1984). Metabolism of methylglyoxal in microorganisms. *Annu. Rev. Microbiol.* **38**, 49–68.

Danson, M. J. (1993). Central metabolism of the archaea. In "The Biochemistry of Archaea (Archaebacteria)" (M. Kates, D. J. Kushner, and A. T. Matheson, eds.), pp. 1–24. Elsevier, Amsterdam.

DeSaizieu, A., Certa, U., Warrington, J., Gray, C., Keck, W., and Mous, J. (1998). Bacterial transcript imaging by hybridization of total RNA to oligonucleotide arrays. *Nature Biotech.* **16**, 45–48.

Doolittle, R. F. (1998). Microbial genomes opened up. *Nature* **392**, 339–342.

Fraenkel, D. G., and Vinopal, R. T. (1973). Carbohydrate metabolism in bacteria. *Annu. Rev. Microbiol.* **27**, 69–99.

Gray, M. W. (1998). Rickettsia, typhus and the mitochondrial connection. *Nature* **396**, 109–110.

Gottschalk, G. (1979). "Bacterial Metabolism." Springer-Verlag, New York.

Gottschalk, G., and Andreesen, J. R. (1979). Energy metabolism in anaerobes. *In* "International Review of Biochemistry, Vol. 21, Microbial Biochemistry" (J. R. Quayle, ed.), pp. 85–115. University Park Press, Baltimore.

Gow, N. A. R., and Gadd, G. M. (1995). "The Growing Fungus." Chapman & Hall, London.

Kengen, S. W. M., Stams, A. J. M., and de Vos, W. M. (1996). Sugar metabolism of hyperthermophiles. *FEMS Microbiol. Rev.* **18**, 119–137.

Lechner, J., and Wieland, F. (1989). Structure and biosynthesis of prokaryotic glycoproteins. *Annu. Rev. Biochem.* **58**, 173–194.

Lessie, T. G., and Phibbs, P. V., Jr. (1984). Alternate pathways of carbohydrate utilization in pseudomonads. *Annu. Rev. Microbiol.* **38**, 359–388.

Morgan, M. J. (1986). "Carbohydrate Metabolism in Cultured Cells." Plenum Press, New York.

Neidhardt, F. C., Curtiss, R., III, Ingraham, J. L., Lin, E. C. C., Low, K. B., Magasanik, B., Reznikoff, W. S., Riley, M., Schaechter, M., and Umbarger, H. E. (eds.) (1996). "*Escherichia coli* and *Salmonella typhimurium*, Cellular and Molecular Biology," 2nd ed., Vols. 1–2. American Society for Microbiology, Washington, DC.

Neidhardt, F. C., Ingraham, J. L., and Schaechter, M. (1990). "Physiology of the Bacterial Cell." Sinauer Associates, Sunderland, MA.

Roberts, I. S. (1996). The biochemistry and genetics of capsular polysaccharide production. *Annu. Rev. Microbiol.* **50**, 285–315.

Robyt, J. F. (1998). "Essentials of Carbohydrate Chemistry." Springer-Verlag, New York.

Selig, S., Xavier, K. B., Santos, H., and Schönheit, P. (1997).

Comparative analysis of Embden-Meyerhof and Entner-Doudoroff glycolytic pathways in hyperthermophilic archaea and the bacterium *Thermotoga. Arch. Microbiol.* **167**, 217–232.

Sonenshein, A. L., Hoch, J. A., and Losick, R. (eds.) (1993). "*Bacillus subtilis* and Other Gram-Positive Bacteria," American Society for Microbiology, Washington, DC.

Warren, R. A. J. (1996). Microbial hydrolysis of polysaccharides. *Annu. Rev. Microbiol.* **50**, 183–212.

Whitfield, C., and Valvano, M. A. (1993). Biosynthesis and expression of cell-surface polysaccharides in gram-negative bacteria. *In* "Advances in Microbial Physiology" (A. H. Rose, ed.), Vol. 35, pp. 135–246, Academic Press, London.

# Carbon and Nitrogen Assimilation, Regulation of

**Alexander J. Ninfa and Mariette R. Atkinson**

*University of Michigan Medical School*

## GLOSSARY

**catabolite repression** Process whereby glucose and certain other sugars prevent the uptake or utilization of lactose, glycerol, and other sugars. The term comes from the hypothesis that products of glucose catabolism bring about repression of gene expression or inhibition of enzyme activity required for utilization of lactose, glycerol, and other sugars. Also known as the glucose effect.

**Cer regulon** The set of genes directly regulated by the complex of cAMP and its receptor, the CAP protein.

**inducer exclusion** Mechanism for inhibition of induction of operons by prevention of the internalization of the inducer. For example, induction of the *lac* operon may be prevented by inhibition of the transport of lactose.

**Ntr regulon** The set of genes directly regulated by the phosphorylated from of the transcription factor NRI (NtrC).

**phosphotransferase system (PTS)** System of proteins that catalyzes the transport and phosphorylation of certain sugars. This system of proteins also participates in catabolite repression and inducer exclusion.

**CARBON AND NITROGEN** constitute the most important nutrients for living organisms, as these elements make up most of the dry mass. Bacterial cells can use a variety of environmental nitrogen and carbon sources. When multiple sources are present, the cells utilize the sources that provide for the fastest growth and prevent the utilization of inferior sources. Furthermore, the rate of assimilation of carbon and nitrogen sources is coordinated to provide for balanced metabolism. In this article we will discuss some of the mechanisms responsible for the regulation of carbon and nitrogen assimilation.

## I. OVERVIEW

We cannot hope to completely cover the regulation of carbon and nitrogen assimilation in this short article for two reasons. First, this regulation is only partially understood, and thus we must necessarily present a progress report that emphasizes those areas where our knowledge is most secure. Second, the study of carbon and nitrogen assimilation historically has played a predominant role in the study of bacterial gene expression and its regulation by environmental signals, and accordingly, the literature in this area is vast and touches most important issues in cell physiology and gene regulation. For example, the concepts of promoters, operons and regulons, gene repression and activation, DNA looping, and protein covalent modification as a signal transduction mechanism were derived in large part from studies of the regulation of bacterial carbon and nitrogen assimilation. In this article, we will emphasize nitrogen metabolism and the global regulatory mechanisms used to coordinate carbon and nitrogen metabolism. Most of our discussion deals with *Escherichia coli* and other enteric bacteria, as these have been the subject of the most intensive studies.

An amazing feature of bacteria is that they can maintain balanced metabolism at a wide variety of growth rates and under a variety of environmental conditions. In part, this is due to the development of specialized cell types to survive extreme conditions. For example, *Bacillus subtilis* and many other bacteria escape unfavorable environments by forming spores. Similarly, it has recently come to be realized that "nondeveloping" bacteria form specialized cell types to survive long-term starvation or extended periods of stationary-phase growth. In both cases, a hallmark of the development of the special cell type is a global alteration in gene transcription and in metabolism, orchestrated by a network of signal transduction systems that regulate the activity of key metabolic enzymes and transcription factors, such as σ factors and transcriptional activators and repressors. The presence of electron acceptors for respiration obviously plays a major role in cellular metabolism, and cells carefully regulate the use of electron acceptors.

We will discuss the coordination of carbon and nitrogen metabolism under nonextreme conditions. Specifically, we are interested in how cells respond to alterations in the carbon and nitrogen sources when growing logarithmically in the presence of oxygen. In order to consider how metabolism is coordinated under such conditions, we will first briefly summarize carbon and nitrogen central metabolic pathways. Next, we will consider some of the regulatory mechanisms that control these metabolic pathways.

## II. OVERVIEW OF CARBON AND NITROGEN METABOLISM IN LOG PHASE AEROBIC CULTURES OF *ESCHERICHIA COLI*

The carbon source is metabolized for biomass production and for energy production. The balance between these competing requirements is regulated in part by the control of the TCA cycle. Under conditions where a carbon source leading to pyruvate (such as glucose) is present at high concentration, the TCA cycle is not run as a cycle, but rather as two branches. One branch provides 2-ketoglutarate, while the other branch provides succinate via oxaloacetate (Fig. 1). These two branches provide intermediates for biomass production. Under such conditions, energy is generated primarily by glycolysis and by substrate-level phosphorylation leading to the excretion of acetate. However, when grown on acetate, the TCA cycle is run as a cycle to generate energy and the glyoxylate shunt is run to provide for biomass production (see Fig. 1). The key enzyme controlling the whether the TCA cycle is run as a cycle is 2-ketoglutarate dehydrogenase (oxoglutarate dehydrogenase, ODH). The key enzyme controlling the flux into the glyoxylate shunt is isocitrate dehydrogenase (ICD). Our understanding of the regulation of ODH is rudimentary. The level of ODH is high in aerobic, acetate-grown cells. It has been known for 35 years that ODH activity is very low in anaerobic cultures and in aerobic glucose-grown cells in log phase. In aerobic glucose-grown cells, ODH increases coordinately with culture density. It is known that, as culture density increases in glucose-grown cells, acetate accumulates in the medium; this accumulation of acetate in the medium may be responsible for the growth-phase regulation of ODH in glucose-grown cells resulting in induction of ODH.

ODH consists of three subunits, one of which is shared with pyruvate dehydrogenase. The two unique subunits, encoded by the *sucAB* genes, are regulated coordinately with the genes encoding succinate dehydrogenase. The transcription of these genes is regulated by the carbon source, with the highest expression occurring when acetate, succinate, or fumarate was the sole carbon source, and the lowest expression occurring when glucose, galactose, or glycerol was the sole carbon sources. The mechanism responsible for this regulation is not known. In addition, transcription of these genes is controlled by the availability of oxygen, and this regulation is due to the ArcA and Fnr proteins.

The ODH enzyme is found as large particles containing many copies of the three subunits. One of the subunits forms a scaffolding structure for the assembly of variable numbers of the other subunits. The enzyme may exist as part of a bifunctional complex with the subunits of pyruvate dehydrogenase.

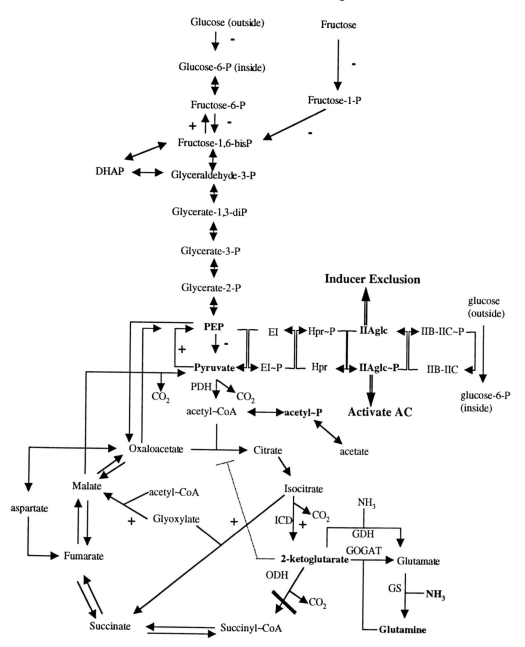

**Fig. 1.** Central metabolism in *E. coli*. Plus and minus signs indicate some of the enzymes whose expression is controlled by FruR. Since the effectors of FruR (fructose-1-P and fructose-1,6,diP) prevent binding of FruR to DNA, these effectors relieve the regulation provided by FruR. For example, the effectors act to increase glycolysis and inhibit gluconeogenesis. The main block in the TCA cycle in cells grown aerobically in glucose is the absence of the step catalyzed by ODH. This is depicted by a bold line. Compounds and processes discussed in the text are shown in bold. AC refers to adenylylate cyclase.

This aspect of the enzyme has hampered the study of its regulation, although the individual subunits and fragments derived from them have been studied in detail. The ODH and PDH enzyme systems are among the most complex enzymatic systems known, with substrate channelling occurring by means of a "swinging arm" mechanism.

Our understanding of the regulation of ICD activity, which plays a key role in the diversion of carbon to the glyoxylate shunt, is clearer. ICD is controlled by reversible phosphorylation catalyzed by a kinase/phosphatase protein, encoded by *aceK*. The phosphorylated form of ICD is inactive. Metabolic signals affecting the kinase and phosphatase activities of the kinase/phosphatase include AMP, which promotes the activation of ICD and thus the diversion of carbon to energy production.

The preferred nitrogen source for *E. coli* is ammonia, which is assimilated by two enzymatic routes (Fig. 1). Glutamate dehydrogenase (GDH) catalyzes the formation of glutamate from ammonia and 2-ketoglutarate. However, this enzyme is only effective at high concentrations of ammonia, due to a high $K_m$ for this substrate. The main route for ammonia assimilation is by the combined action of glutamine synthetase (GS) and glutamate dehydrogenase (glutamine : oxoglutarate amidotransferase, GOGAT). The net result of the combined action of these enzymes is the assimilation of ammonia into glutamate and glutamine. From these compounds, the cell can synthesize all other nitrogenous compounds by transamination and transamidation reactions and by reactions that incorporate amino acids into larger compounds.

The GOGAT enzyme is encoded by the *gltBD* operon of *E. coli*. An understanding of the regulation of this operon is only beginning to emerge. Transcription of the *gltBD* operon is activated by the leucine-responsive protein (LRP). LRP is a global transcription factor that coordinates transcription of genes encoding many metabolic enzymes, as well as genes responsible for other cellular processes, such as the formation of surface appendages. LRP is a dimer of 19 kDa subunits that regulates at least 40 genes in *E. coli*. It may act as a transcriptional activator or repressor, depending on the target gene. Purified LRP binds DNA at specific sites and bends DNA;

binding of leucine to LRP reduces its ability to bind DNA. Many of the regulated genes are only regulated about 2- to 5-fold by LRP. However, a few genes are highly regulated by LRP, including *gltBD*, which is regulated about 44-fold. LRP is highly conserved and found in gram-positive and gram-negative bacteria. Although LRP binds leucine, only about half of the LRP regulated genes are regulated by leucine. It is thought that the promoters with the highest affinity for LRP are insensitive to leucine. The amount of LRP is regulated by control of expression of the structural gene; in part, this control is due to LRP itself. In cells growing on minimal medium, there are at least 3000 molecules of LRP/cell, while in cells grown on rich medium, LRP is almost undetectable. The mechanistic basis for this regulation is not known. Many of the targets of LRP regulation affect amino acid biosynthesis operons and the enzymes of one carbon metabolism. It is thought that, in nature, LRP may play a role in reorganizing metabolism in response to the environmental stimulus of being in a suitable host. This hypothesis is consistant with the observation that LRP also controls the synthesis of bacterial appendages, such as fimbriae, and has a role in the bacterial osmotic response.

In addition to regulation by LRP, *gltBD* has also been reported to be regulated by glutamate, but the mechanism for this regulation is not known.

In contrast to GOGAT, a great deal is known about the regulation of the activity of GS, as will be described. This enzyme is apparently the key enzyme for the regulation of the coordination of carbon and nitrogen assimilation under many conditions. As will be discussed, GS activity is regulated by signals of carbon and nitrogen availability. The main intracellular signal of nitrogen status appears to be the concentration of glutamine. This signal also plays a key role in the regulation of the stringent response. Thus, nitrogen regulation and stringent response are linked.

In the absence of ammonia, *E. coli* can use alternative nitrogen sources, such as certain amino acids. These compounds are catabolized to provide ammonia, which is captured by GS to provide glutamine. Since the GS reaction is the only way for *E. coli* to make glutamine, only nitrogen sources that can be catabolized to ammonia can be utilized as the sole nitrogen source. However, under such conditions GS may not be responsible for all nitrogen assimilation, since some compounds may be catabolized to glutamate, and only some of the glutamate formed need be catabolized further to provide ammonia. Some of the genes required for the import and catabolism of alternative nitrogen sources are regulated by the same signal transduction system that controls GS activity.

## III. CHOOSING AMONG CARBON SOURCES

It has long been known that the presence of glucose in the culture medium prevents the uptake and utilization of less suitable carbon sources. This phenomenon is known as the "glucose effect," although the effect itself is not restricted to glucose. The term "catabolite repression" was applied to describe the observation that one or more catabolites derived from glucose blocked the expression of the *lac* operon and other operons that provided for the use of inferior carbon sources. This effect was amplified when cells were starved for nitrogen. We now know that catabolite repression can be mediated by multiple mechanisms. The mechanistic basis for the linkage between nitrogen metabolism and catabolite repression is not known.

When presented with a choice of carbon sources, *E. coli* selectively uses PTS sugars, which lead to the production of pyruvate. The PTS (*p*hosphotransferase *s*ystem) is a system of proteins that transfers the phosphoryl groups from PEP to transmembrane permeases, which phosphorylate the incoming sugar as it is internalized (Fig. 1). PTS sugars are those sugars transported by the PTS system.

At least two types of control are responsible for preventing the use of less favorable carbon sources that do not directly lead to pyruvate; these are inducer exclusion and gene activation by the complex of cAMP and its receptor, the CAP protein. Inducer exclusion is thought to be entirely due to the PTS system, while the regulation of cAMP levels appears to have both PTS-dependent and PTS-independent aspects. Inducer exclusion is due to the dephosphorylated form of the PTS factor IIa$^{Glc}$ protein, which

directly controls the uptake and/or assimilation of inferior carbon sources (Fig. 1). For example, LacY permease and glycerol kinase, which catalyze the first steps in the utilization of lactose and glycerol, respectively, are inactivated upon binding the dephosphorylated form of IIa$^{Glc}$. IIa$^{Glc}$ is present when environmental glucose is present and is being rapidly internalized (Fig. 1). The inactivation of permeases by IIa$^{Glc}$ requires that the target carbohydrate is present; thus, an inactive ternary complex between the permease, its substrate, and IIa$^{Glc}$ is formed. Such an arrangement prevents the "wasting" of IIa$^{Glc}$ on the inactivation of permeases for which no substrate is present.

The PTS proteins are in equilibrium, such that uptake of any PTS sugar leads to the dephosphorylation of Hpr~P. This, in turn, results in the dephosphorylation of IIa$^{Glc}$~P and inducer exclusion. In this way, PTS sugar other than glucose can also exert inducer exclusion on lactose uptake.

Recent results have indicated that in addition to its dephosphorylation brought about by the internalization of glucose and other PTS sugars (Fig. 1), IIa$^{Glc}$~P may be dephosphorylated when cells grow on non-PTS sugars, such as lactose or glycerol. That is, lactose exerts catabolite repression on its own utilization, by dephosphorylating IIa$^{Glc}$ and, by so doing, inhibiting its own uptake. The mechanism for this phenomenon is not known, but an important observation is that, in the absence of a PTS sugar, the phosphorylation state of IIa$^{Glc}$ is correlated with the ratio of PEP to pyruvate. Carbohydrates, such as lactose, that cannot be taken up or degraded fast enough to PEP reduce this ratio, resulting in a decrease in the extent of phosphorylation of IIa$^{Glc}$.

The utilization of lactose appears to involve the export of glucose and galactose (products of the reaction catalyzed by $\beta$-galactosidase) from the cell, followed by uptake and utilization of the glucose. Thus, cells that cannot transport glucose are also defective in the utilization of lactose. This phenomenon may also account for the ability of lactose to exert inducer exclusion and catabolite repression.

PTS-mediated activation of gene expression is due to the global regulation of gene expression by the complex of cAMP, synthesized by adenylylate cyclase, and the CAP protein. We will discuss gene regulation by the complex of cAMP and CAP. It is thought that the phosphorylated form of IIa$^{Glc}$ is an activator of adenylylate cyclase. Since this species is present when glucose is not being rapidly transported (Fig. 1), a linkage between the transport of glucose and the production of cAMP results. Unfortunately, the regulation of adenylate cyclase has not been demonstrated *in vitro*, despite much effort. One possibility is that perhaps an additional unknown factor is required to mediate the regulation of adenylate cyclase by the phosphorylated form of factor IIa$^{Glc}$. Recent results indicate that there must be additional mechanisms that control the activity of adenylylate cyclase. For example, methods for the measurement of the extent of phosphorylation of IIa$^{Glc}$ have recently been developed and used to study the correlation between the phosphorylation state of IIa$^{Glc}$ and the level of cAMP. These studies have indicated that a strong correlation is only observed when cells are grown on certain sugars, while growth on other sugars results in only a weak correspondence between IIa$^{Glc}$ phosphorylation and cAMP levels. Thus, while IIa$^{Glc}$~P is almost certainly involved in activation of adenylylate cyclase, other regulators of this enzyme must also be present.

More than 20 years ago, a small heat-stable factor was identified in conditioned medium, which counteracted the effects of cAMP. This factor, designated catabolite modulation factor, appeared to act at the level of regulation of transcription of genes activated by cAMP–CAP. Unfortunately, the factor was never identified.

The FruR protein (also known as Cra) is a global regulator of carbohydrate metabolism, which exerts catabolite repression in a cAMP–CAP-independent and PTS-independent manner. This factor is responsible for some, but not all, of the observations of cAMP–CAP-independent catabolite repression in *E. coli*. FruR is a tetrameric transcription factor with similarity to the LacI family of transcription factors. It may act as a transcriptional activator or transcriptional repressor, depending on the target gene. Some of the genes regulated by FruR are indicated in Fig. 1. In general, FruR acts to promote gluconeogenesis and repress glycolysis. While the effects of FruR on target promoters is generally on the order of 2- to 5-fold regulation, by influencing many metabolic steps,

FruR can influence metabolism in a dramatic way. Studies of the purified protein suggest that fructose-1-phosphate or fructose-1,6-bisphosphate may constitute the signal molecule that disables the ability of FruR to bind target promoters. Thus, the presence of this signal, by inactivating FruR, promotes carbohydrate utilization and inhibits gluceoneogenesis. Since the discovery of the role of FruR is recent, it is likely that other mechanisms of regulation of FruR activity are yet to be identified.

In addition to the mechanisms already described, catabolite repression in some cases is due to the regulation of an alternative sigma factor, with promoter specificity partially overlapping that of the main sigma factor. A complex signal transduction system, including a two-component system, controls the stability of the alternative sigma factor and, by so doing, influences the expression of many genes.

Undoubtedly, bacteria contain additional mechanisms of catabolite repression that have yet to be elucidated. For example, there are examples of genes subjected to catabolite repression in *E. coli* that are not regulated by any of the known processes. One curious phenomenon that has been known for over 30 years is that catabolite repression of the *lac* operon affects the relative expression of the three genes of the operon. For this reason, it was thought that at least some part of catabolite repression was due to the regulation of translation. This hypothesis remains largely untested.

In addition to global regulation, the use of various carbon sources is typically regulated by the specific carbon source itself or a closely related compound formed from it. As examples, the *lac*, *gal*, and *ara* operons, encoding the enzyme necessary for uptake and catabolism of lactose, galactose, and arabinose, respectively, are repressed by specific repressor proteins in the absence of the carbohydrate substrate.

## IV. cAMP AND THE GLOBAL REGULATION OF GENE EXPRESSION

As an example of the global regulation of carbon source utilization, we discuss the regulation of gene expression by the complex of cAMP and the CAP protein. This complex participates in the regulation of over 20 genes in *E. coli*. The cAMP–CAP complex has been intensively studied as a paradigm for gene regulation by a global transcription factor. The complex has been crystallized in the presence and absence of a DNA site, and the mechanisms of DNA binding and transcriptional activation have been studied in some detail. It is beyond the scope of this article to cover this large field, but a few interesting conclusions are presented to illustrate the extent of our knowledge.

It has long been known that the level of cAMP in cells is increased in the absence of glucose or other PTS sugars, and that this is due to the regulation of cAMP synthesis by adenylylate cyclase. Adenylylate cyclase is encode by the *cya* gene, which is itself regulated by inverse catabolite repression—glucose stimulates *cya* expression. This is due, in part, to repression of the gene by the cAMP–CAP complex. The receptor for cAMP, the CAP protein (encoded by *crp*), is a dimeric transcription factor that may activate or repress gene transcription when complexed with cAMP. Recent studies suggest that the regulation of *crp* expression is biphasic with respect to cAMP levels, with low levels repressing *crp* expression and high levels activating it. This pattern of regulation is apparently due to the presence of low-affinity and high-affinity sites for the binding of cAMP–CAP, with the binding to these sites having opposite consequences.

Many, but not all, of the genes regulated by cAMP–CAP are involved in carbohydrate utilization, and, thus, this set of operons has been referred to as the carbon and energy (Cer) regulon. However, the cAMP–CAP complex also regulates genes important for the adaptation to stationary phase, as well as the genes required for bacterial motility and chemotaxis and other cellular functions.

The cAMP–CAP complex activates gene expression at different promoters by distinct mechanisms. At many promoters, cAMP–CAP plays a direct role in activation by binding to RNA polymerase and stabilizing the interaction of RNA polymerase with the promoter. In one type of promoters, called Class I promoters, cAMP–CAP binds at position $-61.5$, relative to the transcriptional start site. An example of a Class I promoter is the *lac* promoter. Genetic

and biochemical studies have shown that activation at Class I promoters is the result of an interaction between a part of CAP near amino acid 159, known as activating region 1, and the C-terminal domain of the $\alpha$ subunit of RNA polymerase. In this regard, the cAMP–CAP complex is similar to many other bacterial transcriptional activators, such as the OmpR regulator of porin genes, which also act through the C-terminal domain of the $\alpha$ subunit of RNA polymerase. At Class I promoters, the main role of cAMP–CAP is to stimulate the binding of RNA polymerase to the promoter sequence.

At another class of cAMP–CAP activated promoters, called Class II promoters, cAMP–CAP binds at position $-41.5$ relative to the site of transcription initiation. An example of a Class II promoter is the *galP1* promoter. Two different parts of cAMP–CAP are required for activation at these promoters, activating region 1 and a second region (activating region 2) consisting of amino acids 19, 21, 96, and 101, which are clustered in the CAP structure. Activating region 2 contacts the N-terminal domain of the $\alpha$ subunit of RNA polymerase to promote the formation of the open transcription complex at these promoters. Thus, the mechanism of cAMP–CAP activation is quite different at Class I and Class II promoters.

At other promoters, cAMP–CAP activates transcription by distinct mechanisms. For example, instead of contacting RNA polymerase, cAMP–CAP may serve to stabilize or destabilize the binding of another protein to DNA and, by so doing, indirectly regulate transcription. In the case of the *malK* promoter, cAMP–CAP is thought to promote the formation of a nucleoprotein complex where the DNA is wrapped around several molecules of cAMP–CAP. This nucleoprotein complex then serves as the target for a transcription factor, MalT, that brings about the formation of the open complex.

An interesting feature of cAMP–CAP interaction with DNA is that it promotes severe bending of the DNA. This capacity may influence transcriptional control by several mechanisms; for example cAMP–CAP may permit RNA polymerase to have access to DNA sequence elements distal to the cAMP–CAP binding site. In intact cells, cAMP–CAP may influence gene expression by regulation of the topography of the DNA.

## V. THE REGULATION OF GS ACTIVITY

Glutamine synthetase is a large enzyme, Mr = 600 kDa, consisting of 12 identical subunits (a dodecamer) encoded by the *glnA* gene. The enzyme is regulated in at least three distinct ways. First, the enzyme is subjected to concerted feedback inhibition by a number of different products of nitrogen metabolism. Second, the activity of the enzyme is regulated by reversible covalent modification, adenylylation, catalyzed by the *glnE* product, adenylyltransferase (ATase). Finally, the synthesis of the enzyme is regulated by the control of the rate of transcription initiation of the *glnA* gene. These three mechanisms ensure that the level of GS activity can be accurately and rapidly altered in response to intracellular signals of carbon and nitrogen status.

Concerted feedback inhibition of GS has been reported to involve at least 7 different compounds: alanine, glycine, histidine, glucosamine-6-P, AMP, CTP, and carbamyl phosphate. None of these compounds, in isolation, is able to completely inhibit the enzyme but, in combination, they can cause complete inhibition. The mechanism of this regulation is not understood. Several of the inhibiting compounds compete with substrates for the enzyme, but it is not known if other sites on the enzyme are involved as well.

The regulation of GS activity by covalent adenylylation is a paradigm for enzyme regulation by covalent modification. Adenylylation is on a specific tyrosine residue, thus, GS dodecamers may contain from zero to 12 AMP moieties. It has been reported that the activity of each subunit is controlled independently of the adenylylation state of the other subunits in the dodecamer. Thus, there are 13 steps in the regulation of enzyme activity. Adenylylation of a subunit renders it inactive for the biosynthetic activity of glutamine synthetase. In addition, adenylylation of the enzyme renders it more sensitive to feedback inhibition in a nonphysiological reaction often used to study the enzyme *in vitro*.

The activity of the ATase enzyme, which catalyzes the adenylylation of GS and deadenylylation of GS~AMP, is regulated directly by glutamine and by a sensory system that measures the relative intracellular concentrations of glutamine and 2-ketoglutarate (Fig. 2). This sensory system consists of two

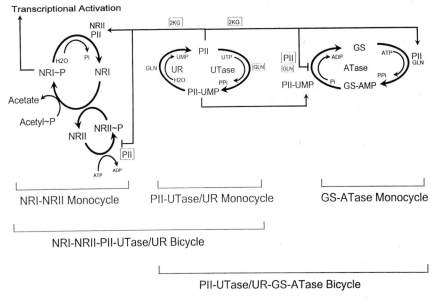

**Fig. 2.** Signal transduction system controlling nitrogen assimilation in *Escherichia coli*. Compounds shown in boxes are inhibitors of the indicated reaction, unboxed compounds are activators. 2KG refers to 2-ketoglutarate, gln refers to glutamine. Reprinted from Integration of antagonistic signals in the regulation of bacterial nitrogen assimilation. Ninfa *et al.* (1999). *Curr. Topics Cell. Regul.* (in press).

proteins, the PII protein and the bifunctional enzyme uridylyltransferase/uridylyl-removing enzyme (UTase/UR; Fig. 2). The UTase/UR enzyme measures the concentration of glutamine, an intracellular signal of nitrogen status, and catalyzes the uridylylation of the PII protein on a specific tyrosine reside. The UTase/UR has a single active site at which both the uridylylation of PII and the deuridylylation of PII~UMP occurs. Glutamine inhibits the uridylylation of PII and activates the deuridylylation of PII~UMP. Thus, under conditions of nitrogen starvation, when the intracellular concentration of glutamine is low, PII is mainly uridylylated, while under conditions of abundant intracellular glutamine, PII is mainly unuridylylated.

The PII protein is a small homotrimer consisting of 112 amino-acid subunits. This protein binds 2-ketoglutarate, a signal of the carbon status, and contains three sites for this effector/trimer. However, the binding of the first molecule of 2-ketoglutarate to the PII trimer results in strong inhibition in the binding of additional molecules. This inhibition is only overcome at high concentrations of 2-ketoglutarate. The binding constants are such that, in cells, PII trimers are always bound by at least one molecule of 2-ketoglutarate, and become fully bound when the intracellular concentration of 2-ketoglutarate reaches the high end of its range. These binding properties of PII have regulatory significance, because the cellular 2-ketoglutarate concentration regulates the interconversion of PII between two conformational states with different regulatory properties (Fig. 3). The singly liganded form of PII interacts with the UTase/UR and with two additional receptors that are bifunctional enzymes, as will be discussed, while the fully liganded form of PII interacts only with the UTase/UR (Fig. 3).

Interestingly, uridylylation of PII reduces the negative cooperativity in 2-ketoglutarate binding. Fully uridylylated PII (three UMP per trimer) should be completely bound by 2-ketoglutarate in cells at all times.

The arrangement described explains how the antagonistic effectors glutamine and 2-ketoglutarate can control the activity of receptors. Glutamine, by acting on the UTase/UR, brings about the deuridylylation of PII~UMP and, thus, increases the concen-

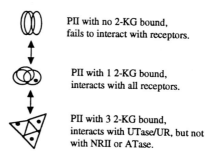

PII with no 2-KG bound, fails to interact with receptors.

PII with 1 2-KG bound, interacts with all receptors.

PII with 3 2-KG bound, interacts with UTase/UR, but not with NRII or ATase.

**Fig. 3.** Allosteric regulation of PII activity by 2-ketoglutarate. The PII protein has three sites for 2-ketoglutarate. Binding of the first molecule of 2-ketoglutarate exerts strong negative cooperativity on the binding of additional effector molecules. This conformation of PII interacts well with the ATase, NRII, and the UTase/UR. At high effector concentrations, the negative cooperativity is overcome, and PII is bound by three molecules of 2-ketoglutarate. The resulting conformation of PII does not interact with the ATase or with NRII, but interacts well with the UTase/UR. Adapted from Jiang P., and Ninfa, A. J. (1999). *J. Bacteriol.* **181**, 1906–1911 (American Society for Microbiology) with permission.

tration of unuridylylated PII (Fig. 2). 2-ketoglutarate converts PII to a conformation that does not interact with receptors (Fig. 3). Thus, PII activity is subject to competing allosteric and covalent control. The allosteric control of PII activity may be more complex than is pictured above. In addition to binding 2-ketoglutarate, PII can bind other effectors at the same site, including oxaloacetate, pyruvate, and glutamate. In general, these effectors bind the 2-ketoglutarate site much less well than does 2-ketoglutarate. However, the binding of these effectors cannot be discounted, because it has been observed that glutamate results in yet another conformation of PII, which interacts with its receptors but not with the UTase/UR. Thus, in cells, other effectors may regulate PII activity in addition to 2-ketoglutarate, and the resulting patterns of regulation may be complex.

The bifunctional ATase that modifies GS is regulated by PII and PII~UMP and by glutamine. PII (bound to a single molecule of 2-ketoglutarate/trimer) and glutamine synergistically activate GS adenylylation and inhibits GS~AMP deadenylylation (Fig. 2). PII and glutamine act synergistically to control ATase. At low concentrations of PII, high concentrations of glutamine are required for activation of adenylylation, while at high concentrations of PII, a low concentration of glutamine can provide full activation of the enzyme. Similarly, at low glutamine, a high concentration of PII is required for full activation, while at high glutamine, a low concentration of PII is required for full activation. Glutamine and PII (bound to a single 2-ketoglutarate/trimer) probably facilitate the binding of each other to the enzyme, but this has not been proven.

Thus, glutamine regulates the adenylylation state of GS at two levels. It acts to control the concentration of unmodified PII by controlling the activities of the UTase/UR, and it acts to promote the binding of PII to the ATase (Fig. 2). This results in very sharp regulation of GS adenylylation state by glutamine when the concentration of 2-ketoglutarate is stable (Fig. 4).

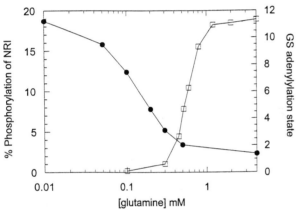

**Fig. 4.** Comparison of NRI and GS control by glutamine. The reactions shown in Fig. 2 were studied *in vitro* with purified components. Filled circles show the regulation of NRI phosphorylation state by glutamine at a fixed concentration of 2-ketoglutarate. Reaction mixtures contained NRI, NRII, UTase/UR and PII, 2-ketoglutarate, and various concentrations of glutamine as shown. Unfilled squares show the regulation of GS adenylylation state in reactions that contained UTase/UR, PII, ATase, GS, 2-ketoglutarate, and various concentrations of glutamine. As shown, regulation of GS adenylylation state by glutamine is sharper than regulation of NRI phosphorylation state and occurs at higher glutamine concentration. Reprinted with permission from Jiang, P., Peliska, J. A., and Ninfa, A. J. (1998). *Biochemistry* **37**, 12802–12810. Copyright American Chemical Society.

PII~UMP activates the deadenylylation of GS~AMP by ATase (Fig. 2). This reaction requires that PII~UMP be bound by 2-ketoglutarate, but at physiological concentrations of 2-ketoglutarate, this binding is saturated and, thus, probably not regulatory. The activation of the deadenylylation activity by PII~UMP is antagonized synergistically by glutamine and PII (Fig. 2). Therefore, this reaction is also controlled at two levels by the glutamine concentration.

## VI. THE REGULATION OF *glnA* AND Ntr GENE EXPRESSION

The UTase/UR and PII protein also play important roles in the regulation of transcription of *glnA* and the operons of the Ntr regulon. These genes are activated by the phosphorylated form of the transcription factor NRI (NtrC), which binds to upstream enhancers and activates transcription by a specialized form of RNA polymerase containing $\sigma^{54}$ instead of the usual $\sigma^{70}$. Transcriptional activation by NRI~P requires the formation of a DNA loop, which brings the distantly bound NRI~P into contact with the polymerase (Fig. 5). This contact activates the isomerization of the polymerase::promoter "closed complex," in which the DNA is double stranded, to an "open complex" in which the DNA is melted near the transcriptional start site. This melting of the DNA requires the cleavage of ATP by NRI~P, although the mechanism of energy coupling remains unknown. Several lines of evidence indicate that the phosphorylation of NRI results in the oligomerization of NRI and that the oligomeric form is the form that can cleave ATP and activate transcription by $\sigma^{54}$-RNA polymerase. The phosphorylation and dephosphorylation of NRI are catalyzed by the bifunctional kinase/phosphatase NRII (NtrB), which is, in turn, regulated by PII (Fig. 2).

NRII is a homodimer of 34 kDa subunits. It catalyzes its own phosphorylation, on a specific histidine residue. The phosphorylation mechanism is curious, in that one subunit in the dimer binds ATP and phosphorylates the other subunit within the dimer. This is a *transintramolecular* mechanism of autophosphorylation. The phosphoryl group is then trans-

Unphosphorylated        Phosphorylated
NRI dimer                NRI dimer

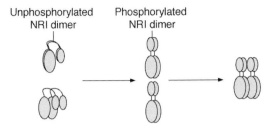

Unphosphorylated NRI dimers become phosphorylated,
resulting in tetramerization

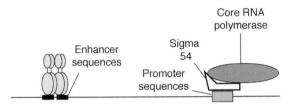

NRI~P binds to the upstream enhancer. RNA polymerase containing sigma 54 forms a stable closed complex at the promoter

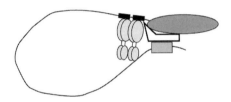

A DNA loop permits the interaction of NRI~P and the
polymerase. This interaction causes RNA polymerase to melt
the DNA strands and begin transcription.

**Fig. 5.** Mechanism of regulation of Ntr gene transcription.

ferred from the histidine residue in NRII to an aspartate residue in the N-terminal regulatory domain of
NRI. This reaction seems to be catalyzed by the N-
terminal domain of NRI, that is, NRI catalyzes its
own phosphorylation with NRII~P as the substrate
(Fig. 2).

When PII (bound to a single molecule of 2-
ketoglutarate/trimer) binds to NRII, it inhibits the
autophosphorylation of NRII and activates a phosphatase activity of NRII that rapidly hydrolyzes
NRI~P. Thus, PII converts NRII from a self-kinase
to a phosphatase and, by so doing, controls the extent
of NRI phosphorylation (Fig. 2). It appears that PII
does not play a direct role in the NRI~P phosphatase
reaction, because mutant forms of NRII have been

obtained that catalyze the dephosphorylation of
NRI~P in the absence of PII.

PII~UMP apparently does not bind to NRII and,
thus, has no role in the regulation of NRII (Fig. 2).
The UTase/UR regulates NRII indirectly, by providing or removing (unuridylylated) PII. NRII itself is
not regulated by glutamine; thus, glutamine only acts
at a single point (control of UTase/UR) to regulate
NRII. Consequently, regulation of NRI phosphorylation state by glutamine is not as sharp as the regulation of GS adenylylation state (Fig. 4).

NRI~P is a global regulator of nitrogen-regulated
genes known as the Ntr regulon. In *E. coli*, the Ntr
regulon consists of relatively few genes involved in
the catabolism of alternative nitrogen sources, such
as amino acids. However, *Klebsiella aerogenes* and
*Klebsiella pneumoniae* have a more extensive set of
Ntr genes and, consequently, can utilize more alternative nitrogen sources than can *E. coli*. For example,
*K. aerogenes* can use urea or histidine as a nitrogen
source, while *K. pneumoniae* can synthesize nitrogenase and fix atmospheric $N_2$ when nitrogen starved.
*E. coli* lacks these capabilities.

Several lines of evidence suggest that the level of
NRI~P is controlled in two ways: by control of the
absolute level of NRI and by the control of the phosphorylation state of NRI. The absolute level of NRI
is controlled by autoregulation of its transcription.
The genes encoding NRII (NtrB) and NRI (NtrC),
*glnL(ntrB)* and *glnG(ntrC)*, respectively, are clustered with *glnA* and regulated coordinately with *glnA*
(Fig. 6). In *E. coli*, these genes comprise a complex
*glnA-glnL-glnG* operon (Fig. 6). This operon contains
three promoters, two upstream from *glnA* (*glnAp1*
and *glnAp2*) and one located between *glnA* and *glnL-
glnG* (*glnLp*). In addition, there is a transcriptional
terminator located immediately downstream from
*glnA*. Under conditions of nitrogen excess, transcription from *glnAp1* and from *glnLp* provides for a low
level of expression of all three genes (Fig. 6). This
transcription is repressed by NRI and NRI~P. Under
conditions of nitrogen starvation, NRI~P activates
transcription from *glnAp2*. A fraction of this transcription proceeds through the terminator between
*glnA* and *glnL*, resulting in transcription of *glnL* and
*glnG* (see Fig. 6). The net result of activation of
*glnAp2* is, thus, an increase in all three gene products.

**A**

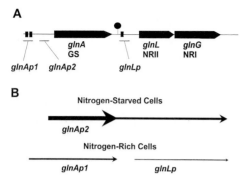

**B**

**Fig. 6.** *glnALG* operon of *Escherichia coli.* (A) Organization of sequence elements. Structural genes are shown as filled arrows, with the gene name and protein name indicated below each arrow. The locations of promoters are indicated by small lines, attached to their labels. Sites at which NRI and NRI~P bind are shown as small squares. The terminator located downstream of *glnA* is depicted with a lollipop symbol. (B) Transcripts observed in nitrogen-starved cells and in nitrogen-rich cells are shown. The source of each transcript is shown underneath the transcript. Relative amounts of each transcript are depicted by variations in the thickness of the lines. Reprinted from Ninfa, A. J., Jiang, P., Atkinson, M. R., and Peliska, J. A. (1999). *Curr. Topics Cell. Regul.* (in press).

A consequence of prolonged activation of *glnAp2* is a 10-fold increase in the concentration of NRI. This increase in NRI concentration is not required for the activation of *glnAp2*, but is required for expression of certain other Ntr genes. In a few cases, this requirement for a high concentration of NRI~P for activation of Ntr promoters has been examined. It was observed that several mechanisms contributed to the requirement for a high concentration of NRI~P; the enhancers for these promoters were not as effective as the *glnA* enhancer in binding NRI~P, the $\sigma^{54}$-RNA polymerase bound to these promoters less well than it bound *glnAp2*, and, in one case, the open complex formed upon activation was unstable and readily decayed back to the closed complex.

The Ntr genes may be thought of as a gene cascade consisting of three levels (Fig. 7). At the top of the cascade is the *glnALG* operon, which must be activated to provide a high intracellular concentration of NRI~P. This high concentration of NRI~P results in the activation of genes at the second level (Fig. 7). In at least two cases, genes at the second level encode regulators of genes at a third level. For exam-

ple, the *nac* protein of *K. aerogenes* is an activator and repressor of genes that are transcribed by the major cellular RNA polymerase containing $\sigma^{70}$. In *K. pneumoniae*, the *nifL* and *nifA* proteins encode regulators of *nif* gene expression encoding the nitrogenase and associated proteins (Fig. 7). The nif genes are transcribed by $\sigma^{54}$-RNA polymerase and activated by NifA, which is related to NRI. Like NRI, NifA binds to an enhancer and must cleave nucleotides to bring about the formation of the open transcription complex.

The regulation of $\sigma^{54}$-RNA polymerase transcription by NRI~P and by NifA requires the formation of a DNA loop that brings the activator and polymerase into proximity (Fig. 5). Factors that affect the formation of the DNA loop can affect regulation of these promoters. For example, the IHF protein, which bends DNA, is required for the formation of

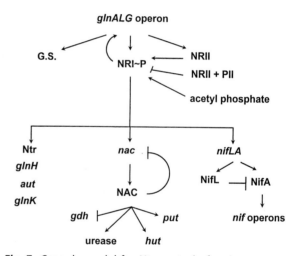

**Fig. 7.** Cascade model for Ntr control of various operons. This figure shows a composite Ntr system from *E. coli, K. aerogenes,* and *K. pneumoniae.* The *glnALG* operon encodes NRI, which becomes phosphorylated in nitrogen-starved cells. Factors controlling the phosphorylation of NRI are shown. Arrowheads symbolize activations, whereas a flat end symbolizes inhibition. At the second level of the cascade are genes activated by NRI~P when this is present at high concentration. These include *nac* and *nifLA.* The products of these genes control genes at the third level as indicated. Reprinted with permission from Ninfa, A. J., Atkinson, M. R., Kamberov, E. S., Feng, J., and Ninfa, E. G. (1995). *In* "Two-Component Signal Transduction" (J. A. Hoch and T. J. Silhavy, eds.), pp. 67–87. American Society for Microbiology, Washington, DC.

the DNA loop in some cases. At the *glnA* promoter, the DNA has a natural curvature in the control region. This may reflect the special position of the *glnALG* operon at the top of the cascade. In other cases, factors that affect DNA loop formation may negatively regulate the target promoter. For example, the Nac protein represses its own expression by binding DNA and bending it in a way that disfavors the formation of the DNA loop required for activation. Clearly, we are only beginning to learn the interplay of regulatory factors that may affect Ntr gene expression in addition to the concentration of NRI~P.

NRI and NRII are related to many other regulatory pairs, which are known as the two-component regulatory systems. The N-terminal regulatory domain of NRI, containing the site of its phosphorylation, is related to the regulatory domains of many other proteins. Signal transduction by these regulatory domains involves their reversible phosphorylation, as with NRI. The kinase and phosphatase activities are encoded by the C-terminal domain of NRII, which is homologous to a similar domain in many regulators. These all contain the autophosphorylation activity and, in many cases, also contain a phosphatase activity, like NRII. *E. coli* contains at least 32 two-component systems, regulating various cellular processes in response to different environmental or internal stimuli.

## VII. THE ROLE OF ACETYL PHOSPHATE IN THE REGULATION OF CARBON AND NITROGEN ASSIMILATION

In addition to its phosphorylation by the transfer of phosphoryl groups from NRII~P, NRI may become phosphorylated by acetyl phosphate (Fig. 2). Acetyl phosphate is formed from acetyl~CoA by the enzyme phosphotransacetylase and from acetate by the enzyme acetate kinase (Fig. 1). Both of these enzymes are reversible, and the substrate level phosphorylation of ADP associated with the excretion of acetate is a major source of energy to *E. coli* growing aerobically on glucose (Fig. 1).

In wild-type cells that contain NRII, the phosphorylation of NRI by acetyl phosphate is counteracted by the NRII phosphatase activity under nitrogen-excess conditions (Fig. 2). However, under nitrogen-limiting conditions, the phosphorylation of NRI by acetyl phosphate contributes to Ntr gene expression, by raising the level of NRI~P above that obtained by NRII acting alone. Some Ntr promoters cannot be activated unless both NRII and acetyl phosphate are available to phosphorylate NRI.

Interestingly, acetyl phosphate also affects the activity of other two-component regulatory systems, by phosphorylating the NRI-homologue. Thus, it has been proposed that acetyl phosphate may comprise a global signal of metabolic stress. In particular, acetyl~P may accumulate when the flux through acetyl~CoA is perturbed. GS activity has a major role in controlling the concentration of acetyl phosphate. Regulatory mutations that decrease GS activity result in the accumulation of acetyl phosphate, while regulator mutations that increase the activity of GS result in very low levels of acetyl phosphate. Thus, GS may contribute to the regulation of many genes indirectly, by controlling the accumulation of acetyl phosphate.

## VIII. OTHER MECHANISMS FOR THE COORDINATION OF NITROGEN AND CARBON METABOLISM

We are just beginning to understand how carbon and nitrogen metabolism is coordinated. In addition to the mechanisms already described, it has been proposed that the PTS directly affects nitrogen regulation via a set of PTS components encoded by genes that are part of the same operon as the gene encoding $\sigma^{54}$. However, as yet a role for these PTS components in the regulation of Ntr gene expression has not been demonstrated. As already noted, the stringent response plays an important role in the regulation of the intracellular glutamine concentration and, thus, is connected to the Ntr signal transduction system. In addition, several recent reports have suggested that nitrogen regulation is somehow tied to the regulation of polyP synthesis, which is also regulated by ppGpp, by the phosphate regulatory system (Pho), and by osmolarity. The mechanisms responsible for these interconnections are not known, and their elucidation will certainly enhance our understanding of how carbon and nitrogen metabolism are coordinated with each other and with the rest of metabolism.

### See Also the Following Articles

GLYOXYLATE BYPASS IN *ESCHERICHIA COLI* • NITROGEN CYCLE • TRANSCRIPTIONAL REGULATION IN PROKARYOTES

### Bibliography

Magasanik, B. (1996). The regulation of carbon and nitrogen assimilation. *In* "*Escherichia coli* and Salmonella, Cellular and Molecular Biology" (F. C. Neidhardt, ed.-in-chief), pp. 1344–1356. ASM Press, Washington, DC.

Ninfa, A. J., Jiang, P., Atkinson, M. R., and Peliska, J. A. (1999). Integration of antagonistic signals in the regulation of nitrogen assimilation in *E. coli. Current Topics in Cellular Regulation* (in press).

Saier, M. H., Jr. (1998). Multiple mechanisms controlling carbon metabolism in bacteria. *Biotechnol. Bioeng.* **58**, 170–174.

Saier, M. H., Jr. (1996). Cyclic AMP-independent catabolite repression in bacteria. *FEMS Microbiol. Lett.* **138**, 97–103.

Ullmann, A. (1996). Catabolite repression: A story without end. *Res. Microbiol.* **147**, 455–458.

# Careers in Microbiology

**Alice G. Reinarz**

*University of Michigan*

## GLOSSARY

**biochemistry and biophysics** Chemical and physical techniques used to study the structure and function of biomacromolecules; study of the mechanism and regulation of molecular biosynthesis, energy conversions, and assembly of cellular structures.

**genetics** Study of the transmission of heritable information in organisms; includes topics such as organization and function of DNA, recombination, and regulation of gene expression.

**microbial ecology** Study of the interactions among microorganisms and the impact of microorganisms on their environment; includes coevolution of species in natural ecosystems; study of the distribution and abundance of microorganisms in nature.

**microbiology** Study of organisms so small that visualization requires a microscope; uses microorganisms as models for basic science and studies their clinical significance in human, animal, and plant disease, with applications in cell biology, physiology, genetics, structural studies, development, and population growth; models include bacteria, fungi, viruses, and cells of the immune response; industrial applications involve making products of value and bioremediation.

**molecular biology** Application of technologies to study and manipulate biomacromolecules; utilized to study biological phenomena at the molecular level; techniques with which genes can be purified, sequenced, changed, and in-

troduced into cells; provides an integrated experimental approach to problems in genetics, biochemistry, and prokaryotic and eukaryotic cell biology.

**WITH EXCITING NEW PROGRESS** in the science of microbiology, many varied career options have developed. Bachelor's-, master's-, and doctoral-level education in microbiology is obtainable at institutions across the United States. Career options for professional microbiologists are found in academic, industrial, and governmental settings. Many microbiologists also choose to work in the health professions. Salary expectations vary with degree of training, location of the job, and position. Professional information is available from organizations such as the American Society for Microbiology and from many publications. The most current information can be found on reliable Internet sites.

## I. WHY CHOOSE MICROBIOLOGY?

In seeking a career, one important consideration is the stimulation and satisfaction that one is likely to derive from the major work interest. For scientists, challenges lie in exploring the unknown, participating in developments that may ultimately benefit humanity, and being part of an enterprise that is truly a worldwide collaboration. Microorganisms are recognized as some of modern biology's most useful models, and microbiologists now work with powerful instruments and techniques, some of which were developed only recently. There is a sense of excitement and enthusiasm among microbiologists as the science enters an unprecedented age of discovery. In fact, microbiologists are encouraged to recruit bright young people into the field.

An element in choosing a discipline is availability of future career options. The well-documented lack of students selecting education in science and engineering is one of the factors suggesting ample opportunities in the natural sciences, including microbiology. Despite strong interest in science and engineering expressed in high school, many students ultimately choose other areas of study. Only a small fraction finish science degrees. Tracking persistence of interest in science and engineering from high school through Ph.D. degrees shows a dramatic decline. University studies on choice of major field of study have demonstrated that a high proportion of college freshmen, after first declaring interest in natural sciences, may switch to other areas. First-year students first choosing business administration or communications switch to natural sciences with less frequency, however.

Recent shifts in expectations regarding availability of jobs and salaries present a particular challenge for a student trying to make well-informed academic and career choices. Particularly for high school and first-year college students, it is impossible to predict job availability as much as 5–10 years into the future. Advisors generally suggest that students follow their own individual interests and talents in making academic selections but with a continuing awareness of changes in professional opportunities. Mentors of undergraduate and graduate students must disseminate accurate information on career prospects. Advisors should seek current information from sources such as "Trends in the Early Careers of Life Sciences," a report by the Board on Biology, National Research Council, and "The Employment Outlook in the Microbiological Sciences," a study prepared by Westat, Inc., for the American Society for Microbiology (see Bibliography).

Because of the concern that too few people, and particularly underrepresented groups such as women, ethnic minorities, and disabled persons, are choosing science careers, many programs have been designed by various organizations to attract students.

Some of these programs provide grants to groups, schools, and colleges to reach out to students (K–12) and encourage their study and career interest in science. Summer institutes for science teachers and talented high school students are supported at some colleges. Both pre- and postdoctoral fellowships are available to underrepresented groups. (For addresses of representative organizations, see Appendix A.) For example, many colleges and universities have listings of scholarships to help students from underrepresented groups to finance their education. The admissions and financial aid offices of various institutions can supply information on opportunities. Relatively more grants are available to graduate than to undergraduate students. Corporations are involved in sponsoring students in university programs, and those particular students are often recruited to industrial jobs after finishing their education. Many universities have special student services directed toward the retention and success of qualified students from underrepresented groups. Information is available from institutions through the Dean of Students or Office of Student Affairs.

Because of its pivotal position among the cellular and molecular sciences, microbiology provides training for many subdisciplines. Microbiologists have backgrounds appropriate to pursue biochemistry, molecular biology, genetics, and cell biology. In addition to the well-recognized professional opportunities for microbiologists, forecasts of the impact of new technology on emerging occupations for the future suggest that many positions will become available in environmental research/applications and with biotechnology firms.

## II. EDUCATIONAL BACKGROUND FOR MICROBIOLOGY

Education in microbiology is available throughout the United States. Institutions that grant degrees in microbiology or in an area of the life sciences with emphasis on microbiology are available most readily by a web search. A site to begin with is the Education and Career Center at Princeton, New Jersey (see Bibliography). It is possible to pursue training in microbiology in virtually all regions of the United States.

To become a microbiologist, choices of appropriate classes should begin in high school so that the student will have a background in sciences (biology, chemistry, physics) and mathematics. In addition, the high school student is well advised to develop skills in logical thinking and in oral and written presentation of arguments. Experience in public speaking, computer skills, and management of group activities will be helpful in the workplace. Many employers cite ethical behavior, commitment to improvement, continuous learning, adaptability to change, and fact-based decision-making as factors they look for in potential employees. Students should be alert, therefore, for opportunities to develop in these areas throughout their education.

The high school student should plan to take the Scholastic Aptitude Test (SAT) or American College Test (ACT) and, for some schools, College Board Achievement Tests in selected subjects. This must be done in ample time to apply to the college or university of choice. The school's Admissions Office will send free information regarding the application procedure. These inquiries should begin at least by the junior year in high school. Early attention to test-taking and investigating various colleges is critical to finding scholarship support.

The length of time that one is willing to commit to education and training is a factor in career options. For students who effectively devote full-time effort to college, the Bachelor of Arts (B.A.) or Bachelor of Science (B.S.) will require approximately 4 years. The Master of Arts (M.A.) or Master of Science (M.S.) typically requires 2 additional years. Some university programs do not require a master's degree if the student chooses to work directly for the doctorate. There is greater variability at this level, but the B.A. or B.S. degree holder can expect to spend 4–6 years, and sometimes more, in gaining the Doctorate of Philosophy (Ph.D.). A main requirement for the Ph.D. is a substantial, independent research project. Other advanced degrees that may be sought include doctorates in Medicine (M.D.), Science (D.Sc.), Public Health (D.P.H.), and Veterinary Medicine (D.V.M.). Following the doctoral degree award, many scientists choose to work with a leader in their field of choice for specialized training. This "postdoctoral" work generally lasts 1–4 years in the laboratory of the mentor.

Students planning graduate study should be aware that there is considerable competition among schools for the best candidates. Various levels of support are available. Descriptions of graduate programs are found at the Web sites of major universities and of appropriate professional organizations (see Appendix B). Having chosen several possible institutions, the student can write the Graduate Advisor or Graduate Studies Committee Chairman for specific program and support information. Particularly at the graduate level, students from underrepresented groups should seek information on unique opportunities through the National Science Foundation and American Association for the Advancement of Science (for addresses, see Appendix A).

For occupations such as directing a research or clinical lab, the doctorate degree will be required. The lab director will be responsible for the productivity and effectiveness of the group. The doctoral degree holder will have the greatest latitude in choice of employment options. The master's degree is generally held by individuals to whom considerable responsibility is given in the daily operation of a laboratory. These individuals have some role in charting the direction and emphasis of their work. Holders of bachelor's-level degrees have the least freedom of choice in their daily work activity but also have less of the stressful responsibility that accompanies the lab operation.

Students are often worried about choosing whether to pursue a B.A. or B.S. degree. In most universities, the programs have many courses in common. The more traditional B.A. degree usually requires four semesters of foreign language. The B.S. degree may require less foreign language but may have additional calculus, computer science, and/or laboratory component plus some additional microbiology course requirements that the B.A. does not have. The B.S. degree is popular at present, particularly among students who plan to pursue graduate work. Choosing a good variety of microbiology classes and attaining a strong background in chemistry, physics, and math is probably more significant than deciding between the B.A. and B.S.

For students planning to enter graduate school, experience gained by working one or two semesters in a research lab is highly recommended by faculty advisors. These opportunities are available through organized (often "honors") courses by faculty mentor invitation. Some universities have a programmatic commitment to undergraduate research that offers a significant number and variety of options. Additionally, many universities and medical schools sponsor summer programs for enrichment. These summer experiences are valuable to students, and the institutions accept only outstanding candidates. Some programs are designed for excellent minority students. Modest stipends to students are provided.

More opportunities are becoming available for research technicians. The large number of public community and junior colleges across the United States have made it relatively convenient and inexpensive for students to finish a 2-year program with an associate's degree. The technician has specific training and specialized work experience in the routine tasks of the research or clinical laboratory.

## III. CAREER OPTIONS FOR MICROBIOLOGISTS

With degree(s) in hand, the microbiologist has many job choices. Location may be an issue. Most scientists are employed on the East or West Coast, but a growing number of positions are becoming available in metropolitan areas and university centers across the United States. Because there are simply more jobs at B.A. or B.S. than at the Ph.D. level, bachelor's degree holders will have a wider choice of location. Advanced degree positions tend to be clustered, but not exclusively, in large cities or in smaller communities that have a university or research consortium.

### A. Academic

For the Ph.D. microbiologist who works in an academic institution, commitment to both teaching and research is required. At universities with graduate programs, the faculty member will be expected to direct, and fund through grants, a research labora-tory for the pursuit of research and the training of graduate students. In addition, organized classes for undergraduate and graduate students are taught by faculty. The teaching labs are typically staffed by graduate student teaching assistants under direction of a faculty member, and these positions are funded by the institution. In the institutions that offer only bachelor's degrees, the faculty member will teach lecture and laboratory courses and will very often carry out a research program with undergraduate students in the lab. In colleges and universities, the promotional track begins at assistant professor. The assistant professor typically holds this position for approximately 6 years and is, at that juncture, promoted or dismissed. The next step, associate professor, has "tenure," which provides considerable freedom in that the tenured faculty member's position cannot be terminated except under the most unusual of circumstances. The next level, professor, carries the highest prestige and salary.

In addition to universities, research and teaching opportunities for microbiologists are found in medical, dental, and veterinary schools. Faculty members (assistant professor, associate professor, and professor) require a Ph.D. or M.D. The faculty's teaching commitment generally involves less classroom contact at health science institutions as compared to universities. The research missions of health science centers typically relate to clinical topics, as contrasted to the basic science research focus of universities.

In a university or health science center, research labs will employ master's- and bachelor's-level personnel as well. These positions—research technician, research assistant, research associate—vary a good deal in responsibility and salary, commensurate with the background and experience of the individual. The research lab director, through grants, also supports graduate students and postdoctoral research associates.

Some microbiologists in academic institutions are also engaged by industrial or governmental units as consultants. The particular expertise of the academician is sought. The duration and extent of the consultantship depends on the situation, and these interactions must be approved by the university's administration. Consulting provides an additional income and collaboration source for the faculty member. In addition, many individuals who are full-time consulting microbiologists may have gained their expertise in industry or in academia.

Appointments for faculty at community and junior colleges involve teaching commitments exclusively. These colleges, all across the United States, provide introductory and survey classes in biological sciences and some more specialized classes, including microbiology lecture and lab. A frequently cited advantage of this occupation is the opportunity to interact with students. A master's or Ph.D. degree is required.

## B. Industry and Research Institutes

Two areas showing particularly rapid growth in opportunities for microbiologists are industry (particularly pharmaceutical and chemical industries) and environmental science. Many new positions are developing in areas of applied microbiology, including water and wastewater technologies, handling of hazardous wastes, bioremediation, and quality assurance for product industries.

Many corporations in the United States and abroad employ microbiologists. These include companies in the food, pharmaceutical (drugs, antibiotics, vaccines), environmental, agricultural, fermentation, and chemical industries. Corporate positions can be found in research and development, production, quality control, management, and marketing. There are positions at all levels (bachelor's, master's, and Ph.D.), with salaries and job flexibility increasing with higher levels of training and experience. In many companies, advancement can occur along the technical or scientific pathway or in a direction of more supervisory or management responsibility. Directors and corporate officers have the greatest responsibility, prestige, and salary. Research done in industrial labs is most often related to the focus of the company and is profit-driven. This includes developing (and patenting) new products, processes, and safety/reliability testing.

Some entrepreneurial microbiologists establish their own businesses with venture capital or with assistance from the federal government's Small Business Association. These companies generally start with only a small number of employees and a limited market. Because of the high rate of failure for all small businesses, this would have to be considered a risky career choice but one that may ultimately provide substantial satisfaction and possibly much greater financial reward than that of salaried microbiologists.

Privately endowed or university-affiliated research institutes employ microbiologists at all degree levels. Doctoral degree holders follow the promotion pathway of assistant professor to associate professor to professor. Some may serve as consultants to industry. In general, no teaching is required, although some institutes are introducing graduate programs. The lab director must seek funds through grants. At some institutes, the research tends to focus in one area, whereas at others, research topics are considerably diverse.

Many private foundations support research through grants to a university or research institute. Regional foundation libraries maintain a reference collection detailing funding opportunities through corporations and foundations.

Industrial or research institute microbiologists may have cross-appointments at a university. They may teach classes in their specialty at the undergraduate or graduate level. Often, their title will bear the term "adjunct" (such as adjunct associate professor) to show their primary employment outside the university.

## C. Federal, State, and Local Government

Government agencies at all levels need microbiologists. For example, the United States government supports research laboratories and regulatory bureaus at the federal level. The employees of these facilities are civil service workers and move through the government service (GS) hierarchy. Greater education and experience credentials enable the person to have a higher GS rank with the most responsibilities and highest salaries. Federal agencies employing microbiologists include the Food and Drug Administration, Department of Agriculture, Department of Energy, Department of Defense, and Environmental Protection Agency. Additionally, the Department of Health and Human Services (HHS) has major programs for research at the many branches of the National Institutes of Health. HHS also supports science education and research through the National Science Foundation. Among the many large laboratory operations of the federal government are the NIH labs in Bethesda, Maryland, and the Centers for Disease Control and Prevention, headquartered in Atlanta, Georgia. Smaller regional labs are scattered across the United States.

At the National Institutes of Health campus, postdoctoral-level scientists conduct research and have clinical opportunities. The Ph.D. and M.D. holders generally have different types of experience and follow different tracks. Some of these persons serve also as consultants to industry. After several years of work, some individuals become "tenured" and are invited to remain in permanent positions. Information about postdoctoral research fellowship opportunities is available from the Office of Education, Building 10, National Institutes of Health, Room IC-129, 10 Center Drive MSC 1158, Bethesda, MD 20892. These labs also employ a significant number of technical personnel at the bachelor's and master's degree level.

State and local governments also have both laboratory and regulatory functions. Microbiologists in these positions might be involved in functions as varied as epidemiology or routine monitoring of water, food, or milk. Public health facilities associated with hospitals and clinics employ microbiologists. Diagnosis and reporting of some infectious diseases are handled in state laboratories. These occupations are generally organized in grades (such as Virologist I through Virologist V), with advancement and salary dictated by training and experience.

## D. Clinical Microbiologists

Many microbiologists choose careers in health-related professions. For example, clinical laboratory directors are often M.D.- or Ph.D.-level microbiologists. The director is responsible for the accuracy of tests performed in the lab and also for interactions with the physicians who require information about their patients' tests. The lab may be affiliated with a hospital or clinic or it may be a private organization. Naturally, this type of career requires considerable management skills as well as expertise in infectious

diseases, instrumentation, and a myriad of diagnostic and immunological tests. The lab director must remain current in understanding and application of rapidly changing technology.

## E. Medical Technologists and Medical Laboratory Technicians

Some students seek a B.S. degree in medical technology or a B.A. in microbiology with the intent of working in a clinical or diagnostic lab. In addition to the degree, professionals in this area take a test for certification by one or more agencies. For example, medical technologists (MTs) and microbiologists who pass the tests are registered by the American Society of Clinical Pathologists and are designated MT(ASCP) and M(ASCP), respectively. The American Academy for Microbiology maintains a national registry. By examination in specialty areas, earned designations are registered microbiologist [RM(AAM)] or specialist microbiologist [SM(AAM)].

MTs collect specimens and perform a variety of tests on patient samples. Labs employing MTs are located in large cities and small towns throughout the country, often housed in hospitals or clinics. This work demands careful, conscientious effort because the diagnosis and treatment regimen to be chosen for the patient often depends on the lab tests.

Reliability and accuracy are critical to the medical laboratory technician (MLT) also. Although the MLT may do the more routine tests of the clinical lab, extreme care and excellent recordkeeping are required. Education in a 2-year program, often a junior or community college, with specialized experience on the job is required for an MLT.

## F. Microbiologists in Medical, Dental, or Veterinary Professions

Many individuals pursue microbiology, including some who receive advanced degrees, and then go to medical, dental, or veterinary school. For example, after graduate work in infectious diseases or immunology (M.A. or Ph.D.), a person may complete medical school (M.D.) and then choose a specialty such as internal medicine, pediatrics, oncology, or pathology. Also, many medical schools offer a M.D.–Ph.D.

training program. Although it requires additional time for completion, the dual-degree recipient has insight and experience both in working with patients and with clinical research.

New opportunities for microbiologists or MTs (B.A. or B.S.) are found in reference labs for veterinary laboratory diagnosticians. This is only one example of emerging professions for individuals with good laboratory skills.

## G. Other Options

With training in microbiology, other opportunities exist outside academic, industrial, government, or health-related jobs. For example, with a degree in microbiology and a law degree, one might be an expert in the patent laws concerning new developments in molecular and cellular science for the biotechnology industry. For microbiologists with appropriate talents and interest, scientific writing and illustration are desirable careers.

Microbiologists may also choose to be science teachers or administrators in secondary schools. With the realization that an adequate supply of scientists depends on training and encouragement of students at elementary, middle, and high school levels, more incentives to enter the teaching profession have been suggested. More competitive fellowships, active recruitment of students from underrepresented groups, and greater access to summer in-service institutes are being suggested to draw talented people into precollege science teaching.

Another option to consider is to finish bachelor's level training in microbiology and then seek a master's in Business Administration (M.B.A.) degree. This background provides managerial opportunities, particularly in industry, as area leaders or laboratory supervisors. In companies that market medical diagnostics or pharmaceuticals, positions are available in technical sales or in the development of new products for the marketplace.

## IV. SALARY EXPECTATIONS

Libraries and career information centers at colleges and universities have resources that give representative salary data for various occupations. Professional organizations (see Appendix B) will send, on request, information describing their discipline, job opportunities, and outlining salary expectations. It is not appropriate to list salary figures here because these data lose their reliability so quickly. Employment outlook and salaries vary significantly as technology and needs of employers change.

As a rule, when one compares salary data, the most significant element is education. In all sectors, beginning wages are least for those with B.A./B.S. degrees, higher for M.A./M.S. holders, and highest for Ph.D. holders. Average salaries at all degree levels increase in the following progression: lowest in academic careers (some difference between public and private schools), next higher in government agencies, next in hospitals or clinics, and highest in industry. At all levels and in all sectors, tremendous variations can occur among individuals depending on their experience, expertise, and relative success in their own career. In addition to salary, other components such as opportunity for travel, to consult, or to write independently are significant. Working hours, retirement, and fringe benefits are important variables.

Salaries paid to microbiologists are adequate for a reasonable standard of living but, clearly, there are other professions that offer more money. Although salary is one tangible reward for work, other factors should be considered. For example, microbiologists can expect good working conditions and anticipate stimulation by personal interactions with coworkers and others in the field. Depending on degree and occupation, freedom to pursue one's interests is often cited as an important factor in career choice among scientists. Additionally, satisfaction can be derived from making contributions: researchers to the body of knowledge, clinical microbiologists to patients, academicians to students, industrial microbiologists to products and services.

## V. RESOURCES

## A. Professional Affiliations

While an undergraduate, a student can participate in campus chapters of preprofessional organizations. The student learns about career options and also has interactions with peers who share the same interests and with faculty in the discipline. The faculty (particularly the organization's advisor) will be available if problems arise and will also be role models for the student.

Microbiologists (at all degree levels) and graduate students in the discipline are eligible for membership in the American Society for Microbiology (ASM). Members receive the monthly publication ASM News and member rates for meetings and primary research journals (e.g., *Journal of Bacteriology, Molecular and Cell Biology, Journal of Virology, Infection and Immunity*). In addition, ASM members receive schedules of all meetings and continuing education workshops involving microbiology and related topics. This international organization promotes exchange of information among professionals and is an effective voice to address legislation (national and state) and public opinion that relates to microbiology. An application for membership can be obtained from the Membership Committee, American Society for Microbiology, 1325 Massachusetts Avenue, NW, Washington, DC 20005 [phone: (202) 737-3600]. For the microbiologist seeking employment, the placement service with on-site interview opportunities and Career Development Forum, held in conjunction with national ASM meetings, are valuable services.

Other professional organizations that may also serve the interests of microbiologists are listed in Appendix B.

## B. Sources of Useful Information

Public school and university libraries have many books that provide interesting reading about microbiology, its practitioners, and its history and milestones. Introductory-level microbiology textbooks provide an overview of the science and are available in college libraries. Biographies of Louis Pasteur and Antony Van Leeuwenhoek are particularly appropriate for younger readers. Reading choices relating to developments in microbiology, new laboratory techniques, and the ethics and regulation of modern technologies can be recommended by librarians.

A multitude of free or very inexpensive materials (booklets, directories, newsletters, books, and teaching aids) relating to science and science education are available. Items can be chosen at levels that are appropriate for youngsters. The Internet is most convenient and up-to-date source of information (for addresses of some sites, see Appendix A).

Many science-oriented periodicals are available by personal subscription or through libraries. These magazines are useful in maintaining a current overview of science and technology. They are appropriate for readers at varied levels of interest and sophistication. Examples, but by no means an all-inclusive list, are *Science, Scientific American, Discover,* and *Omni.*

## APPENDIX A: PROGRAMS TO STIMULATE STUDENT INTEREST IN SCIENCE[1]

American Association for the Advancement of Science
Directorate for Education and Human Resources Programs
1200 New York Avenue, NW
Washington, DC 20005
*ehrweb.aaas.org/her/*

Carnegie Corporation of New York
437 Madison Avenue
New York, NY 10022
*www.carnegie.org/*

Howard Hughes Medical Institute
6701 Rockledge Drive
Bethesda, MD 20817

National Academy of Sciences
2101 Constitution Avenue, NW
Washington, DC 20055
*www2.nas.edu/cpc*

National Science Foundation
4201 Wilson Boulevard
Arlington, VA 22230
*www.nsf.gov/*

---

1. Some grants and fellowships are targeted to groups underrepresented in science.

## APPENDIX B: PROFESSIONAL ORGANIZATIONS THAT MAY SERVE THE INTERESTS OF MICROBIOLOGISTS

American Association of Immunologists[2]
9650 Rockville Pike
Bethesda, MD 20814
*www.scienceXchange.com/aai/*

American Chemical Society
1155 16th Street, NW
Washington, DC 20036
*www.acs.org*

American Institute of Biological Sciences
1444 I Street, NW, Suite 200
Washington, DC 20005
*www.aibs.org*

American Society for Cell Biology[a]
9650 Rockville Pike
Bethesda, MD 20814
*www.ascb.org/ascb/*

American Society for Microbiology
1325 Massachusetts Avenue, NW
Washington, DC 20005
*www.asmusa.org/*

---

2. Organization is part of the Federation of American Societies for Experimental Biology (see *www.faseb.org/*).

Society for Industrial Microbiology
PO Box 12534
Arlington, VA 22209
*www.simhq.org/index1.html*

### *See Also the Following Article*
EDUCATION IN MICROBIOLOGY

### *Bibliography*

"Careers in Science and Engineering. A Student Planning Guide to Grad School and Beyond." (1996). National Academy Press, Washington, DC.

National Research Council. (1995). "Research-Doctorate Programs in the United States: Continuity and Change." National Academy Press, Washington, DC.

National Research Council. (1998). "Trends in the Early Careers of Life Scientists." National Academy Press, Washington, DC.

Peterson's Graduate Programs in Microbiology. (1998). The Education and Career Center, Peterson's, Princeton, NJ at http://www.petersons.com/.

"Profiles of American Colleges." (1998). Barron's Educational Series, Hauppauge, New York.

"Salary and Employment Survey 1998. Employment of Recent Doctoral Graduates in Science and Engineering." (1998). Commission on Professionals in Science and Technology, Washington, DC.

"The Employment Outlook in the Microbiological Sciences." (1996). American Society for Microbiology, Washington, DC.

# Caulobacter, Genetics

## M. R. K. Alley

*Imperial College of Science, Technology and Medicine*

I. Plasmids and Transfer
II. Mutagenesis, Transduction, and Mapping
III. Molecular Genetic Techniques
IV. Practical Use of Genetics to Study the Cell Cycle
V. The Genome Sequence and the Future

## GLOSSARY

**auxotroph** A mutant that requires more nutrients than required by a "wild-type" strain for growth on minimal media.

**conjugation** Transfer of DNA via cellular contact from a donor cell to a recipient cell.

**electroporation** Transfer of DNA into a cell by the appliance of an electrical field.

**generalized transduction** Transfer of random fragments of chromosomal DNA from one cell to another cell via a bacteriophage.

**plasmid** An autonomous replicating unit of DNA that is not essential for the viability of the organism.

**plasmid incompatibility** The inability of a plasmid to be maintained in the same host as another different plasmid.

**predivisional cell** A *Caulobacter* cell prior to cell division.

**stalked cell** A nonmotile cell with a stalk or prostheca, which is DNA replication competent.

**swarmer cell** A motile cell that is unable to replicate its chromosome and must differentiate into a stalked cell to divide.

**transposon** Mobile unit of DNA.

**CAULOBACTER** is a dimorphic gram-negative bacterium of the alpha subdivision of proteobacteria. This article will concentrate on the many different genetic and molecular genetic methods that have been employed to investigate the *Caulobacter* cell cycle.

Genetics has empowered the study of the *Caulobacter* cell cycle and has been the main conduit for understanding how one cell can give rise two different cell types from a single cell division (the generation of asymmetry). *Caulobacter* must go through an obligate asymmetric cell division to yield two functionally distinct progeny (Fig. 1), a stalked cell and a swarmer cell. The stalked cell is the sole cell type capable of initiating DNA replication and cell growth, which leads to the regeneration of the predivisional cell. The swarmer cell type is present for approximately one-third of a generation time before it undergoes an obligate differentiation event to become a stalked cell. The decision to differentiate sets off a series of events, including the loss of the machinery for motility (single polar flagellum and chemotaxis proteins), the acquisition of the ability to initiate DNA replication, and stalk synthesis which is initiated at the site of the ejected single polar flagellum. As the stalked cell grows it must replace the motile machinery required by the swarmer cell in the next cell division event. The synthesis of the flagellar and chemotaxis proteins is coordinately regulated with progression through the cell cycle; any interruption of DNA replication results in inhibition of synthesis of these proteins. Superimposed on the cell cycle regulation of the flagellar and chemotaxis genes is a spatial control, in which flagellar and chemotaxis components are targeted to the flagellated pole of the predivisional cell. Conversely, there is also specific targeting of proteins to the stalked cell portion of the predivisional cell. The growth of the stalked cell accompanied by the synthesis and targeting of the chemotaxis and flagellar proteins culminates in the predivisional cell.

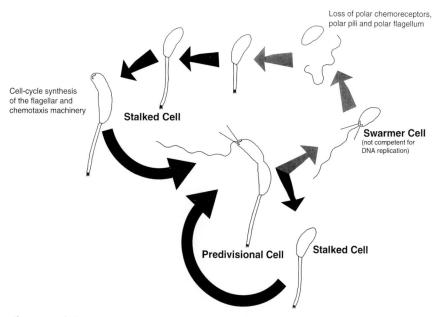

Loss of polar chemoreceptors, polar pili and polar flagellum

Cell-cycle synthesis of the flagellar and chemotaxis machinery

**Stalked Cell**

**Swarmer Cell** (not competent for DNA replication)

**Predivisional Cell**

**Stalked Cell**

***Fig. 1.*** Caulobacter cell cycle. The gray arrows show the development and differentiation of the swarmer cell during the cell cycle, the black arrows denote the progression of the stalked cell through the cell cycle, and the black dots denote chemoreceptor.

The well-developed *Caulobacter* genetic system has been essential in understanding the underlying mechanisms that play an important part in the cell cycle, including cell cycle and spatial control of transcription, protein targeting and proteolysis, DNA replication, and chromosome segregation. Therefore, this article will emphasize the many genetic techniques that can be used to study the *Caulobacter* cell cycle.

## I. PLASMIDS AND TRANSFER

### A. Plasmids

No naturally occurring plasmids have been found in the genetically manipulable *Caulobacter* strain CB15. The commonly used *Escherichia coli* plasmid vectors, based on the replication origins (*oriV*) of the plasmids ColE1 and P15A, are not able to replicate in *Caulobacter*. These plasmids are classified as narrow host range plasmids because of the limited number of bacterial species that are permissive for their replication. However, plasmids from the incompatibility

groups P and Q, which are called broad host range plasmids because they can replicate in a diverse number of gram-negative bacterial hosts, can replicate in *Caulobacter*. The IncP and Q plasmids are present in low copy numbers in *Caulobacter* (two to five copies per cell). However, IncQ plasmids are very unstable and once antibiotic selection for the plasmid is removed they are lost rapidly. Therefore, plasmid vectors for complementation and transcriptional studies have been mainly based on IncP plasmids. Higher copy number plasmids capable of replicating in *Caulobacter* have been isolated from *Bordetella bronchiseptica*, a member of a novel incompatibility group. An important addition to the ability to replicate in one's preferred host is the ability to select for that event, and *Caulobacter* has a distinct advantage in that it is not resistant to many antibiotics—only nalidixic acid, trimethoprim, and ampicillin. The following antibiotics can be selected for by using the appropriate resistance genes: tetracycline, kanamycin, neomycin, gentamicin, chloramphenicol, hygromycin, streptomycin, and spectinomycin. This allows for double or even triple selection of plasmids or insertions in the chromosome. Different resistance genes can also be used to remove resident plasmids by introducing another plasmid of the same incompatibility group but with a different antibiotic resistance gene. For example, selecting for a gentamicin-resistant IncP plasmid will remove a resident IncP tetracycline-resistant plasmid.

## B. Plasmid Transfer

### 1. *Conjugation*

The transfer of plasmids from *E. coli* to *Caulobacter* was first performed by conjugation using a large (60-kb) self-transmissible IncP plasmid RP1, which has also been called RP4 and RK2. IncP-mediated conjugation requires cell to cell contact on a solid substrate, such as filter paper or agar, and transfer rates of 100% can be attained. Conjugal transfer requires a *cis*-acting site called the origin of transfer (*oriT*) and *trans*-acting functions for cell to cell contact; the transfer of the plasmid from donor to recipient occurs as a single-stranded DNA molecule. Some plasmids have evolved to use the IncP-mediated conjugation system because IncQ and ColE1 plasmids can be transferred using RP4. The IncQ and ColE1 plasmids encode a mobilization protein which nicks their respective plasmids at their *oriT* and this acts as a substrate for DNA transfer using the IncP conjugation system. All plasmids can be modified to be transferred using the IncP conjugation system by adding an IncP *oriT* to the plasmid of interest and supplying the transfer functions *in trans* on another plasmid (pRK2013) or in the chromosome, as in the *E. coli* strain S17-1.

### 2. *Electroporation*

Unlike *E. coli*, *Caulobacter* cannot be transformed using CaCl$_2$ or by any other chemical treatment. However, *Caulobacter* can be transformed using electroporation. The frequency of transfer is lower than that by conjugation but it allows plasmids without an IncP *oriT* to be introduced into *Caulobacter*. Electroporation also enables ampicillin to be used as a selection since in conjugation the death of the ampicillin-resistant *E. coli* donor confers resistance on the *Caulobacter* recipient by releasing the ampicillin resistance protein β-lactamase into the media. Since *Caulobacter* is naturally resistant to ampicillin, an ampicillin-sensitive strain must be used for these transformations.

## II. MUTAGENESIS, TRANSDUCTION, AND MAPPING

## A. Mutagenesis and Transposons

The traditional mutagens N-methyl-N′-nitro-N-nitrosoguanidine, ethyl methane sulfonate (EMS), and UV light have been used in *Caulobacter*. However, many kinds of auxotrophs and motile mutants have been obtained without prior mutagenesis using enrichment procedures or by direct selection in the case of antibiotic-resistant mutants. The use of mutagens has mainly been restricted to generating temperature-sensitive mutations in genes essential for viability. The easiest way to mutate non-essential genes in *Caulobacter* is via Tn5 transposon mutagenesis. Tn5 is a composite transposon containing two insertion sequences (IS50L and IS50R) coding for a transposase and transposase inhibitor. The DNA separating the two IS elements codes for the antibiotic-resistant genes to neomycin, streptomycin, and bleomycin (Fig. 2). The Tn5 transposon is introduced by conjugation via a plasmid that can-not replicate in *Caulobacter* and so any neomycin-resistant colony arising from this mating will be due to Tn5 transposition to the chromosome. The other transposons tested in *Caulobacter,* Tn10 and Tn501 do not transpose, whereas Tn7 only transposes to a single specific site on the chromosome. The transposons Tn3 and Tn1 have not been tested. Tn5 transposes randomly in *Caulobacter* and has been used to generate many flagellar and chemotaxis mutants, which can easily be assayed because of their inability to swim in semi-solid agar (Fig. 3). An additional advantage to using Tn5 is that the transposase inhibitor prevents Tn5 transposing; therefore, if an extra Tn5 is introduced into a strain harboring a Tn5, it will integrate by homologous recombination into the resident Tn5. Many different antibiotic-resistant Tn5s have been constructed, so these can be used to exchange the resistance gene in the chromosome by homologous recombination (Fig. 4), thus changing the resistance of the cell.

# Tn5

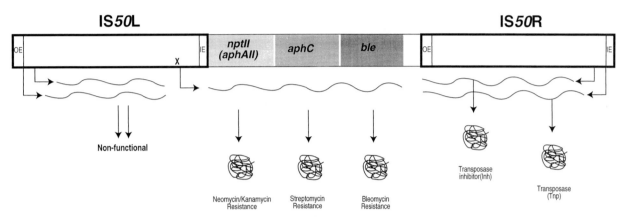

**Fig. 2.** Tn5 transposon. The X denotes a stop codon in the reading frame for the inhibitor and transposase in IS50 L. IE, inside end; OE, outside end, both of these *cis*-acting elements are required for transposition; promoter, ⌐; mRNA, ∿; protein, ▩.

## B. Generalized Transduction and Mapping

Generalized transduction has been shown to occur in *Caulobacter* using the lytic bacteriophage φCR30. The bacteriophage φCR30 does not form lysogens, so transduction of genetic markers from one strain to another requires irradiating the donor lysate with UV light and then infecting the recipient with this irradiated lysate. The basis for the transduction ability of φCR30 is that the bacteriophage is capable of packaging random pieces of the *Caulobacter* chromo-

some, and UV irradiation kills the wild-type bacteriophage. The bacteriophage φCR30 packages approximately 200 kilobase pairs (kb), which is 1/20 of the *Caulobacter* chromosome. The mapping of mutations involves finding a linkage between a known gene (marker) and the mutation. Linkage is determined by the frequency of loss of a recipient marker and the gain of the selected donor marker. Therefore, if two markers are closely linked, the recipient marker will replace the donor marker. To obtain linkages over longer distances than those obtained with φCR30, IncP plasmid-mediated chromosome transfer has to be used. On average, one-sixth of the chromosome can be transferred using this method. Although many different auxotrophs and motile mutants have been isolated and mapped using generalized transduction and chromosome transfer, a circular genetic map has never been obtained. It was not until the advent of pulse-field gel electrophoresis that it was proved that *Caulobacter* had a circular chromosome. Pulse-field gel electrophoresis allows the separation of DNA fragments larger than 20 kb in agarose gel electrophoresis. Because the genome of *Caulobacter* is 69% GC, restriction enzymes that have an AT-rich recognition sequence will cut infrequently. Three restriction enzymes, *Ase*-1, *Dra*-l, and *Spe*-l, were found to cut the genome into 13, 40, and 26 fragments, respectively. The genetic and physical maps were aligned using Tn5 mutants which could

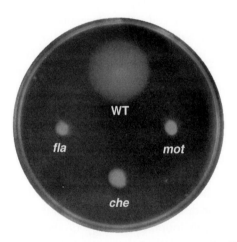

**Fig. 3.** Swarm plate assay. showing swarms of wild-type (WT), a flagellar mutant (fla), a chemotaxis mutant (che), and motility mutant (mot) in semi-solid agar.

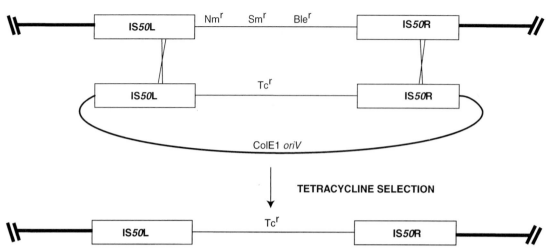

**Fig. 4.** Tn5 resistance replacement: the replacement of a neomycin-resistant Tn5 in the *Caulobacter* chromosome for a tetracycline-resistant Tn5. Nm^r neomycin resistance; Sm^r, streptomycin resistance; Ble^r bleomycin resistance; Tc^r, tetracycline resistance. ColE1 *oriV* is the replication origin for the narrow host range plasmid ColE1, which is unable to replicate in *Caulobacter*.

be mapped by either hybridization or a change in size of the respective restriction fragment (Fig. 5). The circularization of the genome map was performed by converting the Tn5 insertions in *trpE*, *lac*, *cysD*, and *CysB*, which map to either end of the linear genetic map, to tetracycline resistance (Fig. 4). The tetracycline resistance gene contains restriction enzyme sites for *Ase*-l and *Dra*-l allowing for precise localization of the Tn5 in the restriction fragment. Because of the combined physical and genetic map, any *Caulobacter* gene can be mapped by inserting into the genome a cloned gene on a ColE1-derived vector with an ampicillin resistance gene. The ampicillin resistance gene introduces extra *Ase*-l and *Dra*-l sites, which can be mapped precisely using pulsed field gel electrophoresis.

## III. MOLECULAR GENETIC TECHNIQUES

### A. Promoter and Protein Fusions

Once a gene has been identified by mutagenesis it is important to understand how it is regulated. Regulation can occur at the transcriptional or post-transcriptional levels. Construction of fusions to either the promoter or coding sequence to an assayable gene yields data on a gene's regulation. The first genetic studies of promoter regulation in *Caulobacter* were performed using Tn5-VB32, a tetracycline-resistant Tn5 with a promoterless neomycin resistance gene (*nptII*) that replaced most of IS50L except for the outside end. When Tn5-VB32 transposes into a gene with the *nptII* gene downstream of a promoter, this confers kanamycin/neomycin resistance on the cell, but only at a level commensurate with the strength of the *Caulobacter* promoter. The protein NptII is stable throughout the *Caulobacter* cell cycle, therefore, the synthesis of NptII needs to be measured to observe cell cycle expression. Antisera was generated to NptII in order to assay cell-cycle expression using immunoprecipitation of radio-labeled cell extracts. The use of *nptII* as a reporter gene has been supplanted by use of the *lacZ* gene, which codes for β-galactosidase, a more easily assayable enzyme. Additionally, functional protein fusions can be fused to β-galactosidase, enabling post-transcriptional regulation to be measured. By using protein fusions to β-galactosidase and β lactamase (ampicillin resistance protein), the topology of cytoplasmic membrane proteins can be determined. This has been used to determined the membrane topology of the chemotaxis receptor McpA. Although protein fusions to the *lacZ* gene produce active β-galactosidase, they often inactivate the gene that is fused to *lacZ*. Therefore, raising

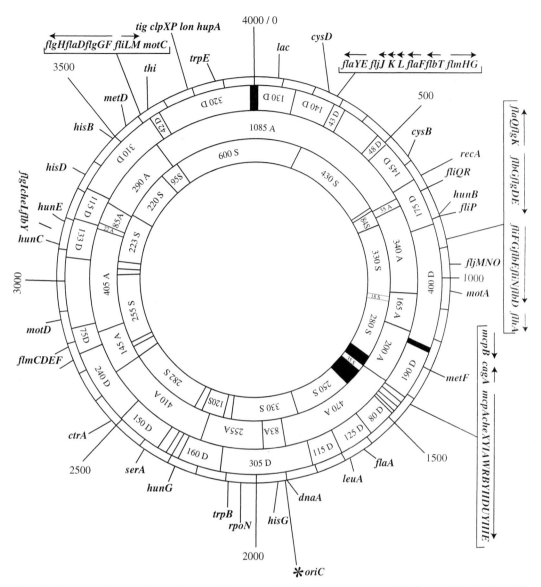

**Fig. 5.** The genetic and physical map of *Caulobacter*. The numbers are in kilobase pairs. A, *Ase* I; D, *Dra* I; S, *Spe* I. The arrows denote transcriptional units or genes. The asterisk denotes the origin of replication (*oriC*).

antisera or generating protein fusions to epitopes (a recognition site for a single monoclonal antibody normally between 6 and -12 amino acids in length) are necessary to study localization or proteolysis of functional proteins.

## B. Counter-Selectable Markers

The problem with transposon insertions is that they are random, an advantage for mutagenesis of the chromosome but a distinct disadvantage for making specific mutations in a certain gene. It is possible to randomly mutate a plasmid bearing a clone gene with Tn5 in *E. coli*. However, trying to introduce the Tn5 insertion back into *Caulobacter* presents a problem in that a single cross-over event is much more frequent than a double cross-over event, which is required for the Tn5-mutated gene to replace the wild-type gene. Transducing the insert to another *Caulobacter* strain can sometimes resolve a single cross-over event, but this is infrequent (only 1% of the transductants) and only works with selectable markers. Tn5 insertions in promoter adjacent genes often effect expression of downstream genes: called a polar effect. Therefore, deletions that remove just one gene are required in order to not perturb the expression of downstream genes. However, these deletions have no selectable marker, which is a problem for resolution of the integrant using the aforementioned transduction technique. This conundrum is solved in *Caulobacter* by the use of a counter-selectable gene *sacB* from *Bacillus subtillis*. The *sacB* gene confers sensitivity to sucrose; therefore, cells that have resolved the single cross-over event will survive (Fig. 6). The *sacB* gene has also been used to remove a Tn5 from the ampicillin resistance gene. All Tn5 insertions excise at a very low frequency, either precisely or imprecisely; therefore, selecting

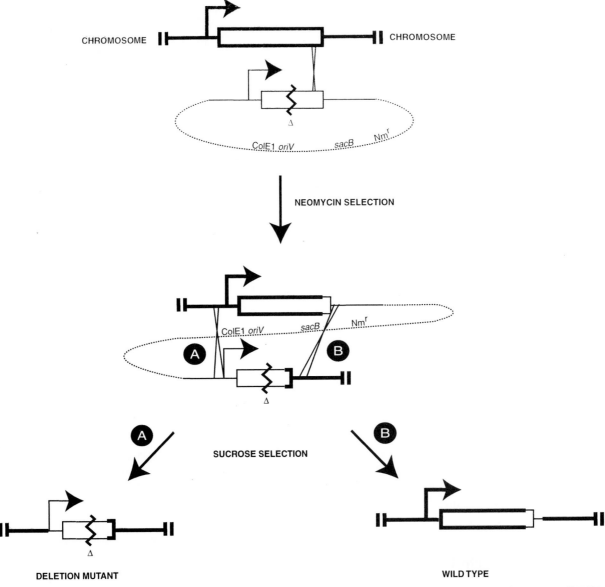

**Fig. 6.** The use of *sacB* counter-selectable marker in *Caulobacter*. The thick black lines denote chromosomal DNA. Pathways A and B are alternative possibilities depending where the cross-over event occurs. ⌐, promoter; ColE1 *oriV* is the origin of replication of the narrow host range ColE1 plasmid; Nmʳ, neomycin resistance gene.

for an imprecise excision of a Tn5 with a *sacB* gene will produce a strain which is ampicillin sensitive and Tn5 negative.

## C. Essential Genes and Inducible Promoters

The generation of temperature-sensitive mutants has been used to isolate conditional mutations in essential genes. This is commonly used in genetic screens; however, if a gene has already been isolated and it is essential for viability, creating a temperature-sensitive conditional mutant can take more time compared to placing a controllable promoter in front of the gene. The regulation of the promoter must be tight and no transcription must occur in the nonpermissive condition for studies of essential genes. Unfortunately, the *E. coli tac* promoter is not tightly regulated by *lacI* in *Caulobacter*, so a native promoter was isolated. A xylose-inducible promoter was isolated by generating random insertions using Tn5*gusA*, which creates promoter fusions to the assayable gene *gusA*. The gene *gusA* codes for *β*-glucouronidase; therefore, mutants were screened that could not grow on xylose but had xylose-inducible *β*-glucouronidase activity. One insertion was isolated and the putative xylose-inducible promoter DNA was cloned by recombining a *gusA*-containing ColE1 plasmid into the Tn5*gusA* insertion.

Chromosomal DNA was isolated from this strain and digested with *Sac*I, and then it was ligated and introduced into *E. coli* by transformation. To test whether the resulting plasmid contained the xylose promoter, it was recombined into the *Caulobacter* chromosome. If the fragment did not contain a promoter and was internal to the gene it would generate a xylose mutant (Fig. 7). However, if the resulting recombinant did not generate a xylose mutant it would contain the xylose promoter (Fig. 7). Final demonstration of its usefulness in *Caulobacter* genetics was shown by fusing it to a promoterless flagellar gene *fliF* and demonstrating that complementation of a *fliF* mutant was xylose inducible.

## IV. PRACTICAL USE OF GENETICS TO STUDY THE CELL CYCLE

### A. Isolation of Flagellar and Chemotaxis Genes

The ease of swarmer cell isolation, and hence the ability to study cell cycle events, has resulted in much emphasis on isolation of flagellar and chemotaxis genes. The isolation of flagellar and chemotaxis mutants is relatively easy, because strains bearing random Tn5 insertions can be screened for motility in semi-solid agar (Fig. 3). Three classes of mutants have been isolated: (a) nonmotile mutants which

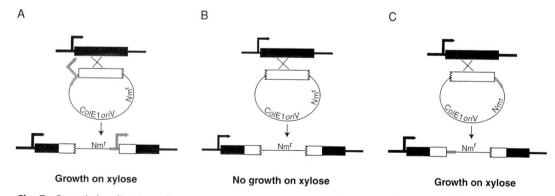

**Fig. 7.** Genetic localization of the xylose promoter. (A) Integration of a ColE1 vector bearing a promoter fragment. (B) Integration of a ColE1 vector bearing an internal fragment of a gene or operon. (C) Integration of a ColE1 vector bearing a 3′ end of a gene or operon. The black thick lines denote chromosomal DNA. The resulting phenotype of the integration event is shown under each integration event. ⌐, promoter; ColE1 *oriV* is the origin of replication of the narrow host range ColE1 plasmid; Nm<sup>r</sup>, neomycin resistance gene.

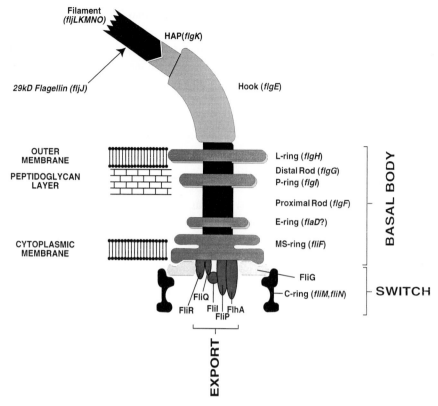

**Fig. 8.** The *Caulobacter* flagellum. The basal body is the flagellum rotor that resides in the cytoplasmic and outer membrane, from the MS-ring in the cytoplasmic membrane to the L-ring in the outer membrane. The E-ring seen in electron micrographs of isolated *Caulobacter* basal bodies has been suggested to be encoded by the *flaD* gene. HAP, hook-associated protein. The switch complex composed of FliG, FliM, and FliN is involved in changing the direction of rotation required for chemotaxis. The export complex is involved in exporting the flagellin subunits up the hollow center of the basal body, hook, and filament.

can be further subdivided into two subclasses—motility mutants that are nonmotile but make a paralyzed flagellum and flagellar mutants that do not make an intact flagellum; (b) general chemotaxis mutants that are motile but cannot reverse swimming direction; and (c) mutants that are motile and reverse swimming direction but produce small swarms in semi-solid agar. Transduction and IncP-mediated chromosome transfer were initially used to identify and map the separate flagellar loci, which were later mapped to the physical map of the *Caulobacter* chromosome using PFGE (Fig. 4). The flagellar mutants were further classified by their effects on flagellar assembly (e.g., the presence of a filament or basal body). Filament and basal body assembly were ob-

served using the electron microscope, whereas synthesis of the flagellins and the hook protein was by immunoprecipitation. Many of the separate flagellar loci have been complemented using IncP plasmids carrying *Caulobacter* DNA. The DNA sequence of the complementing clones has shown that many flagellar loci are in fact operons and contain many flagellar genes (Fig. 5). Some of these genes are homologous to *E. coli* flagellar genes; therefore, the gene names of the homologs were changed in accordance with the *Salmonella typhimurium* and *E. coli* nomenclature. To date, there have been more than 50 flagellar and chemotaxis genes isolated and sequenced. Many flagellar and chemotaxis genes, lie in four clusters around the chromosome (Fig. 5), although there are some flagellar genes distributed throughout the genome. Most of the structural genes that code for the flagellar filament, basal body, switch complex, and export complex have been cloned and sequenced (Fig. 8).

## B. Genetic Hierarchies

The study of the regulation of flagellar and chemotaxis promoters has been greatly aided by the use of promoter fusions. Initially, Tn5-VB32 insertions were generated to observe the effect of flagellar mutations on flagellar promoter fusions to *nptII*, which placed flagellar genes in a transcriptional hierarchy. The flagellar and chemotaxis genes were placed into three classes based on the effect of flagellar mutations on neomycin resistance or β-galactosidase activity from *lacZ* promoter fusions on IncP plasmids (Fig. 9). For example, class III promoters require class II genes for transcriptional activity, and class IV promoters require class III and II genes for expression (Fig. 9). The only exceptions are the chemotaxis genes (*mcpA* operon) and the 29-kDa flagellin gene (*fljJ*), which do not require any class II genes for expression and are not required for expression of other flagellar genes. The essential class I gene *ctrA*, which is a member of the *ompR* class of response regulators, was isolated using a *fliQ–nptII*

promoter fusion and selecting for increased kanamycin resistance at the permissive temperature after EMS mutagenesis and screening for lethality at the non-permissive temperature. Using either this conditional lethal *ctrA* mutant or a strain with a xylose-inducible promoter expressing *ctrA*, it has been shown that *ctrA* is required for correct class II gene expression. The CtrA protein can act as a repressor or activator (Fig. 9) and has been shown to regulate genes other than flagellar and chemotaxis genes, including cell division genes (*ftsZ*), and may possibly be involved in the regulation of DNA replication.

Most class II genes code for either the structural components (Fig. 8) that lie in the cytoplasmic membrane (MS ring, switch, and export complexes) or flagellar transriptional regulators FlbE (kinase), FlbD (response regulator, and RpoN (RNA polymerase sigma factor 54). Class III genes, code for the rest of the basal body and the hook and hook-associated proteins (Fig. 8). The flagellins *fljK* and *fljL* have been classified as class IV genes because of their requirement for class II and III genes for expression, although the structural class II and III genes regulate *fljK* expression post-transcriptionally. The hierarchy of expression is reflected in the differential cell cycle expression of the different classes of flagellar genes (Fig. 10).

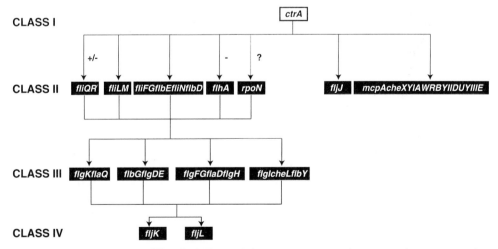

**Fig. 9.** Genetic hierarchy of the flagellar and chemotaxis genes. The arrows denote a requirement for expression, except where there is a − sign or +/− sign. The − sign indicates that ctrA is required for negative regulation, and the +/− sign denotes a requirement for positive and negative regulation.

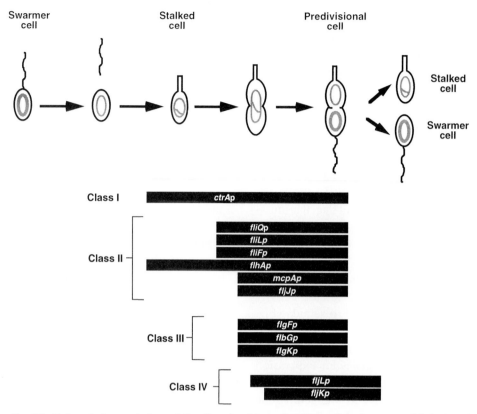

**Fig. 10.** Cell cycle transcription of the flagellar hierarchy. The cell cycle starts with isolated swarmer cells. The length of the boxes denotes the length of transcription during the cell cycle. The gray circles denote the *Caulobacter* chromosome: The thin gray circles denote a chromosome competent for replication, and the thick gray circles denote chromosome incapable of replication.

## C. Generation of Asymmetry-Localized Transcription, Protein Targeting, and Proteolysis

When the stalked cell differentiates into a predivisional cell it synthesizes a single polar flagellum (Fig. 1). The flagellum is constructed at the cell pole opposite the stalk. How is this structure specifically targeted to only one pole of the cell? This generation of asymmetry is produced by a combination of localized transcription, protein targeting, and proteolysis. First, the transcription of class III and IV genes, in particular hook (*flgE*), 25-KDa (*fljK*), and 27.5-kDa (*fljL*) flagellins, is localized in the swarmer portion of the predivisional cell. There is also an additional protein-targeting mechanism, which has been shown for the hook protein. Localized transcription is not

a mechanism used by the class II genes probably because of the time they are expressed in the cell cycle (Fig. 10). Most class II promoters are transcribed earlier in the cell cycle than are either class III or class IV promoters. Therefore, the spatial localization of the class II gene products mainly occurs by protein targeting and in some cases is removed from the stalked portion of predivisional cell by proteolysis. Localization of the chemoreceptor McpA to the flagellated cell pole was first shown using a full-length protein fusion to β-lactamase using immuno-gold electron microscopy. The McpA β-lactamase protein fusion was detected in the electron microscope using a primary rabbit antibody to β-lactamase followed by a secondary goat anti-rabbit antibody labeled with 3-nm particles of gold, an electron-dense element. Although the resolution of immunogold electron microscopy is very high, its sensitivity is low, making observations on proteins less abundant than McpA much more difficult. Therefore, both immunofluorescence and green fluorescent protein (GFP) fusion technologies have been developed to study the many localized proteins in *Caulobacter*. The advantage of using GFP is that the fluorophore is present in GFP so proteins that are fused to GFP can be visualized in a living cell.

## V. THE GENOME SEQUENCE AND THE FUTURE

The *Caulobacter* genome is currently being sequenced. This will enhance the use of genetics to study *Caulobacter*. In the past, mapping a mutation could take weeks, even using pulse-field gels, but because the genome sequence is available one needs only 200 base pairs of DNA sequence from a small complementing clone and the mutation can be mapped to a single gene. The genome sequence will also indicate whether the gene is in a monocistronic or polycistronic operon. Furthermore, additional genetic techniques will be developed, including the use of additional inducible promoters and construction of other counter-selectable markers such as streptomycin resistance and sensitivity.

## See Also the Following Articles

CELL DIVISION, PROKARYOTES • *ESCHERICHIA COLI* AND *SALMONELLA*, GENETICS • MAPPING BACTERIAL GENOMES • TRANSDUCTION: HOST DNA TRANSFER BY BACTERIOPHAGES

## Bibliography

Alley, M. R. K., Gomes, S. L., Alexander, W., and Shapiro, L. (1991). Genetic analysis of a temporally transcribed chemotaxis gene cluster in *Caulobacter crescentus. Genetics* **129**, 333–341.

Alley, M. R. K., Maddock, J. R., and Shapiro, L. (1993). Requirement of the carboxyl terminus of a bacterial chemoreceptor for its targeted proteolysis. *Science* **259**, 1754–1757.

Ely, B. (1991). Genetics of *Caulobacter crescentus. Methods Enzymol* **204**, 372–384.

Gober, J. W., and Marques, M. V. (1995). Regulation of cellular differentiation in *Caulobacter crescentus. Microbiol. Rev.* **59**, 31–47.

Meisenzahl, A. C., Shapiro, L., and Jenal, U. (1997). Isolation and characterization of a xylose-dependent promoter from *Caulobacter crescentus. J. Bacteriol.* **179**, 592–600.

Newton, A., and Ohta, N. (1992). *Caulobacter* differentiation. *In* "Encyclopedia of Microbiology" (J. Lederburg, Ed.), pp. 443–454. Academic Press, San Diego.

Newton, A., Ohta, N., Ramakrishnan, G., Mullin, D., and Raymond, G. (1989). Genetic switching in the flagellar gene hierarchy of *Caulobacter* requires negative as well as positive regulation of transcription. *Proc. Natl. Acad. Sci. USA* **86**, 6651–6655.

Quon, K. C., Marczynski, G. T., and Shapiro, L. (1996). Cell cycle control by an essential bacterial two-component signal transduction protein. *Cell* **84**, 83–93.

# Cell Division, Prokaryotes

## Nanne Nanninga
*University of Amsterdam*

## GLOSSARY

**cell division genes** Genes that encode for proteins that specifically function during the division process.

**constriction, septation** Mode of cell envelope invagination during division. During constriction all envelope layers move inwards simultaneously and the daughter cells move gradually apart; septation involves the ingrowth of the cell envelope forming a T-like structure.

**cytokinesis** In prokaryotes, the process of cell division. By contrast, in eukaryotic cells division also includes mitosis.

**dcw cluster** The cluster of genes involved in division (*d*) and cell wall (*cw*) synthesis. In many prokaryotes this cluster is evolutionary conserved.

**divisome** The macromolecular complex that carries out division at the cell center.

**Fts proteins** Cell division proteins encoded by *fts* genes. In temperature-sensitive (ts) cell division mutants, division is blocked and, because cells continue to grow, filaments (f) are formed.

**BECAUSE OF THE CELLULAR BASIS OF LIFE,** its maintenance and its proliferation require the multiplication of cells. For the individual cell this is achieved by fission of a cell that is on average two times as large as a newborn one. All macromolecular building stones should have been duplicated before fission. Clearly, the most important component of a cell to be replicated is its DNA.

In the prokaryotic research field the fission process is termed cell division. In the eukaryotic field the term cell division includes mitosis—the distribution of chromosomes over two new daughter cells; the process of cellular separation as such is referred to as cytokinesis. Thus, when the term cell division is employed for prokaryotes, what is meant is cytokinesis.

To appreciate the biological context of prokaryotic cell division it is enlightening to compare the size of a prokaryote such as *Escherichia coli* with that of a eukaryote such as a human HeLa cell (Fig. 1). Although the biological purpose of cell division in prokaryotes and in eukaryotic microbes is the same, it should be emphasized that completely different macromolecular components are involved in the two cases.

Prokaryotic cell division represents a very dynamic field of study. Therefore, in presenting this topic, outstanding questions will also be mentioned.

## I. PROKARYOTIC DIVERSITY

### A. Different Model Organisms

Of the many prokaryotic species, only a few have been or are being studied in detail. These are in all cases eubacteria; virtually nothing is known about archaea. For eubacterial cell division a distinction should be made between gram-positive species [*Bacillus subtilis, Enterococcus hirae* (formerly called

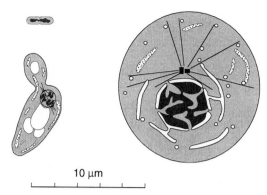

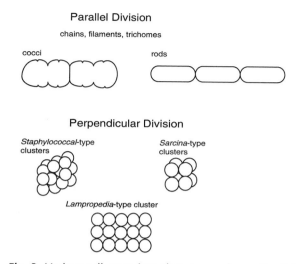

**Fig. 1.** Comparative sizes of the prokaryote *E. coli* (upper left), the yeast *S. cerevisiae* (lower left), and a human HeLa cell (right) (from Nanninga, 1998, used by permission of the American Society for Microbiology journals).

**Fig. 3.** Various cell groupings that occur when cells stick together after division (from Koch, 1985, used by permission of the National Research Council of Canada 1985).

*Streptococcus faecalis* and *Streptococcus faecium*), and *Staphylococcus aureus*], and gram-negative species (*Caulobacter crescentus* and *E. coli*). This distinction is reasonable because the difference in gram staining is based on cell envelope organization, which in turn affects the mode of division. That is, in a gram-positive organisms a circumferential inward-growing septum divides the new daughter cells, whereas in a gram-negative organism the cell constricts in the cell center (Fig. 2). The constriction process, however, also requires local envelope synthesis. To date, *E. coli* has been studied most intensively with respect to cell division, followed by *B. subtilis*. In this article, the focus will be on *E. coli*. In this organism the cell envelope is composed of three layers (Fig. 2). From outside to inside, these are the outer membrane, the peptidoglycan or murein layer, and the cytoplasmic or inner membrane. Because of its rigid nature the peptidoglycan layer serves as an exoskeleton, which maintains the shape of the cell. It prevents cellular

disruption due to osmotic pressure and also plays an active role during the constriction process.

## B. Prokaryotic Cell Division Patterns

The final separation of cells can be blocked or new rounds of division may start before the ongoing ones have been completed, in which case parallel divisions occur that lead to chains of cells. These chains may occur in nature (Fig. 3). When subsequent divisions take place perpendicular to each other, 2D sheets or 3D clusters occur (Fig. 3). An example of the latter is *Staphylococcus*, which actually resembles a cluster of grapes. What determines the successive orientations of the division plane is not clear. However, evidence suggests that it is related to the spatial orientation of the replicating bacterial chromosome or nucleoid in the cell.

## II. SPECIFIC GENE PRODUCTS ARE INVOLVED IN CELL DIVISION

Is division largely a physical process or do specific structural proteins and enzymes play a role? In the first case, this means that cells after having reached sufficient length fission in the middle due to forces that also play a role in the breaking up of a stream of water from the tap. In solving this problem, bacterial

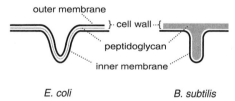

**Fig. 2.** Division by constriction in *E. coli* and by septation in *B. subtilis*. During the constriction process the envelope layers invaginate together; during septation a T structure is formed.

genetics has made a fundamental contribution, aided by the characteristic mutant phenotype of cells impaired in division. Generally, such mutant cells continue to grow and to replicate their DNA. As a consequence, they can become extremely long and the resulting filaments are easily visualized in a standard light microscope. Of considerable importance is the identification of temperature-sensitive cell division mutants and in particular those in which the altered gene product cannot function at high temperature—the nonpermissive temperature of 42°C. Because cells filament at this temperature the respective genes have been denoted as *fts* genes, where *f* stands for filament forming and *ts* for temperature sensitive. Such filaments can be smooth or indented at regular intervals. The first phenotype indicates that the mutation has affected a protein involved in the beginning of division, whereas in the second case this applies to a later step in division process. For instance, the smooth filaments referred to previously are due to a mutation in the *ftsZ* gene, which products an FtsZ protein defective at 42°C. The genetic approach has led to the detection of several *fts* genes and after specific labeling most of their respective gene products have been localized to the site of constriction by fluorescence microscopy. For example, Fig. 4 is an immunofluorescent image of FtsZ located at the cell center . It can be concluded that the division process is carried out by specific cell division proteins.

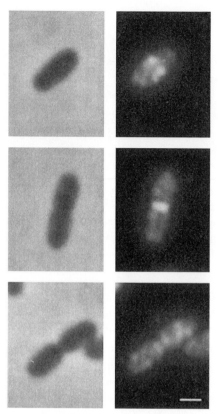

**Fig. 4.** Immunofluorescent image of the FtsZ ring in *E. coli*. FtsZ has been labeled with monoclonal antibody directed against an FtsZ epitope. A secondary antibody containing a fluorophore has been bound to the primary monoclonal antibody. The cells have been arranged according to size. (Left) Phase contrast images; (right) immunofluorescent images. Scale bar = 1 $\mu$m.

## III. ORGANIZATION OF CELL DIVISION GENES ON THE CHROMOSOME

The *E. coli* circular chromosomal map is divided into 100 minutes, whereas in *B. subtilis* it is divided into 360°. Therefore, there is no consistent nomenclature for the chromosomal position of genes in the different species. In *E. coli* most cell division genes are located at 2 min (Fig. 5). Remarkably, many genes encoding enzymes involved in the formation of peptidoglycan precursors and in peptidoglycan assembly are also situated in this region. The 2-min region is therefore also denoted as the *dcw* cluster, where *d* stands for division and *cw* for cell wall. This clustering indicates the existence of a global

regulatory mechanism that guarantees expression of the many genes required for division under a large variety of growth conditions. To fully understand this putative mechanism, information will be required about the cell division-specific expression of the various individual genes. This information is only very slowly emerging and the possible global regulatory mechanism currently is unknown.

For instance, the *ftsQAZ* region (Fig. 5) is probably transcribed as one polycistronic messenger RNA, requiring the differential expression of the genes and regulation of the relative amounts of the encoded gene products. In addition, several potential *ftsZ* promoters have been identified upstream of the *ftsQAZ* region. This complicates the understanding of tran-

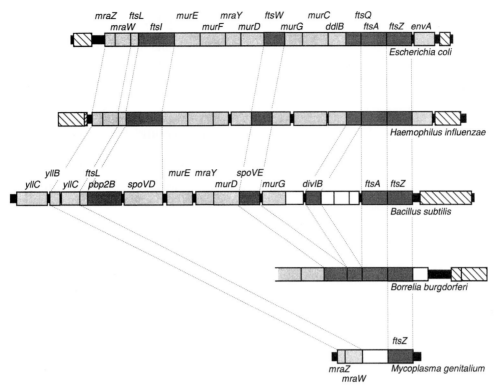

**Fig. 5.** Clustering of genes involved in cell division and cell wall synthesis (*dcw* cluster). The *dcw* cluster is conserved in *E. coli* and in *B. subtilis*. Note its reduction in "primitive" organisms such as *B. burgdorferi* and *M. genitalium*. The dark gray boxes represent cell division genes; the light gray boxes represent genes involved in peptidoglycan synthesis. In the text the *fts* genes of *E. coli* are discussed (from Vicente *et al.*, 1998, used by permission of CMLS Cellular and Molecular Life Sciences **54**).

scriptional expression of this region. Research on the regulation of expression of the *dcw* cluster is certainly an important field, especially because the complete nucleotide sequence of this region has been known for some time.

Because increasingly more prokaryote genomic sequences have been determined, it is of interest to determine whether *dcw* clusters occur in other organisms. As depicted in Fig. 5, *Haemophilus influenzae* has a *dcw* cluster which closely resembles that of *E. coli*. In view of the similarities of these organisms, this is perhaps not unexpected. However, in other gram-negatives the cell division gene arrangement is different. Therefore, one cannot conclude that there is a specific gram-negative *dcw* cluster. Nevertheless, the organization of the *B. subtilis* cluster bears a striking resemblance to that of *E. coli*. In *Mycoplasma genitalium* the *dcw* cluster is very reduced in size,

which is most likely related to its simple envelope structure. A constant feature is the occurrence of FtsZ in all prokaryotes so far investigated, and this also applies to archaea. Interestingly, FtsZ has been detected in chloroplasts, emphasizing the endosymbiotic origin of these organelles.

## IV. THE CELL DIVISION MACHINERY

### A. Compartmentalization of Division Proteins

The Fts proteins are located in specific cellular compartments (Fig. 6). They can be cytoplasmic, periplasmic (in between the outer and inner membrane; Fig. 2), or inserted in the inner membrane. FtsA and FtsZ are cytoplasmic proteins. An FtsZ-

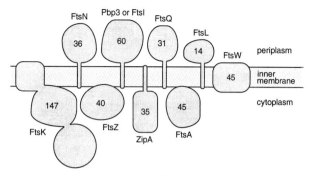

**Fig. 6.** Compartmentalization of *E. coli* cell division proteins. The numbers apply to the molecular weights (KDa). Note that the spatial organization of the proteins with respect to each other is not known. Some are very abundant such as FtsZ, whereas others occur in a very limited number such as FtsQ.

## B. Divisome Assembly and Fission

Genetic and microscopic studies have provided clues about the sequence of events occurring during division. The first gene product recognized at the cell center was FtsZ, and its localization appears to be independent of other cell division proteins. Temperature-sensitive mutants of FtsZ grown at the nonpermissive temperature formed filaments without visible indentations. By contrast, filaments of, for instance, *ftsA, ftsI,* and *ftsQ* mutants had aborted constrictions. This led to the conclusion that the respective gene products act later than FtsZ in the division process. Using a complementary approach, it has been investigated by immunofluorescence microscopy whether cell division proteins can be localized to the cell center in a particular genetic background. For example, FtsZ could be localized in an *ftsI* mutant at the nonpermissive temperature, whereas FtsI did not assemble at the cell center in an *ftsZ* mutant. Such experiments have been carried out in many other combinations and they have led to a general view on the divisome assembly process. FtsZ is the first protein to occupy the future division site. This is followed by the arrival of ZipA and FtsW. FtsA, FtI, and FtsQ are then localized. Subsequent actors are FtsK, FtsL, and FtsN. It should be emphasized that this order is not definitive, and the biochemical function of most of the essential cell division proteins is unknown. It is also unknown whether all components have been detected. To date, FtsI, FtsZ, and FtsA have been most intensively studied. FtsI, also known as PBP3, is a penicillin-binding protein specifically involved in peptidoglycan synthesis. FtsZ resembles eukaryotic tubulin, it binds GTP, and its GTPase activity is needed for polymerization of FtsZ *in vitro*. Less is known about FtsA. It bears some resemblance to actin and as such it can bind ATP. FtsK contains an ATPase domain. Little is also known about how the various proteins are grouped together in the divisome.

interacting protein (ZipA) is located mainly in the cytoplasm; however, in contrast to FtsA and FtsZ, it is anchored to the inner membrane. The periplasmic division proteins are anchored with a single transmembrane sequence to the inner membrane, whereas a short stretch of amino acids protrudes into the cytoplasm [FtsI (PBP3), FtsL, FtsN, and FtsQ]. FtsW contains several transmembrane sequences. This also applies to FtsK, which contains a considerable cytoplasmic component. This orientation of the division proteins (Fig. 6) not only reflects the fact that the cell envelope is involved in division but also that cytoplasmic components play a role. Most notably, this has been demonstrated for FtsZ. Before division, this protein is diffusely located in the cytoplasm; upon division a fraction of the proteins becomes concentrated at the cell center, where they form a cytokinetic ring as revealed by various microscopic techniques (Fig. 4). FtsZ easily polymerizes *in vitro* and it is likely that this also occurs in the living cell.

There is a wide variation in the number of cell division proteins per cell. Whereas FtsZ is ubiquitous protein which occurs on the order of 10,000 copies per cell, a protein such as FtsQ occurs on the order of approximately 100 or less copies per cell. Presumably, the FtsZ ring (Fig. 4) contains subassemblies of other cell division proteins. The cytokinetic ring containing FtsZ and other cell division components has been denoted as divisome.

Concerning the division process, it is clear that the actively ingrowing periplasmic peptidoglycan layer is matched by a cytoplasmic FtsZ ring of continuously decreasing diameter. How this is coordinated is unknown, although it can be expected that components of the inner membrane are instrumental in this process. In addition, physical factors such as surface stress can be expected to play a role. The interplay between biochemistry and physics remains to be determined.

## V. REGULATION OF CELL DIVISION

Prokaryotic cells can adjust to a variety of growth conditions. Under laboratory conditions using defined growth media adjustments with respect to protein synthesis, RNA synthesis, DNA synthesis, and cell size have been studied extensively for *E. coli*. Briefly, at faster growth cells become bigger, reflecting the increased number of active ribosomes and the increased genome content per cell. It has been shown that the start of DNA replication is directly correlated with cell size. This size has been termed initiation mass, and division occurs during a fixed period after initiation of DNA replication. In this way, the rate of division adjusts to growth conditions.

Apart from physiological regulation, cell division comprises at least two other regulatory aspects. How does a cell know where its middle is and what induces the start of division? To date, the first question has only been approached in a speculative way and its solution is unknown. Current thinking on the onset of division encompasses two views. One view emphasizes the role of the elongating cell envelope in triggering division when the cell has acquired a certain length. In the other view, cell division is dependent on the completed replication and partitioning of the chromosome. A definite answer cannot be given, and clearly the two possibilities do not exclude each other.

*Escherichia coli* and *B. subtilis* can divide not only in the cell center but also at their poles. In the latter case, the cells are very small and they have therefore been denoted as minicells. They can perform protein synthesis, but because they lack DNA they cannot perpetuate. Obviously, a system is needed that helps prevent polar division in wild-type cells. Again, *E. coli* has been most intensively studied. Genes coding for proteins involved in minicell formation belong to the so-called *min* operon. Three proteins—MinC, MinD, and MinE—are responsible for minicell formation. Interestingly, MinE has been localized to the cell center independent of FtsZ but dependent on MinD. The regulatory interplay between the minicell-forming system and the normal cell division system remains to be elucidated.

*Bacillus subtilis* as a sporulating organism places an asymmetrically located septum during formation of the so-called forespore. The forespore of course contains DNA and should not be confused with a minicell. In this case, as in all divisions mentioned previously, FtsZ is involved.

### See Also the Following Articles

BACILLUS SUBTILIS, GENETICS • OUTER MEMBRANE, GRAM-NEGATIVE BACTERIA • PROTEIN BIOSYNTHESIS • RIBOSOME SYNTHESIS AND REGULATION

### Bibliography

Helmstetter, C. E. (1996). Timing of synthetic activities in the cell cycle. *In* "*Escherichia coli* and *Salmonella.* Cellular and Molecular Biology". (Neidhardt, F. C., Editor-in-Chief), pp. 1627–1639. American Society for Microbiology, Washington, DC.

Koch, A. L. (1985). How bacteria grow and divide in spite of internal hydrostatic pressure. *Can. J. Bacteriol.* **31**, 1071–1084.

Koch, A. L. (1995). "Bacterial Growth and Form." Chapman & Hall, New York.

Lutkenhaus, J., and Mukherjee, A. (1996). Cell division. *In* "*Escherichia coli* and *Salmonella.* Cellular and Molecular Biology" (Neidhardt, F. C., Editor-in-Chief), pp. 1615–1626. American Society for Microbiology, Washington, DC.

Nanninga, N. (1998). Morphogenesis of *Escherichia coli. Microbiol. Mol. Biol. Revs.* **62**, 110–129.

Neidhardt, F. C., Ingraham, J. L., and Schaechter, M. (1990). "Physiology of the Bacterial Cell." Sinauer Sunderland, Ma.

Vicente, M., Gomez, M. J., and Ayala, J. A. (1998). Regulation of transcription of cell division in the *Escherichia coli dcw* cluster. *Cell Mol. Life Sci.* **54**, 317–324.

# Cell Membrane: Structure and Function

## Robert J. Kadner

*University of Virginia*

## GLOSSARY

**ABC proteins**  Proteins that contain the widely conserved ATP-binding cassette, a motif that couples energy from ATP binding and hydrolysis to various transport processes.

**detergent**  A molecule with polar and nonpolar portions that can disrupt membranes by stabilizing the dispersion of hydrophobic lipids and proteins in water.

**hydrophobic**  Molecules or portions of molecules that cannot form hydrogen bonds or other polar interactions with water.

**hydrophobic effect**  The tendency of hydrophobic regions of molecules to avoid contact with water.

**osmolarity**  The tendency of water to flow across a membrane in the direction of the more concentrated solution.

**proton motive force**  The electrochemical measure of the transmembrane gradient of protons, consisting of an electrical potential due to separation of charge and the pH gradient due to different concentration of protons.

**symporter**  A transport system in which movement of the coupling ion moves in the same direction as the substrate molecule, in contrast to an antiporter or uniporter.

**EVERY CELL POSSESSES A SURFACE MEMBRANE** that separates it from the environment or from other cells. Animal cells and other eukaryotic cells possess, in addition to the plasma membrane, numerous intracellular membranes which form the or-

ganelles that perform specialized metabolic functions. Bacterial and archaeal cells typically lack intracellular membrane organelles and contain only the single cytoplasmic membrane, perhaps surrounded by an outer membrane. The cytoplasmic membrane of bacteria is typically composed of simple phospholipids that form a membrane bilayer, into which are inserted a large number of different proteins. The phospholipid bilayer forms the osmotic barrier that prevents movement of most materials into or out of the cell. The various membrane proteins carry out numerous important functions, including the generation and storage of metabolic energy and the regulation of uptake and release of all nutrients and metabolic products. Membrane proteins recognize and transmit many signals that reflect changes in environmental conditions and trigger an appropriate cellular response. They also play key roles in the control of cell growth and division, bacterial movement, and the export of surface proteins and carbohydrates.

## I. ULTRASTRUCTURE AND THE ROLE OF CYTOPLASMIC MEMBRANE

### A. Ultrastructure of Cell Membranes

Cell membranes are readily visible when thin sections of cells are stained with heavy metals and viewed in the electron microscope. They appear as a characteristic triple-layered structure with two dark electron-dense layers, representing the region of the lipid head groups, surrounding a light layer which reflects the hydrophobic central portion of the membrane bilayer. All cellular membranes appear quite

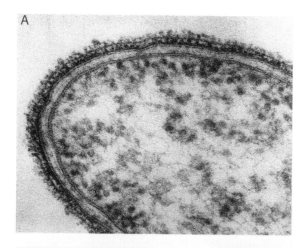

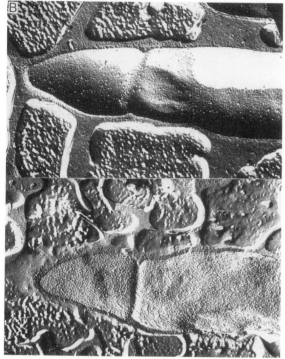

**Fig. 1.** Structure of bacterial membranes. (A) Electron micrograph of a thin section of the fish pathogen, *Aeromonas salmonicida*. Cells were embedded in plastic, cut to a thin slice, stained with heavy metals (uranyl acetate and lead citrate), and visualized by transmission electron microscopy. The cytoplasmic membrane is seen as the triple-layered structure bounding the cytoplasm. Outside the 7.5-nm-thick cytomplasmic membrane is the periplasmic space, the triple-layered outer membrane, and the thick surface S layer. (B) Electron micrograph of a freeze-fractured sample. A suspension of cells of *Bacillus licheniformis* was frozen, and the block was shattered by a sharp blow with a knife edge. The fracture plane ran occasionally

similar by this technique, regardless of the source of the membrane or their protein content (Fig. 1A). Most biological membranes are 4 or 5 nm in width. In the technique of freeze-fracture electron microscopy a knife blow is used to split a frozen sample of cells. The fracture plane often extends along or through the weakly connected central section of a membrane bilayer. This technique can reveal the presence and density of proteins embedded in and spanning through the membrane. Figure 1 supports the fluid mosaic model of membrane structure in which the polar membrane lipids form a lamellar, or leaf-like, bilayer in which their nonpolar portions face each other in the central region and their polar regions are on the outside. Integral membrane proteins span across the bilayer, but can diffuse within the plane of the bilayer and even associate into large complexes. Many peripheral membrane proteins do not span across the membrane and can be transiently bound through hydrophobic anchors or by association with other membrane proteins or the lipid head groups.

## B. Role as Osmotic Barrier

The cytoplasmic membrane is the osmotic barrier of the cell, owing to its ability to restrict the passage of salts and polar organic compounds. If a cell is placed in a medium in which the osmolarity is higher or lower than the osmolarity of the cytoplasm, water will flow across the cytoplasmic membrane out or into the cell, respectively. This osmotic flow of water occurs in response to the natural forces that seek to eliminate gradients or differences in the concentration of water on the two sides of the membrane. Hence, the cytoplasm either shrinks or swells under these two conditions as a result of the loss or gain

though membrane bilayers. A carbon replica of the two faces thus revealed was made, the organic material was etched away with acid, and surface structures were enhanced by shadowing with a beam of platinum atoms. The image is viewed in transmission electron microscope. The two faces show the two halves of the cytoplasmic membrane layer, indicating the presence of particles that are embedded in and span the membranes (courtesy of Terrance Beveridge, University of Guelph, Canada).

of water. In most bacteria, the cell does not change size owing to the presence of its rigid cell wall.

## C. Role as Cell Boundary

The cytoplasmic membrane is the boundary between the cell and its surroundings and thus must regulate the passage of nutrients and metabolic products. The presence of the hydrophobic layer formed by the membrane lipids greatly restricts the passage of any polar molecules and of macromolecules. It prevents the loss of cellular macromolecules and metabolic intermediates.

## D. Regulation of Transport

Transport systems allow the passage of specific molecules, such as ion, nutrients, and metabolic products, either into or out of the cell. Bacteria in general have a large number of very specific transport systems that carry out active transport. They consume some form of metabolic energy to be able to pump their substrate from a low concentration on one side of the membrane to a much higher concentration on the other side. Transport is an integral part of the universal process of bioenergetics, which refers to the formation and consumption of sources of cellular energy, most of which involve transmembrane ion gradients.

## E. Role in Cell Growth and Division

Expansion of the membrane surface is intimately related to growth rate of any cell, and all components must be inserted in a timely manner to allow cells to expand in size. Cell division requires a carefully controlled process whereby the membranes of the parental cell pinch together, fuse, and separate to create two progeny cells, without loss of internal material. The membrane contains export systems of control the release of structural components to the cell surface and other secreted factors beyond the cell. Other membrane-localized protein complexes regulate the process of initiation of DNA replication, separation of chromosomes into the dividing bacterial cells, and in-growth of the cell surface that occurs during cell division.

## II. STRUCTURE AND PROPERTIES OF MEMBRANE LIPIDS

### A. Lipid Composition

The key ingredients of biological membranes are polar lipids, primarily phospholipids. In most bacteria, phospholipids consist of two fatty acids, usually with 16–18 carbon atoms in the hydrocarbon chain with zero or one *cis*-double bond. The fatty acid content changes in response to environmental conditions, particularly temperature. As described later, lower growth temperatures result in a higher degree of fatty acid unsaturation, which has dramatic effects on the membrane's fluidity and function. Some fatty acids are branched or contain cyclopropane rings. Fatty acids are joined in ester linkage to two of the hydroxyl groups of glycerol, usually with a saturated fatty acid at the 1-position and an unsaturated fatty acid at the 2-position. To the third hydroxyl group of glycerol is attached a phosphate moiety and to it the head group. In bacteria, the range of head groups is narrow, and the phospholipids in *Escherichia coli* are approximately 75% phosphatidyl ethanolamine (PE) and 20% phosphatidyl glycerol (PG), and the remainder is cardiolipin (diphosphatidyl glycerol), phosphatidyl serine, and trace amounts of other phospholipids (Fig. 2).

Other bacteria possess more complex types of membrane lipids, although these lipids are usually much less complex than those in the plasma membrane of animal cells. Some bacteria possess phosphatidyl choline, or lecithin, which is characteristic of higher organisms. Other bacteria produce glycolipids, such as monogalactosyl diglyceride. The membrane lipids from archaea are quite different from those in bacteria and eukarya. Their hydrocarbon chains are based on isoprenoid units and these are linked to the glycerol backbone in an ether, rather than ester, linkage. In some archaea, a glycerol backbone and head group are attached to both ends of a pair of isoprenoid units.

Sterols, such as cholesterol in mammalian cells or ergosterol in fungi, are invariant features of membranes in eukaryal cells, in which they appear to stiffen the membrane by increasing the degree of order of the hydrocarbon chains. Sterols are not com-

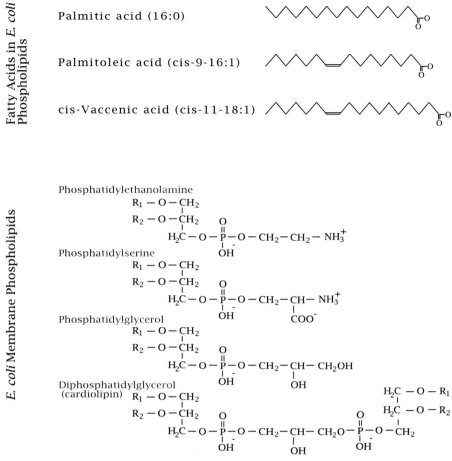

**Fig. 2.** Chemical structures of the fatty acids and phospholipids that comprise the bulk of the membrane lipids in *E. coli*. For the phospholipids, the R groups represent a fatty acid.

monly found in bacteria and archaea, except for the cell wall-less *Mycoplasma*. Very complex lipids, including the very long, branched mycolic acids, are common in *Mycobacterium* but occur in a very thick and rigid outer layer rather than in the cytoplasmic membrane.

## B. Hydrophobic Effect

Phospholipids spontaneously form membranous structures when suspended in aqueous solution. The forces that drive their assembly into a bilayer or more complex structure are called the hydrophobic effect. This organizing force depends on the ability of water molecules to donate and accept hydrogen bonds from one another to form an extensive network of water molecules transiently linked through hydrogen bonds and polar interactions. Polar molecules can participate in this interactive network of water molecules and are thereby able to dissolve in aqueous solution. In contrast, hydrophobic or nonpolar molecules, such as a long hydrocarbon or aromatic chain, are unable to participate in the hydrogen-bonded network of water molecules. For them to dissolve in water would result in loss of the energy resulting from the intrusion in the mobile water bonding and from the organization of water molecules into a cage-like structure around the intruding nonpolar molecule. It is the loss of the energy of interaction between the water molecules and the entropic cost of organizing them that drive the nonpolar molecules to associate with one another, out of contact with the water. Hence, nonpolar lipids tend to form oil droplets in water, so as to pre-

sent the smallest possible hydrophobic surface to the water.

## C. Membrane Bilayer

Polar lipids, such as phospholipids, have chemical structures of two different natures. The hydrophobic acyl chains strive to be sequestered from contact with water, whereas the charged and polar head groups seek contact with aqueous ions to help dissipate their electrical charge and to form a hydrogen-bonded network with water. Thus, polar lipids are driven by basic physical characteristics to form aggregate structures in which the hydrophobic portions are segregated out of contact with water while the head groups face the water. There are numerous ways in which these requirements can be accommodated. Of greatest biological relevance is the lamellar bilayer, in which large flat surfaces of bilayer form with the acyl chains facing each other on the inside and the head groups facing the solution on the outside (Figs. 3 and 4). Other nonlamellar structures, such as hexagonal phases, can form under certain conditions of head group, temperature, and salt concentration. The propensity of different lipids to form nonlamellar

**Fig. 4.** Representation of the orientation of the acyl chains and head groups of a phospholipid in a bilayer. This orientation of phosphatidylethanolamine is seen in crystal structures. The solid circles represent oxygen atoms; the heavy lines represent the glycerol; the thin lines are ethanolamine; and the gray lines are the hydrocarbon chains of the two fatty acids, all in their most extended configuration.

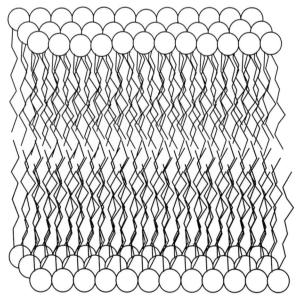

**Fig. 3.** Schematic representation of the lipid bilayer or lamellar arrangement. The polar head groups of the lipids face the water, and the hydrocarbon acyl chains are segregated away from the water in the interior of the bilayer.

bilayers is a function, in part, of the relative cross-sectional areas of the hydrophobic acyl chains in reference to the area of the head group. When the areas of the polar and nonpolar parts are similar, a lamellar bilayer is favored. If the nonpolar part is substantially smaller or larger than the head group, formation of a spherical micelle or an inverted structure, such as the HexII phase (hexagonal phase II), respectively, is favored.

When most biological phospholipids are dried into a film from a solution in an organic solvent and then water is added, the lipids spontaneously form a multilamellar liposome in which concentric bilayers assemble like an onion. When these liposomes are sonicated (disrupted by intense ultrasonic irradiation), they break down into small unilamellar vesicles. These are small spherical particles with a single membrane bilayer surrounding an aqueous cavity.

## D. Lipid Phase Behavior

Above a certain temperature, the lipid molecules in a bilayer can move rapidly within the plane of the membrane but do not move very far in or out of the membrane owing to the hydrophobic effect. In this liquid crystalline state, the acyl chains are parallel to each other but undergo frequent rotations around the carbon bonds to produce kinks in the chain. These kinks provide transient discontinuities in the hydrophobic barrier that allow movement of other lipid molecules within the membrane and of water molecules across the membrane. As the suspension of membranes is cooled below a critical temperature ($T_m$), there is a transition of the lipids from the liquid crystalline phase to the rigid gel phase. In this phase, all the hydrocarbon chains form the all-trans configuration, which increases the bilayer thickness and greatly decreases diffusion of the lipids within the membrane and of permeants across the membrane. This transition reflects the motion and packing of the acyl chains.

The critical temperature at which the gel-to-liquid crystalline phase transition occurs is dependent on the lipid composition, including the nature of the head group and the lipid chains. The longer the hydrocarbon chains, the higher the $T_m$ for transition to the liquid crystalline state. The presence of unsaturated fatty acids with one or more double bonds has a very dramatic effect reducing the $T_m$ by as much as 60°C. The effect of the double bond is greatest when it is in the middle of the acyl chain. The double bond introduces a permanent kink or bend in the chain that interferes with packing of the chains in the gel state. Most cells adjust their lipid composition to the growth temperature to ensure that their membrane remains in the liquid crystalline state. Most membrane proteins are excluded from or are inactive in the rigid gel phase membranes. Another lipid phase transition can occur at temperature higher than $T_m$. This corresponds to the change of certain lipids from a lamellar to a nonlamellar configuration.

## III. STRUCTURE AND PROPERTIES OF MEMBRANE PROTEINS

Although the lipids are very important for determining the barrier functions of the cell membrane, the membrane proteins confer most of the important functions of biological membranes. There are many different types of membrane proteins, reflecting their very different functions. Integral membrane proteins are those that cross the membrane with one or more transmembrane segments and are usually exposed to both sides of the membrane. They cannot be easily removed from the membrane unless detergents are added to disrupt the bilayer structure. Some integral membrane proteins are stably anchored to the membrane, usually by covalent attachment to a lipid such as a fatty acid, isoprenoid, phosphatidyl inositol, or a lipoprotein derivative. The membrane-spanning proteins include most of the functionally important transporters and signal receptors. Peripheral membrane proteins are defined operationally as those that are readily removed from association with the membrane by procedures that do not disrupt the bilayer, such as washing with high salt, urea, or sodium carbonate at pH 11. These proteins generally lack transmembrane segments, although it is recognized that some peripheral proteins can transiently insert a segment across the membrane as part of their normal function.

Some integral membrane proteins possess one or two transmembrane segments only, and the bulk of these proteins is located in the aqueous solutions on one or both sides of the membrane. The nonmembranous segments of these proteins are similar in character to that of a normal soluble globular protein. Charged or polar amino acid residues line the surfaces exposed to the water, and nonpolar amino acid residues form the interior of the domain, driven into this sequestered state by the same hydrophobic effect that stabilizes the membrane lipid structure. The membrane-spanning portion of these proteins has a very limited range of composition and structures. Owing to the very hydrophobic environment of the interior of the membrane bilayer, the presence of charged or polar residues or of unpaired hydrogen bonds is energetically unfavorable. Thus, the amino acid residues that comprise single transmembrane segments are generally highly hydrophobic. In addition, an α helix is the only peptide conformation in which all the hydrogen bonding possibilities of the polypeptide backbone are satisfied. Thus, single or double transmembrane segments are most likely to be nonpolar α-helical segments, with lengths of approximately 20 amino acids (approximately six turns of the helix), which is sufficient to span the width of the membrane.

Many membrane proteins cross the membrane multiple times and insert the bulk of their mass within the membrane. Transport proteins typically have 10–14 transmembrane segments, and a major class of signal receptors have 7 transmembrane segments. These proteins have a very different character than that of the multi-domain proteins described previously. The large surface of the protein that is imbedded in the membrane and exposed to the hydrophobic environment of the hydrocarbon lipid chains is highly hydrophobic and cannot possess charged amino acid residues. Other surfaces of these proteins are exposed to the solution on either side of the membrane. These surfaces, which are composed of the loops joining transmembrane segments, must possess mainly polar residues capable of remaining soluble in water. The presence of the very different surfaces of membrane proteins, two polar belts and one very nonpolar belt, holds the protein tightly within the membrane bilayer and restricts its movement out of the membrane.

The transmembrane segments of such a polytopic protein are α-helical in the very few proteins for which detailed structural information is available (the photosynthetic reaction center, bacteriorhodopsin, and lactose permease). The amino acid residues that comprise transmembrane segments need not be all nonpolar. These residues can be exposed to different environments, namely the lipid hydrocarbon chains, the neighboring α-helical transmembrane segments, and a potential water-filled channel. Thus, the residues of these transmembrane segments exhibit periodic variability, with very nonpolar residues along one face and generally polar residues along the opposite face. In contrast, the transmembrane segments of most bacterial outer membrane proteins are composed of anti-parallel β sheets of approximately eight amino acid residues in length.

Proteins are inserted in cellular membranes in a defined orientation. The orientation of the entire protein appears to be determined by the orientation of its individual transmembrane segments. The orientation of each transmembrane segment is determined mainly by the nature of the charged residues flanking the transmembrane segment rather than by the residues within the transmembrane segment. The "inside-positive" rule seems to govern the orientation of transmembrane segments in bacteria, and it states that relatively short, positively charged loops are retained on the cytoplasmic side of the membrane. The orientation of a protein can be affected by its association with other cellular or membrane proteins or by the presence of a signal sequence that directs the protein into the secretory pathway.

The orientation of a membrane protein can be determined experimentally by detecting the sites of action of proteases or other enzymes added to one side of the membrane. A simpler and more generally informative approach makes use of fusions of a part of the tested protein to a topological reporter, which is an enzyme whose activity depends on which side of the membrane it resides. It has thus been possible to gain a considerable degree of understanding of the structure of many membrane proteins, even without high-resolution crystallographic information.

## IV. FUNCTIONS OF CYTOPLASMIC MEMBRANE

The cytoplasmic membrane of bacteria is a very busy site at which an almost bewildering number of important processes occur. It carries out most of the reactions that are handled by the many organelles of eukaryotic cells. Since bacteria are generally far more metabolically capable and diverse than eukaryotic cells, it is not surprising that an estimated one-fourth of the cell's proteins are membrane associated.

One of the key principles in biology is the basic universality of bioenergetics, which refers to the processes of energy generation, storage, and utilization in cells. The major feature of these processes is the use of ion gradients that are formed across cellular membranes, such as the membranes of mitochondria and chloroplasts in higher organisms or the cytoplasmic membrane of bacteria. In most systems, the gradient of protons is the central factor in bioenergetics, although gradients of sodium ions are used by some bacteria for energy generation and by most eukaryotic cells for cellular signaling and nutrient transport. The chemiosmotic proposal, initially made by Peter Mitchell, that ion gradients are the intermediate between the processes of electron transport and the formation of ATP has been overwhelmingly accepted. In bacteria, ion gradients are also used to drive several types of active transport systems, bacterial motility, and protein secretion.

## A. Energy Generation

Energy generation refers to the trapping in a metabolically useful form of the energy absorbed from sunlight or released by reduction of some inorganic molecule or the oxidation or breakdown of an organic molecule serving as energy source. Bacteria can generate energy by many different processes. In simple fermentative pathways, such as the glycolytic breakdown of glucose to lactate, ATP can be formed during several enzymatic steps by the process of substrate level phosphorylation. Important energy-producing processes use electron transport chains to pass electrons from a carrier of high negative redox potential to carriers of successively lower energy states. During respiration, electrons enter these chains following transfer from an organic molecule and are ultimately transferred to an inorganic electron acceptor. During photosynthesis electrons are excited to a higher energy state following absorption of light by a chlorophyll-related molecule. Figure 5 summarizes several key steps of microbial energy generation.

During the processes of electron transport to carriers of successively higher redox potential, there is a separation of charge across the membrane. This is ultimately coupled to the movement of protons from one side of the membrane to the other, resulting in the formation of a proton motive force (pmf) which has two aspects. Movement of the positively charged proton creates an electrical charge across the membrane, which is termed $\Delta\Psi$. In bacteria and mitochondria, in which electron transport results in the

release of protons, the electrical charge is negative inside and can be 100–200 mV. Proton pumping also results in a difference in proton concentration, or $\Delta$ pH, across the membrane, such that the exterior is usually more acidic than the interior. Photosynthetic or respiratory electron transport thus results in proton pumping and creation of the pmf.

The proton gradient can be tapped to bring about the formation of ATP, which is the ultimate energy source for most energy-requiring processes in the cytoplasm. Synthesis of ATP is carried out by a family of protein complexes, which include the $F_1F_0$ proton-translocating ATPases of mitochondria and bacteria. Related complexes are found in chloroplasts and archaea. These protein complexes contain a membrane-embedded sector, the $F_0$ portion, which includes the pathway to allow the protons to flow back into the cell in response to the chemical and electrical forces acting on them. The $F_1$ portion of the complex contains the sites for conversion of ADP + Pi to ATP, and the energy for this process is coupled to the movement of protons. The stoichiometry of the process is such that entry of three or four protons results in the formation of one molecule of ATP. The individual steps of proton movement through the $F_1F_0$–ATPase and ATP synthesis or hydrolysis are tightly coupled under most conditions to prevent wasteful loss of the pmf or of the ATP pool in the cell and consequent heat generation. In bacteria, this ATP synthase can function in a reversible manner to allow ATP that was generated by substrate-level phosphorylation to drive formation of a proton gradient which can then be used to drive transport systems or motility. It was recently found that movement of protons causes the $F_0$ sector to rotate within the membrane, like the action of a turbine. The rotation of the $F_0$ sector is coupled to changes in the conformation of the nucleotide-binding sites in the stationary $F_1$ sector, which is linked to interconversion of ADP + Pi to ATP.

### 1. Photosynthesis

Photosynthesis traps the energy of sunlight and converts it into metabolically useful forms such as ATP during cyclic electron transport and NADPH during noncyclic electron transport processes. In some organisms, photosynthetic electron transport is

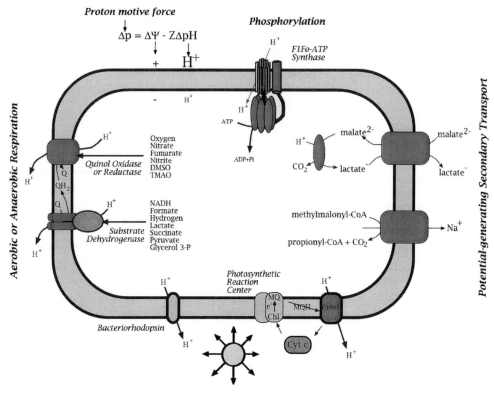

**Photosynthetic Proton Translocation**

**Fig. 5.** Summary of some processes of generation of metabolic energy in bacteria. (Left) Components of respiratory electron transport chains, in which specific substrate dehydrogenases oxidize their substrate, transfer the released electrons to membrane quinones, and in some cases extrude protons to the exterior. The electrons of the reduced quinones are transferred by the terminal oxidase or reductase to the terminal electron acceptor, such as oxygen, with the extrusion of additional protons. (Bottom) Photosynthetic systems whereby absorption of light is converted to a transmembrane gradient of protons. (Right) Two examples in which substrate/product exchange and metabolism result in generation of pmf. (Top) The electrical and chemical components of the proton motive force and a representation of the action of the $F_1F_0$–ATP synthase which interconverts the proton gradient and ATP synthesis or hydrolysis.

coupled to the formation of oxygen from water—the process that is essential for aerobic life. There are numerous pigments in cells that absorb light energy for use in photosynthesis, but the most important of these are the chlorophylls. Chlorophylls are porphyrin molecules, similar to heme, but contain a magnesium atom instead of iron. Some pigments are carried in protein molecules that serve as antennae or light-harvesting complexes, but the key processes occur in a protein complex called the photosynthetic reaction center, which typically consists of three proteins that spread across the membrane and contain bacteriochlorophyll, bacteriopheophytin, menaquinone, and

nonheme iron as electron carriers. The light energy is ultimately absorbed by a chlorophyll molecule and this energy excites an electron to a higher energy level. This excited electron passes through a series of electron-carrying prosthetic groups within the reaction center and then out through the pool of membrane-bound quinones, which transfer the electron to a cytochrome-containing electron transport chain. Passage of the electron through the electron transport chain is coupled to pumping of protons across the specialized membranes containing the photosynthetic apparatus. In cyclic phosphorylation, as carried out in the photosynthetic bacteria, the electron ultimately returns to the chlorophyll molecules after transfer to the periplasmic heme protein, cytochrome c. In the process of noncyclic phosphorylation in plants and cyanobacteria, the electron can be transferred ultimately to pyridine nucleotides for use as a reductant in biosynthetic processes. In this process, the electron can be replaced on chlorophyll by another light-absorption process that removes electrons from water to create oxygen.

A completely different system for conversion of light into metabolic energy is present in *Halobacterium salinarum,* an extremely halophilic archaeon that thrives in very saline environments such as the Dead Sea or brine evaporation ponds. These bacteria produce patches of membrane that are densely packed with the membrane protein, bacteriorhodopsin, having seven transmembrane helices and covalently bound retinal as in the visual pigment in mammalian retina. Light absorption by the retinal causes the isomerization of one of the double bonds in the molecule, causing a change in the conformation of the protein which results in the change of the *pK* of several acidic groups on either side of the membrane. The consequence of these changes is that a proton is released from the bacteriorhodopsin on the outside of the membrane and replaced by one from the cytoplasm. In this way, light is directly converted into a transmembrane proton gradient without the requirement of an electron transport chain.

### 2. Respiration

Respiration is the process whereby electrons from the metabolism of an energy source are transferred through a proton-pumping electron transport chain to some inorganic molecule. The most familiar form of respiration is aerobic respiration, in which oxygen serves as the ultimate electron acceptor. Owing to the ability of oxygen to accept electrons, aerobic respiration is the most energetically favorable, but some partially reduced forms of oxygen, hydrogen peroxide, superoxide anion, and hydroxyl radical, are extremely reactive and thus toxic to the organism. Many bacteria are capable of carrying out anaerobic respiration, in which the electrons are transferred to alternative acceptors, such as nitrate, nitrite, sulfate, or sulfite. These processes yield less energy but can occur in anoxic environments.

All respiratory metabolism uses electron transport chains, whereby electron transfer from the donor to oxygen or other acceptor is coupled to proton movement across the membrane. In *E. coli,* electron donors for respiration include NADH, succinate, glycerol 3-P, formate, lactate, pyruvate, hydrogen, and glucose. Electron acceptors include oxygen, nitrate, nitrite, fumarate, dimethylsulfoxide, and trimethylamine-N-oxide. Typical respiratory systems contain two to four transmembrane protein complexes. These include substrate-specific dehydrogenases, which transfer electrons from the donor to quinones in the membrane. The reduced quinones migrate to another protein complex which accepts electrons from them and transfers the electrons to cytochromes and ultimately to the terminal electron acceptor. The transmembrane protein complexes often contain flavin and/or nonheme iron and are arranged in the membrane in such a way that the passage of electron results in the release of proton to the outside or its consumption from the cytoplasm, i.e., the formation of the pmf.

### 3. Coupled Processes

Some bacteria couple the transport and metabolism of their energy source directly to the production of the pmf. An example of this very simple, but not very energy-rich, process is malo-lactate fermentation in *Leuconostoc.* The substrate malate is transported into the cell and converted to lactate, which leaves the cell in exchange for a new molecule of malate. The net result of this process is the movement of one negative change into the cell and the consumption of one proton inside the cell, which results in the creation of a pmf that is interior negative and alkaline.

## B. Membrane Transport

Biological membranes form the permeability barrier separating the cell from its environment. The hydrophobic barrier of the membrane bilayer greatly restricts passage of polar molecules, although nonpolar molecules can pass. Transport mechanisms exist to move nutrients and precursors into the cell and metabolic products, surface components, and toxic materials out of the cell. Several types of transport mechanisms and families of transporters have been identified.

## 1. Types of Transport Systems

Transport can occur through energy-dependent and energy-independent processes. Several general classes of transport process have been identified. Passive diffusion occurs spontaneously without the involvement of metabolic energy or of transport proteins. It only allows the flow of material down a concentration gradient, and the rate of this process is a linear function of the concentration gradient. The rate of passive diffusion depends on the ability of the permeant to dissolve in the membrane bilayer and thus depends of the polarity of the permeant and its size. These factors are related to the ability of the permeant to fit into transient defects that form in the membrane bilayer. Only water and a few hydrophobic molecules use this mechanism for entry into bacteria.

Facilitated diffusion requires the operation of a membrane protein to provide a mechanism for passage of the permeant across the membrane. These transporters merely provide a route for diffusion of their substrate down its concentration gradient, and thus the concentration of the substrate on both sides of the membrane will be equal. Transport is not dependent on the polarity of the substrate and usually exhibits stereospecificity, in which isomeric forms of the same compound are transported at very different rates. Because of the involvement of the transporter as a catalyst for movement, the rate of transport can be saturated in the same manner as an enzyme-catalyzed reaction. A possible example is the glycerol facilitator GlpF of *E. coli*, a transmembrane protein that allows glycerol and other small molecules to diffuse across the cytoplasmic membrane at rates much faster than those across lipid bilayers. However, this protein may act in the manner of a channel rather than a carrier.

The overwhelming majority of transport systems in bacteria catalyze active transport and expend metabolic energy to allow the accumulation of even very low external concentrations of a nutrient to a much greater concentration inside the cell. Active transport is carried out by a transport protein or complex and thus exhibits substrate stereospecificity and rate saturation. The difference compared to facilitated diffusion is that the substrate can be accumulated at concentrations as much as 1 million times higher than that outside. This accumulation requires the expenditure of energy, and in the absence of energy many but not all transport mechanisms can carry out facilitated diffusion. These active transport systems differ in their molecular complexity and in the mechanism by which metabolic energy is coupled to substrate accumulation. It is important to distinguish active transport, in which the substrate is accumulated in unaltered form, from group translocation, in which the substrate is converted into a different molecule during the process of transport. Some types of transport processes in bacterial cells are summarized in Fig. 6.

## 2. ATP-Driven Active Transport

Several groups of transport mechanisms use the energy gained during ATP hydrolysis to drive active transport. One of these groups is called the P-type ion-translocating ATPases to indicate the fact that a phospho-enzyme is formed as an intermediate in their reaction cycle. Typically, these transport systems consist of a large polypeptide of approximately 100 kDa which spans the membrane and contains the site for ATP binding and the residue that is phosphorylated. A smaller subunit usually participates in the activity. The ATP is used to phosphorylate a specific acidic aspartate residue, and this phosphorylation causes a change in conformation of the transporter that is part of the ion pumping process. Several examples of this type of transport system have been extensively studied. The sodium/potassium ATPase in the plasma membrane of higher organisms is responsible for pumping sodium out and potassium into cells, thereby generating the ion gradients that are necessary for many steps of nutrient transport and for neural signal transmission. The electrical potential that exists across the plasma membrane of mammalian and some other cells is based mainly on the difference in sodium ion concentration that is maintained by the action of this transporter. Similarly, the calcium-translocating ATPase located in the sarcoplasmic reticulum acts to lower the intracellular calcium concentrations that accumulate following the processes that initiate muscle contraction. Other

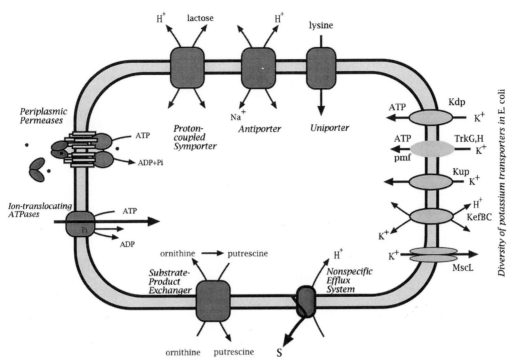

**Fig. 6.** Schematic representation of several types of active transport systems in bacteria. Top, transporters linked to the pmf; left, ATP-driven transports; bottom, examples of systems that carry out release of metabolic products of toxic chemicals. (Right) A presentation of all the transport systems known to mediate uptake or release of potassium in *E. coli*. Some of these transporters are ATP driven; others are coupled to the pmf; and MscL is a channel activated by mechanical stretch of the membrane.

P-type ATPases include the proton-translocating ATPase in the plasma membranes of fungi and plants, which establishes the gradient of protons that is used to drive many of these cells' nutrient transport systems, and some of the transport systems for magnesium or potassium ions in bacteria.

Although P-type ATPases function only in the transport of ions, another family of ATP-driven systems transports a wide range of substrates and is involved in the uptake of numerous types of nutrients and in the efflux of both surface and secreted macromolecules (proteins, carbohydrates, and lipids) and of toxic chemicals. This family of transporters is usually the largest family of any set of related genes in those organisms whose genomes have been completely sequenced. Although the subunit composition of these transporters differs, they are called the ABC family to indicate the presence in at least one subunit of a highly conserved ATP-binding cassette, a protein domain that couples ATP binding and hydrolysis to the transport process. A more descriptive name for these proteins is traffic ATPases.

One subset of the family of ABC transporters includes a large group of nutrient uptake mechanisms present only in bacteria and archaea and called periplasmic permeases. These transport systems, such as those for histidine, maltose, oligopeptides, etc., consist of a heterotetramer in which two highly hydrophobic transmembrane proteins with usually five or six membrane-spanning segments are associated with two subunits that contain the ATP-binding cassette and are mainly exposed to the cytoplasm. A fifth protein subunit is responsible for the substrate specificity of these transport systems. This substrate-binding protein usually has very high affinity for the substrate and allows uptake of nutrients even in nanomolar-range concentrations. The structure of these substrate-binding proteins resembles a clam, with two large lobes hinged in the middle. The substrate binds to specific residues in both lobes, which close around the substrate molecule for carriage to the membrane-bound components and entry into the cell. In gram-negative bacteria, the substrate-binding protein floats freely in the periplasmic space between the cytoplasmic and outer membranes. Gram-positive bacteria lack the outer membrane and, to prevent its loss, the binding protein is tethered to the cytoplasmic membrane by a lipoprotein anchor. The mechanism by which ATP hydrolysis is coupled to the release of substrate from the binding protein and its movement across the membrane is currently being studied. There is evidence suggesting that a portion of the ABC protein becomes exposed to the exterior during the transport process. A striking feature of these transporters is that they act in a unidirectional manner and only allow nutrient to enter the cell but not to be released.

The basic features of the ABC transport process and homologous transport components also operate in the opposite direction in many processes of macromolecular export, including proteins and surface carbohydrates.

### 3. Transporters Coupled to Ion Gradients

In addition to ATP-driven active transport systems, bacteria possess many transporters in which the movement of their substrate is obligately coupled to the movement, in the same or opposite direction, of an ion. In this way, accumulation of a substrate is coupled to the expenditure of the gradient of the coupling ion, which is usually a proton or sodium ion. Transmembrane ion gradients are a very convenient source of energy for active transporters. Entry into the cell of at least three protons must occur for synthesis of one molecule of ATP. It is thus very economical for the cell if it can accumulate a molecule of substrate at the expenditure of one proton rather than having to expend one ATP molecule for the same purpose. Symport refers to the process in which the coupling ion moves in the same direction as the substrate, i.e., when the downhill movement of a proton into the negative and alkaline interior of the cell is coupled to the uptake of substrate. Antiport is the reverse process, in which the two molecules move in opposite directions. If movement

of substrate is coupled to movement of a proton in a 1:1 stoichiometry, then a pmf of $-120$ mV can achieve a 100-fold accumulation of substrate inside the cell. A pmf of $-180$ mV can allow a 1000-fold gradient of substrate. Uniporters allow coupling of the movement of a positively charged molecule to the pmf without movement of any other ion. The cationic molecule is drawn into the negatively charged cell interior simply by electrostatic attraction.

These types of transporters are referred to as secondary active transport systems since they use the pmf that was generated by other means and do not use an immediate source of energy, such as ATP. Ion-coupled transport systems are inhibited by conditions that dissipate or prevent formation of the pmf, such as ionophores which allow ions to distribute across the membrane in response to the electrical and chemical gradients that act on it. An uncoupler or protonophore, such as 2,4-dinitrophenol or carbonylcyanide *p*-trifluoro-methoxy phenylhydrazone, is a hydrophobic molecule that can cross the membrane in either its ionized or its neutral form. Its presence allows protons to equilibrate across the membrane, thereby dissipating both the electrical and the chemical gradients of protons and thus the entire pmf. The ionophore valinomycin carries potassium ions and allows them to distribute across the membrane in response to electrical or chemical gradients. The addition of valinomycin to cells or membrane vesicles that have a pmf allows potassium ions to accumulate inside the negatively charged interior. This accumulation results in dissipation of the electrical potential $\Delta\Psi$. The ionophore nigericin carries protons and sodium or potassium ions across the membrane, but only in the process of exchange. The action of nigericin thus does not result in any net gain or loss of charge and thus does not dissipate $\Delta\Psi$. However, if there is a concentration gradient of protons, $\Delta$pH, nigericin allows the concentration gradient to dissipate, whereas the electrical potential is maintained or even increased.

Ion-coupled transporters typically consist of a single polypeptide chain with 12 transmembrane segments, although examples with 10–14 transmembrane segments have been claimed. It has been proposed that these proteins arose as the result of tandem duplication of a precursor protein with 6 transmembrane segments.

In the well-studied *E. coli* lactose permease LacY, several major experiments demonstrated the coupling of lactose accumulation to the pmf. The magnitude of the pmf affects the magnitude of the accumulation ratio of lactose inside the cell in a direct manner indicative of a 1:1 stoichiometry of lactose and proton. When membrane vesicles are energized by provision of a substrate for the electron transport system, a pmf is generated and lactose is accumulated. Even when a final steady-state level of lactose accumulation is reached, the lactose is in continual movement in both directions across the membrane. At the steady state, the rates in and out of the vesicle are equal, although the internal concentration of lactose is much higher than the external concentration. This indicates that the energy has resulted in a decreased affinity of the carrier for lactose on the inside face of the membrane relative to its affinity on the outside. Instead of using the electron transport system, a transmembrane electrical potential, interior negative, can be generated experimentally by diluting vesicles loaded with a high concentration of potassium ions into a medium of low potassium concentration in the presence of valinomycin. The potassium ions flow out down their concentration gradient, carrying positive charge out of the vesicle and leaving behind an interior negative charge. This negative interior can attract protons into the vesicle through the lactose permease, thereby driving lactose accumulation. Finally, if unenergized vesicles are placed in an unbuffered solution that contains a high concentration of lactose, the lactose will flow into the vesicle, bringing along a proton and thereby causing a measurable decrease in the pH of the medium. All these results provide convincing evidence for the coupled movement of proton and lactose.

These transporters are designed to prevent uncoupled movement of substrate without protons or of protons without substrate. If the latter case occurred, it would result in the operation of an uncoupler and allow the futile dissipation of the pmf. How the binding of a proton affects the affinity or binding of the substrate remains an intriguing and central question. It has been shown that the proton must bind before the lactose. If saturating concentrations of lactose are present on both sides of the membrane, the lactose transporter carries out their very rapid exchange independent of the release or re-binding of the proton. This result indicates that the reorientation of the loaded substrate-binding site from facing the interior to facing the exterior does not require changes in proton binding by LacY. If lactose is present on only one side of the membrane, however, its downhill movement is much slower than in the case of exchange and is strongly influenced by the pH. This result indicates that the bound proton must be released from the carrier to allow the empty carrier to re-orient its substrate binding site to pick up another molecule of lactose. This result is in agreement with the model that the binding of a proton is needed to increase the affinity of the carrier for lactose, and that the low concentration of protons inside the cell or vesicle is the factor that slows the rate of release of lactose and hence drives lactose accumulation.

The lactose permease has been subjected to extensive genetic and biochemical analysis. Surprisingly few amino acid residues are essential for function, although amino acid substitutions that introduce or affect charged residues in the transmembrane region usually interfere with the stability of the protein or its ability to be stably inserted in the membrane. Models for the folding of the transmembrane segments relative to one another have been proposed from genetic and biophysical assays of regional proximity.

### 4. Efflux Systems

The existence and clinical importance of nonspecific drug efflux systems have recently been recognized. An important medical finding was the discovery of an ABC protein that mediates the efflux from cells of nonpolar planar molecules, many of which are used in cancer chemotherapy. Overexpression of this protein, called the P-glycoprotein or multi-drug resistance protein-1 (MDR-1), is often associated with failure of chemotherapy and recurrence of the disease after a previous round of treatment. This protein is a single polypeptide, but it resembles the periplasmic permeases in having two separate transmembrane domains, each with six membrane-spanning segments followed by a domain with the ABC consensus motifs. It is interesting that a homologous protein in mammalian cells, MDR-2, does not mediate drug efflux but is responsible for the translocation of lipids or their flipping from one side of the membrane to the other. Spontaneous flipping of a lipid across membrane bilayers is extremely slow, and hence an ABC transporter may be assigned this function in cells. Another related protein catalyzes bile acid transport out of liver cells. There are probably many more functions for ABC transporters.

It subsequently has become clear that nonspecific efflux systems are widespread in bacteria and account for serious examples of multiple antibiotic resistance. Unlike the ATP-dependence of the MDR carrier, the bacterial efflux systems are coupled to the proton gradient. Most systems possess 4, 12, or 14 transmembrane segments; those with 4 appear to function as a trimer. In *E. coli*, the major nonspecific efflux system is called the Acr system, indicating its initial discovery as a factor that conferred resistance to acriflavins. It comprises three proteins: AcrB, a proton-coupled cytoplasmic membrane transporter; AcrA, a lipoprotein than spans the periplasmic space; and TolC, an outer membrane pore-forming protein. Although not essential for growth, the Acr system can very effectively pump almost any amphiphilic or lipophilic molecule from the cytoplasmic membrane through the outer membrane directly into the medium. This systems is just one example of complex transport systems that act across multiple cellular compartments.

### 5. *Phosphotransferase System*

Many bacterial species, but not archaea or eukarya, possess sugar uptake systems that carry out the simultaneous transport and phosphorylation of the sugar. The phosphoenolpyruvate:sugar phosphotransferase system (PTS) uses phosphoenolpyruvate (PEP) as phosphate donor, which is transferred successively to two proteins that act in common in all PTS systems. The enzyme I protein transfers phosphate from PEP to HPr, a small protein that is phosphorylated on a histidine residue. HPr serves as phosphate donor to the sugar-specific components, which comprise three protein domains that can be linked together in various orders and combinations. The IIC domain spans the membrane and catalyzes transport of the sugar, but only under conditions in which

it is phosphorylated during its passage. The IIA and IIB domains receive phosphate from HPr-P and transfer it to the sugar molecule that is carried by the corresponding IIC domain. This transport mechanism provides a very economical method to combine the phosphorylation that must occur during sugar metabolism with the transport process. Although the PTS allows substrate accumulation, it is not considered active transport because the substrate is modified during transport, and the metabolic energy has been expended in the substrate modification rather than during the transport.

It is interesting that the PTS system plays a major role in the regulation of cellular metabolism, and the transport of PTS sugars inhibits uptake of potential carbon sources through other types of transport systems. Part of this mechanism involves the inhibitory interaction of the IIA component of the glucose PTS with a variety of transporter proteins for other sugars.

### C. Export of Surface Molecules

All organisms must have specialized processes for the secretion or export of proteins or carbohydrates across the cytoplasmic membrane to the cell surface, periplasm, cell wall, outer membrane, or even the external medium. That these components can comprise 10% or more of the weight of the cell indicates the magnitude and variety of macromolecular transport activities that must occur. For peptidoglycan, lipopolysaccharide, and capsular polysaccharide synthesis, the precursor subunits are translocated across the cytoplasmic membrane and assembled on its outer surface. Some of these precursors are flipped across the membrane after they are coupled to a lipid membrane carrier.

There are several specialized mechanisms for secretion of proteins. To be secreted, a protein must carry a suitable secretion signal. The most common of these is the signal peptide, an amino-terminal extension that is removed during secretion. The typical signal peptides in all cell types comprise 20–30 amino acids with positively charged residues at the amino terminus and then a stretch of hydrophobic residues, followed by a more polar stretch and a peptidase cleavage site. Variants of this structure are used to target proteins to specific cellular organelles in eukaryotic cells. The Sec system acts on the majority of translocated proteins in bacteria. It operates along with several cytoplasmic chaperone proteins that help retard the folding of the precursor protein into its stable native structure, which would prevent movement across the membrane. The SecYEG protein complex in the cytoplasmic membrane forms a channel through which the polypeptide chain can move. The SecA protein plays a crucial role by binding to the precursor in the cytoplasm, bringing it to the SecYEG translocation complex, and sequentially inserting approximately 30 amino acid segments to the other side of the membrane. The insertion process requires ATP hydrolysis. Once the signal peptide has appeared on the other side of the membrane, it is cleaved off by the action of a leader peptidase enzyme.

At least three types of transport systems allow export of specific proteins out of the cell. These proteins employ special targeting signals to specify their entry into the appropriate secretory pathway. One of these, the type II secretion system, uses the Sec pathway for initial movement of the precursor into the periplasmic space, where a very complex protein assemblage recognizes the exported protein and moves it across the outer membrane. The type I secretion system resembles the Acr multi-drug efflux system in the simplicity and location of its protein components, except that the cytoplasmic membrane component uses the energy of ATP hydrolysis for its action. The type III secretion systems are of particular interest because they preferentially secrete their substrate proteins directly into a eukaryotic target cell. Other specialized systems exist for the assembly of flagella and fimbrial adhesins (pili and fimbriae) on the cell surface. The number, mechanism, and regulation of the many specialized export systems have only recently begun to be understood.

## D. Cell Growth

### 1. Cell Division

The cytoplasmic membrane plays numerous important roles in the processes of cell growth and division. In ways which are not fully understood, the rate of growth of a cell is determined by the rates of synthesis of its macromolecules, RNA, and protein.

Their continued production produces pressure that drives the expansion of the cytoplasmic membrane, with the insertion of additional membrane proteins and of the phospholipids to maintain a set protein : lipid ratio. Somehow, the pressure of the expanding cytoplasm triggers insertion of additional cell wall material to allow the increase in cell volume. Once the cell volume has reached a critical point, the concentration of a particular protein has reached a certain concentration, or a certain time has passed since the completion of a round of chromosome replication, the process of cell division is initiated. A critical step in cell division is the assembly of a ring of tubulin-like FtsZ proteins from the cytoplasm onto the membrane at the division site. This assembled complex contracts to pull the membrane together at the division septum to close off the two progeny cells.

A poorly understood process of cell division that may require membrane action is the separation and equal partitioning of the bacterial chromosomes into each progeny cell. In one model, the chromosomes attach to a membrane protein and are pulled apart by the growth of the membrane. This model is unlikely to account for the rapidity with which chromosome separation can occur under certain conditions, but no convincing evidence for cytoskeletal components that might pull the chromosomes apart has been presented.

### 2. Signal Transduction

Bacterial gene expression is very responsive to changes in the cell's environment, and many types of regulatory systems allow specific genes to respond to the presence of or need for a wide range of pathway substrates or products. Some regulatory systems are controlled by the binding of the effector molecule to a specific DNA-binding protein that controls the level of expression of the controlled gene. Other systems are controlled by effector molecules that remain outside the cell. Many of these are controlled by two-component regulatory systems, which are widespread in bacteria and archaea and even occur in eukarya. One component of these systems is a transmembrane protein that recognizes its effector molecule in the medium and responds to its binding by a transmembrane signaling event that changes its ability to phosphorylate or to transfer that phosphate.

Phosphorylation of the sensor kinase protein can result in transfer of that phosphate to the second component, which is a response regulator protein. The ability of the response regulator protein to bind to a target DNA sequence or to activate transcription of that gene is directly related to the level of its phosphorylation. This mode of transmembrane signaling by regulation of protein phosphorylation is reminiscent of the myriad signaling processes in eukaryotic cells, although the mechanisms and components are not related.

### 3. Cell Movement

Bacteria exhibit several types of motility. Many rod-shaped bacteria and a few cocci can swim through liquid medium through the use of flagella. Flagella are long, helical filaments that extend from the poles or the periphery of the cell body and are assembled from a single protein subunit, called flagellin. Motility is initiated by the rotation of the flagellar filament, which in the case of bacteria with multiple filaments results in their coalescence into a bundle that acts similar to a propeller. Their rotation is driven by the downhill entry of protons through the flagellar basal body, a complex structure embedded in the cytoplasmic membrane and driven by the pmf.

Spirochetes are spiral-shaped bacteria in which the cell body is wrapped around the flagellar filaments which grow from the cell poles. Their flagella do not extend into the medium but are retained in the periplasmic space where they overlap in the middle of the cell. These bacteria exhibit a characteristic corkscrew motility that is thought to result from rotation of the endo-flagella.

Several types of bacteria are capable of movement on solid surfaces or in very viscous solutions, in which flagella are ineffective. In some types of these bacteria the mechanism of movement is unknown, whereas in some enteric bacteria, such as *Proteus*, this swarming motility is related to differentiation of the cell into very long forms that are covered with a profusion of lateral flagellar filaments.

Motility is a regulated process that allows bacteria to swim toward or away from gradients of nutrients or repellents or physical conditions, such as oxygen or light. Response to chemical attractants or repellents is called chemotaxis and this senses whether a bacteria is moving in a direction which increases or decreases the concentrations of the chemical signal. In the absence of a signal, bacteria exhibit periods of swimming in a straight line followed by short periods in which they tumble aimlessly before setting off in a new direction. Straight-line swimming is associated with counterclockwise (CCW) rotation of the flagellum (viewed toward the cell), and tumbling is associated with clockwise (CW) flagellar rotation. The process of chemotaxis controls the direction of rotation so that when cells are swimming in a favorable direction, their period of straight swimming (CCW rotation) is extended. Movement in an unfavorable direction results in an increased frequency of tumbling (CW rotation). This process is controlled by several chemoreceptors in the cytoplasmic membrane, whose occupancy by substrates indicates the level of the chemical signals. Occupancy of these receptors by their ligands results in changes in the activity of a protein kinase that is typical of the two-component regulatory systems described previously. Changes in the activity of the kinase result in changes in the level of phosphorylation of a small cytoplasmic protein, CheY, whose phosphorylated form signals CW rotation of the flagella. Another form of covalent modification is the methylation of certain glutamate residues on the chemoreceptors which serves to adjust their signaling properties and allow the receptors to respond to changes in the level of the chemicals rather than to their static concentration. This adaptive response allows the bacterium to resume its normal behavior once it finds itself in a steady supply of the chemical attractant and to prepare to set off in response to new signals. Chemotaxis thus provides a well-studied example of transmembrane signaling and communication between protein complexes in the cytoplasmic membrane. Of particular interest is the localization of the chemoreceptors and associated components at the poles of the cell.

## V. ISOLATION OF MEMBRANES

Procedures have been developed for the isolation of cellular membranes from many bacteria. These procedures are modified owing to differences in the composition and content of peptidoglycan cell wall and of the outer membrane or other surface layers. For the gram-negative *E. coli,* membranes are most reliably isolated following disruption of the cell either by decompression in a French pressure cell or by osmotic lysis following disruption of the peptidoglycan cell wall with the degradative enzyme lysozyme. Cytoplasmic membrane vesicles that are used for transport studies are obtained by osmotic lysis of such spheroplasts (or operation of the French pressure cell at low pressure) and generally have only a somewhat smaller volume than that of the intact cell and are mainly in the right-side-out orientation. Membrane vesicles that are prepared by more vigorous cell disruption by sonication or operation of the French pressure cell at high operating pressure tend to be much smaller in volume and in the inside-out or everted orientation.

After unbroken cells are removed by low-speed centrifugation, the total membrane fraction can be collected by ultracentrifugation. Sucrose density gradient centrifugation can be used for removal of ribosomes, peptidoglycan fragments, and other large complexes and for separation of the cytoplasmic and outer membranes. Because of its content of lipopolysaccharide, the density of the outer membrane in *E. coli* is higher than that of the cytoplasmic membrane. In other gram-negative bacteria, the densities of the two membranes are similar, and their separation by this technique is not as effective.

An alternative approach for separation of the proteins from the cytoplasmic and outer membranes in enteric bacteria takes advantage of the resistance of most outer membrane proteins to solubilization by nonionic detergents in the presence of divalent cations. This rapid method cannot be relied on for localization of all membrane proteins since it has been tested only on a limited set of proteins and depends on features that are not necessarily universally maintained. Detergents are amphipathic molecules that are able to associate with and disrupt membrane structure. They allow the lipids to form a spherical micellar structure and provide the membrane proteins with a suitable environment for their nonpolar surfaces in molecular aggregates much smaller than the membrane. Nonionic detergents are useful be-

cause many allow membrane proteins to retain their structure and function.

## VI. MEMBRANE ASSEMBLY AND CONTROL OF COMPOSITION

The process of membrane assembly is becoming increasingly understood. Insertion of integral proteins into the cytoplasmic membrane is determined by the presence of hydrophobic or amphiphilic stretches of amino acid residues that represent potential transmembrane segments. Most cytoplasmic membrane proteins do not have a cleaved signal sequence that directs them to the membrane. The exceptions are proteins which are anchored in the membrane but are mainly exposed to the outside; these undergo processing and removal of a signal sequence. The orientation of the transmembrane segments of an integral membrane protein is determined primarily by the pattern of charged amino acid residues on the two polar loops on either side of the segment, which generally obey the positive-inside behavior. Although most integral membranes can insert spontaneously into lipid bilayers, their insertion in the cell appears to be facilitated by cytoplasmic chaperones, in particular the Ffh and FtsH proteins that are related to the components of the eukaryotic signal recognition system. These chaperones appear to retard folding of the nascent polypeptide in the cytoplasm before it associates with the membrane. The components of the Sec system do not seem to be necessary, unless the protein contains a large (>60 residues) external segment.

Membrane phospholipids are made by cytoplasmic and membrane-associated enzyme pathways. New phospholipids are inserted into the inner face of the cytoplasmic membrane and must flip across to the outer leaflet. This flipping process is extremely slow without the involvement of a protein catalyst. There is a considerable degree of membrane asymmetry in membranes of eukaryotic cells, with a substantially different lipid composition in the two leaflets of the bilayer. Such asymmetry appears less prominent in bacterial membranes but has not been studied in detail.

The lipid composition of cellular membranes changes in response to environmental conditions and growth state. Lower growth temperatures result in the incorporation of fatty acids with a higher degree of unsaturation than those that are present at higher growth temperatures so as to maintain a sufficient level of membrane fluidity. This sensing and response to ambient temperature involves selective synthesis and incorporation of different fatty acids by the appropriate enzymes of lipid biosynthesis rather than changes in levels of these enzymes. When cells of *E. coli* enter the stationary phase of growth, an enzyme is produced that adds a methyl group across double bonds in fatty acids to convert unsaturated fatty acids to the corresponding cyclopropane fatty acids. These cyclopropane fatty acids have similar effects on membrane dynamics as those with double bonds but are more stable to oxidative damage.

Phospholipid head groups determine certain properties of the membrane. The acidic phospholipids in *E. coli,* PE and cardiolipin, are necessary for the incorporation and function of many membrane enzymes and transporters. Anionic phospholipids are essential for stimulating the ATPase activity of the SecA protein during its translocation of proteins across the membrane. These lipids are also necessary for the activation of ATP binding to the DnaA protein, which plays the central role in the initiation of bacterial chromosome replication. Through the use of mutants defective in the various lipid biosynthetic pathways, it was possible to show that a minimal quantity of acidic phospholipids was essential for cell growth, although cardiolipin was dispensable. The other major lipid, PE, is noted for its ability to form nonlamellar structures under certain conditions. Mutants that are completely blocked in the synthesis of PE can grow, but only in the presence of elevated concentrations of divalent cations, which promote nonlamellar structures in cardiolipin. In this

mutant, cardiolipin synthesis is essential for growth. It is thus clear that the membrane can tolerate a wide range in the lipid head group composition, as long as there is a minimal level of acidic phospholipids and of lipids that can form nonlamellar structures. It has proven difficult to determine the effect of changes in lipid composition on individual membrane functions in the intact cell because of the activation of a stress response system under these conditions. The fluid state of the membrane certainly affects the activity of numerous membrane proteins, indicating that acyl chain or lipid mobility are necessary for their proper function or insertion. One expects substantial progress in the future in understanding the structures and interactions of lipids and proteins in the cytoplasmic membrane.

## See Also the Following Articles

ABC Transport • Cell Walls, Bacterial • Energy Transduction Processes • Lipid Biosynthesis • Outer Membrane, Gram-Negative Bacteria • Protein Secretion

## Bibliography

deKruijff, B., Killian, J. A., Rietveld, A. G., and Kusters, R. (1997). Phospholipid structure and *Escherichia coli* membranes. *Curr. Topics Membranes* **44**, 477–515.

Harold, F. M. (1986). "The Vital Force: A Study of Bioenergetics." Freeman, New York.

Konings, W. N., Kaback, H. R., and Lolkema, J. S. (1996). "Transport Processes in Eukaryotic and Prokaryotic Organisms." Elsevier, Amsterdam.

Neidhardt, F. C., Curtiss, R., III, Ingraham, J. L., Lin, E. C. C., Low, K. B., Magasanik, B., Reznikoff, W. S., Riley, M., Schaechter, M., and Umbarger, H. E. (1996). "*Escherichia coli* and *Salmonella.* Cellular and Molecular Biology." ASM Press, Washington, DC.

Pao, S. S., Paulsen, I. T., and Saier, M. J., Jr. (1998). Major facilitator superfamily. *Microbiol. Mol. Biol. Rev.* **62**, 1–3.

Yeagle, P. L. (1993). "The Membranes of Cells," 2nd ed. Academic Press, San Diego.

# Cellular Immunity

## M. S. Rolph and S. H. E. Kaufmann

*Max Planck Institute for Infection Biology*

## GLOSSARY

**adaptive immunity** Adaptive immunity encompasses the immune response that occurs following recognition of specific antigen by B and T lymphocytes and it develops later in the immune response than innate immunity. Also known as specific immunity or acquired immunity.

**antigen** A molecule recognized by specific receptors on B and T lymphocytes.

**chemokine** A subset of the cytokine family distinguished by a characteristic molecular structure and mostly functioning to attract immune cells to the site of infection.

**chemotaxis** The directed migration of cells toward an inflammatory site in response to factors known as chemotaxins.

**cytokine** Cytokines are protein hormones produced by a wide range of cell types. They play an integral role in the regulation and effector function of all stages of the immune response.

**innate immunity** The early stage of an immune response involving cells such as natural killer cells, polymorphonuclear granulocytes, and macrophages and factors such as complement, in which recognition of specific antigen is not involved.

**major histocompatibility complex (MHC)** A gene complex found in all mammals, the products of which are intimately involved in antigen presentation to T cells. The principal components of the MHC are divided into MHC class I and MHC class II.

**monocyte/macrophage** A leukocyte subset derived from bone marrow precursor cells which subsequently migrate into the blood, where they are identified as monocytes, and then to tissue sites where they differentiate to become macrophages. Macrophages are characterized by a strong phagocytic capacity and numerous potent antimicrobial mechanisms.

**opsonization** The process by which foreign particles are coated with factors known as opsonins, such as antibody and complement, facilitating their uptake by phagocytes.

**phagocytosis** The process in which large material, such as microorganisms, is engulfed by cells.

**polymorphonuclear granulocyte** A leukocyte group comprising neutrophils, eosinophils, and basophils.

**T lymphocyte** A class of lymphocyte (the other class being B lymphocytes). T lymphocytes develop in the thymus and subsequently migrate into lymphoid and other tissue sites, where they play a central role in the adaptive cellular immune response.

**INFECTION WITH MICROORGANISMS** presents a profound challenge to host survival, in which the capacity of the microorganism to replicate and/or persist in the host is pitted against the host immune response. The immune response is frequently divided into two separate arms: humoral and cellular immunity. For the purposes of this chapter, cellular immunity is defined as that part of the immune response mediated by cells. Major players in cellular immunity include neutrophils, macrophages, natural killers cells, and T lymphocytes. Humoral immunity is mediated by antibodies and is not considered in this article.

The early phase of the cellular immune response is known as **innate immunity** and is characterized by broad and nonspecific recognition of foreign material by neutrophils and macrophages and later by natural killer cells. Subsequently, **acquired** or **adap-**

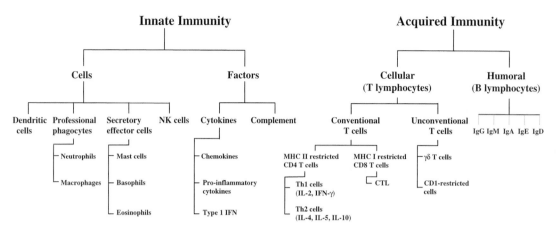

**Fig. 1.** The major components of the cellular immune response.

tive **immunity** develops whereby T lymphocytes are activated following recognition of specific **antigen**. Antigen is foreign material that is specifically recognized by the immune system and is presented to T lymphocytes as peptide in association with major histocompatibility complex (MHC) molecules on the cell surface. All stages of the immune response are regulated by cytokines, which are small proteins that serve as signal transmitters within the immune system. In this article we first describe the cells and the cytokines that participate in the cellular immune response against infectious agents. Subsequently, the functional activities expressed by the innate and acquired immune response are described, with emphasis on two major functions—target cell lysis and microbial killing by activated macrophages. Finally, we discuss different aspects of the immune response to infectious agents using examples from human infections and experimental animal systems. In doing so, we attempt to show that the immune system has adapted to different pathogen strategies so that the most appropriate response is elicited by a given type of pathogen. The major players in the cellular immune response are depicted schematically in Fig. 1.

## I. CELLS OF THE IMMUNE RESPONSE

### A. Polymorphonuclear Granulocytes

The polymorphonuclear granulocytes (PMNs) are a group of leukocytes characterized by a multilobed nucleus (hence "polymorphonuclear") and numerous cytoplasmic granules (hence "granulocyte"). Based on their staining characteristics with routine hematological stains, PMNs are divided into three groups: neutrophils, eosinophils and basophils.

### 1. Neutrophils

Neutrophils represent the major PMN subset. They enter inflammatory sites from the bloodstream by a process known as chemotaxis. Chemotaxis is the directed migration of cells in response to factors ("chemotaxins") such as bacterial products, molecules from the complement pathway, or a large range of other inflammatory proteins. Neutrophils play an extremely important role in acute infections and inflammatory processes, and they are central players in the earliest phases of the innate immune response. The principal antimicrobial function of neutrophils is to engulf foreign materials, a process known as phagocytosis. Once phagocytosed, foreign matter is exposed to a vast and potent array of antimicrobial molecules, such as nitric oxide, reactive oxygen intermediates, defensins, and lactoferrin. The process of phagocytosis is discussed further in Section III.

### 2. Eosinophils

Eosinophils represent 2–5% of blood leukocytes. In response to many different stimuli, such as antibody-coated parasites, and cytokines including interleukin (IL)-3, IL-5, granulocyte-macrophage colony-stimulating factor (GM-CSF), tumor necrosis factor (TNF), and type 1 interferon (IFN), eosinophils will release their granules into the extracellular space. These granular molecules, which include cationic proteins such as major basic protein, can be highly cytotoxic and are effective in killing large extracellular parasites that are too large to be phagocytosed. Activated eosinophils can also produce large quantities of reactive oxygen intermediates (see Section III.B) and are major effector cells against helminths, although their contribution to defense against most other infectious agents is small.

### 3. Basophils

Basophils represent a minor subset of the PMNs, and their role in the cellular immune response to microorganisms is also minor. They mostly act to further the inflammatory response during some parasitic infections.

## B. Natural Killer Cells

Natural killer (NK) cells are a subset of cytotoxic cells with the morphological appearance of large lymphocytes and characterized by the presence of numerous cytoplasmic granules. Despite their appearance, NK cells do not express typical B or T lymphocyte cell surface markers, and they do not express rearranged immunoglobulin or T cell receptor genes. The means by which NK cells recognize target cells is an area currently under intensive investigation. A general feature of target cell recognition is that killing by NK cells is inversely related to major histocompatability complex (MHC) class I expression on the target cell.

Following target cell recognition, NK cells release their cytoplasmic granules within the extracellular space between the NK cells and the target cells. The contents of the granules, which include proteins such as perforin and granzymes, are capable of punching holes in the target cell membrane and of inducing apoptotic cell death of target cells. In addition to their cytotoxic function, NK cells are important sources of cytokines such as IFN-$\gamma$, TNF, and IL-1.

NK cells are prominent during the later phase of innate immunity and are considered important in controlling infection prior to the full development of the adaptive immune response. In addition to their effector function, NK cells, through their capacity to produce cytokines, play a significant role in regulating and amplifying the developing immune response.

## C. Macrophages

Macrophages are bone marrow-derived cells that are integral to the induction and effector activities of cellular immunity. Macrophage precursors leave the bone marrow via the peripheral blood, where they are known as monocytes. Upon entering tissue sites (particularly in response to various inflammatory stimuli), monocytes mature into tissue macrophages. They are located throughout the body, particularly in sites such as the liver, lung, and spleen, where they are most likely to encounter particulate matter. Large numbers of macrophages, derived from recently immigrated monocytes, also accumulate in inflammatory sites.

A key feature of macrophages is their potent phagocytic capacity. This is an important function during the innate immune response. Detection and uptake of foreign material, such as sugar residues on bacteria (including mannose, fucose, or galactose), can be mediated by so-called pattern recognition receptors. Alternatively, phagocytosis may be facilitated by the process of opsonization—coating of antigen with molecules (opsonins) such as antibodies and products of the complement pathway which can then be taken up via specific receptors on the macrophage. Macrophages are armed with a variety of antimicrobial effector mechanisms which can kill or deactivate phagocytosed microorganisms. This represents an important early line of defense, which is frequently sufficient for control of infection.

Another consequence of uptake or detection of foreign substances by macrophages is the release of a wide range of biologically active mediators, including cytokines and chemokines. For example, macrophage release of chemokines and proinflammatory cytokines, such as IL-1, IL-6, and TNF, acts to amplify the innate immune response and assists in the initiation of adaptive immunity. A critical event in the induction of adaptive immunity is the release of IL-12 and IL-18 by macrophages. These cytokines direct the development of T helper cells that are necessary for the control of infections with intracellular pathogens (see Sections I.D and III.E).

Finally, macrophages are one of the major cell types involved in the presentation of antigenic peptides to T helper lymphocytes (see Section III.C) and are thus critical for the initiation of the adaptive immune response. Macrophages are also important effector cells in the adaptive immune response. Activated T lymphocytes produce a range of cytokines, in particular IFN-$\gamma$, that act to further enhance macrophage antimicrobial function. Indeed, for many infections, activation by T lymphocytes is required before macrophage killing becomes fully effective.

## D. T Lymphocytes

Lymphocytes are a leukocyte subset involved in the recognition of antigen and are broadly divided into T and B lymphocytes (commonly termed B and T cells). B cells develop in the bone marrow and produce antibodies. T cells develop in the thymus and recognize antigenic peptide presented by MHC molecules (see Section III.C). Within the peripheral T cell system there exists considerable heterogeneity. The majority of T cells (approximately 90%) express the $\alpha\beta$ T cell receptor (TCR). These $\alpha\beta$ TCR-positive cells can be broadly divided into those with cell surface expression of CD4 (CD4$^+$ T cells), which recognize antigen presented by MHC class II, and those with expression of CD8 (CD8$^+$ T cells), which recognize antigen presented by MHC class I.

### 1. CD4$^+$ T Lymphocytes

CD4$^+$ T cells are the central regulatory cells in antigen-specific immunity and are frequently described as T helper (Th) cells. Through production of cytokines, and also through expression of cell surface ligands, CD4$^+$ T cells are important regulators of antibody production, cytotoxic CD8$^+$ T cell activation, and macrophage activation. CD4$^+$ T cells may also have a direct effector function through production of cytokines such as IFN-$\gamma$ and TNF as well as the elaboration of cytotoxic activity. On the basis of cytokine production, CD4$^+$ T cells can be broadly divided into Th1 cells, which produce cytokines such as IL-2 and IFN-$\gamma$, and Th2 cells, which preferentially produce IL-4, IL-5, and IL-10. This is an important functional distinction which is discussed further in Section III.E.

### 2. CD8$^+$ T Lymphocytes

CD8$^+$ T lymphocytes are known as cytotoxic T lymphocytes (CTLs) because of their capacity to kill target cells following recognition of specific antigen. CD8$^+$ T cells recognize peptide antigen in association with MHC class I molecules on the surface of an infected cell. Due to the nature of the MHC class I antigen processing pathway, CD8$^+$ T cells are specialized for the detection and elimination of cells infected with viruses and other intracellular microorganisms as well as tumor cells. In addition to their cytotoxic activity, CD8$^+$ T cells can exert effector function through the production of a wide range of cytokines, particularly IFN-$\gamma$ and TNF, both of which play critical roles in the effector phase of cellular immunity.

### 3. Unconventional T Cells

The remaining 10% of T cells are often grouped together as "unconventional T cells" although this appellation does not do justice to the heterogeneity found within the group. Prominent within the unconventional T cell group are T cells that express a $\gamma\delta$ TCR and T cells restricted through CD1 molecules.

#### a. $\gamma\delta$ T Cells

The $\gamma\delta$ TCR is expressed on a small subset of $\alpha\beta$ TCR-negative peripheral T cells. Several features of $\gamma\delta$ T cells distinguish them from conventional $\alpha\beta$ T cells. First, the $\gamma\delta$ TCR structure is quite different from that of the $\alpha\beta$ TCR, sharing more similarity with immunoglobulin. Second, the distribution of $\gamma\delta$ T cells is different from that of $\alpha\beta$ T cells, with a greater concentration of $\gamma\delta$ T cells in epithelial sites. Third, the type of antigen recognized by $\gamma\delta$ T cells differs from that recognized by $\alpha\beta$ T cells. For example, mycobacterial phospholigands can stimulate a large proportion of all human $\gamma\delta$ T cells, apparently without the aid of any known antigen-presenting molecule.

The precise role of $\gamma\delta$ T cells in cellular immunity awaits full clarification. Due to their epithelial location, direct recognition of bacterial components, and relatively early activation during the immune response, it has been suggested that $\gamma\delta$ T cells may bridge the gap between the innate immune response and the highly specific response mediated by $\alpha\beta$ T cells. A regulatory role of $\gamma\delta$ T cells has also been suggested in experiments using mutant mice deficient in $\gamma\delta$ T cells. Following infection of these mutant mice with *Mycobacterium tuberculosis* or *Listeria monocytogenes,* a slight exacerbation of infection compared to normal mice was observed; interestingly, however, the histological picture was considerably different. In contrast to the characteristic granulomas that developed following infection of mice with intracellular bacteria (see Section IV.E), the lesions in the $\gamma\delta$ T cell-deficient mice were characterized by inflammatory abscess-like lesions.

### b. CD1-Restricted T Cells

CD1 molecules are a group of cell surface proteins with some homology to MHC molecules, and like MHC class I they are expressed at the cell surface in association with $\beta_2$-microglobulin. They are not encoded within the MHC region but can present peptide (and other) antigen to T cells. A major difference between MHC and CD1 molecules is that CD1 molecules are nonpolymorphic.

Two major groups of CD1-restricted T cells have been identified. One group reacts with bacteria-derived molecules such as mycolic acids from *M. tuberculosis* and lipoarabinomannan from *M. leprae.* These cells produce IFN-$\gamma$ and are cytolytic, suggesting that they play a protective role during infection. A second group of CD1-reactive T cells has been identified whose members coexpress the $\alpha\beta$ TCR and an NK cell marker, NK1. Following stimulation through their TCRs, these TCR $\alpha\beta^+$/NK1$^+$ cells rapidly release cytokines, especially IL-4, and it has been proposed that they play a role in the regulation of the cellular immune response.

## E. Dendritic Cells

Although numerically a minor cell population, dendritic cells (DCs) deserve their own section due to their importance in the initiation of T cell responses. DCs have a characteristic, dendritic morphology and are specialized for the uptake, processing, and presentation of antigen to T cells (see Section III.C). They are found throughout the body, particularly at sites where they are likely to encounter antigen (e.g., in the skin or in the T cell areas of lymphoid tissue). DCs are the most potent antigen-presenting cells (APCs), and this is at least partially related to their high level of expression of MHC class I and class II as well as costimulatory molecules (see Section III.D). In comparison to other APCs, DCs are particularly effective in activating naive T cells—that is, those T cells that have not previously encountered antigen. The following scenario is envisaged for DC function. DCs patrol sites in which contact with foreign antigen is likely, such as epithelial/mucosal surfaces. Following capture of antigen, DCs migrate via the afferent lymph to the local lymph nodes, where they are available to initiate a T cell response following recognition of specific antigen by the T cells. It should be noted that DCs have only a limited phagocytic capacity, and that uptake of microbial antigen may occur only after initial phagocytosis and degradation of microbial products by macrophages.

## II. CYTOKINES

Cytokines are a group of low-molecular-weight proteins with regulatory and effector functions in the immune response. Typically, the action of cytokines is restricted to the local microenvironment, in which they operate in an autocrine or paracrine fashion. However, in some situations, such as strong inflammatory reactions, endocrine function may also be observed. Cytokine biology is complex: There are numerous cytokines, each with a broad range of activities; in many cases there is a considerable degree of functional overlap and redundancy between different cytokines; cytokines positively and negatively regulate their own expression as well as that of other cytokines; receptors for some cytokines are ubiquitously expressed, whereas others can have very restricted distributions; and the level of receptor expression can be regulated by many different factors. In this article, the major cytokines will be briefly discussed.

## A. IL-1

IL-1 is a proinflammatory cytokine with a broad spectrum of biological activities both within and without the immune system. There are two genes for IL-1 (IL-1$\alpha$ and IL-1$\beta$) with similar biological activities despite sharing only 26% homology at the protein level. Numerous cell types can produce IL-1, including monocytes/macrophages, T cells, dendritic cells, neutrophils, smooth muscle cells, and keratinocytes. Macrophages and keratinocytes are considered to be the major producers of IL-1 *in vivo*. Within the immune response, IL-1 enhances T cell proliferation; stimulates production of proinflammatory mediators including IL-1, IL-6, IL-8, TNF, and prostaglandins from macrophages; enhances the ability of APCs to induce T cell proliferation; and enhances IL-12-mediated NK cell activation. IL-1 also has a major role in fever induction.

## B. IL-2

IL-2 is a T cell-derived cytokine that acts directly on T cells, in a paracrine or autocrine fashion, and plays a central role in the development of T cell responses, where it is important in the induction of clonal expansion. Naive T cells do not normally express the high-affinity IL-2 receptor and thus do not respond to IL-2. Following antigen recognition, expression of the high-affinity IL-2 receptor is induced, enabling the T cell to proliferate in response to IL-2. IL-2-induced proliferation is critical in the induction of a T cell response because prior to activation T cells of any given specificity are present in the body in very low numbers. Clonal expansion induced by IL-2 is important in increasing the population of T cells with the correct specificity to the level required to deal with an invading microorganism. In the absence of IL-2, activated T cells will die. IL-2 can act on cells other than T cells, including macrophages, NK cells, and T cells. For each of these cells, IL-2 is an activating cytokine.

## C. IL-4

IL-4 is an 18- to 20-kDa cytokine produced by T cells, basophils, mast cells, and some bone marrow cells. Nearly all cell types, through their expression of the IL-4 receptor, can respond to IL-4, but the important target cells for the immune response are macrophages, T cells, and B cells. IL-4 induces B cell maturation and promotes immunoglobulin isotype class switching in B cells and can enhance T cell proliferation. It plays a critical role in regulating the immune response by favoring humoral immunity while blocking cell-mediated immunity (see Section III.E).

## D. IL-6

IL-6 is a pleiotropic cytokine produced by numerous cell types, including macrophages, T cells, keratinocytes, and fibroblasts. IL-6 is an important cytokine in the acute phase response (the systemic response to foreign material such as bacterial products), the induction of fever, and the production of numerous hepatocyte-derived serum proteins. Within the immune response, IL-6 stimulates growth and maturation of B cells and can enhance T cell activation.

## E. IL-10

Macrophages, B cells, and T cells represent the major sources of IL-10. Many of the effects of IL-10 are inhibitory: It can block cytokine production by macrophages, NK cells, and Th1 cells. In the case of macrophages, IL-10 can directly suppress production of cytokines such as TNF, IL-1, IL-6, IL-8, and GM-CSF and other macrophage products such as nitric oxide. The ability of IL-10 to block cytokine production by Th1 cells is less direct and is mediated by a downregulation of the ability of macrophages to potentiate T cell function. In contrast, IL-10 directly stimulates B cell function.

## F. IL-12

IL-12 is a heterodimeric cytokine consisting of 35- and 40-kDa subunits, and it is produced by macrophages and B cells. The principal targets of IL-12 are CD4$^+$ and CD8$^+$ T cells and NK cells. Some of the functions of IL-12 include induction of IFN-$\gamma$ production by T cells and NK cells, regulation of the development of cell-mediated immunity by enhancing the activation and proliferation of Th1 cells, and enhancement of cytotoxicity in T cells and NK cells.

## G. IL-18

IL-18 is a recently identified cytokine that is produced by activated macrophages and shares several functions with IL-12. It can induce IFN-$\gamma$ production by Th1 T cell clones, splenocytes, and liver lymphocytes. It also activates NK cells and enhances the proliferation of activated T cells. IL-18, especially in combination with IL-12, enhances the development of Th1 cells.

## H. Type I IFN

Interferons were first discovered in 1957 as a result of their ability to interfere (hence "interferon") with virus replication. Interferons can be broadly divided into two groups: type I interferons (comprising interferon-$\alpha$ and interferon-$\beta$) and type II interferons (interferon-$\gamma$). In response to virus infection and numerous other cellular insults (e.g., bacteria, fungi, parasites, and their products) most cell types can produce type I interferons. The most important consequence of type I IFN release is the induction of an antiviral state in neighboring cells. However, type I IFN also plays a role in regulating the immune response, and it can activate NK cells and macrophages and increase cell surface expression of MHC class I.

## I. IFN-$\gamma$

IFN-$\gamma$ is a homodimeric cytokine produced principally by NK cells and CD4$^+$ and CD8$^+$ T cells. IFN-$\gamma$ has some intrinsic antiviral activity but has many other more important functions in the immune response. It is a crucial cytokine for macrophage activation because it is a potent stimulus for the production of macrophage effector molecules such as nitric oxide and reactive oxygen intermediates, and it stimulates the production of macrophage-derived cytokines such as IL-1 and TNF. Presentation of antigen to CD4$^+$ and CD8$^+$ T cells is enhanced by the capacity of IFN-$\gamma$ to increase cell surface expression of MHC class II and MHC class I. Other important functions of IFN-$\gamma$ in cellular immunity include stimulation of NK cell activity and promotion of Th1 cell development.

## J. TNF

TNF is a highly pleiotropic molecule produced by a range of cell types, principally macrophages, T cells, NK cells, and mast cells. There are two receptors for TNF, the p55 and p75 forms, which mediate different cellular functions of TNF. Both receptors are present on essentially all cell types. Among the processes of cellular immunity, TNF plays an important role in macrophage activation: It stimulates production of chemokines and other proinflammatory cytokines, such as IL-1 and IL-6, and synergizes strongly with IFN-$\gamma$ for macrophage activation. TNF also enhances the activity of NK cells, neutrophils, and eosinophils.

## K. Chemokines

The chemokines represent a structurally related family of low-molecular-weight molecules with chemotactic function. Based on structure, chemokines are divided into several groups. Alpha chemokines are characterized by a structurally conserved motif with two cysteine residues separated by an intervening residue. A wide range of cell types can produce alpha chemokines, including macrophages, lymphocytes, PMNs, and other nonimmune type cells. The major target cell for the alpha chemokines is the neutrophil, although some alpha chemokines also target lymphocytes and monocytes. Examples of alpha chemokines include IL-8, interferon-inducible protein-10, and Gro. Beta-chemokines have two adjacent cysteine residues in the conserved motif, are produced mostly by activated T cells, and act principally on T cells, monocytes, and eosinophils but not neutrophils. Beta chemokines include macrophage inflammatory protein-1$\alpha$, monocyte chemotactic protein-1, and RANTES.

## III. FUNCTIONAL ASPECTS OF CELLULAR IMMUNITY

### A. Phagocytosis

Phagocytic uptake of foreign material (including live microorganisms) represents a critical early line of host defense and is mediated by several distinct pathways (Fig. 2). Phagocytosis may be initiated directly following recognition via pattern recognition receptors, or uptake may be facilitated by the process of opsonization. For direct phagocytic uptake, several different types of pattern recognition receptors have been described. There is a group of lectin-like receptors—the mannose-type receptor, the galactose-type receptor, and the fucose-type receptor—whose members recognize mannose, galactose, and fucose, respectively. These sugar molecules are common microbial components but are not found on mammalian cells, thus allowing for a broad structural discrimination between host and foreign material. Another pattern recognition receptor is CD14, which recognizes glycolipids such as lipopolysaccharide (LPS), a component of gram-negative bacteria.

Opsonized material is a significant target for phagocytic uptake. Major opsonins include antibody, complement components, and fibronectin. Specific antibody binds to microorganisms and uptake is facilitated through Fc receptors (a class of receptor

which binds to the constant region of antibody) on the phagocytes. Foreign material frequently activates the complement cascade, one consequence of which is that several complement components may bind to the surface of the particles. This allows for phagocytic uptake mediated via a group of cell surface molecules on the phagocyte known as complement receptors which bind complement components. Fibronectin works in a similar way, binding to some foreign components, thus facilitating uptake via the fibronectin receptor.

## B. Intracellular Killing

Foreign material taken up by phagocytosis is enclosed in vesicles and exposed to a wide range of toxic and degradative molecules as it progresses from the early phagosome to the late phagosome and finally, following vesicular fusion with lysosomes, to the phagolysosome. The phagocytic killing mechanisms employed depend on the type and activation state of the phagocyte, and their efficacy of killing varies for different microorganisms. The major killing mechanisms are discussed in the following sections and illustrated in Fig. 2.

### 1. Nitric Oxide

Nitric oxide (NO) is a short-lived free radical gas involved in an enormous range of physiological and pathophysiological processes. Most cell types in the body have the capacity to produce NO in response to a variety of stimuli, and such NO production has a wide range of consequences based on the ability of the molecule to interact with many different molecular targets. The enzymes responsible for NO production are called nitric oxide synthases (NOS). There are at least three types of NOS. $NOS_1$ and $NOS_3$ are constitutively expressed and produce small bursts of NO that mediate a wide range of physiological processes. These isoforms are not typically considered to be part of the immune system. $NOS_2$ is an inducible isoform, found in macrophages and other cell types, that can produce high levels of NO and has an important role in antimicrobial defense.

Many stimuli can induce macrophage expression of $NOS_2$, the most important of which is IFN-$\gamma$, produced by NK cells and CD4$^+$ and CD8$^+$ T lympho-

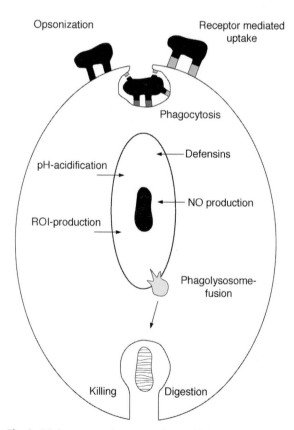

**Fig. 2.** Major macrophage uptake and killing mechanisms.

cytes. TNF synergizes strongly with IFN-$\gamma$ for production of NO by NOS$_2$. Of note, a wide range of microbial products such as human immunodeficiency virus (HIV) gp 120, outer surface lipoproteins of *Borrelia burgdorferi,* glycosylphosphatidylinositol toxin of *Plasmodium* sp., and killed *Staphylococcus aureus* can act alone or in synergy with IFN-$\gamma$ to stimulate NO production in macrophages.

There are several consequences to the high level of NO production that occurs following NOS$_2$ expression. Of paramount importance is the direct antimicrobial activity of this free radical; it is effective against bacteria, protozoa, fungi, helminths, and viruses. The mechanism of antimicrobial activity is in many cases not known, but given the diverse range of agents against which NO can act there are probably numerous biochemical targets. NO binds to, and inactivates, iron–sulfur centers, a mechanism that could potentially target a wide range of pathogen and host protein targets. Other biochemical activities of NO that may be involved in its antimicrobial functions include *S*-nitrosylation of proteins, direct damage of DNA, and interaction with oxygen radicals to form highly toxic molecules such as peroxynitrite.

Since the initial studies in the mid- to late 1980s characterizing the biochemical pathway leading to NO production there has been considerable controversy over the capacity of human macrophages to produce NO. Most studies were performed using mouse macrophages which can be readily stimulated to produce NO. It proved more difficult to stimulate NO production in human macrophages. However, recent studies using macrophages taken directly from *in vivo* inflammatory reactions indicate that human macrophages can produce high levels of NO, although the stimuli required to induce NO in human macrophages are probably different from those in rodent macrophages.

### 2. Reactive Oxygen Intermediates

Reactive oxygen intermediates (ROIs) are produced in the macrophage by the action of the enzyme NADPH oxidase. The principal cell types capable of producing ROIs are macrophages, neutrophils, and eosinophils. Production of ROI is induced by the binding of IgG to Fc receptors or by stimulation with cytokines such as IFN-$\gamma$ and/or microbial products

such as LPS. ROIs include superoxide anion, hydrogen peroxide, hydroxyl radical, and hypochlorite and are capable of damaging DNA, membrane lipids, and proteins. As with NO, however, the biochemical pathway resulting in antimicrobial activity is not always clear. The importance of ROI is illustrated by patients with chronic granulomatous disease (CGD) who have a defect in NADPH oxidase and hence have limited capacity to produce ROIs. CGD is characterized by increased susceptibility to staphylococci and several other types of bacteria and fungi.

### 3. Other Effector Molecules

Other antimicrobial molecules produced by phagocytes that can act against ingested microorganisms include defensins and other cationic proteins, acid hydrolases, and lactoferrin. The acidification of the phagosome that occurs principally to optimize conditions for the activity of various enzymes can also have direct antimicrobial activity.

## C. Antigen Processing and Presentation to T Cells

In contrast to the ability of B cells to directly recognize soluble antigen, T cells require their antigen to be processed and presented by APCs. The end result of antigen processing is the presentation of short peptide fragments in association with MHC class I or class II molecules for recognition by CD8$^+$ or CD4$^+$ T cells, respectively. Although there are many similarities between presentation of peptide antigen on MHC class I and class II, and the subsequent recognition by CD8$^+$ and CD4$^+$ T cells, the processing steps leading to the presentation of peptide antigen differ substantially between the two pathways.

### 1. MHC Class I Antigen Processing Pathway

MHC class I molecules are cell surface glycoproteins made up of a heavy chain bound noncovalently to $\beta_2$-microglobulin. The MHC class I pathway presents endogenous protein antigen and thus allows the immune system to monitor the interior of cells for foreign antigen. Such foreign antigen may be derived from viral, bacterial, fungal, or protozoal proteins or may arise as a result of neoplastic transformation. Due to the near ubiquitous expression of MHC class I, the intracellular environment throughout essentially the entire body can be monitored by means of this system.

The first step in the processing of cytosolic proteins for presentation by MHC class I molecules is protein degradation. This is a constant but highly regulated process in which cytosolic (host and foreign) proteins are degraded by large multiprotein complexes with proteolytic activity, called proteasomes. From the cytosol, degraded protein peptide fragments are transported to the endoplasmic reticulum, which is the site of association with MHC class I molecules. The passage of these peptide fragments across the membrane of the endoplasmic reticulum is facilitated by "transporters associated with antigen processing" (TAP) molecules. Following transport into the lumen of the endoplasmic reticulum, the peptide fragments associate with MHC class I molecules and $\beta_2$-microglobulin to form a stable structure which is then transported to the cell surface for recognition by antigen-specific CD8$^+$ T cells.

## 2. MHC Class II Antigen Processing Pathway

MHC class II molecules are heterodimeric glycoproteins consisting of a heavy ($\alpha$) chain and a light ($\beta$) chain. While the MHC class I pathway is specialized for the presentation of endogenous antigen, the MHC class II pathway is specialized for presentation of exogenous antigen. For this reason, the pathways are quite distinct. Furthermore, expression of MHC class II is considerably more restricted than that of MHC class I. The principal cell types expressing MHC class II, and hence the principal APCs for CD4$^+$ T cells, are DCs, monocytes/macrophages, and B cells.

MHC class II molecules are initially found in the rough endoplasmic reticulum bound to a polypeptide called the invariant chain. They then move through the Golgi apparatus before entering an endosomal/lysosomal compartment called MIIC. Here, the invariant chain is proteolytically cleaved from MHC class II, leaving behind a 24-amino acid remnant

called class II-associated invariant chain peptide (CLIP) in the MHC class II peptide binding cleft. CLIP is subsequently removed, allowing binding of peptide fragments derived from degraded proteins that have been taken up by endocytosis. The peptide–MHC complex is then transported to the cell surface where it may be recognized by antigen-specific CD4$^+$ T cells.

## D. T Cell Activation

Activation of antigen-specific T cells represents the central step in the induction of the adaptive immune response. Recognition of peptide antigen in the context of MHC class I or class II is necessary but not sufficient for T cell activation. For both CD4$^+$ and CD8$^+$ T cells, further signals, known as costimulatory signals or costimulation, are required for efficient T cell activation. Cytokines such as IL-1, IL-6, and IL-12 can provide costimulatory signals, but of paramount importance are various ligand–receptor interactions between the T cell and APCs. These interactions are mediated by costimulatory molecules expressed on the surface of APCs that interact with surface molecules on the T cell. Costimulatory molecules include CD80/CD86, LFA-1, and LFA-2 on the APCs which interact with CD28/CTLA-4, ICAM-1, and CD2, respectively, on the T cell. The interaction between CD28 and CD80/CD86 is the most crucial for optimal T cell activation. Costimulation is particularly important for the activation of naive T cells, and a naive T cell that encounters cognate antigen in the absence of appropriate costimulation may not simply fail to be activated but may be directly inactivated. In contrast, the requirement for costimulation in activated and memory T cells is not as stringent.

Once activated, T cells undergo clonal expansion. Because the frequency of precursor cells within the peripheral T cell pool that are specific for a given antigen is relatively low, this is a necessary step to provide sufficient specific T cells for the immune response. The principal growth factor for proliferation of T cells is IL-2. Activated T cells increase transcription of the IL-2 gene while at the same time increasing expression of the high-affinity IL-2 receptor. This positive feedback loop allows for a rapid increase in T cell numbers. Although IL-2 is clearly the major factor responsible for T cell proliferation, other cytokines, including IL-4, IL-7, and IL-15, are also involved.

## E. Th1 and Th2 Cells

An extremely broad range of pathogenic agents can infect the human host, including bacteria, viruses, protozoa, helminths, and fungi. These agents differ in the area of the body that they colonize; some are extracellular and some intracellular; some produce toxins and some directly kill cells; some proliferate widely and will kill the host unless they are killed first, whereas others establish an equilibrium with the host and a chronic infection ensues; and others become almost completely quiescent, resulting in latency. The immune response must be able to cope with all these pathogen strategies, and different types of immune response are efficacious against different pathogen strategies. Thus, the immune system does not comprise one single effector mechanism but involves many different effector functions with different modes of action and different target microorganisms.

In determining the most appropriate type of immune response, a crucial distinction is that between intracellular and extracellular habitats. For those organisms that reside in extracellular locations, exposure to phagocytes, antibody, complement, eosinophils, and basophils is one of the major effector mechanisms. In contrast, the intracellular habitat provides a refuge from these effector mechanisms. Two principal strategies are available for control of established intracellular infections. First, in response to activation signals (such as cytokines) the host cell may be able to kill the invading microorganism. However, the majority of cell types do not possess the full range of intracellular killing mechanisms and this strategy is most effective when the infected cell is a professional phagocyte such as a macrophage. Second, cytotoxic CD8$^+$ T cells can detect and lyse infected cells following recognition of antigen in the context of MHC class I. Lysis of the host cell releases the microorganism into the extracellular milieu and exposes it to antibody, complement, and phagocytes and, for virus infection, also acts to prevent the completion of virus replication.

Rather than induce the full range of immune effector mechanisms, the particular type of host response that is most effective for the specific pathogen is usually emphasized. CD4$^+$ T cells are central to the selection of an appropriate and effective type of immune response. CD4$^+$ T cell populations can be broadly divided into T helper 1 (Th1) and T helper 2 (Th2) cells based on the pattern of cytokines that they produce. Th1 cells tend to produce IFN-$\gamma$, IL-2, and TNF, and these cytokines are important in stimulating cell-mediated immunity and some antibody classes. For example, IFN-$\gamma$ and TNF are both crucial activating cytokines for macrophages, and IL-2 is important in the development of a CTL response. Thus, Th1 cells are the most appropriate cell type for combating infections with viruses and other intracellular microorganisms. On the other hand, Th2 cells produce IL-4, IL-5, IL-6, IL-9, IL-10, and IL-13. These cytokines are important in inducing antibody responses and activating eosinophils and basophils, and they are particularly effective against extracellular microorganisms. The role of Th1 and Th2 cells in regulating cellular immunity is illustrated in Fig. 3.

The factors that determine whether a CD4$^+$ T cell develops into a Th1 or Th2 cell are diverse and not fully characterized. The most important factor appears to be the prevailing cytokine microenvironment in which the CD4$^+$ T cell first becomes activated. IL-12 in the local environment favors the induction of a Th1 response, whereas IL-4 induces a Th2 cell response. Other factors that are important in determining whether Th1 or Th2 cells develop include antigen dose and the type of APC (including the type of costimulatory molecules that it expresses) that activates the helper cell. An important feature of the regulation of T helper cell responses is that a Th2 response, particularly through the production of IL-4, not only enhances subsequent Th2 responses but also blocks the development of a Th1 response. Similarly, the type of environment that favors a Th1 response also acts to block the development of a Th2 response. One consequence of this is that in many cases the immune response is predominantly either Th1 or Th2.

It is important to note that mounting an inappropriate immune response can have serious conse-

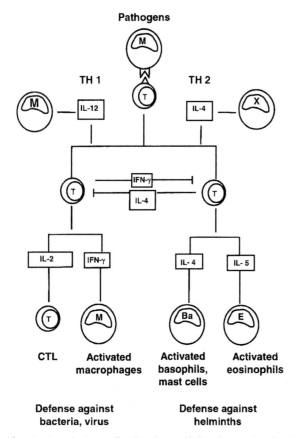

**Fig. 3.** Regulation of adaptive cellular immunity by T helper 1 and T helper 2 cells. (Note that T helper cells also have a crucial role in the regulation of antibody production.)

quences for the host. The best characterized example is the experimental infection of resistant and susceptible mouse strains with the protozoan pathogen *Leishmania major*. C57BL/6 inbred mice respond to *L. major* infection with a classical Th1-type response, characterized by production of IFN-γ and IL-12, and potent macrophage activation. This response is entirely appropriate, and C57BL/6 mice exhibit robust resistance to infection with *L. major*. In contrast, mice of the BALB/c strain mount a Th2-type response to *L. major* infection and are highly susceptible. However, BALB/c mice can be made at least partially resistant to *L. major* infections by a range of experimental interventions designed to promote a Th1 response and/or block a Th2 response.

## F. Target Cell Killing by CTL and NK Cells

The intracellular habitat protects microorganisms from the effector mechanisms that are most effective against extracellular pathogens, principally phagocytes, antibody, and complement. For this reason, killing of target cells is an important mechanism in the control of viruses and other intracellular pathogens.

Both NK cells and CTL use similar mechanisms of target cell killing. Killing involves intimate contact with the target cell, mediated through target cell recognition receptors, plus further interactions between killer and target cell surface ligands. There are two major biochemical pathways leading to cell lysis, the most important of which for the control of infection is the granule exocytosis pathway. In the granule exocytosis pathway, cytotoxic cells release the contents of their cytoplasmic granules into the narrow extracellular space between killer cell and target cell. Chief among the granule contents are perforin, which once released polymerizes to literally bore a hole in the target cell outer membrane, and the granzymes, which appear to mediate their cytotoxic effect once inside the target cell. A second mechanism of cytotoxicity involves the Fas/Fas ligand pathway. This involves binding of Fas ligand on the surface of the killer cell to Fas on the surface of the target cell, and it induces a series of biochemical events leading to target cell death by a process known as apoptosis. This pathway of cytotoxicity is important in maintaining homeostasis in the immune system, but its role in defense against intracellular pathogens is not clear.

In the case of viruses, killing of infected target cells is most efficacious when it occurs prior to completion of virus replication. This is due to the absolute requirement for the intracellular habitat in order for viral replication to occur. For many intracellular bacteria and parasites, the major consequence of target cell killing is exposure to immune mechanisms such as antibody, phagocytosis, and complement from which the pathogen was formerly protected while in its intracellular habitat. Recent evidence, however, has indicated that intracellular bacteria may be directly killed as a result of lysis of their host cell.

## G. Immunological Memory

In response to specific antigen, lymphocytes undergo clonal expansion and differentiate into effector cells. Once the antigen has been successfully cleared from the body, the majority of the specific lymphocytes die. However, a minority persists for long periods and can respond rapidly following subsequent exposure to the same antigen. These cells are termed "memory cells" and account for immunological memory, in which the response to the second (and subsequent) exposure to an antigen is always more rapid and more effective than the first. Immunological memory is the basis for vaccination and is a feature of both T and B cells.

## IV. CELLULAR IMMUNITY DURING INFECTION

In the following sections, some aspects of cellular immunity during infection will be discussed using examples from human infections and experimental animal systems.

## A. Innate Immunity

Phagocytes are a major component of the innate immune response to infection. As discussed previously, phagocytes enter sites of infection in response to chemotactic stimuli and phagocytose foreign material directly via pattern recognition receptors or indirectly with the assistance of opsonins. Following ingestion, microorganisms (and other material) are exposed to a vast array of microbicidal processes. The important role of the neutrophil subset of phagocytes is revealed in neutrophil-deficient animal models of infection. Here, following depletion of neutrophils, mice are substantially more susceptible to a range of infectious agents, including viruses, bacteria, and parasites.

The most important event in the innate immune response to virus infection is the production of type

I IFN by virus-infected cells. In addition to establishing an antiviral state in neighboring cells, IFN production amplifies other aspects of the immune response, particularly NK cell activation. Prior to the induction of antigen-specific immunity, NK cells play a pivotal role in the control of virus infection by lysing infected cells and producing the macrophage-activating antiviral cytokine IFN-$\gamma$. The importance of NK cells is well illustrated in animal models of virus infection; mice that do not have functional NK cells have heightened susceptibility to infection with a range of viruses.

## B. The Central Role of Cytokines

Cytokines play a pivotal role in all aspects of the cellular immune response by regulating development, proliferation, activation, and migration of immune cells as well as by having direct effector activity. The importance of cytokines in infectious disease is clearly illustrated in human and experimental immunodeficiency states characterized by disruption of cytokine production or signaling. For example, mutations in the receptors for IFN-$\gamma$ and IL-12 are associated with extreme susceptibility to infections with normally nonvirulent mycobacteria and salmonellae. The generation of mutant strains of mice deficient in the production of defined cytokines is a powerful approach for elucidating the role of cytokines in the cellular immune response to infection. Mice deficient for signaling or production of a wide range of cytokines, including IL-4–IL-6, IL-10, IL-12, IL-13, TNF, type I IFN, and IFN-$\gamma$, and numerous chemokines have all demonstrated altered susceptibility to infection with at least some subsets of pathogens.

Administration of exogenous cytokines is a possible therapeutic approach for treating infectious disease. IFN-$\gamma$ alone or in combination with other therapeutic drugs was shown to have a beneficial effect in cutaneous and visceral leishmaniasis and lepromatous leprosy. IL-12 has a therapeutic effect in many experimental infections, such as *L. major* and *L. monocytogenes,* and it has also been proposed as an adjuvant for vaccination.

## C. Macrophages

Activated macrophages are central to the cellular immune response because they mediate effector function, produce cytokines and other biologically active mediators, and present antigen to T cells. Although macrophages become activated early during the innate response, IFN-$\gamma$ production by antigen-activated T cells is frequently necessary for maximal macrophage activation. For example, in many experimental models of infection, production of one of the major macrophage effector molecules, NO, is substantially reduced in the absence of T cells. The importance of macrophage-derived NO is well illustrated in experimental infections of mice in which NO production is blocked by chemical inhibitors or in mice rendered deficient in NO production. In the absence of NO, enhanced susceptibility to numerous bacteria, viruses, and parasites has been recorded. For example, mice in which the $NOS_2$ gene has been genetically deleted show extreme susceptibility to *M. tuberculosis* infection.

## D. Cytotoxic T Lymphocytes

CTLs are central elements in the control of primary virus infections. Peptides derived from endogenously synthesized virus proteins are presented to CTLs by MHC class I molecules on the surface of the infected cell. CTLs are most effective when they recognize peptide fragments derived from viral proteins that are synthesized during the early phase of virus replication. In this case, the infected cell can be lysed prior to the assembly of infectious virus particles. Production of cytokines such as IFN-$\gamma$ also contributes to the antiviral function of CTLs. The importance of CTLs in the control of virus infection is illustrated in many animal models of virus infection, in which depletion of CTLs results in an exacerbation of the course of infection. Although CTLs are strongly activated during virus infections of humans, it has been difficult to determine whether human CTLs have a protective function. Recently, however, evidence that CTLs play an important role in virus infection in humans has been accumulating. For example, in the case of HIV infection, there is an inverse correlation between CTL activity and plasma RNA viral load, suggesting that CTLs are capable of reducing viral load. The observation that during natural infection HIV mutants arise that can escape recognition by CTLs provides further support for a protective role of CTLs during HIV infection.

The importance of CTLs in the control of virus infection is well illustrated by the number of viruses [e.g., herpes simplex virus (HSV), human cytomegalovirus, adenovirus, and HIV] that encode molecules that interfere with recognition of infected cells by CTLs. For example, the HSV gene product ICP47 binds to and blocks the activity of TAP molecules (see Section III.C), thus reducing the cell surface expression of MHC class I molecules.

Some infections with nonviral intracellular microorganisms are also controlled by CTLs, including *L. monocytogenes*, *M. tuberculosis*, and *Plasmodium* sp. In some cases, lysis of the target cell may result in direct pathogen killing. Otherwise, lysis of infected cells releases the organisms into the extracellular milieu, exposing them to aspects of the immune response to which they are not normally exposed and to which they may be susceptible. Cytokine production by CD8$^+$ T cells is also important in activating killing mechanisms in infected cells.

## E. The Granulomatous Response

Many pathogens, especially those that reside in an intracellular habitat, are relatively resistant to phagocytic killing. One consequence of this is that infection frequently follows a chronic course. A number of factors may account for resistance to phagocytic killing, such as the presence of a waxy outer layer, or direct interference with phagocytic function. Persistence of microorganisms or their antigens results in chronic activation of the cellular immune response and may frequently result in the formation of a characteristic lesion called a granuloma. The persistent organism or antigen is located in the center of the lesion and is surrounded and engulfed by activated macrophages, which sometimes take on the appearance of epithelial cells and are known as "epithelioid cells" or may fuse together giving rise to "multinucleated giant cells." Surrounding the macrophages is a band of T cells producing cytokines, such as IFN-$\gamma$ and TNF, that serve to maintain the macrophages in a state of chronic activation. Fibrosis is also a feature of the granulomatous lesion. Infections with a range of intracellular bacteria (e.g., mycobacteria, brucellae, and listeriae), intracellular fungi (e.g., *Cryptococcus neoformans*), and parasites (e.g., *Schistosoma mansoni*) are associated with granulomas.

## F. Immunopathology: Cellular Immunity Can Be Damaging

Unchecked, the cellular immune response has the capacity to severely damage the host. Granulomas provide a good example of how a protective immune response can also cause damage to the host. In the case of granuloma formation in response to infection with *M. tuberculosis,* the granuloma acts to wall off the infectious agent and prevents further spread of the infection. However, the lesion is associated with substantial necrosis and fibrosis, and it is this response, rather than direct mycobacterial toxicity, that is largely responsible for the respiratory impairment of tuberculosis infections. Several mechanisms are available for dampening potentially damaging immune responses, e.g., the production of suppressive cytokines such as IL-10 and transforming growth factor-$\beta$.

## G. Evasion of Cellular Immunity by Pathogens

Evolutionary pressures on pathogens and the immune systems of their hosts are inextricably linked, and it is becomingly increasingly clear that the immune response exerts considerable selective pressure on microorganisms. Many pathogens have developed strategies to evade or interfere with the host immune response. The types of evasion strategies employed are diverse and include antigenic variation, escape from phagocytic vacuoles into the cytoplasm, masking of pathogen antigens with host molecules, and antigen shedding. Additionally, microorganisms may interfere more directly with the immune response. Mycobacteria can inhibit phagolysosome fusion and

thus interfere with killing by macrophages, and a wide range of microorganisms can induce lymphocyte unresponsiveness in their host. Some microorganisms impair the generation of ROI following their uptake by macrophages. Many viruses have acquired host DNA sequences that may interfere with the immune response. For example, Epstein–Barr virus encodes an IL-10-like molecule that may enhance virus survival through the downregulatory effects of IL-10 on cellular immunity. Numerous viruses have acquired sequences for cytokine receptors, and these are thought to block host cytokine activities by diverting the cytokines from their physiological receptors. As discussed in Section IV.D, some viruses can interfere with antigen processing and presentation, thus interfering with T cell activation.

### Acknowledgments

We thank Caitlin McCoull and Daniella Groine-Triebkorn for excellent secretarial assistance and for preparing the figures.

### See Also the Following Articles

ANTIBODIES AND B CELLS • CHEMOTAXIS • INTERFERONS • VIRUS INFECTION

### Bibliography

Abbas, A. K., Lichtman, A. H., and Pober, J. S. (1997). "Cellular and Molecular Immunology," 3rd ed. Saunders, Philadelphia.

Finkelman, F. D., Shea-Donohue, T., Goldhill, J., Sullivan, C. A., Morris, S. C., Madden, K. B., Gause, W. C., and Urban, J. F., Jr. (1997). Cytokine regulation of host defense against parasitic gastrointestinal nematodes: Lessons from studies with rodent models. *Annu. Rev. Immunol.* 15, 505–533.

Kaufmann, S. H. E. (1993). Immunity to intracellular bacteria. *Annu. Rev. Immunol.* 11, 129–163.

Ramshaw, I. A., Ramsay, A. J., Karupiah, G., Rolph, M. S., Mahalingam, S., and Ruby, J. C. (1997). Cytokines and immunity to viral infections. *Immunol. Rev.* 159, 119–135.

Reiner, S. L., and Locksley, R. M. (1995). The regulation of immunity to *Leishmania major. Annu. Rev. Immunol.* 13, 151–177.

# Cellulases

## Pierre Béguin and Jean-Paul Aubert[1]

*Institut Pasteur*

I. Structure of Lignocellulose
II. Diversity, Ecology, and Physiology of Cellulolytic Microorganisms
III. Biochemistry of Cellulases
IV. Regulation of Cellulase Synthesis
V. Applications of Cellulases in Biotechnology

## GLOSSARY

**carboxymethyl cellulose** Amorphous derivative of cellulose; soluble forms with a degree of substitution of about 0.7 are commonly used as substrates for endoglucanases.

**cellobiohydrolase** 1,4-β-D-Glucan cellobiohydrolase (E.C. 3.2.1.91); cleaves cellulose chains from the reducing or nonreducing end, liberating a cellobiose molecule at each step.

**cellobiose** β-1,4-D-Glucopyranosyl-glucopyranose; a dimer of glucose.

**cellulosome** A high-molecular-weight, multienzyme complex, in which cellulases and hemicellulases are non-covalently bound to a multivalent scaffolding protein.

**cohesin domain** A receptor domain which binds dockerin domains. Cohesin domains of type I bind dockerin domains of type I borne by catalytic subunits of the cellulosome. They are reiterated several-fold within the sequence of the cellulosome scaffolding subunit. Cohesin domains of type II bind the dockerin domain of type II borne by the cellulosome scaffolding subunit. They are borne by exocellular proteins present in the cell envelope.

**dockerin domain** A conserved, non-catalytic domain, which binds to cohesin domains. Dockerin domains of type I are borne by cellulase and hemicellulase subunits of the cellulosome; a dockerin domain of type II is borne by the scaffolding subunit of the *Clostridium thermocellum* cellulosome.

**endoglucanase** 1,4-β-D-Glucan glucanohydrolase (E.C. 3.2.1.4); cleaves cellulose chains randomly at multiple internal sites within the molecules.

**β-glucosidase** β-D-Glucoside glucohydrolase (E.C. 3.2.1.21); cleaves β glucosidic bonds in cellobiose and other β glucosides.

**CELLULASES** constitute a family of enzymes that hydrolyze β-1,4 glucosidic bonds in native cellulose and derived substrates. Their action on nonsubstituted cellulose leads to the formation of cellobiose, which can be further hydrolyzed by β-glucosidases. By hydrolyzing cellulose, the most abundant form of organic carbon synthesized by plants, cellulases play a key role in the carbon cycle of the biosphere. Cellulases will also be required if biological conversion of plant biomass into fuels and basic chemicals is to become economically feasible.

## I. STRUCTURE OF LIGNOCELLULOSE

Cellulose is the major carbohydrate polymer synthesized by plants. Cellulose fibrils have a high tensile strength, which has been used in the textile industry since the dawn of history and which endows secondary plant cell walls (Fig. 1) with the capacity to withstand mechanical stress, including osmotic pressure. Cellulose is a linear polymer made of glucose subunits held together by β-1,4 bonds. Stereochemically, however, the basic repeating unit is cellobiose (Fig. 2).

Cellulose is totally insoluble in water. In most

---

1. Deceased.

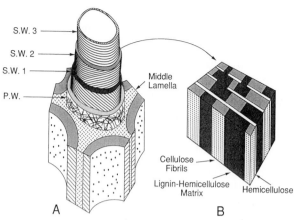

***Fig. 1.*** Schematic illustration of the molecular architecture of woody tissue showing a cutaway view of the cell wall layers (A) and the probable relationship of lignin and hemicellulose to the cellulose fibrils in the secondary walls (B). The diameter of each cell is approximately 25 $\mu$m. P.W., primary wall; S.W. 1–S.W.3, secondary cell walls (adapted from Kirk, 1988).

forms of native cellulose, the carbohydrate chains, which contain between 100 and 14,000 glucose residues, form bundles, or microfibrils, in which the molecules are oriented in parallel and held together by hydrogen bonds. Such microfibrils consist of highly ordered, crystalline domains interspersed by more disordered, amorphous regions. The degree of crystallinity can vary between 0%, as in the case of acid-swollen cellulose or chemically derivatized, soluble cellulose such as carboxymethylcellulose (CMC), and nearly 100% in the case of cellulose isolated from the cell walls of the alga *Valonia.* Cellulose from cotton is approximately 70% crystalline, and most commercial celluloses are between 30 and 70% crystalline. Several forms of crystalline cellulose have been identified. For example, the native form

of cellulose, termed cellulose I, actually consists of two types of crystal lattice which occur in characteristic proportions in cellulases from different sources. Cellulose I$\alpha$, with triclinic symmetry, predominates in the cell walls of some algae (e.g., *Valonia, Cladophora,* and *Laminaria* spp.) and in the cellulose produced by the bacterium *Acetobacter xylinum.* Cellulose I$\beta$, which is monoclinic, is the most abundant form in higher plants and is the only form found in animal cellulose from tunicates.

In most cases, cellulose fibrils present in plant cell walls are embedded in a matrix of hemicellulose and lignin (Fig. 1). Hemicellulose designates a set of complex carbohydrate polymers, with xylans and mannans as the main components. The xylan backbone carries a variety of side chains, including acetyl, arabinofuranosyl, and methylglucuronyl groups. Phenolic components, including ferulic (4-hydroxycinnamic) and *p*-coumaric acids, are covalently bound to the side chains, and some are thought to be involved in cross-links between hemicellulose and lignin mediated by ether linkages.

Lignin is a phenylpropanoid polymer produced by the free-radical condensation of aromatic alcohols. The resulting compound is an amorphous, highly branched random polymer which is highly resistant to biodegradation and protects cellulose fibers against enzymatic attack by microbes.

## II. DIVERSITY, ECOLOGY, AND PHYSIOLOGY OF CELLULOLYTIC MICROORGANISMS

Cellulolytic microorganisms are abundant in nature and play an important role in the carbon cycle

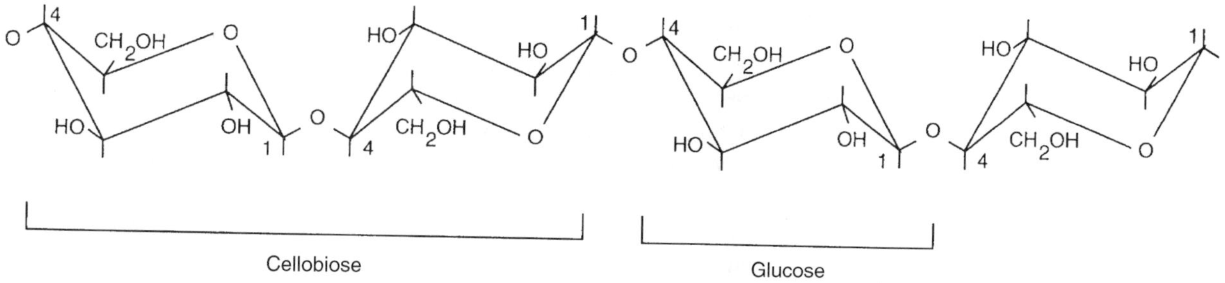

***Fig. 2.*** Chemical structure of cellulose.

by recycling $CO_2$ fixed by photosynthesis. It is likely that they evolved with the appearance of cellulose in plants. Indeed, it is conceivable that some cellulase genes were actually borrowed from plants, in which they appear to play a role in morphogenesis and developmental processes (e.g., in the ripening of fruits such as the avocado).

Cellulose degradation occurs in a variety of ecological niches where plant residues accumulate. Thus, cellulolytic microorganisms include a variety of aerobes and anaerobes, mesophiles, and thermophiles. Fungi and bacteria are the main natural agents of cellulose degradation. However, protozoa living in the hindgut of termites have long been known to digest cellulose; in addition, in higher termites cellulase activity appears to be produced by the midgut tissue and the salivary gland of the termite. Indeed, an endoglucanase gene was cloned recently using cDNA generated from termite salivary gland mRNA.

As a general rule, cellulolytic microorganisms found in natural habitats constitute mixed populations, including several cellulolytic and noncellulolytic species, which interact synergistically. These interactions lead to efficient cellulose degradation with formation of $CO_2$ and $H_2O$ in aerobiosis or $CO_2$, $CH_4$, and $H_2O$ in anaerobiosis.

The soil surface is the most important aerobic environment in which dead plant material (wood, leaves, straw, etc.) accumulates. The most recalcitrant substrate is wood, which is highly lignified. White-rot fungi, such as the well-studied basidiomycete *Phanerochaete chrysosporium,* can degrade both lignin and cellulose and play a major role in wood decay. Other aerobic fungi are devoid of ligninase activity but are efficient cellulose degraders. This is the case, for example, for *Trichoderma reesei,* whose cellulase system has been extensively studied. Aerobic cellulolytic bacteria have long been known to be present in soil. Cellulolytic species found in soil include *Cellulomonas, Cytophaga, Pseudomonas,* bacilli, and many actinomycetes. Some cellulolytic actinomycetes are thermophilic, such as *Thermomonospora* and *Microbispora;* furthermore, several actinomycetes, including nocardiae and rhodococci, can attack lignocellulose.

Cellulose-rich material is also found in anaerobic habitats, including the rumen and intestinal tracts of animals, sewage sludge digestors, composts, freshwater and seawater muds, and sediments. Cellulolytic and noncellulolytic microorganisms living in such environments have in general a fermentative metabolism, and they are frequently associated with methanogens.

In the rumen system, anaerobic fungi such as *Neocallimastix frontalis* are associated with cellulolytic bacteria, in particular *Ruminococcus flavefaciens, Ruminococcus albus,* and *Fibrobacter succinogenes.* Fermentation products formed are butyrate, propionate, acetate, lactate, formate, succinate, ethanol, $CO_2$, and $H_2$. These products are partly used as food by the animal. Residual acetate, formate, $CO_2$, and $H_2$ are converted into $CH_4$ by methanogens.

In other anoxic environments, cellulose degradation seems to be due mainly to bacteria—for example, *Acetivibrio cellulolyticus* and various *Clostridia,* either mesophiles such as *C. cellulolyticum* and *C. cellulovorans* or thermophiles such as *C. thermocellum* and *C. stercorarium.* The main fermentation products formed by these bacteria are lactate, acetate, ethanol, $CO_2$, and $H_2$. In addition, cellobiose, glucose, and some cellodextrins of low molecular weight, resulting from cellulose hydrolysis, are produced in excess. These sugars are fermented by other noncellulolytic saprophytic bacteria, such as *Clostridium thermohydrosulfuricum* and *Thermoanaerobacter ethanolicus,* with formation of additional amounts of low-molecular-weight fatty acids, lactate, acetate, ethanol, $CO_2$, and $H_2$. The removal of excess sugars derived from cellulose hydrolysis increases the efficiency of various cellulase systems.

The accumulation of fermentation products and $H_2$ inhibits most fermentation processes. Thus, the conversion of fermentation products arising from the metabolism of carbohydrate-utilizing organisms into $CO_2$ and $CH_4$ is an essential part of the anaerobic food chain. Fermentation products such as butyrate and propionate are oxidized into acetate, with the concomitant release of $H_2$. The reaction is endergonic under normal conditions, and organisms deriving their energy from it can only do so under syntrophic conditions, when the partial pressure of $H_2$ is maintained sufficiently low by hydrogen-consuming microorganisms. $H_2$ can be scavenged by acetogenic bacteria, such as *Clostridium thermoaceticum,* which use the Wood pathway to generate acetate from $CO_2$ and $H_2$, and by methanogens such as *Methanobacterium thermoautotrophicum* and *Methanosarcina barkeri*, which convert acetate, $CO_2$, and $H_2$ into $CH_4$. Thus, the action of a complex mixed population of bacteria finally transforms cellulose into $CO_2$, $CH_4$, and $H_2O$. Once $CH_4$ reaches aerobic zones, it can be oxidized into $CO_2$ by methylotrophic bacteria.

"True" cellulolytic organisms, able to grow at the expense of crystalline cellulose, produce a complete cellulase system constituted of several enzymes, each with a different specificity. However, many other bacteria, unable to use cellulose as a carbon source, synthesize enzymes endowed with cellulase activity. For example, enzymes that can hydrolyze CMC have been characterized in *Bacillus subtilis* and related species and in phytopathogens. The significance of these systems is not entirely elucidated. In phytopathogens, a restricted cellulolytic action may be sufficient and/or required for penetration of the bacteria into the plant tissue. In saprophytic bacteria, limited cellulase activity could be useful for the utilization of soluble cellodextrins resulting from the action of true cellulolytic organisms with whom they are associated.

Due to the extreme insolubility of lignocellulose and cellulose, enzymes that can digest these compounds must be either secreted into the medium, as in fungi, or bound to the cell surface, as in several cellulolytic bacteria. In addition, the compact structure of wood restricts the accessibility of the enzymes to their substrates. This is probably why fungi, rather than bacteria, are the main degraders of wood. Indeed, the hyphae produced by these organisms give them the ability to penetrate cracks and to progress inside the wood as branched tiny threads, which deliver *in situ* a mixture of different depolymerizing enzymes. No organism known to date can grow only on lignin. Thus, it is thought that a white-rot fungus growing inside wood first degrades exposed cellulose and hemicellulose sectors. This supplies soluble sugars and nutrients. Once the fungus starts to starve, its metabolism shifts toward lignin degradation, thereby exposing new cellulose and hemicellulose sectors, and the process continues. Several bacteria, in particular *Cellulomonas* and *Clostridia,* have been shown to bind to cellulose fibers. This property confers on these microorganisms an obvious selective advantage over other saprophytic bacteria living in the vicinity, because they have direct access to the soluble sugars released by cellulose hydrolysis.

## III. BIOCHEMISTRY OF CELLULASES

Although the hydrolysis of a linear homopolymer such as cellulose may seem straightforward, the conversion of cellulosic material into glucose is a process of considerable complexity.

First, cellulose occurs in multiple forms differing in crystallinity, degree of polymerization, and pore size distribution. This is also true of chemically pure, commercial cellulose preparations, which are heterogeneous with respect to physical parameters. Furthermore, the physicochemical parameters of the substrate change during the course of degradation. As a consequence, enzymology is difficult to study rigorously, except by using low-molecular-weight, soluble substrates such as cellodextrins and their chromogenic derivatives. Second, as already mentioned, natural cellulose rarely occurs in pure form. The matrix of hemicellulose and lignin embedding cellulose fibers severely restricts the access of cellulolytic enzymes to the substrate. Thus, most cellulolytic organisms also possess hemicellulases (xylanases, acetyl xylan esterases, mannanases, etc.). Hydrolysis of hemicellulose appears to favor delignification, possibly through the removal of lignin bound by ether linkages to aromatic components of the hemicellulose side chains. The degradation of lignin has been most extensively studied in the white-rot fungus *P. chrysosporium.* The process involves the generation of aryl cation radicals catalyzed by lignin peroxidase and Mn-peroxidase, followed by spontaneous, nonenzymic decay into a variety of final products. Several actinomycetes also attack lignocellulose. Lignin degradation by actinomycetes involves a much less extensive mineralization to $CO_2$ than in the case of fungi. Lignin solubilization possibly proceeds through a set of reactions involving limited oxidation of lignin and cleavage of cross-links between lignin and hemicellulose.

All microorganisms that are known to degrade crystalline cellulose produce many cellulases with different specificities and modes of action. The activity of each individual component can usually be assayed on soluble model substrates, but hydrolysis of the native substrate requires the synergistic action of several components. The biochemical complexity of cellulase systems arises both from the presence of different genes encoding different polypeptides and from posttranslational modifications (glycosylation and proteolysis).

## A. Cellulolytic Systems

Cellulase systems are probably as manifold as the organisms that produce them; however, a few systems have been investigated extensively and currently serve as paradigms for the interpretation of other, less thoroughly characterized cellulase systems. Two such systems will be discussed here. In the first, cellulolytic enzymes are found as individual proteins in the extracellular medium; in the second, the enzymes are physically associated to form high-molecular-weight complexes maximizing synergistic interactions.

### 1. Unassociated or Transiently Associated Cellulases

Historically, unassociated cellulase systems produced by filamentous fungi, such as *T. reesei*, *Trichoderma koningii*, or *Phanerochaete chrysosporium*, were the first to be characterized in detail. Later on, very similar cellulase systems were found to be produced by Actinomycetes; such as *Microbispora bispora* and *Thermomonospora fusca*, or by *Cellulomonas fimi*, which belongs to the Coryneforms. The main features of such systems are indicated in Fig. 3. They are composed of three major types of enzymes: endoglucanases, cellobiohydrolases, and β-glucosidases. Most systems contain a variety of endoglucanases, which act almost exclusively on the noncrystalline regions of the substrate. It is thought that the role of endoglucanases is to create start sites for cellobiohydrolases, which degrade cellulose chains stepwise from the ends, generating cellobiose at each step. For a long time, cellobiohydrolases were thought to start exclusively from the non-reducing ends of the chains. It is now known that many systems contain a pair of cellobiohydrolases, one acting

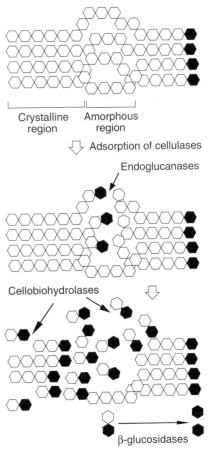

**Fig. 3.** Schematic representation of the synergistic action of *Trichoderma reesei* cellulases. Glucose residues are represented by hexagons; glucose residues carrying reducing ends are shown in black.

from the non-reducing end and the other from the reducing end. Such a complementary specificity probably accounts for the so-called exo–exo synergism between different cellobiohydrolases which was previously unexplained. Because cellobiohydrolases are capable of hydrolyzing crystalline cellulose, they are regarded as key enzymes for the degradation of the native substrate. β-Glucosidases hydrolyze cellobiose and other low-molecular-weight, soluble cellodextrins to yield glucose. The action of β-glucosidases prevents the build-up of cellobiose, a competitive inhibitor of cellobiohydrolases. The model fits well with the known properties of individual enzymes, but it is nonetheless an oversimplification. It is still not clear, for example, why some endoglucanases are more competent than others to synergize with cellobiohydrolases. Furthermore, the degree of synergism is also dependent on the nature and the degree of saturation of the substrate with enzyme.

## 2. Permanently Associated Cellulases: The Cellulosome Concept

The concept of physical association between cellulolytic components has become central to the understanding of cellulase systems from several anaerobic microorganisms. These organisms produce cellulase systems with a very high specific activity, in which most individual components are associated in high-molecular-weight complexes termed cellulosomes. The most extensively studied example is the thermophilic, anaerobic bacterium *C. thermocellum*. Several other cellulolytic clostridia, such as *C. cellulolyticum*, *C. cellulovorans*, and *C. papyrosolvens*, produce similar cellulase systems. A possibly related complex exists in the rumen bacterium *R. albus*. Furthermore, highly efficient, high molecular-weight complexes are produced by anaerobic rumen fungi such as *Neocallimastix patriciarum* and *Piromyces equi*.

The cellulase complex of *C. thermocellum* is composed of both a low-molecular-weight fraction, with $M_r < 100,000$, corresponding to unassociated endoglucanases, and a high-molecular-weight, multienzyme complex, or cellulosome, of approximately 2–4 MDa. Hydrolysis of crystalline cellulose is almost exclusively associated with the high $M_r$ fraction. Up to 26 different components have been resolved by sodium dodecyl sulfate-polyacrylamide gel electrophoresis, including many endoglucanases, several xylanases, and two cellobiohydrolases. The cellulosome is normally quite stable, but it can be dissociated under mildly acidic conditions in the presence of EDTA and low concentrations of sodium dodecyl sulfate. Dissociated subunits retain activity on amorphous cellulose but are much less active than the complex on crystalline cellulose. Activity on crystalline cellulose can be recovered, at least in part, on reassociation of the complex, which may be achieved by restoring neutral pH, removing detergent, and adding back $Ca^{2+}$.

Two factors may contribute to the higher cellulolytic activity of cellulosome components when they are associated. On the one hand, complex formation entails binding of the catalytic subunits to a 250-kDa scaffolding component, termed CipA, which acts at the same time as a cellulose-binding factor. Indeed, available data indicate that the activity of individual components is enhanced upon binding to CipA. On the other hand, it is quite possible that clustering the various catalytic components close to each other enhances their synergism. The possibility that synergism of the kind observed for nonassociated cellulase systems may occur within the cellulosome is supported by the presence in the complex of the same types of enzymes (endoglucanases and cellobiohydrolases). In fact, with artificial complexes reconstituted from subunits purified by preparative gel electrophoresis, the highest activity is observed on mixing CipA with an endoglucanase and a pair of cellobiohydrolases.

## B. Association of Cellulases with the Cell Surface and Attachment of Cellulolytic Organisms to Cellulose

Because cellulose particles are much too large to be transported inside cellulolytic microorganisms, cellulases must be secreted, and they can usually be recovered from the culture medium. However, it is of obvious advantage for cellulose degraders to be as close as possible to the degradation site, and many do so by carrying cell-bound cellulases and by adhering to the substrate. For example, the rumen bacterium *Fibrobacter succinogenes* clings tightly to cellulose and appears to dig itself into cellulose fibers, with little erosion of the substrate occurring outside of the contact zone.

The surface of many cellulolytic bacteria features protuberances which contain cellulolytic enzymes and contribute to the attachment of the cells to the substrate. In *C. thermocellum*, cellulosomes are associated with such protuberances, which are part of a thick, amorphous outer layer surrounding the cells. Upon making contact with the substrate, protuberances form filamentous protractions connecting bacteria with the cellulose fibrils. Particles also appear to be shed off from the protuberances into the medium. The presence of protuberance is not restricted to bacteria producing cellulosomes or cellulosome-like complexes. For example, protuberances are present on the surface of *Cellulomonas* or *Thermo-*

*monospora* which produce unassociated cellulase systems. In addition, the formation of protuberances can also be associated with exoenzymes hydrolyzing other polysaccharides, such as xylanases or pectinases.

## C. Structure–Function Relationships in Components of Cellulolytic Systems

Recombinant DNA technology introduced in the 1980s has generated an enormous amount of primary sequence data concerning cellulases and xylanases: More than 200 cellulase sequences are currently recorded in the databases. Fortunately, comparative sequence analysis shows that the various modules, or subdomains, composing these enzymes can be classified into a limited number of families, which in all likelihood share common structural properties. As a consequence, it is possible to focus structural and functional studies on relatively few enzymes, which can serve as a paradigm after which the basic features of other related enzymes could be modelled. The next step involves a more detailed understanding of enzyme–substrate interactions responsible for the activity and the specificity of the enzymes. In parallel, the principles governing the quaternary organization of cellulosomes and cellulosome-like complexes have been elucidated.

### 1. Modular Structure of Cellulases

When compared with each other, the most striking feature of cellulases and hemicellulases is that many of them are composed of similar basic modules which are arranged in variegated combinations in different enzymes. In many cases, the study of truncated polypeptides generated by proteolytic cleavage or genetic deletion has demonstrated that such modules correspond to individual protein domains, which are able to fold and function independently. Various types of domains have been identified.

#### a. Catalytic Domains

Catalytic domains are an essential part of cellulases since they perform the hydrolysis of $\beta$-glucosidic bonds. Two possible hydrolysis mechanisms were predicted by Koshland as early as 1953 (Fig. 4), and both have been borne out by numerous examples. In both cases, hydrolysis requires the participation of two catalytic residues. One is a proton donor, which protonates the glucosidic oxygen and facilitates the departure of the leaving group. The other is a carboxylate ion acting as a base. In the first case, the carboxylate interacts directly with the anomeric carbon, leading to the formation of a glycosyl enzyme intermediate. The latter must then be hydrolyzed in a second step, in which the proton donor recovers its proton from a water molecule, generating the $OH^-$ ion required for the second substitution. The outcome is a double nucleophilic substitution leading to retention of configuration at the anomeric carbon. In the second case, the base promotes the ionization of a water molecule, forming an $OH^-$ ion which acts as a nucleophile and substitutes for the departing glucosidic oxygen. The outcome is a single-step nucleophilic substitution, leading to inversion of configuration at the anomeric carbon.

Based on hydrophobic cluster analysis of polypeptide sequences, Henrissat first classified cellulases and xylanases into six broad families, designated A–F. Since then, these families have been redesignated by numbers and integrated into a broader classification of glycosyl hydrolases. Cellulases are thus represented by families 5–8, 12, 26, 44, 45, and 48 of glycosyl hydrolases, xylanases by families 10 and 11, and $\beta$-glucosidases, which hydrolyze cellobiose and low-molecular-weight cellodextrins, by families 1 and 3. With the exception of families 11 and 12, which contain approximately 200–250 amino acids, most catalytic domains range in size between 300 and 500 residues. It was predicted that, within each family, enzymes would share a common folding pattern, a conserved topology of the active site, and a similar catalytic mechanism. The prediction has been borne out by all available evidence. Three-dimensional structures are currently available for at least one member of each cellulase and xylanase family, except families 26 and 44. The most represented fold is the $\alpha_8/\beta_8$ barrel, originally described for triose isomerase, which is typical of families 1, 5, and 10. Indeed, these families are part of a very large "clan" of glycosyl hydrolases, which also includes families 2 ($\beta$-galactosidases) and 17

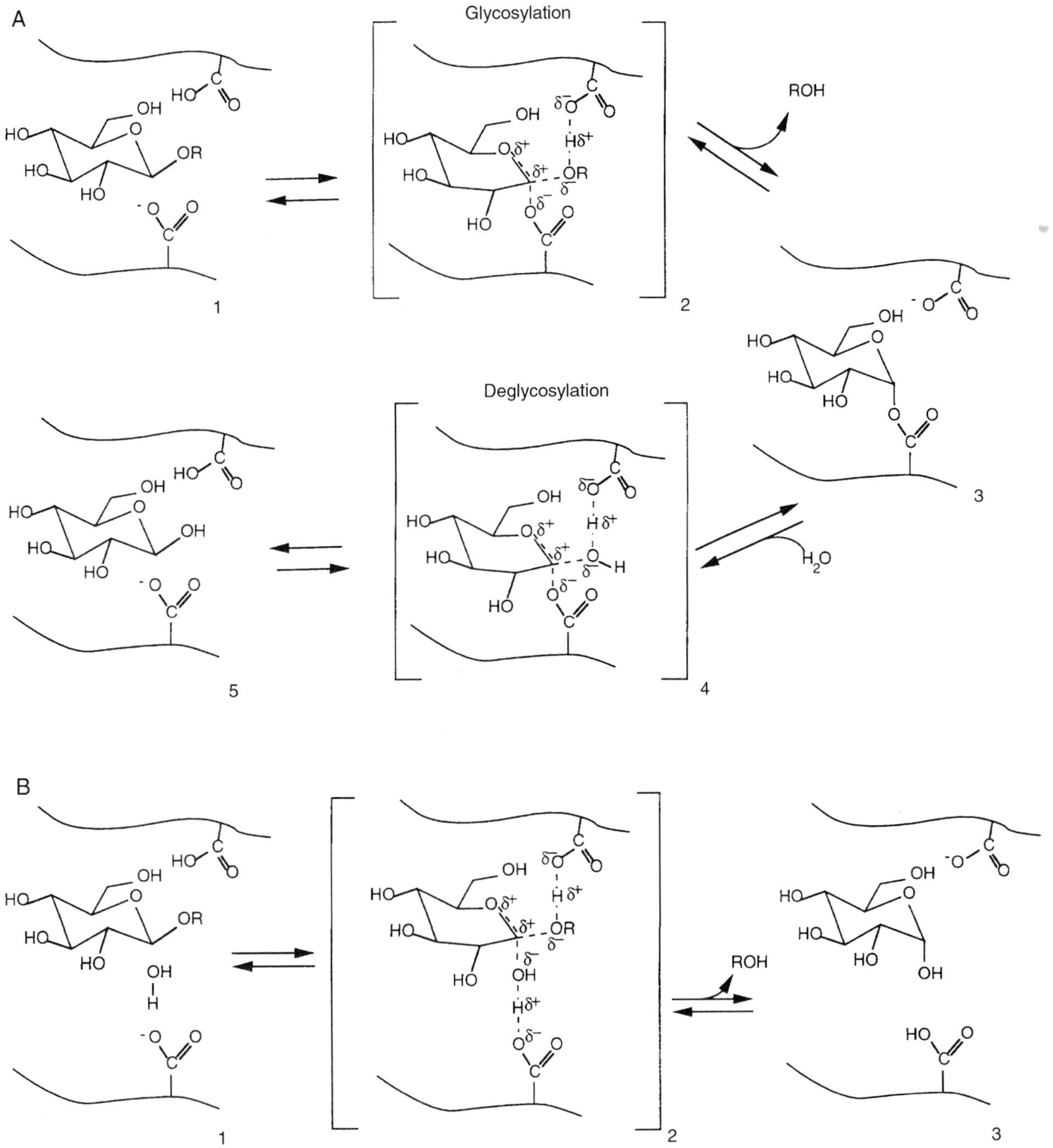

**Fig. 4.** Basic mechanisms of β-glucosidic bond hydrolysis. (A) Two-step mechanism leading to retention of the β configuration at the anomeric carbon. (B) One-step mechanism leading to inversion of configuration at the anomeric carbon.

(β-1,3-1,4-glucanases) and probably families 30 (glucocerebrosidase), 35 (β-galactosidase), 39 (β-xylosidase), and 42 (β-galactosidase) as well. All these enzymes hydrolyze β-glycosidic linkages via a double-substitution mechanism leading to retention

of configuration. In all cases, the observed or predicted structure of the catalytic site is quite similar, with conserved catalytic residues located at similar positions. In other cases, the same framework is shared by enzymes whose relatedness is much more distant. For example, the folding of cellulases of families 8, 9, and 48 is an $\alpha_6/\alpha_6$ barrel, but the build-up of the active site is different in the three families, with catalytic residues being located at non-equivalent positions in the structure.

Structural analysis has provided interesting insights concerning the mode of action of different cellulases. It has long been known that some cellulases, termed endoglucanases, tend to attack cellulose randomly along the glycan chains, whereas others, termed exoglucanases or cellobiohydrolases, have a much more processive mode of action and will preferentially hydrolyze the substrate stepwise from the end of the chains. Endo- and exoglucanases may belong to the same family and share similar overall structures. However, the shape of the active site shows a striking difference. In exoglucanases, the active site is shaped like a tunnel with polypeptide loops closing around the active center so that the glucan chain has to be threaded from the end through the enzyme. In endoglucanases, the loops are shorter and fail to enclose the catalytic site completely so that the latter is shaped like an open cleft, which can straddle the substrate anywhere along the glucan chain.

The crystallographic analysis of enzyme–substrate complexes, with the substrate chain lying across the catalytic center, has provided important clues about the mechanism by which cellulases facilitate the cleavage of $\beta$ glucosidic bonds. This has been made possible by studying mutant enzymes lacking the proper catalytic residues and complexes with nonhydrolyzable analogs in which the oxygen forming the glucosidic bond is replaced by sulfur. In *T. reesei* cellobiohydrolase I, *Fusarium oxysporum* endoglucanase I, and *C. thermocellum* endoglucanase CelA, the glucosyl residues of the substrate chain bind to several subsites on either side of the cleavage site. This forces the glucan chain into a strained conformation at the level of the catalytic center. The $-1$ glucosyl residue, which bears the glucosidic oxygen, adopts a distorted shape which makes the $C_1$ carbon more accessible for the substitution reaction with the nucleophile.

### b. Cellulose-Binding Domains

Many cellulolytic enzymes possess cellulose-binding domains (CBDs), which are generally connected to the catalytic domain by a glycosylated linker segment containing a high proportion of proline, serine, and threonine. CBDs are capable of binding independently and promoting binding of fusion polypeptides to cellulose, which makes them attractive as affinity tags for the immobilization of enzymes or for affinity chromatography.

Like catalytic domains, CBDs can be classified in families according to their sequence similarity. Approximately 11 families are currently recorded, with families I–III encompassing the vast majority of CBD sequences known to date. With a size of approximately 35 residues, family I CBDs are the smallest; they are typically found in fungal cellulases. Most bacterial CBDs, encompassing all other families, range between 100 and 180 residues.

Three-dimensional structures have been determined by nuclear magnetic resonance or X-ray diffraction for CBDs belonging to families I–V. All display all-$\beta$ sheet folds, with families I and V forming a single antiparallel $\beta$ sheet and families II and III a $\beta$-sandwich. Unlike catalytic domains, which can be cocrystallized with soluble substrates and substrate analogs, it is generally impossible to visualize directly the interaction between CBDs and the cellulose chains. One exception is the family IV CBD of *C. fimi* endoglucanase CenC, which binds amorphous cellulose and soluble cellotetraose. Nevertheless, in most cases, CBDs feature a flat face or strip with conserved aromatic residues. *In silico* docking of these residues with the known structure of cellulose shows that they are adequately located to participate in stacking interaction with the glucosyl residues of the cellulose chains. In several cases, the participation of the conserved residues in cellulose binding was further confirmed by mutagenesis studies.

Removal of the CBD from cellulases generates core enzymes which retain full activity against soluble model substrates, such as chromogenic cellobiosides, but are impaired in their activity towards native cellulose. Conversely, the activity of cellulases devoid of a CBD may be enhanced by grafting a CBD by means of genetic engineering. Two effects may contribute to the increase in efficiency afforded by CBDs. One is to tether the enzyme to the substrate while the catalytic moves from one cleavage site to the next one. Indeed, the connecting peptide linking the CBD to the catalytic domain is probably sufficiently flexible to allow "inchworm"-like movement of the enzyme on the surface of the substrate. Furthermore, some CBDs may also enhance the activity of cellulases by improving the accessibility of the substrate. Although no CBD has been demonstrated to disrupt the packing of individual cellulose chains within cellulose crystallites, some CBDs appear to affect the gross features of cellulose fibers. Thus, the CBD derived from *C. fimi* CenA induces exfoliation of the surface layers of cotton or ramie fibers, which become rough and release small particles composed of bundles of microfibrils. In addition, the fibers become more permeable and show increased penetration by and labeling with fluorescein isothiocyanate-labeled CBD. This may explain why the CBD of CenA is capable of enhancing the activity of the catalytic domain of CenA even when it is added separately from the core enzyme.

CBDs also occur frequently in hemicellulases, such as xylanases, xylan esterases, and arabinofuranosidases. As observed with cellulases, the activity of truncated hemicellulases devoid of CBD is maintained with soluble substrates but reduced with cell wall material containing highly substituted xylan. In these cases, the main role of the CBD is probably to enhance the attachment of the enzymes to the plant cell wall.

## 2. Dockerin Domains, Cohesin Domains, and the Quaternary Structure of the Cellulosome

Although catalytic subunits of the *C. thermocellum* cellulosome feature a variety of catalytic domains, they share a conserved domain of approximately 65 residues, termed the dockerin domain. Dockerin domains mediate the association of proteins to the scaffolding protein CipA. Indeed, fusion of dockerin domains to noncellulosomal proteins such as endoglucanase CelC or thioredoxin is sufficient to promote binding of the latter to CipA. Dockerin domains comprise two highly similar, conserved segments of 22 residues each which are connected by a linker peptide showing much lesser sequence conservation. The $NH_2$-terminal sequence of each duplicated segment contains residues that are conserved in the EF-hand motif of calcium-binding proteins. Indeed, the presence of $Ca^{2+}$ strongly enhances the affinity of

catalytic subunits for CipA, presumably because it stabilizes the conformation of dockerin domains.

The sequence of CipA comprises a CBD of type III and nine reiterated domains of approximately 145 residues linked together by Pro/Thr-rich, glycosylated linker segments. The reiterated domains, termed cohesin domains, act as receptor domains which bind the dockerin domains borne by the catalytic subunits. The three-dimensional structures of two cohesin domains have been determined. They both fold into a nine-stranded $\beta$ sandwich with an overall "jelly roll" topology resembling that observed for CBDs of types II and III, although direct sequence similarity with the CBDs is not detectable.

The cohesin domains of CipA are even more highly conserved than the dockerin domains of the catalytic subunits. Accordingly, there is no detectable specificity in the interaction between the dockerin domains of the catalytic subunits and the different cohesin domains of CipA. Each dockerin domain can bind to all the cohesin domains of CipA with a comparable affinity and vice versa. Consequently, the topology and stoichiometry of binding of the catalytic subunits along the different cohesin domains of CipA is probably quite flexible, resulting in a highly heterogeneous population of complexes.

The cellulosomes produced by other cellulolytic clostridia, such as *C. cellulolyticum*, *C. josui*, or *C. cellulovorans*, are organized in a very similar manner, with scaffolding proteins and dockerin domains resembling those found in *C. thermocellum*, although they are not mutually compatible. Dockerin domains of *C. cellulolyticum* cannot bind to the cohesin domains of *C. thermocellum* and vice versa. Recently, duplicated sequences resembling clostridial dockerin domains were found in an endoglucanase from *R. albus* and in two xylanases from *R. flavefaciens*, indicating that Ruminococci probably also contain cellulosomes. The high-molecular-weight cellulase complexes produced by the anaerobic rumen fungi *N. patriciarum* and *P. equi* are an interesting example of converging evolution. Several cellulases, xylanases, or mannanases from these organisms comprise a conserved segment of approximately 40 residues, which is usually repeated two or three times. Although the sequence of this segment bears no similarity to the clostridial dockerin domains, it probably has the same function. Fusion of the reiterated domain of *P. equi* xylanase XYLA to glutathion-*S*-transferase produces a hybrid protein which binds specifically to 97- and 116-kDa polypeptides present in the multicellulase complexes from *P. equi* and *N. patriciarum*, respectively. The sequence of these putative scaffolding polypeptides has not been determined, however.

### 3. Interactions Involved in Anchoring Cellulosomes to the Cell Surface

In *C. thermocellum*, the COOH terminus of the scaffolding protein CipA consists of a dockerin domain whose sequence diverges strongly from those of the dockerin domains borne by the catalytic subunits of the cellulosome. Binding studies indicate that the dockerin domain of CipA interacts with a set of proteins that are different from CipA. Several genes encoding such proteins have been cloned. The corresponding polypeptides contain one to four copies of a new type of cohesin domain, termed cohesin domain of type II, in contrast with the cohesin domains of type I borne by CipA. Both types have very low sequence similarity, although analysis suggests that they share the same folding pattern. All type II cohesin domains known so far belong to polypeptides which also contain a triplicated segment of approximately 60 residues termed the SLH domain. SLH domains have been found in many exocellular proteins, such as S-layer proteins and polysaccharidases, which are located in the cell envelope from a variety of bacteria. Fusion and deletion analysis, as well as *in vitro* binding studies, indicate that SLH domains are directly involved in binding proteins to the cell surface by interacting with cell envelope-associated polysaccharides. Indeed, SdbA and OlpB, two of the *C. thermocellum* polypeptides harboring N-terminal type II cohesin domains and C-terminal SLH domains, have been located on the outer layer of the cell envelope by immunochemical labeling and electron microscopy. Thus, as shown in Fig. 5, it is likely that *C. thermocellum* cellulosomes are bound to the cell surface by means of a type II cohesin–

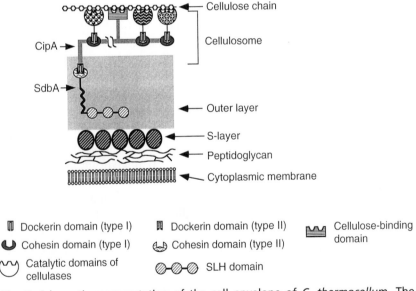

**Fig. 5.** Schematic representation of the cell envelope of *C. thermocellum*. The catalytic subunits of the cellulosome are anchored to the cohesin domains of the scaffolding protein CipA. Only three of the nine cohesin domains of CipA are shown, together with the attached catalytic subunits. The cellulose-binding domain of CipA makes contact with a cellulose fiber and promotes attachment of the complex to the substrate. CipA is bound to the type II cohesin domain of SdbA by means of its dockerin domain. SdbA is a component of the outer layer (see text for details) (reprinted with permission from Béguin and Alzari, 1998).

dockerin interaction between CipA and cell envelope polypeptides containing SLH domains. However, different determinants must be responsible for anchoring the cellulosomes of *C. cellulolyticum* or *C. cellulovorans* since the scaffolding proteins of these complexes contain no recognizable dockerin domain.

## IV. REGULATION OF CELLULASE SYNTHESIS

Many studies investigating the physiological conditions required for cellulase biosynthesis in various organisms have established that cellulase synthesis is controlled by two basic regulation mechanisms. Low $M_r$ substrates that are more easily metabolized than cellulose repress cellulase synthesis. In addition, in many systems, cellulase biosynthesis is induced in the presence of cellulose. Although the exact nature of the true inducers is controversial, it is generally accepted that they derive from soluble degradation products that are generated by low, constitutive amounts of cellulase.

Probes derived from cloned genes have been used to characterize the transcripts of individual cellulase genes. Such studies have been useful in mapping and identifying transcription start sites and putative promoters. They have shown that transcription of the same gene can start at different promoters according to culture conditions, with some promoters being inducible and some constitutive. They have also shown that, within the same species, transcription of cellulase genes is not strictly coordinated some of the genes have more or less elevated levels of constitutive expression. Gel retardation assays have also been performed, for example, in *T. fusca*, to demonstrate the presence of putative regulatory proteins binding to specific sequences located upstream of cellulase genes.

In most cellulolytic microorganisms, genetics is limited to random mutagenesis and screening of mutants with interesting phenotypes. In practical terms, this approach has been quite useful to obtain industrial strains of *T. reesei* that are no longer subject to catabolite repression and produce massive amounts of cellulase. Recently, however, the possibility of performing targeted genetic manipulations has made *T. reesei* the organism of choice to study the regulation of cellulase genes at the molecular level.

Repression of *T. reesei* cellulase gene transcription by glucose is effected by the glucose repressor CRE1, which is similar to the homologous genes CREA present in *Aspergillus nidulans* and *Aspergillus niger*. The CRE1/CREA glucose repressors contain a conserved DNA-binding region with two $Cys_2His_2$ zinc fingers. It appears that the CRE1 repressor is partially deleted in the industrial strain Rut-C30, which was isolated as a hypercellulolytic strain in which expression of several cellulase and hemicellulase genes is no longer sensitive to glucose repression. Complementation of Rut-C30 with the wild-type *cre1* gene restores glucose repression of these genes, showing that CRE1 acts as a pleiotropic regulator. A site located 500 bp upstream from the start codon is required for glucose repression of the *cbh1* gene. This site contains several determinants similar to the homologous sites recognized by the CREA repressor in *A. nidulans*.

The presence of a specific induction mechanism is suggested by the observation that growth on nonrepressing substrates, slow feeding of glucose, or mutations affecting catabolite-type repression fail to induce cellulase biosynthesis. Cellulase induction requires the presence of cellulose and of low, constitutive amounts of cellulases, which release soluble products required for induction. Insertional inactivation of specific cellulase genes, such as *cbh2* and *egl2,* prevents the induction of transcription of other cellulase genes in cultures grown in the presence of cellulose. Among soluble sugars, the most potent inducer of cellulase synthesis is sophorose ($\beta$-1,2-glucobiose), which is formed by the transglycosylating activity of $\beta$-glucosidases. Inhibition of $\beta$-glucosidase activity or inactivation of $\beta$-glucosidase genes reduce or abolish induction of cellulase genes by cellulose but not by sophorose. Two genes have recently been shown to activate transcription from the *cbh1* promoter expressed in yeast. The encoded proteins, termed ACE I and ACE II (activator of cellulase expression), contain three $Cys_2His_2$ and one $Zn_2Cys_6$ zinc fingers, respectively. Whether ACE I- and II-mediated expression is dependent on sophorose has not been reported, however.

## V. APPLICATIONS OF CELLULASES IN BIOTECHNOLOGY

### A. Cellulose as a Renewable Carbon Source for the Production of Fuels and Chemicals

Since the days of the first oil crisis, considerable efforts have been devoted to the conversion of biomass to petroleum substitutes, which could serve either as fuels or as raw material for the chemical industry. The interest of biotechnologists was drawn by the vast supply of cellulose, which could potentially be used for the production of glucose, which can in turn be fermented into alcohols, acetone, and volatile fatty acids. Excitement abated significantly during the 1980s due to the decrease in oil price and to the realization that long-term basic and applied research would be required before commercial exploitation of most natural cellulosic materials could become economically feasible. Recently, however, concern about global climatic warming due to $CO_2$ emissions from the burning of fossil fuels has stimulated a renewed interest in the use of biomass for the production of energy. Switching from fossil to biomass-derived fuels would indeed reduce the net output of $CO_2$ from energy production close to zero. Thus, in the long term, there is still the prospect that cellulosic biomass may contribute significantly to the production of fossil fuel substitutes, but much fundamental and applied research is still needed. Recent studies indicate that although the cost of feedstock is unlikely to decrease substantially, strong reductions in the cost of processing may be expected from the development of advanced technologies, particularly concerning substrate pretreatment and biological conversion.

### 1. Pretreatment of Cellulosic Materials

Most of the cheaply available supply of cellulose is in the form of lignocellulose. Although a balance exists in nature between synthesis and degradation of lignocellulose, degradation is too slow for industrial applications. Hence, many efforts have been devoted to the development of chemical and physical pretreatments that enhance the digestibility of natural lignocellulosics. Rather than reducing the degree of crystallinity of cellulose, the critical factor appears to be the increase in surface area available for enzymatic attack. Increasing the accessibility of the substrate to cellulolytic enzymes may be brought about by mechanical disruption and/or partial removal of the lignin and hemicellulose matrix. The hydrolysis of hemicellulose can be acid catalyzed at high temperature, either in the presence of added acid or due to the release of acetic acid from the acetyl groups of xylan. As hydrolysis of hemicellulose proceeds, associated lignin forms clumps that separate from the cellulose fibers. Various pretreatment procedures have been developed, including alkaline swelling, ball milling, mild acid hydrolysis, delignification with oxidizing agents, steam explosion, and high-pressure, high temperature treatment with water or dilute methanol. Several points must be considered in the assessment of a pretreatment process: (i) efficiency (i.e., suitability of the pretreated product as a substrate for enzymatic hydrolysis); (ii) price, including cost of environmentally sound operation (treatment of effluents); and (iii) yield, which is influenced by factors such as recovery of carbohydrates solubilized during pretreatment and losses due to the formation of by-products (e.g., furfural and hydroxymethylfurfural). Another problem is the inhibitory effect of by-products on the fermenting microorganisms used to convert glucose into the desired final products. Currently, high-pressure, liquid hot water pretreatment and steam explosion appear promising. In contrast to dilute-acid technology, they do not require extensive milling of the substrate and obviate to a large extent the need to neutralize effluents and the concomitant problem of gypsum disposal.

### 2. Biological Conversion

Current processes for the conversion of cellulose to ethanol are based on simultaneous saccharification and fermentation (SSF). In such processes, hydrolysis of cellulose and fermentation of glucose are performed in the same vessel, whereas cellulases required for hydrolysis are produced separately. Extensive efforts have addressed the improvement of cellulase production by *T. reesei*. Wild-type *T. reesei* is already a remarkable cellulase producer; hyperproducing mutants were obtained after screening for insensitivity to catabolite repression and for enlarged clearing zones when grown on plates containing cellulose powder. Further increase in cellulase production was obtained by careful design of fed-batch cultivation. For example, *T. reesei* strain CL-847 can convert lactose to cellulase with a protein yield on lactose of approximately 40% and with final extracellular concentration in excess of 30 g/liter. Nevertheless, the cost of cellulase production remains a limiting factor for SSF processes. Not only does the cost of cellulase add to the total cost but also cost optimization of the enzyme : substrate ratio requires that cellulase be added in low amounts, resulting in long fermentation times and correspondingly high reactor operating costs. Hence, an attractive alternative is the direct microbial conversion (DMC), in which cellulase production, cellulose hydrolysis, and hexose fermentation occur at the same time in a single bioreactor. Although cocultures may be envisaged, ideally DMC would be best performed by a single organism combining high cellulolytic activity and high ethanol yields. No such organism has been found, however. Two approaches are currently followed to improve existing strains. One is to transfer cellulase genes into organisms known to ferment hexoses with a high yield and a high tolerance to ethanol. The other is to coax good cellulolytic microorganisms into producing high yields of ethanol. In the first case, the difficulty lies in transferring all the genes required for cellulolysis and getting them expressed in a foreign host. In the second case, ensuring that all available sugars are funnelled into ethanol fermentation would require inactivation of alternative metabolic pathways leading to production of acetate, lactate, or formate by knocking out the appropriate genes.

## B. Modification of Lignocellulosic Materials

In addition to complete hydrolysis of cellulose into glucose, cellulases and hemicellulases can be utilized for many applications involving the modification, without complete hydrolysis, of various lignocellulosic materials.

In the food-processing area, cellulases are already being used to soften fruit pulp and increase the recovery of oil and fruit juices. Pretreatment of animal

feed has also been the topic of numerous studies. The situation is complex. Many factors must be taken into account, such as the physiology of ruminants, including the influence of fiber length on the residence time of cellulosic material in the rumen. Certainly, total saccharification is not a prerequisite, nor even desirable. Pretreatment with cellulase has also been considered for the production of silage. Partial attack of cell wall polysaccharides would release soluble carbohydrates, both from the hydrolyzed substrate and from intracellular cell sap, thereby speeding up the onset of lactic acid fermentation and preventing butyric fermentation by clostridia. Recombinant lactic acid bacteria containing cloned cellulase genes have been constructed. The economic viability of silage pretreatment with cellulase remains to be assessed, however. Cellulases and hemicellulase preparations are also used to upgrade feedstuffs for chicken by hydrolyzing glucans and xylans, which increase the viscosity of the bowel content, reduce nutrient uptake, and lead to the "sticky faeces" problem.

The use of cellulases and hemicellulases in the paper industry has been studied intensively. One major negative effect to be avoided is the loss of pulp viscosity due to the activity of endoglucanases, which is detrimental to the tensile strength of the paper. However, some aspects of pulp processing can benefit from the action of hemicellulases and cellulases. The action of chlorine bleach on lignin results in the release of polychlorinated phenols in paper mill effluents, which is increasingly considered unacceptable. The addition of xylanases significantly reduces the amount of chlorine required for bleaching due to the disruption of the lignin–hemicellulose matrix, which causes partial delignification. Some cellulases, such as *T. reesei* cellobiohydrolase I, can contribute to the mechanical refinement of paper pulp, in which coarse fibers are mechanically disrupted to form fines consisting of microfibrils with improved inter-fiber bonding properties.

Cellulases are also included as additives to laundry detergents. Repeated washings cause cotton fabrics to assume a dull, felt-like aspect and a rough texture due to the appearance of microfibrils from the wear and tear of cotton fibers. Limited action by cellulases removes the microfibrils and contributes to restoring the original aspect and texture of the fabric. In the same vein, treatment with cellulases is used to remove excess dye in denim fabric in pre-faded blue jeans ("biostoning").

The potential uses of cellulases are therefore many and divergent. They are valuable in various specialized niche applications, even if their use for the bulk commercial conversion of wood depends on further technological advances.

## See Also the Following Articles

Acetogenesis and Acetogenic Bacteria • Lignocellulose, Lignin, Ligninases • Rumen Microbiology • Timber and Forest Products

## Bibliography

Bayer, E. A., Morag, E., and Lamed, R. (1994). The cellulosome—a treasure-trove for biotechnology. *Trends Biotechnol.* **12**, 379–386.

Béguin, P., and Aubert J.-P. (1994). The biological degradation of cellulose. *FEMS Microbiol. Rev.* **13**, 25–58.

Béguin, P., and Alzari, P. M. (1998). The cellulosome of *Clostridium thermocellum. Biochem. Soc. Trans.* **26**, 178–185.

Claeyssens, M., Nerinckx, W., and Piens, K. (Eds.) (1998). "Carbohydrases from *Trichoderma reesei* and Other Microorganisms. Structures, Biochemistry, Genetics, and Applications." Royal Chemical Society, Cambridge, UK.

Davies, G., and Henrissat, B. (1995). Structures and mechanisms of glycosyl hydrolases. *Structure* **3**, 853–859.

Eriksson, K.-E., Blanchette, R. A., and Ander, P. (1990). "Microbial and Enzymatic Degradation of Wood and Wood Components." Springer-Verlag, Berlin.

Henrissat, B., and Bairoch, A. (1996). Updating the sequence-based classification of glycosal hydrolases. *Biochem. J.* **316**, 695–696.

Kirk, T. K. (1988). Biochemistry of lignin degradation by *Phanerochaete chrysosporium. In* "Biochemistry and Genetics of Cellulose Degradation" (J.-P. Aubert P. Béguin, and J. Millet, Eds.), pp. 315–332. Academic Press, London.

Koshland, D. E., Jr. (1953). Stereochemistry and the mechanism of enzymatic reactions. *Biol. Rev.* **28**, 416–438.

Kubicek, C. P., Messner, R., Gruber, F., Mach, R. L., and Kubicek-Pranz, E. M. (1993). The *Trichoderma reesei* cellulase regulatory puzzle—From the interior life of a secretory fungus. *Enzyme Microb. Technol.* **15**, 90–99.

Ljungdahl, L. G., and Eriksson, K.-E. (1985). Ecology of microbial cellulose degradation. *Adv. Microbial Ecol.* **8**, 237–299.

Teeri, T. T. (1997). Crystalline cellulose degradation—New insight into the function of cellobiohydrases. *Trends Biotechnol.* **15**, 160–167.

Tomme, P., Warren, R. A. J., and Gilkes, N. R. (1995). Cellulose hydrolysis by bacteria and fungi. *Adv. Microb. Physiol.* **37**, 1–81.

Wilson, D. B. (1992). Biochemistry and genetics of Actinomycete cellulases. *Crit. Rev. Biotechnol.* **12**, 45–63.

# Cell Walls, Bacterial

## Joachim-Volker Höltje

*Max-Planck-Institut für Entwicklungsbiologie*

## GLOSSARY

**autolysins** Endogenous murein hydrolases, which cleave bonds in the peptidoglycan sacculus that are critical for the mechanical strength of the structure and thus cause lysis (autolysis) of the bacterium.

**cell envelope** A multilayered structure that engulfs the cytoplasm. The innermost layer, the cytoplasmic membrane, is stabilized by an exoskeleton of peptidoglycan (murein). Gram-negative bacteria have a second lipid bilayer, called the outer membrane, making the envelope of gram-negative bacteria less permeable compared to that of gram-positive bacteria.

**Gram stain** Iodine–gentian violet complex that is retained by some bacteria (called gram-positive) but is released from the envelope by acetone or ethanol from another group of bacteria (called gram-negative). Whereas gram-positive bacteria have a multilayered shell of peptidoglycan, gram-negative bacteria have a thin (monolayered) peptidoglycan and a second membrane, the outer membrane.

**lipoproteins** Proteins carrying at their amino terminus a cysteine to which glycerol is linked that has its hydroxyl groups substituted by fatty acids. In addition, the amino group of Cys is also modified by a fatty acid. A murein lipoprotein is covalently attached to the cell wall of gram-negative bacteria with its carboxyl terminus and at the same time is inserted with its lipophilic amino terminus into the outer membrane, thereby connecting murein and the outer membrane.

**lysozyme** $\beta$-1,4-N-acetylmuramidase that hydrolyses the $\beta$-1,4 glycosidic bond between N-acetylmuramic acid and N-acetylglucosamine in peptidoglycan. It is found in many bacteria, where it is involved in the growth processes of the cell wall. It is also present in various tissues and secretions of higher organisms (e.g., hen egg white lysozyme), where it functions as a powerful antibacterial agent.

**murein** Synonym for peptidoglycan, a cross-linked biopolymer of poly-(N-acetylglucosamine-$\beta$-1,4-N-acetylmuramic acid) that is cross-linked by peptide bridges that are linked to the lactyl group of the muramic acid residues (from *Murus*, a Latin word meaning wall).

**murein sacculus** The bacterial exoskeleton that forms a bag-shaped macromolecule completely enclosing the cell. It endows the cell with mechanical strength and confers the specific shape to the bacterium.

**penicillin-binding proteins** Enzymes that covalently interact with penicillin by forming a penicilloyl–enzyme complex. The family of penicillin-binding proteins consists of bifunctional transglycosylase–DD-transpeptidases, DD-transpeptidases, DD-endopeptidases, and DD-carboxypeptidases.

**periplasm** A specific cellular compartment of the cell envelope of gram-negative bacteria confined by the cytoplasmic membrane and the outer membrane.

**teichoic acid** Anionic polyol-phosphate polymer covalently bound to the muramic acid of peptidoglycan in gram-positive bacteria. Ribitol- and glycerol teichoic acids are known.

**THE BACTERIAL CELL ENVELOPE** is a complex structure consisting of different layers that have to fulfill many critical functions for the cell. Besides being a protective shield against the hostile environment, it must allow communication with the surroundings in order for the bacteria to find optimal conditions for growth. This highly developed cell organelle has to be mechanically stabilized to withstand the high intracellular osmotic pressure of approximately 2–25 atm. Eubacteria as a rule reinforce their cell envelope by an exoskeleton made of peptidoglycan (murein), a cross-linked biopolymer that is extremely well suited to endow the cell with sufficient strength. In order to achieve this, the murein forms a closed bag-shaped structure, called sacculus, completely wrapping up the cell. Importantly, the murein sacculus, also referred to as the cell wall, not only stabilizes the cytoplasmic membrane but also maintains the specific shape of the bacterium. Morphogenesis of bacteria can therefore be studied by analyzing the metabolism of a single macromolecule—the murein sacculus.

## I. CELL ENVELOPE STRUCTURE

On the basis of a special staining procedure bacteria can be subdivided in essentially two groups, the gram-positive and the gram-negative bacteria. Interestingly, this reflects a fundamental difference in the general construction of the cell envelope (Figs. 1 and

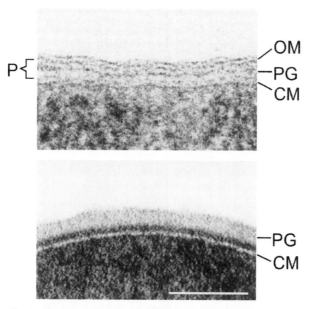

**Fig. 1.** Electron micrographs of negatively stained sections of bacterial cell walls. (Top) Gram-negative bacterium *Escherichia coli;* (bottom) gram-positive bacterium *Staphylococcus aureus*. P, periplasmic space; OM, outer membrane; PG, peptidoglycan; CM, cytoplasmic membrane. Scale bar = 0.1 mm (courtesy of Drs. H. Frank and H. Schwarz).

2). The staining method by Christian Gram consists of two steps. First, the heat-fixed cells are stained with a dark-blue iodine gentian violet dye complex. In the second step, the cells are extracted with ethanol. If the cells are destained during this step they are referred to as gram-negative bacteria, and if the stain remains within the cell envelope the bacteria are called gram-positive.

A typical gram-positive envelope consists of a cytoplasmic membrane and a thick, multi-layered murein shell (20–50 nm thick) which is decorated by teichoic acids (Fig. 2). The gram-negative bacterium is enclosed by two bilayers, a cytoplasmic membrane and an outer membrane confining a unique compartment called the periplasmic space (Fig. 2). The murein sacculus of gram-negative bacteria is embedded into this space and is characteristically extremely thin, forming only one continuous layer (approximately 3 nm thick). The outer membrane and the murein layer are connected by a lipoprotein that has its fatty acid-substituted amino terminus immersed in the outer membrane and its carboxyl terminus covalently linked to the murein (Figs. 2 and 4). Unlike the cytolasmic membrane, the outer membrane is a highly asymmetric lipid bilayer structure with an inner leaflet consisting of phospholipids and an outer leaflet of lipopolysaccharides. Typically, the outer membrane contains pore-forming proteins, known as porins.

The most important structural distinction between gram-positive and gram-negative bacteria is the presence in the latter group of a second bilayer system, the outer membrane. Due to this additional permeability barrier, gram-negative bacteria show significantly higher minimal inhibitory concentration values for many antibiotics than do gram-positive bacteria. As a consequence, some otherwise quite powerful antibiotics are of no therapeutic use for the treatment of gram-negative infections. Besides a general hindrance to the uptake of hydrophilic compounds, the existence of a second permeability barrier has many additional consequences for cell wall metabolism. It allows the cell to reduce the thickness of its murein to just one single layer and makes it possible to efficiently recycle the valuable murein turnover products that accumulate during growth in the periplasmic space.

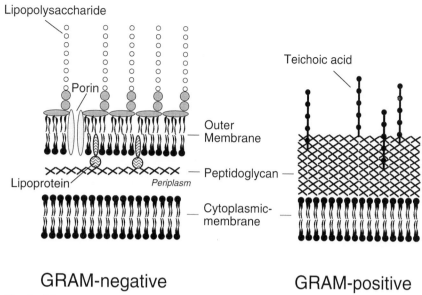

**Fig. 2.** Schematic view of the construction of the cell envelope of gram-positive and gram-negative bacteria.

## II. CHEMISTRY OF BACTERIAL CELL WALLS

The structural principle that glycan strands are cross-linked by peptides in order to form a strong latticework for a bacterial exoskeleton has been invented in nature twice, in Archaea and in Eubacteria. Archaea contain a compound called pseudomurein. Although the architectural style is the same in pseudomurein and in murein, the building materials are different.

### A. Peptidoglycan (Murein)

The murein of Eubacteria consists of glycan strands that are cross-linked by peptides (Figs. 3 and 7). The amino sugars N-acetylglucosamine (GlcNAc) and N-acetylmuramic acid (MurNAc) are polymerized by β-1,-4 glycosidic bonds in an alternating order; thus, the glycans have one GlcNAc and one MurNAc terminus. The latter represents the reducing end of the polysaccharide. In some species the terminal MurNAc residue is modified to a non-reducing 1,6-anhydromuramic acid (Fig. 3). The lactyl group of the muramic acid is substituted by a short peptide consisting of L- and D-amino acids in an alternating sequence. The presence of LD and DD peptide bonds renders the peptides resistant to the majority of peptidases. Cross-linkage of two peptides is made possible by the presence of a diamino acid, such as L-lysine, *meso*-diaminopimelic acid, or L-ornithine. This allows the formation of a tail to tail bridging peptide bond between the terminal carboxyl group of a D-Ala in position 4 of one peptide moiety and the non-alpha amino group of the diamino acid at position 3 of another peptide side chain (Figs. 3 and 7). In many gram-positive bacteria the cross-linkage is not a direct one but is mediated by an additional peptide called "Intervening peptide." A pentaglycine, for example, is inserted between the D-Ala and the L-Lys in the case of *Staphylococcus aureus*. In contrast to the types of cross-linkages referred to as group A, in which the cross-linkage is between positions 4 and 3 of two peptides, the linkage in group B is via an intervening peptide containing one diamino acid that allows for a cross-linkage between the alpha-carboxyl group of the D-Glu in position 2 of one peptide to the carboxyl group of D-Ala in position 4 of another peptide (Fig. 3). In general there are only a few modifications of the sugar part. The glycans can be $O_6$-acetylated, which makes the murein resistant towards the action of hen egg white lysozyme, or they can be de-N-acetylated, as is the case in *Bacillus cereus*.

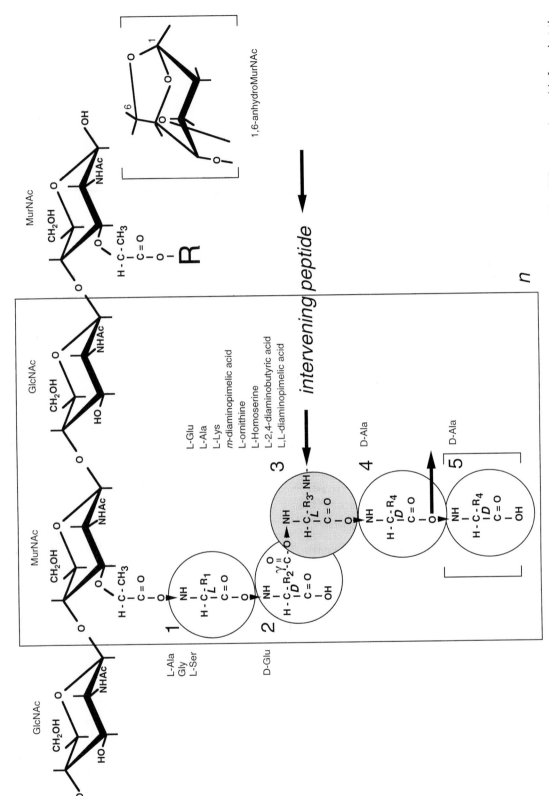

**Fig. 3.** Generalized chemical structure of peptidoglycan (murein). The box indicates the subunit of the polymer. The different amino acids found at the indicated sites of the pentapeptide moiety in various peptidoglycans are listed. R, peptidyl-moiety; GlcNAc, *N*-acetylglucosamine; MurNAc, *N*-acetylmuramic acid. The arrows indicate the donor and acceptor sites for cross-linkage. The intervening peptide that occurs in many gram-positive bacteria is explained in the text.

## B. Murein Lipoprotein

The murein of gram-negative bacteria is substituted by a lipoprotein that on average is attached to every tenth muramic acid residue. The linkage is from the epsilon amino group of the lysine at the carboxyl terminus to the carboxyl group at the L-center of *meso*-diaminopimelic acid (Fig. 4). The murein lipoprotein is a member of the superfamily of lipoproteins that are characterized by a typical consensus processing site (LLLAGCSSNS). The unmodified prolipoprotein that carries a typical amino-

terminal leader is exported to the periplasmic side of the cytoplasmic membrane where the SH group of the Cys is substituted by glycerol (Fig. 4). Two fatty acids are added to the hydroxyl groups of the glycerol moiety to yield the diglyceride proliprotein. A specific signal peptidase (signal peptidase II) cleaves the leader, releasing the amino group of the Cys to which a third fatty acid is linked. The free form of the mature lipoprotein is hooked to the murein by an unknown adding enzyme. Globomycin specifically inhibits the signal peptidase II.

The function of the lipoprotein is probably to connect the outer membrane with the murein sacculus (Fig. 2). Although mutants in Lpp are viable, they often show blebs of outer membrane vesicles at the site of cell division where all three layers of the envelope, the outer membrane, the murein, and the cytoplasmic membrane have to be contracted simultaneously. When the Lpp mutation is combined with a defect in the major outer membrane protein OmpA, *Escherichia coli* can no longer maintain its rod shape and grows as spheres, but only when sufficient $Mg^{2+}$ is added.

## C. Teichoic Acid

An anionic polyol-phosphate polymer, called teichoic acid, constitutes the outermost part of the peptidoglycan shell of gram-positive bacteria. The polyol can be either ribitol or glycerol. Most glycerol teichoic acids are 1,3-linked. Many substitutions, such as D-alanine, L-serine, glycine, glucose, and GlcNAc can occur. Teichoic acids are linked via a special linkage unit by a phophodiester to the $C_6$ of the muramic acid. Because of the equally spaced phosphate groups, teichoic acids strongly bind magnesium ions. It has been speculated that teichoic acids function as a kind of ion exchanger. Thus, the teichoic acid layer forms a type of cell compartment that may have a function similar to that of the periplasmic space of gram-negative bacteria.

Upon transfer to phosphate-limiting growth conditions, teichoic acid synthesis rapidly decreases and synthesis of a teichuronic acid takes over. Unlike teichoic acids, teichuronic acids lack the phosphate group in the repeating units. The teichuronic acid of *Micrococcus luteus* is formed from the disaccharide

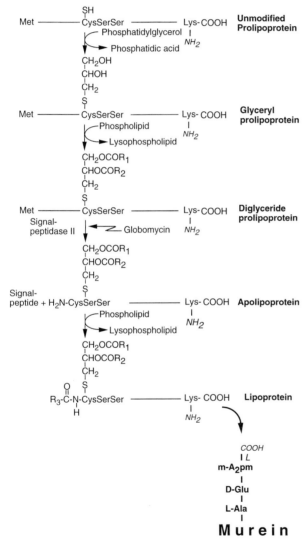

**Fig. 4.** Biosynthetic pathway of the murein lipoprotein. $R_1$–$R_3$ indicate fatty acids with a composition similar to that of the phospholipids of the bacterium.

D-N-acetylmannosaminuronic acid-β-1,6-D-glucose that is polymerized by α-1,4-glycosidic bonds up to 10–40mers. The teichuronic acid of *Bacillus lichenformis* consists of equimolar amounts of N-acetyglactosamine and D-glucuronic acid.

## D. Pseudomurein

Pseudomurein resembles murein in that it has the same structural engineering as murein. However, the glycan strands consist of GlcNAc or N-acetylgalactosamine and N-acetyltalosaminuronic acid, linked together by β-1,-3 glycosidic bonds. The peptide bridges that are hooked to the carboxyl group of the talosaminuronic acid contain L-amino acids, including Lys, Glu, Ala, Thr, and Ser. As a consequence of this different chemical set-up, the synthesis of pseudomurein is not inhibited by D-cyloserine, vancomycin, or penicillin, which are typical inhibitors of murein synthesis.

## III. BIOSYNTHESIS OF PEPTIDOGLYCAN (MUREIN)

### A. Cytoplasmic Reaction Steps

The biosynthetic pathway of the murein sacculus involves three cellular compartments: synthesis of soluble murein precursors in the cytoplasm (Fig. 5), transport of the lipid-linked murein precursors across the cytoplasmic membrane (Fig. 6), and insertion of the precursors into the pre-existing murein sacculus in the extracellular space or, in the case of gram-negative bacteria, in the periplasmic space (Figs. 6 and 7).

The first biosynthetic intermediate that is specific for murein is UDP-N-acetylmuramic acid (UDP-MurNAc). It is formed by a transfer of enolpyruvate from phosphoenolpyruvate to UDP-N-acetylglucosamine (UDP-GlcNAc), followed by NADPH catalyzed reduction of the intermediate UDP-GlcNAc-enolpyruvate to the lactate-substituted glucosamine known as muramic acid (Fig. 5). The antibiotic fosfomycin (phosphonomycin, L-cis-1,2-enolpropylphosphoric acid) is a potent inhibitor of the UDP-GlcNAc-enolpyruvyl transferase. The lactate moiety

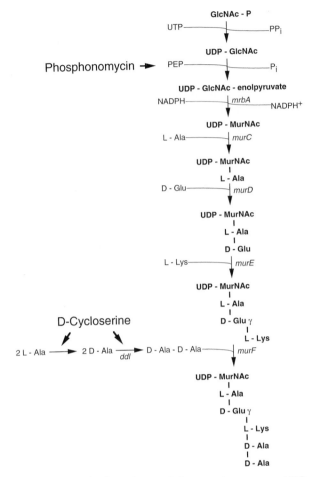

**Fig. 5.** Biosynthetic pathway of the murein precursor UDP-N-acetylmuramyl pentapeptide.

of muramic acid functions as an acceptor for the first amino acid of the pentapeptide side chain. The additional amino acids are added sequentially by specific synthases that couple the cleavage of ATP to the formation of a peptide bond. The correct sequence of the pentapeptide, an alternating succession of L- and D-amino acids, is determined by the substrate specificity of the synthases. However, the L-alanine adding enzyme also accepts L-serine and glycine and the *meso*-diaminopimelic acid adding enzyme from *E. coli* also accepts the sulfur-containing diaminopimelic acid analog, lanthionine. Interestingly, the last two amino acids, both of which are D-alanine, are added in the form of the D-alanyl–D-alanine dipeptide pre-synthesized by a D-alanine ligase. The D-Ala–D-Ala adding enzyme completes the synthesis of

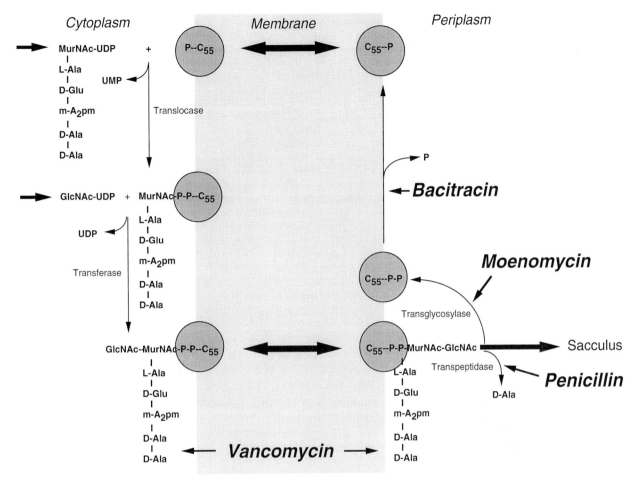

**Fig. 6.** Formation of the lipid-linked murein precursors and their translocation across the cytoplasmic membrane. $C_{55}$, undecaprenol.

the UDP-MurNAc-pentapeptide precursor. Other DD-dipeptides in addition to D-Ala–D-Ala can be added by the ligase; in particular, glycine and D-lactate can substitute for one of the D-Ala residues. Both the L-alanine racemace and the D-alanine racemace are inhibited by D-cycloserine and related compounds such as *O*-carbamoyl-D-serine, haloalanines, and alaphosphin (L-alanyl-L-1-aminoethyl phosphonic acid).

## B. Membrane Translocation of Murein Precursors

For insertion into the murein sacculus the activated precursors UDP-GlcNAc and UDP-MurNac-pentapeptide must be transported across the cyto-

plasmic membrane (Fig. 6). The details of this important step are poorly understood. An undecaprenylphosphate ($C_{55}$-isoprenoid) molecule, also called bactoprenol, functions as a vehicle (lipid carrier) to shuffle the hydrophilic precursors from the inner to the outer side of the cytoplasmic membrane. A translocase, phospho-N-acetylmuramyl pentapeptide translocase (MurY), transfers the phosphoryl-muramyl pentapeptide to undecaprenyl-phosphate to yield the so-called lipid intermediate I, undecaprenyl-diphosphoryl-N-acetylmuramyl pentapeptide. The translocase reaction is fully reversible and is inhibited by tunicamycin. This enzyme also catalyzes an exchange reaction between UMP and UDP-MurNAc pentapeptide. In a second step, catalyzed by the transferase N-acetylglucosamine trans-

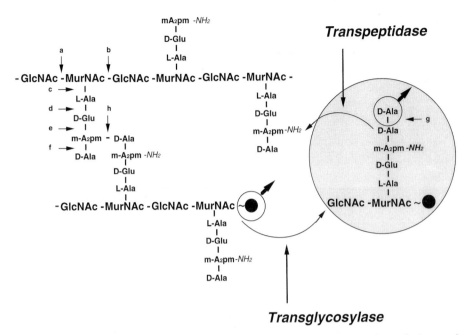

**Fig. 7.** Polymerization of the lipid intermediate II of *E. coli* by transglycosylation and transpeptidation. The black circles represent the undecarenyl pyrophosphate moiety. The lipid intermediate II is highlighted by a gray circle and the leaving groups of the polymerization reactions are encircled and marked with an arrow. The sites of action of specific murein hydrolases are indicated by small letters: a, *N*-acetylglucosaminidase; b, muramidase (lysozyme); c, *N*-acetylmuramyl-L-alanine amidase; d, L-alanyl-D-glutamyl-endopeptidase; e, D-glutamyl-L-diaminopimely-endopeptidase; f, LD-carboxypeptidase; g, DD-carboxypeptidase; h, DD-endopeptidase; GlcNAc, *N*-acetylglucosamine; MurNAc, *N*-acetylmuramic acid; A₂pm, *meso*-diaminopimelic acid.

ferase (MurG), GlcNAc is transferred from UDP-GlcNAc to lipid I to form the final murein precursor undecaprenyl-diphosphoryl-*N*-acetylmuramyl(pentapeptide)-*N*-acetylglucosamine, also called lipid intermediate II. Both translocase and transferase are bound to the inner side of the cytoplasmic membrane thus, the final murein precursor accumulates at the inner side of the membrane to which it is anchored via the undecaprenylphosphate moiety. To be available for insertion into the murein sacculus, the lipid-linked precursor has to be translocated across the cytoplasmic membrane. The antibiotic vancomycin interferes with this step by binding to the D-Ala–D-Ala terminus of the precursor. It is unlikely that a spontaneous flip-flop of the lipid intermediate II would be fast enough to match the rate of murein. Therefore, it is expected that the process is facilitated by auxiliary proteins.

## C. Insertion of Murein Precursors into the Wall

The murein disaccharide pentapeptide is inserted into the existing murein net by the formation of glycosidic and peptide bonds (Fig. 7). A transglycosylase first catalyzes the cleavage of the phosphodiester bond by which a nascent glycan strand is still linked to the undecaprenyl pyrophosphate and then catalyzes the transfer of the glycan strand onto the $C_4$ hydroxyl group of the GlcNAc residue of a lipid-linked disaccharide pentapeptide precursor. The glycolipid antibiotic moenomycin specifically inhibits the transglycosylation reaction. The released bactoprenol pyrophosphate is then processed to bactoprenol monophosphate in order to be accepted again by the translocase (Fig. 6). Bacitracin, an antibiotic that binds strongly to the bactoprenol pyrophosphate, inhibits the recycling of the lipid carrier. The formation of the cross-linkage of the peptide side chains to acceptor peptide side chains in the sacculus is catalyzed by a transpeptidase. Like transglycosylation, transpeptidation is also a two-step transferase reaction. First, the terminal D-Ala–D-Ala peptide bond of the pentapeptide precursor is cleaved, the terminal D-Ala is released, and a substrate–enzyme intermediate is formed. In a second reaction step the murein peptidyl moiety is transferred to a free amino group on an acceptor peptide side chain. As a consequence of transglycosylation and transpeptidation, the precursors are polymerized in two directions yielding the characteristic net structure of murein. Interestingly, in some bacteria, bifunctional enzymes combining a transglycosylase domain with a transpeptidase domain are responsible for the polymerization of the murein precursors.

Penicillin inhibits murein transpeptidases because of its analogy to the D-alanyl–D-alanine terminus of the murein precursor (Fig. 8A). The inhibition depends on the enzymatic interaction of the enzyme with the antibiotic. In analogy to the cleavage of the D-Ala–D-Ala bond (Fig. 7), the $\beta$-lactam ring is cleaved by the enzyme and a covalent substrate (penicilloyl)–enzyme intermediate is formed that involves a Ser in the catalytic site (Fig. 8B). This intermediate is inert and does not react further. Thus, the enzyme is blocked by the covalently linked penicillin molecule, which may be considered a "suicide substrate" for the transpeptidases. Not only the DD-transpeptidases but also other enzymes specifically recognizing D–D peptide bonds, including DD-carboxypeptidases and DD-endopeptidases, are penicillin-sensitive enzymes. These proteins are collectively referred to as penicillin-binding proteins (PBPs). Since inhibition of the PBPs by penicillin is due to the formation of a covalent enzyme–penicillin intermediate (Fig. 8), a simple assay allows the identification of all PBPs of a given strain. Incubation of whole cells or cell fractions with a labelled (e.g., radioactively) penicillin followed by sodium dodecyl sulfate (SDS)-polyacryl-

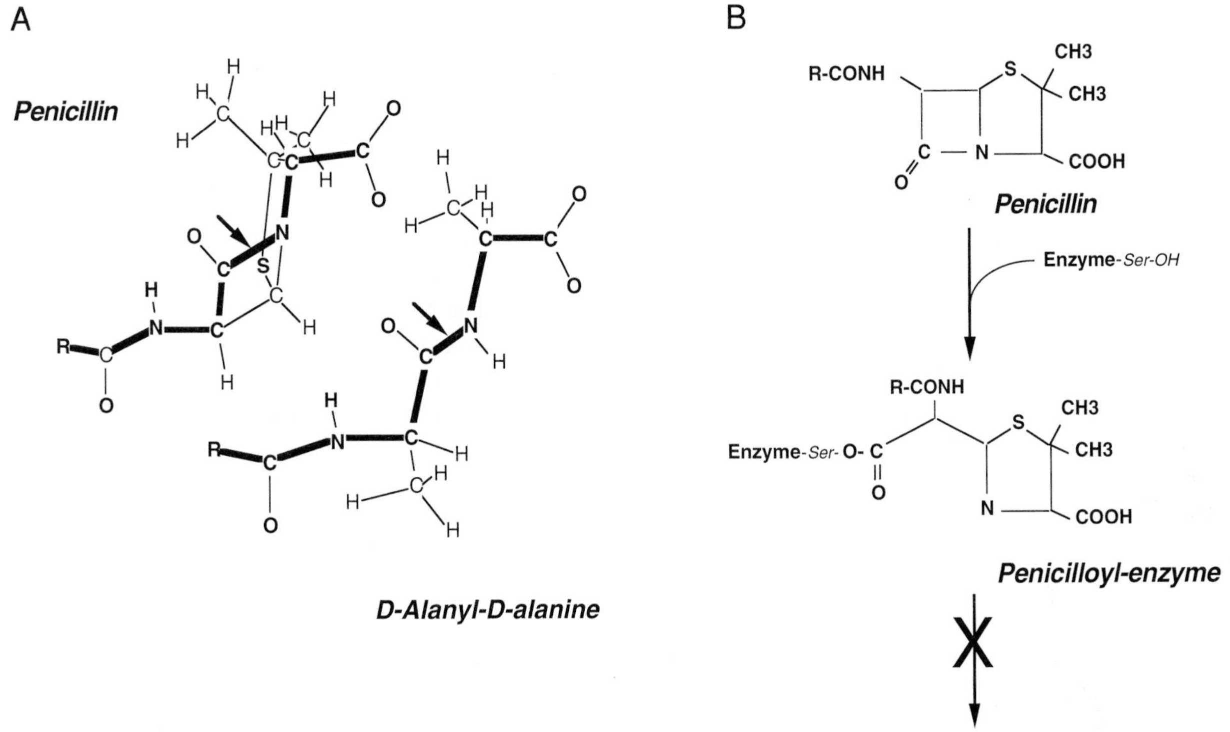

**Fig. 8.** (A) Structural analogy between penicillin and D-alanyl–D-alanine. The arrows indicate the bonds cleaved by penicillin-sensitive DD-transpeptidases, DD-endopeptidases, and DD-carboxypeptidases. (B) Formation of the penicilloyl–enzyme intermediate.

amide gel electrophoresis results in a species-specific PBP pattern.

## IV. ARCHITECTURE OF THE MUREIN SACCULUS

### A. Structure of Murein Sacculi

The cell wall can be isolated in the shape of the intact murein sacculus by boiling cells in 4% SDS. When inspected by electron microscopy the final sacculi preparation shows empty bag-shaped structures that reflects the shape of the cells from which they have been isolated. The murein structure (i.e., its composition of muropeptide subunits) can be analyzed by a complete hydrolysis of isolated murein sacculi using a muramidase, followed by separation of the products by reversed-phase high-pressure liquid chromatography.

X-ray diffraction data indicate that the disaccharide units in the strands are twisted in relation to one another, forming a four- to five-fold helix structure. As a result, the peptide moieties protrude alternatingly upwards, to the left, downwards, right, and so forth. This arrangement allows a strand to be cross-linked to both neighboring strands in one layer and strands in an upper and lower level, thus forming a perfect three-dimensional framework. The average length of the glycan strands can be calculated when the total number of disaccharide subunits and the number of reducing ends are known. For gram-positive bacteria, lengths between 40 and 80 units have been observed. The average length of the glycan strands in the gram-negative *E. coli* was found to be approximately 21 disaccharide units. For *E. coli* the length distribution could be determined by separating the glycan strands that were released from the sacculus by amidase treatment. The majority (70%) of the glycans were found to be short, with a length of approximately 7–9 disaccharide units.

The orientation of the glycan strands in the murein sacculus is still a matter of debate. In the case of rod-shaped bacteria, the glycan strands could either be running along the shorter circumference or arranged parallel to the long axis of the cell. A rhombic, "Chinese finger puzzle-like pattern" can also be en-visaged, and even a completely unordered structure cannot be discounted. Despite the lack of clear-cut experimental data, it is tempting to speculate that some kind of order must exist in order to facilitate (assist) the ordered growth of the shape-maintaining structure of the bacterium.

The murein structure is endowed with a great degree of flexibility. In particular, the peptide bridges can be stretched by a factor of four. By contrast, the glycan strands are quite stiff and show almost no elasticity. As a consequence, the sacculus can increase in surface when under stress and shrink when relaxing, as is the case for isolated murein sacculi.

### B. Barrier Function of Murein

Because of the latticework of murein the sacculus represents a molecular sieve for larger compounds. The smallest mesh, also called a tessera, in a systematically constructed murein latticework would have a length of a peptide bridge and a width of approximately four disaccharide units. Thus, in the case of *E. coli* it measures approximately $1-4 \times 4$ or 5 nm. The meshes in the net may not just form rectangles; due to the tension in the wall, they may be stretched into a honeycomb-like hexagon. The exclusion limit for the passage of molecules across the net has been determined *in vitro* to be approximately 50–60 kDa and to be almost the same for the multilayered murein of gram-positive and the thin murein of gram-negative bacteria. For bulky proteins with greater mass, murein is an effective barrier and therefore a localized opening of the murein net is a prerequisite for such molecules to pass through the sacculus. Consequently, the participation of specific murein hydrolases has been proposed for processes such as the export of bulky proteins (i.e., pili and flagellar assembly) and transfer of DNA during conjugation.

## V. BACTERIAL CELL WALL GROWTH

### A. Cell Wall Metabolizing Enzymes

The vast number of enzymes involved in murein metabolism reflects the complexity and importance of growth of the cell wall in bacteria. Different and distinct processes are involved. First, the biosynthetic pathway leads to the formation of activated murein precursor molecules. Second, the precursors are inserted into the preexisting murein sacculus. Due to the lattice structure of murein, a concerted action of murein hydrolases and synthases is needed in order to enlarge the surface of the sacculus. Depending on the mechanism employed, many bacteria release surprisingly large quantities of turnover products during growth (see Section III.D). Therefore, a third set of enzymes are specifically involved in degrading and trimming these valuable murein turnover products into structures suitable for recycling for *de novo* murein synthesis. Further complexity is added by the performance of two fundamental processes during growth of the bacterial cell wall: the general expansion of the surface (in the case of rod-shaped bacteria elongation of the cylindrical middle part) and subsequent formation of the septum (see Section V.B). Different enzyme systems seem to be responsible for these two processes. Due to the importance of the perfect execution of cell wall growth and division for cell viability, regulatory enzymes, backup enzymes, and repair enzymes are likely to be involved.

Specific enzymes exist that can cleave all covalent bonds in murein (indicated in Fig. 7). Glycosylases have only two specificities. *N*-acetylglucosaminidases cleave the β-1,-4 glycosidic bond between GlcNAc and MurNAc. Muramidases (lysozymes) split the β-1,-4 glycosidic bond between MurNAc and GlcNAc. A unique type of muramidase, called lytic transglycosylase, combines the cleavage of the glycosidic bond with a concomitant formation of a 1–6-anhydro ring at the released muramic acid residue (see Fig. 3).

Because so many different peptide bonds are present in murein, the number of peptidases is correspondingly high. *N*-acetylmuramyl-L-alanine amidases cleave the amide bond between the lactyl group of the MurNAc and the L-Ala of the peptide side chain. DD-Endopeptidases specifically hydrolyze the bridging peptide bond between the D-Ala of one peptide and the D-center of the dibasic amino acid of another peptide. Whereas DD-endopeptidases are penicillin sensitive (see Section III.C), LD-endopeptidases that specifically hydrolyze the LD-peptide bonds

are not inhibited by most β-lactams. DD-Carboxypeptidases remove the terminal D-Ala residue from pentapeptides and LD-carboxypeptidases split off the D-Ala residue in position 4. DD-Carboxypeptidases are sensitive towards β-lactam antibiotics however, LD-carboxypeptidases are inhibited only by β-lactams that carry a D-amino acid in their side chains, such as nocardicin A and cephalosprin C.

With the exception of the carboxypeptidases, murein hydrolases that cleave bonds in the murein sacculus are potentially autolytic enzymes and are thus also referred to as autolysins. Although potentially suicidal, these enzymes are essential for growth. Cleavage of bonds in the preexisting murein net by hydrolases that allows the insertion of new subunits is a prerequisite for the enlargement of the latticework. In addition, cell separation depends on the splitting of the murein septum by murein hydrolases. It is this group of autolysins that is responsible for antibiotic-induced bacteriolysis. The mechanisms that control the murein hydrolases are not fully understood.

## B. Growth and Division of the Murein Sacculus

Growth and division of the murein sacculus are a risky enterprise since the stress-bearing structure that is essential for the cell's integrity has to be enlarged and split into two daughter sacculi. These operations have to be executed while maintaining both the mechanical strength of the wall and the specific shape of the cell. Whereas shape maintenance remains poorly understood, the mechanical stability of the wall during growth is thought to be preserved by a mechanism that enlarges the sacculus by an inside-to-outside growth mechanism. Accordingly, new material is first hooked in a relaxed state underneath the existing stress-bearing layers of the wall and, in a second step, is exposed to stress by the cleavage of critical bonds in the old material; this is a strategy called "make-before-break." This mechanism may even result in the release of old material from the sacculus, a phenomenon known as murein turnover. Growth of the thin, mostly monolayered murein of gram-negative bacteria is a far more delicate process. Therefore, it very likely also follows the safe make-before-break strategy. One model proposes that first a murein triplet (i.e., three cross-linked glycan strands) is covalently attached to the cross bridges on both sides of a so-called docking strand of the murein layer under tension. Specific removal of the docking strand by the action of murein hydrolases provokes insertion of the murein triplet into the stress-bearing sacculus.

Growth of spherical bacteria (i.e., cocci) occurs exclusively at the equator of the cell, the future site of cell division (Fig. 9). The role of the FtsZ protein in placing the division site at the midpoint of the

cell is discussed elsewhere. New material is added in a sharp growth zone to the leading edge of the nascent cross wall. Splitting and peeling apart of the newly added murein results in the material being pushed outwards, thereby causing an increase in the surface of the coccus. The newly synthesized wall is then strengthened by the attachment of additional murein (thickening). Inhibition of the splitting process blocks further pushing outwards of the added material but triggers annularly closing of the cross wall. On completion of the cross wall, a precise cutting of the septum that may involve murosomes (lytic enzymes wrapped into vesicles) allows for cell separation. Murein turnover appears not to occur in gram-positive cocci.

In rod-shaped bacteria the sites of wall growth alternate during the cell cycle (Fig. 10). First, the sacculus is elongated while strictly maintaining the diameter. This process occurs as a result of incorporation of new material all over the cylindrical part of the wall, with the poles being metabolically silent.

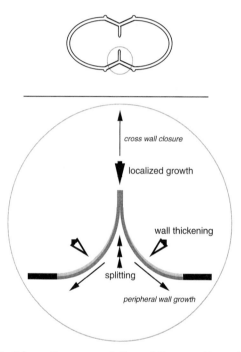

**Fig. 9.** Schematic representation of the growth modus of cocci. The encircled area of a dividing coccus (top) is shown in detail (bottom). The large, solid arrowhead indicates the addition of new material at the leading edge of the septum. The group of three small arrowheads marks the site of action of the murein hydrolases that split the newly added material. As a result, the material is pushed outwards, thereby increasing the surface of the two daughter hemispheres. The two open arrowheads point to the thickening process of the newly formed peripheral wall. Arrows indicate the two processes of peripheral wall enlarging and centripetal cross-wall extension. Old peptidoglycan is shown in black, newly synthesized material in gray, and the murein added during the thickening process in light gray (modified from Higgins and Shockman, 1976).

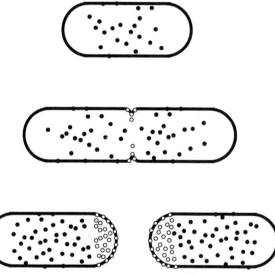

**Fig. 10.** Schematic representation of the growth modus of rod-shaped bacteria. Solid circles represent the random insertion of new material into the cylindrical part of the cell during cell elongation. Note that the diameter of the cell does not change. Open circles represent incorporation of new material in a zonal growth zone at the site of cell division. As a result, the new polar caps formed after cell division are exclusively made of murein synthesized in the growth zone.

The growth mechanism is also different from that of cocci because it gives rise to an enormous amount of murein turnover. Almost 50% of the murein is released from the sacculus per generation. In the case of gram-positive bacteria the material newly added to the cylindrical part of the rod is passed on step by step from the inner layers to the outermost layers from where it is finally removed by murein hydrolases. In the case of gram-negative bacteria, it may be the release of the docking strands that is responsible for murein turnover. Septum formation involves a switch to localized incorporation of new material at the equator of the cell, which is defined by the FtsZ protein that forms a ring structure at the site of cell division.

## Acknowledgment

I thank David Edwards for a critical reading of the manuscript.

## See Also the Following Articles

AMINO ACID FUNCTION AND SYNTHESIS • CELL MEMBRANE: STRUCTURE AND FUNCTION

## Bibliography

Archibald, A. R., Hancock, I. C., and Harwood, C. R. (1993). Cell envelope. *In* "*Bacillus subtilis* and Other Gram-Positive Bacteria" (A. L. Sonensheim, J. A. Hoch, and R. Losick, Eds.). ASM Press, Washington, DC.

Ghuysen, J.-M., and Hakenbeck, R. (1994). Bacterial cell wall. *In* "New Comprehensive Biochemistry Vol. 27" (A. Neuberger and L. L. M. van Deenen, Eds.). Elsevier, Amsterdam.

Higgins, M. L., and Shockman, G. D. (1976). Study of a cycle of cell wall assembly in *Streptococcus faecalis* by three-dimensional reconstructions of thin sections of cells. *J. Bacteriol.* **127**, 1346–1358.

Höltje, J.-V. (1998). Growth of the stress-bearing and shape-maintaining murein sacculus of *Escherichia coli*. *Microbiol. Mol. Biol. Rev.* **62**, 181–203.

Koch, A. L. (1995). "Bacterial Growth and Form." Chapman & Hall, New York.

Nanninga, N. (1998). Morphogenesis of *Escherichia coli*. *Microbiol. Mol. Biol. Rev.* **62**, 110–129.

Park, J. T. (1996). The murein sacculus. *In* "*Escherichia coli* and *Salmonella*" (F. C. Neidhardt *et al.*, Eds.), pp. 48–57. ASM Press, Washington, DC.

Rogers, H. J., Perkins, H. R., and Ward, J. B. (1980). "Microbial Cell Walls and Membranes." Chapman & Hall, London.

Schleifer, K. H., and Kandler, O. (1972). Peptidoglycan types of bacterial cell walls and their taxonomic implications. *Bacteriol. Rev.* **36**, 407–477.

Shockman, G. D., and Barret, J. F. (1983). Structure, function and assembly of cell walls of gram-positive bacteria. *Annu. Rev. Microbiol.* **37**, 501–527.

# *Chemotaxis*

## Jeff Stock and Sandra Da Re

*Princeton University*

I. Response Strategy
II. Genetics of Bacterial Behavior
III. Role of Protein Methylation in Adaptation
IV. Mechanism of Signal Transduction in Chemotaxis
V. Phylogenetic Variations

## GLOSSARY

**adaptation**   The return to a preset behavioral state following a response to an altered environmental condition.

**attractant**   A chemical that causes a positive chemotaxis response.

**excitation**   A behavioral response.

**information**   A significant perturbation in a signal transduction system.

**intelligence**   The ability to respond successfully to a new situation.

**learning**   The acquisition of altered sensibilities from previous experience.

**memory**   An internal record of past experience.

**receptor**   A protein that specifically interacts with a particular stimulus to generate a signal that leads to a cellular response.

**repellent**   A chemical that causes a negative chemotaxis response.

**sensing**   The acquisition of information.

**CHEMOTAXIS** in microbiology refers to the migration of cells toward attractant chemicals or away from repellents. Virtually every motile organism exhibits some type of chemotaxis. The chemotaxis responses of eukaryotic microorganisms proceed by mechanisms that are shared by all cells in the eukaryotic kingdom and generally involve the regulation of microtubule-

and/or microfilament-based cytoskeletal elements. In this article, we will be concerned only with bacterial chemotaxis.

All bacteria share a conserved set of just six different regulatory proteins that serve to direct cell motion toward favorable environmental conditions. The same regulatory system operates irrespective of whether motility involves one or several flagella, or whether it occurs by a mechanism such as gliding motility that does not involve flagella. The same basic system mediates responses to a wide range of different chemicals including nutrients such as amino acids, peptides, and sugars (which are usually attractants) and toxic compounds such as phenol and acid (generally repellents). The same proteins also mediate responses to oxygen (aerotaxis), temperature (thermotaxis), osmotic pressure (osmotaxis), and light (phototaxis). As a bacterium moves it continuously monitors a spectrum of sensory inputs and uses this information to direct motion toward conditions that are optimal for growth and survival. To accomplish this task, the chemotaxis system has developed molecular correlates of processes such as memory and learning that are widely associated with sensory motor regulation by higher neural systems.

## I. RESPONSE STRATEGY

### A. Biased Random Walk

In a constant environment, motile bacteria generally move in a random walk of straight runs punctuated by brief periods of reversal that serve to randomize the direction of the next run. The chemotaxis system functions by controlling the probability of a reversal. If, during a run, the system determines that conditions are improving, then it sends a signal to the motor that suppresses reversals so that the cell tends to keep moving in the preferred direction. If, on the other hand, the system determines that conditions are getting worse, then it sends a signal for the motor to change direction. The effect is to bias the random walk so that cells tend to migrate toward attractants and away from repellents (Fig. 1). Thus, bacterial chemotaxis is effected by the simple strategy of using environmental cues to modulate the probability of random changes in direction. By using this mechanism, individual cells never have to determine in which direction they want to move. Instead, they simply determine whether they want to continue on course or change direction. The biased random walk strategy is essential to bacterial chemotaxis because it provides a mechanism whereby bacteria can direct their motion despite the fact that bacterial cells are far too small to have a sense of direction.

## B. Temporal Sensing and Memory

Bacterial cells are generally only a few micrometers long. This is too small to possibly measure differences in attractant or repellent concentration over the length of their bodies. In the early 1970s, through the work of Macnab, Koshland, Berg, and others, it

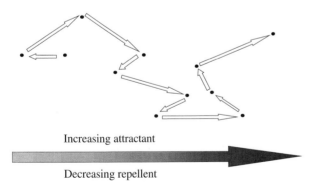

Increasing attractant

Decreasing repellent

**Fig. 1.** Chemotaxis is accomplished by a biased random walk mechanism. Bacterial swimming behavior involves a series of runs (indicated by arrows) punctuated by motor reversals that randomize the direction of the subsequent run. Cells migrate toward attractants and away from repellents by increasing their average run lengths in the preferred direction.

was shown that bacteria solve this problem by sensing changes in attractant and repellent concentration in time rather than in space. In other words, chemotaxis depends on a temporal rather than a spatial sensing mechanism. As a cell moves it constantly compares its current surroundings to those it has experienced previously. If the comparison is favorable, the cell tends to keep going; if not, it tends to change direction. This mechanism implies a memory function whereby the present can be compared with the past to determine whether conditions are getting better or worse as time (and movement in a given direction) proceeds.

## C. Excitation and Adaptation

One of the ways it was shown that bacterial chemotaxis works by a temporal rather than spatial sensing mechanism was to suddenly transfer a population of randomly moving bacteria from one spatially uniform environment into another that contained a uniform distribution of an attractant or repellent chemical. In this type of experiment there are no spatial gradients; cells are exposed only to a temporal change in their environment. As expected from a temporal sensing mechanism, when cells are suddenly exposed to attractants the entire population determines that it is on a good course and the tendency to change direction is uniformly suppressed (Fig. 2a). The opposite effect is seen when cells are suddenly exposed to repellents. All the individuals in the population, despite the fact that they are moving many different ways, suddenly determine that they need to change the direction of their motion. This result clearly shows that bacteria must have a way of comparing the past with the present—they must have memory.

After a period of time, bacteria that have been transferred to a new environment gradually adapt so that their behavior returns precisely to the same random walk as that before they were exposed to the attractant or repellent stimulus. This occurs despite the fact that the attractant or repellent is still present. Thus, bacteria do not respond to absolute concentrations of attractant and repellent chemicals. They respond only to changes.

There is a close relationship between memory and adaptation. If one moves a population of bacteria

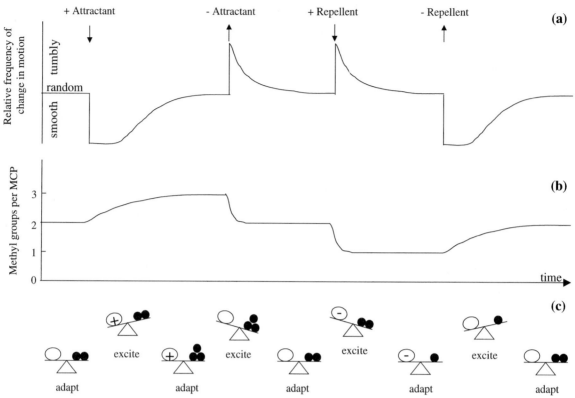

**Fig. 2.** Excitation and adaptation in bacterial chemotaxis. (a) Addition of attractant causes cells to continue swimming smoothly without changing direction until they adapt back to their prestimulus random behavior, removal of attractant causes cells to frequently change direction or tumble until adaptation restores random behavior, adding repellent causes the same tumbling response as removing attractant, and removing repellent causes the same swimming response as adding attractant. (b) In the absence of attractants or repellents a typical MCP has approximately two of four possible methylated glutamates, addition of a saturating attractant stimulus causes addition of approximately one methyl group, removal of the attractant causes loss of this group, addition of a saturating repellent stimulus causes loss of one more methyl groups, and removal of repellent causes addition of a methyl group. (c) MCP signaling depends on the balance between stimulus (O, no stimulus; +, attractant; −, repellent) and the level of methylation (●, one methyl group; ●●, two methyl groups, etc). A sudden change in stimulus causes an imbalance that leads to excitation, and the level of methylation then changes to restore the balance.

that has adapted to an environment with an attractant back to an environment lacking attractant, the cells think they are moving in a bad direction so they all change course as if they had been exposed to a repellent. The opposite happens with cells that are adapted to a repellent. Thus, an increase in attractant concentration is equivalent to a decrease in repellent concentration and vice versa.

In bacterial chemotaxis, the sense and degree of excitation in response to a new place in time are only determined in relation to the memory of the old one, with the memory for the past environment being set by the process of adapting to it. In effect,

there must be two core mechanisms at work in chemotaxis: an excitation mechanism that controls the probability of a motor reversal and an adaptation mechanism that modulates the sense and degree of excitation with respect to a preset default value.

## II. GENETICS OF BACTERIAL BEHAVIOR

### A. Chemotaxis Mutants

The most common strategy that has been used to isolate mutants that are defective in chemotaxis has involved selecting for cells that cannot swarm from a colony inoculated into the center of a dish filled with semisolid nutrient agar. Chemotactic cells form a colony at the point where they are initially inoculated, and the growing cells consume nutrients in the culture media creating attractant gradients that cause them to swarm outward from the center. Mutant cells that are deficient in chemotaxis are left behind at the center. This strategy produces several different classes of mutant strains. By far the most common are strains that are not motile. In bacteria whose motility depends on flagella, these nonmotile strains can be subdivided into two classes: Fla mutants, which have lost the ability to make flagella, and Mot mutants, which make flagella that are paralyzed. Mutant strains that are unable to swarm but are fully motile are categorized into two additional subclasses: Che mutants, which are generally nonchemotactic, and blind mutants, which are unable to swarm in semisolid agar with one type of nutrient but can swarm normally in agar that contains other nutrients.

## B. Genetic Analysis of *Escherichia coli* Chemoreceptors

It was through the selection and characterization of blind mutants from *E. coli* that Julius Adler and colleagues first demonstrated that chemosensing in bacteria is mediated by specific receptors in the cell envelope rather than by some other mechanism such as nutrient utilization. The first chemoreceptors to be identified genetically were the galactose and ribose binding proteins that had previously been shown to function in the transport of their respective sugar ligands. The selection of ribose and galactose transport mutants with normal chemosensing abilities established that uptake and metabolism were not required for chemotaxis. Further genetic analysis indicated that ribose and galactose sensing required another component, termed Trg (taxis to ribose and galactose). Early work on the ribose and galactose receptors revealed another important aspect of chemotaxis—the possibility that bacterial cells could exhibit a simple form of learning. The galactose and ribose receptors are specifically induced by growth in the presence of galactose and ribose, respectively. Thus, whereas a naive cell is unable to respond to

either sugar, once it is allowed to grow on ribose or galactose the corresponding receptor is induced and the cell has now learned to respond to that sugar.

In addition to the sugar receptors, Adler's group identified two *E. coli* genes, *tar* and *tsr,* that were required for responses to amino acids and several repellents. Tar was required for sensing of the attractants aspartate, glutamate, and maltose and the repellents cobalt and nickel. The maltose response also required an inducible maltose binding protein similar to the ribose and galactose binding proteins that had been shown to be mediated by Trg. Tsr was required for chemotaxis to serine, alanine, and several other amino acids and repellents. In contrast to the genes that encode binding proteins, *tar, tsr,* and *trg* are expressed in the same regulon as the flagellar genes of *E. coli* so that as long as a cell is motile it can sense aspartate and serine.

## C. Che Genes

The principal task of analyzing the *E. coli* Che mutants fell to a former colleague of Adler's, John S. Parkinson, who determined that there were two major Che complementation groups in *E. coli*, designated *cheA* and *cheB*. Later studies by Parkinson and others established that the CheA locus was composed of two genes (*cheA* and *cheW*), whereas the CheB locus was composed of four genes (*cheR, cheB, cheY,* and *cheZ*). Strains defective in *cheA, cheW, cheY,* or *cheR* exhibited a smooth swimming phenotype, never changing their direction of motion. In contrast, *cheB* and *cheZ* mutants had a constantly changing, tumbly pattern of swimming behavior. Whereas the ability of *cheB* and *cheZ* mutants to change direction was still suppressed by the addition of attractants, and *cheR* mutants could still reverse in response to repellent stimuli; *cheW, cheA,* and *cheY* mutants were completely unresponsive. From these results Parkinson was able to conclude that the CheW, CheA, and CheY proteins were essential for excitation, whereas CheR, CheB, and CheZ were involved in adaptation (for a summary of the Che genes and their protein products see Table I). The fact that mutants defective in excitation were invariably smooth swimming suggested that the excitation mechanism produced a signal that caused a change in the direction of mo-

### TABLE I
### E. coli Che Genes

| Gene | Protein $M_r$ (kDa) | Function |
|------|------|----------|
| cheR | 32 | Methylation of MCPs |
| cheB | 36 | Demethylation of MCPs |
| cheW | 18 | Coupling CheA to MCPs |
| cheA | 73 | Histidine kinase |
| cheY | 14 | CheY-P binds to flagellar switch to cause change in swimming direction |
| cheZ | 24 | CheY-P phosphatase |

tion, and that in the absence of this hypothetical signal the cell would rarely, if ever, change its direction.

## III. ROLE OF PROTEIN METHYLATION IN ADAPTATION

### A. Methionine Requirement for Chemotaxis

One of the most important discoveries from Adler's pioneering work on the E. coli chemotaxis system was the serendipitous finding that methionine was required for chemotaxis. In his initial characterization of E. coli chemotaxis, Adler employed an assay that had first been developed in the late nineteenth century by the great German microbiologist and botanist, Pfeffer. This method, called a capillary assay, simply involves placing the tip of a glass capillary tube that contains an attractant chemical into a suspension of bacteria. As the attractant diffuses from the capillary tip, an attractant gradient is established which the cells follow up into the capillary tube. After about 1 hr the capillary is withdrawn and the bacteria inside are counted to provide a measure of the chemotaxis response. Unlike with swarming on semisolid agar, capillary assays do not require cell growth, and they are generally performed with cells suspended in a defined buffer solution. Adler observed that when he performed this type of assay with a mutant E. coli strain that required methionine for growth, the chemotaxis responses to attractants

were generally depressed. Among all the amino acids, this effect was specific for methionine. Further analysis showed that as cells became starved for methionine they lost the ability to adapt so that addition of attractants such as aspartate or serine caused a smooth swimming behavior similar to that observed with cheR mutants.

### B. Methylaccepting Chemotaxis Proteins

Subsequent studies established that the effect of methionine depletion stemmed from a requirement for the universal methyl donor, S-adenosylmethionine (AdoMet), which is produced from methionine and ATP through the action of AdoMet synthase:

$$\text{ATP} + \text{methionine} \rightarrow \text{AdoMet} + \text{PP}_i + \text{P}_i$$

AdoMet is required for the methylation of a wide range of different macromolecules, including proteins, DNA, and RNA, as well as numerous different small molecules. It was shown that in chemotaxis the requirement for AdoMet is to methylate a set of ~60-kDa membrane proteins that were termed methylaccepting chemotaxis proteins (MCPs). These proteins were identified with the products of genes such as tar, tsr, and trg that had been implicated in chemosensing. In fact, Tar and Tsr were shown to bind aspartate and serine, respectively, and to act directly as the membrane receptors for these attractants. Trg, on the other hand, acts indirectly as a receptor for ribose and galactose through interactions with the corresponding periplasmic binding proteins. Furthermore, maltose is detected by Tar via the periplasmic maltose binding protein. Thus, each MCP can detect several different stimuli either by binding a stimulatory ligand directly or through indirect interactions that are mediated by periplasmic binding proteins.

Methylation studies, analyses with anti-MCP antibodies, and, most important, DNA sequencing have shown that the MCPs are a large and highly conserved family of proteins that are invariably associated with bacterial chemosensing. There are five different MCPs encoded in the E. coli genome (Fig. 3), including Tar, Tsr, and Trg as well as a sensor for cellular redox potential termed Aer that is responsi-

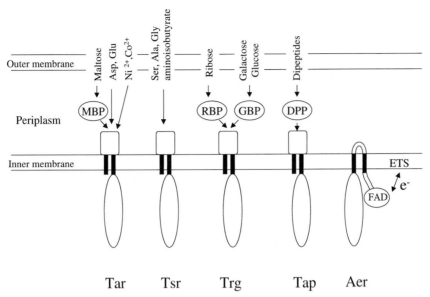

**Fig. 3.** *Escherichia coli* chemoreceptors. There are five MCP receptors in *E. coli:* Tar, Tsr, Trg, Tap, and Aer. These transmembrane proteins either bind stimulatory ligands directly or interact with ligand-bound periplasmic binding proteins (MBP, maltose binding protein; RBP, ribose binding protein; GBP, galactose binding protein; DPP, dipeptide binding protein). Aer differs from other MCPs in that it has an intracytoplasmic sensing domain with an associated flavin cofactor, FAD. It is thought that Aer senses cellular oxidative potential through redox interactions with the electron transport system in the membrane.

ble for aerotaxis and a receptor that mediates responses to dipeptides termed Tap. Chemotaxis systems in other species of bacteria have an equivalent or larger number of different MCPs.

## C. Structural and Functional Organization of Sensing and Signaling Domains of Receptor MCPs

The MCPs are the principal sensory receptors of the bacterial chemotaxis system. They have a structural organization, membrane topology, and mode of function that is typical of type I receptors in all cells, including important vertebrate type I receptors such as the insulin, growth hormone, and cytokine receptors. In recent years, the Tar protein from *Salmonella typhimurium* has emerged as both the archetypal MCP and as a model to understand general principles of type I receptor function. Tar has the typical membrane topology of a type I receptor with an N-terminal extracytoplasmic sensing domain connected via a hydrophobic membrane-spanning sequence to an intracellular signaling domain. The sensing and signaling domains can function independently of the membrane and independently of one another. Most MCPs have this structural organization. Sequence comparisons indicate that, as one might expect, the extracytoplasmic sensing domains tend to be highly variable, whereas the cytoplasmic signaling domains, which interact with the Che proteins, are highly conserved. In fact, the tools of genetic engineering have been used to construct several different hybrid receptors with one MCP's sensing domain connected to another's signaling domain. In every case the hybrids exhibit sensory specificities equivalent to those of the MCP that contributed the N-terminal portion.

The sensory and signaling domains can also be produced as independent soluble protein fragments. This approach has been used with many type I receptors to produce protein fragments that are free of the membrane and can therefore be much more easily crystallized for X-ray diffraction studies. Determination of the X-ray crystal structure of the sensing domain of Tar in the presence and absence of aspartate revealed a dimer of two $\alpha$-helical bundles with aspartate binding at the subunit interface.

The structure of the signaling domain has not been defined in detail, but it too is predominantly $\alpha$-helical. The signaling domain is composed of a highly conserved central region that binds the CheW and CheA proteins and thereby connects the receptor to the remainder of the chemotaxis signal transduction system. This region is flanked on both sides by methylated $\alpha$-helices that together contain four or more potential sites of glutamate methylation and demethylation. Attractants cause increases in the level of methylation and repellents cause decreases. These changes are responsible for adaptation to attractant and repellent stimuli (Fig. 2b).

## D. Receptor Methylation Enzymology

The MCP receptors are methyl esterified at several specific glutamate residues. The methylation reaction is catalyzed by an AdoMet-dependent methyltransferase encoded by the *cheR* gene. Receptor methyl groups are removed through the action of a specific methyl esterase encoded by the *cheB* gene. CheR and CheB are both soluble monomeric proteins. Their structures have recently been determined by X-ray crystallographic methods. CheR is tethered to Tar and Tsr via a tight interaction with the C-terminal four amino acids, which are identical in these two MCPs but are absent in Trg, Tap, and Aer. Tar and Tsr are present in cells at about 10-fold higher levels than Trg, Tap, and Aer, and considerable evidence suggests that the latter, so-called minor receptors, function in higher order complexes with the major receptors, Tar and Tsr. CheR tethering to major receptors puts the enzyme in position to methylate the associated minor receptors.

The active site of CheB contains a Ser–His–Asp catalytic triad that is characteristic of serine hydrolases. An N-terminal regulatory domain occludes the active site so that the enzyme is relatively inactive. CheB is activated to remove receptor methyl groups by the same signal that causes a change in the direction of cell movement in response to repellent stimuli. This provides a feedback mechanism that contributes to the adaptive phase of the chemotaxis response. Thus, repellent addition or attractant removal produce an excitatory signal to change direction. At the same time, this signal activates CheB, leading to a rapid decrease in the level of methylation that causes adaptation. The converse is true with attractant addition or repellent removal. It is as if the receptor signaling system functions as a balance between the effects of stimulatory ligands and methylation (Fig. 2c). Addition of attractant or repellent offsets the balance to produce a positive or negative excitatory signal, and changes in methylation restore the balance to effect adaptation.

## IV. MECHANISM OF SIGNAL TRANSDUCTION IN CHEMOTAXIS

### A. Receptor–CheW–CheA Signaling Complexes

The CheA protein is a kinase that binds ATP and catalyzes the phosphorylation of one of its own histidine residues. The rate of autophosphorylation of the isolated CheA protein is very slow. The physiologically relevant form of CheA seems to be in a stable complex with CheW and the MCP receptors. The rate of CheA autophosphorylation in these receptor-signaling complexes can be elevated at least 100-fold or completely inhibited depending on the level of receptor methylation and the binding of stimulatory ligands. Attractants such as serine or aspartate have an inhibitory effect, whereas increased levels of methylation cause dramatic increases in kinase activity. Because of the dimeric nature of the receptor sensing domain and the fact that CheA is a dimer, it was assumed that the receptor–CheW–CheA signaling complex had a 2:2:2 stoichiometry. Recent results indicate a much more complex architecture, with the thousands of receptors in a cell clustering together in a higher order complex with CheW and CheA (Levit *et al.*, 1998). It has been hypothesized that packing interactions within these signaling arrays function to control kinase activity in response to the binding of stimulatory ligands or changes in the level of receptor methylation.

## B. Motor Regulation and Feedback Control

The level of phosphorylation of the CheY protein controls the probability that a cell will change its direction of motion. CheY is a 14-kDa monomeric enzyme that catalyzes the transfer of a phosphoryl group from the phosphohistidine in CheA to one of its own aspartate residues. CheY phosphorylation induces a conformational change in the protein that causes it to bind to switching proteins at the flagellar motor. Repellent-induced increases in the rate of CheA phosphorylation produce elevated levels of phospho-CheY that bind to the motor to enhance the probability of motor reversal. Phospho-CheY spontaneously dephosphorylates to terminate the response. In *E. coli* this autophosphatase reaction is dramatically enhanced by the CheZ protein. Thus, addition of attractants inhibits CheA autophosphorylation, and CheZ activity leads to a rapid decrease in the level of phospho-CheY, a reduction in the level of phospho-CheY bound to the motor, and a decrease in the probability that a cell will change direction.

The CheY protein is homologous to the regulatory domain of the CheB protein and, like CheY, the regulatory domain of CheB acts to transfer phosphoryl groups from the phosphohistidine in CheA to one of its own aspartate residues. Phosphorylation of CheB causes a dramatic increase in demethylation activity that leads to a decrease in receptor methyla-

tion and a concomitant decrease in the rate of CheA autophosphorylation. Thus, the same mechanism that acts to produce a motor response feeds back to cause adaptation. The signal transduction mechanism that mediates *E. coli* chemotaxis is summarized in Fig. 4.

## V. PHYLOGENETIC VARIATIONS

Most of our understanding of bacterial chemotaxis has come from studies of the system in *E. coli*. Other motile bacteria that have been investigated have MCPs and all the same Che proteins as those in the *E. coli* system except for CheZ, which has only been found in enterics. There appear to be a number of variations on the *E. coli* scheme, however. Studies in *Bacillus subtilis* indicate that in this species the system is reversed so that attractants activate CheA, and CheY phosphorylation suppresses the tendency for the cell to change direction. The *B. subtilis* system also appears to have additional components that are not found in *E. coli*.

Many species have several copies of one or more of the chemotaxis genes. In some instances, it is apparent that there are multiple chemotaxis systems functioning in different cell types. The best example of this is provided by *Myxococcus xanthus*, in which different systems operate at different stages of development to control different types of motility. In con-

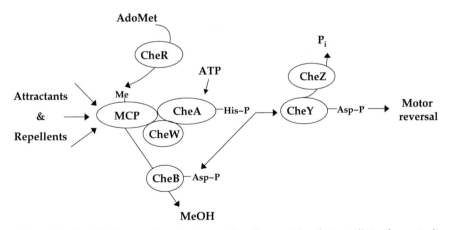

**Fig. 4.** Biochemical interactions between the Che proteins that mediate chemotaxis responses in *E. coli*.

trast, two CheY proteins in *Rhodobacter sphaeroides* seem to supply divergent functions in one signal transduction network. One CheY interacts with the motor to control swimming behavior, whereas the other CheY functions as a CheA phosphatase to drain phosphoryl groups out of the system.

The chemotaxis system seems to be eubacterial in origin. There is no evidence for any of the chemotaxis components in eukaryotic cells. Although homologous systems are found in archaea such as *Halobacterium salinarum* and *Archaeoglobus fulgidus,* the sequences of the component proteins are so closely related to those of *B. subtilis* that one can be fairly certain that they originated by lateral transfer from a *B. subtilis* relative.

## See Also the Following Articles

*Bacillus subtilis*, Genetics • *Escherichia coli*, General Biology • Flagella

## Bibliography

Adler, J. (1975). Chemotaxis in bacteria. *Annu. Rev. Biochem.* **44**, 341–356.

Berg, H. C., and Brown, D. A. (1972). Chemotaxis in *Escherichia coli* analysed by three-dimensional tracking. *Nature* **239**, 500–504.

Djordjevic, S., and Stock, A. M. (1998). Structural analysis of bacterial chemotaxis proteins: Components of a dynamic signaling system. *J. Struct. Biol.* **124**, 189–200.

Levit, M. N., Liu, Y., and Stock, J. B. (1998). Stimulus response coupling in bacterial chemotaxis: Receptor dimers in signalling arrays. *Mol. Microbiol.* **30**, 459–466.

Macnab, R. M., and Koshland, D. E., Jr. (1972). The gradient-sensing mechanism in bacterial chemotaxis. *Proc. Natl. Acad. Sci. USA* **69**, 2509–2512.

Milburn, M. V., Prive, G. G., Milligan, D. L., Scott, W. G., Yeh, J., Jancarik, J., Koshland, D. E., Jr., and Kim, S. H. (1991). Three-dimensional structures of the ligand-binding domain of the bacterial aspartate receptor with and without a ligand. *Science* **254**, 1342–1347.

Parkinson, J. S. (1977). Behavioral genetics in bacteria. *Annu. Rev. Genet* **11**, 397–414.

Springer, M. S., Goy, M. F., and Adler, J. (1979). Protein methylation in behavioural control mechanisms and in signal transduction. *Nature* **280**, 279–284.

Stock, J. B., and Surette, M. G. (1996). Chemotaxis. *In* "*Escherichia coli* and *Salmonella:* Cellular and Molecular Biology" (F. C. Neidhardt, Ed.), pp. 1103–1129. ASM Press, Washington, DC.

# Chlamydia

## Jane E. Raulston and Priscilla B. Wyrick

*University of North Carolina School of Medicine*

## GLOSSARY

**elementary bodies (EB)** Infectious, extracellular chlamydial forms that are metabolically inert and unable to grow and divide.

**inclusion** The unique intracellular, membrane-enclosed organelle that supports the growth of chlamydia.

**reticulate bodies (RB)** Noninfectious, intracellular chlamydial forms that grow and divide by binary fission.

**zoonoses** The transmission of infectious agents from animals or birds to humans, resulting in disease.

**THE CHLAMYDIA** are small, coccoid eubacteria that can grow only within eucaryotic cells. All isolates are pathogenic and are highly adapted for infection within a certain mammalian or avian host. Because the chlamydiae grow slowly within their natural host, actual disease syndromes often do not materialize until much later in the infectious process. Much of the eventual damage to tissues is mediated by the host's own immune response. This clever strategy of prolonging the health of the infected host and, thus, ensuring their continued propagation and transmission means that the chlamydiae are among the most insidious pathogenic bacteria.

## I. TAXONOMY

Although accurate descriptions of chlamydial infections were recorded as early as 1500 B.C., it was only as recently as 1957 that these organisms were first isolated *in vitro* by growth within embryonated eggs and confirmed as bacteria rather than protozoa or viruses. Since this time, all isolates have been traditionally grouped within a single order, Chlamydiales, a single family, Chlamydiaceae, and a single genus, *Chlamydia*. The reader should be aware that present, ongoing molecular analyses may lead to a reclassification within Chlamydiaceae in the near future that will be more definitive and reflective of the diversity of these organisms. At present, there are four designated species: *C. trachomatis, C. pneumoniae, C. psittaci,* and *C. pecorum*. Humans are the predominant natural hosts for the first two species, whereas a variety of hosts, including humans, can become infected by the latter two species.

Isolates of *C. trachomatis* are well known as the most common cause of bacterial sexually transmitted infections worldwide, but were first identified as the agents of the blinding eye disease, trachoma. *C. trachomatis* is subdivided into four biological variants based on the associated disease syndrome. Biovariant trachoma includes (1) serovariants A through C that cause trachoma and (2) serovariants D through K that cause sexually transmitted infections most common to developed countries, such as the United States, Canada, and Western Europe. Biovariant Lymphogranuloma venereum (LGV) includes three serovariants (L1, L2, and L3) that elicit an invasive sexually transmitted disease syndrome more common to underdeveloped or developing countries. The third biovariant contains a single murine isolate termed mouse pneumonitis (MoPn) and a fourth biovariant encompasses isolates from swine. The other species of *Chlamydia* have not been serotyped to this extent, but it is clear that at least four subdivisions exist within *C. psittaci* including (1) a guinea pig isolate, (2) a feline isolate, (3) abortion-inducing isolates from sheep and cattle, and (4) a number of isolates from avian populations.

## II. MORPHOLOGY AND GROWTH

The hallmark characteristic of chlamydiae is their continual transition between two distinct morphological forms. Infection is initiated by chlamydial elementary bodies, or EB, that attach to and enter into susceptible host cells. These small, rigid particles are osmotically stable but metabolically inert; thus, EB are designed to exist in the extracellular environment until a suitable host cell is available for intracellular growth. Reticulate bodies, or RB, are the larger, replicative, intracellular chlamydial forms that divide within a highly unique membrane-bound vesicle, termed an inclusion. Osmotically fragile and unable to attach to eucaryotic cells, chlamydial RB are not infectious. Intermediate forms are observed during the transitional stages of EB to RB and during condensation of RB to EB prior to release of new EB progeny into the environment. This overall mechanism of infection, growth, maturation, release, and reinfection is termed the chlamydial developmental cycle (Fig. 1A).

The chlamydial envelope contains both a cytoplasmic membrane bilayer and a lipopolysaccharide-containing outer membrane, suggesting that these organisms are gram-negative (Fig. 1B). However, the chlamydiae exhibit variability using the Gram staining procedure and, therefore, staining with the Giemsa reagent has served as a more traditional means for identification of these organisms (Fig. 1C). In recent years, fluorescence microscopy using species-specific monoclonal antibodies against certain chlamydial protein epitopes has become the most convincing means for positive identification and illustration of the chlamydiae (Fig. 1D).

One noteworthy enigma regarding the chlamydial envelope is that an assembled peptidoglycan layer is not biochemically detectable, even though the chlamydiae do synthesize penicillin binding proteins and do respond to penicillin exposure. Further, the recently completed *C. trachomatis* serovar D genome sequence indicates that the genetic machinery necessary to encode for peptidoglycan is indeed present. Exposure of chlamydia-infected cells to penicillin leads to the presence of enlarged RB within inclusions that do not divide by binary fission. This observation is one example of how these organisms may exist in a state of persistence (i.e., viability is maintained, but RB do not mature to EB unless the penicillin is removed from the culture medium). Persistent RB are also observed following exposure of infected cells to the potent cytokine interferon-gamma.

## III. CELLULAR AND MOLECULAR BIOLOGY

At the cellular level, it is clear that the chlamydiae grow and develop within a highly selective environment. Following entry, the early intracellular chlamydiae-containing vesicles do not acidify or fuse with lysosomes; the pH stabilizes at a value of approximately 6.6 and these vesicles expand to become an inclusion. The term "inclusion" is traditionally used when chlamydiae-containing vesicles become visible by light microscopy. Many research interests are directed toward understanding the properties and composition of the inclusion membrane; recent studies show that molecules as small as 520 daltons do not freely diffuse across this protective barrier. The chlamydiae are known to obtain ATP and certain essential amino acids from the host cell. How these nutrients and cofactors are transported across the inclusion membrane is yet unknown.

Diversity among different species of *Chlamydia* is readily apparent within the single infected cell. For example, early EB-containing vesicles of *C. trachomatis* and *C. pneumoniae* fuse with one another within hours of entry and lead to the development of a single inclusion per host cell (Fig. 1B and D). Con-

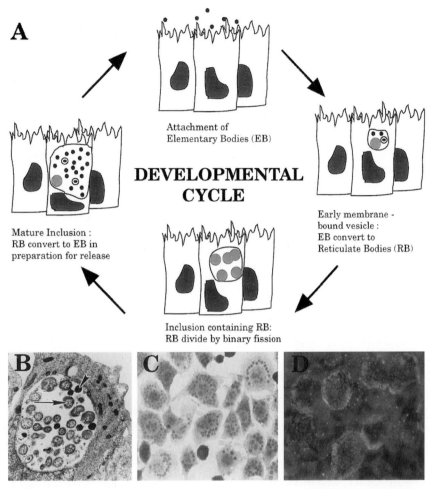

**Fig. 1.** Schematic of the chlamydial developmental cycle and visualization of intracellular inclusions. The developmental cycle (A) begins with the attachment of elementary bodies (EB) to susceptible host cells. After entry, EB convert to reticulate bodies (RB) that grow and divide within the membrane-bound intracellular inclusion. RB eventually convert back to infectious EB in preparation for release and infection of neighboring host cells. (B) Electron microscopic view of an intracellular inclusion of *C. trachomatis* containing both EB (arrowhead) and RB (arrow). (C) Visualization of multiple *C. psittaci* inclusions per host cell using the Giemsa staining procedure; inclusions appear as "grape-like" clusters surrounding the nucleus. (D) Visualization of single *C. trachomatis* inclusions per host cell by fluorescence microscopy using a chlamydia-specific antibody. See color insert.

versely, *C. psittaci* vesicles do not fuse and give rise to multiple inclusions within each infected cell (Fig. 1C). Inclusions containing *C. trachomatis* often exhibit an accumulation of glycogen during growth and division; this property is not observed with other chlamydial species. The inclusions formed by *C. psit-* *taci* are unique in that mitochondria become closely associated with the outer leaflet of the inclusion membrane; such an intimate relationship is not as apparent for other chlamydiae. These examples represent only a few of the properties that are unique among various isolates of the chlamydiae. One might imagine that, if we understood more about these differences at the cellular level, such knowledge might extend to understanding the diversity of disease syndromes that the chlamydiae elicit at the level of the infected host.

Because of their requisite growth within eucaryotic host cells, a system for direct genetic analyses in the chlamydiae has not yet been developed. The fusion of multiple EB-containing vesicles of *C. trachomatis* into a singular inclusion makes clonal selection a challenge. Further, since many, if not most, chlamydial genes are developmentally regulated and the growing microcolony matures in an asynchronous fashion, the time frame for addition of a selective reagent becomes complicated. Other bacteria are commonly used as surrogate genetic hosts for determining chlamydial gene function, but such systems are often limited in the extent of information that can be obtained. For example, it is known that the chlamydiae are more permissive in initiating transcription from promoter regions preceding chlamydial open reading frames (ORF). More stringent criteria, or consensus sequences, are used by the *Escherichia coli* transcriptional apparatus, which partly explains why so few chlamydial genes are readily transcribed in *E. coli* recombinant libraries. Nevertheless, continual efforts are made to develop a genetic system. With the exception of *C. pneumoniae,* the chlamydiae have a conserved 7.5 kb plasmid and certain isolates of *C. psittaci* harbor bacteriophage; these extrachromosomal elements represent likely vectors for transformation. Moreover, there is evidence that recombination does occur within the chlamydiae *in vivo*.

Perhaps one of the most exciting recent advances in chlamydial molecular biology is the complete genomic sequencing of several prototype isolates. Sequencing of the 1.045 Mb *C. trachomatis* serovar D chromosome is now completed and 894 open reading frames (ORF) have been tentatively identified. It is interesting that, for a prokaryote, an unusually high number of chlamydial genes show relatedness with eucaryotic genes. Further, when the putative *C. trachomatis* proteins encoded by each ORF are compared with *E. coli* and *Bacillus subtilis* proteins, the number of matches are low and do not favor either

Gram-positive or Gram-negative; this observation substantiates the placement of the chlamydiae within their own evolutionary order.

## IV. HUMANS AS A PRIMARY HOST

### A. Ocular Infections

*C. trachomatis* is the culprit in the world's leading cause of preventable blindness. The World Health Organization estimates that there are approximately 150 million people in the world today with active infectious trachoma. Such infections are concentrated in countries with poor sanitary conditions and, unfortunately, the primary reservoir is young children. It is estimated that there will be more blindness due to trachomatous infection in the year 2020 than exists today. If initial infections are left untreated, trachoma causes a follicular conjunctivitis that progresses to neovascularization of the cornea; the formation of scar tissue in the eye is the ultimate reason for blindness. In developed countries, genital isolates of *C. trachomatis* are transmitted from infected mothers to infants during birth and cause both ocular and respiratory infections.

### B. Genital Infections

The chlamydiae are perhaps best known as agents of sexually transmitted infections (STI). Indeed, these organisms are responsible for an estimated 90 million new infections worldwide each year. Four million of these infections are in the United States and, alarmingly, the most significant factor associated with chlamydial genital infections is age. The Centers for Disease Control (CDC) estimates that among women with genital chlamydial infections, 46% are 15 to 19 years of age; one out of every 10 adolescent girls tested for chlamydia is positive. Women of ages 20 to 24 years represent an additional 33% of infections. One primary reason for such high infection rates is attributable to the silent nature of chlamydial infection in the early stages; approximately 75% of women and 50% of men exhibit no initial symptoms and, therefore, do not seek treatment.

Similar to ocular infections, the fundamental mechanism of chlamydial genital disease involves immune-mediated damage and scar tissue formation. Women bear a special burden because of adverse reproductive consequences. Left untreated, 40% of women with genital chlamydia infections will develop pelvic inflammatory disease (PID); 20% will become infertile, 18% will experience chronic pelvic pain, and 9% will have a life-threatening tubal pregnancy. The primary agents are *C. trachomatis* serovariants D through K, which exhibit a slow, ascending process in the genital tract. In women, the organisms first infect mucosal epithelial cells in the cervix and spread laterally to the endometrium, fallopian tubes, and, eventually, the peritoneal cavity. In men, urethritis, epididymitis, and prostatitis are common sequelae.

Lymphogranuloma venereum (LGV) is a highly invasive STI caused by the L1 through L3 serovariants of *C. trachomatis*. Although infections by these agents are found worldwide, they are more concentrated in certain countries, such as Southeast Asia, India, and Africa. The infection begins with the appearance of a small genital lesion that is relatively painless. However, the organisms rapidly penetrate into the genital submucosae, becoming systemic, and a regional lymphadenopathy soon develops.

## C. Respiratory Infections

Many chlamydial species are capable of causing respiratory infection, including genital *C. trachomatis* (during birth) and *C. psittaci* (see following). However, *C. pneumoniae* is the most common agent of chlamydial pneumonia. While asymptomatic carriers are thought to be common, *C. pneumoniae* infections can become life-threatening. Systemic infections may arise from organisms within mononuclear leukocytes that exit the lung and are distributed by circulation. Estimated percentages of adults that either have been or are infected with *C. pneumoniae* range from 50 to 90%. Individuals with mild or acute infections

typically exhibit a prolonged cough; rhinitis, sinusitis, otitis media, and pharyngitis are also observed. Roughly, 10% of infections progress to pneumonia that is preceded by pharyngitis; hoarseness, a persistent dry cough, and low fever are classic symptoms.

## D. Associated Disease Syndromes

As stated earlier, much of the destructive pathology observed by chlamydial infection is immune-mediated. This is the primary reason that efforts to develop a protective vaccine have been hampered. Chlamydial infections are associated with the eventual development of arthritis, as well as bronchitis and other chronic respiratory syndromes. However, the most notable recent finding is an association between *C. pneumoniae* and coronary artery disease, or atherosclerosis. There is little doubt among investigators that these organisms are indeed present and detectable within atheromatous lesions, but their precise role, if any, in atherosclerotic disease is not yet known.

## E. Diagnosis and Treatment

For many years, chlamydial infections were confirmed by actually isolating the organisms in cell culture; this approach was not only tedious and slow, but required scraping cells from the site of infection in patients. Infection rates in men have been particularly difficult to determine due to the discomfort of intraurethral swabbing. However, the amplification of chlamydia-specific nucleic acids by either polymerase chain reaction (PCR) or ligase chain reaction (LCR) has improved the detection sensitivity and reduced the time involved. Further, these techniques are > 90% accurate using urine specimens. Other available diagnostic techniques involve the use of specific antibodies in fluorescence microscopy or enzyme-linked immunoassays.

*Chlamydia* are responsive to antimicrobial therapy; the traditional drugs of choice include tetracycline (or doxycycline), erythromycin (or other macrolides), and sulfonamides. However, high infection

***TABLE I***
**Chlamydial Infections in Other Hosts and Zoonoses**

| Species | Host symptoms and disease | Consequences | Human disease from zoonotic transmission |
|---|---|---|---|
| *C. psittaci* | | | |
| **Avian isolates** (>130 species) | Parakeets—chronic infection resulting in appetite and weight loss, diarrhea (yellow droppings), sinusitis, respiratory distress | occasionally fatal | pneumonia (dry cough), systemic disease (high fever) |
| | Turkeys—acute infection resulting in air saculitis, nasal adenitis, pneumonia, pericarditis, peritonitis, hepatitis | occasionally fatal, egg production is decreased (60 to 10%) | pneumonia (dry cough), systemic disease (high fever) |
| **Abortion isolates** | Sheep, cattle, goats—wide range of symptoms. Inapparent intestinal infection, enteritis, conjunctivitis, mastitis, orchitis, polyarthritis, encephalitis, genital tract infection | decrease in milk and wool production, abortion, occasionally fatal | gestational psittacosis, abortion in pregnant women assisting with lambing |
| **Feline isolate** | Cats—nasal discharge, conjunctivitis, coughing, sneezing, severe rhinitis, genital tract infection | transmission in catteries, reproductive complications | unknown |
| **Guinea pig isolate** | Guinea pigs—conjunctivitis, urethritis, cervicitis, ascending genital tract infection, pneumonia | sexual transmission and transmission to newborns | unknown |
| *C. pecorum* | Wide range of mammalian hosts (sheep, goats, koalas, swine)—wide range of symptoms. Inapparent intestinal infection, enteritis, pneumonia, polyarthritis, encephalitis, genital tract infection | abortion? | unknown |
| *C. trachomatis* | Swine—wide range of symptoms. Inapparent to chronic intestinal infection, genital tract infection, mastitis, arthritis | abortion | unknown |

rates persist partly due to patient noncompliance. The antimicrobial target of these protein synthesis-inhibiting antibiotics is the metabolically active reticulate body and, therefore, compounds must traverse four membrane layers: (1) the host cell plasma membrane; (2) the inclusion membrane; (3) the chlamydial outer membrane, and (4) the chlamydial cytoplasmic membrane. In addition, because the chlamydiae grow slowly and develop in an asynchronous fashion, bactericidal concentrations of antibiotics must be maintained for an extended period of time—usually two or more weeks with multiple daily dosages. Fortunately, new macrolide derivatives have been designed, such as azithromycin, that have the unique biophysical property of a long tissue half-life. Because these compounds are not rapidly cleared via circulation, patients only require one or two biweekly doses.

## V. OTHER HOST RESERVOIRS AND ZOONOTIC TRANSMISSION

Of the more than 60 strains of *Chlamydia* that infect birds and animals, including humans, five groups are particularly important to veterinarians, farmers, slaughterhouse or poultry-processing workers, and pet owners: *C. psittaci*-avian isolates that primarily infect birds; *C. psittaci*-abortion isolates; *C. psittaci*-feline isolates; and *C. pecorum* and *C. trachomatis*-swine isolates that infect mammals (Table 1). The diseases produced in birds and mammals vary from clinically inapparent infections to severe systemic infections. In the latter cases, economic losses to farmers and aviarians can approach millions of dollars annually. Spread of diseases from birds or animals to humans (zoonoses) can occur; even though such transmissions are sporadic, via occupational hazards or to pet owners, some consequences can be serious, such as endocarditis from bird-acquired pneumonia or abortion in pregnant women assisting in the delivery of infected lambs. A more recent concern, resulting from the overexposure of poultry flocks and animal herds to tetracycline-containing feed, is the isolation of chlamydia strains (especially *C. trachomatis* swine) resistant to tetracycline, the recommended antibiotic of choice for treating human chlamydial infections.

## VI. SUMMARY

The enormous number of chlamydial infections worldwide is not attributed simply to population growth. Therefore, these pathogens are not necessarily "emerging" infections; they have already reached epidemic proportions. The United States spends an estimated $2.4 billion dollars each year in treatment of chlamydial diseases. Improved diagnostic and antibiotic treatment measures are anticipated to lower infection rates. It is hoped that education and the use of protective barrier methods for sexual activities will also lower the incidence of chlamydial STI. However, the ultimate measure would be the development of a protective vaccine. From past experience, it is clear that we must first differentiate between chlamydial antigens that are protective versus destructive. Although there is documented evidence for natural protective immunity, it is of a short duration and appears restricted to related chlamydial species or isolates. This natural protection appears largely due to the production of protective antibodies, but it is becoming quite clear that an effective long-term vaccine would involve programming the cell-mediated immune response, as well as the production of protective antibodies.

### See Also the Following Articles

CELL DIVISION, PROKARYOTES • DEVELOPMENTAL PROCESSES IN BACTERIA • LIPOPOLYSACCHARIDES • ZOONOSES

### Bibliography

Bavoil, P. M., Hsia, R.-C., and Rank, R. G. (1996). Prospects for a vaccine against *Chlamydia* genital disease I.—Microbiology and pathogenesis. *Bull. Inst. Pasteur* 94, 5–54.

Beatty, W. L., Morrison, R. P., and Byrne, G. I. (1994). Persistent chlamydiae: From cell culture to a paradigm for chlamydial pathogenesis. *Microbiol. Rev.* 58, 686–699.

Black, C. M. (1997). Current methods of laboratory diagnosis of *Chlamydia trachomatis* infections. *Clin. Microbiol. Rev.* 10, 160–184.

Hackstadt, T. (1998). The diverse habitats of obligate intracellular pathogens. *Curr. Opin. Microbiol.* 1, 82–87.

Hackstadt, T., Fischer, E. R., Scidmore, M. A., Rockey, D. D., and Heinzen, R. A. (1997). Origins and functions of the chlamydial inclusion. *Trends Microbiol.* 5, 288–293.

Hatch, T. P. (1998). Chlamydia: Old ideas crushed, new mysteries bared. *Science* 282, 638–639.

Hatch, T. P. (1996). Disulfide cross-linked envelope proteins: The functional equivalent of peptidoglycan in chlamydiae? *J. Bacteriol.* 178, 1–5.

Institute of Medicine. (1997). The hidden epidemic: Confronting sexually transmitted diseases. (T. R. Eng and W. T. Butler, eds.). National Academy Press, Washington, DC.

Kalman, S., Mitchell, W., Marathe, R., Lammel, C., Fan, J., Hyman, R. W., Olinger, L., Grimwood, J., Davis, R. W., Stephens, R. S. (1999). Comparative genomes of *Chlamydia pneumoniae* and *C. trachomatis*. *Nature Genetics* 21(4), 385–389, Apr.

Kuo, C.-C., Jackson, L. A., Campbell, L. A., and Grayston, J. T. (1995). *Chlamydia pneumoniae* (TWAR). *Clin. Microbiol. Rev.* 8, 451–461.

McClarty, G. (1994). Chlamydiae and the biochemistry of intracellular parasitism. *Trends Microbiol.* **2**, 157–164.

Peeling, R. W., and Brunham, R. C. (1996). Chlamydiae as pathogens: New species and new issues. *Emerg. Infect. Dis.* **2**, 307–319.

Rank, R. G., and Bavoil, P. M. (1996). Prospects for a vaccine against *Chlamydia* genital disease II.—Immunity and vaccine development. *Bull. Inst. Pasteur* **94**, 55–82.

Raulston, J. E. (1995). Chlamydial envelope components and pathogen-host cell interactions. *Mol. Microbiol.* **15**, 607–616.

Rodolakis, A., Salinas, J., and Papp, J. 1998. Recent advances on ovine chlamydial abortion. *Vet. Res.* **29**, 275–288.

Sinai, A. P., and Joiner, K. A. (1997). Safe haven: The cell biology of nonfusogenic pathogen vacuoles. *Ann. Rev. Microbiol.* **51**, 415–462.

Stephens, R. S., Kalman, S., Lammel, C., Fan, J., Marathe, R., Aravind, L., Mitchell, W., Olinger, L., Tatusov, R. L., Zhao, Q., Koonin, E. V., and Davis, R. W. (1998). Genome sequence of an obligate intracellular pathogen of humans: *Chlamydia trachomatis. Science* **282**, 754–759.

# Cholera

## Claudia C. Häse, Nicholas Judson, and John J. Mekalanos

*Harvard Medical School*

## GLOSSARY

**biotype** Different strains of the same bacterial species distinguished by a specified group of phenotypic and genetic traits.

**pathogenicity island** A chromosomal region containing many pathogenicity-related loci that may have been acquired by horizontal gene transfer.

**reactogenicity** Undesired symptoms produced by a vaccine strain.

**regulon** A set of genes that are coordinately controlled by the same regulatory protein(s).

**serogroup** Bacteria of the same species with different antigenic determinants on the cell surface.

**serotype** A subdivision of serogroup; bacteria with different proportions of the same antigenic determinants on the cell surface.

**virulence factor** Phenotype required for full pathogenicity of the bacteria; loss of which results in attenuated strains.

**CHOLERA** is a disease that has affected mankind for centuries. It is a severe and potentially lethal diarrheal disease caused by the gram-negative bacterium *Vibrio cholerae*. Upon ingestion, the bacteria colonize the small intestine, in which they produce a toxin (cholera toxin) that causes the secretion of large amounts of water into the intestine, resulting in the profuse watery diarrhea characteristic of cholera. *Vibrio cholerae* is a waterborne bacterium that commonly causes epidemics in areas of the world where there is overcrowding and poor sanitation.

## I. INTRODUCTION

The modern period of cholera epidemics began in 1817 with a pandemic that started in the Ganges river delta in India (now Bangladesh). Although there are descriptions dating back to seventh-century Sanskrit writings of dehydrating diarrheal diseases resulting in death that may have been due to cholera, the pandemic of 1817 was the first instance of an epidemic form of the disease that spread beyond India and Asia. The emergence of epidemic cholera from India and Asia resulted in the disease being named Asiatic cholera. Since 1817, there have been seven cholera pandemics. The last pandemic, which started in 1961, continues today.

Cholera is the most severe of many diarrheal diseases that affect humans. It is unusual in the speed with which dehydration and death can occur. In severe cases, patients may develop hypovolemic shock and acidosis and can die in as short a period as 24 hr. Mortality rates in untreated patients can reach 70%. In the past 40 years, since the discovery of cholera toxin in 1959 by two independent researchers and their colleagues in India (S. N. De, a pathologist in Calcutta, and N. K. Dutta, a pharmacologist in Bombay), there have been great advances

*Encyclopedia of Microbiology, Volume 1*
SECOND EDITION

**789**

in our understanding of the disease. Along with our understanding of how the disease works has come knowledge of how to treat it. Morbidity and mortality from cholera are extremely preventable—dehydration is the main concern with cholera patients. The introduction in the 1960s of oral rehydration therapy for patients of diarrheal illnesses has greatly reduced the mortality rate associated with cholera and other diarrheal diseases. We have also come to understand the mechanism of action of cholera toxin and much about the regulation of virulence factors in *V. cholerae*.

Infection with *V. cholerae* results in long-lasting immunity. Adults in endemic areas, such as Bangladesh, have been shown to be 10 times less likely to die from a cholera infection than children between 1 and 5 years old. This is presumably due in part to protective immunity that is established by surviving a childhood infection. This strong and long-lasting immunity indicates that the development of an effective vaccine is feasible. Vaccine research has included work toward killed whole cell approaches as well as live-attenuated approaches. Several vaccines have been developed, but problems with efficacy for the killed whole-cell vaccines and reactogenicity (unwanted symptoms) for the live-attenuated strains mean that we still do not have a safe and effective vaccine for cholera.

## II. HISTORICAL BACKGROUND

Descriptions of severe diarrheal diseases exist in ancient writings, but the first pandemic thought to be due to *V. cholerae* of the O1 serogroup started in 1817. There are more than 150 different serogroups of *V. cholerae*, but only 2 serogroups cause epidemic disease: the O1 and O139 serogroups. Serogroups are distinguished by the antigenic regions on the surface of the bacteria, with different serogroups having different antigenic properties. In addition to the O1 and O139 serogroups, there are two biotypes of *V. cholerae* that cause epidemic disease—classical and El Tor. The classical biotype of *V. cholerae* O1 is thought to have caused the first six pandemics, whereas the pandemic which started in 1961 and continues today is caused by the El Tor biotype.

*Vibrio cholerae* was first described in 1849 in Tuscany upon the examination of the intestinal contents of cadavers by an Italian physician, Filippo Pacini. He described the characteristic curved shape of *V. cholerae* in his published findings in 1854. There was, however, no etiological relationship demonstrated and the findings remained obscure for almost a century. His discovery was recognized by the Judicial Commission of the International Commission on Bacterial Nomenclature in 1965.

The toxic effects of *V. cholerae* were first postulated by Robert Koch in several reports between 1883 and 1885. He isolated the bacterium in pure culture and noted that it satisfied the criteria of the postulates that he had formulated in his studies on anthrax and tuberculosis. The bacteria were present in all cases of the disease, were found in the environment only in association with cholera patients, were able to cause disease when given to guinea pigs, and were present in the small intestine of infected guinea pigs. In 1884, he proposed that the toxic effects of cholera were due to the presence of a toxin produced by the bacteria, but it was not until 1959 that this enterotoxin was actually discovered.

The El Tor biotype was first described in 1905 by Gotschlich, who isolated it at a quarantine station in El Tor on the Sinai Peninsula from the bodies of dead pilgrims returning from Mecca. They died with no symptoms of cholera, but intestinal examination revealed the distinctive comma-shaped *V. cholerae*. The fact that they did not produce disease symptoms and that the bacteria were found to have hemolytic activity (the ability to lyse red blood cells) meant that the bacterium was originally thought to be a different species. It was named *Vibrio eltor*. We have since learned that El Tor and classical strains are the same species, but that there are some significant genetic differences between the two biotypes. In addition, the El Tor biotype typically causes a milder form of the disease than the classical biotype: Approximately one in seven cases are severe compared with one in two cases for classical.

One of the distinctions between the history of cholera before 1817 and afterwards is that it is thought that the pandemic of 1817 was the first time that *V. cholerae* O1 caused epidemic disease. Although there are no clinical isolates from the first four pandemics, it is known that the fifth and sixth pandemics were caused by classical *V. cholerae* O1. It is thought that the emergence of epidemic cholera at the beginning of the *nineteenth* century was due to the emergence of the O1 serogroup. Historical accounts of cholera-like illness exist in ancient Indian writings, but the pandemic of 1817 was the first occurrence that spread into the Western world. There is some dispute regarding the exact dates of the first six pandemics, but the most widely followed dates (and the ones followed here) are those that are laid out in the first monograph on cholera written by R. Pollitzer (1959). For a more complete historical description, there are several extensive books and reviews on the subject (Pollitzer, 1959; Barua and Greenough, 1992).

Since 1817, there have been seven pandemics of Asiatic cholera. The first pandemic started in India in 1817 and lasted for 5 years. During that time it spread into Asia and the Middle East, reaching east into islands of Indonesia and west to Syria's border with Egypt.

The second pandemic, from 1829 to 1851, spread much farther. It also originated in India but spread into Russia, Europe, Great Britain, and North America.

The third through sixth pandemics (1852–1859, 1863–1879, 1881–1896, and 1899–1923) affected all areas of the world, leading to a global awareness of the problem that cholera presented and the need for adequate sanitation and sewage systems. The establishment of an adequate sewage and water supply system in Great Britain by the 1890s led to the eradication of cholera in Great Britain, with the last indigenous case reported in 1893.

The pandemic that continues today started in Indonesia on the island of Celebes (Sulawesi) in January 1961. This pandemic is different than the previous ones in that it is caused by the El Tor biotype of *V. cholerae*. Although the El Tor biotype had previously caused sporadic cases of mild cholera-like disease, it had never caused widespread disease. However, this changed in the 1960s as the pandemic spread through Indonesia, reaching Calcutta by 1964. The El Tor biotype completely replaced classical *V. cholerae* in India by the end of the year. For unknown reasons, the classical biotype remained predominant in Bangladesh until 1972 when it was replaced by the El Tor biotype. A classical strain re-emerged in 1982 in Bangladesh; since then, both classical and El Tor *V. cholerae* have been isolated from patients. The current pandemic surged forward in 1970, reaching into Africa and Europe. In 1991, an outbreak occurred in Peru, marking the first time that cholera had been present in South America since 1895.

In October 1992, a new serogroup of *V. cholerae* emerged in Bengal, *V. cholerae* O139. This emergence has been described as the beginning of a new pandemic of cholera and was a concerning development in cholera epidemiology. The new epidemic strain is most closely related to O1 El Tor strains, but it is encapsulated with different antigenic determinants on the surface of the bacteria. Pre-existing immunity to *V. cholerae* O1 strains did not confer protection against *V. cholerae* O139. Consequently, adults and children were equally susceptible to the new serogroup and *V. cholerae* O139 continues to cause disease today.

## III. ORGANISM

*Vibrio cholerae* is a gram-negative, oxidase-positive, facultative anaerobe. Microscopic examination of *V. cholerae* reveals a highly motile curved rod with a single polar flagellum. The characteristic curved shape, along with the rapidity with which it moves, is the basis of the diagnostic analysis of wet-mount preparations.

The surface of gram-negative bacteria is made predominantly of a coat of lipopolysaccharide (LPS). This coat provides bacteria with protection against hydrophobic compounds and detergents. It can also provide a surface for immune recognition. The outermost part of the LPS molecule is the primary antigenic region, known as the O antigen. This antigenic region is used to classify different serogroups of bacteria. There are more than 150 different serogroups of *V. cholerae*, only 2 of which cause epidemic disease.

The O1 serogroup of both classical and El Tor strains can be further divided into serotypes. Serotypes are distinguished by the antigenic molecules that make up the O1 antigen of the LPS molecule.

There are three parts to the O1 antigen: A–C. The A antigenic moiety is thought to be made up of 3-deoxy-L-glycerotetronic acid, and the B and C components have not been characterized. The serotype of the different strains depends on the ratio of expression of these three antigenic moieties. There are two main serotypes, known as Ogawa and Inaba. A third, rarer, serotype also exists, known as Hikojima. Ogawa strains express A and B antigens and to a lesser extent the C antigen, Inaba strains express only the A and C antigens, and the Hikojima strain expresses all three. It has been theorized that the Hikojima strain represents strains that are seroconverting between the Ogawa and Inaba serotypes.

Although both classical and El Tor *V. cholerae* O1 can exist as all three serotypes, there are important genetic differences between the two biotypes. Different strains of *V. cholerae* have different sized genomes. The El Tor strain N16961, which is currently being sequenced, has a genome of approximately 4 megabases (Mb) distributed over two chromosomes. Classical strain genomes range in size from 3.2 to 3.6 Mb, and the O139 serogroup strain SG24 has a genome size of 3.6 Mb. The reason for and the consequences of the differences in genome size are not understood.

Several different phenotypes have been used to distinguish classical and El Tor biotypes. The five tests that have been used (and the results for classical strains of *V. cholerae*) are hemolysis of sheep erythrocytes (non-hemolytic, although most El Tor strains are now non-hemolytic), mannose-sensitive hemagglutination of chicken erythrocytes (negative), polymyxin B sensitivity (sensitive), classical IV bacteriophage sensitivity (sensitive), and the Voges–Proskauer reaction (negative).

The O139 serogroup of *V. cholerae* is most closely related to El Tor O1 strains. The new serogroup is thought to have arisen from a recombination event that resulted in the partial deletion of the O antigen biosynthesis region (the *rfb* operon) and the insertion of a 35-kb region containing genes encoding a novel serogroup antigen and a polysaccharide capsule. The inserted region of DNA most closely resembles the organization found in the *V. cholerae* O22 genome, and it has been hypothesized that this region was transferred horizontally from the O22 to the O1 serogroup of *V. cholerae*.

As mentioned previously, there are more than 150 different serogroups of *V. cholerae*, only 2 of which have caused epidemic disease. The serogroups that do not cause epidemic disease are referred to as non-O1 serogroups. Some non-O1 strains of *V. cholerae* have given rise to sporadic cases of cholera, but the majority of non-O1 serogroups do not possess the genes encoding cholera toxin, the major virulence determinant of *V. cholerae*, and so do not cause disease.

## IV. TRANSMISSION OF THE DISEASE

*Vibrio cholerae* is present in the environment in coastal waters throughout the world. It infects the human host by colonizing the small intestine after ingestion of contaminated food or water. The gastric acid barrier plays an important role in our defense against cholera as well as against other enteric pathogens. Studies with human volunteers have shown that neutralization of the stomach acid reduces the required infectious dose by as much as five orders of magnitude from $10^{11}$ to $10^{6}$ organisms.

The role of water in the transmission of cholera was first described during the epidemic of 1852. In 1854, John Snow, a British physician, was the first to demonstrate this role. He analyzed the patterns of illness and death from cholera in London and noted that there were two water companies supplying households in the affected neighborhoods of London. The incidence of disease correlated with those households that were supplied by the water company Southwalk and Vauxhall, but those supplied by another company, the Lambeth company, were much less likely to have disease. The two companies got their water from different sources. Based on this observation, John Snow argued successfully to have the handle from the pump supplying houses with cholera cases—the Broad Street pump—removed. The outbreak of cholera in London was already on the downswing, but this action undoubtedly helped bring the epidemic to an end. In 1855, he documented his reasoning in the second edition of his book *On the Mode of Communication of Cholera*.

The environmental reservoir for *V. cholerae* is not known. There are seasonal differences in when

V. *cholerae* can be isolated from the environment, but what happens to the bacteria during the times that it cannot be isolated is unknown. One hypothesis is that some individuals are carriers: They are chronically infected but do not suffer from disease symptoms. This would enable the bacterium to stay sequestered in the human host, periodically reemerging to cause disease. Another possibility is that V. *cholerae* is present in the environment but in a form such that traditional methods for isolating it are not effective. It was commonly thought that V. *cholerae* existed predominantly in the human host, having a relatively short survival time outside the host. This belief was mainly due to the inability to isolate toxigenic V. *cholerae* from environmental samples. Work by Colwell and colleagues at the University of Maryland has shown that it is possible to identify V. *cholerae* in environmental samples by use of the polymerase chain reaction when it is not possible to culture these organisms on traditional laboratory media. These non-culturable V. *cholerae* may represent a mechanism by which cholera can survive in the environment during intra-epidemic periods.

The El Tor biotype has a longer environmental survival time than classical strains of V. *cholerae* (it can be recultured from environmental samples for a longer time). This may have contributed to the replacement of the classical form of the disease by the El Tor biotype.

## V. PATHOGENESIS

The disease cholera usually begins with the ingestion of V. *cholerae* in contaminated food or water. Those bacteria that survive the acidic stomach must colonize the small intestine and elaborate a powerful enterotoxin, cholera toxin (CT), that is directly responsible for the severe diarrhea characteristic of cholera. A surface structure on the bacteria, called toxin-coregulated pilus (TCP), is important in the colonization process. Transcription of the genes encoding CT and TCP are coordinately regulated via a cascade of regulatory proteins.

## A. Virulence Factors

### 1. *Cholera Toxin*

CT is a proteinaceous enterotoxin secreted by V. *cholerae* into the extracellular milieu. The structure of CT is well understood and is of the $AB_5$ subunit type (Fig. 1). The B subunit forms a pentameric "doughnut" structure that serves to bind CT to the receptor on the eukaryotic cells, the ganglioside $GM_1$. The A subunit of CT contains the enzymatically active portion of the toxin. Proteolytic cleavage of the A subunit results in the generation of the $A_1$ and $A_2$ peptides which initially remain linked via a disulfide bond. Following internalization of CT into the eukaryotic cells, the disulfide bond is reduced. The $A_1$ subunit contains an ADP-ribosyltransferase activity and covalently modifies the G protein that regulates adenylate cyclase. Adenylate cyclase mediates the formation of cyclic AMP (cAMP) which is an important intracellular messenger for various cellular pathways. The ADP-ribosylating activity of the $A_1$ peptide is stimulated by some cellular GTP binding proteins, termed ADP-ribosylating factors (ARFs), that appear to act as allosteric activators of $A_1$. Transfer of the ADP-ribose moiety of NAD to the $G_{s\alpha}$ protein by the $A_1$ subunit of CT results in the constitutive activation of adenylate cyclase and thus increased levels of intracellular cAMP. Increased cAMP levels in turn activate a protein kinase, resulting in protein phosphorylation, altered ion transport, and

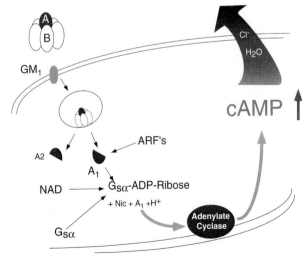

**Fig. 1.** Mechanism of action of the cholera enterotoxin.

ultimately diarrhea. The genes encoding CT, *ctxAB*, are part of a larger genetic element on the *V. cholerae* chromosome (Fig. 2) that was only recently recognized to be the genome of a filamentous phage, CTX φ. The A and B subunits are encoded by two separate but adjacent open reading frames (ORFs), *ctxA* and *ctxB*, that form an operon. Transcription of the *ctxAB* genes is regulated by several proteins in response to external signals. Unlike most filamentous phages, the CTX φ genome can integrate into the host genome at a specific attachment site, *attRS*, or replicate as a double-stranded plasmid. The "core" region of CTX φ carries several phage morphogenesis genes as well as the *ctx* genes and is flanked by repeated sequences (RSs) that encode genes necessary for the replication and integration of the phage DNA. Interestingly, the receptor for CTX φ is TCP, which is essential for efficient colonization of the intestinal tract by *V. cholerae*. The requirement for the host strain to express TCP in order to be infected by CTX φ has important epidemiological and evolutionary implications.

## 2. Toxin-Coregulated Pili

Efficient colonization of the human intestinal tract by *V. cholerae* requires the expression of TCPs. TCPs are expressed on the surface of *V. cholerae* cells and are composed of long laterally associated filaments 7 nm in diameter. The major pilin subunit, TcpA, is a 20.5-kD protein that belongs to the type IV class of pilins. TCPs function as receptors for the cholera toxin encoding phage CTX φ. No receptor for TCP

**Fig. 3.** Organization of the TCP–ACF pathogenicity island.

on intestinal cells has been identified. Most of the genes important for TCP production are clustered on a pathogenicity island in the chromosome of *V. cholerae* (Fig. 3). The *tcpA–F, tcpJ*, and the physically unlinked *tcpG* (*dsbA*) genes are important in the processing and assembly of the pilus structure, whereas some of the other *tcp* genes are involved in the coordinate regulation of virulence gene expression. Passive immunization with antibodies directed against TcpA epitopes confers protection against infection in an experimental infant mouse model. Although expression of TCP is critical for intestinal colonization, the adherence of *V. cholerae* to epithelial cells is probably multifactorial.

## 3. Other

Several other proteins produced by *V. cholerae* are potentially involved in its virulence, but the precise role of these proteins in pathogenesis is not known. Culture supernatants of *V. cholerae* contain an activity that results in increased tissue conductivity and altered tight junctions in rabbit ileal tissue. This zona occludens toxin (Zot) and another protein, accessory cholera enterotoxin (Ace), which increases the potential difference across mounted epithelial cells, are believed to be encoded on the CTX φ genome (Fig. 2). The Zot and Ace proteins appear to have dual functions and may be involved in phage morphogenesis and have toxic activities on eukaryotic cells. Strains of *V. cholerae* deleted for the *ctx* genes are known to cause some diarrhea and other symptoms referred to as "reactogenicity". Factors that may possess such secondary secretogenic properties might include hemolysins, proteases, or as yet unrecognized toxins. Putative adhesins, other than TCP, include the accessory colonization factor (ACF) that is also encoded on the TCP–ACF pathogenicity island (Fig. 3). *Vibrio cholerae* produces several hemagglutinins, such as a mannose-sensitive hemagglutinin

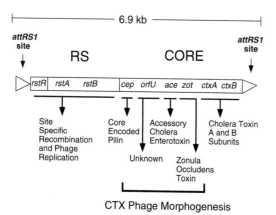

**Fig. 2.** Organization of the CTX genetic element.

(MSHA), also a type IV pilus, and a mannose–fucose-resistant hemagglutinin that may be important in the adherence of the bacteria. However, a knockout of the MSHA does not result in attenuation in human volunteers.

A large-scale effort to screen for colonization-defective mutants of *V. cholerae* in an animal model resulted in the identification of several genetic loci that were previously not known to be critical for colonization. Mutations in genes important in purine, biotin, and LPS biosynthesis were found to cause severe colonization defects. Other identified loci had no similarity to any known genes. Although it is clear that the colonization of the human intestinal tract by *V. cholerae* is a complex process, only the role of TCP in this important step in the pathogenesis of cholera has been conclusively established. Studies in different animal models have provided conflicting reports about whether motility is an important virulence property of *V. cholerae*. A confounding factor in these studies may be an observed inverse relationship between motility and expression of CT and TCP.

## B. Regulation of Virulence Factors

Expression of the two main virulence factors of *V. cholerae*, CT and TCP, *in vitro* is strongly influenced by changes in culture conditions, including temperature, pH, osmolarity, and composition of the growth medium. Transcription of the genes encoding CT and TCP (*ctx* and *tcp*, respectively), is coordinately regulated by several regulatory proteins via a cascade in which ToxR and TcpP control expression of ToxT, which is a transcriptional activator that directly controls expression of several virulence genes (Fig. 4). ToxR and TcpP are inner-membrane proteins with cytoplasmic DNA-binding domains. The periplasmic domains of ToxR and TcpP are thought to interact with other transmembrane regulatory proteins (ToxS and TcpH, respectively), that stimulate their activities. The ToxR/S proteins are not only required for transcription of the *toxT* gene but also important for *ctx* transcription and regulation of the expression of the OmpU and OmpT outer-membrane proteins. The TcpP/H proteins were only recently recognized to be necessary for *toxT* tran-

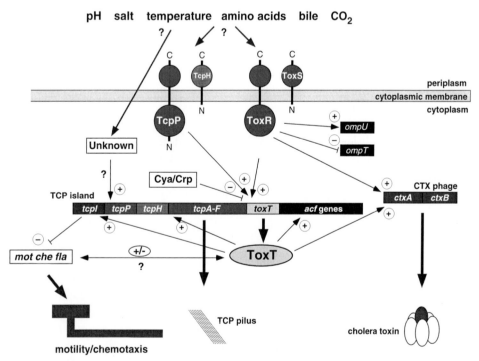

**Fig. 4.** Regulatory pathways of virulence gene expression (adapted with permission from Skorupski and Taylor, 1997).

scription and act synergistically with ToxR/S at the *toxT* promoter. Although transcription of the *toxRS* genes is moderately affected by temperature, no other environmental conditions known to modulate the "ToxR regulon" *in vitro* affect the amount of ToxR protein in the cells. In contrast, transcription of the *tcpPH* genes is believed to be regulated in response to several environmental stimuli by an unidentified protein(s). The ToxT protein is an AraC-like transcriptional activator that activates transcription of several genes in the ToxR regulon, including *ctx* and *tcpA*. Other proteins, such as adenylate cyclase (Cya) and the catabolite-receptor protein (Crp), are known to modulate *toxT* transcription. Recently, a mutation in the *nqr* gene cluster, encoding a sodium extrusion system, was found to result in increased *toxT* transcription. A screen for mutants that display elevated levels of a ToxT–LacZ reporter construct resulted in the identification of several genes that were not previously recognized to be important in *toxT* transcription, such as *hns*, *fumA*, and *glmS*. The mechanisms of these other regulatory interactions are not understood. It is interesting that several of the proteins in the ToxR regulon show similarity to proteins involved in motility or chemotaxis and *V. cholerae* mutants in these proteins as well as ToxR mutants display altered swarming behavior. Conversely, mutants of *V. cholerae* that have either increased or severely reduced motility also exhibit altered expression of CT and TCP. It is not understood how this inverse correlation of expression of the ToxR regulon and motility is mediated.

Although the regulatory cascade leading to expression of CT and TCP is well understood in classical biotype *V. cholerae,* less is known about these signal transduction events in the El Tor biotype. El Tor *V. cholerae* strains also have the ToxR/S, TcpP/H, and ToxT regulatory proteins but do not express CT and TCP as readily in laboratory media as do classical biotype strains. It has been suggested that differences in the levels of *toxT* transcription, possibly due to the TcpP/H proteins, may be responsible for this effect.

The regulatory networks described for *V. cholerae* are among the most complex to have been characterized in bacteria. Although many of the key players in this cascade of regulatory proteins have been identified, we still do not fully understand the signal transduction events leading to the coordinate expression of virulence factors in *V. cholerae*.

## VI. DIAGNOSIS

Successful treatment of cholera and other diarrheal diseases requires rapid rehydration. Although laboratory diagnosis is useful for epidemiological concerns, treatment of severe dehydration does not require such a diagnosis. Rehydration therapy should be started as soon as possible.

The symptoms and signs of a typical cholera case may include diarrhea, vomiting (with intestinal cramps and sometimes nausea), cold and clammy skin, a weak (often undetectable) pulse, tachypnoea (rapid breathing), and other signs of dehydration, such as sunken eyes and a pinched face, shriveling of the skin on the feet and hands, poor skin turgor—manifested by the inability of the skin to retract when pinched, and cyanosis of the nail beds. The onset of diarrhea is sudden and can reach volumes of 10 ml per kilogram per hour. Initially, the diarrhea may contain mucus and fecal matter, but as the disease progresses the stool takes on the characteristic milky color of rice water. Advanced dehydration leads to hypovolemic shock (shock induced by low blood volume) and acidosis (due to the loss of bicarbonate ions in the stool). Some patients may experience feelings of altered consciousness. Children are susceptible to hypokalemia (low blood potassium levels) and hypoglycemia (low blood sugar levels), which can result in seizures. Hypoglycemic patients should be treated immediately with intravenous glucose; however, death still occurs in approximately 40% of affected children. Other complications that can occur are acute renal failure and persistent vomiting. Oral rehydration therapy (ORT) is important for treatment of all these complications, but additional measures may need to be taken.

Many methods for clinical diagnosis of *V. cholerae* exist. A complete listing can be found in Wachsmuth *et al.,* (1994). Some examples of commonly used methods are the examination of a stool sample under a dark-field microscope, plating samples onto selective media, such as thiosulfate–citrate–bile salts–sucrose agar or tellurite taurocholate gelatin agar, tests for agglutination with polyvalent and monovalent O1 or O139 antiserum, the string test, and the oxidase test.

## VII. TREATMENT

Cholera is an extremely treatable disease. Early diagnosis and initiation of treatment are extremely important in preventing morbidity and mortality. Rehydration of an infected patient allows the patient to clear the bacterial infection even if no antibiotics are available.

ORT is the treatment of choice for diarrheal dehydration. Cholera and other severe cases of diarrhea can be treated by this regimen. ORT consists of two phases: (i) Rehydration of the patient with oral rehydration solution (ORS), which is a solution of water and electrolytes and (ii) maintenance, in which continued fluid loss is replaced by an equivalent volume of ORS and dietary intake is started. Severe cases of dehydration may require intravenous rehydration, but this is followed by ORT as soon as the patient is able to drink.

Antibiotic treatment can reduce the length and severity of a cholera case by approximately 50% however, it does not make a life-saving difference. The drug of choice is tetracycline, given orally at a dose of 500 mg every 6 hr for 48–72 hr. Other drugs that have been successfully used are doxycyline, furazolidone, erythromycin, and a combination of trimethoprim and sulfamethoxazole.

Rehydration was first recognized as a method to treat cholera in the 1830s by several researchers. Herman, a chemist in Moscow, observed that the blood of severely dehydrated individuals appeared to be more concentrated. He was the first to attempt to treat a dehydrated patient with an iv injection. The injection initially revived the patient, but treatment was not continued and the patient subsequently died. When cholera arrived in England in 1832, similar treatment was tried independently by two physicians, the Irish physician William O'Shaughnessy and the Scottish physician Thomas Latta. The medical journal *Lancet* described Latta's treatment of 15 patients as life-saving, but the fact that only 5 survived was viewed badly by the medical community.

Experiments with iv treatment were discontinued until the turn of the century, mainly because the medical community did not recognize the dehydration for what it was and preferred other more traditional treatments, such as venesection, cathartics, and the use of leeches (which must have exacerbated the dehydration process). At the turn of the century, iv treatment of cholera patients was again established by Rogers, when he used a hypertonic saline solution and managed to reduce case mortality rates. Experimentation with rehydration, however, did not seriously begin until the 1930s when the development of an appropriate iv solution by Hartman and the increased understanding of the importance of sterility broadened the use of iv treatment.

The first ORSs were developed in the 1940s by two independent researchers, Harrison and Darrow. Chemical analysis of the composition of stool from dehydrated patients allowed the formulation of physiologically relevant solutions, but iv treatment was the main treatment method for cholera through the 1950s and 1960s. However, the cost associated with iv treatment was prohibitive for widespread use in poverty-stricken areas. In 1958, in work unrelated to dehydration due to cholera, Riklis and Quastel discovered that the absorption of a sodium ion at the intestinal brush border was linked to the absorption of a glucose molecule. The discovery of this cotransport phenomenon was incorporated into treatment remedies for acute diarrhea. It was shown in 1964 by R. Phillips that the addition of glucose to a saline solution increased the net absorption of water and electrolytes in cholera patients. The cotransport phenomenon has also been shown to occur with other organic molecules, such as amino acids, dipeptides, and tripeptides. Studies in Dhaka and Calcutta extended and refined the use and composition of (ORSs).

In 1975, the World Health Organization (WHO) and the United Nations International Children's Emergency Fund recommended the use of a single solution (WHO-ORS) for the treatment of all diarrhea [(sodium, 90 mM); potassium, 20 mM; chloride, 80 mM; bicarbonate, 30 mM; and glucose, 111 mM (2%)]. The single solution has a lower sodium concentration than initial formulations that were specifically for use in treating cholera patients, but it has been shown to be effective for all types of diarrhea, cholera induced and otherwise. In another commonly used ORS solution the base is replaced with 10 mM citrate. This solution has a longer shelf life and is at least as effective as the bicarbonate-containing solution. ORT is an extremely cost-effective treatment for cholera and the benefits of a single formulation of a solution are easy to see. It is distributed as a powder that can be used for any type of diarrhea, regardless of the initial cause, age of the patient, or initial sodium levels in the patient. ORS is used in many countries with varying levels of general education and medical expertise, but the ease of formulation and the low cost associated with its preparation and distribution makes it an extremely effective treatment. Diarrhea is easy to diagnose, and the amount of fluid given should replace the volume lost due to diarrhea.

The main concern with making ORS is correct dilution of the powder. To address this issue, the WHO sent health care workers to villages in India, Bangladesh, and other affected countries to teach people how to formulate the mixture correctly. The main problem that was encountered was the ability to accurately measure an appropriate volume of water. This problem was eliminated by having each person bring a vessel to the health care worker, who would then fill that vessel with an appropriate volume of water and mark the inside of the vessel. Enabling people in remote villages to treat themselves greatly reduced the cost to the villages of bringing a sick individual to a hospital, accelerated recovery of the patient, and reduced mortality.

Formulations in addition to WHO-ORS have also been shown to be effective. A mixture of cooked rice powder and water with salt provides effective rehydration therapy. This mixture is often used in areas where there is no ready source of glucose. Nutritional intake should be started soon after the patient has begun recovery from rehydration. It was previously thought that fasting was an appropriate treatment for diarrheal patients; however, controlled studies have shown that the reintroduction of food reduces both the volume and duration of diarrhea.

Situations that may complicate ORT include severe dehydration, bloody diarrhea (which indicates the presence of underlying complications such as a bacte-

rial or parasitic infection that will require antibiotic treatment), and severe vomiting, in which case ORS should be administered in multiple small (5–10 ml) doses in 5- to 10-min intervals.

## VIII. EPIDEMIOLOGY

Cholera cases occur predominantly in developing countries and in refugee camps where crowding and malnourishment promote the spread of disease. In endemic areas, cholera is also often found after periods of flooding when sewage systems overflow and contaminate drinking water. Without treatment, mortality rates can reach as high as 70%, with death occurring in as little as 24 hr. It is estimated that the cholera pandemics at the beginning of the nineteenth century resulted in the deaths of millions of people worldwide and that in India between 1900 and 1950 approximately 100,000 people died yearly from cholera. The incubation period is between 12 and 72 hr. with most cases occurring 24–48 hr after exposure. With iv treatment or ORT, however, mortality rates are reduced to less than 0.5%, with complete recovery in 2 or 3 days.

Some interesting data link blood type with severity of cholera symptoms, with the O blood group having a higher susceptibility to cholera than other blood types. The reason for this susceptibility is unknown.

## IX. VACCINES

Work toward the development of a vaccine for cholera began more than a century ago. Clinical infection with *V. cholerae* produces a long-lasting protective immunity. Because only the O1 and, *recently* the O139 serotypes of *V. cholerae* cause large-scale epidemics, the development of a safe and effective vaccine against cholera seems very feasible. An ideal cholera vaccine should produce long-lasting protective immunity against O1 and O139 strains of *V. cholerae* following a single dose and should be safe, inexpensive to produce, and easy to administer. Several parenterally administered killed whole cell vaccines that have been tested induce only weak and short-lived immunity. Parenteral vaccines for cholera have been largely abandoned because they do not generate an adequate local immune response at the site of cholera infections, the mucosal surface. Attention has focused on the development of oral cholera vaccines, with both live-attenuated and killed whole cell vaccines being pursued. Limitations of whole cell oral vaccines include the need for multiple-spaced doses of the vaccine, the relative expense for preparing the preparation, and a lower protection in children and persons of blood group O.

The possibility of generating a live-attenuated cholera vaccine was initially shown with a *V. cholerae* strain called Texas Star-SR that produced the immunogenic B subunit, but not the enzymatically active A subunit of CT. Recently, recombinant DNA technology has been used to generate similar but genetically stable, live-attenuated *V. cholerae* vaccine strains. The first recombinant live oral vaccines tested in human volunteers expressed neither the A nor the B subunit of CT (JBK70) or only expressed the non-toxic B subunit (CVD101). Although both strains were effective immunogens, they were also very reactogenic, causing symptoms such as mild to severe diarrhea, cramps, nausea, and anorexia. The reasons for this reactogenicity are currently not understood, but it is possible that *V. cholerae* may secrete additional toxins. Alternatively, the mere colonization of the intestinal tract by the bacteria may somehow disturb intestinal function and lead to the observed side effects. A recombinant oral vaccine strain that was well tolerated and immunogenic (CVD103-HgR), has been tested extensively in clinical trials. Various rates of success have been observed with this strain, but no efficacy was found in a recent large-scale clinical trial in Indonesia.

Recent efforts to generate vaccine constructs have focused on the O139 and O1 (El Tor biotype) serogroups because most of the cases of cholera in the current pandemic are caused by these strains. As a precautionary measure, the region carrying the CTX genetic element has been deleted, resulting in the loss of the *ctxAB* genes as well as the RS and *attRS* sequences. This deletion should prevent the strains from re-integrating the CTXφ phage into the chromosome. To confer another level of safety the *recA* gene has also been deleted from these strains. Overexpression of the B subunit of CT may have an adjuvant effect as well as elicit an antitoxic immune response, therefore, the *ctxB* gene has been introduced under the control of the powerful heat shock promoter. Furthermore, these strains are non-motile, a trait that may account for the remarkable lack of reactogenicity observed with these vaccine strains in volunteers. A safe and effective oral live attenuated cholera vaccine might become available for public use in the near future.

## X. CONCLUSIONS

Cholera is an ancient disease, with a colorful history that has shaped mankind in various ways. The severe and potentially lethal diarrhea associated with cholera is characteristic of the disease. The causative agent of cholera, *V. cholerae*, is a gram-negative bacterium that colonizes the human intestinal tract and elaborates a powerful enterotoxin, (CT), the activity of which is directly responsible for the symptoms observed in cholera patients. TCPs are essential for colonization. As in many pathogenic bacteria, the genes encoding the two main virulence factors of *V. cholerae*, CT a TCP, are located on distinct genetic elements. It was only recently recognized that the *ctx* genes are part of the genome of a filamentous phage that uses TCP as its receptor. The genes for biogenesis of TCP also reside on a genetic element that has been recognized as a "pathogenicity island." Thus, horizontal gene transfer and *in vivo* expression of virulence factors are remarkably linked in the emergence of *V. cholerae* as a pathogen.

Furthermore, the expression of CT and TCP is coordinately regulated by a regulatory cascade of transcriptional activators. Understanding how the different regulatory proteins interact may tell us something about the evolution of virulence gene regulation. Although the origin of the TCP pathogenicity island is not known, it appears that it is responsible for transfer of the genes necessary for biogenesis of TCP, a set of regulatory proteins (TcpP/H and ToxT), and several proteins that can interact with the motility apparatus. Whereas most *Vibrio* species have ToxR/S homologs, the TCP island is absent in most environmental isolates of *V. cholerae*. Therefore, in pathogenic strains, this acquired element has integrated the regulation of its genes into the signal transduction network of the host bacterium. As we continue to study the mechanisms affecting virulence gene expression in this organism, we will gain a better understanding not only of the basic biology of signal transduction and regulation but also of the evolution of such a remarkable integration.

## See Also the Following Articles

Enteropathogenic Bacteria • Vaccines, Bacterial • Water, Drinking

## Bibliography

Barua, D., and Greenough, W. B. (1992). "Cholera." Plenum, New York.

Kaper, J. B., Morris, J. G., and Levine, M. M. (1995). Cholera. *Clin. Microbiol. Rev.* **8**, 48–86.

Pollitzer, R. (1959). "Cholera," Monograph No. 42. World Health Organization, Geneva.

Skorupski, K., and Taylor, R. K. (1997). Control of the ToxR virulence regulon in *Vibrio cholerae* by environmental stimuli. *Mol. Microbiol.* **25**, 1003–1009.

Van Heyningen, W. E., and Seal, J. R. (1983). "Cholera: The American Scientific Experience. 1947–1980." Westview, Boulder, CO.

Wachsmuth, K., Blake, P. A., and Olsvik, Ø (1994). "*Vibrio cholerae* and Cholera: Molecular to Global Perspectives." ASM Press, Washington, DC.

Waldor, M. K., and Mekalanos, J. J. (1996). *Vibrio cholerae:* Molecular pathogenesis, immune response, and vaccine development. *In* "Enteric Infections and Immunity" (L. J. Paradise, Ed.), pp. 37–55. Plenum, New York.

# Cholera, Historical

### Christopher D. Meehan and Howard Markel

*University of Michigan Medical School*

## GLOSSARY

**anticontagionism** The belief that disease originates not from the transmission of germs from person to person but rather from interaction with an unsuitable environment, contact with rotting or deteriorating organic material, inhalation of polluted or contaminated air, or immoral behaviors.

**contagionism** The belief that disease is transmitted by direct or indirect contact between living organisms, especially humans, in the form of microscopic living entities (e.g., germs).

**miasma** Literally, foul or bad air arising from decaying animal or vegetable matter, thought by anti-contagionists to cause disease.

**quarantine** Originates from the Italian words *quarantina* and *quaranta giorno*, referring to the 40 day period ships entering the port of Venice were required to remain in isolation before any disembarkment. Defined by public health authorities in the nineteenth century as the process of inspecting all ships, cargos, and passengers for evidence of contagious diseases.

**sanitarians** Public health officials who worked to eradicate disease by disinfecting the environment and imposing sanitary restrictions on citizens.

**CHOLERA** is an acute diarrheal disease in which *Vibrio cholerae*, serogroup 1, found only in humans, are present in large numbers in the small intestine. Marked by severe abdominal pains and rapid dehydration, cholera has brought horrific and untimely death to millions as it swept the world in as many as seven pandemics in the past two centuries. Cholera's modern history as a worldwide pandemic disease begins in 1817. Long endemic in India, cholera at this time began to make its way out of the subcontinent and spread as far as the United States by 1832. Cholera, described by one historian as "the classic epidemic disease of the nineteenth century," has played a major role in medical history, particularly due to its widespread physical and emotional effects on individuals, societies, and cultures. The disease manifests with little warning, induces frightfully painful symptoms in its victims, and kills between 30 and 80% of those infected. Moreover, the cholera pandemics spanned generations, crossed political and geographic boundaries, and fueled fears of disease during a time of dramatic growth in the life sciences, public health, and international migration.

## I. ETYMOLOGICAL CONSIDERATIONS

The Greek word *kholera*, meaning "bile" or "to flow," is found in sources as early as the Hippocratic corpus. Classical writers such as Celsus (first century AD) used the term "cholera" to describe illnesses marked by sporadic diarrhea, vomiting, and gripping abdominal pain. Although the term cholera has been in use for millennia, the term was applied in various ways to describe a variety of conditions. For example, the term "choleric," meaning "easily moved to anger," is also derived from *kholera*, but was a concept employed by humoralists to describe the condition resulting from vitiated humors. It was not until 1669 that Thomas Sydenham first used the term "cholera morbus" to distinguish sporadic and endemic diarrhea from the choleric concept. By the early nineteenth century, when cholera reached global epidemic proportions, the term "cholera nostras" had come to designate diseases with symptoms similar to sporadic and endemic cholera (i.e., profuse diarrhea, dehydration, and cramps), whereas cholera morbus described the more virulent occurrences of epidemic cholera. Other terms synonymous with epidemic cholera are cholera asiatica, malignant cholera, cholera asphyxia, and cholera spasmodica.

## II. PATHOGENESIS, SIGNS, AND SYMPTOMS

The disease called cholera today occurs when the etiological organism *Vibrio cholerae* is ingested and passes through the stomach into the small bowel, where it colonizes and multiplies. The *V. cholerae* is an acid-sensitive bacterium and a human must ingest a relatively large inoculum for sufficient numbers to evade the acidic environment of the stomach and reach the small intestine. The organism then releases a toxin which enters the epithelial cells, disrupting the absorption of electrolytes, and results in copious, watery discharges relatively free of fecal material accompanied by shedded mucous and epithelial cells giving it a characteristic "rice water" appearance.

The signs and symptoms of cholera are the result of a rapid loss of fluid and electrolytes. Symptoms begin with the victim's sense of generally not feeling well. This condition lasts only a few hours and is then followed by a violent bout of vomiting and diarrhea. The victim experiences painful spasms of the abdominal muscles as a result of forceful propulsions of the gut, and matters only worsen as hypovolemic shock ensues. The effects of dehydration are painfully apparent on the face of the victim; the skin becomes blue and tight, the eyes sunken deeply in their sockets, and the lips and mucus membranes of the mouth are dry and cracked. As diarrhea and vomiting continues, patients become increasingly more disoriented and eventually lapse into convulsion and/or coma. From 30 to 80% of all cholera cases end in death.

## III. ETIOLOGY

From antiquity until well into the nineteenth century, the medical theory of the cause of cholera was relatively static. For the most part, illness was perceived as an imbalance in the bodily humors due to poor diet, change in weather or seasons, geographic environment, or exposure to poisoned air or miasmas, such as the foul air caused by rotting organic material or animal and human waste. Although humoral theory waned during the nineteenth century, miasmatic theory and environmental influences continued to serve as explanations for disease. In a world still influenced largely by religious morality, people also often invoked metaphysical conceptions to explain cholera and other diseases. In America during the 1830s, for example, many ministers, moralists, and physicians agreed that those suffering from cholera had engaged in sinful activities and thereby predisposed themselves to sickness.

When the second pandemic reached Europe and the United States (1832), delegations of scientists and physicians were sent out to study the spread of cholera, and questions about its contagious nature slowly began to surface. Germ theory was far from well established at this time, but burgeoning interests in contagionism and increasing knowledge of microorganisms stirred the imagination of medical scientists to search beyond the traditional metaphysical and environmental explanations of disease.

Perhaps one of the greatest challenges to miasmatic theories on the cause of cholera came from John Snow, a British physician and epidemiologist. In the summer of 1849 he published a pamphlet "On the Mode of Communication of Cholera," in which he proposed that cholera was a water-borne disease. In 1854, his theory would be put to the test. He mapped incidences of cholera which occurred near Golden Square in London and noted that many cases were clustered around a particular water pump on Broad Street. After careful analysis, his cholera pamphlet was expanded and reprinted in 1855, reporting findings that sewage had seeped into the well which the recent victims of cholera used and concluding that contaminated water was the "predisposing cause" of cholera. Although Snow was unaware of the causative agent, he posited that *materis morbi* (poisonous matter) must have caused the infection. Although many papers and pamphlets were published on studies similar to Snow's (such as the work of William Budd) and some measures were taken to avoid contaminated water, many medical and scientific elites who subscribed to anti-contagionist theories, such as the German public health expert Max Von Pettenkofer, remained resolute in their belief that cholera was caused by imbalances in the air, soil, and environment or exposure to human and animal filth in overcrowded cities. Shortly after Snow announced his findings, Italian microscopist Filippo Pacini reported his discovery of a microorganism with a terminal flagellum, isolated from the excreta of a cholera victim. This report, however, did not attract much interest among the medical community. Moralist ideas and claims about miasmatic theory were slow to die.

Anticontagionism, however, steadily lost scientific credibility as the nineteenth century progressed. For example, in 1868, the French chemist Louis Pasteur first articulated the germ theory when he elucidated the microbial cause of silkworm diseases. Fifteen years later, the famed microbiologist Robert Koch isolated the *V. cholerae* during the cholera epidemics in Calcutta and Alexandria. Indeed, Koch's studies confirmed that cholera is transmitted in drinking water and food contaminated with fecal matter from those infected with cholera.

The acceptance of germ theory and rapid growth in the science of bacteriology yielded more advances in the field of cholera research at the turn of the century. Recent investigation has elucidated the existence of 60 or more serogroups of *V. cholerae*, of which only a single group, serogroup 1, is responsible for the epidemic cholera; others are responsible for sporadic diarrhea and symptoms similar to epidemic cholera. Serogroup 1 of the *V. cholerae* exists as two serotypes, Ogawa and Inaba, each characteristic of different somatic antigen structures in the organism. *Vibrio cholerae* also occur as two major biotypes: the classic (first described by Koch) and El Tor. The El Tor vibrio was discovered in 1905, during the sixth pandemic, in the El Tor quarantine camp in Egypt.

Six unusual strains of vibrios were isolated from the dead bodies of pilgrims returned from Mecca. Gotschlich, who isolated the strains, performed tests that revealed the reactions of classic *V. cholerae*, though the victims did not show any signs of the cholera disease post mortem or while they were alive. Upon reexamination of the strains, Kraus and Pribram found that the El Tor vibrios produced a haemotoxin found to be lethal in experimental animals. They hyothesized that variability in the biotypes could be responsible for individual cholera epidemics. This was clearly demonstrated in the 1960s when El Tor was found to be the cause of many cholera outbreaks throughout the world.

The previous hypothesis was further supported in early 1993 when a *V. cholerae* strain, with an antigenic structure differing from that of El Tor, was found responsible for a large outbreak in India. The existence of the newly identified strain, named O139 Bengal, demonstrates that epidemic potential is not exclusive to the classic and El Tor vibrios bearing the O1 antigen. The existence of O139 Bengal is indicative of an emerging level of complexity in the relationship of genetic and epidemiological factors facing today's researchers and public health officials.

## IV. THE PANDEMICS

### A. First Pandemic

In 1817, northeastern India experienced a particularly heavy rainfall that brought deluge to the state of Bengal and other regions between the Ganges and Brahmaputra Rivers. Floods resulted in failed crops and destroyed villages, and following the devastation cholera appeared with extraordinary virulence. In July of that year, cholera broke out in several districts in Bengal. Within a month, 25,000 people in Calcutta were being treated for the disease, 4000 of whom perished. This episode marks the beginning of cholera as a worldwide pandemic disease. Only 3 months later the province of Bengal was consumed by the disease, and by 1818 cholera extended in all directions to Nepal, Burma, and further into India: Delhi, Bombay, and as far as Ceylon. Although cholera affected these regions in the past, the rapidity with which it spread and the numbers mortally endangered in 1817 cast a shadow over any previous record of the disease. By 1820, the disease had spread by sea and land routes to Southeast Asia, moving from Burma to Siam's (Thailand) capital city of Bangkok and to Indonesia, where as many as 100,000 people succumbed to the cholera menace.

By 1822, incidences of cholera began to subside in India, although the disease was widely established outside the subcontinent. Ships traveling from Southeast Asia carried the epidemic to China, where it had been previously introduced by land travelers as early as 1817. Soon after, the British army landed infected troops from Bombay into Oman, Arabia, from where the disease spread and was established in Muscat by 1821. In the same year, 15,000–18,000 people were killed along the Persian Gulf in port cities such as Basra. From this region cholera continued on, moving across the Mediterranean region, carried by caravans into countries such as Syria, where it raged until the end of 1823. The spread of cholera was greatly facilitated by Persian troops victoriously returning home to present-day Iran after warring with Turks; they served as vectors for the deadly vibrio, disseminating cholera in areas between the Tigris and Euphrates Rivers.

After raging across the Far and Middle East for as many as three or four seasons, cholera subsided but remained active in Lower Bengal, India. Some have posited that control measures may have been responsible for cholera's retreat in the early 1820s, although others have ascribed its decline to a severe winter during 1823 and 1824.

## B. Second Pandemic (1829–1837)

By 1824 cholera settled back in its home, the endemic area of the Ganges Delta in Bengal, India. There the disease remained active until 1827, when it was reported to have moved west to the Punjab. Cholera continued to exist in isolated regions outside of India during the interpandemic period; therefore, when the disease spread to the north and west of the Caspian Sea, into Russia and neighboring countries, it was thought that the pandemic's origin came from Astrakhan, Azerbaijan, where cholera had persisted throughout the 1820s. However, cholera did not disperse from Astrakhan until 1830, although it was observed to be a problem in Orenburg, Russia as early as 1829. Reports from that period in China demonstrated that the second pandemic made its way back into areas of China, particularly in and around Peking, via India, and from there gradually extended into Russia. Similarly, cholera was creeping across Persia from Afghanistan into Russia by way of caravans. Although these scenarios might not explain cholera's appearance in Orenburg, they demonstrate the vast space through which cholera steadily advanced early in the second pandemic.

Well established in Russia by 1830 in cities such as Moscow and Kharkov, cholera was then introduced into Poland by the Russian army. A ship transported the disease from Riga to the Prussian city of Danzig, resulting in a wave of infection that soon spread to Berlin, Vienna, and Hamburg by late 1831. At this time, some of the first cases of cholera were appearing in England in the port city of Sunderland, which had shipping connections with Germany. Cholera effectively made its way through England in 1832, infecting as many as 15,000 people and leaving more than one-third of them dead. That same year cholera visited Ireland and France. All of Paris' districts were reportedly overcome with the disease and as many as 7000 people died in 18 days. By early 1832, much of Europe was suffering from the devastating effects of cholera. Having traveled from Asia through the Near East and into Europe, it crossed the Atlantic and released its fury in North America. On June 8, a ship from Dublin carried 173 passengers to Quebec City and Montreal, of which 42 died before reaching port. On June 23, cholera appeared in New York, and 2 weeks later it surfaced in Philadelphia. From the north the epidemic spread to Mexico, Latin America, and the Caribbean. It was not until 1837 that the second cholera pandemic finally subsided.

## C. Third Pandemic (1846–1855)

Scholars have long debated the dates of the second and third pandemics. Authorities such as Pollitzer considered the second pandemic to have run until 1851, marking the commencement of the third in 1852. Others, however, noting the significant decrease in cases of cholera and its withdrawal in some areas during the period of the mid-1830s to the mid-1840s, have concluded that the resurgence of the disease in 1846 marks the beginning of a third pandemic.

In 1846 cholera again erupted in and around the endemic regions of south Asia. Having already extended into Persia and central Asia during 1844 and 1845, Europe was again invaded by cholera by 1848 in much the same fashion as the disease progressed during the second pandemic. In that same year, New York and New Orleans were miserably reacquainted with cholera. From these cities cholera spread rapidly across North America, reaching as far as California in 1850. Present throughout Europe since 1849, cholera continued its course, eventually surging in 1854, making this year one of the worst on record.

## D. Fourth Pandemic (1863–1879)

In the fourth pandemic, cholera flourished in the same regions as it had in past pandemics, but it infiltrated Europe via new routes. Instead of moving from Asia, across Persia and the Caspian Sea, and into the heart of Europe, cholera traveled across Arabia. In Mecca, for example, 30,000 of 90,000 pilgrims died in 1865. The scourge progressed throughout the Mediterranean regions from Alexandria, Egypt, and this time entered Europe through Italy and southern France. From Egypt, Africa's countries along the eastern coast were ravaged as far south as Mozambique. When cholera traveled north in 1866, some of the worst episodes occurred in Germany; where up to 115,000 deaths were reported. In Berlin, approximately 5,500 deaths occurred out of 8000 cases. It has been suggested that Austria's wars with Germany and Italy may have contributed to cholera's dissemination.

In 1866, the United States was just recovering from the Civil War when cholera returned for a third American epidemic. New Orleans was hit by several waves of cholera through 1868 and the disease spread through the South and the Midwest via the extension of the railway system. However, the outbreaks were mild in comparison to previous epidemics. In New York, measures such as the cleaning of city streets and the isolation of the ill were successful in pre-

venting the further transmission of disease. Cholera resurfaced again in New York and New Orleans in 1873–1875, though casualties were minimal. Russia, Persia, Arabia, Africa, India, and much of East Asia, however, suffered repeated serious attacks of cholera during this period. Central Europe also had its share of cases, but epidemics were less widespread due to the increasing awareness of public health.

## E. Fifth Pandemic (1881–1896)

Many of the early epidemics of this period occurred in Asia, particularly China, and around the Mediterranean. However, in 1892 Hamburg suffered a huge outbreak of cholera due to the contamination of unfiltered water from the Elbe River; approximately 7500 deaths occurred. In North America, potential epidemics were again prevented due to advanced notice and modern sanitary measures, although isolated cases were recorded, particularly in New York City.

## F. Sixth Pandemic (1899–1923)

Cholera recrudesced in India in 1899, marking the start of the sixth pandemic. Cholera never disappeared completely from China and other regions of Asia after the previous pandemic, as was also the case for Egypt. From these regions, cholera spread to Persia, Arabia, and Afghanistan. During this period, America and most of Europe were largely unaffected, although sporadic cases occurred in southern Europe and Hungary.

## G. Seventh Pandemic (1961–Present)

Many of the epidemics occurring in the present era have been traced to the El Tor biotype. El Tor was isolated in Indonesia and China in 1961 and in 1962 the World Health Organization recommended the inclusion of diseases caused by El Tor to appear in the definition of cholera. Both the classical and El Tor biotypes were detected in Afghanistan, from where the El Tor spread to neighboring Iran. An upsurge of cholera infection was also documented to have spread into Europe and Africa in 1970 and 1971. Since 1972, the number of countries affected in any one year has declined. However, in South America, where nearly a century had passed since the last reported cholera cases, the disease broke out violently in Peru in early 1991. El Tor was found responsible for this episode and for the recurrent Latin American epidemics that followed in the early 1990s. In late 1992, cholera-like disease appeared in Madras, India. The outbreak spread north into Bangladesh, where 100,000 cases were reported in the next 6 months. The new strain of *V. cholerae*, O139 Bengal, was the source of this epidemic that subsequently spread to Pakistan, Nepal, and regions of Southeast Asia. Cholera remains endemic in areas of Asia, Africa, and many countries of South and Central America, and rarely isolated cases of cholera have been imported to America and Europe. One relatively recent occurrence was reported in Los Angeles in 1993 after a woman returned from a 6-week visit to Hyderabad, India.

### H. Geographical Considerations

Cholera owes much of its geographical distribution to pilgrimage, the industrial revolution, international shipping, traveling armies, and immigration. For example, large religious festivals in India convene near sacred sights, usually along the banks of sacred rivers. Upon people's return home from such festivals, where thousands camped and used the same water supplies, cholera often followed. A similar process has been observed during the Islamic pilgrimages to Mecca. As transportation, such as with the steamship, became more efficient and continental and intercontinental railways linked city and village, the dissemination of the disease accelerated. The need for large work forces during the industrial revolution and the desire of many to emigrate because of either political or religious persecution contributed to the crowding of cities and the contamination of water supplies.

## V. CONTROL, PREVENTION, AND TREATMENT

Some of the most significant topics explored in the history of medicine, such as the modern-day understanding of contagious diseases, the rise of san-

itation and public health institutions, and developments in medical therapy, find context in the history of cholera. For much of the nineteenth century, doctors found that they could do very little to prevent or cure cholera. Revolutions in industry and transportation brought about the rapid growth of urban populations. It was in this setting, including the living conditions of crowded and dirty cities, contaminated water supplies, and large-scale migration of peoples, that cholera proliferated before traveling into bucolic areas. Before the 1830s, city officials had little interest in public health. With news of cholera moving from East to West, however, both European and American newspapers and popular magazines reported the spread of the disease, raising the attention of civic leaders and the public. Physicians and public health officials published pamphlets and articles and posted signs encouraging personal hygiene. Anti-contagionists such as Von Pettenkofer warned of bad air and soil and encouraged proper nourishment and sanitary measures. John Snow, on the other hand, encouraged attention to maintaining clean water and Koch's discovery of the etiology of cholera, *V. cholerae*, led to the development of modern public health policies and sanitation procedures and techniques that continue to maintain health in much of the industrialized world.

One of the initial responses to cholera's appearance or impending crossing of borders was the use of quarantine. For example, soon after it was reported that cholera broke out in Canada in 1832, both Canadian and United States ports issued quarantine measures on all shipping and goods. In 1892, an epidemic of cholera was effectively prevented by the quarantining of ships in New York Harbor, where infected passengers were found. Entire vessels were quarantined for days until it was certain that no cholera would be introduced to the population on land. As a result of bacteriologists' increasing abilities to recognize organisms and epidemiologist's facility to track disease, scientists, physicians, and public health officials have been successful in controlling the spread of cholera.

Treatment of cholera before and during the early nineteenth century employed the use of emetics, purgatives, and even bloodletting. Such practices probably only worsened the conditions of the ill. As early as 1830 research in fluid balance led physicians to attempt injecting water into terminally ill cholera patients. Many of these patients demonstrated the return of a strong pulse, but soon died. Injections of salt water proved slightly more helpful, although determining a proper and effective solution was not always possible. Hence, such a treatment did not become successful until the early decades of the twentieth century when physicians had a clearer understanding of water and electrolyte balance. After the discovery of antibiotics in the 1940s, their use and a carefully planned regimen of fluid replacement greatly improved the therapeutic resources of physicians.

## VI. CHOLERA AND SOCIETY

Epidemics are commonly viewed as crises and engender massive reactions by physicians, public health workers, and lay-people. One unfortunate theme in the history of cholera (as with other epidemic diseases) is the scapegoating of those people and social groups perceived to be the vectors of the epidemic in question. The history of immigration illustrates such examples, where massive movements of peoples resulted in the transmission of disease across borders. In large cities that attracted great numbers of immigrants, such as New York City, the meeting of various ethnic groups and cultures set the stage for dramatic shifts in civic and social organization. When dealing with the cholera menace, societies, governments, and groups such as public health organizations at times did not hesitate to point the finger at marginalized peoples, labeling them as the bearers of disease. Immigrants were perceived to be predisposed to disease based on the association with the relatively few immigrants who did arrive in U.S. ports ill with cholera and hence stigmatized. In reality, cholera was a social leveler that attacked people of all social classes and backgrounds. Nevertheless, the fear of cholera often inspired certain majority social groups to scapegoat and blame minority groups, such as immigrants and the urban poor.

On the other hand, the cholera pandemics in the nineteenth century helped solidify ideas and sentiment towards concerns for public health in a time of scientific, economic, and societal growth. During this period, the pandemics also inspired the formation of the first international health agency (the International Sanitary Conferences), demonstrating that epidemics also have the power to bring nations together. Hence, the history of cholera illustrates that epidemic disease is an intimate part of social organization and change.

### See Also the Following Articles

Plague • Typhoid, Historical

### Bibliography

Bilson, G. (1980). "A Darkened House: Cholera in Nineteenth-Century Canada." Univ. of Toronto Press, Toronto.

Delaporte, F. (1986). "Disease and Civilization: The Cholera in Paris, 1832." MIT Press, Cambridge.

Evans, R. J. (1987). "Death in Hamburg: Society and Politics in the Cholera Years, 1830–1910." Oxford University Press, Oxford.

Kudlick, C. J. (1996). "Cholera in Post-Revolutionary Paris: A Cultural History." Univ. of California Press, Berkeley.

Longmate, N. (1966). "King Cholera: The Biography of a Disease." Hamilton, London.

Markel, H. (1997). "Quarantine! East European Jewish Immigrants and the New York City Epidemics of 1892." Johns Hopkins Univ. Press, Baltimore.

McGrew, R. E. (1965). "Russia and the Cholera (1823–1832)." Univ. of Wisconsin Press, Madison.

Morris, R. J. (1976). "Cholera, 1832: The Social Response to an Epidemic." Holmes & Meier, New York.

Pollitzer, R. (1959). "Cholera." World Health Organization, Geneva.

Rosenburg, C. E. (1962). "The Cholera Years, the United States in 1832, 1849, 1866." Univ. of Chicago, Chicago.

Snow, J. (1936). "Snow on Cholera: Being a Reprint of Two Papers" (B. W. Richardson, Ed.). Milford, London.

Snowden, F. M. (1995). "Naples in the Time of Cholera, 1884–1911." Cambridge Univ. Press, Cambridge, UK.

# Chromosome, Bacterial

## Karl Drlica

*Public Health Research Institute and New York University*

## Arnold J. Bendich

*University of Washington*

## GLOSSARY

**DNA supercoiling** A phenomenon occurring in circular, covalently closed, duplex DNA molecules when the number of turns differs from the number found in DNA molecules of the same length but containing an end that can rotate. Supercoiling creates strain in closed DNA molecules. A deficiency of duplex turns generates negative supercoiling; a surplus generates positive supercoiling.

**DNA topoisomerases** Enzymes that change DNA topology by breaking and rejoining DNA strands. Topoisomerases introduce and remove supercoils, tie and untie knots, and catenate and decatenate circular DNA molecules.

**nucleoid** A term for the bacterial chromosome when it is in a compact configuration, either inside a cell or as an isolated structure.

**origin of replication** A location on the chromosome (*oriC*) where initiation of replication occurs. For *Escherichia coli*, *oriC* is approximately 250 nucleotides long, and during initiation it specifically interacts with several proteins to form an initiation complex.

**recombination** A process in which two DNA molecules are broken and rejoined in such a way that portions of the two molecules are exchanged.

**replication fork** The point at which duplex DNA separates into two single strands during the process of DNA replication. Associated with replication forks are DNA helicases to separate the strands and DNA polymerases to synthesize new DNA strands.

**BACTERIAL CHROMOSOMES** are intracellular repositories of genetic information. In molecular terms, chromosomes are composed of (i) large DNA molecules that store information, (ii) RNA molecules in the process of copying information from specific genes, and (iii) proteins that repair DNA damage, duplicate the DNA, and control patterns of gene expression. Proteins also fold and bend the DNA so it fits in the cell. In many bacteria, chromosomal DNA appears to be circular, but examples of linear chromosomes have also been found. An individual cell can contain multiple identical copies of a single chromosome. Two and three distinct chromosome types have been observed in some species. When cells contain very large plasmids, the distinction between plasmid and chromosome blurs if both carry genes essential for cell growth. Chromosomal DNA has fewer duplex turns than would be found in linear, B-form DNA under the same conditions, and this deficiency of turns places torsional (superhelical) strain on the DNA. The strain lowers energy barriers for strand separation, and in this sense the chromosome is energetically activated. DNA replication begins at a precise point and continues bidirectionally until the two replication forks meet in a region 180° from the origin in circular DNA or until they reach the ends of linear DNA. As DNA is replicated, attached proteins pull the daughter chromosomes apart while other proteins untangle the DNA. Nucleotide sequence analysis of many bacterial genomes reveals that chromosomes have a rich evolutionary history of sequence rearrangements, which are due largely to fragments of DNA moving into and out of chromosomes.

## I. HISTORICAL INTRODUCTION

Bacterial chromosomes were discovered much later than their eukaryotic counterparts because they do not exhibit the striking condensation at metaphase that makes eukaryotic chromosomes so easy to visualize. By the 1940s evidence that bacteria undergo spontaneous mutation finally emerged, and this established that bacteria must have mutable genes, the functional elements of chromosomes. At about the same time, Avery and associates uncovered the chemical nature of genetic material with a transformation experiment in which a character for polysaccharide synthesis was transferred from one strain of *Pneumococcus* to another using extracted DNA. At the time, the result was not universally accepted as evidence for genetic exchange, partly because the so-called "transforming principle," DNA, exerted its effect after an unknown number of steps and partly because there was no molecular framework for explaining how DNA could function as genetic material. In 1952, Hershey and Chase announced that phage DNA, not protein, is injected into bacterial cells during infection, and a year later Watson and Crick provided the structural framework for DNA. At that point DNA became widely accepted as the carrier of hereditary information. By 1956, nucleoids, as bacterial chromosomes are sometimes called, could be seen in living cells as discrete, compact structures (a modern view is shown in Fig. 1). Gentle extraction methods eventually yielded large, intact DNA molecules, and by the early 1970s it became possible to isolate a compact form of the chromosome for biochemical study (Fig. 2). DNA supercoiling was discovered in the mid-1960s, and within a decade

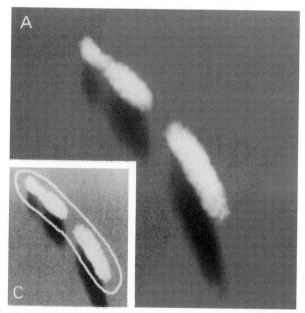
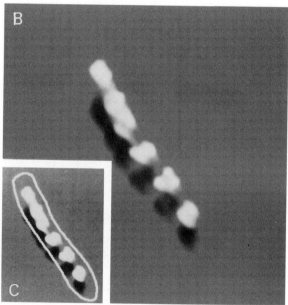

**Fig. 1.** Bacterial nucleoids. Nucleoids of *Escherichia coli* K-12 were visualized in a confocal scanning laser microscope as developed by G. J. Brankenhoff (1985). Elongated cells were obtained by growth in broth. Then the nucleoids were stained with the DNA-specific fluorochrome DAPI (0.1 $\mu$g/ml) added to the growth medium. Under these conditions the stain had no effect on growth. The cells were observed either alive (A) or after fixation with 0.1% osmium tetroxide (B). Since the cell boundary is not easily visualized, it has been sketched in for reference (C). Multiple nucleoids were present because these fast-growing cells contain DNA in a state of multifork replication. In live cells the nucleoid has a cloud-like appearance and a smooth boundary with the cytoplasm (protuberances, if present, would be smaller than 200 nm). Magnification = 9000 × (courtesy of Dr. Conrad Woldringh, Department of Molecular Cell Biology, University of Amsterdam, The Netherlands).

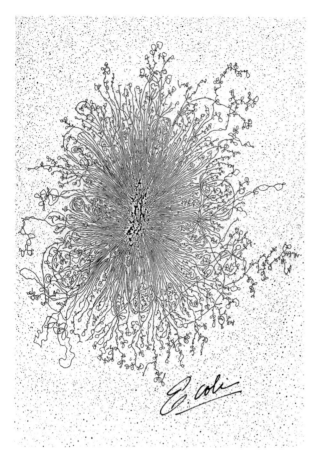

**Fig. 2.** Isolated bacterial chromosome. Electron micrograph of a purified, surface-spread *E. coli* chromosome by Ruth Kavenoff and Brian Bowen. The line under the *E. coli* signature represents 2.5 $\mu$m (copyright 1983 with all rights reserved by DesignerGenes, P.O. Box 100, Del Mar, CA 92014, in trust for the Julius Marmur Memorial Fund, Biochemistry Dept., Albert Einstein College of Medicine, Bronx, NY, 10461, USA.).

enzymes that introduce and remove supercoils had been characterized by Wang, Gellert, and Cozzarelli. The existence of these enzymes, DNA topoisomerases, gave credence to the idea that chromosomal DNA is under torsional tension. During the 1980s, the dynamic, regulated nature of supercoiling emerged as a major structural feature that needed to be considered whenever the activities of the chromosome were discussed. The development of rapid methods for determining nucleotide sequences led in the 1990s to complete sequences for many bacterial genomes. Information from DNA sequence analyses made it likely that all living organisms share a com-

mon ancestor, and inferences could be drawn about the nucleotide sequence history of chromosomes.

An emerging theme is the dynamic nature of bacterial chromosomes. In terms of nucleotide sequence, massive gene shuffling has occurred over the course of evolution. With respect to three-dimensional structure, portions of the genome move to particular regions of the cell at specific times during the cell cycle, even as the bulk of the DNA threads through stationary replication forks. At the level of DNA conformation, changes can occur within minutes after alteration of cellular environment. All three types of change are influenced, and in some cases directed, by protein components of chromosomes. In this article, we discuss major concepts concerning chromosome structure and point out unanswered questions. We conclude by describing a speculative model of the chromosome that may help put some of the details in perspective.

## II. CHROMOSOME FORM AND NUMBER

Bacterial DNA has been found in both circular and linear forms. For *Escherichia coli*, chromosomal circularity is supported by three lines of evidence. First, circles were observed when radioactively labeled DNA was extracted from cells and then examined by autoradiography. In these experiments almost all the molecules were so tangled that their configurations were unclear, but a few appeared as large circles more than 1 mm in length (cells are only 1 or 2 $\mu$m-long). This chromosomal length is approximately that expected from DNA mass measurements combined with the assumption that *E. coli* contains a single chromosome. Second, genetic mapping studies are most easily interpreted as if the genes are arranged in a circle, although a linear interpretation is still possible (mapping can be ambiguous since a large linear bacteriophage DNA is known to have a circular genetic map). Third, two replication forks emerge from a single origin of replication and move bidirectionally toward a single terminus located 180° opposite the origin on the circular map. Replication data, which clearly reflect the whole cell population, are the strongest of the three lines of evidence. Conclusive evidence for circularity, which is still lacking, would be visualization of circular images of most of the DNA molecules present.

In 1989, chromosomal DNA molecules of *Borrelia burgdorferi* were found to have a linear form. Linear chromosomes were subsequently observed in *Streptomyces* species, *Rhodococcus fascians*, and *Agrobacterium tumefaciens*. With *Streptomyces*, DNA ends contain repetitive sequences as well as terminal proteins that prime synthesis complementary to the 3′ end of the DNA. In *B. burgdorferi,* the ends are hairpins that facilitate complete replication. Thus, bacteria have chromosomal ends that function similarly to the telomeres of linear chromosomes in eukaryotic cells.

Most bacteria carry all their genes in a single genetic linkage group, as if they have a single type of chromosome. However, there is a growing list of species in which useful or essential genes are found on two or more chromosomes. The number of large, circular-mapping molecules is two for *Vibrio* species, *Leptospira interrogans*, *Rhodobacter sphaeroides,* and *Brucella* species, three for *Rhizobium meliloti,* and two to four among isolates of *Burkholderi (Pseudomonas) capecia*. Some *Agrobacterium* species contain one circular- and one linear-mapping chromosome. Thus, the idea that prokaryotes contain only one circular chromosome has been abandoned. Indeed, those with more than one chromosome (genetic linkage group) may constitute a sizable class since the vast majority of bacterial species has yet to be examined.

It is occasionally difficult to distinguish between chromosomes and plasmids since some plasmids are very large and contain genes essential for cell growth. Moreover, some large plasmids integrate into, and excise from, chromosomes. Thus, chromosome number in some species may be variable.

The existence of multiple copies of chromosomal regions, as well as entire chromosomes (multiploidy), is well-known in eukaryotes. In addition, a eukaryotic cell can contain thousands of copies of mitochondrial and chloroplast genomes. Multicopy genes and chromosomes are also common among bacteria. For example, *E. coli* contains approximately 11 genome equivalents per cell when growing rapidly in rich medium, whereas this number is between 1 and 2 during slow growth. In this organism high copy number may facilitate rapid cell doubling (see Section VII). For *Deinococcus radiodurans*, the ploidy levels are 10 during exponential growth and 4 during stationary phase. Even slowly growing cells, such as *Borrelia hermsii* (minimum doubling time 8 hr), can be multiploid. This bacterium contains 8–11 genome copies when grown *in vitro* and up to 16 copies when grown in mice. *Azotobacter vinlandii* represents a more extreme example. Its ploidy in rich medium increases from 4 to 40 and then to >100 as the culture progresses from early exponential through late exponential to stationary phase. Ploidy level then decreases at the start of a new growth cycle. This spectacular increase in chromosome copy number in *Azotobacter* is not observed with cells grown in minimal medium. The current record holder is *Epulopiscium fishelsoni*. Its DNA content varies by four or five orders of magnitude among individuals at different stages of the life cycle. Perhaps the increase represents an example in which DNA is used as a stored nutrient, much as fat and starch are used by other organisms. Regardless of the reason for polyploidy, it is clearly not restricted to eukaryotic cells. Indeed, bacterial and eukaryotic chromosomes can no longer be considered different with respect to form (both types can be linear), ploidy levels (both types can be multiploid), and number of linkage groups (bacteria, which often have one, can have several; eukaryotes, which usually have many, can have only one, as seen with the ant *Myrmecia pilosula*).

## III. GENE ARRANGEMENTS

Gene mapping in bacteria was originally based on the ability of an externally derived, genetically marked fragment of DNA to recombine with the homologous region of a recipient's DNA. The frequency with which two nearby markers recombine is approximately proportional to the distance between them. Mutations were collected for a variety of purposes, and characterization usually included determining map position on the chromosome. The resulting genetic maps revealed relationships among genes such as operon clusters, showed orientation preferences that might reflect chromosomal activities, and suggested that some chromosomal information may have been derived from plasmids and phages. The discovery of restriction endonucleases led to a quantum advance in genetic mapping since these enzymes allowed the accurate construction of maps in terms of nucleotide distances. Practical nucleotide sequencing methods, which became available in the late 1970s, are expected to yield the complete nucleotide sequences for at least 100 bacterial species by the Year 2000. Data are being obtained at three levels: (i) the genetic map, with the genes and their map locations correlated with the role of the gene products in cell metabolism, structure, or regulation; (ii) the physical map in terms of locations of restriction sites; and (iii) the nucleotide and corresponding protein amino acid sequences. It is becoming clear that all living organisms probably arose from a common ancestor. Thus, information on nucleotide sequence and gene function in one organism can be applied to many other organisms.

One of the conclusions from genome studies is that large families of genes exist. For example, in *E. coli* there is a family of 80 membrane transport proteins, and half the protein-coding genes of *Mycobacterium tuberculosis* have arisen through duplication. These observations support the idea, which originated from analysis of eukaryotic genomes, that new genes arise from the duplication and modification of old ones.

The conservation of gene structure makes it possible to use nucleotide sequence information for comparison of genetic maps among bacterial species. One of the features revealed is clustering of related genes. For example, the genetic maps of *Bacillus subtilis*, *E. coli*, and *S. typhimurium* show a grouping of many genes for biosynthetic and degradative pathways. Such grouping could be for purposes of coordinated regulation since some adjacent genes produce polycistronic messages. A completely different view of the same data maintains that functionally related genes move horizontally (from one organism to another) as clusters because the products of the genes work well together, increasing the probability of successful transfer. Both ideas are likely to be accurate.

It is becoming increasingly clear that bacterial genomes can be quite malleable, even at the level of large rearrangements. For example, comparison of

the genomic maps of *E. coli* and *S. typhimurium* reveals that a large inversion has occurred. Similar comparisons of *S. typhimurium* LT2 and *S. typhi* Ty2 show that these two genomes differ by at least three inversions. In a study of 21 *P. aeruginosa* isolates, nine inversions were detected. Many comparisons make it possible to divide bacteria into two groups based on genomic stability. Representatives of the stable genome group are *E. coli*, *S. typhimurium*, and *Halobacterium salinarum*. Highly rearranged genomes are found in *S. typhi*, *Helicobacter pylori*, and *P. aeruginosa*. The reasons for differences among organisms are not clear. Some rearrangements, such as insertions or deletions, may be more deleterious for certain bacteria, or perhaps the opportunity for rearrangements, such as the occurrence of recombinational hot spots, is greater in some organisms than others. The latter explanation appears to be more likely for chloroplast and mitochondrial chromosomes, which in many ways resemble bacterial chromosomes. After approximately 300 million years of evolution, the order of chloroplast genes is highly conserved among most land plants, including mung bean. However, chloroplast gene order is completely scrambled in pea, a plant closely related to beans. Massive rearrangement of genes is also evident when mitochondrial chromosome maps are compared among types of maize. Thus, gene order in organelles appears to have little functional significance, and it can be subject to frequent recombination if the opportunity arises.

As complete genomic nucleotide sequences become increasingly available, new questions will be raised. For example, what is the minimal number of genes required for independent life? Organisms of the genus *Mycoplasma* have the smallest cellular genomes, probably because many of the needs of these obligate parasites are supplied by their hosts. Genomic comparison of *M. genitalium* with a free-living pathogen, *Hemophilus influenzae*, indicates that the minimal set of genes to sustain a cell may be approximately 250. Nucleotide sequences should also help identify genes involved in pathogenicity by comparison of virulent and avirulent strains of a pathogen. Such an approach has uncovered a "pathogenicity island," a collection of virulence genes, in *H. pylori*. The island is bounded by 31-base pair direct repeats, as if it had been transferred horizontally into an ancestor of *H. pylori*. In some bacteria, horizontal transfer may have been quite extensive. For example, in *E. coli* as much as 15% of the genome, (700 kbp) may have been acquired from foreign sources such as integrative bacteriophages, transposons in plasmids, and conjugative transposons (genetic elements that cannot replicate independently but cause conjugation, a form of cell-to-cell DNA transfer, to occur).

## IV. RECOMBINATION

Intracellular DNA experiences a variety of perturbations that must be repaired to maintain the integrity of the genome and to allow movement of replication forks. Cells have several ways to repair DNA damage, one of which involves recombination (recombination is a process in which DNA molecules are broken and rejoined in such a way that portions of the two molecules are exchanged). Damaged sequences in one molecule can be exchanged for undamaged ones in another (Fig. 3). It is now thought that the raison d'être for recombination is its role in DNA repair, a process that occurs thousands of times per cell generation.

Recombination is also involved in DNA rearrangements arising from the pairing of repeated sequences. When the repeats are in direct orientation, duplications and deletions occur; inversions occur when the repeat is inverted. In *B. subtilis* a cascade of sequential rearrangements has been identified in which large transpositions and inversions have been attributed to recombination at specific junction points in the chromosome. Several other examples are found with the *rrn* clusters, sets of similar assemblies of ribosomal and transfer RNA genes. Rearrangements at the three *rrn* clusters of *Brucella* are thought to be responsible for the differences in chromosome size and number among species of this genus. Other repeated sequences that facilitate rearrangements are the *rhs* loci (recombination *hot spot*), duplicate insertion sequences, and experimentally introduced copies of the transposon Tn10.

A third consequence of recombination is the insertion of genes from mobile elements into chromo-

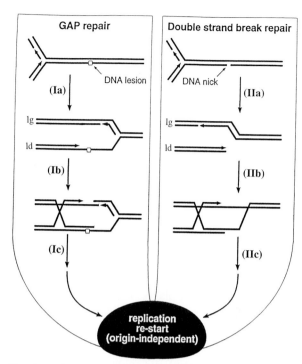

**Fig. 3.** Major pathways for recombinational DNA repair in bacteria. The principal function of recombination in bacteria is to restart replication forks stalled at sites of DNA damage. Two pathways are depicted. First, gap repair: (Ia) A DNA lesion blocks movement of the leading strand (Id), causing disassembly of the replication fork. (Ib) The RecA and RecFOR proteins replace the lesion with parental DNA from the lagging strand (Ig) side of the fork by recombination. (Ic) The recombination intermediates are then resolved by the RuvABC and RecG proteins so replication can restart. Second, double-strand break repair: (IIa) A single-strand break (nick) blocks movement of the leading strand (Id), causing disassembly of the replication fork. (IIb) The RecA and RecBCD proteins regenerate the fork by recombination with parental DNA from the lagging strand (Ig) side of the replication fork. (IIc) The recombination intermediates are then resolved and repaired by the RuvABC and RecG proteins so replication can restart (adapted from Cox, 1997, *Proc. Natl. Acad. Sci. USA* **94**, 11765, copyright 1997 National Academy of Sciences, U.S.A.).

somes. These elements, which include transposons, plasmids, bacteriophages, integrons, and pathogenicity islands, move from one cell to another and sometimes from one species to another. In a spectacular example of gene transfer and its evolutionary effects across kingdoms, the acquisition of a symbiosis island of 500 kbp converts a saprophytic *Mesorhizo-*

*bium* into a symbiont of lotus plants. Because they mediate such sweeping change, mobile genetic elements may represent the most important means for generating the genetic diversity on which selection operates. For mobility, and thus generation of genetic diversity, such genetic elements require recombination activities.

## V. DNA TWISTING, FOLDING, AND BENDING

### A. DNA Supercoiling

Circular DNA molecules extracted from bacteria that grow at moderate temperature have a deficiency of duplex turns relative to linear DNAs of the same length. The deficiency places strain on DNA, causing it to coil. This coiling is loosely referred to as negative supercoiling (an excess of duplex turns would give rise to positive supercoiling). The strain is spontaneously relieved (relaxed) by nicks or breaks in the DNA that allow strand rotation; consequently, supercoiling is found only in DNA molecules that are circular or otherwise constrained so the strands cannot rotate. Since processes that separate DNA strands relieve negative superhelical strain, they will tend to occur more readily in supercoiled than in relaxed DNA. Among these activities are initiation of DNA replication and initiation of transcription. Negative supercoiling also makes DNA more flexible, facilitating DNA looping, wrapping of DNA around proteins, and the formation of cruciforms, left-handed Z-DNA, and other non B-form structures. In a sense, negatively supercoiled DNA is energetically activated for most of the processes carried out by the chromosome.

Negative supercoils are introduced into DNA by gyrase, one of several DNA topoisomerases found in bacteria. DNA topoisomerases act through a strand breaking and rejoining process (Fig. 4) that allows supercoils to be introduced or removed, DNA knots to be tied or untied, and separate circles of DNA to be linked or unlinked. The action of gyrase is modulated by the relaxing activity of topoisomerase I. Since gyrase is more active on a relaxed DNA substrate and topoisomerase I on a highly negatively supercoiled one, the two topoisomerases tend to reduce variation in supercoiling under stable growth conditions. In addition, lowering negative supercoil-

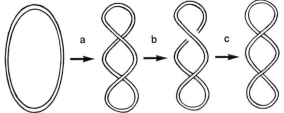

**Fig. 4.** Negative supercoils. Gyrase generates negative supercoils by passing one duplex strand through the other. In the scheme shown, the enzyme binds to the DNA and creates a positive and a negative node (a). At the upper, positive node the duplex is broken (b). The bottom strand is then passed through the break, which is then sealed (c). [Reprinted from *Trends in Genetics* **6**, Drlica, Bacterial topoisomerases and the control of DNA supercoiling, p. 433, copyright 1990, with permission from Elsevier Science.]

ing increases gyrase expression and decreases topoisomerase I expression. Thus, negative supercoiling is a controlled feature of the chromosome.

Supercoiling is influenced by the extracellular environment. For example, when bacteria such as *E. coli* are suddenly exposed to high temperature, negative supercoiling quickly drops (relaxes), and within a few minutes it recovers. The reciprocal response is seen during cold shock. Presumably these transient changes in DNA supercoiling facilitate timely induction of heat and cold shock genes important for survival. Supercoiling is also affected by the environment through changes in cellular energetics. Gyrase hydrolyzes ATP to ADP as a part of the supercoiling reaction; ADP interferes with the supercoiling activity of gyrase while allowing a competing relaxing reaction to occur. Consequently, the ratio of [ATP] to [ADP] strongly influences the level of supercoiling reached. Changes in oxygen tension and salt concentration are examples in which cellular energetics and supercoiling change coordinately. Collectively, these observations indicate that chromosome structure changes globally in response to the environment.

Supercoiling is influenced locally by transcription. During translocation of transcription complexes along DNA, RNA polymerase does not readily rotate around DNA. Consequently, transcription generates positive supercoils in front of complexes and negative supercoils behind them. Since topoisomerase I removes the negative supercoils and gyrase the positive ones, transcription and similar translocation processes have only transient effects on supercoiling. However, there are cases in which induction of very high levels of transcription results in abnormally high levels of negative supercoiling. In such situations transcription-mediated changes in supercoiling provide a way for specific regions of a DNA molecule to have levels of supercoiling that differ greatly from average values. Problems can occur because excessive negative supercoils behind a transcription complex allow nascent transcripts to form long hybrids with the coding strand of DNA. Such structures, called R-loops, probably interfere with gene expression. Problems also occur as a result of a buildup of positive supercoils in front of a transcription complex since helix tightening will slow transcription. This is probably why strong gyrase binding sites are scattered throughout the chromosome immediately downstream from active genes.

## B. Chromosome Folding

Multiple nicks are required to relax chromosomal supercoils. Consequently, it was concluded that the DNA must be constrained into topologically independent domains. Current estimates place the number at approximately 50 domains per genome-quivalent of DNA in *E. coli,* or approximately 1 per 100 kb of DNA. Since superhelical tension and topological domains are detected in living cells, it is unlikely that the domains are an artifact of chromosome isolation. From a functional point of view, dividing the chromosome into domains prevents a few DNA nicks or gaps from relaxing supercoils in the entire chromosome. The existence of domains also makes it possible to introduce supercoils into the chromosome before a round of replication finishes; in the absence of domains, the gaps following replication forks would relax any supercoils that gyrase might introduce. Thus, the domains allow the bulk of the chromosome to maintain a supercoiled state.

How the domains are established is unknown. They are present after cells are treated with rifampicin, an inhibitor of RNA synthesis; thus, they are not simply the by-products of DNA–RNA polymerase–RNA complexes. Even after exhaustive deproteinization, fluorescence microscopy shows that nearly every nucleoid in preparations from both exponential- and

stationary-phase *E. coli* appears as a rosette or loose network of 20–50 large loops. Networks probably also occur in the linear chromosomes of *B. burgdorferi.* When examined by pulsed-field gel electrophoresis and fluorescence microscopic imaging of individual DNA molecules, some, and occasionally most, of the DNAs are in an electrophoretically immobile network larger than the size of the genome (some *B. burgdorferi* DNA also behaves as unit length linear molecules). Discovering the nature of the bonding in the apparently all-DNA networks may be central to understanding bacterial chromosome structure.

## C. DNA Bending

Associated with the chromosome are five small proteins that either bend DNA or bind to bends and stabilize them. The most abundant is HU, a protein with long flexible arms that reach around DNA and force it to make a U-turn. HU does not recognize a specific nucleotide sequence; therefore, it is considered to provide a general bending activity. Several examples have been found in which HU serves as an architectural protein, assisting in the formation of DNA–protein complexes that carry out site-specific recombination. HU also provides the DNA bending needed for certain repressors to bring distant regions of DNA together in loops that block initiation of transcription.

HU was initially classified as a histone-like protein on the basis of its amino acid composition and its ability to wrap DNA into nucleosome-like particles *in vitro.* Nucleosomes, which have long been a distinctive feature of eukaryotic nuclei, are ball-like structures in which approximately 200 bp of DNA is wrapped around histone proteins. They occur at regular intervals along DNA, giving nuclear chromatin a "beads-on-a-string" appearance and compacting the DNA by a factor of approximately seven. True bacteria (eubacteria) do not have true histones or nucleosomes, although some archaebacteria (archaea) do. It is unknown whether HU wraps intracellular DNA or just bends it.

Closely related to HU is a bending protein called IHF (integration host factor). It too can cause DNA to turn 180° on itself, but unlike HU, IHF recognizes specific nucleotide sequences. There are many examples in which IHF helps form a DNA loop between promoters and transcription activators bound far upstream from promoters, thereby facilitating initiation of transcription. IHF also participates as an architectural protein during the formation of site-specific DNA–protein complexes. The best known of these is the intasome generated by bacteriophage lambda during integration into the bacterial chromosome.

Two other bending proteins, FIS (factor for inversion stimulation) and LRP (leucine-responsive regulatory protein), serve as sensors and global regulatory agents. FIS senses the bacterial growth phase, and its expression is sharply elevated shortly after a culture begins growing. In older cultures the rate of FIS synthesis decreases to almost zero. FIS binds to specific nucleotide sequences, some of which are so close to a promoter that FIS acts as a repressor. In other cases, FIS acts as an upstream activator of transcription. LRP responds to the nutrient status of the cell, particularly amino acid levels. It acts as a repressor for many genes involved in catabolic (breakdown) processes and an activator for genes involved in metabolic synthesis. Both FIS and LRP also have architectural roles when they bend DNA to form protein–DNA complexes for site-specific recombination.

The fifth protein is called H-NS (histone-like nucleoid structuring protein). Unlike the other four, it does not actively bend DNA. Instead, it binds to DNA that is already bent. If an appropriate bend is near the promoter of a gene, H-NS will bind and act as a mild repressor. It is likely that 100 genes are affected in this way. H-NS action appears to be a general way to keep the expression of many genes down-regulated until their products are needed.

It is not known whether a bending protein is involved in packaging the chromosome as a whole. It is interesting to note that when H-NS is expressed at very high levels, the chromosome compacts. Although such an event is lethal, it may reflect a moderate compacting action by H-NS at normal concentration. Also relevant may be the observation that cells do not tolerate the absence of HU, IHF, and H-NS together, although cells are viable when only one of the three proteins is present. Perhaps at least one of these DNA-bending proteins is needed for chromosome compaction.

## VI. CHROMOSOME INACTIVATION

In eukaryotic cells large portions of genomes are rendered transcriptionally inactive by heterochromatinization, a local DNA compaction that is readily observed by light microscopy. Bacterial chromosomes are too small for locally compacted regions to be seen; consequently, we can only guess about their existence. However, evidence is accumulating that bacteria have systems that condense entire chromosomes. In *Caulobacter crescentus* two cell types exist: swarmer cells and stalk cells. When a swarmer cell differentiates into the stalked form, the nucleoid changes from a compact to a more open structure, possibly reflecting an activation of the genome. In a second example, a histone H1-like protein in *Chlamydia trachomatis* probably causes chromosomal condensation during the conversion of the metabolically active reticulate body to the inactive, extracellular elementary body form. Another example occurs during sporulation in *Bacillus*. In this case the chromosome of the spore is bound with new proteins as its transcriptional activity ceases. Still another case is when the cells of the archaebacterium *Halobacterium salinarium* progress from early to late exponential phase of growth. In this prokaryote, the nucleoid obtained by gentle lysis procedures changes from a form containing naked DNA to one having a beads-on-a-string appearance typical of nucleosomal DNA; this change, seen by electron microscopy, is also reflected in nucleoid sedimentation properties. Finally, fluorescence measurements of DNA and RNA within the enormous cells (up to 500 $\mu$m long) of *Epulopiscium fishelsoni* suggest that decondensation and dispersion of the nucleoid are accompanied by increased transcriptional activity. The molecular events that occur during the condensation–decondensation process should prove very interesting to study.

## VII. CHROMOSOME DUPLICATION

The major features of chromosome replication have been established for many years. Semiconservative replication was demonstrated by density-shift experiments in 1958, and a few years later the autoradiograms prepared by Cairns revealed a partially replicated circle containing a large replication "eye." In the early 1970s it became clear that bidirectional replication begins at a fixed origin (*oriC*) and that the two forks proceed in opposite directions until they reach a terminus 180° around the chromosome. Under conditions of rapid growth, bacterial chromosomes can contain more than one pair of replication forks. It is the presence of multiple forks that allows multiple chromosomes to be present, which in turn enables *E. coli* cells to double at shorter intervals than required for the forks to traverse the chromosome.

Initiation of replication has long been a focus of attention since knowledge of its control is expected to lead to an understanding of the regulation of the cell cycle. Early in the study of initiation, heat-sensitive mutations were obtained in genes called *dnaA* and *dnaC*. They made it possible to uncouple initiation from the elongation phase of replication. Then the origin was cloned by its ability to confer replication proficiency to a plasmid lacking an origin of replication. The availability of the origin on a small piece of DNA and purified initiation proteins allowed Kornberg to develop an *in vitro* initiation system. From this system it was learned that initiation involves the specific binding of the DnaA protein to *oriC* and the wrapping of origin DNA around DnaA. Local DNA strand separation then occurs at the origin, and single-stranded binding protein attaches to the separated strands. This helps stabilize what appears to be a single-stranded bubble in duplex DNA. The DnaB helicase, helped by the DnaC protein, binds to the replication bubble and enlarges it. Then DNA polymerase binds, and new strands are synthesized as one replication fork moves away from the origin in the clockwise direction and a second fork moves in the counterclockwise direction.

When the replication forks approach the terminus of replication, they slow drastically. Present at the replication terminus are nucleotide sequences that act as traps to halt fork movement in an orientation-specific manner, apparently functioning as binding sites for a termination protein that acts as an antihelicase. Flanking the traps are zones containing additional terminators arranged to block replication forks that pass through the primary terminators and head back toward the origin.

Sensitive probes for specific regions of the chromosome have provided support for two major cytological concepts. First, fluorescent labelling of DNA polymerase revealed that replication forks are located at the center of the cell, where they appear to remain throughout most of the cell cycle. When multifork replication occurs, two additional replication centers, each probably containing a pair of forks, can be seen situated between the mid-cell forks and the cell poles. What holds the replication apparatus in place is unknown, although circumstantial evidence implicates an attachment to the cell membrane. The fixed nature of replication forks supports the idea that replicating bacterial DNA threads through a stationary replication apparatus, a notion that has long been advocated for eukaryotic cells.

The second concept focuses on the origin of replication (*oriC*), which can be located by fluorescent antibodies directed at proteins that bind to repeated nucleotide sequences placed near *oriC* (or any other specified region). In newly formed cells, *oriC* and the replication terminus are located at opposite poles of the nucleoid. During replication, *oriC* moves briefly toward a mid-cell position. Then two copies of *oriC* become visible at the nucleoid pole, apparently having been drawn back after replication. Later, one copy abruptly moves to the opposite edge of the nucleoid. The replication terminus then migrates to a mid-cell position, and late in the cell cycle two termini can be seen pulling apart. The septum that separates the new daughter cells forms between the termini. The localization of *oriC* and its rapid movement, which is about 10 times faster than cell elongation, indicate that bacterial chromosomes undergo a form of mitosis.

Although the details of bacterial "mitosis" are poorly understood, several proteins exhibit properties expected of mitotic proteins. For example, in *B. subtilis* the Spo0J protein appears to participate in chromosome partitioning by binding to multiple sites on the chromosome near *oriC*. Ten related, 8-bp inverted repeat DNA sequences are scattered across approximately 800 kb of the 4200-kb chromosome. Eight of these sites are bound *in vivo* to Spo0J. Such distribution of bacterial centromere-like DNA elements is similar to the most common type of distribution of functional centromeric DNA in eukaryotes, the *CEN*-containing regional centromeres. Thus, SpoOJ may hold the new and old copies of *oriC* near one pole of the nucleoid until one copy of *oriC* is moved to the opposite pole. Chromosome condensation, which is probably too slight to see with current methods, may involve the action of the Smc protein, a homolog of a eukaryotic protein family known to participate in DNA condensation. When *smc* is mutant in *B. subtilis,* the SpoOJ protein is not found at its polar position on the nucleoid, and newly formed septa cut some daughter chromosomes in a guillotine-like manner. Since mitosis is expected to be an essential activity, it is surprising that mutations in *spoOJ, smc,* and *mukB,* an *E. coli* gene postulated to be involved in chromosome movement, are not lethal. Clearly there is much more to learn about the segregation of sister chromosomes to daughter cells.

We believe that as replicated chromosomes are pulled apart, DNA tangles must occur. The double-strand passing activities of gyrase and topoisomerase IV are well suited to resolve the tangles. Consistent with this idea, both enzymes are distributed around the *E. coli* chromosome, as judged by DNA cleavage induced by the quinolone inhibitors of topoisomerases. In *E. coli,* DNA cleavage occurs at approximately 100-kbp intervals for gyrase and 200-kbp intervals for topoisomerase IV. Replication is also expected to leave daughter chromosomes catenated (interlinked). Plasmid studies indicate that unlinking may be a function of topoisomerase IV, but bacteria such as *M. tuberculosis, Treponema pallidum,* and *H. pylori* appear to lack this enzyme. Other possible sources of decatenation are gyrase and, when nicks or gaps are present, topoisomerases I and III.

## VIII. SPECULATIONS ON CHROMOSOME PACKAGING DYNAMICS

In the past two decades our understanding of bacterial chromosomes has advanced remarkably along two fronts. First, a combination of genetics and biochemistry has taught us a great deal about the proteins that manipulate DNA. Second, we now have complete genomic sequences for many bacteria, and

more will soon be available. These sequences indicate that bacterial genomes are quite flexible with respect to gene order. However, few experiments bear on how the long chromosomal DNA molecule is compacted to fit inside a cell. Here, we offer a speculative scheme that may help form a framework for understanding future discoveries.

One key concept is that cytoplasmic proteins and other large cytoplasmic molecules are at such high concentration that they compact DNA through macromolecular crowding. This idea, which has recently been refined by Zimmerman, requires no specific DNA compacting proteins, and so it accommodates the apparent absence of nucleosome-like particles in eubacteria. We envision that chromosomal activities involving bulky protein complexes occur at the edges of the nucleoid (Fig. 5). For example, the replication apparatus, which is likely to be attached to a multienzyme complex that supplies deoxyribonucleoside triphosphates, is probably situated at the edge of the compacted portion of the chromosome, especially if replication proteins are bound to the cell membrane. Likewise, transcription, which in bacteria is coupled to translation, also probably occurs on DNA emerging from the compacted mass of nucleoid DNA because ribosomes are seen only outside the nucleoid (extrachromosomal localization is especially likely when transcription–translation complexes are bound to the cell membrane via nascent membrane proteins). Consistent with this idea, pulse-labeled nascent RNA is preferentially located at the nucleoid border, as is topoisomerase I (as noted previously, topoisomerase I may serve as a cytological marker for transcription since it is probably localized behind transcription complexes to prevent excess negative supercoils from accumulating).

If the replication and transcription–translation machinery are located on the surface of the nucleoid, DNA movement must occur to allow access to all nucleotide sequences. Replication-based movement probably occurs by DNA threading through stationary replication forks. Such movement would not be sufficient for transcriptional access to the whole genome since some genes can be induced when DNA replication is not occurring. Perhaps compacted DNA is sufficiently fluid that genes frequently pass from interior to exterior. At any given moment, in some

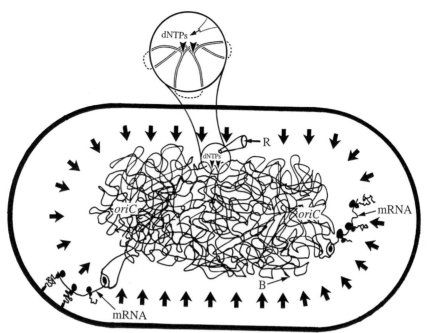

***Fig. 5.*** Overview of bacterial chromosome structure. The figure shows a schematic representation of a bacterial cell and its chromosomal DNA (nucleoid). The replication apparatus is located at the edge of the nucleoid at a mid-cell position. Two replication forks (arrowheads) are shown in close proximity. DNA is thought to thread through a stationary replication apparatus. The funnel-like structure represents a multienzyme complex responsible for synthesis of deoxyribonucleoside triphosphates (dNTPs) from ribonucleoside diphosphates (R). In the enlargement of the replication apparatus the dashed lines outside the circle represent the connections between the DNA strands masked by the large amount of DNA in the cell. The polar distribution of *oriC* regions is indicated. Macromolecular crowding (arrows) contributes to DNA condensation, with additional packing occurring from protein-induced DNA bending (B) at many points on the chromosome (only one bending point is labeled). Two examples of coupled transcription–translation are shown to occur at the edge of the nucleoid. In the lower left, nascent protein is bound to the cell membrane, drawing a region of DNA out of the compact part of the nucleoid. To provide transcriptional access to all regions of the genome, the interior and exterior regions of the nucleoid are assumed to exchange rapidly.

fraction of the cell population each gene may be at the surface of the nucleoid and available for transcription. Capture of a gene by the transcription–translation apparatus would hold that gene on the surface. During induction of gene expression, the fraction of cells in which a particular gene is captured would increase until most of the cells express that gene. For the chromosome as a whole, many genes would be expressing protein during active growth, and therefore many regions would be held outside the nucleoid core by the

transcription–translation apparatus. Kellenberger suggested that such activity explains why the nucleoid appears more compact when protein synthesis is experimentally interrupted. The idea of gene capture for expression requires that the replication apparatus be strong enough to pull the DNA through itself even when genes are bound to ribosomes via mRNA and to the cell membrane via nascent proteins still attached to ribosomes. A fixed RNA polymerase must also pull DNA.

Capture of the *oriC* region by the replication apparatus might be similar to gene capture for transcription. With the fluid chromosome hypothesis, some replication proteins would assemble at mid-cell, whereas others would assemble with the centromere-like DNA elements and Spo0J (in *B. subtilis*) at the poles and dislodge *oriC* from its polar connection. Once liberated, a mobile *oriC* would be captured by the replication apparatus at mid-cell. As *oriC* and nearby regions are drawn through the replication forks and replicated, new binding sites for a chromosome partition protein (Spo0J) would be created. Once these sites were filled, the two daughter *oriC* regions might pair through Spo0J–Spo0J interactions and return to the polar position. Other proteins would later disrupt the Spo0J–Spo0J interactions as the new Spo0J–*oriC* complex is moved to the other pole of the nucleoid.

Movement of DNA must generate tangles, just as loops in fishing line snarl when reels are not carefully attended. The decatenating activities of the type II topoisomerases, DNA gyrase and topoisomerase IV, are available to remove the tangles, explaining in part why these two enzymes are found at many spots on the chromosome. The movement of the daughter chromosomes to opposite cell poles would provide the directionality needed by the topoisomerases to untangle the loops.

The core of a compacted chromosome need not be impenetrable to proteins. Indeed, DNA compacting generated by polyethylene glycol facilitates the DNA condensing action of HU. The abundant DNA bending proteins, such as HU, IHF, and H-NS, probably facilitate chromosome compaction in a dynamic manner by rapidly exchanging between DNA-bound and unbound states. Likewise, the topoisomerases probably respond rapidly to local perturbations in supercoiling to maintain the proper level of supercoiling throughout the chromosome.

An important feature of a fluid model for bacterial chromosome structure is that fixed topological domains are not easily accommodated since they require specialized, pulley-like structures to allow the DNA movement needed for replication. Transient domains could be generated by recombination intermediates, provided that recombination occurs often enough to maintain approximately 50 domains per genome. However, chromosomes exhibit structures (large loops) resistant to extensive protease and ribonuclease treatment even when isolated from *recA* mutants. Thus, the source of the all-DNA looped structure found in isolated chromosomes is unknown.

## IX. CONCLUDING REMARKS

Many of the features found in bacterial chromosomes are remarkably similar to those of eukaryotic chromosomes: linear maps, one or more dissimilar chromosomes [the number can be as high as four among bacteria and as low as one in eukaryotes ($2N = 2$)], high ploidy (copy number) levels, and a mitotic-like apparatus used in cell division. Consequently, the prevalent belief that profound differences exist between prokaryotic and eukaryotic chromosomes is gradually eroding. A major distinction, other than the presence of a nuclear membrane in eukaryotes, revolves around histones and their compaction of DNA into nucleosomes. True bacteria lack histones and nucleosomes, and so DNA compaction must occur by other means. However, some archaea have histones and stable nucleosomes, whereas some unicellular eukaryotes lack both. Thus, at the chromosome level the difference between prokaryotes and eukaryotes may not be as extensive as generally thought.

### Acknowledgments

We thank M. Gennaro and G. L. G. Miklos for critical comments on the manuscript. The authors' work was supported by grants from the National Science Foundation, the American Cancer Society, and the National Institutes of Health.

### See Also the Following Articles

### Bibliography

Brankenhoff, G. J., van der Voort, H., van Spronsen, E., Linnemans, W., and Nanninga, N. (1985). Three-dimensional chromatin distribution in neuroblastoma nuclei shown by confocal scanning laser microscopy. *Nature* 317, 748–749.

Cox, M. (1997). Recombinational crossroads: Eukaryotic enzymes and the limits of bacterial precedents. *Proc. Natl. Acad. Sci. USA* **94**, 11764–11766.

Cozzarelli, N. R. (1980). DNA gyrase and the supercoiling of DNA. *Science* **207**, 953–960.

Drlica, K. (1990). Bacterial topoisomerases and the control of DNA supercoiling. *Trends Genet.* **6**, 433–437.

Drlica, K., and Zhao, X. (1997). DNA gyrase and topoisomerase IV as targets of the fluoroquinolones. *Microbiol. Mol. Biol. Rev.* **61**, 377–392.

Kolsto, A. B. (1997). Dynamic bacterial genome organization. *Mol. Microbiol.* **24**, 241–248.

Lemon, K., and Grossman, A. (1998). Localization of a bacterial DNA-polymerase: Evidence for a factory model of replication. *Science* **282**, 1516–1519.

Pettijohn, D. E. (1996). The nucleoid. *In "Escherichia coli* and *Salmonella typhimurium"* (F. Neidhardt *et al.,* Eds.), pp. 158–166. ASM Press, Washington, DC.

Reeve, J. N., Sandman, K., and Daniels, C. J. (1997). Archael histones, nucleosomes, and transcription initiation. *Cell* **89**, 999–1002.

Zimmerman, S. B., and Murphy, L. D. (1996). Macromolecular crowding and the mandatory condensation of DNA in bacteria. *FEBS Lett.* **390**, 245–248.

# Chromosome Replication and Segregation

## Alan C. Leonard and Julia E. Grimwade

*Florida Institute of Technology*

I. Prokaryotic and Eukaryotic Chromosomes: Replication Origin Placement and Initiation Timing
II. Structure of Replication Origins
III. Assembly and Disassembly of Nucleoprotein Complexes at Replication Origins
IV. Chromosome Partition Systems in Prokaryotic and Eukaryotic Microbes

## GLOSSARY

**autonomously replicating sequences (ARSs)** Yeast chromosomal sequences that provide a replicator function to plasmids and produce high-frequency transformation. ARSs are the most thoroughly studied replication origins in yeast.

**centromere** *cis*-Acting sequences that control movement and segregation of chromosomes. In eukaryotic microbes, centromeres are attached to microtubules of the mitotic spindle apparatus. In prokaryotic microbes, the centromere and its attachment structure are less well defined.

**DNA unwinding element (DUE)** Regions of double-stranded DNA where the helix is easily destabilized to achieve a single-stranded state. The DUE is associated with replication origins and is rich in A-T base pairings.

**equipartition** Allocation of one from each pair of newly replicated chromosomes into each progeny cell.

**fluorescence in situ hybridization** Microscopy technique used to locate specific genetic sites within an intact cell. DNA probes tagged with a fluorescent protein are hybridized to fixed cells and the position of the glowing spot is determined relative to intracellular structures or other genetic sites.

**nonrandom segregation** Oriented distribution of chromosomes into progeny cells; cosegregation of chromosomes and conserved cell structures.

**origin of replication** Chromosomal sites that interact with specific proteins to produce unwound DNA regions re-quired to start polymerization of new DNA from existing template.

**sister chromosomes** The two products of chromosome duplication, each containing a newly polymerized DNA strand and a template strand formed during an earlier round of DNA replication.

**CHROMOSOME REPLICATION AND SEGREGATION** are key events during the microbial cell cycle that must be completed before a cell divides. To reproduce successfully, every cell is obliged to replicate its chromosome(s) and distinguish nascent sister chromosomes from one another. Each sister chromosome must then be physically segregated into one of two new cells prior to completion of cell division. These are not simple tasks considering the large size of microbial genomes (0.2–5 mm) and the extremely limited space these genomes occupy (0.1–10 $\mu m^3$). However, errors (production of chromosome-less cells) are rare ($<10^{-5}$/ cell division in *Escherichia coli* and *Saccharomyces cerevisiae*). To ensure a low error rate, microbial cells require complex and precise regulatory mechanisms to both properly time new rounds of replicative DNA synthesis and orient newly synthesized DNA with respect to fixed intracellular locations. This article focuses on the nature of molecular mechanisms that regulate chromosome replication and segregation in prokaryotic and eukaryotic microorganisms. Most examples are taken from the bacterium *E. coli* and the budding yeast *S. cerevisiae*. Emphasis is placed on assembly of DNA–protein complexes at replication origins and localization of specific chromosomal sites during segregation.

# I. PROKARYOTIC AND EUKARYOTIC CHROMOSOMES: REPLICATION ORIGIN PLACEMENT AND INITIATION TIMING

Chromosomal DNA replication initiates from specialized sites termed origins of replication. The premise of a specialized replicator site that binds initiator proteins was formalized in the Replicon model presented in 1963 by Jacob, Brenner, and Cuzin. This model remains essentially correct, although many details of the initiation triggering process in bacteria and yeast are not completely understood. It is instructive to compare and contrast current knowledge about the location, arrangement, and number of replication origins on bacterial chromosomes and yeast chromosomes. This simple comparison reveals fundamental similarities and differences between the control mechanisms in these cell types.

## A. Bacteria

Bacterial genomes, with very few exceptions, are double-stranded, circular, supercoiled DNA molecules. The genome contains a unique fixed site, termed *oriC*, from which DNA replication initiates. Once every cell cycle, two newly initiated DNA replication forks proceed from *oriC*, moving bidirectionally until the entire chromosome is duplicated. The majority of gene transcription is symmetrically divergent from the replication origin. Replication forks move predominantly in the same direction that RNA polymerase transcribes genes on the chromosome. In most species of bacteria, the fixed position of *oriC* is closely associated with gene products that play a direct role in the regulation of DNA replication. *Escherichia coli*'s *oriC* remains an exception because it is positioned between genes that are not directly involved in DNA synthesis—ATP synthetase and asparagine synthetase.

Since there is only one *oriC* locus on the chromosome, the number of intracellular copies of *oriC* might be expected to fluctuate from one to two during the cell cycle. This is indeed the case for slow-growing bacteria. However, bacteria may harbor multiple replication origins while still maintaining normal growth physiology. During rapid growth under nutrient-rich conditions, bacterial doubling times are shorter than the time needed to complete chromosome replication and septation. For example, *E. coli* doubling times are approximately 20 min in broth containing beef extract, but approximately 60 min is required after initiation of DNA replication to produce a complete copy of the 4600-kilobase (kb) genome and to finish cell division. Therefore, in order to produce two chromosomal copies to be segregated at division, bacteria must trigger new rounds of chromosome replication from *oriC*s before previously initiated rounds are completed. As a result, fast-growing bacteria have dichotomously forked chromosomes that contain more copies of *oriC* per cell (as many as eight in *E. coli* at cell division) than slower growing cells. Despite the unusual appearance of the chromosomes in fast-growing *E. coli* (Fig. 1), each copy of *oriC* is identical and functionally equivalent to all others. Replication initiates synchronously from all available copies of *oriC* at the start of the DNA synthesis phase (C period) of the cell cycle.

It is possible to further increase the number of functional copies of *oriC* per cell by introducing minichromosomes, plasmids whose sole origin of replication is a cloned copy of *oriC*. Minichromosomes are governed by the same regulatory mecha-

A          B

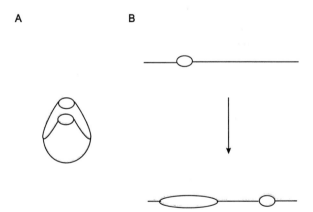

***Fig. 1.*** Multiple origins of replication in bacteria and yeast. (A) In rapidly growing bacteria, multiple origins initiate chromosome replication synchronously. All origins fire before the previous round of replication is completed, resulting in dichotomous replication forks on a single chromosome. (B) In eukaryotic microbes, not all origins initiate replication synchronously. A single origin functions only once during S phase, and no reinitiations are possible until the chromosome has finished replicating.

nisms as chromosomal copies of *oriC* (i.e., all *oriC* copies replicate coincidentally with cell cycle specificity). Although one might expect the copy number of minichromosomes to be equivalent to the number of chromosomal *oriCs,* minichromosomes are defective for equipartition at division (see Section IV) and are inherited as though they are clumped together. The result is that, at cell division, half the cells receive the majority of minichromosomes and half receive few or none. After sufficient numbers of generations under selective growth conditions to remove minichromosomeless cells, minichromosome copy number increases. Regardless of copy number, all *oriC* copies initiate coincidentally, and the cell can support more than 20 copies of *oriC* without perturbation of growth physiology. Clearly, based on these observations, the mechanism that regulates bacterial chromosome replication is capable of synchronously triggering DNA replication from large numbers of origins. In addition, it is clear that the regulatory mechanism that initiates new rounds of replication from *oriC* does not sense completion of previously initiated rounds, nor does it sense cell division. Initiation of DNA replication is coupled to cellular growth rate, and mechanistically it must depend on the accumulation of sufficient numbers of at least one *oriC* binding protein required for initiation (DnaA protein).

## B. Yeast

Bidirectional replication also ensues from origins on eukaryotic chromosomes, although characterization of these sites is a far more difficult task due to the large size of most eukaryotic genomes. *Saccharomyces cerevisiae* contains 16 linear chromosomes, ranging from 250 to 2000 kb with a total genomic content that is three times larger than that of *E. coli.* Despite the larger amount of DNA, the time required to replicate the yeast genome in rich media is nearly identical to the time needed to duplicate the *E. coli* chromosome. This is because the yeast genome has between 250 and 400 different origins placed 40–90 kb apart. Unlike *oriC* copies, yeast origins of replication do not all fire synchronously at the start of the DNA synthesis (S) phase of the cell cycle. In some adjacent origins, as much as 20-min differences in firing times have been measured (Fig. 1). This is a

remarkable burden to place on the initiation triggering mechanism because origins that fire late must be identified amid an ever-increasing background of origins that have already initiated DNA replication. Obviously, reinitiations in any single S phase are not permitted.

Many yeast replication origins are available for study as autonomously replicating sequences (ARSs). ARS-containing DNA fragments are sufficiently different from one another that they do not cross hybridize, although common sequence modules exist. It is not clear what specific qualities distinguish early firing origins from late firing ones. Clearly, differences in nucleotide sequence could affect the timing of one origin relative to another given the fact that key sequences bind the same regulatory proteins. Alternatively, the orientation of an origin on the chromosome, relative to the overall nuclear architecture, might constrain initiation to mid- or late S phase.

## C. Summary

Both prokaryotes and eukaryotes are capable of triggering DNA synthesis from multiple replication origins. In this sense, the regulatory mechanisms governing initiation are fundamentally similar. The mechanisms are different in that yeast origins are not triggered synchronously. This finding suggests that, unlike the identical origins in prokaryotes, eukaryotic origins exist in easily triggered or delayed states. Thus, the initiation triggering system in eukaryotic microbes must remain active for a considerable fraction of S phase. Powerful origin activation mechanisms must be countered by equally powerful repression mechanisms that monitor the state of every replication origin on eukaryotic genomes. In these circumstances, it is reasonable to suggest that the number of functional origins on eukaryotic chromosomes is dynamic, increasing or decreasing depending on developmental or physiological conditions that modify chromatin.

## II. STRUCTURE OF REPLICATION ORIGINS

The primary function of replication origins is to provide regions in which double-stranded DNA is easily unwound in response to a cell growth-regulated signal. This signal is mediated by the interaction of one or more specialized proteins with binding sites within the replication origin. Ultimately, protein–DNA interactions produce an unwound DNA substrate suitable for the assembly of a DNA polymerization machine to copy template strands. Once new replication forks are assembled, the initiation complex must be disassembled or inactivated and reset.

What are the features of replication origins that distinguish them from other sites found on microbial genomes? Surprisingly, only a short stretch of DNA is required for replication origin function. *Escherichia coli oriC* comprises only 245 bases (Fig. 2). Although less thoroughly defined, the function of yeast ARSI on chromosome IV requires only 120 bases. Mutation analysis of these and other origins reveals that they are composed of nucleotide sequences that serve one of three functions: (i) binding to origin-recognition proteins that assemble the initiation complex, (ii) unwinding or destabilizing the helix, and (iii) fixing the distance between protein binding sites. The general arrangement of functional modules within the limited size of replication origins is described in the following sections.

## A. Binding Sites for Primary Initiation Proteins

Both bacterial and yeast origins contain short stretches of nucleotides that bind to key regulatory proteins. Once specific recognition proteins bind the replication origin, additional regulatory proteins are recruited to assemble replication forks.

In *E. coli* and other bacterial species, DnaA is the most convincing candidate for the origin-binding initiator protein. All viable *E. coli* strains harboring mutations in the *dnaA* gene are temperature sensitive for growth. In most cases, these mutant strains complete all rounds of previously initiated DNA replication when shifted to nonpermissive temperature but do not initiate new rounds. There are also DnaA mutants that overinitiate when cultures are incubated at temperatures lower than 37°C. Overproduction of DnaA protein triggers spurious initiations from *oriC*, although the replication forks produced do not necessarily finish a round of synthesis.

The ATP-bound form of DnaA binds to four copies of the 9-mer 5′-TTATC/ACAC/AA-3′ in *oriC*. These sites are termed R boxes. However, DnaA does not bind all R boxes with equal affinity; R4 has the strongest affinity and R3 the weakest. Although the specific

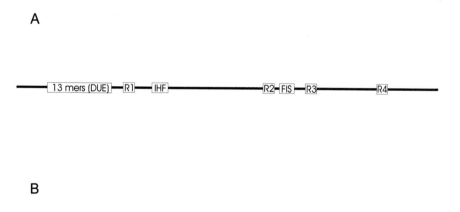

**Fig. 2.** Structure of replication origins. (A) Schematic map of *oriC,* the *E. coli* replication origin. Relative locations of the consensus sequences for DnaA (R1–R4), FIS, and IHF binding are indicated. The site of unwinding at initiation is also shown (DUE). (B) Schematic map of *S. cerevisiae* ARS1. Relative locations of the A domain, containing the ACS consensus sequence, and the B domains are shown.

manner in which DnaA interacts with *oriC* is unclear, *in vitro* analysis with purified components revealed that 20–40 monomers of DnaA produce a nucleosome-like complex with approximately 220 bp of DNA. In the presence of ATP at 38°C, this DnaA–*oriC* complex is sensitive to single-strand scission agents. This result suggests that DnaA binding alone is sufficient to unwind the origin and trigger initiation at *oriC*.

In yeast, the best studied candidate for initiator is a tight complex of proteins termed origin recognition complex (ORC). ORC forms from six different proteins in the presence of ATP. Functional *orc* genes are required for viability, and temperature-sensitive mutations in *orc2*, *orc3*, and *orc5* show cell cycle defects in DNA replication as well as plasmid loss. ORC is reported to be limiting in living *S. cerevisiae* (approximately one ORC complex per origin). In an analogous fashion to R sites for DnaA in *E. coli*, ORC binds to an 11-bp core sequence known as ACS. 5′-A/TTTTATA/GTTTA/T-3′, which lies within a region called domain A (Fig. 2). In ARS1, the ACS is not sufficient for origin function. Approximately 100 bp of 3′ DNA are also required. This region is termed domain B (Fig. 2) and is further divided into essential subdomains (e.g., B1–B3) based on linker substitution mutagenesis. There is a great deal of sequence variability in the B domain among different ARSs isolated to date. Domain B1, nearest to the ACS, is the most highly conserved. ORC binding extends over B1, based on *in vivo* footprinting experiments. In addition, mutations in the B element reduce the frequency of origin firing. The B domain is reported to carry the replication origin's easily unwound region (see Section II.C).

## B. Additional Protein Binding Sites in Bacterial and Yeast Origins

In *E. coli*, DnaA is not the only protein with a specific binding site in *oriC*. Two additional, histone-like proteins are known to bind to *oriC*. These proteins are integration *host factor* (IHF) and *factor for inversion stimulation* (FIS). They are not required for *oriC* function *in vivo* and are therefore considered accessory proteins. IHF and FIS appear to facilitate efficient synchronous assembly of the nucleoprotein complex that triggers initiation. In addition to their role in chromosome replication, both FIS and IHF are associated with higher order DNA–protein complexes produced by integration, recombination, and transposition systems. Both proteins also function as transcription regulators at a wide variety of genetic sites throughout the chromosome.

IHF binds to the left half of *oriC* (Fig. 2) between R1 and R2. Binding of IHF protects approximately 30 bp of *oriC* immediately rightward of R1 from *in vitro* Dnase I digestion. In the right half of *oriC*, between R2 and R3, is a binding site for FIS. FIS binding protects the R3 region from Dnase I digestion. Binding of FIS and binding of DnaA to R3 are incompatible. The most significant known function of FIS and IHF is their ability to severely bend DNA. There is evidence that in *E. coli*, these bending proteins bind *oriC* with cell cycle specificity, producing precisely timed changes in DNA conformation and in DnaA accessibility at weak R boxes.

In yeast ARS1, an accessory protein was also identified that binds within the replication origin. This ARS binding factor (ABF1) binds to the B domain most 3′ to the ACS, subdomain B3. ABF1 is a multifunctional protein analogous to FIS or IHF in that it is involved in transcription regulation and is not required for ARS function. Like IHF and FIS, ABF1 acts as an enhancer of origin function by producing changes in DNA conformation.

In addition to ORC and ABF1, other yeast proteins, such as Cdc6, Cdc45, and Mcm associate with the origin of replication at specific times in the cell cycle. However, although the presence of these proteins in the origin region alters the pattern of nuclease sensitivity caused by ORC binding, most data suggest that they interact with components of ORC rather than binding directly to DNA.

## C. DNA Unwinding Elements

All known microbial origins contain discrete modules that are highly A-T rich and easily unwound. These regions are termed DNA unwinding elements (DUEs). Placement of the DUE within the replication origin differs for prokaryotic and eukaryotic origins of replication. The left half of *E. coli*'s replication origin contains three tandem repeats of a 13-base sequence whose consensus is GATCTNTTNTTTT (Fig. 2). In DnaA-dependent initiation, unwinding of *oriC* is restricted to the 13-mer region, with primary unwinding in the rightmost 13-mer. Analysis of single-strand nuclease hypersensitivity, and thermodynamic helical stability indicate the presence of DUEs in the B domain of well-studied ARSs. However, a consensus sequence for yeast ARS DUE is more difficult to ascertain due to variation in nucleotide sequence adjacent to the ACS.

## D. Spacer Sequences

There are stretches of origin DNA sequence that play no role in protein recognition or DNA unwinding. However, these regions are important, and are needed to separate protein binding and unwinding sites. Mutagenic analysis reveals that in *E. coli*, the spacing between R sites as well as the distance between the right 13-mer and R1 are necessary for origin function. Apparently, critical DNA conformational changes are produced within the left half of *oriC* during assembly of the initiation nucleoprotein complex. The right half of *oriC* appears to be less sensitive to changes in the numbers of bases between R2 and R3 or R3 and R4, as long as helical phasing between these R sites is unperturbed. DnaA protein bound at one R site must be oriented so that it can interact directly with DnaA or nucleotides at other R sites. Based on linker substitution mutagenesis in yeast ARS, the placement of the ACS relative to the B domain also appears to be critical for function, presumably so that appropriate DNA–protein and protein–protein complexes can assemble to produce key conformational changes in the origin.

## E. Regulation of Origin Function by Methylation

*Escherichia coli's oriC* contains 11 GATC sites, and the placement of 8 of these sites is conserved among enterobacterial origins. The adenosine within GATC is methylated by deoxyadenosine methyltransferase (Dam methylase). Methylation is critical for proper initiation timing, and mutant strains deficient in Dam methylase are not capable of synchronous initiation. After initiation, fully methylated GATC sites are replicated, and the double-stranded DNA produced is temporarily hemimethylated. Hemimethylated GATCs stimulate association of the protein SeqA, which appears to "sequester" *oriC* from Dam methylase and other proteins, including DnaA, for approximately one-third of a generation. In this sequestered state, a new round of replication cannot be triggered. Thus, SeqA plays the role of a negative regulator of initiation in *E. coli* and SeqA mutant strains are defective for initiation control.

Hemimethylation produces a cell cycle-specific condition that could not only limit the accessibility of *oriC* to initiator protein, but also may play a role in bacterial chromosome segregation. When hemimethylated, *oriC* binds to membrane fractions, although the mechanism of binding is not well understood. There are no clear data that suggest methylation regulates initiation or segregation in eukaryotic microbes.

## III. ASSEMBLY AND DISASSEMBLY OF NUCLEOPROTEIN COMPLEXES AT REPLICATION ORIGINS

### A. Overview

The assembly of DNA–protein complexes at replication origins is a dynamic, multistep process that is critically timed in the cell cycle. Both *E. coli* and *S. cerevisiae* replication origins are converted from preinitiation to initiation and finally to postinitiation states (Fig. 3). The preinitiation complex must serve two interrelated roles: (i) to ensure the proper, ordered assembly of the initiation complex and (ii) to prohibit any spurious initiation that could be accidentally triggered by altered complex formation. Thus, preinitiation complexes are both enhancers and repressors of initiation. The preinitiation complex progresses to an initiation complex via displacement of some proteins and recruitment of new proteins. Activation of proteins in the complex induces helix unwinding. At this point DNA synthesis begins, as replication forks are set into motion. Replication origins then form a post initiation complex, whose primary function is to make the origin refractory to further initiations within a single cell cycle. Follow-

**A**                                      **B**

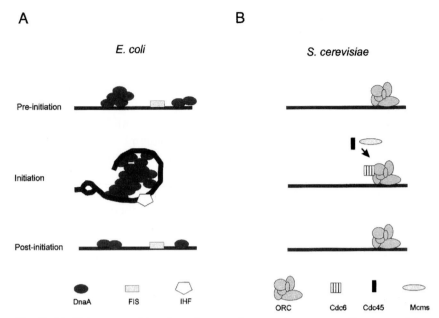

**Fig. 3.** Multistep assembly of nucleoprotein complexes at replication origins. (A) Progression of pre-initiation to initiation and post-initiation complexes in *E. coli*. Binding of DnaA, FIS, and IHF is indicated. (B) Model of initiation complex formation at ARS1 in *S. cerevisiae*. Continuous binding of ORC, as well as recruitment of Cdc6, Cdc45, and Mcm proteins, is indicated.

ing the refractory period, replication origins are reactivated or licensed to enter the prereplicative state once more. In *E. coli*, *oriC* is likely to reform the preinitiation complex immediately after sequestration ends. In eukaryotic nuclei, licensing requires passage through mitosis. Specific features of the molecular transitions of *E. coli* and yeast replication origins through the cell cycle are presented in the following sections.

## B. *Escherichia coli*

A complex of proteins bound to *oriC* is detected almost throughout the entire cell cycle. This preinitiation complex includes DnaA binding to R1 and R4, as well as FIS binding to its *oriC* site. When bound, FIS partially covers the lower affinity DnaA binding sites R2 and R3. Its most likely function is to ensure that initial loading of DnaA onto *oriC* is restricted to the R1 and R4 sites. As new DnaA is synthesized during the cell cycle, it accumulates at *oriC*. At a critical DnaA concentration, two events can be measured: (i) FIS is displaced from its site, allowing

DnaA access to the R2 and R3 sites and (ii) IHF binds to its site between R1 and R2. The initiation complex is formed by these events. Although this remodeling of *oriC* is catalyzed by DnaA, the mechanism controlling the conversion from FIS-bound to IHF-bound complex is not known. The accessory proteins appear to function as switches, changing the conformation of the origin rapidly as the correct concentration of DnaA is achieved for initiation. Mutant strains deficient in FIS or IHF demonstrate asynchronous initiations and have variable but generally increased mass at initiation. These data suggest that, in the absence of FIS or IHF, initiation requires, on average, more DnaA, but the amount of DnaA might vary from origin to origin. Thus, the FIS to IHF switch appears to be necessary for setting the precise level of DnaA needed for proper initiation timing.

At initiation, the 13-mer region is unwound, and DnaA protein interacts with the 13-mer region and recruits the DnaB–DnaC complex. DnaB helicase protein is loaded onto the DNA followed by DNA polymerase. After forks begin their journey, a postinitiation complex represses further initiations and allows for more gradual remodeling back to the pre-initiation state. FIS rebinds *oriC,* accompanied by loss of IHF and DnaA, within several minutes after initiation. It is not clear what removes DnaA and IHF from the origin. It is possible that the replication fork knocks these proteins off, or perhaps SeqA binding resets the origin. The fate of DnaA is not clear. It may be inactive (ADP bound), actively degraded, or moved to a different cellular location. Certainly, much data indicates that existing DnaA is no longer functional after initiation, and DnaA must be synthesized *de novo* each cell cycle. After return to the FIS-bound complex, *oriC* remains hemimethylated for nearly one-third of the cell cycle. During this time, SeqA may inhibit binding of new DnaA protein to the origin. After sequestration, newly synthesized DnaA binds to the FIS-bound complex and another cycle is set into motion.

## C. Yeast

Based on footprint analysis, yeast replication origins form at least two different complexes during the cell cycle. A pre-replicative (preRC) complex is detected from the end of mitosis to the time DNA synthesis begins. This complex protects significantly more of the B domain than is possible for ORC alone, indicating the presence of additional proteins. A post-replicative complex (postRC), which apparently contains only ORC, appears between the time DNA synthesis begins and the end of mitosis. The postRC converts to the preRC during $G_1$, and this conversion involves both cell cycle-specific synthesis and recruitment of proteins to the ORC complex. Certain preRC proteins are activated by cell cycle-regulated protein kinases. This activation triggers initiation of DNA replication in S phase. After initiation, proteins (except ORC) are removed, reforming the preRC complex. Although it is not clear that all preRC proteins have been identified, strong experimental evidence suggests that Cdc6, Cdc45, and MCM proteins, encoded by conditional lethal cell division cycle genes *cdc6* and *cdc45* and minichromosome maintenance genes (*mcm* 2–7), respectively, are components of the preRC.

A primary step in preRC assembly is association of *cdc6* with existing ORC, apparently via interaction with Orc5. Cdc6 is critical for assembly and maintenance of the preRC, and in temperature-sensitive *cdc6* mutant strains only the ORC-containing postRC is observed at nonpermissive temperature. These mutants also fail to progress from $G_1$ to S phase at nonpermissive temperature. Cdc6 expression is strictly under cell cycle control, with mRNA levels peaking at mitosis and rapid degradation of Cdc6 protein at the $G_1$/S transition.

Loading of ORC-bound origins with Cdc6 protein in $G_1$ allows the next step of preRC assembly, the loading of an oligomeric complex of six different Mcm proteins. Mcms are conserved among eukaryotes and each carries a 240-amino acid region similar to DNA-dependent ATPases. Direct interaction between Mcms and ORC–Cdc6 has been difficult to measure, although it appears that the ORC–Cdc6 complex must be present for Mcms to function since *de novo* synthesis of Cdc6 is necessary for tight binding of Mcms to chromatin. In addition to binding, Mcms must be activated by phosphorylation before cells can exit $G_1$ and initiate DNA replication in S phase. Mcm phosphorylation appears to be regulated by a cell cycle-specific protein kinase, termed Cdc7–Dbf4. (Cdc7–Dbf4 is activated by a $G_1$-specific cyclin-dependent kinase.)

The final step in assembly of the preRC is binding and activation of the Cdc45 protein, which requires functional Cdc6 protein and phosphorylated Mcms. In addition, Cdc45 activity in the initiation complex requires another cell cycle-specific kinase, termed Clb–Cdc28. (Like Cdc7–Dbf4, Clb–Cdc28 is activated by a $G_1$ cyclin-dependent kinase.) When Cdc45 binds and is phosphorylated by Clb–Cdc28, the resulting complex appears to be sufficient to trigger initiation. After initiation, Mcm and Cdc45 proteins may associate with the replication fork. Some evidence suggests that although it is a member of the replication fork complex, Mcms may provide helicase function. Following initiation and throughout S phase, the Cdc6–ORC complex is disrupted by Clb–Cdc28 kinase, which prevents Cdc6 function and blocks reinitiation of DNA replication. Thus, activation and suppression of the initiation complex are controlled by cell cycle-specific kinases. $G_1$ cyclin-dependent kinases activate downstream protein kinases, including Cdc7–Dbf4 and Clb–Cdc28.

Cdc7–Dbf4 controls assembly of the preRC through phosphorylation of Mcms, and activation of the preRC-bound origin is under control of Clb–Cdc28, via phosphorylation of Cdc45. After initiation, Clb–Cdc28 prevents Cdc6 from stimulating reformation of the preRC until Cdc28 is degraded at mitosis.

## D. Summary

Both prokaryotic and eukaryotic microbes control initiation of chromosome replication by multistep, ordered assembly of a nucleoprotein complex at an origin of replication. In bacteria, the rate at which the initiator protein DnaA accumulates at the origin determines the frequency of initiation, and cell cycle-specific expression of *oriC* binding proteins is not necessary for proper initiation timing. Loss of active DnaA, hemimethylation of *oriC*, and the mechanism of sequestration automatically prohibit reinitiation in the critical moments following origin firing. In contrast, yeast cells contain cell cycle-specific kinases that regulate all aspects of origin function, such that key components are present and/or functional during a discrete time period of the cell cycle. The processes of initiation, chromosome replication, and segregation are separated temporally, and this separation is governed by a series of molecular checkpoints. With such a sophisticated regulatory network in place, it is not surprising that the yeast cell rarely commits an error. In fast-growing *E. coli,* DNA replication and segregation are ongoing when new rounds of replication initiate from *oriC.* If bacteria are to maintain the survival advantages resulting from rapid growth, they apparently cannot afford the luxury of restricting times that DNA may replicate. Instead, bacterial cells have evolved an initiation control mechanism that may be operational at any time during the cell division cycle. This mechanism is more streamlined than that found in eukaryotic microbes, but it is no less precise.

## IV. CHROMOSOME PARTITION SYSTEMS IN PROKARYOTIC AND EUKARYOTIC MICROBES

After successfully replicating their genomes, microbes must ensure that each new daughter cell re-

ceives its complement of chromosomes after cell division. Mechanistically, this is not a trivial process and there are obviously many steps in which errors could lead to the production of nonviable cells. A successful segregation system requires several components: (i) a mechanism to identify the location of each nascent daughter chromosome, (ii) a means for physical attachment to chromosome copies, and (iii) a polarized motor activity to pull chromosome copies into separate physical spaces destined to become new cells. During mitosis in eukaryotic microbes, structures for physical separation of chromosomes, the spindle pole bodies (SPBs), are visible with the aid of a microscope. The vehicle for segregation is not so obvious in bacteria. Bacteria contain few visible intracellular structures, and until recently there has been no evidence of centromeres and intracellular organization. In addition, the segregation mechanism in bacteria must, under rapid growth conditions, be functional, whereas DNA replication is ongoing. Because of these clear differences, it was expected that bacteria and yeast would segregate their chromosomes via markedly different mechanisms. However, there is evidence that localized segregation proteins do exist in bacteria. Furthermore, although the physical force separating bacterial chromosomes has yet to be identified, such a force must exist. Current data suggest that in some ways, eukaryotic and bacterial microbes use similar strategies to segregate chromosomes. The properties of both systems are discussed in the following sections.

## A. Chromosome Segregation in Budding Yeast

After replication, as the cell enters mitosis, yeast chromosomes are paired and condensed, held together by specialized adhesive forces. In mitosis, sister chromatids achieve bipolar attachment to the spindle, which is composed of interdigitated microtubules emanating from the SPBs. Next, during the transition from metaphase to anaphase, the forces holding sister chromatids together are synchronously dissolved and the chromatids are pulled to opposite poles by motor proteins. Although this scenario seems simple, the molecular machinery of segregation in yeast is complex. It must include protein–DNA interactions that control cohesion and condensation of sister chromatids as well as the assembly of a multicomponent DNA–protein structure, termed the kinetochore, that associates microtubules and motor proteins with centromere DNA. Failure to assemble or disassemble these components of the segregation system results in cell cycle arrest.

After chromosome replication, sister chromatids are maintained as a linked complex. This linkage in metaphase is beneficial and obviates the need to localize each sister chromatid individually before bipolar attachment to spindle microtubules. DNA intertwining, generated by replication, initially produces physical linkage of sister chromatids. These DNA catenanes are removed by DNA topoisomerase II, which is part of the condensed chromosome scaffold. After decatenation, cohesion proteins, termed cohesins and condensins, ensure that sister chromatids do not separate until anaphase. In *S. cerevisiae*, several cohesion proteins have been identified, including MCD1/SCC1 and several members of the SMC (structural *m*aintenance of *c*hromosomes) family. SMC proteins are conserved among some bacteria and most eukaryotes, including humans. SMCs are putative ATPases, containing an NTP-binding motif in their N-terminal domains. In addition to their role in cohesion, SMCs may also function in DNA recombination and repair. Surprisingly, in the prokaryote *B. subtilis*, SMC homologs are involved in chromosome partitioning.

Attachment of sister chromatids to spindle microtubules requires assembly of kinetochores, which contain centromere DNA and centromere binding proteins. Centromeres of *S. cerevisiae* chromosomes are quite small (120 bp) relative to other eukaryotic centromeres (which are contained in megabase domains of repetitive DNA). The *S. cerevisiae* centromere consists of three nucleotide sequence elements, termed CDEI–CDEIII. There is an 8-bp homology among all budding yeast chromosomes in CDEI and a 25-bp homology in CDEIII. A 78- to 86-bp sequence that is more than 90% A-T rich separates CDEI and CDEIII. CDEI and CDEIII are essential for chromosome segregation since deletion of CDEI increases chromosome loss 10-fold and deletion or point mutations of CDEIII destroy centromere function.

In contrast to the centromere sequence, centromere-binding proteins of *S. cerevisiae* show little similarity to analogous proteins in other yeasts and higher eukaryotes. In *S. cerevisiae*, a four-protein complex, termed Cbf3, binds specifically to CDEIII and initiates kinetochore assembly. After binding to CDEIII, one of the Cbf3 proteins, p58, is activated by phosphorylation and later degraded by ubiquitin-mediated proteolysis. By this mechanism, assembly of the kinetochore can be limited to one per chromatid and assembly can be restricted to a limited time during the cell cycle.

*Saccharomyces cerevisiae* kinetochores achieve bipolar attachments to single microtubules so that each sister chromatid is pulled in opposite directions. The microtubules emanate from an SPB to form the mitotic spindle. The yeast SPB is embedded in the nuclear membrane throughout the cell cycle. Duplication of the SPB occurs prior to the onset of S phase in *S. cerevisiae*. Surprisingly, the spindle (SPB with microtubules) first appears during S. phase in budding yeast, suggesting that chromosome replication and spindle assembly comprise two separate regulatory pathways. Spindle elongation and subsequent chromatid separation requires kinesin-related proteins Kip1 and Cin8 and a dynein-related protein Dyn1 to provide both pushing and pulling forces. There is also evidence for mechanochemical motor activity associated with the kinetochore.

It is likely that only one of the sister chromatids initially becomes attached to a spindle microtubule. The attachment, however, causes the movement of both chromatids, which oscillate as the microtubule grows and shrinks. This oscillation may prevent the remaining centromere from attaching to other microtubules from the same SPB. Only binding of the remaining centromere to a microtubule from the opposite SPB can produce the bidirectional force required to trigger dissolution of adhesions holding the chromatids together. Since this dissolution is a synchronous event, a checkpoint signal that inhibits chromosome segregation must be removed when all chromatids are properly attached to microtubules. Although the signal has not been identified, a protein termed anaphase promoting complex (APC) is implicated in dissolving sister chromatid cohesion. APC ligates ubiquitin to target proteins, thus marking them for proteolysis. APC mutant cells do not separate sister chromatids. APC is also involved in ubiquitinization/destruction of B-type cyclins in anaphase; thus, a relationship exists between chromatid separation and progression through the cell cycle. After removal of the forces holding them together, chromatids disjoin during anaphase and are segregated by movement along microtubules toward each SPB.

## B. Segregation in Prokaryotes

There is little obvious structural organization within the cytoplasm of *E. coli* cells, and certainly no structure equivalent to the mitotic spindle has been observed in prokaryotic cells. However, bacterial cells must have a highly effective chromosome partitioning system since anucleate cells are rarely produced. This perplexing situation has resulted in models for chromosome segregation in *E. coli* that utilize the cell surface as part of the segregation machinery. The 1963 Replicon hypothesis proposed by Jacob, Brenner, and Cuzin suggested that the replication origin could act as the centromere and sites at which the origin attached to the membrane could function as an SPB (centrosome) in *E. coli*. In this model, *oriC* is attached to the cell surface at midcell. After initiation of chromosome replication, both copies of *oriC* become surface attached. A signal is then sent to induce growth of the cell envelope between the attached origins. Localized surface growth is the physical force separating chromosomes into progeny cells. This clever model remains the working hypothesis for partitioning mechanisms of *E. coli* chromosomes, although recent studies suggest modifications will be necessary.

In *E. coli, oriC* attachment to cell membrane is measurable. Hemimethylated *oriC* binds specifically to the outer membrane. After initiation of replication, *oriC* remains hemimethylated (and presumably membrane bound) for one-third of the generation time, and it seems reasonable to propose that *oriC* attachment around the time of initiation of replication persists long enough to form the basis for a chromosome partitioning mechanism. There is also recent evidence that replication origins are localized in bacteria, although they do not appear to bind the cell surface at midcell as Jacob *et al.* proposed. Studies performed in *E. coli, Bacillus subtilis*, and *Caulobacter crescentus* have used several elegant methods to local-

ize *oriC*. One approach is to insert DNA cassettes containing multiple copies of the *lac* operator into the chromosome. Genetic locations are visualized within the cell using green fluorescent protein linked to Lac repressor. Partition proteins were also localized during the cell cycle using fluorescent antibody as an *in situ* probe. Other groups have used DNA probes for fluorescence *in situ* hybridization to fixed cells on microscope slides. The results are summarized as follows. For cells growing with doubling times equivalent to their chromosome replication time, *oriC* localizes to the cell poles in newborn cells, fixing the orientation of nucleoids "back to back," with the terminus region at midcell. Origin duplication occurs at the polar location and one of the newly replicated copies is rapidly translocated to midcell, where a future pole will form. Several proteins involved in chromosome segregation, such as Spo0J in *B. subtilis*, and ParB in *C. crescentus*, are also localized to the poles, associated with the *oriC* region of the chromosome. It has been suggested that these proteins may be needed for *oriC* localization.

The force that separates chromosomes in bacterial cells prior to division remains elusive. Little experimental evidence supports the model that cell surface growth is localized between the attached *oriC*s. In fact, the strongest evidence supports the idea of diffuse growth throughout the lateral envelope. Most recent data indicate that the conformation of the bacterial chromosome in a condensed structure termed the nucleoid plays a role in segregation. Studies in *B. subtilis* suggest that chromosome condensation proteins form part of the segregation machinery. Mutations in the *smc* gene of *B. subtilis*, a homolog of the yeast *smc* genes, produce less condensed nucleoids, 10% anucleate cells, and altered localization of Spo0J. Although no clear SMC homolog exists in *E. coli*, at least 11 bacteria harbor this protein and it is likely to play an important role in bacterial chromosome biology.

An active, spindle-like mechanism to physically move bacterial chromosomes has also been proposed. Such a mechanism would require bacterial proteins that have spindle-like or motor function. A search for partitioning mutants (anucleate cells) in *E. coli* identified the Muk family of proteins (encoded by *mukB, -E*, and *-F*). These mutant strains are defective in correct folding and condensation of daughter chromosomes. MukB is a 177-kDa protein. In solution it appears as an elongated molecule with globular domains at both N- and C- termini and a hinged rod connecting region. It has structural features in common with myosin and kinesin motor proteins. MukB binds ATP and GTP but does not hydrolyze these nucleotides. MukB also binds to DNA, but specific binding sites have not been identified. It remains to be determined whether MukB forms higher order structures similar to the spindle in eukaryotes or whether MukB is a motor protein that pulls or pushes DNA along a structure associated with the cell surface. Despite these uncertainties, MukB remains the best candidate for a motor protein component of the putative bacterial cytoskeleton.

Based on observations discussed previously, a revised model for partitioning of bacterial chromosomes can be proposed. A partition protein, such as SpoOJ, localizes *oriC* to a polar location. After duplication of *oriC*, one copy is actively translocated, perhaps via a motor protein such as MukB, to the site that will become a new pole. Interestingly, there is a probabilistic aspect to segregation in *E. coli*. Each round of DNA replication produces two origins that are distinguishable from one another because each template strand used to produce the new origins has a different age (templates were polymerized in different cell cycles). Experimental data indicate that the chromosome with the oldest template will segregate into the daughter cell with the oldest pole with a probability $> 0.5$. In other words, there is a greater chance that the oldest *oriC* will stay at its site and the younger *oriC* will move to the site that will become a new pole. Although the reason for this segregation pattern is not known, current models suggest that the translocation mechanism is likely to be responsible for this phenomenon, assuming the precise location of *oriC* is always at the poles.

Despite recent advances, many questions about the mechanism of chromosome segregation in bacteria remain unanswered. In particular, the localization of *oriC* near the pole raises some intriguing questions about the existence of specifically localized surface receptors. Although it is unlikely that the well-defined segregation structures seen in eukaryotic cells will be found in bacteria, an increasing body of evidence suggests that the segregation mechanism may be more similar between prokaryotes and eukaryotes than was previously believed. The notion of a bacterial "cytoskeleton," which helps localize and move macromolecules inside the cell, now seems plausible.

## See Also the Following Articles

CELL DIVISION, PROKARYOTES • CELL MEMBRANE: STRUCTURE AND FUNCTION • DNA REPLICATION

## Bibliography

Diffley, J. F. X. (1996). Once and only once upon a time: Specifying and regulating origins of DNA replication in eukaryotic cells. *Genes Dev.* **10**, 2819–2830.

Heck, M. M. S. (1997). Condensins, cohesins, and chromosome architecture: How to make and break a mitotic chromosome. *Cell* **91**, 5–8.

Hiraga, S. (1993). Chromosome partition in *Escherichia coli*. *Curr. Opin. Genet. Dev.* **5**, 789–801.

Koshland, D. (1994). Mitosis: Back to the basics. *Cell* **77**, 951–954.

Leonard, A. C., and Helmstetter C. E. (1989). Replication and segregation control of *Escherichia coli* chromosomes. *In* "Chromosomes: Eukaryotic, Prokaryotic, and Viral" (K. Adolph, Ed.), Vol. 3, pp. 65–94. CRC Press, Boca Raton, FL.

Levin, P. A., and Grossman, A. D. (1998). Cell cycle: The bacterial approach to coordination. *Curr. Biol.* **8**, R28–R31.

Masuda, H. (1995). The formation and functioning of yeast mitotic spindles. *Bioessays.* **17**, 45–51.

Messer, W., and Weigel, C. (1998). Initiation of chromosome replication. *In* "*Escherichia coli* and *Salmonella typhimurium*" (F. C. Neidhardt, J. Ingraham, K. B. Low, B. Magasanik, M. Schaechter, and H. Umbarger, Eds.), 2nd ed., pp. 1579–1601. ASM Press, Washington, DC.

Newlon, C. S. (1988). Yeast chromosome replication and segregation. *Microbiol. Rev.* **52**, 568–601.

Newlon, C. S. (1997). Putting it all together: Building a prereplicative complex. *Cell* **91**, 717–720.

Page, B. D., and Snyder, M. (1993). Chromosome segregation in yeast. *Annu. Rev. Microbiol.* **47**, 231–261.

Toone, W. M., Aerne, B. I., Morgan, B. A., and Johnson, L. H. (1997). Getting started: Regulating the initiation of DNA replication in yeast. *Annu. Rev. Microbiol.* **51**, 125–149.

Wake, R. G., and Errington, J. (1995). Chromosome partitioning in bacteria. *Annu. Rev. Genet.* **29**, 41–67.

Wheeler, R. T., and Shapiro, L. (1997). Bacterial chromosome segregation: Is there a mitotic apparatus? *Cell* **88**, 577–579.

# Clostridia

## Eric A. Johnson

*University of Wisconsin, Madison*

I. Basic Aspects of the Clostridia
II. Pathogenesis and Applications of Clostridia
III. Conclusions

**vaccine** Any antigenic preparation administered to humans or animals to stimulate protective immunity in the recipients to specific pathogens and/or toxins.

## GLOSSARY

**acetone–butanol fermentation** A bacterial fermentation carried out by certain sugar-metabolizing species of *Clostridium*. The typical end-products include acetone, *n*-butanol, acetic acid (collectively referred to as "solvent").

**anaerobe** An organism that has the ability to grow in the absence of oxygen.

**biocatalysts** Biochemical compounds (particularly enzymes) that catalyze chemical reactions.

**bioremediation** Conversion of pollutants to nontoxic compounds by microorganisms and enzymes.

**botulism** The rare paralytic disease of humans and other animals caused by the potent neurotoxin produced by the bacterium *Clostridium botulinum*.

**clostridium** Obligate anaerobic, endospore-forming eubacteria that occur widely in soils and in the intestines of humans and other animals.

**endospore** Resistant bodies formed by certain genera of bacteria, including *Bacillus* and *Clostridium*.

**fermentation** Energy-yielding metabolism in which an energy substrate is metabolized without the molecular involvement of an external electron acceptor, such as oxygen.

**gas gangrene** A rapidly spreading disease which results from the infection of a wound by certain anaerobic bacteria, particularly from the genus *Clostridium*.

**tetanus** The extremely painful spastic disease (commonly called lockjaw), affecting humans and animals, that is produced by the bacterium *Clostridium tetani*.

**toxins** Microbial products or components that cause injury or disease in multicellular organisms, including humans and animals.

**THE CLOSTRIDIA** have a rich history in industrial and medical microbiology. The genus *Clostridium* comprises a large and diverse group of anaerobic or aerotolerant gram-positive, rod-shaped eubacteria that form resistant endospores. The endospores are usually wider than the vegetative organisms in which they arise giving the characteristic spindle shapes, or clostridium forms. The clostridia are widely distributed in nature by virtue of their ability to form environmentally resistant endospores.

The clostridia appear to reside mainly in two habitats: soils throughout the world and the intestines of animals. Many clostridia cause devastating diseases of humans and animals, such as botulism, tetanus, and gas gangrene, through the production of protein toxins. Other species are important in the formation of solvents and organic acids by anaerobic fermentations or as a source of unique enzymes for biocatalysis. Most clostridia lack heme and cytochromes and have evolved as strict anaerobes, consequently they obtain cellular energy by fermentation of carbon and nitrogen substrates.

Although life without oxygen was envisioned as early as 1680 by Antonie van Leeuwenhoek, the discovery of anaerobiosis is attributed to Pasteur, who showed in the mid-1850s that butyric acid fermentation occurred in the absence of oxygen. Pasteur devised anaerobic culture conditions by boiling the medium to drive out absorbed oxygen and adding inert gases back to the culture medium. He isolated an organism that only grew and produced butyric acid under anaerobic conditions, which he called "*Vibrion butyrique,*" which probably corresponds to *Clostridium butyricum,* the type species of the genus *Clostridium.* In 1877, Pasteur and Joubert also described the first pathogenic anaerobe of humans and animals, now known as *Clostridium septicum.*

The study of the clostridia has had tremendous impacts on various facets of microbiology. The importance of anaerobic clostridia in medical and industrial microbiology contributed significantly to the advent of important techniques and equipment for isolation of anaerobes and for anaerobic culture. The discovery of the roles of clostridial protein toxins in causing diseases contributed to the concept of vaccination with detoxified forms of toxins to produce immunity in animals and humans. The importance of clostridia in industrial fermentations was demonstrated before World War I, when an industrial process was developed for butanol as a precursor of butadiene (for synthetic rubber) and of acetone, used in the manufacture of munitions. Currently, clostridia are being investigated as sources of novel enzymes for biotransformations and as organisms for production of solvents and organic acids by industrial fermentation, as well as for their capabilities to cause diseases in humans and animals.

## I. BASIC ASPECTS OF THE CLOSTRIDIA

### A. Taxonomy of the Genus *Clostridium*

The genus *Clostridium* is a highly diverse assemblage of gram-positive eubacteria with more than 100 species currently recognized. Clostridia are classified on the basis of morphology, disease association, physiology, serologic properties, DNA relatedness, and ribosomal RNA gene sequence homologies. The clostridia have certain common properties: (a) a gram-positive cell wall structure (though many species stain gram-negative during early stages of culture); (b) formation of resistant endospores that generally swell the cell; (c) an anaerobic and fermentative metabolism; and (d) the inability to reduce sulfate to sulfide. The vast majority of clostridia have

a rod-shaped morphology and are motile by peritrichous flagella. Several taxonomic groups of *Clostridium* have been described on the basis of nucleic acid homologies, sequencing of macromolecules, particularly 16S rRNA, mol% G + C, cell wall structure, production of toxic and antigenic proteins, and type of anaerobic metabolism. Eighteen groups of *Clostridium* species have been proposed, based on sequences of the genes coding for 16S rRNA.

Historically, clostridia causing diseases in humans and animals have been classified on the basis of production of potent protein toxins and the neutralization of toxicity by specific antitoxins. Botulinum and tetanus toxins are the most poisonous substances known to man. While several species of clostridia are known to produce botulinal neurotoxin, they are all artificially classified as *Clostridium botulinum,* since the production of the neurotoxin is the outstanding character of these organisms. For this reason, it is unlikely that a natural classification system and delineation of numerous species will be utilized by most medical and industrial scientists working with clostridia.

### B. Metabolic Properties of Clostridia

Clostridia carry out a fermentative metabolism and do not utilize oxygen for energy production or biosynthesis. Some clostridial species, such as *C. novyi,* tolerate low concentrations of oxygen, while, for other species, oxygen is highly toxic. Most *Clostridium* species lack defenses against reactive oxygen species such as hydrogen peroxide, superoxide anion, hydroxyl radical, and singlet oxygen. These organisms lack heme pigments and are catalase negative. For others, oxygen is toxic by interfering directly with vital enzyme systems. Clostridia lack enzyme pathways that utilize oxygen for the synthesis of many classes of secondary metabolites, such as antibiotics.

The genus *Clostridium* contains species that can grow over a wide range of pHs and temperatures. Most species prefer growth over the pH range of 6–7, but some grow at pHs below 4 or above 8. Most clostridia favor temperatures of growth from 25–37°C, but several species of psychrophilic clostridia grow below 10°C and several thermophilic species grow above 60°C. The psychrophiles are important in food spoilage, while many of the thermophilic clostridia are valuable as sources of durable enzymes for industrial processes.

Most clostridia have complex nutritional requirements and need several amino acids, vitamins, and a carbohydrate to achieve high numbers of cells in culture. Synthetic culture media are available for many clostridial species and these are useful for studying physiology and gene regulation. Although most clostridia are saccharolytic or proteolytic, and grow on sugars or proteins as their main sources of carbon and energy, some species are able to use carbon dioxide, simple organic acids such as formate or acetic, or nitrogen-containing substrates such as amino acids, purines, or pyrimidines as their sole carbon source for growth. Many clostridia are proteolytic and obtain nutrients from proteins and carry out a putrefactive fermentation of the derived peptides and amino acids. Some clostridia, such as *C. pasteurianium*, are able to fix molecular nitrogen and convert it to organic nitrogen cellular components. Other species are able to ferment cellulose and other complex polysaccharides as their sole carbon and energy source.

Special considerations are needed for isolation and cultivation of clostridia. First, since most species are strict anaerobes, specialized equipment and methodologies are required to provide an anaerobic environment for growth. Anaerobic jars, specialized culture tubes, glove boxes, and reduced media are needed to exclude oxygen and provide the needed redox environment. Second, clostridia tend to grow as mixed cultures with other anaerobes and strict attention is needed to affirm the purity of the culture under study or used in an industrial process. Many clostridia are subject to bacteriophage infection that will decrease solvent, enzyme, or toxin yields. Safe laboratory practices and immunization of personnel is needed for study of toxigenic species such as *C. botulimum* and *C. tetani*.

## C. Spores of Clostridia

Clostridia produce specialized structures, referred to as endospores, which are very resistant to heat, radiation, drying, and chemicals. All *Clostridium* species are able to form spores, but there is considerable

variation in which it occurs in nature and in the laboratory. Spores can be visualized by phase-contrast microscopy. The clostridial spores released from the mother cell are distinct in structure and resistance properties. They are low in water content, possess distinct layers and compartments, and resist inactivation by heat, other physical treatments, and exposure to chemical agents. Certain clostridia, such as *C. botulinum*, produce spores of extraordinary heat resistance, and spores of resistant strains of type A *C. botulinum* (Fig. 1) have heat resistances of $D_{121}C \leq 0.23$ min and $D_{100}C \sim 30$ min. Inactivation of *C. botulinum* spores or control of spore germination and outgrowth provides the basis for many food processing technologies and food regulation laws. Survival of spores of nonpathogenic heat-resistant mesophilic and thermophilic spores during processing of foods can lead to large economic losses. The heat resistance of spores is often used to advantage in isolation of clostridia from mixed cultures or from clinical or environmental samples.

## D. Genetics of Clostridia

The genetic study of the clostridia is in its infancy but significant advances have been made in recent years. The application of molecular biology techniques has enabled the genome size to be estimated for a limited number of clostridial strains. Considerable variation exists between species and even among strains of the same species. *Clostridium perfringens* is the best genetically characterized clostridial species. It contains a single circular chromosome of about 3600 kbp, with essential genes, such as those encoding tRNAs and rRNA operons, having an arrangement analogous to that in *Bacillus subtilis*. The solvent-producing species *Clostridium acetobutylicum* has a genome size of about 6500 kbp, and several genes involved in fermentative metabolism have been mapped and sequenced. Genetic analysis is also advancing in the species *C. botulimum*, *C. difficile*, *C. pasteurianum*, *C. thermocellum*, and *C. tyrobutyricum*. Gene transfer technology using transformation (usually electroporation) or conjugation has been developed for *C. perfringens*, *C. acetobutylicum*, *C. difficile*, and *C. botulinum*, and genetic manipulation to understand virulence and to improve industrial processes is becoming increasingly available. Since the coding

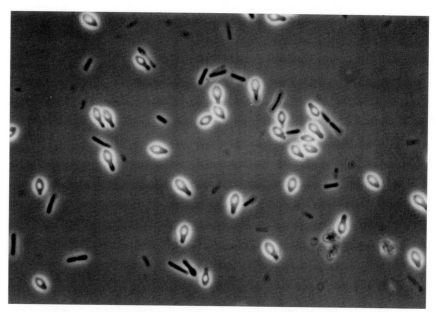

**Fig. 1.** Characteristic spindle morphology of *C. botulinum* and presence of endospores. The photograph shows a phase contrast visual micrograph (×750) of a culture of *C. botulinum* type A.

genomic DNA of most clostridial species is A–T rich, it is often difficult to express cloned clostridial genes in well-characterized heterologous hosts, such as *Escherichia coli* or *Saccharomyces cerevisiae,* due to the limited availability of the required cognate tRNAs for protein synthesis.

Plasmids and bacteriophages are commonly found in clostridia, particularly in pathogenic species. Although most plasmids encode unknown (cryptic) functions, some have been demonstrated to possess genes for virulence and antibiotic resistance. Bacteriophages are widespread in pathogenic and industrial strains of clostridia. In certain pathogens, phages carry genes for toxins that can be transferred to normally nonpathogenic clostridia by infection. Phage infection and culture lysis have been a continual problem of clostridial cultures used for solvent production. Strain degradation and the loss of capacity of clostridia to produce high yields of solvents has also been problematic for industrial processes.

## II. PATHOGENESIS AND APPLICATIONS OF CLOSTRIDIA

Several clostridial species are of practical importance or interest (Table I). Many species are patho-genic to humans and animals, mainly through the production of protein toxins and enzymes during infection. Other species have beneficial aspects in biotechnology, such as production of valuable metabolites, formation of enzymes catalyzing bioconversions, secretion of enzymes and proteins that convert wastes to higher-value products, and formation of enzyme systems that metabolize pollutants or detoxify xenobiotics under anaerobic conditions (Table I). One of the most remarkable applications of the clostridia in industrial microbiology is the utilization of botulinum neurotoxin for the pharmacological treatment of a myriad of human disorders characterized by involuntary or hyperactive muscle movements. The practical importance of these clostridial groups is briefly described.

### A. Toxigenic Clostridia

One of the most fascinating features of the clostridia is their production of a wide array of biologically active antigens, many of which cause diseases in humans and animals. The clostridia produce a greater number of protein toxins than any other bacterial genus. About 20 clostridial species produce protein toxins that are lethal for animals and/or hu-

**TABLE I**
**Clostridial Processes Affecting Human Welfare**

| Property or role | Important products and species |
|---|---|
| Cause of disease in humans and animals, e.g., botulism, tetanus, gas gangrene, wound infections | Neurotoxins, cytotoxins, collagenases, lipases, lecithinases, DNAses, RNAses, ADP-ribosyltransferases, hyaluronidases, hemolysins, others |
| Spoilage of foods | *Clostridium tyrobutyricum,* psychrophilic *Clostridium* sp., putrefactive clostridia |
| Production of solvents and organic acids | Acetone, butanol, ethanol, propanediol, acetate, butyrate, *C. acetobutylicum* |
| Source of industrial enzymes | Cellulases, amylases, pullulanases, proteases, nucleases, stereospecific enzymes for biotransformations and bioconversions, *C. thermocellum* |
| Degradation of pollutants and xenobiotics | Various enzymes |
| Source of pharmaceuticals | Botulinum toxin, *C. botulinum* |

mans. Some of the toxins are notable for their extreme potency; for example, botulinum and tetanus toxins are the most lethal poisons known. Botulinum toxin can be preformed in foods and cause a true intoxication, whereas most of the other pathogenic clostridia produce toxins and inflict damage during infection of the host.

## B. Food Spoilage and Food Poisoning

The spores of clostridia resist minimal food processing procedures and they can later germinate and cause spoilage or safety problems in foods. Two clostridial species, *C. botulinum* and *C. perfringens,* are the major species causing food poisonings. Several other clostridial species can spoil foods by forming gas from organic acids or carbohydrates or by carrying out putrefactive degradation of food proteins.

## C. Solventogenic Clostridia

Clostridia produce fermentation end-products of industrial importance, including acetone, butanol, ethanol, 1,2- and 1,3-propanediol, acetate, and butyrate. The acetone–butanol fermentation process employing *C. acetobutylicum* was used for about 30 years on a large industrial scale, but, due to economic constraints, these solvents are now mostly produced by chemical synthesis. Ethanol synthesis from thermophilic clostridia growing on waste feedstocks, such as cellulose, has attracted much interest but the

process is limited by low ethanol yields and formation of side-products. Industrial interest in clostridial metabolites currently is focused on products that are difficult to prepare in good yields by chemical synthesis, such as chiral compounds.

## D. Industrial Enzymes from Clostridia

Certain thermophilic clostridia produce remarkably stable, highly efficient enzymes that selectively degrade inexpensive substrates, including cellulose, xylan, pectin, pullulan, collagen, and starch. These enzymes are being developed for industrial uses in food processing and production, in detergents, and for other applications. Proteases from clostridia are used for chillproofing of beer and for other applications in food processing.

Clostridia also produce enzymes of value in bioconversions and in degradation of pollutants and xenobiotics. Oxidoreductases catalyze the stereospecific reduction of organic acids such as cinnamate to useful chiral compounds. Clostridial enzymes are also being developed for steroid bioconversions in pharmaceutical manufacture. It has been discovered in recent years that certain clostridia possess enzyme systems for anaerobic degradation of pollutants and xenobiotics, including aromatic compounds and halogenated chemicals, such as herbicides. Thus, the clostridia appear to have important roles in environmental bioremediation.

## E. Use of Clostridial Toxins as Pharmaceuticals

Botulinum neurotoxin is the most poisonous substance known on earth. Botulinum toxin has become an important pharmaceutical for the treatment of involuntary movement disorders, spasticity, pain syndromes, and various other neuronal disorders. Selective injection of botulinum toxin into nerve–muscle regions produces a local weakening of proximal muscles, providing relief from excessive involuntary muscle contractions and pain or disfigurement. The outstanding properties of botulinum toxin as a pharmacological agent are its extreme specificity for nerves and its long duration of action. Other clostridial toxins or fragments of the entire toxins are being developed for drug delivery to the nervous system, prevention of food poisoning, prevention of inflammatory responses, and stimulation of the immune system. It is remarkable that nature's most poisonous substances are being employed as therapeutics to benefit humans.

## III. CONCLUSIONS

The clostridia are ancient evolutionary ancestors of the gram-positive eubacteria. Their outstanding biological properties include the strict anaerobic metabolism, the formation of resistant endospores, and the synthesis of a wide array of distinctive toxins and enzymes. Although clostridia have been known for centuries to cause devastating diseases in humans, such as tetanus, botulism, and gas gangrene, they also are a source of metabolites and enzymes that have considerable utility in biotechnology.

### *See Also the Following Articles*

ANAEROBIC RESPIRATION • BACTERIOPHAGES • BIOCATALYSIS FOR SYNTHESIS OF CHIRAL PHARMACEUTICAL INTERMEDIATES • FOOD SPOILAGE AND PRESERVATION • PLASMIDS

### Bibliography

Fenchel, T., Finlay, B. J. (1995). "Ecology and Evolution in Anaerobic Worlds." Oxford Univ. Press, Oxford, UK.

Hatheway, C. L., and Johnson, E. A. (1998). *Clostridium:* The spore-bearing anaerobes. *In* "Topley and Wilson's Microbiology and Microbial Infections" 9th ed. Vol. 2. Systematic Bacteriology (L. Collier, A. Balows, and M. Sussman, eds.), pp. 731–782. Arnold, London, UK.

Hippe, H., Andreesen, J., Gottschalk, G. (1992). The genus *Clostridium*—Nonmedical. *In* "The Prokaryotes" (A. Balows, H. G. Trüper, M. Dworkin, W. Harder, K.-H. Schleifer, eds.). (2nd ed.). Springer-Verlag, New York.

Hurst, C. J., Knudsen, G. R., McInerney, M. G., Stetzenbach, L. D., Walter, M. V., ed. (1997). "Manual of Environmental Microbiology." American Society for Microbiology, Washington, DC.

Johnson, E. A. (1999). Anaerobic fermentations. *In* "Manual of Industrial Microbiology and Biotechnology" (2nd ed). (A. Demain and J. Davies, eds.) American Society of Microbiology, Washington, DC.

Johnson, E. A. (1999) Clostridial toxins as therapeutic agents. *Annu. Rev. Microbiol.* **53,** 551–575.

Minton, N. P., and Clarke, D. J., (eds.), (1989). "Clostridia. Biotechnology Handbooks," Vol. 3. Plenum Press, New York and London, UK.

Montecucco, C. (ed.), (1997). "Clostridial Neurotoxins. The Molecular Pathogenesis of Tetanus and Botulism." Springer-Verlag, Berlin.

Morris, J. G. (1994). Obligately anaerobic bacteria in biotechnology. *Appl. Biochem. Biotechnol.* **48,** 75–106.

Rood, J. I., McClane, B. A., Songer, J. G., Titball, R. W. (eds.), (1997). "The Clostridia. Molecular Biology and Pathogenesis." Academic Press, San Diego.

Sebald, M. (ed.), (1993). "Genetics and Molecular Biology of Anaerobic Bacteria." Springer-Verlag, New York.

Willis, A. T. (1969). "Clostridia of Wound Infection." Butterworths, London, UK.

Woods, D. R. (ed.). (1993). "The Clostridia and Biotechnology." Butterworth-Heinemann, Boston.

Zehnder, A. J. B. (ed.). (1988). "Biology of Anaerobic Microorganisms." Wiley & Sons, Inc., New York.

# Coenzyme and Prosthetic Group Biosynthesis

**Walter B. Dempsey**

*VA Medical Center and University of Texas Southwestern Medical Center*

## GLOSSARY

**common metabolite**   A metabolite that is a precursor to more than one other metabolite.

**first committed step**   The first step in a biosynthetic pathway that converts a common metabolite to a specific metabolite.

**dedicated pathway**   The entire series of biosynthetic steps, beginning with the first committed step, that converts a common metabolite to a specific metabolite.

**salvage pathways**   Enzymatic reactions which allow an organism to utilize a partially preformed coenzyme or prosthetic group that originates either from the external environment (growth medium) or from intracellular degradation. A common example of "salvage" is phosphorylation of a coenzyme that had become dephosphorylated.

**COENZYMES AND PROSTHETIC GROUPS** are generally small, non-peptidyl molecules which form part of specific proteins and participate in specific biochemical reactions. The distinction between the two terms can be unclear and occasionally is not of great utility. Prosthetic group is the more general term. It applies to compounds that are either tightly bound to their associated proteins or covalently linked to them without regard to whether the protein is an enzyme.

An example of a prosthetic group is the heme in hemoglobin, myoglobin and the cytochromes. Certain metal ions are also considered prosthetic groups.

By their name, coenzymes are obviously associated with enzymes. Typically, they are less tightly bound than prosthetic groups. The original coenzyme, coenzyme I (later known as DPN and now known as NAD), is not tightly bound but behaves as a substrate. Other compounds, once called coenzymes, are so tightly bound to their enzymes that they are frequently considered prosthetic groups.

## I. RELATIONSHIP TO VITAMINS

The exploration of the biosyntheses of coenzymes and prosthetic groups was initiated with the discovery of vitamins. Early vitamin research showed that most of the water-soluble vitamins required for human nutrition were made by bacteria and that the vitamins were used in both bacteria and humans to synthesize compounds that served catalytically in enzyme reactions. This led to an association of the term "Vitamins" with the term "coenzymes."

Among the vitamins found in a typical multivitamin capsule, the following serve as precursors to coenzymes or prosthetic groups: thiamine (thiamine pyrophosphate), pyridoxine (pyridoxal 5'-phosphate), pantothenic acid (acetyl coenzyme A), biotin (biotin), niacin [nicotinamide adenine dinucleotide (NAD)], riboflavin [flavine adenine dinucleotide (FAD, FMN)], folic acid (tetrahydrofolate), and vitamin $B_{12}$ (cobalamin). None of these vitamins can be synthesized in humans, but most common bacteria make their associated coenzymes or prosthetic groups routinely. Many of the vitamins can be used by bacteria to make coenzymes or prosthetic groups, but the pathway by which that chemistry is accomplished is frequently a salvage pathway. We now know that many of the compounds we call vitamins are not biosynthetic intermediates but instead arise in bacteria as degradation products which can be reused or salvaged. Typical examples of this are seen in the biosyntheses of thiamine pyrophosphate and pyridoxal 5′-phosphate. In both these syntheses, bacteria use phosphorylated intermediates and retain the phosphate group throughout the syntheses, never making the free, nonphosphorylated vitamin. The free vitamins that appear in bacterial media are the result of degradation.

## II. WHY SOME BIOSYNTHESES ARE UNKNOWN

The biosynthetic schemes for many coenzymes and prosthetic groups are not worked out. Individual reasons are many, but the overriding one is that coenzymes and prosthetic groups are notable for their very low concentration in cells when compared to common metabolites such as the metabolites of carbohydrate or amino acid metabolism. The amounts are so low that they led McIlwain (1946) to calculate that the amounts of any coenzyme in bacteria could easily be explained by a single molecule of each enzyme on its biosynthetic pathway if the enzymes had turnover numbers in the normal range. (His other hypothesis, that the amounts of enzyme were normal, but their turnover numbers were very sluggish, has proved to be the case.) These very low amounts of metabolites, together with the remarkably sluggish enzymes that synthesize them, have led to a great practical difficulty in studying the biosynthetic pathways of this class of compounds, namely, it has often been extremely difficult to accumulate enough intermediates to isolate and identify them, thereby leaving many of the pathways still unknown.

Several advances have led to the recent elucidation of biosynthetic pathways for some coenzymes. One has been the publication of the complete DNA sequences of several microorganisms, particularly that of the well-studied *Escherichia coli*. Adroit use of information in this data-base has clarified several pathways. Another is the return of skillful organic chemists to this field. Their use of modern organic synthetic methods and their isolation and analyses of micro amounts of coenzymes and precursors labeled in different atoms resolved several steps in several pathways and turned conjecture into reality. A third advance has been the development of analytical hardware of greater sensitivity and sophistication, which has allowed isolation and identification of very small amounts of chemicals. A fourth advance has been the discovery of new metabolic pathways which provide hitherto unknown compounds as starting material for coenzyme biosyntheses.

## III. SCHEMES

In the schemes presented in the following sections, the biosynthetic steps leading to most common metabolites are not shown. Pathways leading to most of the common metabolites are generally well-known and can be found in basic biochemistry books if not elsewhere in this encyclopedia. An interesting common metabolite is 1-deoxy-D-xylulose-5-phosphate, a precursor of isoprenoids, pyridoxal 5′-phosphate, and thiamine pyrophosphate. It is unusual in that, as a precursor of thiamine pyrophosphate, it requires thiamine pyrophosphate for its synthesis. The scheme for its synthesis is shown in Fig. 1.

Descriptions of individual molecules are provided in the following sections. The active molecule is listed first and the related vitamin is given in parentheses.

### A. Biotin (Biotin)

The biosynthesis of biotin begins with pimeloyl coenzyme A (CoA). (Pimelic acid is a six-carbon-long dicarboxylic acid. The exact steps leading to pimeloyl CoA have not been studied but are presumed to arise from fatty-acid-like synthesis.) In the first committed step alanine is added by replacing the CoA to form 7-keto-8-aminopelargonic acid. S-adenosyl methionine reacts with this to convert it to 7,8-diaminopelargonic acid. $CO_2$ is added between the two amino groups to form dethiobiotin. The last step involves the addition of S to dethiobiotin to form biotin. Details of the addition of S are not known.

Biotin serves as a prosthetic group. When it func-

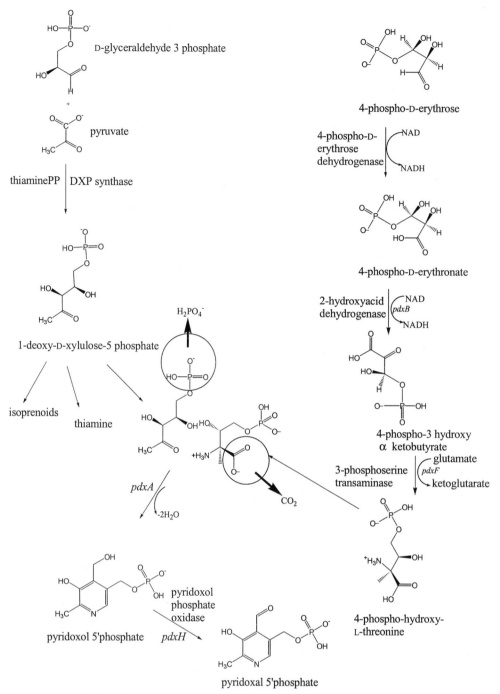

**Fig. 1.** Biosynthetic scheme of 1-deoxy-D-xylulose-5-phosphate and the coenzyme pyridoxal 5-phosphate. (Left) The scheme for the biosynthesis of the common metabolite 1-deoxy-D-xylulose-5-phosphate. It is made from two common metabolites, pyruvate and D-glyceraldehyde 3-phosphate, and is a precursor of isoprenoids, pyridoxal 5'-phosphate, and thiamine pyrophosphate. (Right) The dedicated biosynthetic pathway for pyridoxal 5-phosphate which begins with 4-phospho-D-erythrose. The third step, catalyzed by 3-phosphoserine transaminase, requires pyridoxal 5'-phosphate for activity. Its product reacts with the common metabolite 1-deoxy-D-xylulose-5-phosphate to form pyridoxol 5' phosphate. The italicized symbols are the genes

tions on an enzyme, it is always covalently attached to the enzymes in which it serves by forming an amide bond with the ε amino group of a lysyl residue of the enzyme. Biotin enzymes serve to facilitate adding or removing carboxyl groups. The average amount of biotin in a bacterial culture is 0.15 μ mol/ g dry weight of cells.

## B. Cobalamin (Vitamin B₁₂)

Cobalamin is not synthesized in all bacteria. For example, it is synthesized in *Salmonella typhimurium* but not in *E. coli*. In the former species it is only synthesized under anaerobic conditions. In those bacteria that do synthesize it, all the details of cobalamin biosynthesis are not known. Its synthesis is best viewed as being a coming together of three pieces: dimethylbenzimidazole (DMB), ATP, and cobinamide. The dedicated synthesis of DMB begins with riboflavin. ATP provides an adenosyl group. Cobinamide is a large heme-like structure containing cobalt rather than iron. Its dedicated synthesis begins with the common metabolite uroporphyrinogen III.

Cobalamin participates in several different reactions in different organisms, including methionine synthetase. In this reaction, methionine is synthesized from homocysteine and methyl-THF via a cobalamin-dependent enzyme. Another is acetyl CoA synthesis from CoA, methyl-THF, and carbon monoxide in anaerobic bacteria. A third is propanediol dehydratase. In this reaction propanediol is converted to propionaldehyde via a cobalamin-dependent enzyme.

## C. Coenzyme A (Pantothenic Acid)

Coenzyme A biosynthesis begins with the biosynthesis of pantothenic acid. Pantothenate biosynthesis begins with a common metabolite, α-ketovalerate, an intermediate in the biosynthesis of valine. The first committed step is the addition of a methylol group from 5, 10-methylene THF to form ketopan-

toate. This is reduced to pantoate via NADPH. Pantoate then forms an amide bond with β-alanine (derived from the decarboxylation of aspartate) to form pantothenate. Pantothenate is phosphorylated via ATP and then forms an amide bond with the amino group of cysteine. The carboxyl group is removed via a decarboxylase to yield 4′-phosphopantotheine. This is adenylylated by ATP to form dephospho coenzyme A and finally phosphorylated by another ATP to form CoA.

CoA serves in the transfer of active carbon units in the metabolism of carbohydrates and lipids. Examples of commonly found CoA derivatives are acetyl CoA, succinyl CoA, and malonyl CoA. The sulfhydryl group added by the incorporation of cysteine during the biosynthesis of CoA is the site of attachment of the active acyl groups. The average amount of pantothenate in a bacterial culture is 1.9 μmol/g dry weight of cells.

## D. FMN and FAD (Riboflavin)

The biosynthesis of the flavin moiety begins with the common metabolite GTP. The first committed step involves opening the imidazole ring of the guanine and loss of the methylene carbon as formate. The ribose group is reduced to a ribityl group and 3,4-dihydroxy-2-butanone 4-phosphate, derived from ribulose-5′-phosphate, is added to form 6,7-dimethyl-8-ribityllumazine. Two molecules of this last compound interact with each other to form one molecule of riboflavin and one of an aminopyrimidine by-product. The ribityl group of riboflavin is phosphorylated by ATP to form the coenzyme FMN. The phosphate group of FMN is then adenylylated by another molecule of ATP to form FAD.

Both FMN and FAD serve as prosthetic groups in electron transfer. Both are usually very tightly bound to their respective enzymes and do not function as "substrates." The average amount of riboflavin in a bacterial culture is 0.48 μmol/g dry weight of cells.

---

associated with the enzyme indicated. The circles and thick arrows indicate the two groups that leave during the condensation of 1-deoxy-D-xylulose-5-phosphate with 4-phosphohydroxy-L-threonine and the subsequent aromatization of the product. Note that the phosphate of the starting material, 4-phospho-D-erythrose, becomes the phosphate group of PALP.

### E. Lipoic Acid

The biosynthesis of lipoic acid appears to begin with octanoic acid which can be synthesized from acetyl CoA. This is converted stepwise to the 8-mercapto derivative and then to lipoic acid. Details of the addition of the sulfur atoms are not known.

The active prosthetic group is linked by an amide bond to an $\varepsilon$ amino group of a lysyl residue of the protein involved and is then sometimes referred to as lipoamide. Lipoic acid is found in $\alpha$-keto acid dehydrogenase multienzyme complexes. Its role is that of a temporary acceptor of acyl groups and electrons.

### F. NAD (Nicotinic Acid)

The biosynthesis of NAD begins with the synthesis of nicotinic acid mononucleotide (NaMN). Neither free nicotinamide nor free nicotinic acid are intermediates in the bacterial synthesis of NAD, but they can be incorporated via salvage pathways. The biosynthesis of NaMN begins with aspartate. In the first committed step, aspartate is oxidized to iminoaspartate and then combined with dihydroxyacetone phosphate to form quinolinic acid. The quinolinic acid then combines with phosphoribosyl pyrophosphate to form NaMN with the release of carbon dioxide. NaMN is then adenylylated by ATP to form deamido NAD. The final step in NAD biosynthesis is the amidation of the nicotinic acid moiety with $NH_3$ and ATP.

NAD participates in oxidation-reduction reactions. It is one of the coenzymes that behaves more like a substrate, being freely dissociable from enzymes. The average amount of nicotinic acid in a bacterial culture is 3.6 $\mu$mol/g dry weight of cells.

### G. Pyridoxal 5'-Phosphate (Vitamin B$_6$)

The biosynthesis of pyridoxal 5'-phosphate (PALP) begins with 4-phospho-D-erythrose (Fig. 1). In the dedicated pathway, this phospho-erythrose is oxidized in two steps to 4-phospho-3-hydroxy $\alpha$-ketobutyrate. This is transaminated to 4-phospho-hydroxy-L-threonine (4-PHT) via 3-phosphoserine transaminase. The phosphate on 4-PHT remains to become the 5'-phosphate on the coenzyme. 4-PHT then condenses with the common metabolite 1-deoxy-D-xylulose-5 phosphate (DXP) to form pyridoxol 5'-phosphate (POLP). POLP is then oxidized to PALP. The fact that PALP biosynthesis requires a transaminase which has PALP as a prosthetic group suggests that there must be an alternate way of completing this synthesis either in *E. coli* or in some other organism.

The coenzyme PALP participates in many enzymic reactions that involve the bonds attached to the $\alpha$-carbon atom of amino acids. The most common of these enzymes are the transaminases. In its role as coenzyme for transamination, PALP is first converted to pyridoxamine 5'-phosphate (PAMP) by accepting an amino group from a donor amino acid. PAMP is then converted back to PALP by donating the amino group to a recipient $\alpha$ keto acid to complete the transamination. The active coenzyme in transaminases is therefore considered to be both PALP and PAMP. In other PALP-requiring enzymes (e.g., decarboxylases), PALP is the only active form. In the PALP form, the coenzyme is frequently linked by a reversible covalent bond to its associated transaminase, making PALP a prosthetic group. The average amount of vitamin B$_6$ in a bacterial culture is 0.26 $\mu$mol/g dry weight of cells.

### H. 5,6,7,8-Tetrahydrofolate (Folic Acid)

The biosynthesis of 5,6,7,8-tetrahydrofolate (THF) begins with the common metabolite GTP. It uses ATP for energy and directly incorporates both L-glutamate and *p*-aminobenzoate (PABA). (PABA is synthesized from chorismate, one of the intermediates in the biosynthesis of aromatic amino acids.) The first committed step involves opening the five-membered imidazole ring of GTP, loss of the imidazole methylene carbon, and reclosing the ring as a six-membered pyrazine by adding the C1 and C2 from the ribose of the original GTP. Ensuing steps remove the C4 and C5 atoms of the original ribose and add *p*-aminobenzoate to the C3 of the original ribose molecule. Next, the carboxyl of the PABA forms an amide bond with the amino group of glutamate, and the product 7,8-dihydrofolate is reduced to THF. THF is active in bacteria, but the usual

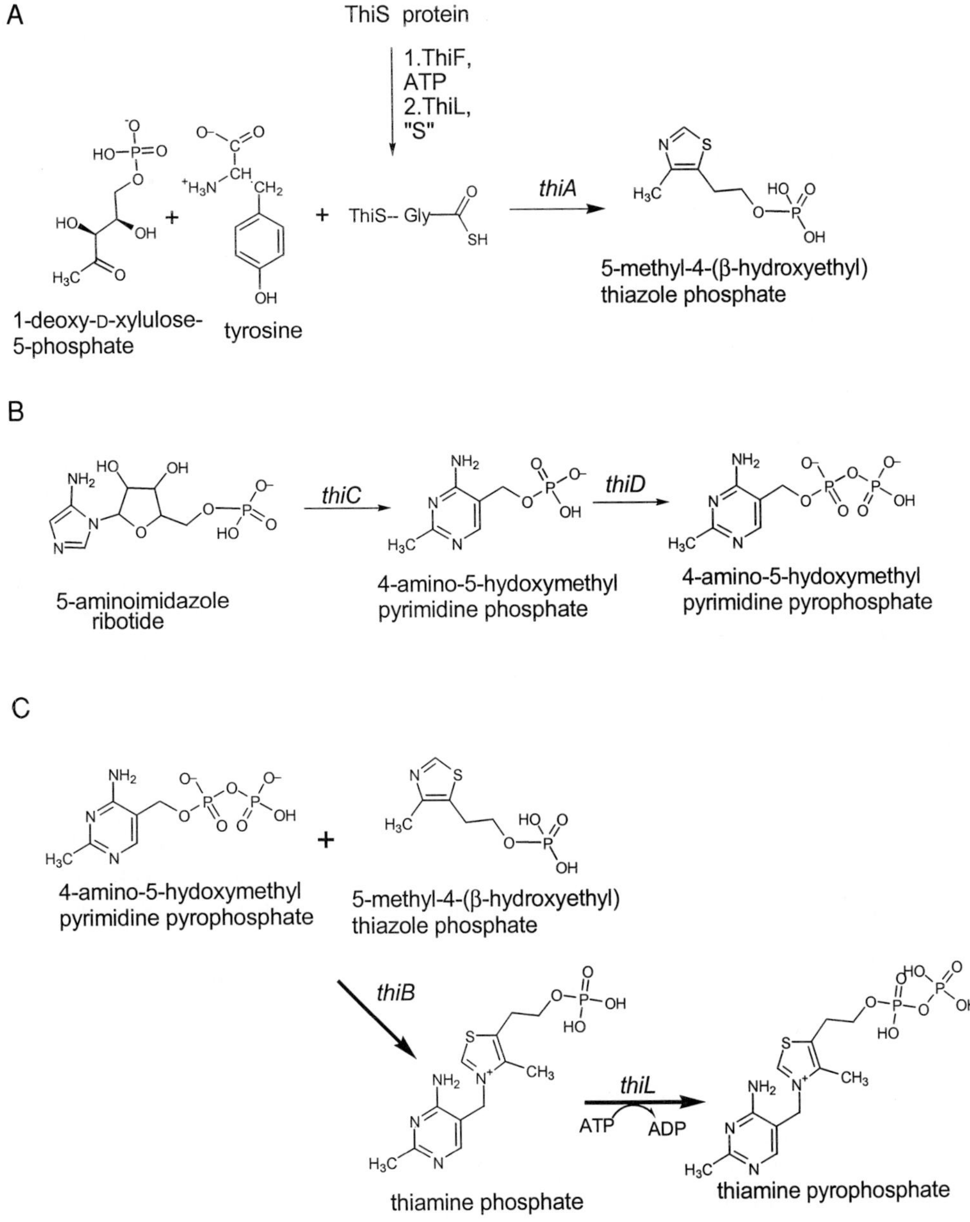

**Fig. 2.** The biosynthesis of thiamine pyrophosphate. (A) The common metabolites 1-deoxy-D-xylulose-5-phosphate and tyrosine react with the specially activated form of the small, thiamine-specific protein ThiS to form the thiazole moiety of thiamine. The detailed mechanism by which one of the oxygens of the terminal glycyl residue is replaced by sulfur is unknown. It is this sulfur which becomes the sulfur of the thiazole ring. (B) The scheme of synthesis from the common metabolite 5-aminoimidazole ribotide. (C) The end products of A and B combine to form thiamine phosphate (arrows), which is then phosphorylated to form TPP. The italicized symbols are the genes associated with the enzyme indicated. Note that the phosphate group of 1-deoxy-D-xylulose-5-phosphate is retained as the phosphate of thiamine phosphate.

form of the coenzyme has a string of five glutamates attached rather than just one.

THF is active as a donor and acceptor of one-carbon units. It is not involved in moving $CO_2$ but is involved in the metabolism of carbon at the level of formate, formaldehyde, and methanol. Typical reactions requiring THF are the biosynthesis of thymidylate from uridylate (thymidylate synthetase) and the biosynthesis of serine from glycine (serine hydroxymethyltransferase). In both of these reactions, 5,10-methylene-tetrahydrofolate is the one carbon donor. In the former, the tetrahydrofolate is oxidized during the reaction to dihydrofolate in order to reduce the hydroxymethyl group to methyl. The average amount of folic acid in a bacterial culture is 0.16 $\mu$ mol/g dry weight of cells.

## I. Thiamine Pyrophosphate (Thiamine and Vitamin B₁)

Thiamine pyrophosphate (TPP) biosynthesis has two dedicated pathways. Each makes one-half of the TPP. The whole process is shown in Fig. 2. The first dedicated pathway (Fig. 2A) starts with the common metabolites tyrosine and DXP. Tyrosine donates its nitrogen and one carbon to DXP. The glycine at the C-terminal end of a small protein called ThiS has one of its carboxyl oxygens replaced with S. This activated S, in a still unclear series of steps, adds to the DXP–tyrosine pair to form 5-methyl-4($\beta$-hydroxyethyl) thiazole phosphate (5MHTP). The second dedicated pathway (Fig. 2B) begins with the common metabolite 5-aminoimidazole ribotide (5AIR from purine biosynthesis). In the first committed step of this pathway, the imidazole ring of 5AIR opens and rearranges, incorporating some of the attached ribose atoms to form in two steps 4-amino-5-hydroxymethyl pyrimidine pyrophosphate (4AHP). 4AHP

then condenses with 5MHTP to form thiamine pyrophosphate in two steps. Just as PALP biosynthesis contains one step that uses PALP as a coenzyme, TPP biosynthesis requires TPP in the condensation of pyruvate and erythrose-4-phosphate to make the common metabolite DXP. Again, this requirement of the end product for its own synthesis suggests that there must be a way to bypass the need for TPP in DXP biosynthesis either in *E. coli* or some other organism.

TPP participates in reactions that involve forming activated aldehydes as intermediates. Typical reactions include pyruvate decarboxylase and transketolases. The average amount of thiamine in a bacterial culture is 0.14 $\mu$mol/g dry weight of cells.

## J. Coenzymes and Prosthetic Groups Whose Biosyntheses Are Unknown

There are a limited number of other coenzymes and prosthetic groups whose biosyntheses are not considered here. The biogenesis of heme-based coenzymes is widely known. Coenzymes and prosthetic groups such as methanofuran, coenzyme M, F420, and F430 are found in some methanogenic organisms. They have been relatively recently discovered and their biosynthetic schemes remain unknown.

### See Also the Following Article
Vitamins and Related Biofactors, Microbial Production

### Bibliography
David, S., and Estramareix, B. (1997). Sugars and nucleotides and the biosynthesis of thiamine. *Adv. Carbohydrate Chem. Biochem.* **52**, 267–309.

Machlin, L. J. (1984). "Handbook of Vitamins." Dekker, New York.

McIlwain, H. (1946). The magnitude of microbial reactions involving vitamin-like compounds. *Nature* **158**, 898–902.

# Conjugation, Bacterial

## Laura S. Frost

*University of Alberta*

## GLOSSARY

**plasmid** An extrachromosomal DNA segment, usually circular, which is capable of autonomous replication via a segment of the plasmid called the replicon.

**transconjugant** A general term for a recipient cell that has successfully been converted to donor cell by conjugation.

**transposon** A segment of DNA that is replicated as part of a chromosome or plasmid. It encodes a mechanism, called transposition, for moving from one location to another, leaving a copy at both sites.

**BACTERIAL CONJUGATION** was first described by Lederberg and Tatum in 1946 as a phenomenon involving the exchange of markers between closely related strains of *Escherichia coli*. The agent responsible for this process was later found to be a site on the chromosome called the F ("fertility") factor. This finding was the basis of bacterial genetics in the 1940s and 1950s and was used extensively in mapping the *E. coli* chromosome, making it the pre-eminent prokaryotic organism at that time. It was also shown that F could excise out of the chromosome and exist as an extrachromosomal element which was capable of self-transfer to other bacteria and that mobilization of the chromosome was the serendipitous function of F integrated randomly into its host's DNA. The F sex factor of *E. coli* also imparted sensitivity to bacteriophages which required the F pilus, encoded by the F transfer region, as an attachment site during infection.

In the 1960s many other conjugative plasmids were isolated, many of which carried multiple antibiotic resistance markers. These plasmids were termed R ("resistance") factors and were found in many instances to repress pilus expression and conjugation by F, a process termed fertility inhibition (fi$^+$). The number of conjugative plasmids has increased tremendously in the past few decades and includes self-transmissible plasmids isolated from gram-negative and -positive bacteria as well as mobilizable plasmids. Conjugative transposons, which move between cells using a conjugative mechanism, excise and integrate into the host chromosome via a process reminiscent of lysogenic phage, whereas an example of a conjugative phage has been described for *Staphylococcus aureus*.

In general, the transfer and replication functions of these mobile elements are often physically linked and the type of transfer system is closely aligned with the nature of the replicon which is described by incompatibility groups (Inc). An excellent summary of the properties of many conjugative plasmids is given in Shapiro (1977).

Bacterial conjugation is now known to be one of the principal conduits for horizontal gene transfer among microorganisms. The process is extremely widespread and can occur intra- and intergenerically as well as between kingdoms (bacteria to yeast or to plants). The effect of this process on evolution has been immense, with bacteria rapidly acquiring traits both good (hydrocarbon utilization) and bad (antibiotic resistance, toxins). Once again, bacterial conjugation is at the forefront of microbiology, but this time the emphasis is on the process rather than its utility as a geneticist's tool. Excellent reviews of the topic are provided in the book *Bacterial Conjugation* by Clewell (1993).

## I. THE CONJUGATIVE PROCESS

Unlike the other processes contributing to horizontal gene transfer, transformation, and transduction, conjugation can be characterized by two important criteria. There must be close cell-to-cell contact between the donor and recipient cells and DNA transfer must begin from a specific point on the transferred DNA molecule, be it a plasmid, transposon, or chromosome (Fig. 1). This point is encoded within the origin of transfer (*oriT*) called *nic*. The proteins which act on this site are encoded by *tra* (transfer) or *mob* (mobilization) regions. In general, each conjugative element encodes an array of proteins for mating pair formation (Mpf), whereas another set of proteins are involved in processing and transferring the DNA (Dtr). The Mpf genes can further be classified into the genes for pilus formation or mating pair stabilization (Mps) in gram-negative bacteria or aggregate formation in gram-positive cocci. A system to prevent close contact between equivalent donor cells is called surface exclusion. The gene products that process the DNA in preparation for transfer usually include a protein (relaxase) that cleaves the DNA in a sequence- and strand-specific manner at *nic* and remains covalently bound to the 5' end in all cases that have been examined. This nucleoprotein complex, plus other auxiliary proteins bound to the *oriT* region, is called the relaxosome, whereas the complex formed between the relaxosome and the transport machinery is known as the transferosome. A process which prevents the transfer of DNA into the recipient cell after Mpf has occurred is called entry exclusion. Previously surface and entry exclusion were used interchangeably; however, as the details of the process are refined, it is important to make this distinction.

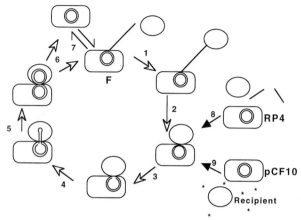

**Fig. 1.** Summary of the mating process for universal (plasmid F) and surface-preferred (plasmid RP4) conjugation systems in gram-negative bacteria and the pheromone-activated system of *Enterococcus faecalis* (plasmid pCF10). In universal systems, the pilus attaches to a receptor on the recipient cell surface (1) and retracts to form a stable mating pair or aggregate (2). DNA transfer is initiated (3), causing transport of a single strand in the 5' to 3' direction (4). Transfer is associated with synthesis of a replacement DNA strand in the donor cell and a complementary strand in the recipient (5). The process is terminated by disaggregation of the cells, each carrying a copy of the plasmid (6). The transfer systems of conjugative plasmids in gram-negative bacteria can be repressed (7) or derepressed (constitutive; 8). Cells carrying RP4 and related plasmids express pili constitutively but the pili are not seen attached to the bacteria. Such cells form mating pairs by collision on a solid surface (8). In gram-positive bacteria, such as the enterococci, the donor senses the presence of pheromone (*), released by the recipient cell, which triggers mating pair formation and DNA transfer (9). Donor cells are shown as oblongs and recipient cells as ovals.

In gram-negative bacteria, the process of DNA transfer is triggered upon cell contact, whereas in *Enterococcus faecalis* and T-DNA transport by *Agrobacterium tumefaciens,* contact between cells induces a complex program of gene expression leading to DNA transport. Although the sequences for many conjugative elements have been completed and comparisons have revealed information on the evolution of conjugative elements, a study of the conjugative process has only been done in some depth for IncF, IncP, Incl, and the Ti plasmid of *A. tumefaciens* in gram-negative bacteria and for the pheromone-responsive system found for some plasmids in *E. faecalis*. Some information is available for the integration/excision process of conjugative transposons as well as the role of the *mob* genes in mobilizable plasmids. In addition, conjugation in *Streptomyces* has been studied in detail but is quite different than that described and may use a DNA transport mechanism related to the process of DNA partition during septation in *Bacillus subtilis* (see Section V,B).

## II. PHYSIOLOGICAL FACTORS

The level of transfer efficiency varies dramatically among the various systems. For derepressed or constitutively expressed systems such as F (IncFl) or RP4 (IncP$\alpha$) maximal levels of mating (100% conversion to plasmid-bearing status) are possible within 30 min. Plasmids undergoing fertility inhibition usually have a 100- to 1000-fold reduction in mating efficiency, whereas other plasmids, especially the smaller plasmids of gram-positive bacteria and conjugative transposons, mate at barely detectable levels in the best of circumstances. These factors include temperature with very precise optimums usually being the rule. For instance, F and RP4 mate optimally at 37–42°C and IncH plasmids and the Ti plasmid at approximately 20–30°C. Other factors, such as oxygen levels, nutrient availability, and growth phase, contribute to mating efficiency. $F^+$ cells in late stationary phase are known as $F^-$ phenocopies because they are able to accept incoming F DNA and are not subject to surface or entry exclusion. Where information is available, conjugation appears to be maximal over a short temperature range in nutrient-rich environments with good aeration for aerobic organisms.

### A. Liquid versus Solid Support

The ability of some conjugative systems to mate equally well in liquid media or on a solid support is one of the hallmarks of conjugation. Although all conjugative elements can mate well on a solid support, usually a filter placed on the surface of a prewarmed nutrient agar plate, many transfer systems, including those of the IncF group and the phero-

mone-responsive plasmids of *Enterococcus*, mate very efficiently in liquid media. This difference can be traced to the nature of the mating pair formation process, with thick, flexible pili of gram-negative bacteria associated with systems that mate well in liquid media, whereas rigid pili, not usually seen attached to the cells (e.g., IncP$\alpha$), require a solid support for efficient mating. The aggregation substance of *E. faecalis* allows high levels of transfer in liquid media but other gram-positive systems and conjugative transposons mate at low levels and absolutely require a solid support. In general, it appears that mating systems requiring a solid support depend on collision between donor and recipient cells, whereas systems that mate well on either medium have a mechanism for initiating contact between freely swimming cells (thick, flexible pili, aggregation substance). Description of the media requirements for many gram-negative plasmid transfer systems is given in Bradley *et al.* (1980).

## III. CONJUGATIVE ELEMENTS

Naturally occurring conjugative elements include plasmids, conjugative transposons, and either of these incorporated into the host chromosome to allow chromosome mobilization ability (CMA) resulting in high frequency of recombination (Hfr). Free plasmids can be divided into self-transmissible (Mpf plus Dtr genes) or mobilizable (Dtr or Mob genes) and can vary in size from a few kilobases to large plasmids of 100–500 kb.

### A. Plasmids

In general, gram-negative transfer systems are approximately 20–35 kb in size and reside on plasmids from 60 to 500 kb, whereas mobilizable plasmids are less than 15 kb. The transfer or mobilization regions often represent half or more of the coding capability of the plasmid. Table I contains a list of selected plasmids and their characteristics, including their pilus type and mating medium preference. In nonfilamentous gram-positive plasmids, the smaller plasmids (<30 kb) usually have a requirement for a solid support during mating and mate at low levels,

***TABLE I***
**Selected Conjugative/Mobilizable Plasmids and Conjugative Transposons**

| Mobile element | Size (kb) | Inc group/pheromone | Copy no. | Mating surface/pilus type | Mating efficiency/host range |
|---|---|---|---|---|---|
| **Gram-negative bacteria** | | | | | |
| F | 100 | IncFI | 1–2 | Liquid/flexible (II) | High (derepressed)/narrow |
| RP4 | 60 | IncPα | 4–6 | Solid/rigid (II) | High (constitutive)/broad |
| ColIB-P9 | 93 | IncI1 | 1–2 | Liquid/rigid (II), thin (IV) | Low (repressed)/narrow |
| pTiC58 | ~200 | HSL | 1–2 | Solid/? | Low (repressed)/narrow |
| *vir* | 25 (T-DNA) | Plant exudate | 1 | Plants/rigid (II) | — |
| **Gram-positive bacteria** | | | | | |
| pAD1 | 60 | cAD1 | | Liquid | High ($10^{-2}$/donor)/narrow |
| pAMβ1 | 26.5 | — | 3–5 | Solid | Low ($10^{-4}$/donor)/broad |
| pIJ101 | 8.8 | *Streptomyces* | ~300 | Solid | High/broad (actinomycetes) |
| **Mobilizable plasmids** | | | | | |
| ColE1 | 6.6 | — | ~10 | Liquid | High (IncF, -P, -I)/narrow |
| RSF1010 | 8.9 | IncQ | ~10 | Solid | High (IncP)/broad |
| pMV1158 | 5.5 | — | | Solid | Low (pAMβ1)/broad |
| **Conjugative transposons** | | | | | |
| Tn916 | 18.5 | — | — | Solid | Low (~$10^{-8}$/donor)/broad |
| Tc$^R$Em$^R$ DOT | 80 | *Bacteroides* | — | Solid | Low (~$10^{-5}$/donor)/narrow |

whereas the larger plasmids mate efficiently in liquid media and express genes for aggregate formation (e.g., *Enterococcus, Staphylococcus, Lactobacillus,* and *Bacillus thuriengensis*). *Streptomyces* is able to mate at high frequency and has the added property of CMA. Each large self-transmissible plasmid can supply the needed Mpf functions for many mobilizable plasmids. These mobilizable plasmids have been used to construct vectors which are maintained in the recipient cell or deliver their cargo of DNA via mobilization but are unable to replicate in the new host (suicide vectors). This has been a boon to the genetics of otherwise recalcitrant bacteria.

## B. Chromosome Mobilization

F undergoes integration into the chromosome via four transposable elements (IS2, IS3a and -b, and Tn*1000*) which either mediate cointegrate formation via a transposition event or more frequently undergo homologous recombination between these sequences and similar elements on the chromosome. Once incorporated into the chromosome, the F replicon is

suppressed by the chromosomal replication machinery allowing stable maintenance of the Hfr strain. Like F, which was found incorporated into the host chromosome, other examples of naturally occurring Hfr strains have been reported in the literature. Hfr strains have also been constructed using homologous gene segments shared by a plasmid and its host for mapping the host's genome. Since the advent of pulsed-field gel electrophoresis for mapping chromosomes and large-scale sequencing facilities, the utility of Hfr strains has waned. The procedure for using Hfr strains for chromosome mapping requires that F integrate near a locus with a few genetically defined markers. The direction of transfer of the chromosome and the time of entry of the markers into the recipient cell are functions of the position and orientation of F in the chromosome and its distance from each marker. By laboriously measuring the time of entry of each marker (e.g., antibiotic resistance and amino acid biosynthesis), which must be able to recombine into the recipient's chromosome in such a way as to announce its presence, a map of the chromosome can be generated. The process of mobilizing the entire *E.*

*coli* chromosome takes approximately 90 min and markers that are distal from F *oriT* are transferred much less efficiently than those more proximally located, a process called the "gradient of transmission." The last portion of the chromosome to be transferred contains the F transfer region; consequently, the recipient cells in an Hfr mating are seldom, if ever, converted to F⁺ (Hfr) status.

Another related property of F is imprecise excision out of the chromosome with adjoining chromosomal sequences being incorporated into the circular F element which are often large enough to encode complete operons. These elements are known as F′ factors, such as F*lac*, F*gal*, and F*his*.

## C. Conjugative Transposons

The first conjugative transposon was isolated from *E. faecalis* (Tn*916*; Table I) in Clewell's lab in 1981 and expressed *tet*(M) (tetracycline) resistance. This element excises from the chromosome, circularizes into a nonreplicative intermediate, and expresses functions for transfer to a wide range of recipient cell types at low frequency on solid surfaces (Salyers *et al.*, 1995). The enzymes responsible for excision and integration (Int and Xis) are related to the corresponding enzymes in lambda phage. The absence of a small repeated sequence flanking the conjugative transposon as well as a non-random site selection mechanism for integration suggests that these elements are evolutionarily more related to phage than true transposons. Excision of the element results in staggered ends which form a heteroduplex structure upon circularization. This heteroduplex is derived from flanking sequences in the chromosome ("coupling sequences"). Through mapping and sequencing the site of insertion and determining which end of the heteroduplex is inherited in the recipient, a model involving single-stranded DNA transfer has been proposed. A second important group of conjugative transposons has been found in the anaerobic gram-negative genus *Bacteroides*. These elements are usually associated with antibiotic resistance (*tetX* and *erm*). The interesting property of increased transfer proficiency in the presence of tetracycline has been noted by Salyer's group.

Conjugative transposons demonstrate amazing versatility in mobilizing DNA. They can mobilize coresident plasmids directly or form cointegrates with plasmids or the chromosome. They are also able to harbor other mobile elements such as transposons and move them between cells. In the case of *Bacteroides*, the conjugative transposons are able to excise and mobilize small nonconjugative, nonreplicative segments of DNA found in the chromosome called NBUs (non-replicating *Bacteroides* units). Although conjugative transposons have been identified in many genera of bacteria, especially in gram-positives, the details of the conjugation process remain obscure. A possible *oriT* region in Tn*916* and a relaxase homolog in *Bacteroides* have been identified but the nature of the proteins involved in Mpf are unknown.

## IV. GRAM-NEGATIVE CONJUGATION

With the exception of *Bacteroides*, all gram-negative transfer systems encode a conjugative pilus (type II) which is essential for mating pair formation and DNA transport (Fig. 1). In thick, flexible pilus mating systems, the pili are easily found attached to the donor cell and examples of the pilus mediating contact between the donor and recipient cell are easy to visualize in the electron microscope. In the case of rigid pilus mating systems, pili are rarely seen attached to cells but are seen as bundles of pili accumulating in the medium. Although there is considerable homology between all the transfer systems examined to date within the gram-negative group of organisms, two broad classes can be identified. These include IncF-like and IncP-like plasmids, which also represent mating systems categorized by their ability to mate in liquid versus solid media or systems encoding thick, flexible pili versus rigid pili. The relaxase, and the protein that energizes DNA transport, is conserved throughout these systems, as are the genes encoding pilus assembly. The principal systems studied to date include IncF (F, R100-1, and R1) and IncHI 1, which are F-like (Firth *et al.*, 1996), and IncP (RP4 and R751; Pansegrau *et al.*, 1994), IncI1 (Collb-P9 and R64), IncN (pCU1 and pKM101), IncW (R388), and the Ti plasmid of *A. tumefaciens*, which are IncP-like.

## A. The Pilus

### 1. Structure

The conjugative pilus is a thin filament expressed in relatively low numbers (one to three per cell) which has no set length (usually ∼1 μm) and is randomly distributed on the surface of the cell (Fig. 2). The diameter of the pilus is approximately 6–11 nm, with most pili having a diameter of approximately 9 nm (Paranchych and Frost, 1988). Pili isolated from cells usually contain a "knob" at the base of the pilus which represents unassembled pilin subunits derived from the inner membrane of the cell. They also often have a pointed tip, suggesting an unusual configuration of pilin subunits at the tip, and can aggregate into large bundles which can be

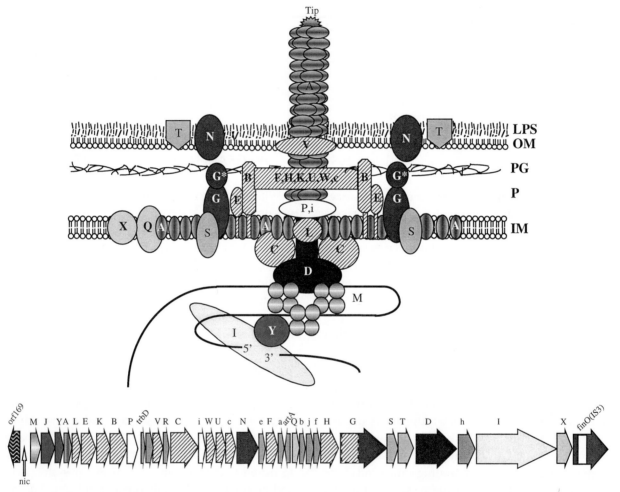

**Fig. 2.** The F transfer region. The organization of the F transfer region is shown below the relaxosome/transferosome complex showing the cellular location of the Tra proteins. The DNA processing genes are TraD, TraI (relaxase) and TraM. TraY is a regulatory protein that is required for relaxosome formation. TraA (pilin), TraQ (pilin chaperone), TraX (N-acetylation of pilin), TraV (lipoprotein), and TraL, -E, -K, -B, -C, -W, -U, -F, -H, TrbC, and TraG (N-terminal domain) are involved in F pilus assembly. TraN and the C-terminal domain of TraG are involved in mating pair stabilization. TraS and TraT are responsible for entry and surface exclusion, respectively. The nature of the F pilus tip is unknown but is inferred to be important in establishing contact with the recipient cell. Orf169, a putative transglycosylase, and the regulatory protein TraJ are not shown. The functions of the other genes are unknown. *tra* genes are shown as capital letters and *trb* genes are shown as lower-case letters. The site of cleavage within *oriT* is shown as *nic* with *orf169* being the first gene to enter the recipient cell.

pelleted in an ultracentrifuge. The pilus is usually composed of a single repeating subunit of pilin arranged in a helical array with a hollow lumen clearly visible in negatively stained electron micrographs. F pili, which are the best studied, have a diameter of 8 nm with an inner lumen of 2 nm. The pilin subunits are arranged as repeating layers of five subunits with each layer rising 1.28 nm. There are 25 subunits in two turns of the helix and a crystallographic repeat of 3.2 nm.

The F pilus is expressed as a propilin of 121 amino acids (*traA*) which requires TraQ, a putative chaperone, for insertion in the inner membrane, where it is stored in a pool of approximately 100,000 subunits. The 51-amino acid leader peptide is cleaved by host leader peptidase (LepI) and the pilin subunit is acetylated at the N terminus by TraX. Transposon insertion studies have revealed that mature pilin is oriented within the inner membrane as two $\alpha$-helical transmembrane segments with the N and C termini facing the periplasm. Assembly by the TraL, -E, -K, -B, -V, -C, -W, -U, -F, -H, and -G and TrbC proteins results in the subunits oriented within the fiber such that the acetylated N terminus is buried within the structure and the C terminus is exposed on the sides. The pilus appears to assemble at its base rather than at the tip based on evidence using the slowly assembled pili expressed by the IncHI1 plasmid R27.

The RP4 pilin subunit is expressed as a 15-kDa prepilin polypeptide (*trbC* in Tra2) which is processed three times to give a 7.5-kDa mature product. The cleavage reactions at the N and C termini are undertaken by LepB (N terminus) of the host as well as by a pilin-specific LepI homolog, TraF, expressed by RP4 which cleaves at least once at the C-terminus. The RP4 transfer region is separated into two parts, Tra1 and -2. In addition to *traF* of Tra1, the essential genes *trbD–L* of Tra2 are required for pilus assembly, with TrbK being involved in entry exclusion. A homolog of TraX is present in RP4 (TraP), although its substrate and function are unknown.

## 2. Phage Attachment

Conjugative pili act as the primary receptor for a wide range of bacteriophages (Frost, 1993). These phages can be divided broadly into those that bind to the pilus tip and those that bind to the sides of the pilus. The structure of the phages includes the single-stranded DNA filamentous phages, the small isometric RNA phages, and the complex double-stranded DNA tailed phages which usually attach near the pilus tip. The filamentous phages specific for F-like pili (Ff phages; M13, f1, and fd) attach via a defined region of the pill attachment protein to an unknown receptor at the pilus tip. RNA phages such as R17 and Q$\beta$, which belong to different phage groups, bind to specific residues in F pilin exposed on the pilus sides. For RP4 (IncP$\alpha$), the filamentous phage Pf3 binds to the sides of the pilus as does the RNA phage PRR1. Tailed phages such as PRD1 and PR4 bind to the pilus tip and have a broad host range, including cells bearing IncP, -W, -N, and -I plasmids.

Although the pilus is required for initial attachment, the transfer region is not necessarily required for phage penetration or growth. The Ff phages are thought to contact the cell surface via the process of pilus retraction where they interact with the TolA protein and penetrate the cell via the TolQRA pathway. RNA phages R17 and Q$\beta$ (have differing requirements for the TraD protein, which energizes the transport of nucleic acid through the conjugation pore, suggesting that R17 is imported via the F transfer machinery, whereas Q$\beta$ is taken up by another pathway.

## 3. Role in Conjugation

The role of the pilus in conjugation has been controversial. It clearly has a role in Mpf, but whether it has a role in initiating DNA transfer or is part of the transfer apparatus has been difficult to determine genetically. Mutations that affect pilus formation block Mpf and DNA transfer. Mutations that affect mating pair stabilization (TraN and -G) allow the initial contacts to form between cells via the pilus and also allow the initiation of DNA synthesis in the donor cell but block DNA transport into the recipient cell. Although indirect, this is the best evidence that the pilus is involved in the signalling process and the Mps genes are involved in transport possibly by forming the conjugation pore. Whether pore formation also requires an intact pilus remains unknown. Other experiments in which donor and recipient cells were not allowed to establish cell-to-cell contact suggested that mating was possible through the extended pilus, and the homology between the pilus assembly genes and protein transport systems also argues for a role for the pilus in DNA transfer.

## B. Mating Pair Formation

The pilus is thought to identify a receptor on the recipient cell surface which triggers retraction of the pilus into the donor cell, although the route of the pilin subunits in this process is unknown. Pilus outgrowth is thought to require energy, whereas retraction occurs by default in the absence of assembly. Thus, factors that negatively affect cell metabolism (temperature, poisons, and carbon source) cause retraction. Whether pilus outgrowth and retraction are ongoing processes or whether binding of recipient cells or phage trigger retraction is unknown.

Early studies identifying mutations in the recipient cell that affected conjugation (Con⁻) revealed that various components of the heptose-containing inner core of the lipopolysaccharide (LPS) were generally important in Mpf, whereas OmpA was required for efficient conjugation by the F transfer system. The F-like systems were each affected by different mutations in the *rfa* (now *waa*) locus in the recipient cell, whereas the IncH plasmids seemed to recognize a generalized negative charge on the recipient cell surface. The requirement for OmpA by F as well as for specific side chains in the LPS appears to be a function of the outer membrane protein TraN, and the idea that the pilus recognizes negatively charged moieties non-specifically remains a possibility. A second protein identified in F that is involved in Mps is TraG. Mutations in *traG* can be categorized into two classes with ones near the 5′ end affecting pilus formation and others affecting mating pair stabilization (Mps) in the 3′ portion of the gene.

An interesting variation on Mps has been identified for the IncI1 transfer systems (R64 and Collb-P9) which express two types of pili: thin flexible pili which are required for Mps and thick rigid pili that are required for DNA transfer. Research on the thin pili of R64 by Komano's group has revealed that they are composed of type IV pilin (similar to the pili found in pathogens such as *Neisseria gonorrhoeae*) of 15 kDa (*pilS*). These pili have a protein at their tip (pilV) whose gene undergoes rearrangement via site-specific recombination by the *rci* gene product to form seven possible fusion proteins, each recognizing a specific LPS structure (e.g., *pilVA′*). Whether these pili retract in order to bring the donor and recipient cells together is unknown, but this is a general feature of type IV pili. Aside from these two cases (F and R64 thin pili), little is known about Mpf in other gram-negative systems.

### 1. Surface/Entry Exclusion

Surface or entry exclusion reduces redundant transfer between equivalent donor cells. Such transfer is thought to be deleterious to the donor cell and is exemplified by the phenomenon of lethal zygosis which occurs when a high ratio of Hfr donor to recipient cells is used. Multiple matings with a single recipient cell result in its death because of severe membrane and peptidoglycan damage as well as induction of the SOS response resulting from the influx of a large amount of single-stranded DNA. The surface exclusion genes were first identified as the *ilz* locus (immunity to lethal zygosis).

The mechanism of entry or surface exclusion is unknown, although an exclusion mechanism has usually been found to be associated with the transfer systems studied to date. One exception is the conjugative transposons, which transfer at such low frequency that redundant transfer might not be a factor. Surface exclusion in the F system involves TraT, a lipoprotein found in the outer membrane, that forms a pentameric structure and blocks mating pair stabilization. Whether it interacts with the pilus or another component of the F transfer system is unknown. The TraS protein of F is an inner-membrane protein which blocks the signal that DNA transfer should begin and is thus associated with the property of entry exclusion. TrbK, a lipoprotein found in the inner membrane of RP4-containing cells, is also thought to cause entry exclusion.

## C. DNA Metabolism

### 1. Organization of oriT

In gram-negative transfer systems, the origin of transfer (*oriT*) can be ~40–500 bp in length and contains intrinsic bends and direct and inverted repeats which bind the proteins involved in DNA transfer. The *nic* site, which is a strand- and sequence-specific cleavage site, is cleaved and religated by the relaxase. In most cases, the relaxase requires an auxiliary protein(s) which directs the relaxase to the *nic* site and ensures the specificity of the reaction. The sequences of the *nic* sites identified to date reveal four possible sequences represented by IncF, -P, and -Q and certain gram-positive plasmids such as pMV1158. In addition, there is usually a protein that binds to multiple sites within *oriT* forming a higher order structure in the DNA which is essential for the process. This protein also appears to have a function in anchoring the relaxosome to the transport machinery (Lanka and Wilkins, 1995).

### 2. Mechanism of DNA Transfer

After mating pair formation, a signal is generated that converts the relaxosome from the cleavage/religation mode to one in which unwinding of the DNA is coupled to transport through the conjugation pore in an ATP-dependent manner. The transfer rate is ~750 nucleotides per second, with the F plasmid (100 kb) transferred in approximately 2 min.

In IncF plasmids, TraI is the relaxase/helicase enzyme which binds to a site near *nic* and generates an equilibrium between cleavage and religation. This reaction requires supercoiled template DNA and $Mg^{2+}$ as well as the auxiliary proteins F TraY and host integration host factor (IHF) *in vitro*. The signal that triggers the helicase activity of TraI which is essential for DNA transfer is unknown, as is the function TraI* produced by a translational restart in the *traI* mRNA. TraY binds near *nic*, whereas TraM binds to multiple sites, in conjunction with IHF, to form a nucleoprotein complex required for transfer to be initiated. TraM also binds to the protein that energizes transport, TraD, which is an inner-membrane protein that utilizes ATP probably via its two NTP binding domains.

In RP4, a similar arrangement of proteins at *oriT* exists except that there is no role for the host protein, IHF. The relaxase protein, called TraI, cleaves at *nic* as a complex with TraJ, whereas TraH stabilizes the TraI, J complex. TraK binds and bends the DNA at *oriT* to form the nucleosome-like structure thought to be needed to initiate DNA replication.

In all cases, the 5′ phosphate generated by the cleavage reaction remains covalently bound to the relaxase enzyme via a tyrosine residue which is similar to the initiation of replication by the rolling circle mechanism in some phage and plasmid replicons. The DNA is transferred in a 5′ to 3′ direction, with the first genes to enter the recipient cell called the leading region. Transfer seems to be a precise process with termination of transfer after one copy of the plasmid has been delivered to the recipient cell. A sequence in *oriT*, near *nic*, is important for termination by the relaxase in a religation reaction. The DNA is released into the recipient cell and both strands are replicated in a manner dependent on *Pol*III enzyme using discontinuous synthesis in the recipient and continuous synthesis either from the free 3′ end at *nic* or from an RNA primer in the donor. Although synthesis and transport are coupled in conjugation, DNA synthesis does not drive, nor is it required, for DNA transfer.

In RP4 and IncI plasmids, the transport of a primase protein, Pri (*traC* encoded in TraI), or Sog in RP4 or IncI plasmids, respectively, has been demonstrated to occur simultaneously with the transport of the DNA, with hundreds of copies being transferred. This protein appears to initiate DNA synthesis in the recipient cell via primer formation, although it is not essential for conjugation. In F, no primase is transferred and DNA synthesis is thought to begin via a mechanism utilizing *ssi* sites for single-stranded initiation.

### 3. Leading Region Expression

The first genes to enter the recipient cell in the leading region include genes for preventing the SOS response (*psi*) and for plasmid maintenance via poison–antidote systems such as CcdAB and Flm in F, Hok/Sok in R1, and Kil/Kor in RP4. Another gene that is highly conserved in the leading region of conjugative plasmids is *ssb*, a single-stranded DNA binding protein that is not essential to the process. Another interesting but nonessential gene is *orf169* in F or TrbN in RP4 which is related to transglycosylases such as lysozyme. Perhaps this gene, which is the first to enter the recipient cell during F transfer, has a role in establishing a new transferosome in the recipient cell, especially in strains of bacteria in the natural environment which might require a transglycosylase to rearrange the peptidoglycan in preparation for pilus assembly and DNA transfer.

## D. Regulation

The regulation of the genes involved in conjugation has been extensively studied in F, RP4, and Ti (see Section VII) and in gram-positive conjugation, but there is little information on other systems. The regulation of F transfer gene expression depends on both host and plasmid-encoded factors, whereas the regulation of RP4 appears to be independent of the host. Also, F is unusual in that there is no evidence for coregulation of transfer and replication, a salient feature of other conjugation systems.

In F there are three main transcripts encoding *traM*, *traJ* (the positive regulator of transfer operon expression), and *traY–I* (33 kb). The $P_{Y-I}$ promoter is controlled by a consortium of proteins, including the essential TraJ protein; TraY, the first gene in the operon; and IHF and SfrA (also known as ArcA) encoded by the host. TraY also controls *traM* expression from two promoters which are autoregulated by TraM. The translation of the *traJ* mRNA is controlled by an antisense RNA FinP which requires an RNA binding protein FinO for activity (fertility inhibition; see Section IV.D.1). Certain mutations in *cpxA* also affect TraJ accumulation probably via an indirect mechanism involving upregulation of factors that respond to stress applied externally to the cell.

In RP4, transfer is tied very closely to replication with the main replication promoter for TrfA divergently oriented and overlapping with the first of two promoters for the Tra2 transfer region, $P_{trbA}$ and $P_{trbB}$. In this system, the *trfA* promoter is activated first in the transconjugant, promoting plasmid replication. The $P_{trbB}$ promoter and the promoters in Tra1, which express the genes for Dtr, are also activated in order to establish a new transferosome. Eventually, the main global regulators KorA and KorB repress expression from these promoters and allow transcription from $P_{trbA}$ which maintains the level of Tra2 proteins in the donor cell. TrbA is a global regulator that represses $P_{trbB}$ and the three promoters in Tra1 encoding the genes for Dtr. Thus, conjugation leads to a burst of transcription that establishes the plasmid in the new donor cell followed by transcription from either the *trfA* or the *trbA* promoters during vegetative growth.

### 1. Fertility Inhibition

Fertility inhibition (Fin) is a wide-spread phenomenon among related plasmids which limits the transfer of competing plasmids coresident in a single cell. The fertility inhibition system of F-like plasmids (R factors) represses F and also autoregulates the expression of their own transfer regions. These systems have two components, the antisense RNA FinP and the RNA binding protein, FinO, which together prevent translation of the *traJ* mRNA, with TraJ being the positive regulator of the $P_{Y-I}$ promoter. FinO protects FinP antisense RNA from degradation by the host ribonuclease, RNase E, allowing the FinP concentration to increase sufficiently to block *traJ* mRNA translation. Although *finP* is plasmid-specific, *finO* is not and can be supplied from many F-like plasmids. This is the basis of the fi+ phenotype noted in the 1960s for various R factors. F lacks FinO since *finO* is interrupted by an IS3 element and consequently is constitutively derepressed for transfer.

In F-like plasmids (FinOP+), 0.1–1% of a repressed cell population expresses pili. If conjugation is initiated, the transconjugant is capable of high frequency of transfer (HFT) for approximately six generations until fertility inhibition by FinOP sets in. This phenomenon, in addition to surface/entry exclusion, contributes to the epidemic spread and stable maintenance of a plasmid in a natural population of bacteria.

Other Fin systems are specified by one plasmid and are directed against another. For instance, F encodes PifC, which blocks RP4 transfer, whereas RP4 encodes the Fiw system, which blocks the transfer of coresident IncW plasmids. Each system has a unique mechanism which has made the study of Fin systems more difficult and has tended to downplay the importance of this phenomenon in the control of the dissemination of plasmids in natural populations.

## V. GRAM-POSITIVE CONJUGATION

Conjugative elements in nonfilamentous gram-positive bacteria can be subdivided into three groups: Small plasmids (<30 kb), usually associated with MLS resistance, exhibit moderate transfer efficiency on solid surfaces over a broad host range (pAMβ1 and pIP501); large plasmids (>60 kb), which mate efficiently in liquid media over a narrow host range and undergo clumping or cell aggregate formation (pAD1 and pCF10 in *Enterococcus*; pSK41 and PGO1 in *S. aureus*); and conjugative transposons.

There is no evidence for pili in gram-positive conjugation. In the few systems studied in detail, detection of a recipient cell results in expression of an aggregation substance (AS, Agg, or Clu) which covers the surface of the donor cell and results in the formation of mating aggregates which are visible to the naked eye. This "fuzz" is the result of a complex pattern of gene expression which has been studied in detail only rarely, mostly in the large plasmids of *E. faecalis*. This group of plasmids responds to pheromones expressed by the recipient cell, whereas the signal that triggers mating aggregate formation in other systems is poorly understood. Plasmids in *S. aureus* produce pheromones that trigger transfer by *E. faecalis*, suggesting a mechanism to broaden the host range for the plasmids of this latter organism.

## A. *Enterococcus faecalis*

The first conjugative plasmid identified in grampositive bacteria was pAD1, which carried a hemolysin/bacteriocin determinant responsible for increased virulence and which caused clumping or aggregation 30 min after the addition of plasmid-free cells (Dunny and Leonard, 1997). Later it was shown that aggregation and subsequent plasmid transfer were induced by pheromones produced by the recipient cell and released into the medium. These pheromones are hydrophobic peptides of seven or eight amino acids with a single hydroxyamino acid. Each recipient cell releases several pheromones, with plasmids from a particular incompatibility group recognizing a specific pheromone in which specificity resides in the N terminus of the peptide. In addition to their role in conjugation, the function of these pheromones is unknown, as is their source. Once the plasmid has become established in the transconjugant, expression of the pheromone is repressed by preventing its synthesis in or release from, the donor

cell. Picomolar amounts of pheromone added to donor cultures can induce the expression of the transfer genes. Usually the concentration is approximately 1–10 n*M* and a slight increase in pheromone levels is sufficient to induce clumping. Pheromones are named after the transfer system that recognizes them; thus, pAD1 recognizes cAD1 and produces iAD1, an inhibitory peptide that blocks accidental induction of transfer.

The pheromone is recognized by a plasmid-encoded protein and imported into the cell via the host Opp system (oligopeptide permease). In pAD1, it binds to a repressor, TraA, inactivating it and allowing transcription of TraE1, a positive regulator required for induction of transfer gene expression. In pCF10, the pheromone cCF10 causes anti-termination of transcription of the *prg* genes (pheromone responsive gene) generating the 530 nt RNA $Q_L$ and the mRNA for aggregation substance and transfer proteins. The $Q_L$ RNA, in conjunction with the pheromone, associates with the ribosome causing preferential translation of the transfer genes. In either case, transcription of the aggregation substance (AS or Asa1 for pAD1 and Asc10 for pCF10) ensues, and this substance is deposited asymmetrically on the surface of the cell until the cell surface is covered. This binds to the binding substance (BS; lipoteichoic acid) on the recipient cell to give the mating aggregates so characteristic of conjugation. Interestingly, both AS and BS have been associated with increased virulence in a rabbit endocarditis model, with AS having RGD motifs (arginine–glycine–aspartic acid) which are known to promote binding to the integrin family of cell surface proteins.

Once the pCF10 transferosome is established in the transconjugant, a cytoplasmic membrane protein binds pheromone and prevents its release. The inhibitory peptide, iCF10, is synthesized from a shorter version of $Q_L$ called $Q_S$. A surface exclusion protein, Sea1 or Sec10 (for pAD1 or pCF10, respectively), is also expressed to reduce aggregation between donor cells and provides a second level of control to prevent redundant mating between plasmid-bearing cells.

There also seems to be a close relationship between replication and transfer in these plasmids, with the replication protein PrgW embedded within a region that negatively regulates transfer in pCF10. The replication protein also appears to have a requirement for pheromone that is not understood. Similarly, the *oriT* for pAD1 is within the *rep* gene for plasmid replication initiation.

## B. *Streptomyces*

The transfer systems found on conjugative plasmids in the large genus *Streptomyces* differ significantly from those of both non-filamentous, gram-positive bacteria and gram-negative systems in that there is only a single essential transfer protein and no evidence for a relaxase or *nic* site has been found. *Streptomyces* are a medically important source of antibiotics and other therapeutic compounds and are thought to be a major reservoir for antibiotic resistance mechanisms which protect these bacteria from the arsenal of antibiotics they produce.

The conjugative plasmids of *Streptomyces* range in size and structure from the circular 9-kb plasmid pIJ101 to the large linear plasmid SCP1 (350 kb). The phenomenon of conjugation in this genus was first identified because of the ability of certain integrating plasmids to mobilize chromosomes (CMA). One such plasmid, SLP1 (17 kb), excises and integrates at the 3′ end of an essential tRNA^Tyr gene in *S. lividans,* with tRNA genes providing the loci for integration of many phage and plasmids.

Streptomycetes are soil microorganisms that undergo a complex differentiation program whereby spores germinate and form substrate mycelia that penetrate into the support surface followed by the erection of aerial hyphae which are multinucleate mycelia. These mycelia eventually septate and form spores. As the cells enter the hyphal stage, they begin to produce the array of secondary metabolites characteristic of the organism and also enter a phase in which they are competent for conjugation between substrate mycelia or mycelia and other organisms such as *E. coli.*

The intermycelial transfer of a plasmid requires one essential protein (e.g., Tra in pIJ101) which has homology to the protein SpoIIIE. This protein is located at the asymmetric septum of sporulating *B. subtilis* cells and ensures that a copy of the chromosome enters the forespore. Since no relaxase protein has been found associated with pIJ101, it is tempting to speculate that this might be a conjugation system

closely related to partitioning mechanisms involving double-stranded DNA.

Once the DNA has been transferred to one compartment of a long mycelium, the plasmid is distributed to all compartments by the *tra* and the *spd* gene products. This process slows the growth rate of the cell, and areas in which plasmids are being spread via inter- and intramycelial transfer form "pocks" of more slowly growing cells which resemble plaques on a phage titer plate. This phenomenon has been useful in identifying cells containing conjugative plasmids.

## VI. MOBILIZATION

Mobilization is a widespread phenomenon whereby a smaller plasmid encoding its own *nic* site and Dtr genes (*mob*) utilizes the transport machinery of a usually larger plasmid to effect its own transfer. Many plasmids can be mobilized by plasmids from many Inc groups. For instance, ColE1 can be mobilized by plasmids from IncF, -P, and -I groups and less effectively and with different requirements by IncW plasmids. The Mob proteins of ColE1 consist of MbeA (relaxase) and MbeB and -C, which aid in relaxosome formation. MbeD is an entry-exclusion function. In the vector pBR322, derived from ColE1, the *mob* genes are deleted and only an *oriT* region for IncP plasmid mobilization remains. Although ColE1 requires TraD from F for mobilization, the closely related plasmid CloDF13 supplies its own TraD-like protein, a difference which is commonly seen among mobilizable plasmids.

The most remarkable mobilizable plasmid is RSF1010 and its relatives (~8.6 kb in size) from the IncQ group. These plasmids are mobilized very efficiently by plasmids from the IncP group into an extremely broad group of recipients, including bacteria, yeast, and plants. This plasmid encodes three Mob proteins, with MobA being the relaxase. Like ColE1, it requires the TraG protein of RP4, an F TraD homolog, for efficient conjugation. The *oriT* region is a mere 38 bp in size and is homologous to *oriT* regions in plasmids from gram-positive bacteria, all of which use a rolling circle mechanism during transfer. RSF1010 can be mobilized into plants and between agrobacteria by the *vir* region (not *tra;* see Section VII) and between strains of *Legionella* using the virulence determinants encoded by the *dot* and *icm* loci involved in macrophage killing (see Section VIII).

Small gram-positive plasmids are also mobilizable by self-transmissible plasmids but less is known about them. The utility of conjugative transposons as genetic tools in gram-positives has overshadowed interest in these plasmids, which tend to be mobilized at low frequencies over long time periods. One plasmid, which replicates and transfers via the rolling circle mechanism using different origins, is pMV1158. It encodes a relaxase (MobM) which cleaves at a *nic* sequence unique to a group of mobilizable plasmids found in gram-positive bacteria representing the fourth class of *nic* sequences.

## VII. TRANSFER TO PLANTS

The phenomenon of DNA transfer from the bacterium *A. tumefaciens* to plant cells has features of both gram-negative (pilus expression) and gram-positive (induction of *tra* gene expression) and has been dealt with here separately (Fig. 3). *Agrobacterium tumefaciens* carrying large conjugative plasmids such as Ti (tumor-inducing) or Ri (root-inducing) of >200 kb in size cause crown gall disease in plants whereby they induce the formation of tumors at the site of infection. The Ti plasmid encodes a sensor–response regulator system, VirA and VirG, respectively, which in conjunction with ChvE, a chromosomally-encoded periplasmic sugar binding protein, process signals from wounded plant tissue. The phospho-transfer reaction from VirA to VirG induces gene expression from the *virA, -B, -D, -E,* and *-G* operons on the Ti plasmid. In addition, the *virC, -F,* and *-H* operons are induced but these operons express nonessential gene products that affect host range or the degree of virulence. The signals generated by the plant include phenolic compounds, simple sugars, and decreased pH or phosphate content.

The *virB* region encodes 11 proteins which are homologous to the gene products in the Tra2 region of RP4 and distantly related to the gene products of F. They encode the gene for prepropilin (VirB2)

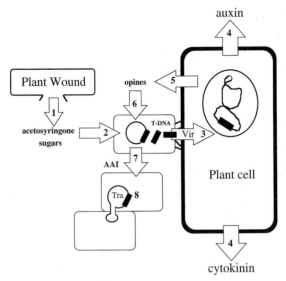

**Fig. 3.** The signalling pathway used to stimulate T-DNA complex transfer to the plant nucleus and Ti conjugative transfer between agrobacteria. Wounded plant tissue releases phenolics (acetosyringone) and sugars (1) that are detected by the VirA, G two-component regulatory system (2). This induces expression of the *vir* genes which transports the T-DNA to the plant nucleus (3). The T-DNA is incorporated into the plant genome and produces the phytohormones auxin (indoleacetic acid) and cytokinin (4) which trigger tumorigenic growth of the plant tissue. The plant also produces opines (5), whose synthesis is encoded on the T-DNA. These unusual amino acids serve as a food source for *Agrobacterium* and also result in the induction of synthesis (6) of the conjugation factor, *N-β*-oxo-octanoyl-homoserine lactone (AAI; 7). AAI allows "quorum sensing," which determines cell density with respect to Ti-plasmid-bearing cells resulting in conjugative transfer to other agrobacteria (8).

which is processed to pilin via a mechanism similar to that for RP4 pilin. A potential peptidase, homologous to TraF in RP4, has been identified (VirF) but its role has not been proven. The assembly of the VirB pilus is very temperature dependent, with an optimum of 19°C and a corresponding optimum for the transfer process.

The specific segment of single-stranded DNA that is transferred to the plant nucleus is called the T-DNA and can be characterized by the right (RB) and left (LB) borders which are direct repeats of 25 bp. The T-DNA of nopaline-producing Ti plasmids is approximately 23 kb in length and contains genes for plant hormone expression (13 kb), a central region of unknown function, and a region for opine (nopaline) biosynthesis (~7 kb). The relaxase, VirD2, in conjunction with VirD1, which is similar to RP4 TraJ, cleaves at RB and subsequently LB in a TraI-like manner and remains attached to the 5′ end. VirC1, which binds to an "overdrive" sequence near the RB, and VirC2 of certain Ti plasmids enhance T-intermediate formation. Unlike other transfer systems, many copies of the T-DNA segment accumulate in the cytoplasm suggesting replacement replication is important in this system. The accumulation of T-DNA strands has been puzzling but might represent a strategy by the bacterium to ensure infection of the larger, more complex plant cell.

The DNA in the VirD2–T-DNA complex (T-complex) is coated with the single-stranded DNA binding protein, VirE2, in preparation for transport through a conjugation pore composed of the VirB proteins (VirB2–VirB11). These proteins are very homologous to the Tra2 gene products for pilus synthesis in RP4 (Christie, 1997), again suggesting the importance of the pilus to DNA transport. One of the Vir proteins, VirB1, which is nonessential, resembles the transglycosylase of F (Orf169) and RP4 (TrbN), whereas a truncated version of VirB1 (VirB1*) is excreted into the rhizosphere and mediates adhesion between the bacterium at the site of transfer and the plant. The process is energized by an RP4 TraG homolog, VirD4, which has NTP binding motifs that are required for its activity. Once the T-complex has entered the plant cytoplasm, the DNA is transported to the nucleus via nuclear localization signals on the VirE2 and VirD2 proteins. The T-DNA is randomly integrated into the plant genome whereupon it begins to elicit signals for plant hormone production resulting in tumor formation. The T-DNA encodes for the synthesis of auxin (indoleacetic acid) and cytokinin isopentenyl adenosine, plant hormones that elicit uncontrolled growth at the site of infection. The bacteria derive nutrients from the tumor by the devious method of opine (unusual amino acid) production encoded by the T-DNA. Opines can be classified into approximately nine different types of compounds, including octopine, nopaline, and agrocinopine, with up to three different opines being encoded by a particular T-DNA. Thus,

Ti plasmids are often referred to as octopine- or nopaline-type plasmids, for instance, depending on the opine they specify. The opines are excreted from the plant and taken up by the *A. tumefaciens* bacteria encoding a region on the Ti plasmid involved in opine utilization. The genes for opine catabolism (e.g., *occ* for octopine catabolism) match the genes for the synthesis of that class of opines on the T-DNA.

An interesting aspect of Ti plasmid biology is the induction of conjugative transfer between agrobacterial cells in response to the presence of opines. The genes for this process (*tra*) are distinct from the genes for T-DNA transfer (*vir*) and encode a transfer region with homology to RP4 as well as the *vir* region.

Conjugative transfer by Ti has a narrow host range, limited to the genus of *Agrobacterium*. However, the host range can be extended to *E. coli* if an appropriate replicon is supplied, suggesting that it is plasmid maintenance and not conjugative functions that affect host range.

The process of inducing conjugative transfer in these bacteria is unique and fascinating (Fuqua et al., 1996). Initially, there is a low level uptake of opines which activates the regulatory protein OccR in octopine-type plasmids and inactivates the repressor protein AccR in nopaline-type plasmids such as pTiC58. This leads to increased expression of the *tra* and opine utilization genes by activation of TraR. TraI (not to be confused with the relaxase proteins of F and RP4 plasmids) is a LuxI homolog which synthesizes a signalling compound, N-β-oxo-octanoyl-homoserine lactone (*Agrobacterium* autoinducer; AAI) belonging to a diverse class of homoserine lactone-like compounds involved in quorum sensing or gene activation in response to cell density (Fig. 3). TraR is a LuxR-like regulatory protein which detects increased levels of AAI and induces transfer gene expression to maximal levels. The result is the dissemination of the genes for opine utilization among the agrobacteria in the rhizosphere. Thus, the system demonstrates a certain degree of chauvinistic behavior since the original colonizer of the plant cell shares its good fortune with its neighbors who then out-compete other bacteria in the rhizosphere.

## VIII. EVOLUTIONARY RELATIONSHIPS

With the advent of high-throughput sequencing and easily available databases, comparison of gene sequences has become routine. Considering that the mechanism for conjugation varies surprisingly little among the systems described previously, the high degree of relatedness of these systems with one another is expected (Table II). However, the remarkable finding that there is homology between conjugative systems and transport mechanisms for many toxins and virulence determinants has generated increased interest in these systems. These is almost gene-for-gene homology between the transport system for pertussis toxin of *Bordetella pertussis* (*ptl*) and the *virB* region of the Ti plasmid, which is in turn, homologous to the genes for pilus synthesis in IncN, -P, and -W transfer systems and is distantly related to those of F-like plasmids. Recently, five *vir* homologs (VirB4, -9, -10, and -11 and VirD4) have been found in the *cag* pathogenicity island of *Helicobacter pylori.* Also, some of the Dot/Icm proteins involved in the pathogenesis of *Legionella pneumophila,* which can mobilize RSF1010, are homologous to genes in the

Tra2 region of RP4 as well as the Trb region of the IncI1 plasmid R64.

## IX. CONJUGATION IN NATURAL ENVIRONMENTS

Although the process of conjugation is thought to be relevant to the adaptation of organisms to environmental conditions such as the acquisition of antibiotic resistance under continuous pressure for selection, there is much to be learned about the process in nature. Conjugation can be demonstrated in the gut of animals, biofilms, soil, aquatic environments including wastewater, on the surface of plants and animals, etc. However, the level of transfer is usually very low. Most experiments have utilized common lab strains and plasmids which are good model systems for study but might be irrelevant in nature. Considering the diversity of bacterial species, their vast numbers, and the time scale for their evolution, we have only scratched the surface of this phenomenon in the natural environment. However, studies on "domesticated" lab strains and plasmids have allowed

### TABLE II
#### Similarities/Homologies Shared by Pilus Synthesis and Transport/Virulence Systems[a]

| Function | IncF | IncP | Ti | Ptl | IncN | Cag[b] | IncI[c] | Dot[c] |
|---|---|---|---|---|---|---|---|---|
| Pilin | TraA | TrbC | VirB2 | PtlA | TraM | | | |
| Pore | TraL | TrbD | VirB3 | PtlB | TraA | | | |
| Pore | TraC | TrbE | VirB4 | PtlC | TraB | Cag544 | | |
| Pore | TraE | TrbF | VirB5 | | TraC | | | |
| Pore | | TrbL | VirB6 | PtlD | TraD | | | |
| Pore | | | VirB7 | PtlI | TraN | | | |
| Pore | | | VirB8 | PtlE | TraE | | | |
| Pore | | | VirB9 | PtlF | TraO | Cag528 | | |
| Pore? | TraK | TrbG | | | | | | |
| Lipoprotein | TraV | TrbH | | | | | | |
| Pore | TraB | TrbI | VirB10 | PtlG | TraF | Cag527 | | DotG |
| Transport | | TrbB | VirB11 | PtlH | TraG | Cag525 | | DotB |
| Pore? | | | | | | | TrbA | DotM |
| Pore? | | | | | | | TrbC | DotL |
| Transport | TraD | TraG | VirD4 | | | Cag524 | | |

[a] Based on Christie (1997). IncF, F; IncP, RP4; Ptl, *Bordetella pertussis* toxin secretion; IncN, pKM101.

[b] Cag open reading frames are taken from Tomb *et al.* (1997).

[c] Comparison of IncI1 (R64) gene products to *dot* virulence determinants from *Legionella pneumophila* are taken from Vogel *et al.* (1998).

predictions about the conditions that favor transfer. Most conjugative systems require actively growing cells in exponential phase and have a fairly precise temperature optimum. The majority of systems studied to date mate more efficiently on solid media. Those systems that mate efficiently in liquid media seem to be found in enteric bacteria and might be associated with diseases which are transmitted via the water supply. More information is required on the natural hosts for conjugative elements and their contribution to the evolution of these elements in an ecological niche. In addition, the most likely route of transmission, which appears to involve many intermediate organisms, is usually impossible to predict or detect because of the complexity of the system and the unknown role of nonculturable organisms in this process. Thus, we can isolate a plasmid from its environment and we can find evidence for its transfer to a new species, but we cannot, at this time, follow the plasmid as it makes its way in the world.

## See Also the Following Articles

AGROBACTERIUM • FIMBRIAE, PILI • HORIZONTAL TRANSFER OF GENES BETWEEN MICROORGANISMS • STREPTOMYCES, GENETICS • TRANSPOSABLE ELEMENTS

## Bibliography

Bradley, D. E., Taylor, D. E., and Cohen, D. R. (1980). Specifications of surface mating systems among conjugative drug resistance plasmids in *Escherichia coli* K-12. *J. Bacteriol.* **143**, 1466–1470.

Christie, P. J. (1997). *Agrobacterium tumefaciens* T-complex transport apparatus: A paradigm for a new family of multifunctional transporters in eubacteria. *J. Bacteriol.* **179**, 3085–3094.

Clewell, D. B. (1993). "Bacterial Conjugation." Plenum, New York.

Dunny, G. M., and Leonard, B. A. B. (1997). Cell–cell communication in gram-positive bacteria. *Annu. Rev. Microbiol.* **51**, 527–564.

Firth, N., Ippen-Ihler, K., and Skurray, R. A. (1996). Structure and function of the F factor and mechanism of conjugation. *In* "*Escherichia coli* and *Salmonella:* Cellular and Molecular Biology" (F. C. Neidhardt *et al.,* Eds.), pp. 3277–2401. ASM Press, Washington, DC.

Frost, L. S. (1993). Conjugative pili and pilus-specific phages. *In* "Bacterial Conjugation" (D. B. Clewell, Ed.), pp. 189–221. Plenum, New York.

Fuqua, C., Winans, S. C., and Greenberg, E. P. (1996). Census and consensus in bacterial ecosystems: The LuxR–LuxI family of quorum-sensing transcriptional regulators. *Annu. Rev. Microbiol.* **50**, 727–751.

Lanka, E., and Wilkins, B. M. (1995). DNA processing reactions in bacterial conjugation. *Annu. Rev. Biochem.* **64**, 141–169.

Pansegrau, W., Lanka, E., Barth, P. T., Figurski, D. H., Guiney, D. G., Haas, D., Helinski, D. R., Schwab, H., Stanisich, V. A., and Thomas, C. M. (1994). Complete nucleotide sequence of Birmingham IncPα plasmids. Compilation and comparative analysis. *J. Mol. Biol.* **239**, 623–663.

Paranchych, W., and Frost, L. S. (1988). The physiology and biochemistry of pili. *Adv. Microbial Physiol.* **29**, 53–114.

Salyers, A. A., Shoemaker, N. B., Stevens, A. M., and Li, L. Y. (1995). Conjugative transposons: An unusual and diverse set of integrated gene transfer elements. *Microbiol. Rev.* **59**, 579–590.

Shapiro, J. A. (1977). Bacterial plasmids. *In* "DNA Insertion Elements, Plasmids, and Episomes" (A. I. Bukhari, J. A. Shapiro, and S. L. Adhya, Eds.), pp. 601–670. Cold Spring Harbor Laboratory Press, Cold Spring Harbor, NY.

Tomb *et al.* (1997). The complete genome sequence of the gastric pathogen *Helicobacter pylori. Nature* **388**, 539–547.

Vogel, J. P., Andrews, H. L., Wong, S. K., and Isberg, R. R. (1998). Conjugative transfer by the virulence system of *Legionella pneumophila. Science* **279**, 873–876.

# Conservation of Cultural Heritage

## Orio Ciferri

*University of Pavia*

*"Blessed were the ancients, for they had no antiquities"* (Italian saying)

## GLOSSARY

**cultural heritage** The term has supplanted and encompasses established categories—works of art, antiquities, specimens, artifacts—to cover the immensely diverse mass of documents of all types on which our societies confer a particular artistic, historic, or ethnologic value.

**THE AIM OF CONSERVATION** is to provide conditions and/or treatments that protect cultural heritage from all sorts of injuries, including microbial colonization. Conservation should arrest, or at least slow down, the progressive degradation of cultural objects and delay for as long as possible the restoration interventions.

Microorganisms contribute significantly to the deterioration of cultural heritage. Indeed, it is now widely accepted that growth of microorganisms leads to the defacement, structural and aesthetic, of all types of works of art. Paintings, sculpture, masonry, books, etc. represent substrates on which different members of the microbial flora of soil find suitable nutritional sources and ecological niches adapted for their growth.

Damages inflicted by microorganisms to cultural heritage may be aesthetic and/or structural. Obviously, the two types of damage are closely related because structural degradation results in the defacement of an artistic object. Microbial colonization leads to the appearance of spots, streaks, and patinas of different color (from white efflorescences to black crusts) depending on the organism, the nature of the substrate, the environmental conditions, and, often, the changing of seasons. These aesthetic variations are accompanied by transformations in the chemical, physical, and mechanical properties of the materials making up art objects. Microorganisms may cause, for instance, weathering of lithic materials, dissolving certain salt constituents, inducing loss of cohesion, and leading to the gradual destruction of the stone. Similarly, they may cause crumbling of painted layers and degradation of supports (the cellulose of paintings, books, and wooden objects, the proteins of parchment and silk, etc.) as well as the other ingredients (pigments, glues, binders, etc.) that may be present. Finally, growth of microorganisms may reduce the life span of cultural heritage by exacerbating the damages caused by environmental factors (water, temperature, and light and also other variables such as pollution and seismic activity).

We expect cultural heritage to last, in its pristine conditions, for centuries or even millennia. This is if not impossible at least rather unlikely. Suffice to recall here that, up to a few years ago, we believed that reinforced concrete was indestructible. Much to our surprise, we discovered that this material undergoes chemical and mechanical degradation and that microorganisms are among the agents responsible for this process.

## I. THE SUBSTRATE

It is quite obvious that the range of objects that compose cultural heritage is extremely wide: from archaeological sites (often covering square miles) to miniatures, from historical monumental complexes to illuminated books, from religious objects to stuffed animals, from stained glasses to phonographic records etc. This wide range is accompanied by extreme variations in the chemical constituents of these artifacts and in the inorganic and organic molecules present in the environment and deposited on the surface of these artifacts especially outdoors: dust and other pollutants such as the oxides of nitrogen and sulfur, hydrocarbons, fertilizers, bird droppings, etc. Indoors, one also has to consider the chemicals brought about by workmen and visitors or originating from their metabolism (breath and sweat) or by certain human activities (e.g., burning of candles). Thus, the microbial flora that may colonize and, as a consequence, deface cultural heritage varies considerably. It may be safely stated that only objects kept in environments in which temperature, moisture, light, and pollution are kept under control, such as museums, are protected from microbial attack. In any other environment, sooner or later cultural heritage will undergo colonization by microorganisms.

Regarding the chemical composition of art-works, it is possible, with a certain degree of superficiality, to distinguish two groups: those composed essentially of inorganic constituents (stones, bricks, masonry, etc.) and those made up essentially of organic compounds (easel paintings, wooden sculptures and other wood artifacts, books, etc.). This division is not completely accurate because, for instance, organic compounds are present in stones, bricks, etc. and more so in buildings (e.g., wooden beams). Similarly, most of the pigments used in paints are inorganic, but the support of easel paintings (the cellulose of canvas, wood, paper, the proteins of silk, wool, parchment, etc.) and all other components of paintings (binders, glues, etc.) are organic. In any case, one may as a first approximation subdivide the substrates into the two categories, inorganic and organic, each being colonized by a specific microbial flora. In general, the inorganic substrates are colonized by chemolithotrophic microorganisms and, when light

is available, by photoautrophs, whereas the organic ones are attacked by chemoheterotrophs. Again, this is not totally correct since, especially in the case of the inorganic substrates, heterothrophic microorganisms are present and multiply on them by utilizing the metabolic products and the dead cellular structures of the first colonizers. However, we shall use the terms inorganic and organic substrates to identify operationally in the first group monuments, buildings, and other artifacts whose main constituents are stone, bricks, plaster, glass, metals, etc. and, in the second one, the objects composed essentially of cellulose, proteins, and other organic compounds.

## II. THE FLORA

Unless kept under closely controlled conditions, the surface of any art object bears a rich microflora. The chemical composition of the object operates a profound selection on the environmental flora and only relatively few of the innumerable microbial species present in the environment are able to colonize a given substrate. For instance, it is clear that the species composing the microflora, mainly fungal but also bacterial, developing on books and prints are very few compared to the aeroflora present in the rooms housing these materials. Thus, although the environment contains an extremely rich variety of microorganisms, only a small fraction may be isolated from any given substrate. Furthermore, only a few of the microorganisms isolated from the substrates are responsible for damaging it. One of the key problems in studying the microbial deterioration of cultural heritage is differentiating the microorganisms present on cultural heritage but that do not contribute to its degradation and those that are responsible for it. Even species present in relatively high cell concentrations may not be responsible for degradation because they are simply saprophytes living at the expenses of the colonizer species.

A large variety of microbial species have been isolated from art-works: bacteria, fungi, algae, and lichens. In certain cases, members of each of these four broadly defined groups may be found on a given artifact, whereas in other cases only representatives of one group may be present. These variations are a function of the chemical nature of the artifact and of the environmental conditions. For examples, lichens are found essentially only on the exterior of buildings, on the surface of sculptures, and on other objects kept outdoors. On these artifacts growth of heterotrophic microorganisms is very reduced when not outright impossible. Similarly, growth of lichens, cyanobacteria, and algae on books or manuscripts is practically impossible in libraries and in other surroundings in which light is very reduced.

## A. Inorganic Substrates

On the exterior of buildings and monuments and on stone sculptures and other artifacts kept outdoor, lichens, eukaryotic algae, and cyanobacteria are the most common colonizers. Often, their colonization has a seasonal variation, being most prominent in spring and fall. Similarly, growth is more pronounced on surfaces facing north than on those facing south and, in the case of the interior of buildings and hypogean sites, in proximity of the source of natural or artificial illumination. For instance, the Lascaux cave, world famous for its prehistoric drawings, was opened to the public in 1948 and closed to it in 1963 because of the massive growth of a single organism, the chlorophyte *Bracteacoccus minor*. Similarly, a bloom of cyanobacteria and chlorophytes developed very soon after hypogean Roman remains were opened to the public and an illumination system installed. The flora was composed essentially of two *Leptolyngbya* species accompanied by chlorophytes in the genera *Pseudococcomixa* and *Pseudopleurococcus* and, to a lesser extent, species of *Chlorella*.

Except for areas where chemical pollution is high, lichens are ubiquitous on outdoor monuments. For instance, an investigation of the lichen flora of 16 archeological sites throughout Rome led to the isolation of 276 different species. Lichens are very adapted to grow on lithic surfaces and are able to cause compositional changes of the thin layer immediately underneath the lichens' thallus by the excretion of different organic acids (e.g., oxalic acid, whose total content in certain species may be up to 50% of the lichen's weight). These acids chelate chemical elements present on the stone, especially Ca that is accumulated inside the thalli. The chemical changes

are accompanied by physical damages due to penetration of hyphae into the stone and to the contractions and swelling of thalli in accordance with changes in weather and season' variations. As a consequence, lichens corrode stones, causing pitting, etchings, and formation of fissures on the surface of stones. These cavities provide pockets in which water and environmental pollutants are collected, giving rise to chemically rich ecological niches that other microorganisms may utilize for growth. The group of so-called crustose lichens (species of the genera *Protoblasteria*, *Verrucaria*, *Caloplaca*, *Aspicilia*, *Lecanora*, and *Xanthoria*) appears to be the most widespread on lithic materials and cause more damage than the foliose or fructose species. Lichens are slow growers (on average the colony's diameter increases by 1 cm per year) but they profoundly affect the surface of the material that they colonize so that, even after their removal, a permanent defacement is evident. This is especially important in the case of sculptures, bas-reliefs, friezes, terracottas, and other ornate elements.

In addition to being phycobionts in many lichens, cyanobacteria have been found to colonize the exterior of buildings and other masonry artifacts and are considered by many as the major agents responsible for weathering of stones and defacing of buildings and monuments. Some of the cyanobacteria colonizing cultural heritage can withstand extreme conditions such as high light irradiance, high temperatures, and prolonged periods of drought. The most common species are in the genera *Calothrix*, *Chroococcus*, *Plectonema*, *Synechococcus*, *Lyngbya*, *Scytonema*, and *Nostoc*. The presence of nitrogen-fixing species of *Nostoc* in algal mats covering murals is a further indication that cyanobacteria are pioneer organisms since they may colonize substrates in which insufficient combined nitrogen is available to permit growth of other microorganisms, such as eukaryotic algae, that require a source of combined nitrogen. The filamentous cyanobacteria have well-developed sheaths that may help the adhesion of the organism to the substrates and the formation of uniorganismic or pluriorganismic biofilms. The high water retention may confer to the cyanobacterial mats the capacity to survive even during periods of prolonged drought. Furthermore, this high water content may give rise to significant volume alterations during cyclical periods of drought, moistening, and freezing so that it has been postulated that such variations may be responsible in part for stone weathering and degradation. In at least one case, laboratory experiments have demonstrated that pure cultures of a cyanobacterium, *Microcoleus vaginatus,* colonized sterilized limestone samples forming a well-developed biofilm on the stone's suface and adhering to it through the penetration of trichomes into the stone's upper layer. Finally, the slimy surface of cyanobacterial mats may trap environmental airborne pollutants such as dust, carbon particles from combustion processes, pollen, and spores that increase the aesthetic defacement and contribute to the hardening of the microbial biofilm.

Among the eukaryotic algae, the most common and important groups found on stone, marble, masonry, murals, etc. are the green algae (*Chlorophyta*), mostly unicellular soil inhabitants. Species of the genera *Chlorella, Chlorococcus, Haematococcus, Pleurococcus, Scenedesmus, Stichococcus,* and *Trebouxia* are most frequently isolated from inorganic substrates. Because these microorganisms are in general obligate photoautotrophs, their growth requires the presence of light. However, in the previously mentioned case of *B. minor* growing on the paintings of the Lascaux cave, it was found that the alga could also grow heterotrophically in the dark utilizing the organic substrates present in soil particles brought into the cave by workmen and visitors as well as those excreted through people's breath and perspiration. The damages, aesthetic and structural, inflicted by *Chlorophyta,* as well as by the less frequently encountered members of *Bacillariophyta* (diatoms) and *Chrysophita* (brown algae), are analogous to those caused by cyanobacteria. Actually, often the eukaryotic algae are present together with cyanobacteria forming microbial mats that, at times, may reach a thickness of a few centimeters.

The bacteria most frequently encountered on inorganic substrates are characterized by the capacity to utilize inorganic chemicals as a source of energy (chemolithotrophs) and, quite often, carbon dioxide as a source of carbon. Nitrifying bacteria are probably the most common; they utilize ammonia (species of *Nitrosovibrio* and, to a lesser extent, *Nitrosomonas* and *Nitrosospira*) or nitrite (species of the genus

*Nitrobacter*) as electron donors with the production of nitrites and nitrates, respectively. The substrates come from different sources, including industrial and automotive pollutants, fertilizers, and bird excrement, deposited on the surface of the artifacts. The nitric and nitrous acids produced attack different lithic substrates, such as calcium carbonate. In the case of carbonates, the acids lead to the liberation of $CO_2$ and the formation of nitrites and nitrates of calcium, more soluble than the original carbonates. A second group of chemolithotrophs that seems to participate in the defacement of external surfaces is that of the sulfur-oxidizing bacteria (*Thiobacillus* spp.) that utilize hydrogen sulfide and other sulfur compounds as a source of energy. In addition to the aesthetic defacement produced by the bacterial population, the sulfuric acid produced reacts with calcium carbonate to form water-soluble calcium sulfate.

The presence of chemoorganotrophic microorganisms, such as fungi and the majority of bacteria, has often been reported on inorganic substrates. Whereas it is quite likely that these organisms may participate in the defacement of inorganic substrates through the production of pigments or different organic acids, almost certainly they are not the primary colonizers of these materials and often their colonization follows that of the pioneer species (cyanobacteria, algae, lichens, and litotrophic bacteria).

## B. Organic Substrates

With a few exceptions, such as wooden elements on the facades of buildings, these substrates general remain indoors and comprise an extremely wide range of objects: paintings, wooden objects, books, prints, tapestry, manuscripts, garments, etc. With the exception of murals, all are characterized by being composed solely or essentially of organic compounds. As a consequence, chemoorganotrophic organisms are the main colonizers of these substrates. Of course, if enough light is available, photoautotrophs may also be present, such as cyanobacteria and green algae growing on indoor murals. However, it may be assumed that the organic substrates are colonized essentially by bacteria and fungi. In general, these microorganisms are the most ubiquitous soil inhabitants so that the fungal species most frequently isolated are in the genera *Penicillium, Aspergillus, Chladosporium, Chaetomium, Stemphylium, Alternaria, Aureobasidium,* and *Phoma* and, in the case of eubacteria, *Bacillus, Pseudomonas, Streptomyces, Arthrobacter, Norcardia,* and *Micrococcus.* Many lists of fungi and, less often, bacteria isolated from cultural heritage have been published. Some of these lists report up to 100 different species, but little effort has been made to differentiate the species that are colonizing and, therefore, defacing objects and those that are present occasionally or living at the expense of the colonizing organisms. Thus, it has been reported that from two fifteenth-century frescoes located in the same building, different fungal species were isolated from each fresco. In other cases one single species has been reported to be present. Even more disturbing is the fact that some authors consider the genus *Cladosporium* as the main agent responsible for the defacement, whereas other believe that the genus, although frequently present, does not contribute significantly to the degradation of cultural heritage. Nevertheless, it is widely accepted that fungal colonization may cause profound aesthetic modifications and significant chemical alterations of art objects. In general, bacterial colonization is less conspicuous than that by fungi, but nevertheless it is equally dangerous and bacteria may cause as much aesthetic and structural damages as fungi. Actually, it is unlikely that a defaced substrate is colonized only by fungi or by bacteria even if published reports give the impression that the observed damage was due to colonization by only one group of microorganisms. This impression results from the fact that the majority of the reports are limited to analyses of a single group of organisms (in general fungi). In cases in which the microbial colonization was investigated more thoroughly, it became clear that a rich microbial community was almost always present and that this community was composed of both fungi and bacteria. Unfortunately, there are very few data that demonstrate which species are the first colonizer of a given substrate and which others attach to the substrate at a later time, possibly utilizing some of the products originated from the degradation of the substrate caused by the first colonizers. In other words, except for very few laboratory experiments,

there have been few attempts to elucidate the microbial succession occurring during colonization of a given substrate since, in general, what is seen is a climax community. Nevertheless, even if the role of fungi and bacteria in the defacement of cultural heritage has not been firmly established (in the sense that, with very few exceptions, the causative agents have not been identified), there is general agreement that chemoheterotrophic microorganisms contribute significantly to the degradation of cultural heritage.

## III. MECHANISM OF MICROBIAL DEGRADATION AND DAMAGE EVALUATION

Depending on the nature of the object, the environment surrounding it, and other variables, microbial degradation is accomplished through various mechanism, at times complementary and, in other cases, resulting from one another. The following are the main mechanisms:

1. Production on the artifact's surface of a microbial biofilm resulting in the formation of stains, crusts, or spots, often of different colors due to the production of intracellular or extracellular pigments.

2. Growth of the microbial population into the object through the formation of filaments spreading on the object's surface and entering holes and fissures resulting in the chemical and physical decomposition of materials (e.g., weathering of stones). On painted surfaces, microorganisms may penetrate the painted layer, causing crumbling and exfoliation that lead, eventually, to the detachment from the support of portions of the painting.

3. Production of metabolites, often acidic in nature, and of extracellular enzymes that further contribute to the chemical and aesthetic degradation. In addition, many of these metabolites may be utilized as substrates for growth of other microbial species, thus increasing the "microbial load" of the object.

If possible, surveys to identify the areas apparently damaged by microbial growth should be carried out more than once to evaluate the defacement's extent and progression. Especially on outdoor monuments, it is advisable to perform such surveys in different seasons to establish the seasonal fluctuations of microbial colonization. Sampling may be accomplished by either scraping the surface or removing a small portion of the artifact (stone, wood, painted layer, etc.) from the areas showing defacement presumed to be of microbial origin. Of course, sampling by removal of portions of artifact's surface does not present an obstacle in the case of buildings and monuments (no one would object to the removal a small fragment from a stone in the facade of a church nor to that of a sliver from a wooden beam), whereas it requires greater care when it is not outright impossible in the case of other objects (e.g., paintings). From smaller and more delicate objects, a portion of the microbial biofilm may be recovered by pressing an adhesive tape on the object's surface or by rubbing with a sterile cotton swab. Analysis by light or electron microscopy of the samples recovered by any of the previously reported methods allows one to detect the presence of microorganisms and provides a first, approximate idea of the main groups of microorganisms that may be present. Transfer of these samples to growth media enables one to isolate and identify, using standard microbiological techniques, the main species present on the object. This gives only presumptive evidence that the identified microorganisms may play a role in the defacement of the artifact and does not establish which microorganisms, among those isolated, are responsible for the degradation (parasites) and which ones are present only occasionally or always present but grow by utilizing residues of the parasitic species or other chemicals from the substrate and/or the environment (the saprophytes). Simple as it may seem, this differentiation has not often been made since, as already noted, most of the papers published are simple lists of the different microbial taxa isolated from a given substrate. Identification of the causative agent(s) may be achieved only when pure cultures of the microorganisms isolated from the damaged substrate are individually tested in laboratory experiments. In these experiments, sterile, well-defined samples, identical or as similar as possible to the damaged artifact, are exposed to pure cultures of the different microbial species isolated from the artifact. After a suitable incubation time, one evaluates which microorganisms grow on the test samples and which ones produce the structural and aesthetic damages observed *in situ*. In one case, direct proof of the defacing effect of bacteria isolated from a damaged fresco was obtained by applying to an undamaged portion of the same fresco cotton pads containing suspensions of the different bacterial cultures isolated from the defaced areas. After incubation for a few weeks, many of the bacterial species tested were found to produce on the fresco's surface colored spots and patinas similar to those observed on the defaced fresco. Analogous experiments were performed in which samples of calcitic and dolomitic limestones were incubated for a few weeks with pure fungal or bacterial cultures. Scanning electron microscopy demonstrated that the stones were covered by a microbial biofilm that severely etched the stones' surface. In the case of silk, it was shown that only a few soil bacteria could grow on the protein and that a pure culture of one of these species was able to induce in the laboratory the same reduction of the mechanical properties and the same alterations of the fiber's morphology that were observed on naturally degraded silk or when samples of silk were buried in soil or treated with soil extracts.

In conclusion, the time is ripe for abandoning the strictly descriptive stage (which organisms are isolated from a given substrate) and moving to an experimental one. The latter approach will make possible the identification of the microorganisms responsible for the damages observed on a given substrates and give more accurate information for the disinfestation interventions.

## IV. PREVENTION AND CONTROL OF MICROBIAL COLONIZATION

Methods to control and eradicate microorganisms defacing cultural heritage vary according to the nature of the artifact, its dimensions and location, the environmental conditions, and many other variables. Therefore, quite often, microbial colonization of cultural heritage is controlled through trial and error.

First, it is necessary to distinguish between movable objects, such as easel paintings, sculptures, and books, and fixed, immovable ones, such as archaeological sites, buildings, and monuments. This subdivision echoes in part the subdivision made in Section II between inorganic and organic substrates since, with regard to the chemical composition, most of the immovable objects are essentially inorganic (stone, masonry, etc.) and most of those that are movable are essentially organic. However, there are obviously exception, such as certain stone artifacts (e.g., sculptures) that are movable and may be kept indoors. Similarly, organic substances (e.g., wood ornaments) may be integral parts of monumental complexes and thus immovable.

Humidity is probably the most important environmental factor conditioning microbial colonization of cultural heritage since water is essential for the development of microorganisms. Indeed, it is well-known that in humid climates microbial colonization of cultural heritage is more abundant than in arid ones and that, in the case of buildings, the portions more susceptible to microbial defacement are those more exposed to direct water contact through rain, water seepage, or condensation. It is generally assumed that a relative humidity between 50 and 65% is sufficient to prevent microbial colonization and it may even arrest further growth of microorganisms on objects already inhabited by microorganisms. It is obvious that the humidity of the environment housing cultural heritage should not be decreased below a certain level (in general 50%) because a too dry environment may have deleterious effects by altering the mechanical properties of certain components (wood, canvas, paper, painted layers, etc.). Temperature also influences the growth of microorganisms since higher ambient temperatures favor microbial colonization as demonstrated, for instance, by the fact that cultural heritage is defaced by microbial colonization more rapidly in the tropics than in the northern latitudes. A temperature of approximately 16–20°C is considered optimal for preserving artifacts from biological aggression. In addition to museums, in any closed environment it is relatively easy (e.g., through air-conditioning) to control humidity, temperature, and other factors that favor microbial colonization: light and environmental contaminants such as chemical pollutants, dust, and dirt. This type of control is impossible in the case of, for instance, the exterior of a building and monumental or archeo-

logical complexes disseminated over a large area. Nevertheless, there exists a series of preventive or protective actions, a predisinfestation, that may reduce, if not completely eliminate, the detrimental effects of humidity: construction of covers (such as those protecting archeological remains), repairs and maintenance of roofs, mounting of spillways, dampproofing of foundations and walls, treatment of exposed surfaces with water-repellant resins, etc. Similarly, covers or screens may decrease the amount of sunlight reaching the surface of buildings and monuments and therefore reduce growth of photosynthetic microorganisms. When, as often occurs, these interventions are insufficient to achieve complete control of microbial aggression, disinfection should be carried out to eliminate the microorganisms that are present and prevent, for as long as possible, further microbial growth.

The following are methods that may be utilized for disinfection and control:

1. Mechanical removal: This consists of the manual removal of the biological structures (e.g., lichens' crusts or microbial mats) present on the artifact. This method of intervention is often utilized in the case of lichens that may seriously deface outdoor monuments. The treatment does not eliminate completely the lichen thalli and the portions remaining on the monuments act as an inoculum for resumption of growth of the organisms. However, given the extremely slow growth of lichens, this re-growth is hardly noticeable for years and, as a consequence, has little negative impact. To prevent the possibility of re-growth, it is possible to proceed with mechanical removal of lichens after the organisms have been killed by a preliminary chemical treatment. Notwithstanding the aesthetic and the structural damages caused by these organisms, lichens may give some protection from atmospheric pollution, rain, and variations in temperature and moisture. Thus, it is conceivable that lichen crusts may be kept *in situ* to act as a cover protecting the object's surface.

2. Physical methods: The application of UV radiations and of gamma rays has been proposed especially for indoor structures: however, these methods have been utilized very little, even for movable objects. Gamma radiations has been utilized for the disinfec-

tion of mummies but attempts to utilize this method for other objects have been hampered by the finding that the radiations may have negative effects on some of the molecules that constitute the object (e.g., the cellulose of books). Laser radiations, utilized for removal of soot, dirt, and other environmental pollutants from the facades of buildings, sculptures, and other lithic artifacts, may be used to remove so-called "black crusts," patches formed by fungal species, often in the family Daematiaceae, producing melanin-like black pigments.

3. Chemical methods: These are the most commonly utilized and rely on the application, by different techniques, of chemical compounds endowed with biocidal activity (see Table I). The chemicals that are utilized may be active on all types of microorganisms (e.g., formaldehyde) or have a narrower spectrum of biological activity (e.g., fungicides). It is obvious that, unless chemicals with a very large spectrum of activity are utilized (detergents, formaldehyde, etc.), the choice of the biocide to be utilized

depends on the microbial flora present on the object. This requires the identification of at least the main microbial groups (lichens, algae, fungi, and bacteria) colonizing the objects. In any case, it is always advisable to perform preliminary tests in the laboratory to evaluate which chemicals prevent growth in solid or liquid media of pure cultures of the microbial species isolated from the defaced substrate. If feasible, tests should also be carried out *in situ* by treating small areas of the defaced object with different biocidal agents and evaluating, after a suitable time interval, which agent has been most effective in reducing or eliminating microbial colonization. In addition to the specificity of its biological activity, the choice of the active ingredient to be utilized must meet certain requirements, such as lack of color, inertness towards the object *in toto* and its components, lack of toxicity for the persons applying the treatment and visitors, ease of application, cost, and long-lasting effect. This last condition has been disputed since, on the one hand, the ideal treatment should

### TABLE I
**Chemicals Used to Control Microbial Colonization of Cultural Heritage**

| Category | Chemical | Active against | Utilized for |
|---|---|---|---|
| Inorganic | Na fluoride | Fungi, bacteria | Storerooms, timber, as preservative in glues |
| | Na hypochlorite | Algae, fungi, lichens | Fountains and other water basins, stone, masonry |
| | Na tetraborate | Algae, lichens | Stone, masonry |
| | Hydrogen peroxide | Algae, bacteria, fungi, lichens | Stone, masonry, plaster |
| Organometallic | Tri-*n*-butyl-stannous oxide | Algae, bacteria, fungi, lichens | Stone, masonry, plaster, murals |
| | Phenylmercuric acetate | Algae, bacteria, fungi | Paintings, prints, books |
| Organic | Formaldehyde | Algae, bacteria, fungi | Rooms, caves, murals |
| | Dimethyldithiocarbamates | Algae, bacteria, fungi, lichens | Stone, masonry, murals |
| | *p*-Chloro-*m*-cresol | Bacteria, fungi | Books, prints, murals |
| | Pentachlorophenol | Algae, fungi, lichens | Stone, masonry, murals |
| | Na sorbate | Fungi | Paintings, as preservative in glues |
| | Benzalkonium chloride[a] | Algae, bacteria, fungi, lichens | Stone, masonry, plaster, murals |
| | Dichlorophenyldimethylurea | Algae, lichens | Stone, masonry, murals |
| | *o*-Phenylphenol | Bacteria, fungi, lichens | Stone, masonry, murals, as preservative in glues |
| | *p*-Dichlorobenzene | Fungi | Textiles, storerooms |
| | Thymol | Bacteria, fungi | Books, textiles, wood, murals |

[a] Also, other quaternary ammonium compounds.

be the one that theoretically lasts forever but, on the other hand, there exists the possibility that, in the long run, the chemical residues remaining on the object may lose their biological activity and become substrates for growth of other microorganisms. Especially in the case of buildings and monuments, it is often convenient that, after the disinfestation treatment, the surface be protected with water-repellent compounds (e.g., silicones) which impermeabilize the external portion, maintaining it in a condition of dryness sufficient to prevent further microbial growth.

Fumigation is one of the best methods for disinfecting a wide range of art objects and it has been utilized for sculptures in wood, paintings (on canvas, paper, and wood), textiles, books, and prints. Fumigation ensures good penetration of the active principle inside the object, and it may be easily performed if the object can be transferred to especially designed fumigation chambers or if the rooms in which the objects are kept can be tightly sealed. One of the compounds that has been most frequently utilized for fumigation is formaldehyde, which has been used in the disinfestation of libraries and of the already mentioned Lascaux cave. However, its toxicity has curtailed its use. In the past, ethylene oxide was also used extensively, often mixed with $CO_2$, Freon, or other inert gases to reduce the risks of explosion. However, due to its toxicity and the fact that it has been found to react with linseed oil and some pigments to produce a darkening of colors, its use has been discontinued. Carbon disulfide is often used to kill insects on wood, but it has also been employed to control microbial growth on paintings on wood and other painted wooden objects with no deleterious effects on the painted areas. In this case, toxicity of the gas and the fact that, when mixed with air, it becomes explosive have limited its use. Thymol vapors, produced in air-tight, heated cabinets, have been extensively utilized for paintings and wooden and paper objects. However, on paper, in the presence of light, thymol was found to undergo a rapid photo-oxidative polymerization resulting in the production of a yellow color. In addition, the reported interference with certain materials (e.g., oil paints and parchment) and the high volatility of the chemi-

cal that therefore does not confer a long-lasting protection have severely diminished its use. Occasionally, other compounds such as hydrocyanide and methyl bromide have been used to disinfect rooms by fumigation, but their toxicity requires great care in their utilization.

Spraying of solutions, in water or in organic solvents, of compounds with biocidal activity has been employed on the exterior of buildings and stone artifacts as well as for murals or easel paintings on which deterioration of the superficial layer was evident. Alternatively, spraying may be substituted by application of the biocide solution with a brush or by blotting. It is quite likely that with the latter methods the solution penetrates the object more deeply than when applied by spraying. Control of lichens and algae on lithic substrates has been achieved, for instance, by washing the monuments' surface with an aqueous solution of a quaternary ammonium and an organic tin compounds. The treatment appeared to be capable of eradicating the microbial populations from stones and masonry, even if, to obtain a continuous protection, subsequent treatments with solutions of quaternary ammonium compounds had to be applied periodically. In certain specific cases, such as in the case of wood-rotting fungi, the biocide-containing solution may be injected directly in the object.

Of the inorganic compounds, only hypochlorite is still extensively utilized for the control of algal and fungal growth mostly in fountains and other water basins. Sodium fluoride in water solution is now used essentially only for treating wood, such as soaking timber, since on other substrates (e.g., paintings) fluoride reacts with calcium to give insoluble calcium fluoride devoid of biological activity. The salt, however, is still commonly utilized as a solid in storage rooms and as a preservative added to the glues utilized in the re-lining of paintings. Salts of boric acid have been used as algicides, but the possibility that the acid may react with cations of the substrates to give water-soluble borates has discouraged its use. Similarly, hydrogen peroxide's use is very reduced because of its capacity to oxidize compounds present on the substrates, giving rise to stains of different colors.

One of the most effective and most long-lasting

disinfectants is *p*-chloro-*m*-cresol (once employed in combination with phenylmercuric acetate, which has been abandoned because of its toxicity) dissolved in turpentine and acetone since neither the compound nor the solvents interact with the pigments, the substrates, or the other components that may be present (e.g., glues). In the case of paintings on paper, drawings, prints, etc., the two chemicals have been used to disinfect these substrates simply by keeping for a few days the material to be disinfected at room temperature in a polyethylene bag containing filter papers saturated with either of the two chemicals. Pantachlorophenol, dissolved in white spirit or other solvents, has been extensively utilized, although some authors believe that it should be used on canvas and paper with great care since, under conditions of high humidity, it liberates chloride ions that may attack and depolymerize cellulose.

Currently, ammonium quaternary salts, such as benzalkonium chloride, benzenthonium chloride, and cetyltrimethyl ammonium bromide are probably the most widely employed biocides since treatment with these compounds appears to quite efficiently control growth of all microorganisms on almost any surface. Furthermore, quaternary ammonium compounds are easily soluble in water, do not interact with substrates, and possess a very low toxicity. The only problem is that these compounds do not afford a long-lasting protection so that treatments have to be repeated periodically.

Antibiotics, such as penicillin and streptomycin, have been used to control bacterial growth on murals and stones and nystatin in the case of fungi. Currently, these (and other) antibiotics are rarely utilized since, in addition to high cost, they do not afford a long-lasting control of microbial population and, after a certain period of time (a few months or years), microbial growth resumes.

The chemicals most commonly utilized are shown in Table I. The list must be cosidered a simple indica-tion of the compounds that are or have been used, at times in combination, to eradicate specific groups of microorganisms colonizing specific substrates. Given the complexity of and variations in the system substrate/microorganisms/environmental conditions, only *ad hoc* investigations may provide the reliable informations necessary to achieve disinfestation and control of microbial colonization.

## See Also the Following Articles

## Bibliography

Allsopp, C., and Allsopp, D. (1983). An updated survey of commercial products used to protect materials against bio-deterioration. *Int. Biodeterioration Bull.* **19**, 99–146.

Bock, E., and Sand, W. (1993). The microbiology of masonry biodeterioration. *J. Appl. Bacteriol.* **74**, 503–514.

Griffin, P. S., Indictor, N., and Koestler, R. J. (1996). The biodeterioration of stone: A review of biodeterioration mechanisms, conservation case histories, and treatment. *Int. Biodeterioration* **28**, 187–207.

Koestler, R. J., Warscheid, T., and Nieto, F. (1997). Biodeterioration: Risk factors and their management. *In* "Saving Our Architectural Heritage: The Conservation of Historic Stone Structures" (N. S. Baer and R. Snethlage, Eds.), pp. 25–36. Wiley, Chichester, UK.

Ortega-Calvo, J. J., Hernandez-Marine, M., and Saiz-Jimenez, C. (1993). Cyanobacteria and algae on historic buildings and monuments. *In* "Recent Advances in Biodeterioration and Biodegradation" (K. L. Garg, N. Garg, and K. G. Mukerji, Eds.), pp. 173–203. Naya Prokash, Calcutta.

Strzelczyk, A. B. (1981). Paintings and sculptures. *In* "Microbial Deterioration" (A. H. Rose, Ed.), pp. 203–234. Academic Press, London.

Urzi, C., and Krumbein, W. E. (1994). Microbiological impacts on the cultural heritage. *In* "Durability and Change: The Science, Responsibility and Cost of Sustaining Cultural Heritage" (W. E. Krumbein, P. Brimblecombe, D. E. Cosgrowe, and S. Staniforth, Eds.), pp. 107–135. Wiley, Chichester, UK.

# Continuous Culture

## Jan C. Gottschal

*University of Groningen*

I. Principles of Continuous Culture
II. Basic Continuous Culture Equipment
III. Ecological and Physiological Applications
IV. Concluding Remarks

## GLOSSARY

***auxostat*** A continuous culture system in which a growth-dependent parameter is held constant and all other parameters, including the specific growth rate, vary accordingly.

***chemostat*** A continuous culture system in which the dilution rate, and hence the specific growth rate, is set externally and all other parameters vary accordingly.

***dilution rate (D)*** Flow rate of incoming fresh medium divided by the actual volume of the culture in the continuous culture vessel.

***half-saturation constant for growth ($K_s$)*** Substrate concentration at which the specific growth rate equals half the maximum specific growth rate ($\mu_{max}$).

***specific growth rate ($\mu$)*** Rate of increase of biomass relative to the biomass already present ($1/x \cdot dx/dt$).

***steady state*** Condition of a continuous culture in which changes in density and physiological state of the cells are no longer detectable.

***yield coefficient (Y)*** Quantity of cells produced per substrate consumed.

**A CONTINUOUS CULTURE** is an "open" system in which a well-mixed culture is continuously provided with fresh nutrients. Its volume is kept constant by continuous removal of culture liquid at the same rate at which fresh medium is supplied.

Several types of continuous cultures can be constructed. By far the most common type is the chemostat, in which the growth rate of the culture is fixed by the rate at which medium is fed to the chemostat. At steady state the dilution rate ($D$) of the culture equals the specific growth rate ($\mu$) of the cells. The cell density is set by the concentration of the limiting nutrient ($S_r$) present in the reservoir medium. The dilution rate can be varied over a large range of values from close to the maximum specific rate of growth ($\mu_{max}$) to a small fraction (typically as low as 1–5%) of this maximum value. Over this range of dilution rates, steady states can be obtained during which the growth of microorganisms is exactly balanced by the rate of removal of cells from the culture. At dilution rates approaching the maximum specific growth rate, cell densities become progressively lower, and growth at $\mu_{max}$ is not possible. The only way to maintain cultures at (near) maximum rate of growth is to switch over to some kind of internal control of the supply rate of fresh medium. Such a control mechanism is often based on continuous monitoring of growth-dependent parameters, e.g., biomass, end products of metabolism, or residual concentration of one of the growth substrates in the culture. Although continuous cultures are not synonymous to chemostats, in practice most continuous culture studies have focussed on chemostats.

Continuous cultures are ideally suited for studying the properties of microorganisms under strictly controlled environmental conditions over extended periods of time. Their value is also recognized for studies on interactions between different species grown as mixed cultures under single- and multiple-nutrient limitations.

## I. PRINCIPLES OF CONTINUOUS CULTURE

### A. Single Substrate-Limited Growth

In a substrate-limited continuous culture, a chemostat, the fresh medium is supplied at a constant rate ($F$). Because the culture liquid, including the cells, is removed at the same rate a constant volume ($V$) is maintained. The dilution rate ($D$) of the chemostat is defined as $F/V$. The composition of the inflowing medium is such that, in the most simple case, growth in the chemostat results in (almost) complete consumption of only one of the nutrients, the growth-limiting substrate, with a concentration of $S_r$ in the feed. The specific rate at which growth proceeds will at first be maximal, but upon depletion of the limiting nutrient this rate will rapidly decline; this may conveniently be described by the following well-known empirical relationship proposed by Monod (as early as 1942):

$$\mu = \mu_{max} \cdot s/(K_s + s) \qquad (1)$$

where $\mu$ (the specific growth rate) $= (1/x)(dx/dt)$, where $x$ represents biomass, $s$ is the actual concentration of the growth-limiting nutrient in the culture, and $K_s$ is the half-saturation constant for growth, numerically equal to the substrate concentration at which $\mu = \frac{1}{2}\mu_{max}$. Due to the supply of fresh medium, growth does not stop completely but continues at a rate determined by the feed rate. The combined effect of growth and dilution eventually leads to a steady state in which $\mu = D$:

Change in biomass with time = growth − output
$$dx/dt = \mu x - Dx = (\mu - D)x = 0 \qquad (2)$$

From this formulation, it will be clear that if $\mu = D$, the biomass concentration in the culture remains constant with time ($dx/dt = 0$) and a steady-state situation has been obtained. Such a steady state appears to be, to some extent, self-adjusting with respect to small changes in dilution rate. Thus, if $\mu > D$, the substrate consumption rate will exceed its supply rate, leading to a decrease in the residual substrate concentration in the culture. According to Eq. (1), this will cause a decrease in the specific growth rate, a process that continues until $\mu = D$.

A similar situation exists if initially $\mu < D$. In this case, an increasing concentration of growth-limiting substrates results in an increase in the specific growth rate. Steady states can be obtained for values of $D$ below the critical dilution rate ($D_c$), which in most cases is close to $\mu_{max}$, because $S_r$ is usually much larger than $K_s$:

$$D_c = \mu_{max}[S_r/(K_s + Sr)] \qquad (3)$$

Operation of a chemostat at dilution rates above this critical dilution will, of course, result in complete washout of the biomass and in a substrate concentration equal to that in the fresh medium.

Under steady-state conditions, the change in substrate concentration is given by the following balance:

$$ds/dt = DS_r - Ds - \mu x/Y = 0 \qquad (4)$$

where $Y$ is a yield coefficient defined as the quantity of cells produced per substrate consumed. From Eq. (4), solved for $X$, it follows that

$$x = Y(S_r - s) \qquad (5)$$

and from Eq. (1), solved for $s$, it can be seen that

$$s = K_s D/(\mu_{max} - D) \qquad (6)$$

From Eq. (5), it is clear that the steady-state cell density is determined primarily by the concentration of the growth-limiting substrate in the reservoir medium ($S_r$), whereas Eq. (6) indicates that $s$ is a direct function of the dilution rate, with the assumption that the parameters $Y$, $\mu_{max}$, and $K_s$ are constants for a given organism. This is most clearly illustrated in Fig. 1, in which arbitrarily chosen values for $Y$, $K_s$, and $\mu_{max}$ have been used. Although the assumption that $\mu_{max}$ and $K_s$ are constants for a given organism and growth substrate is often correct, this is less evident for the yield coefficient. This parameter may vary significantly not only due to growth on different substrates, but also due to accumulation of intracellular reserve materials, changes in cell composition and viability, and variability in the energy requirements for maintenance of cell integrity, especially at very low dilution rates.

Also illustrated in Fig. 1 is the important fact that at dilution rates well below $D_c$ relatively high cell

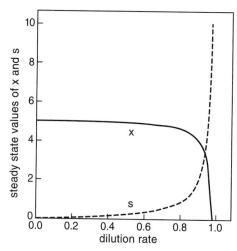

**Fig. 1.** Theoretical relationship between the dilution rate and the steady-state values of cell-density (*x*) and substrate concentration (*s*). Data were calculated assuming the following growth parameters: $\mu_{max} = 1.0$ hr$^{-1}$, $Y = 0.5$ g/g, $K_s = 0.2$ g/liter, and $S_r = 10$ g/liter.

densities can be obtained in the presence of very low, growth-limiting substrate concentrations. This aspect of continuous cultivation, plus the fact that cells are maintained in an active, relatively well-controlled physiological state, has made chemostats extremely useful for both physiological and ecological studies.

Chemostats can also be used quite effectively for accurate determination of basic growth kinetic parameters. For example, $\mu_{max}$ can often be determined more reliably than in a batch culture because (i) prior to the determination of $\mu_{max}$ the culture can be grown at a rate close to $\mu_{max}$, ensuring that all cells are optimally adapted to growth at their near-maximum rate; (ii) lag phases will not interfere with the measurement; and (iii) possible influences of changing substrate and product concentrations are minimized. For the actual measurement, the dilution rate is increased (in one step) from a value slightly below $\mu_{max}$ to a value of 20–50% above the critical dilution rate. This results at once in alleviation of the substrate limitation and in gradual washout of the culture. The rate at which this washout proceeds can be expressed as follows:

$$-dx/dx = (\mu - D)x \qquad (7)$$

which after integration gives

$$\ln x = (\mu - D)t + \ln x_0 \qquad (8)$$

where $x_0$ represents the cell density at the start of the washout period. Because the substrate is no longer limiting, the culture grows at $\mu_{max}$ and a plot of $\ln x$ versus $t$ yields a line with a slope of $(\mu - D)$. Because $D$ is fixed at a known value, $\mu_{max}$ can be determined.

Another important growth parameter, the yield coefficient, can be obtained very easily from cultures in steady state at any dilution rate. According to Eq. (5), the steady-state cell density is a function of $Y$, $S_r$, and $s$. Thus, $Y$ can be obtained directly by dividing the steady-state cell density by the reservoir substrate concentration, assuming that $s \ll S_r$. This gives a yield value at a particular dilution rate, and it is important to remember that its value may vary with the dilution rate and often will be significantly different from values obtained in batch culture. First, bacteria tend to accumulate reserve materials when grown with an excess of substrates (batch culture); therefore, it is important to decide how to express the biomass quantity (as protein, dry weight, total nitrogen, total organic carbon, etc.). Second, in most cases, the cell yield will decrease with decreasing dilution rate (especially under carbon and energy limitations) as a result of increasing "maintenance-energy" requirements (a discussion of these factors is beyond the scope of this article but can be found in some of the specialized literature given in the Bibliography). A third growth parameter, perhaps most decisive for the ability of microorganisms to grow successfully at low substrate concentrations, is the half-saturation constant for growth ($K_s$), as used in Eq. (1). With most organisms and for many substrates this parameter has a very low value (typically in the micro- to nanomolar range). For this reason, direct determination of $K_s$, by measuring the steady-state substrate concentration ($s$) at half-maximum growth rate, often causes significant technical problems. Although for certain substrates (e.g., sugars) reliable direct measurements have been accomplished, it is more common to obtain such data by extrapolation from measurements obtained at relatively high growth rates, resulting in higher steady-state residual substrate concentrations. In analogy with measurement of the Michaelis–Menten constant for half-saturation of enzymes, $K_s$ may thus be obtained from a Lineweaver–Burk type of plot, a linearized form of the "Monod" equation (Eq. 1). Unfortunately, this is not a very accurate plot because those points obtained at the low end of the substrate concentration range (which usually are the most inaccurate ones) put most weight on the position of the line in such a plot. For this reason, the so-called direct linear plot has been introduced and has generally been accepted as being far superior (more accurate) to the Lineweaver–Burk plot. For such a direct linear plot the Monod equation is converted into a linearized form as follows:

$$\mu_{max}/\mu = K_s/x + 1 \qquad (9)$$

Subsequently, substrate concentrations in steady-state cultures at two or more different dilution rates (= specific growth rates) are measured and plotted as shown in Fig. 2. Note that the specific growth rates corresponding to the various substrate concentrations are plotted along the y axis through $s = 0$. From the crossing point of the plotted lines, the projection is made on the x axis, which directly gives the value of $K_s$ in the same units as s. Moreover, from this same plot one can estimate the $\mu_{max}$ as the projection of the crossing point on the left y axis.

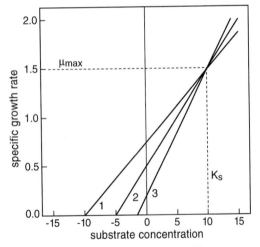

**Fig. 2.** Example of a direct linear plot assuming the following arbitrary combinations of dilution rates (D) and steady-state substrate concentrations: $s = 10 \ \mu M$, $D = 0.75 \ hr^{-1}$ (line 1); $s = 5 \ \mu M$, $D = 0.5 \ hr^{-1}$ (line 2); $s = 1.54 \ \mu M$, $D = 0.2 \ hr^{-1}$ (line 3).

## B. Mixed and Multiple Substrate-Limited Growth

When microorganisms are grown under substrate-sufficient conditions in batch culture in a medium with, for instance, two useable carbon sources, the substrate that supports the highest growth rate is often used preferentially, whereas synthesis of enzymes involved in the utilization of the second substrate remains repressed. As a result, sequential utilization of the substrates occurs and so-called diauxic growth takes place. Although this sequential growth pattern has been described frequently in the past, recent studies have clearly shown that many exceptions do exist. Both the microbial species and the actual combination of growth substrates are crucial factors in determining whether simultaneous or sequential substrate consumption will occur. Based on the (relatively limited number of) studies known to date it is not possible to predict which combinations will result in either of these growth responses. However, a more uniform pattern emerges with respect to the response of microorganisms grown on mixtures of various substrates if these substrates are present in relatively small amounts, i.e., at milligram per liter rather than at gram per liter concentrations. For example, various combinations of glucose + galactose or glucose + fructose are used sequentially in *Escherichia coli* cultures when supplied in grams per liter, whereas at concentrations of less than approx. 5 mg/liter simultaneous utilization was observed. Those few examples of batch culture studies in which more complex but defined mixtures of substrates have been used also indicate that at low concentrations simultaneous substrate utilization is a rule rather than the exception. However, for detailed studies of the physiological response of cultures grown on mixtures of substrates continuous cultures, chemostats in particular are indispensable. Such studies have amply demonstrated that two and many more substrates can be used simultaneously, all being truly growth limiting. Particularly with combinations of substrates serving similar physiological functions, repression of the synthesis of one set of enzymes by the presence of very low concentrations of another does not occur. Moreover, it has now been demonstrated for various combinations of different carbon and energy sources used simultaneously as growth-limiting substrates that the steady-state concentration of one substrate is progressively decreased by the presence of increasing amounts of a second substrate. With varying combinations of two sugars, glucose and galactose, it has been elegantly demonstrated that the steady-state concentration of glucose decreases linearly with increasing amounts of galactose in the substrate mixture and vice versa (Fig. 3). This same effect is even further enhanced if more than just one growth-limiting substrate is used and it has been shown for several bacterial species and some yeasts. The most logical and simple explanation for this phenomenon is that the maximum uptake velocity for the individual sugars in the chemostat culture is not at all or very little affected by the presence of additional substrates. Hence, by maintaining a high cell density at the expense of additional substrates this culture will now have a much larger enzymatic overcapacity for the consumption of the decreased supply of the first substrate.

The situation of simultaneous substrate consumption is less obvious in the case of substrates, which do not fulfill similar physiological functions (e.g.,

oxygen + carbon substrate, carbon source + nitrogen, phosphate + nitrogen). In such cases, one would expect only one substrate to be truly growth limiting. However, the concentration of the second substrate may be made so low that it does affect normal functioning of a specific metabolic process (e.g., the synthesis of phospholipids in the cell membrane, accumulation of reserve materials, and induction–repression of certain enzymes). Although this might influence the precise cellular composition, it does not necessarily affect the overall rate of growth. In other words, the culture could be limited by more than one distinctly different substrate, but the specific growth rate might still be controlled by just one of them. Experimental evidence for the occurrence of multiple nutrient-limited growth (i.e., simultaneous limitation by two or more nutrients serving physiologically dissimilar functions) has been obtained with cultures of bacteria, yeasts, and micro-algae. The pattern observed under these growth conditions is that the transition from limitation by one nutrient to that by a second (or a third nutrient) is characterized by a transition zone, with both nutrients present at growth-limiting concentrations, extending over a range of nutrient ratios in the feed. For example, in a well-studied case of carbon and nitrogen limitation in chemostat cultures of a *Hyphomicrobium* sp. at a constant growth rate, it was shown that within the transition zone the cellular composition depended on the carbon : nitrogen ratio in the feed, whereas outside this zone cell composition remained unaltered with either one of these nutrients being the sole growth-limiting factor. Thus, protein and carbon-reserve material changed with the C : N ratio, as did the activities of at least three different enzymes involved in ammonium assimilation. It was further demonstrated that the boundaries of such a transition zone are determined by the difference in biomass yields between growth under limitation by carbon or nitrogen alone, which is known to be most significant at very low growth rates. This implies that in chemostats maintained at low dilution rates and in many natural environments microbes are likely to be limited simultaneously by two or more different nutrients over extended ranges of available nutrients, whereas this is less likely to occur at high growth rates and in natural environments with high nutrient fluxes.

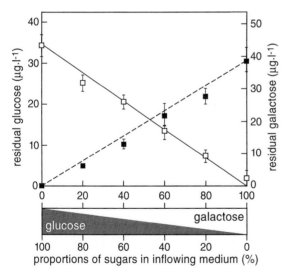

**Fig. 3.** Steady-state concentrations of glucose (□) and galactose (■) during growth of *E. coli* at a constant dilution rate of 0.30 hr⁻¹ in carbon-limited chemostat culture with different mixtures of two sugars. The proportion of the sugars in the mixture fed to the culture is given as weight percentages. The total sugar concentration in the feed was held at 100 mg/liter (redrawn from Egli, 1995).

## C. Substrate-Limited Growth in Mixed Cultures

If two (or more) different bacteria are grown in a chemostat under limitation of one or more nutrients, and if they share the ability to metabolize one or more of these limiting nutrients, these organisms will compete for these nutrients; only those bacteria that manage to maintain a specific growth rate equal to or higher than $D$ will remain in the culture. Initially, when the chemostat has been inoculated with a mixture of bacteria, unrestricted growth is possible for some time until the primary substrate is (nearly) exhausted. During this initial period, the specific growth rate of each species will approach its maximum value because $s \gg K_s$. Competition for the available amount of substrate is thus dominated by the value of $\mu_{max}$ of the individual species. Upon reduction of the substrate concentration, the specific growth rate will decrease according to the respective $\mu$–$s$ relationships. When at this point the supply of fresh medium is started at a rate lower than the maximum rate of growth of at least one member of the mixed culture, a substrate-limited mixed continuous culture will be established. The competitive success of each species will depend on its $\mu_{max}$, its $K_s$, and the imposed dilution rate ($D$). This is seen most clearly by examining Eq. (6) and by recalling

that the organism that attains the highest specific growth rate at a given substrate concentration will eventually eliminate its competitor. This may be visualized by comparing the $\mu$–$s$ relationships of the competing species (Fig. 4). In Fig. 4A, two arbitrary $\mu$–$s$ relationships of two organisms, A and B, are presented, indicating that at any given substrate concentration (i.e., at any $D$ in continuous culture) the specific growth rate of organism A will be higher than that of organism B. However, in Fig. 4B, the two $\mu$–$s$ relationships intersect, which means that the specific growth rate of organism A exceeds that of organism B to the left of the intersection, whereas organism B exhibits the higher specific growth rate to the right of the intersection. Thus, as shown in Fig. 4A, organism A will, in due time, outcompete (i.e., outnumber) organism B at any dilution rate, whereas in the second example (Fig. 4B) this is true only for dilution rates resulting in $s$ values below the intersection. At higher dilution rates, organism B will take over.

Two important comments must be made. First, it should be emphasized that because the cell yield does not appear in the equations describing the $\mu$–$s$ relationships, this parameter does not affect the outcome of the competition in these mixed cultures. Second, this discussion of competition for one limiting substrate assumes cases of pure competition:

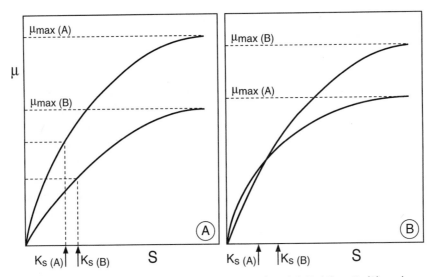

***Fig. 4.*** $\mu$–$s$ relationships of two organisms A and B. (A) $K_s$ (A) $<$ $K_s$ (B) and $\mu_{max}$ (A) $>$ $\mu_{max}$ (B). (B) $K_s$ (A) $<$ $K_s$ (B) and $\mu_{max}$ (A) $<$ $\mu_{max}$ (B).

No other interactions between bacterium A and B should occur. In practice, this will not very often be the case and, as a result, elimination of one species by the other is often incomplete or may not comply very accurately with the predictions based on the $\mu$–$s$ relationships. In fact, this latter situation may be the rule rather than the exception because many examples of coexistence of species grown with just one primary limiting nutrient have been reported. In some cases, this is explained by inhibitory of stimulatory interactions between the competing species, and often it can be attributed to the presence of secondary growth substrates resulting from the metabolism of the competing organisms.

## D. Non-Substrate-Limited Growth in Continuous Culture

In continuous cultures operated as chemostats, the growth rate of bacteria is controlled by setting the rate at which fresh medium is fed to the culture. Although this rate can be varied over a large range of values, growth rates close to $\mu_{max}$ are difficult to achieve in conventional chemostats. The cell density decreases steeply when the critical dilution rate is approached, making cultivation in such circumstances inherently unstable. To overcome this problem, one must switch over to an internal control of the supply rate of fresh medium. In other words, feedback control of the rate at which the medium is fed to the culture is needed to prevent washout of the culture. The best known example of a strictly growth-dependent feedback system is based on continuous measurement of the turbidity as a measure of cell density. Unfortunately, reliable construction of such a "turbidostat" has always been difficult due to problems of fouling of the sensors used to measure turbidity. Therefore, over the years several other growth-dependent parameters have been proposed and tested as alternatives for biomass, such as $CO_2$, inhibitory substrate concentrations (e.g., sulfide), light, oxygen, carbohydrates, and protons. Any continuous culture, based on feedback regulation of a growth-dependent parameter, may be called an "auxostat." The pH-auxostat in particular has proven very useful because it relies on a feedback control based on changes in pH. Briefly, the basic theory of a pH-

auxostat is as follows. Assuming that during growth protons are excreted into the culture liquid, the change in their concentration can be expressed as follows:

$$dH^+/dt = \mu xh + D[H_R^+] - D[H_C^+] - DB_R \quad (10)$$

where $x$ is the culture density (g dry weight of cells per liter), $h$ is the stoichiometry of proton formation per gram dry weight of cells, $[H_R^+]$ is the proton concentration in the culture, and $B_R$ is the buffer capacity of the reservoir medium. For the simplest situation, in which only a small difference exists between the pH of the medium and that of the culture, Eq. (10) reduces to

$$dH^+/dt = \mu xh - DB_R \quad (11)$$

and in steady state with $\mu = D$ the following expression for the cell density is the result:

$$x = B_R/h \quad (12)$$

This shows that the steady-state cell density is a linear function of the buffering capacity of the medium, assuming that $h$ is independent of $B_R$. Combining Eq. (12) with the general nutrient balance for continuous culture, (Eq. 4), yields the following expression for $s$ in steady-state cultures:

$$s = S_r - B_R/hY \quad (13)$$

Finally, solving the conventional Monod expression (Eq. 1) for the obtained steady-state values of $s$ allows a plot of the specific growth rate ($\mu$), the steady-state substrate concentration ($s$), and the steady-state cell density ($x$) as a function of the buffering capacity ($B_R$) (Fig. 5). As can be seen from this illustration, the specific growth rate of the cells remains at a value close to $\mu_{max}$ over a large range of buffering capacities but, of course, will decrease at high buffering capacities due to the decreasing concentration of remaining growth substrate. Obviously, this effect will be most prominent with cells possessing relatively high $K_s$ values for the substrate used. In principle, this will provide the opportunity to choose the buffering capacity such that the substrate concentration becomes strongly growth rate limiting, thus creating an overlap with the conven-

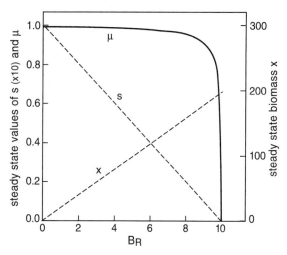

**Fig. 5.** Major growth parameters in a pH auxostat. Residual substrate concentration $s$, specific growth rate $\mu$, and cell density $x$ as a function of the buffering capacity $B_R$ in the reservoir medium. Arbitrarily chosen values: $Y = 20$, $h = 0.05$, $S_r = 10$, and $\mu_{max} = 1$.

tional mode of substrate-limited growth in a chemostat.

## II. BASIC CONTINUOUS CULTURE EQUIPMENT

From the preceding theoretical treatment of continuous culture systems, it is evident that the only fundamental design requirement of a continuous culture system is that the culture be kept growing by a continuous input of fresh medium and an output of culture liquid at the same rate. As already explained, this can be accomplished either through external control of the pump rate (chemostat-type of operation) or by internal control of the flow rate through feedback based on growth-dependent parameters (auxostat-type of operation). Over the years, an enormous number of practical concepts of such fermentor systems have appeared, with sizes ranging from just a few milliliters to several thousands of liters. It is beyond the scope of this article to elaborate on the actual design of continuous culture systems (see Bibliography), but several general considerations are briefly summarized here because they are important for the construction of most general-

purpose (research) chemostats. In Fig. 6, an example is given of a bench-scale (~500 ml working volume) continuous culture system that has proven its effectiveness and flexibility of operation over many years of laboratory practice. Some of its design characteristics are as follows:

1. It can be used for both anaerobic and aerobic cultivation. Because the lid is made of black neoprene rubber (at least 10-mm thickness with a very low

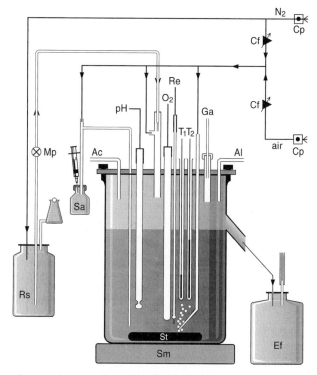

**Fig. 6.** Schematic drawing of a small-scale (500-ml working volume), low-cost glass chemostat. All gases pass through cotton wool filters (not shown) before entering the fermentor. For anaerobic cultivation the $N_2$ is freed of traces of oxygen by passage over heated copper turnings. Rs, reservoir medium; Mp, medium supply pump; Sa, sampling bottle; Ac and Al, acid and alkaline titration inlets, respectively; pH, autoclavable pH electrode; $O_2$, autoclavable polarographic oxygen electrode; Re, redox electrode; $T_1$ and $T_2$, temperature sensor and heating element; Ga, sampling outlet for head-space gas analysis; Cf and Cp, constant flow and pressure regulators, respectively, for maintaining a stable (mixed) flow of $N_2$ and air over and through the culture; St and Sm, magnetic stirring bar and motor unit, respectively; Ef, effluent from the culture.

permeability for most gases), holes can be drilled easily to fit glass tubing and probes of various sizes.

2. Sterility is easily maintained because the entire setup can be autoclaved and mixing is done with a magnetic stirring bar, which eliminates difficulties with sealing of a stirring shaft through the lid of the fermentor.

3. Rubber tubing is made of butyl rubber for anaerobic cultivation and silicon tubing is usually used for aerobic cultures for more flexibility and durability.

4. The medium is supplied by means of a peristaltic tube pump using silicon tubing or marprene rubber especially for anaerobic cultivation. The culture volume is maintained at a constant level as it flows out freely through a side arm together with the outflowing gas (e.g., air and $N_2$).

5. The design of the medium inlet is of critical importance because it should ensure a regular flow of small droplets (to minimize discontinuity in the supply of fresh medium) in such a way that contamination of the reservoir with the organisms grown in the culture does not occur. To this end, the inlet is designed such that the medium droplets fall freely and directly into the culture through a relatively wide glass tube which is kept dry on the inside by a continuous flow of sterile gas to avoid back-growth from the culture along the wall of this inlet tube.

Clearly, this type of continuous culture will need to be adapted to any specific needs. For example, for very volatile or hydrophobic substrates, an open gas phase is not appropriate. Although neoprene rubber is poorly permeable for most gases, it is quite feasible that a number of substrates or products (e.g., chlorinated aliphatic and aromatic solvents) may pass through this barrier, in which case the rubber may need to be replaced by stainless steel. Also, due to the use of a rubber lid, the vessel cannot be pressurized, which for some applications will be an absolute requirement. For example, for growth of hyperthermophiles under elevated pressures, continuous cultures have been made entirely of stainless steel. Finally, aeration may easily become insufficient at very high densities, especially in combination with high dilution rates, and this problem will also become evident at low cell densities if this type of fermentor

is scaled up to volumes well above 1 liter. Not surprisingly, it has become quite common for commercial continuous culture equipment to be equipped with autoclavable oxygen probes because it is known that insufficient aeration quite easily remains unnoticed without permanent monitoring.

## III. ECOLOGICAL AND PHYSIOLOGICAL APPLICATIONS

### A. Pure Culture Studies

In most natural, especially oligotrophic, environments microorganisms will experience a strong limitation of one or more essential nutrients, particularly carbon, nitrogen, phosphorus, oxygen, and sometimes certain metal ions, vitamins, or specific precursors of cell components that cannot be synthesized by the organism. Therefore, if we want to understand and predict the behavior of microorganisms in nature, it is absolutely necessary to study the mechanisms which have evolved to cope with restricted nutrient availability. It is thus not surprising that continuous culture systems in which growth is continuous but rate limited by one or more nutrients is most often the preferred tool for both ecological and physiological studies of bacteria.

Adjusting the dilution rate over a large range from near $\mu_{max}$ to well below 0.01 hr$^{-1}$ can result in changes in nutrient concentrations from near-saturation levels to far below the $K_s$ value of the organism for that particular substrate. In response to such dramatic decreases in substrate availability, many microorganisms apparently maintain the highest possible rate of metabolism and growth by adjusting their nutrient uptake potential through an increase in the $V_{max}$ of their nutrient uptake systems. Similarly, substantial increases have been noted in the levels and activities of other intracellular enzymes, particularly those involved in the initial steps of the catabolism of the growth limiting nutrients. This enhanced induction and/or depression appears to be a common response and probably represents a general solution to maintaining relatively high metabolic fluxes even in the presence of very low extracellular substrate concentrations. Such derepression also may occur with enzymes that are not even involved in the metabolism of the growth-limiting substrate. For example, in *Alcaligenes eutrophus*, a facultatively autotrophic hydrogen-oxidizing organism, hydrogenases appear at low dilution rates under succinate-limiting conditions, which do not at all require hydrogenase activity. Even ribulose–bisphosphate carboxylase, a key enzyme in the $CO_2$-fixing pathway for autotrophic growth of this organism, increases when the dilution rate decreases during heterotrophic, succinate-limited growth.

An interesting observation with chemostat cultures in response to a decreasing nutrient supply is a change in morphology resulting in increased surface to volume ratios. For example, *Arthrobacter* species have been shown to change from spheres into rods, *Caulobacter* species are known to produce long stalks when grown under severe nutrient limitation, and most rod-shaped organisms tend to grow longer and very much thinner with decreasing dilution rates. Increased surface to volume ratios are believed to facilitate nutrient flux into the cell due to a relatively high content of solute uptake systems in the cell surface in combination with the strongly decreased cell volume. An additional well-documented mechanism of enhancing metabolic activity at very low nutrient levels is the switch over to different pathways with similar functions but with much higher overall substrate affinities (usually a combination of lower $K_m$ values and increased enzyme levels). This type of phenotypic adaptation is particularly well-known for the metabolism of sugars, glycerol, and nitrogen sources. A special and intriguing adaptation is found in anaerobic fermentative bacteria (lactic acid bacteria and clostridia are well-known for this) is the ability to change their fermentation routes, such that the overall energy yield per amount of substrate used increases with decreasing substrate availability.

The phenomenon of simultaneous consumption of two and more substrates has been demonstrated many times and apparently is the rule rather than the exception during growth under nutrient limitation. Particularly interesting are substrate combinations such as formate + acetate, formate + oxalate, formate + mannitol, thiosulfate + acetate, methylamine + glucose, methanol + glucose, and $H_2$ + lactate, which all can be used to generate energy and,

if present alone, result in autotrophic, methylotrophic, or heterotrophic growth. The microorganisms capable of utilizing these different substrates simultaneously under carbon and/or energy limitation grow "mixotrophically." In other words, they can combine autotrophic ($CO_2$ serves as the carbon source), methylotrophic ($C_1$ compounds other than $CO_2$ are the carbon source), and heterotrophic ($C_{2-n}$ compounds are used as carbon source) modes of metabolism. This mixotrophic metabolism has been studied in chemostats by supplying the cultures with variable mixtures of these different substrates. Oxidative potentials and $CO_2$ fixing capacities were shown to respond to the ratio of the "autotrophic" or "methylotrophic" and "heterotrophic" substrates in the inflowing medium in such a way that the organisms optimized their biomass yield. In these particular cases, the observed increase in growth efficiency is explained by the energy-saving effect which is gained by the utilization of an organic substrate compared with synthesis of cell material on the basis of $CO_2$ fixation.

One of the major advantages of chemostat cultivation may also be viewed as the greatest conceptual problem for using this technique in ecological research because it is unlikely to find many natural habitats that show a degree of constancy of growth conditions that are as strict as those established in chemostats at steady state. Fortunately, however, due to another very important feature of chemostat cultivation—precise control of the growth environment—the chemostat also offers excellent possibilities to study microbial cultures under controlled discontinuous conditions. To allow for this type of growth control, the standard chemostat equipment needs to be extended with timing and switching devices to make changes to dilution rate, type of medium, light irradiance, aeration, pH, temperature, etc. in a controlled manner. In fact, sophisticated, gradual changes in growth conditions are possible using computer-controlled equipment in combination with proper software specifically designed for this purpose. Some studies on the effects of controlled short-term environmental changes have revealed the enormous phenotypic adaptability of microorganisms to variations in their environment. However, knowledge about the rate and extent of genotypic adaptation to such environmental challenges is very limited. To date, it appears that some organisms can grow on many different substrates over a wide range of temperatures, oxygen partial pressures, and pH values, whereas others are to be considered specialists because of their dependence on just one type of energy source usually under very specific physicochemical conditions.

Conditions of non-growth and the phases of transition between growth and starvation can be studied effectively in continuous cultures. Thus, in substrate-limited continuous cultures the interruption of the medium supply (by switching off the feed pump) in principle will induce starvation conditions instantaneously without a need to manipulate the cells as in batch cultures. For example, studies with *Streptococcus cremoris* in lactose-limited chemostats, subjected to starvation periods of various lengths and a subsequent renewed supply of lactose, have indeed shown that a sustained intracellular pool of phosphoenolpyruvate may be responsible for the rapid reestablishment of growth following periods of complete starvation. In other studies, using *Thiobacillus versutus* grown in thiosulfate- and/or acetate-limited chemostats, the metabolic flexibility of this bacterium was demonstrated. The organism is capable of growth with acetate or thiosulfate alone but also with mixtures of these two substrates when both are growth limiting. Switching between acetate and thiosulfate limitation or from starvation to thiosulfate-limited growth revealed that as long as enzymes required for catabolism of the new substrate following a switch-over were still present in the cells, growth resumed without a detectable lag. Moreover, very rapid restoration of growth at the expense of thiosulfate was also observed with cells, which had completely lost their thiosulfate-oxidizing capacity during starvation or during growth on acetate, as long as a directly usable substrate or reserve material was present along with the new substrate. The survival value of such metabolic properties can be shown most clearly in experiments with chemostat-grown mixed cultures.

## B. Mixed Culture Studies

In most natural environments microbial populations will have to compete for limiting nutrients and as a result this must be considered a major interaction between microbes. In most of the earlier studies, examples of "pure competition" between two bacteria with only one growth-limiting nutrient were investigated. Not surprisingly, in those cases in which no additional interactions were involved, the outcome of the competition clearly confirmed the competitive exclusion principle. However, despite these seemingly straightforward results of pure competition, a significant number of studies have shown that stable mixed cultures could be maintained in chemostats limited by only one primary substrate. In these cases, in which competition may not have been so "pure," the occurrence of additional relationships between the competing organisms usually accounts for the observed coexistence.

Perhaps one of the most remarkable illustrations of the occurrence of such interrelationships was observed during investigations on the occurrence of genotypic and phenotypic changes in a pure culture of *E. coli* during glucose-limited growth in chemostats for at least 800 generations. Apparently, a strain evolved under these conditions which was a specialist on glucose but excreted significant amounts of acetate and some glycerol. The strain used initially would normally take up these excretion products, but gradually two other strains evolved which specialized in uptake of these secondary metabolites, outcompeting the primary strain with respect to uptake of these secondary substrates. As a result of these evolutionary events a mixed culture was created with three distinctly different strains of *E. coli* which coexisted with only glucose as the single primary substrate.

Other classic examples of this phenomenon include those in which fermentative bacteria produce useable fermentation products or in which vitamins or other growth requirements excreted by two distinct species give rise to stable commensalistic or mutualistic relationships. For example, reciprocal stimulation of two species in mixed culture was demonstrated during attempts to produce yogurt by continuous cultivation. In this case *Lactobacillus bulgaricus* produced amino acids (from casein) that stimulated the growth of *S. thermophilus*, which in turn produced small quantities of formic acid, which in turn stimulated growth of *L. bulgaricus*. Of course, these latter types of interactions may also be studied in batch culture systems, but the significant advantage of doing it in continuous culture is the degree of constancy of the growth conditions that can be obtained and the avoidance of interfering lag phases, substrate exhaustion, variations in product accumulation, and changes in biomass, which are so characteristic of batch culture experimentation. These same factors also make continuous culture the method of choice in some detailed studies on interspecies hydrogen transfer. For example, the sulfate-reducing bacterium *Desulfovibrio vulgaris* growing at the expense of lactate or pyruvate requires sulfate as an electron acceptor in batch culture. However, stable mixed cultures of *D. vulgaris* and *Methanosarcina barkeri* (a hydrogen-consuming methanogen) could be obtained in chemostats with lactate (or pyruvate) as the limiting substrate in the absence of sulfate. The methanogen acted as "the electron acceptor" for *D. vulgaris* and kept the hydrogen partial pressure below a detectable level.

Bacteria with seemingly conflicting physicochemical requirements have also been grown in stable mixed chemostat cultures. Thus, a strictly aerobic species, *Pseudomonas* sp., and an obligate anaerobe, *Veillonella* sp., were grown with lactate as the growth substrate under oxygen-limiting conditions. The anaerobic organisms fermented lactate to acetate, propionate, hydrogen, and carbon dioxide, whereas the aerobic species metabolized part of these substrates to carbon dioxide and water, using oxygen as its electron acceptor, thus preventing growth inhibition of the anaerobe. Perhaps the most striking example of this type of cocultures is illustrated by the cocultivation of highly oxygen-sensitive methanogens with strictly aerobic heterotrophs in continuous cultures maintained under rigorously oxygen-limiting conditions. This kind of sensitive mutualistic interacting mixed cultures would be very difficult or impossible to study in batch culture systems, in which the oxygen demand changes significantly with time.

Whereas the preceding examples all represent well-defined mixed cultures of a very limited number of species, it is of course quite feasible to maintain multi-species, undefined mixed populations in continuous culture systems. This has indeed been done, often in an attempt to reproduce entire communities as they occur in their natural habitats. Communities can indeed be maintained, but it seems very unlikely that the selective pressures and environmental constraints exerted on these communities are close to those occurring in their natural environment. It should therefore be borne in mind that this type of investigations will probably do little to obtain a better understanding of the respective ecosystems and the communities therein. Continuous cultures are very useful tools for studying many aspects of microbial life, but they are entirely inappropriate to simulate the actual *in situ* natural situation.

## C. Enrichment and Selection

In selective enrichment cultures, a (natural) sample containing many different microorganisms is kept under conditions that selectively aim at stimulating growth of a particular physiological type of organism, population, or community and allowing them to increase in number relative to physiologically different types of microorganisms. Invariably, the mechanism involved is that the chosen growth conditions allow the favored organisms to grow faster than any of the other microbes present in the same inoculum. The "art" of enriching for certain bacteria has been exploited for many years, usually in order to obtain pure cultures of microorganisms. In batch culture enrichments, the selection pressure is directed toward organisms that exhibit the highest maximum specific growth rate during repeated transfers in media containing relatively high substrate concentrations. This is still the most widely employed technique for obtaining microbes with specific physiological properties and a high $\mu_{max}$. Although repeated transfers offer some degree of continuity during the selection process, the actual growth conditions are continuously changing due to changes in biomass, (inhibitory) product formation, changing substrate concentrations, substrate depletion, and significant changes in physicochemical conditions. The major advantage over methods with more control over the actual growth conditions is its obvious simplicity. If the goal of the enrichment is indeed to obtain populations or communities with the highest possible rates of growth and/or substrate conversion, as is often the case in industrial applications, then this procedure remains the method of choice in most cases. However, the selective pressure of this type of enrichment culture can be enhanced enormously by using continuous cultures based on the principles of the auxostat. Because the dilution rate of such cultures is automatically set by the $\mu_{max}$ of the dominant population in the culture, strong selection takes place based on maximum specific rate of growth. Slower growing strains will wash out from the culture. Moreover, this type of approach permits a more precise choice of the actual selective conditions because a specific set of growth conditions can be constantly maintained over a long period of time. To date, however, this technique has not been used often.

Especially in ecological studies, the major disadvantage of growth in batch cultures or auxostats is the use of unrealistically high substrate concentrations which are usually employed in order to establish sufficiently high culture densities. Therefore, if the objective is to obtain organisms that are adapted to growth under a regime of nutrient limitation and not necessarily have a high $\mu_{max}$, the obvious choice is to use substrate-limited chemostats. This procedure may be seen as one of the best ways of obtaining microorganisms more representative of those prevailing in natural (aquatic) environments. In addition to selecting for organisms on the basis of high nutrient uptake affinities, the enrichment conditions may be varied in a controlled way, resulting, for example, in defined patterns of continued environmental changes such as light–dark cycles, pH, temperature, and oxic/anoxic or osmotic transitions. This clearly adds enormously to the precision of the selective pressure that may be applied.

Another particularly important aspect of chemostat enrichments is the possibility to select organisms under conditions of multiple-substrate limitation. Enrichment in such circumstances has demonstrated that metabolically versatile bacteria were selected that are specialized in using several different substrates at the same time if present at growth-limiting concentrations. Because such bacteria usually display lower maximum growth rates relative to more specialized species, they will, in most cases, be missed by employing batch-type enrichment techniques, even if mixtures of several substrates are used, because this would select for maximum rates of growth due to sequential utilization of the substrates present at high concentrations.

Experimental (spatial) heterogeneity, typical for most natural ecosystems, is sometimes deliberately introduced by connecting two or more continuous cultures to each other. This has been done, for example, to study predation by protozoa. In such cases the first fermentor is often used to grow a bacterial culture, and the outlet of this fermentor serves as the inlet (the bacterial feed) of the second fermentor containing the bacterivorous protozoa. In other applications, two or more fermentors are connected in the same way, with the purpose of transferring bacteria, substrates, and products to the next fermentor, in which the growth environment is maintained in a different condition (e.g., oxic/anoxic, denitrifying, sulfate-reducing, methanogenic, and phototrophic). However, another approach in which natural heterogeneity has been simulated used two or three chemostats which were connected by dialysis membranes, allowing solute exchange but no cells.

Chemostat enrichments also provide excellent possibilities for selective enrichment of entire microbial communities. Mixed cultures of bacteria, representing simple microbial food chains, or more complex food webs, will usually manifest themselves in batch cultures as successions of populations. However, in continuous flow systems many of these populations may be maintained simultaneously for extended periods of time and interrelationships may thus be studied more easily.

Fascinating examples of enrichments of complex microbial communities can be found in the literature concerning food-related fermentations and microbial degradation of (man-made) recalcitrant compounds such as herbicides and various halogenated aromatics. Particularly with respect to this latter category of substrates, it should be recognized that in some cases the substrates involved are toxic, even for the organisms capable of degrading them. Obviously, this adds to the advantages of using substrate-limited selective enrichments in chemostats. Subsequent application of selection pressure on the basis of maximum growth or conversion rates by employing auxostat cultivation clearly has great potential for further strain "improvements" to obtain useful industrial production strains and specialized xenobiotics degrading microbes.

## V. CONCLUDING REMARKS

Continuous culture systems represent excellent tools for studying microorganisms under carefully defined growth conditions. In particular, the possibility to maintain cells for long periods of time in the same circumstances ensures that the physiology of these cells is accurately and reproducibly tuned to the conditions chosen. Moreover, exploiting the possibilities of using continuous cultures in a controlled discontinuous mode greatly adds to its usefulness in studying microbial phenotypic and genotypic adaptability and flexibility.

Despite attempts to mimic the natural growth conditions as closely as possible, it should always be remembered that natural environments are far more heterogeneous and dynamic than continuous cultures will ever be able to reproduce. Only a limited selection of individual items of the large spectrum of environmental constraints can be studied using continuous cultures, but at least they can be studied in a controlled manner and in great detail.

Proper choice and combination of the different types of continuous culture offer a very powerful tool for physiological and ecological studies of microbes and also allows for "tailor-made" selection and strain improvement of microorganisms for biotechnological applications.

### See Also the Following Articles

Low-Nutrient Environments • Stock Culture Collections and Their Databases • Strain Improvement

### Bibliography

Caldwell, D. E., Wolfaardt, G. M., Korber, D. R., and Lawrence, J. R. (1997). Do bacterial communities transcend Darwinism? *Adv. Microbial Ecol.* **15**, 105–191.

Dykhuizen, D. E., and Hartl, D. L. (1983). Selection in chemostats. *Microbiol. Rev.* **47**(2), 150–168.

Egli, T. (1995). The ecological and physiological significance of the growth of hetetrotropic microorganisms with mixtures of substrates. *Adv. Microbial Ecol.* **14**, 305–386.

Gottschal, J. C. (1986). Mixed substrate utilization by mixed cultures. *In* "Bacteria in Nature" (E. R. Leadbetter and J. S. Poindexter, Eds.), Vol. 2, pp. 261–292. Plenum, New York.

Gottschal, J. C. (1990). Different types of continuous culture in ecological studies. *In* "Methods in Microbiology" (J. R. Norris and R. Grigorova, Eds.), Vol. 22, pp. 87–124. Academic Press, London.

Wimpenny, J. W. T. (Ed.) (1988). "Handbook of Laboratory Model Systems for Microbial Ecosystems," Vols. 1 and 2. CRC Press, Boca Raton, FL.

# Cosmetic Microbiology

### Daniel K. Brannan

*Abilene Christian University*

I. Background and Importance of Cosmetic Microbiology
II. Sanitary Manufacture
III. Sanitization
IV. Preservation
V. Test Methods

## GLOSSARY

**adulteration** The addition of any harmful substance that may make a product harmful to users under usual conditions of use. Adulterated products contain filthy, putrid, or decomposed substances. Products are adulterated if packed or held under insanitary conditions or if the container is unsafe.

**antimicrobial** A compound that kills or inhibits the growth of microbes; used as a disinfectant or preservative.

**class II recall** Recalls of products are classified from I to III. Class I is an emergency situation in which the consequences are life threatening. Class II is a priority situation in which the consequences may be immediate or long-range and possibly hazardous to health or life threatening. An example is contamination of a cosmetic with a potential pathogen.

**cosmetics** Articles that someone applies to, sprinkles on, or rubs into their body to cleanse, beautify, or promote attractiveness or alter their appearance. The product must not affect normal bodily function or structure. This definition excludes ordinary soap.

**disinfect** Killing microbes on surfaces to levels that are not harmful to health or the quality of the product.

**preservative** A chemical agent used to prevent microbial growth in finished products. It prevents their multiplication or kills them to prevent spoilage or contamination of the product with pathogens.

**sanitizer** A chemical agent used to disinfect equipment.

**COSMETIC MICROBIOLOGY** is a subdiscipline of microbiology. Within this field, microbiologists study how to produce cosmetics free of pathogens and to prevent spoilage due to microorganisms. The cosmetic microbiologist's goal is to improve the safety and aesthetic quality of cosmetics. The cosmetic microbiologist must understand microbial physiology, pathogenic microbiology, and microbial ecology. In addition to microbiology, the cosmetic microbiologist understands organic and physical chemistry, toxicology, engineering, and regulatory/environmental laws.

## I. BACKGROUND AND IMPORTANCE OF COSMETIC MICROBIOLOGY

Cosmetic manufacturers invest considerable effort to reduce the risks of microbial contamination in their products since the economic effects are great. Contamination requires having to scrap spoiled product, conduct class II recalls, and handle litigation from harmed consumers.

For those few, less reputable, cosmetic firms that are unaware of the role of microorganisms in their products, the discovery that their cosmetic contains contaminating microorganisms creates a reactive, problem-solving flurry of activity. As they become more aware of the microbial world, this activity finally becomes proactive prevention. Microbiologists can solve such preventable problems. In fact, the joy of solving such problems provides a kinship with the microbiological masters of old. The techniques that Pasteur used to solve the spoilage problems of French wines are still the same: Get all information on the subject, formulate a hypothesis for why the problem exists, test it, and then provide a practical solution for the problem.

Even the novice microbiologist can identify and quantify microbial contaminants in a cosmetic. However, it takes considerable expertise and experience to eliminate the contaminant and prevent it from occurring again. The novice just adds more biocide, a guaranteed way to adapt the contaminant to the biocide and compound the problem. The experienced cosmetic microbiologist finds the sources of the contamination, cleans them up, redesigns the product preservative system in case of tolerance, and even helps determine how to reclaim or scrap the bad product in an environmentally safe manner.

## A. Regulations and History

In 1938, Congress passed an administrative bill regulating cosmetics: the Food, Drug, and Cosmetic Act of 1938. This action was the culmination of a sequence of events. The existing 1907 Drug Act was considered too weak to ensure effective drug and food safety. A stronger bill was proposed in 1933 but it did not pass both the House and Senate at that time. In 1937, a company marketed an oral tonic made with a poisonous ingredient. The resulting deaths prompted Congress to pass the act in 1938. The act gave the Food and Drug Administration (FDA) a means of regulating and defining cosmetics. The act also defined adulteration and allowed the FDA to request recalls. If a manufacturer fails to conduct the recall, the agency can seize the product. Finally, Congress passed tighter regulatory control on label claims, ingredient listings, and product safety warnings (the Fair Packaging and Labeling Act of 1973–1975).

The cosmetics industry thrived in the 1930s. The only microbial problem was preventing visible mold growth with parabens. When high-volume manufacture of cosmetics in the 1940s increased, so did bacterial and mold spoilage. Companies began including bacteria in their preservative challenge tests and using bactericidal preservatives.

In 1943, the Toilet Goods Association (later called the Cosmetics, Toiletries and Fragrance Association: CTFA) established its scientific section. Member companies also founded the Society of Cosmetic

Chemists to discuss formulation and preservation on a scientific level.

Physicians used antibiotics indiscriminately in the 1950s. Industry also overused antimicrobials in cosmetics ranging from deodorants and soaps to toothpastes and shampoos. Our preoccupation with germs drove the market for products that killed germs. Often, there was an unclear distinction between whether the biocide was used to provide a functional antimicrobial in the cosmetic or used as a preservative. Soon, *Staphylococcus* spp., *Streptococcus* spp., *Pseudomonas* spp., *Serratia* spp., *Enterobacter* spp., and *Klebsiella* spp. caused contamination problems as they developed tolerance to biocides. Contaminated cosmetics were found at higher rates than ever before on store shelves in the 1960s.

The FDA conducted 25 drug and cosmetic product recalls during 1966–1968. In a 1969 sampling the FDA found contamination in 20% of 169 cosmetics tested. Thus, the least regulated of all consumer products came under fire. Rather than face enforced and impractical regulations, the industry launched a cooperative CTFA/FDA relationship of self-regulation. In 1967, the CTFA formed the Microbiology Committee from member companies to address these contamination problems. The committee conducted a survey of almost 4000 products to show that cosmetics, at least from the reputable companies, were free of objectionable microorganisms. This committee developed test methods and conducted collaborative studies to improve manufacture of microbially-free cosmetics. They issued technical guidelines covering good manufacturing and microbiological practices. With microbiological test methods and good manufacturing practices in place, the industry satisfied one of the FDA's chief concerns.

However, in 1974, instances of blindness occurred from use of mascaras contaminated by the user with *Pseudomonas* spp. The next concern of the FDA was whether a cosmetic product could withstand microbial insults added during consumer use. In the 1980s, the FDA rephrased this concern to ask if preservative challenge tests predicted the risks of in-use contamination. Preservative challenge tests are methods used to determine how well the biocide in a product kills microorganisms. The CTFA Microbiology Committee in conjunction with the FDA and the Association of Official Analytical Chemists arranged for a variety of university and industry collaborations to compare laboratory methods of assessing the preservative efficacy of eye area cosmetics. They found that a variety of laboratory methods for measuring preservative adequacy in eye area cosmetics were satisfactory. Although none of the tests were found to be predictive of consumer contamination, they were shown to be statistically reproducible and reliable.

## B. Future Expectations

Government regulation of cosmetics is increasing. The FDA prefers that cosmetics have premarket clearances, product banning, and mandatory labeling for potential risks. The FDA would like to have inspectional powers. With cosmetics, the FDA has the burden to prove lack of safety rather than the manufacturer having to prove safety to the FDA. In contrast, drug manufacturers have to prove risk–benefit to the FDA. The FDA will likely become far more active in promoting more "drug-like" legislation of cosmetics. This may take the form of drug listing for cosmetics, adverse reaction reports, and establishment of good manufacturing practices (GMPs) for cosmetics.

## II. SANITARY MANUFACTURE

## A. Good Manufacturing Practices

Sanitary manufacture of cosmetics is critical to prevent microbial spoilage and to protect the consumer from potential pathogens. It allows cosmetic plants to voluntarily meet the appropriate sections of current food and drug regulations (21 CFR parts 110, 210, 211). Congress established the requirement for GMPs in 1969 and revised them in 1980.

The GMP rules define the FDA's expectations of manufacturers of food, drugs, and medical devices. The act states that such companies must pack, hold, or prepare such products under conditions where they cannot become contaminated. This requirement typically implies suitable premises, equipment, raw materials, record keeping, sample retention, stability testing, environmental control, and trained personnel who operate using approved procedures. Companies who manufacture their products under conditions whereby they may have become contaminated or where potential contamination was not prevented are subject to fines, recalls, and even seizure. Note that it is only the potential for contamination (or even just the perception of the potential for contamination) that is required for legal action to occur. Proof of contamination, or the presence of microorganisms, is not required—only the perception of unsanitary manufacture. The microbiological deficiencies most cited by the FDA when doing a facility inspection are citations for water contamination, inappropriate or absent testing of final product, and lack of validated methods or validation records.

Even though these regulations are voluntary for cosmetics, most reputable companies follow them, especially those companies that manufacture products that are between cosmetics and drugs (e.g., cosmeceuticals).

## B. Water

Cosmetic plants classify water as "raw" or processed. Raw water comes from either the city or the plant's own well for use in personal hygiene, cooling, toilets, or drinking. Processed water is water for making product. This water is softened, deionized, distilled, or reverse osmosis treated.

A variety of organisms, such as *Escherichia coli* and *Pseudomonas* spp., can contaminate raw water. In storage tanks the numbers of bacteria may rapidly increase to $1 \times 10^6$ colony-forming units per milliliter (CFU/ml). This occurs due to chlorine depletion, particularly during warmer months. Softened and deionized water also contain gram-negative bacteria. In brine-regenerated resins, *Bacillus* and *Staphylococcus* spp. also may grow. These bacteria are in raw water at low levels but multiply rapidly in the ion-exchange resins that serve as fluidized bed bioreactors. Distilled and reverse osmosis water is free of microbes as it leaves the still or membranes. It rapidly becomes contaminated with gram-negatives in storage and distribution. This contamination occurs because of microorganisms that grow back from the various outlets to enter the storage tank and grow throughout the water system.

Biofilms then form on the surfaces of the tanks, pumps, and pipes of the water distribution system. This colonization provides a microbial reservoir that contaminates the water passing through. The shear force of the passing water causes intermittent biofilm sloughing. Nonattached microorganisms also may grow in unused sections of the pipelines called dead-legs. Turbulence of the water passing by carries the organisms into the main water line.

## C. Raw Materials

Most raw materials used in cosmetics are dry powders, natural gels, or surfactants. A few examples of these are talc and quaternized clay, aloe vera, and ammonium lauryl sulfate. These illustrate the key concerns and ways to handle raw materials. In dry powders and natural gels such as aloe vera, the primary contaminant is a spore-forming *Bacillus* or *Clostridium* spp. In surfactants, a wide variety of gram-negative bacteria may grow.

In thickening agents and talc, the spore-formers begin growing during wet portions of their manufacture. Fortunately, most of the spore-forming organisms involved are nonpathogenic *Bacillus* spp. Washing the talc provides an ideal setting for spore-forming bacteria to grow in the moist powder. Drying of the talc preserves the spores. The microbial content will be low if the process time is reduced. One can cool the moist powder to below 25°C or heat it above 45°C until the drying step, but the energy costs to do so are high. One highly effective means of eliminating spores is use of gamma irradiation. Manufacturers refer to irradiated quaternized clays and talc as "cosmetic grade." Although the only issues associated with use of irradiation are for foods, one should be cautious of the regulatory considerations regarding the use of irradiated raw materials in cosmetics.

Aloe vera is also notorious for harboring spore-formers. Manufacturers harvest aloe in dry, dusty areas. Therefore, it has a high bioburden of spore-laden dust. Other organisms that contaminate aloe are *Erwinia* and *Pectobacterium* spp. Manufacturers pasteurize aloe once. This only destroys vegetative cells. Since food manufacturers also use aloe, they use food-grade biocides. These are not sporicidal.

Therefore, it is common to receive aloe with counts as high as $10^5$ or $10^6$ CFU/ml.

The solution is Tyndallization—double or even triple pasteurization. However, slow cooling between each pasteurization provides a warm environment (25–45°C) permitting growth for periods of 4–8 hr. This can actually compound the problem because the spores that survive can germinate and grow, forming even more spores. Germination without growth is desirable. This allows the next pasteurization to work against vegetative cells. Thus, one should flash pasteurize the aloe, cool it rapidly, and repeat within 24 hr to get a microbially free product.

Surfactants are difficult to keep uncontaminated. The exceptions are ammonium xylene sulfonate and sodium lauryl sulfate. These are hostile due to pH extremes and usually require no preservation. The only precautions that must be taken is to keep the domes of the storage tanks free of condensation because this is where microbes grow. When the condensate drips down onto the surfactant, it spreads microbes as a thin film. Use of circulating fans on the tank domes controls this condensation. The fans force air across dust filters and UV lights and then circulate it across the top of the dome.

Other surfactants, such as ammonium lauryl sulfate (ALS), are highly susceptible to microbial attack and require preservation. Some companies use isothiazolinones (Kathon) at 5–10 ppm. Formaldehyde at 100–150 ppm is also effective. This preservative can fail, however, since many organisms easily develop formaldehyde tolerance. If the manufacturing stream is not scrupulously clean, surfactants can become contaminated.

Surfactants support a succession of microbes similar to the ecological succession of microbes in milk. *Pseudomonas* spp. are the primary invaders. They have an inducible formaldehyde dehydrogenase. However, *Enterobacter* or *Klebsiella* spp. can also be primary invaders because of their capsule-producing capacity. These organisms eliminate formaldehyde either by enzymatic means or by non-specific reaction with polysaccharide capsular material. Several organisms succeed *Pseudomonas* or *Enterobacter*. *Serratia* sp. is the first. The surfactant may even turn pink. *Proteus* sp. then follows. It reduces the sulfate portion of ALS to hydrogen sulfide.

Thus, one should know what the primary invader species is to solve these problems. If it is *Pseudomonas* spp., one will have to use a completely different preservative in the surfactant. If it is *Enterobacter*, simple addition of EDTA at 0.05–0.1% will be enough to destroy the capsule. This allows formaldehyde to penetrate the capsule and kill the organism. A simple capsule stain and oxidase test can save countless hours of preservative development.

## D. Personal Hygiene

Topics to discuss when training for hygienic manufacture include personal hygiene, operator-borne contamination, and ways of preventing cross-infection. Personal hygiene includes washing hands, wearing clean clothing, and keeping hair/beards covered. For aseptic manufacturing, the manufacturer may use pre-sterilized single-piece suits, foot coverings, hair and beard covers, face masks, and gloves.

Washing the hands often is the most important and inexpensive way to prevent contamination. Employees should not wear jewelry. They should wash their hands every time they leave and return to the process area. Even a brief 15-s hand-washing period will cause a significant decrease in microbial numbers compared to unwashed hands. However, a thorough scrubbing with warm water (32–43°C) and bactericidal soap for at least 1 min is best.

It is aesthetically displeasing to the consumer to find human hair in a product. To prevent such contamination, hair and beard coverings should be used in all areas of manufacture. Employees should wear disposable hair covers that completely block all hair from exposure. Personnel should put on their hair cover first, then wash their hands. The employee replaces the hair cover each time he or she leaves and returns to the work area.

Clothing must be clean and without adornment. Uniforms are a good means of controlling compliance and actually help promote good attitudes toward sanitation. Light-colored uniforms or lab coats show a need for cleaning much earlier than dark-colored ones. Pockets on the uniforms should have button-down flaps. This prevents materials in them from falling into the product or process machinery.

## E. Sanitary Design of Buildings

Roominess, simplicity, bright lighting, no clutter, and even a fresh clean-smelling environment give a positive perception of cleanliness. This perception creates the correct attitude within the organization to promote compliance with sanitation rules. The FDA regulations written for food and drug plant design are often used by most reputable cosmetic companies as a model since there are no cosmetic GMPs. These regulations require adequate and separate space for equipment and materials storage. They require separate areas for operations that could contaminate the cosmetic. Also required are adequate lighting, ventilation, plumbing, and protection from pests.

The grounds surrounding a well-designed plant should be neat. Keep decorative landscaping features such as ponds, fountains, and sites that provide nesting for birds and rodents at least 30 ft away from the building. A 3-ft perimeter of gravel should surround the building. Trim all trees, shrubs, and lawns to avoid insects that may find harborage in the long grass and unkempt shrubbery. Keep the driveways, docks, refuse sites, and parking lots free of debris. Also, keep these areas drained. Use a perimeter fence around the plant grounds to filter paper and debris.

The building should be a simple, box design with no adornments, ledges, or architectural details to encourage bird nesting. Instead, it should have coved or sloped ledges. The exterior walls and foundations should have no cracks or holes. Avoid porous and cracked walls. Avoid or at least caulk baseboards so there are no spaces that harbor insects. Roofs should have positive slopes of 1 in. per 8 ft and have exterior drainspouts to take water away from the perimeter of the building. Screen all vents on the roof.

Ceilings should have limited overhead pipes. These trap dust and provide pathways for insect movement. Cove, round, or slope overhead beams to ease cleaning. Give inside and outside ledges on windows a 20° slope. The ceilings should be easy to clean, nonporous, and painted with epoxy paint. A plant may use suspended ceilings if inspected regularly. Use load-bearing walls instead of columns on the interior of the building. If using columns, they should be cylindrical or at least sloped at the floor to help cleaning.

Floors should be impervious to water, free of cracks and crevices, and resistant to chemicals. Tiled floors are desirable but expensive. Concrete is satisfactory but must be water sealed. Surround edges of upper mezzanines and wherever pipes pass through the floor with 4-in. curbs or sleeves. This prevents water from passing to the processes below. Keep floors dry. In areas where water is frequently on the floors, use epoxy or urethane coatings on the concrete to prevent water saturation. Provide adequate drainage by using trench drains set in floors sloped at 1/8 to 1/4 in. per foot. When using circular floor drains, place them every 400 ft². However, it is typically difficult to direct water toward these types of drains. Drains and troughs should drain well since moist areas provide ideal harborage of insects. Screen all floor drains to keep rodents from entering via sewers.

Loading docks should be at least 3 ft above grade and entrances into the plant opened only when needed. Screen all windows and doors with 16-mesh screen or keep them closed. Doors should fit well, have automatic closures, and be made of metal. Protect large openings with air curtains. These should sweep air from the top to the bottom of the opening at a rate of 4400 ft³ per minute and at a 25–30° angle. Equip ventilation systems with HEPA (high-efficiency particulate) filters capable of removing 90% of particles that are 1–5 $\mu$m in diameter.

Provide hand-washing facilities in the rest rooms and near entrances to the manufacturing area. Surgical-style washing facilities are showy but superfluous and expensive. Instead, they should be easy to use, easy to find, convenient, and accessible. They should be at least 8 ft away from any process stream to prevent contamination of the product.

## F. Sanitary Design of Equipment

Manufacturers of cosmetics rely on sanitary design of equipment developed by food sanitarians. Their standards for sanitary equipment design apply to cosmetic equipment design. Engineers should design equipment with sanitation in mind.

The material used for pipelines should be smooth to prevent biofilm formation. Stainless steel such as AISl 302 or 316 with sanitary pipe junctions (dairy fittings) should be used. Pipe interiors should be smooth without rough seams. Keep bends smooth and rounded without sharp right angles. The centerline radius of pipe bends should never be less than the outside diameter of the pipe. Slope all pipes 1/8 in. per foot away from tanks to permit proper drainage. Avoid sags or depressions that will trap stagnant fluids. Plastic or polyvinylchloride (PVC) piping is undesirable.

Cosmetic plants should use only diaphragm, plug-cock, or butterfly valves. Each of these has advantages and disadvantages. The key concern is that disassembly is easy to permit cleaning. Washers, O-rings, and diaphragms provide microenvironments particularly susceptible to microbial colonization. Ones made of silicone rather than natural rubber are more resistant to microbial growth.

Use tanks made of stainless steel. Interiors should have no sharp corners to complicate cleaning. Welds should be flush and ground to 120-grit compatible with the surface finish of the rest of the tank. Tank roofs should be domed and their bottoms rounded. Openings into tanks should have protective lips surrounding them. Hatches, covers, and lids should be overlapping to prevent debris from entering into the tank. Protrusions into the tank, such as thermometers, pressure sensors, and spray balls, should form smooth welded junctions. Viewing ports should be flush with the tank interior. Never place a well or depression anywhere in a tank, because these trap stagnant product.

Seal all bearings on stirring devices and keep them oil-free. Drains should be flush with the tank wall and ground smooth. Design inlet pipes to the tank with air gaps to prevent back siphonage. Fit them with flared protective shields directly above the gap to prevent contamination from the environment. Never seal pipes into the top of the tank. They will serve as reflux columns to permit microbial growth in the condensate that drips back into the tank.

Peristaltic and diaphragm pumps are more sanitary than rotary positive displacement or reciprocating pumps. Pumps should be self-draining and free of pockets or crevices that trap product. The most important criterion for pumps is that they are easy to disassemble and clean. Pumps bolted together require tools to take them apart so personnel will clean them less. Clamped pumps are more amenable to cleaning. Product contact parts should be stainless steel and without bearings that directly contact the product stream. Rotors attached to their shafts only by pressure contact are superior to those that use bolts, cotter pins, or hexagonal screws. Pipes entering and leaving pumps should be in smooth curves. Allow plenty of space around the pump to help cleaning and maintenance.

## G. Gaining Employee Commitment

The only way to get employees involved in sanitary manufacture is to get the managers involved. If the employees see the managers wearing hair coverings and washing their hands, then the employees will also obey the rules. People's communal instincts will compel them to cooperate when their superiors set the pace. One achieves cooperation through education, training, and dedication to a sanitary program. Achieving this dedication is sometimes not possible until people experience the negative impacts of ignoring sanitary manufacture. Unfortunately, management views the microbiologist as a roadblock to profitable manufacture. This attitude changes rapidly when consumer complaints, regulatory action, or the expense of scrapping product occurs. Sometimes, this is the only way to gain the attention and cooperation of an uneducated management.

The ideal situation is to have everyone cooperate at the start. This occurs best with an organization scheme in which the microbiologist reports to the quality assurance (QA) manager. The QA manager reports directly to a vice-president. The production manager reports to a manager of manufacturing who also reports to a vice-president. It is unwise to have the production manager and QA manager report to the manufacturing manager. The QA manager is responsible for good quality product; the production manager is responsible for producing it profitably. Short-sighted individuals view these two goals as conflicting. Some cannot see that long-term unsanitary manufacture is typically far more expensive than maintaining a quality product.

The ongoing commitment of managers, and their employees, to proper sanitation is facilitated by an active and knowledgeable QA manager. Typically, the most successful QA functions are those in which the QA manager's reporting relationships are independent of day-to-day manufacturing needs. This allows the QA manager to direct appropriate activities such as employee practices and training and product testing with the primary objective of maintaining product quality.

A corporate microbiologist is also needed to enforce QA and to audit a plant's conformance to GMPs. The corporate microbiologist is responsible for problem-solving support and developing test methods and preservation systems for products. A company concerned with total quality allows the plant microbiologist and the corporate microbiologist to communicate directly with each other. Plant management may think this communication leads to whistle-blowing about sanitation problems. As a result, the microbiologist frequently is accused of "not being a team player." Actually, this is one of the finest accolades for a microbiologist. One knows he or she is doing the job correctly when he or she is not popular.

The corporate microbiologist is also responsible for training and education. This can be through classes with outlines and books, or through clever use of visual aids such as posters and films. Management and employees should attend these training sessions. Training should cover the regulatory requirements for clean manufacture and the illnesses that can result from products contaminated with microorganisms. This training includes personal hygiene, good housekeeping/sanitation, and sanitary equipment design. Training is effective only if the employee is given valid reasons for the hygienic principles taught. This means that he or she will need a basic understanding of microbiology without a scientific, esoteric approach. The rapid nature of microbial growth, their ability to adapt, their small size, and their ubiquity should be taught in easy to understand terms.

## III. SANITIZATION

Several elements of effective cleaning and sanitizing are important in cosmetic microbiology, including the types of cleaning and sanitizing agents used, the kinds of equipment, the type of soil to be removed, when to clean, and how frequently to clean. Typically, cleaning and sanitizing are done at the end of a production run. Other times for cleaning and sanitizing may be after a set number of manufacturing hours or between shift changes.

Base the choice of when to clean and sanitize on facts rather than convenience. Such facts are gained by monitoring the system for microbial contamination during production. The first detection of microbial counts is the maximum length of time to go between sanitizations.

## A. Cleaning

Immediately before washout, one should pump the system free of all product. Sometimes a "pig" (a foam rubber bullet) is air-blown through long lines to remove traces of product. Detergent-based cosmetics, such as shampoos, rarely use cleaning agents. Typically, the system is only washed out with hot water followed by sanitization. Use detergents or caustic materials for cosmetics with an oily nature, emulsions, and powders. These lift and suspend the oily portions by reducing interfacial and surface tension.

Factors that govern choice of cleaning agent are whether it is safe and effective, non-damaging, and compatible with the formulation. Alkaline cleaning agents remove the lipid portions of cosmetics. Other cleaning agents for mineral scale or very fatty materials may be acid or solvent based, respectively. For heavy-duty cleaning, use concentrations as high as 2000 or 3000 ppm. Concentrations of solutions for clean-in-place detergents range from 1000 to 1500 ppm. Chlorinated cleaners enhance cleaning but are not sanitizers. Many companies sell chlorinated sanitizing cleaners. Cleaning agents work well at a pH greater than 9. Chlorine works well at a pH range of 4–7. Mix them together and you have either an ineffective cleaner or an ineffective sanitizer.

The water used for cleaning is as critical as the cleaner used. It should be potable, low in hardness, and hot (70°C) for fatty residues or at least warm (43–54°C) for most other cleaning operations. Control of hardness can be done using softeners or ion-exchange columns. Check and service these routinely so high bacterial counts (>100 CFU/ml) are avoided. Alternatively, one can use detergents with organic chelators or phosphates. Regardless of the cleaning agent used, make routine checks for microbial growth. Quaternary detergents are especially susceptible to pseudomonads, but all detergents can support growth if not frequently changed.

Use physical methods to clean, especially for hard to clean systems. Probably the most effective physical method is scrubbing by hand with a brush and detergent-in-water solution. Use plastic brushes with synthetic fibers–never sponges and rags. Dry using air rather than drying cloths. Unfortunately, this is labor-intensive, costly, and dependent on the attitude of the one doing the scrubbing.

Alternatives to hand scrubbing are use of high-pressure cleaning and clean-in-place methods. High-pressure spray systems can deliver from 500 to 1000 psi. Clean-in-place (CIP) systems are by far the most popular methods. These are line loops connecting the various tanks and equipped with a CIP pump that can deliver 2 or 3 gallons per minute at 400–800 psi. Cleaning agent, sanitizer, or rinse water should be pumped through the system. High flow rates (four or five times the product flow rate) provide shear that will strip biofilms from the inner pipe surfaces. Locate spray balls in the tops of tanks. Ensure that they rotate with the pressure of the solution so the spray reaches all points inside the vessel. The critical points to check are the shear flows and that the cleaning agent and the sanitizer contacts every surface.

## B. Sanitizing

For some cosmetics, a thorough cleaning of the manufacturing equipment will be adequate to provide microbial control. Microorganisms are controlled by physical removal or by removing the nutrients required for growth. Some cosmetics require that the manufacturing equipment is sterile.

The perfect sanitizing agent should be safe for use by the plant personnel and act rapidly under conditions of use. It should not interact with the cosmetic or leave a residue that could interact with it. The agent should be easy to use and be inexpensive. Of the various types of chemical sanitizers, none meet all aspects. The major types of chemical sanitizers available for use in cosmetics are halogens, quaternary ammonium compounds, phenolics, aldehydes, and alcohols.

The most commonly used halogen in the cosmetics industry is chlorine in the form of hypochlorous acid. A variety of chlorine sources exist, including sodium hypochlorite, calcium hypochlorite, chloramines, chlorocyanurates, and gaseous chlorine. Use these at concentrations that will provide from 100 to 200 ppm available chlorine. The pH of the chlorine solution should be at or just slightly below 6.5. A pH below 3.5 may corrode the metal or even give off chlorine gas. One should assay used solutions after a sanitization for free chlorine. Significant decreases to less than 20 ppm indicate that the system was improperly cleaned and contains materials that provide a chlorine demand. In this case, repeat the cleaning and sanitization before production begins.

Cosmetic plants use glutaraldehyde as a disinfectant rather than formaldehyde due to the potential carcinogenicity of formaldehyde vapors. Glutaraldehyde used at 2% and buffered to pH 7.5–8.5 is active against gram-positive and gram-negative bacteria, fungi, viruses, and spores. It acts within 10 min. Formaldehyde used as a preservative is not carcinogenic, but some consumers have a negative perception of its use.

Quaternary ammonium compounds (quats) are cationic surface-active agents that are particularly effective against gram-positive bacteria but ineffective against gram-negatives. In fact, dilute in-use solutions serve as selective media for *Pseudomonas* spp. Plants use quats to sanitize small coupling pieces, associated piping, and exterior surfaces of tanks. Make and use the solutions daily to avoid adaptation problems. One advantage of quats is that they are substantive and therefore provide residual antibacterial activity on treated surfaces. Apply quats at 500–1000 ppm without rinsing. They are most effective at higher temperatures and a pH of 10.

The cosmetics industry uses phenolics only for floor, wall, and ceiling disinfection. The activity of phenolics diminishes markedly in the presence of organic material on surfaces. Therefore, clean the floors with an alkaline detergent and rinse before sanitizing. Phenolics are most effective at acid pH. They are effective against vegetative bacteria and molds.

Use alcohols as surface disinfectants for tank tops and other working surfaces around packing lines.

The most commonly used alcohols are ethanol (70% aqueous) and isopropanol (50% aqueous). Due to volatility, their action is brief and limited to vegetative cells.

Disinfectant suppliers have tried developing combination detergent–sanitizers. Mixtures of quats and nonionic detergents, or solutions of anionic detergents plus chlorine-releasing compounds, are most common. Usually, the combination results in either an ineffective cleaner or an ineffective sanitizer. Rarely are the two completely compatible with each other. The better approach is to apply a cleaning compound to the system followed by a rinse and then the sanitizing agent.

The most effective sanitizing agent is heat. Exposure of the making system to 180°F (82°C) for 15–30 min is effective. The advantage in using heat over chemical sanitizers is that heat penetrates the biofilm where chemical sanitizers do not.

## C. Water System

It is critical to design water systems that permit effective sanitization. Holding tanks and associated piping should be stainless steel. Avoid using pipes made of copper or galvanized piping. Never use PVC or black iron pipe. Water lines entering making tanks should not permit back siphonage of the tank contents into the water system. This is easily done by providing a shielded air gap. Prevent back siphonage in the system when pressure drops in the water line by avoiding cross connections. Construct filters in the water system in parallel. This allows a filter needing service to be isolated from the rest of the system.

Supply water treatment systems with chlorinated city water. This treated water should go directly into the stainless-steel storage tanks and be periodically heated to 180°F. Circulate the heated water through the system and into the storage tank. An alternative to heat sanitation of water is ozonation. Use UV lights at the point of use to remove the ozone and further sanitize the water.

## IV. PRESERVATION

Both clean manufacture and preservation should compliment each other. One should never use preservation to mask unsanitary manufacture. Instead, preservation is primarily a way to protect the consumer during use of the cosmetic product. In addition, preservation is an aid to extend the shelf life of the product.

Cosmetics are such complex products that their preservation is more of a subjective art than an objective science. There is such a complexity of interacting factors in the cosmetic that using ones intuition to select a preservative is often more successful than relying on isolated facts. The formulation factors to consider when choosing a preservative include pH, oil–water partitioning, and interaction with raw ingredients. In addition, preservatives may localize in an emulsion and even react with the container.

Some of the more common and effective preservatives in use today are isothiazolinones (Kathon), hydantoins (Glydant), imidazolidinyl or diazolidinyl urea (Germall), oxazolidines (Nuosept C), formalin, and parabens. One chooses a preservative based on effectiveness as determined in a preservative challenge test. Other considerations should be safety, compatibility with the aesthetics of the product, cost, ease of formulation, and availability. Several choices of preservative systems for a cosmetic should be available in case tolerance to the preservative develops. Some microbiologists like to use combinations of several different preservatives; the logic is to prevent microbial tolerance development to a preservative. This logic is based on an assumption that preservative tolerance develops similarly to antibiotic resistance. This assumption is false since preservatives often act on multiple non-specific targets, as opposed to antibiotics which act on specific molecular targets. This practice is also unnecessary in plants in which sanitation standards are high. It also can create more safety risks and be expensive. If the microbiologist insists on using multiple preservative systems, he or she should at least be sure that the combination acts on different targets. For example, it makes no sense to use two different formaldehyde donors since they both ultimately work in the same way despite having two different chemical formulae.

## V. TEST METHODS

There are two major test methods for the cosmetic microbiologist: the preservative challenge test (PCT) and the microbial content test (MCT). All the other test methods are variations of these two basic tests. In addition, the microbiologist needs to know the basic microbiological techniques that support the conduct of these two tests.

## A. Preservative Challenge Tests

The basic way to conduct a PCT is simple. Inoculate a product and see how long it takes to eliminate or reduce the inoculum to an acceptable level. Variations of the PCT include its adaptation for use in water-miscible and -immiscible products and eye area products. Additional variations are those designed by several groups such as the United States Pharmacopaeia (USP). The Association of Official Analytical Chemists (AOAC) is developing a standardized PCT in collaboration with CTFA and the FDA. As opposed to the USP, which set PCT methods based on collective anecdotal experiences, the work by the AOAC/CTFA/FDA collaborative will base the test on rigorous scientific testing. Unfortunately, the test will still not predict consumer contamination. No test can do this since there are too many variables to predict.

There are many variations to this simple technique. Some of these variations include which organisms to use, the concentration of the organisms, single versus multiple inoculation, and how often or how long to follow the elimination process. Other variations include if the product should be diluted, if the challenge organisms should be a mixed or pure inoculum, and what diluents/plating media are best.

The most used PCT tests are summarized here. For additional information on these tests the reader should see the bibliography. The most used PCT methods are those of the CTFA and the Society of Cosmetic Chemists of Great Britain. For pharmaceuticals, the USP and the British Pharmacopoeia (BP) have developed PCT methods. Other PCT methods include those being developed by the AOAC and a variety of rapid test methods that are simple adaptations of *D*-value methods to cosmetics.

Nearly all the methods include *Pseudomonas aeruginosa, Staphylococcus aureus, Candida albicans,* and *Aspergillus niger*. In addition to these, USP includes *Escherichia coli*. CTFA includes *E. coli, Bacillus sub-*

tilis, *Penicillium luteum,* and spoilage isolates. Only the Society of Cosmetic Chemists of Great Britain (UK test) makes specific inoculum recommendations for each type of cosmetic product.

The levels of inoculum range from $10^5$–$10^6$ CFU/per milliliter or gram and a single challenge for the USP test to $10^6$–$10^7$ CFU/ml with several challenges for the UK test. Interpretations of the tests also vary. The CTFA test makes no formal recommendations but requires that the test continue for at least 28 days. The USP test requires a 3 log reduction of bacteria within 2 weeks. Yeasts and molds should remain at or below the initial count. During the 28-day period, all organisms are to remain at these levels.

The BP test requires that a 3 log reduction of the bacterial load occurs. It requires a 2 log reduction of yeasts and molds within 7–14 days. The BP test expects shampoos to be "self-sterilizing" in 7 days, creams and lotions to "show drastically reduced counts," and eye cosmetics to be "bactericidal to *P. aeruginosa.*"

Criticisms of these tests include improper selection of challenge organism, microbial load of the challenge, number of challenges, and the end-points stipulated. The FDA's chief criticism is that PCT methods do not predict whether consumers can contaminate the product during use. As a result, Brannan in 1987 and Lindstrom in 1986 attempted to develop methods that were predictive of consumer contamination potential. These are the only methods with published data claiming the ability to predict the potential for consumer contamination.

## B. Microbial Content Tests

These tests detect the numbers and sometimes the types of organisms present in the cosmetic. Most tests for microbial content are plate-counting methods. However, one can use other techniques.

Plate-counting methods are also known as aerobic plate counts or total plate counts. For plate-count methods, use an appropriate diluent to neutralize the preservative and any other antimicrobial ingredient in the cosmetic. A variety of neutralization agents are available; however, not all are effective or non-toxic to the organism needing detection. If neutralization via some agent is not possible, then one should use physical dilution or membrane filtration. Similarly, the medium for plating the product is critical for accurate recovery of the microorganisms potentially present in the product.

Use either spread plates or pour plates, and use as low a dilution as possible. For example, a 1 : 10 dilution of the product will yield a better detection limit than a 1 : 100 dilution. Once inoculated into the agar plate, incubate for 1–5 days. Count the viable colonies that form and record the number as colony forming units. There are several sources of error using this method. The biggest error is that no single medium will detect all types of microbes in all types of products.

Other methods for enumerating microbes in cosmetics are the direct microscopic count, the most probable number, radiometric methods, and impedance measurements. In the direct microscopic count, one spreads a known amount of cosmetic on a slide and counts it. The advantage of this technique is that it is fast. It counts both living and dead cells and is only good for heavily contaminated products. Also, the products interfere with seeing the microbes and the technician will be highly susceptible to fatigue.

In the most probable number (MPN) technique, the technician places various dilutions of the product in replicate tubes of nutrient medium. He or she then compares the number of replicates showing growth to a standard MPN table. From this, he or she estimates the number of bacteria in the sample. This method is useful when the organisms do not grow well using standard plating techniques.

Radiometric methods rely on the organisms present in the product to degrade a $^{14}C$-labeled substrate into $^{14}CO_2$. The $^{14}CO_2$ evolved is related to total microbial levels in the product. The radiolabeled substrate used is typically glucose. Use $^{14}C$-glutamate or $^{14}C$-formate instead of $^{14}C$-glucose to detect *Pseudomonas.* The major drawback of this technology is the expense; however, it offers rapid results (6–8 hr) compared to traditional plating methods.

Impedance measurement is a widely used method for detecting microorganisms in cosmetics. It is especially useful for following microbial activity during preservative challenge testing. One can also use impedance methods to approximate microbial numbers in finished product. The method uses the ability of the growing microbial culture to produce changes in impedance of electrical current as it metabolizes the nutrients in the medium. This method will estimate microbial activity within 5 hr. The major drawbacks of this method are the cost and poor detection limits: 10,000 CFU/g of product.

Plate counts will always be the benchmark of quality control in the cosmetic microbiology lab. They are easy to do, inexpensive, and result in numbers of microbes to which most people can easily relate. However, even plate counts do not accurately quantify the numbers of microbes present. First, microbes typically clump together. A colony forming unit is likely not a result of a single microbe but, instead, from one to several thousand microbes.

Reliance on plate count methods should be reevaluated. Regardless of the method used, the key for microbial monitoring is to show relative microbial levels and trends during the process. One should base such monitoring on a system in control. The data should be used to keep the system within total quality limits. Since total quality concepts and just-in-time production require rapid turnaround, the use of rapid methods may one day replace time-consuming plate-counting methods.

## See Also the Following Articles

BIOCIDES • FOODS, QUALITY CONTROL • WASTEWATER TREATMENT

## Bibliography

Block, S. S. (Ed.) (1991). "Disinfection, Sterilization, and Preservation," 4th ed. Williams & Wilkins, Media, PA.

Brannan, D. K. (Ed.) (1997). "Cosmetic Microbiology: A Practical Handbook." CRC Press, Boca Raton, FL.

Hugo, W. B., and Russell, A. D. (1983). "Pharmaceutical Microbiology," 3rd ed. Blackwell, Oxford.

Russell, A. D., Hugo, W. B., and Ayliffe, G. A. J. (1992). "Principles and Practice of Disinfection, Preservation, and Sterilization." Blackwell, Cambridge, MA.

Troller, J. (1983). "Sanitation in Food Processing." Academic Press, Orlando, FL.

# Crystalline Bacterial Cell Surface Layers

## Uwe B. Sleytr and Paul Messner

*Centre for Ultrastructure Research and Ludwig Boltzmann Institute for Molecular Nanotechnology*

## GLOSSARY

**crystalline surface layers**  In prokaryotic organisms, layers composed of protein or glycoprotein subunits.

**glycoproteins**  Proteins occurring as monomolecular arrays on surfaces of archaea and bacteria.

**two-dimensional protein crystals**  Regular arrays of (glyco)proteins present as outermost envelope component in many prokaryotic organisms.

**SURFACE LAYERS (S LAYERS)**  are surface envelope components on prokaryotic cells consisting of two-dimensional crystalline arrays of (glyco)protein subunits. S layers have been observed in species of nearly every taxonomical group of walled bacteria and represent an almost universal feature of archaeal envelopes. As porous crystalline arrays covering the cell surface completely, S layers have the potential to function (i) as protective coats, molecular sieves, and molecule and ion traps; (ii) as structures involved in cell adhesion and surface recognition, and (iii) in archaea, which possess S layers as exclusive wall components, as a framework that determines and maintains cell shape.

## I. INTRODUCTION

The different cell wall structures observed in prokaryotic organism, particularly the outermost envelope layers exposed to the environment, reflect evolutionary adaptations of the organisms to a broad spectrum of selection criteria. Crystalline cell surface layers (S layers) are now recognized as common features of both bacteria and archaea.

Most of the currently known S layers are composed of a single (glyco)protein species endowed with the ability to assemble into two-dimensional arrays on the supporting envelope layer. S layers, as porous crystalline membranes completely covering the cell surface, can apparently provide the microorganisms with a selective advantage by functioning as protective coats, molecular sieves, molecule and ion traps, and as a structure involved in cell adhesion and surface recognition. In those archaea which possess S layers as exclusive envelope components outside the cytoplasmic membrane, the crystalline arrays act as a framework that determines and maintains the cell shape. They may also aid in cell division. In pathogenic organisms S layers have been identified as virulence factors.

S layers, as the most abundant of bacterial cellular proteins, are important model systems for studies of structure, synthesis, assembly, and function of proteinaceous components and evolutionary relationships within the prokaryotic world. S layers also have considerable application potential in biotechnology, biomimetics, biomedicine, and molecular nanotechnology.

## II. LOCATION AND ULTRASTRUCTURE

Although considerable variation exists in the complexity and structure of bacterial cell walls, it is possible to classify cell envelope profiles into the following main groups on the basis of structure, biochemistry, and function (Fig. 1).

1. Cell envelopes formed exclusively of a crystalline S layer composed of (glyco)protein subunits external to the cytoplasmic membrane (most halophilic, thermophilic, acidophilic, and gram-negative archaea; Fig. 1A).

2. Gram-positive cell envelopes of bacteria with a rigid peptidoglycan containing sacculus of variable thickness outside the cytoplasmic membrane and gram-positive cell envelopes of archaea with a rigid sacculus composed of pseudomurein or other polymers (Fig. 1B).

3. Gram-negative envelopes of bacteria with a thin peptidoglycan sacculus and an outer membrane (Fig. 1C).

Although not a universal feature as in archaea, crystalline arrays of (glyco)proteins have been detected as outermost envelope components in organisms of most major phylogenetic branches of gram-positive and gram-negative bacteria.

Currently, the most useful electron microscopical preparation procedure for detecting S layers on intact cells is freeze-etching (Fig. 2). S layers completely cover the cell surface at all stages of cell growth and division in both archaea and bacteria. High-resolution electron microscopical and scanning force microscopical studies revealed that S-layer lattices can have oblique (p1 and p2), square (p4), or hexagonal (p3 and p6) symmetry (Fig. 3) with a center-to-center spacing of the morphological units (composed of one, two, three, four, or six identical monomers) of approximately 5–35 nm. Among archaea, hexagonal lattices were shown to be predominant. S layers are generally 5–25 nm thick and have a smooth outer and a more corrugated inner surface. Since S-layer lattices are monomolecular assemblies of identical subunits they exhibit pores of identical size and morphology (Fig. 3). S layers can display more than one type of pores. From high-resolution electron microscopical and permeability studies, pore sizes in

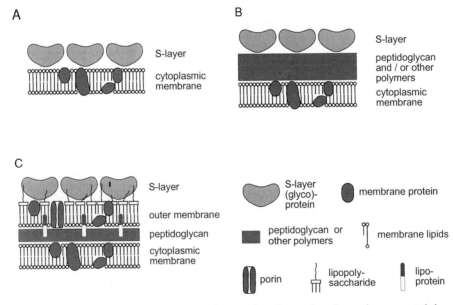

**Fig. 1.** Schematic illustration of major classes of prokaryotic cell envelopes containing crystalline cell S layers. (a) Cell envelope structure of gram-negative archaea with S layers as an exclusive cell wall component. (b) The cell envelope as observed in gram-positive archaea and bacteria. In bacteria the rigid wall component is primarily composed of peptidoglycan. In archaea other wall polymers are found. (c) In gram-negative bacteria the S layer is closely associated with the outer membrane (modified from Sleytr *et al.*, 1996).

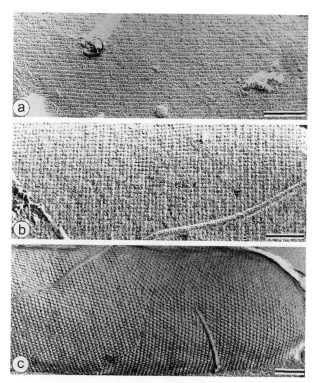

**Fig. 2.** Electron micrographs of freeze-etched preparations of intact bacteria. (a) *Lactobacillus acidophilus* SH1, (b) *Thermoanaerobacterium thermosaccharolyticum* D120-70, and (c) *Thermoanaerobacter thermohydrosulfuricus* L111-69. The oblique (a), square (b), and hexagonal (c) S layer completely covers the cell surface. Scale bars = 100 nm.

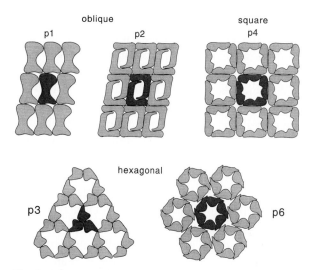

**Fig. 3.** Schematic illustration of the space groups found for S-layer lattices. The unit cells which are the building blocks of the lattice are composed of mono-, di-, tri-, tetra-, or hexamers.

the range of approximately 2–8 nm and a porosity of the protein meshwork between 30 and 70% have been estimated.

Comparitive studies on the distribution and uniformity of S layers have revealed that in some species individual strains can show a remarkable diversity regarding lattice symmetry and lattice dimensions. In some organisms, two or even more superimposed S-layer lattices have been identified.

## III. ISOLATION, CHEMICAL CHARACTERIZATION, AND ASSEMBLY

S layers of different bacteria may vary considerably with respect to their resistance to disruption into their monomeric subunits, and a wide range of meth-

ods have been applied for their isolation and purification. The subunits of most S layers interact with each other and with the supporting envelope layer through noncovalent forces. Additionally, secondary cell wall polymers have been recognized as components which facilitate a weak but specific interaction between the S-layer monomers and the cell shape determining peptidoglycan sacculus. Most commonly, in gram-positive bacteria, a complete disintegration of S layers into monomers can be obtained by treatment of intact cells or cell walls with high concentrations of H-bond-breaking agents (e.g., urea or guanidine hydrochloride). S layers from gram-negative bacteria frequently disrupt application of metal chelating agents (e.g., EDTA and EGTA), cation substitution (e.g., $Na^+$ to replace $Ca^{2+}$), or pH changes (e.g., pH < 4.0). From extraction and disintegration experiments it can be concluded that the bonds holding the S-layer subunits together are stronger than those binding the crystalline array to the supporting envelope layer. There are some indications that S layers of some archaea (e.g., *Thermoproteus* species, and *Methanospirillum hungatei*) are stabilized by covalent bonds between adjacent subunits.

Most S layers are composed of a single, homogeneous protein or glycoprotein species. Sodium dodecyl sulfate polyacrylamide gel electrophoresis (SDS-PAGE) revealed apparent molecular masses for subunits in the range of approximately 40 to 220 kDa.

Comparison of amino acid analyses and genetic studies on S layers from both archaea and bacteria have shown that the crystalline arrays are usually composed of weakly acidic proteins. Typically they contain 40–60% hydrophobic amino acids and possess a low portion, if any, of sulfur-containing amino acids. The isoelectric points p$I$ are in the range of 4–6 but for *Methanothermus fervidus* and for lactobacilli p$I$ values in the range of 8–10 have been determined.

A few post-translational modifications are known to occur in S-layer proteins, including protein phosphorylation and protein glycosylation. In an S-layer (termed A layer) mutant of *Aeromonas hydrophila* the presence of phosphotyrosine residues has been detected by a comparison of the molecular masses obtained from SDS-PAGE and the DNA sequence. A more frequently observed modification of S-layer proteins from archaea as well as bacteria is their glycosylation. Whereas amongst archaea most S layers appear to be glycosylated, evidence for S-layer glycoproteins in bacteria is limited to members of the Bacillaceae. The glycan chains and linkages of these bacterial and archaeal glycoproteins are significantly different from those of eukaryotes. Most archaeal S-layer glycoprotein glycans consist of only short heterosaccharides, usually not built of re-peating units. The predominant linkage types are N-glycosidic bonds such as glucose → asparagine and N-acetylgalactosamine → asparagine. The opposite situation can be found with bacterial S-layer glyco-proteins. Most of the glycans are assembled of identical repeating units with up to 150 monosaccharide residues. The sugar chains are attached mainly by O-glycosidic linkages. Among these, novel linkage types such as β-glucose → tyrosine and β-galactose → tyrosine have been observed (Fig. 4). Structurewise, they are comparable to lipopolysaccharide O-antigens of gram-negative bacteria.

Isolated S-layer subunits of gram-positive and gram-negative bacteria have also shown the ability to recrystallize on the cell envelope fragments from which they had been removed, on those of other organisms, or on untextured charged or uncharged inanimate surfaces.

To date, the most detailed self-assembly and reattachment experiments have been performed with S layers from Bacillaceae. S layers of these organisms reveal a high anisotropic charge distribution. The inner surface is negatively charged, whereas the outer face is charge-neutral, approximately pH 7. This characteristic of the S-layer subunits appears to be essential for the proper orientation during local insertion in the course of lattice growth.

Detailed studies have been performed to elucidate the dynamic process of assembly of S layers during

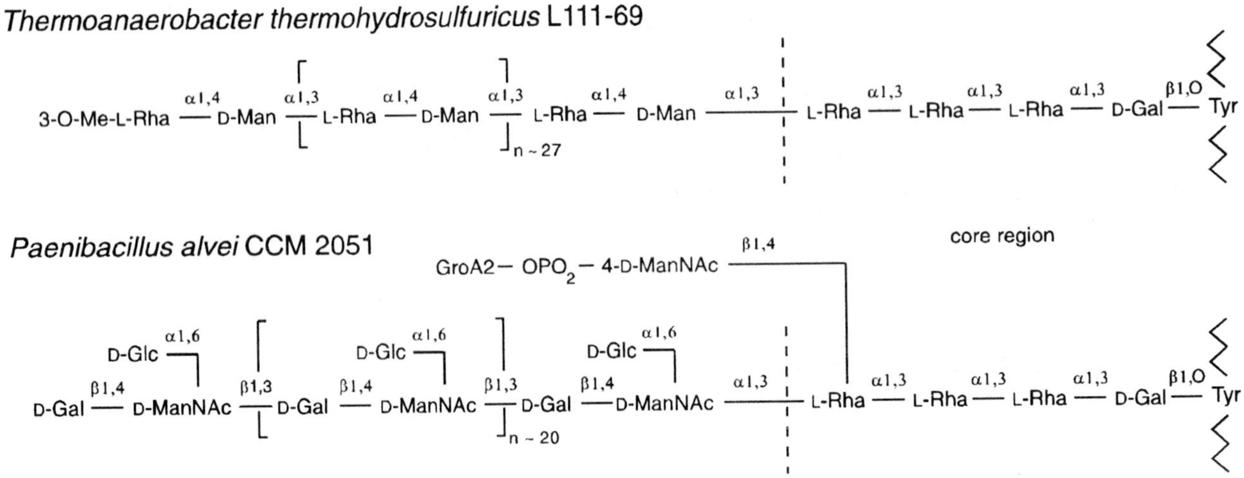

**Fig. 4.** Complete glycan structure of S-layer glycoproteins showing the linkage region to the S-layer polypeptide, the core region, and the O-antigen-like S-layer glycan (modified from Messner *et al.*, 1995).

cell growth. Freeze-etching preparations of rod-shaped cells generally reveal a characteristic orientation of the lattice with respect to the longitudinal axis of the cylindrical part of the cell (Fig. 2). For maintenance of such a good long-range order during cell growth, S-layer protomers must have the ability to recrystallize on the supporting envelope layer. Labeling experiments with fluorescent antibodies and colloidal gold/antibody marker methods indicated that different patterns of S-layer growth exist for gram-positive and gram-negative bacteria. In gram-positives, growth of the S-layer lattice primarily occurs on the cylindrical part of the cell by insertion at multiple bands or helically arranged bands; in gram-negatives, incorporation of new subunits occurs at random. In both types of organisms entirely new S-layer material also appears at regions of incipient cell division and the newly formed cell poles.

## IV. GENETICS AND BIOSYNTHESIS

An intact, "closed" S layer on an average-sized, rod-shaped cell consists of approximately $5 \times 10^5$ monomers. Thus, at a generation time of approximately 20 min, at least 500 copies of a single polypeptide species with a $M_r$ of approximately 100,000 have to be synthesized, translocated to the cell surface, and incorporated into the S-layer lattice per second.

During the past decade a substantial amount of information on the biosynthesis and the genetics of S layers has accumulated. Insight into the molecular organization of S-layer biosynthesis was obtained from cloning experiments and sequencing studies. Sequence comparison of S-layer genes from different archaea and bacteria have revealed that homologies between nonrelated organisms are low, although their amino acid compositions show no significant differences. High homology scores are usually explained by evolutionary relationships but other factors, such as growth conditions and environmental stress, may also be determinative for structural homologies of S-layer genes.

Since S layers are the predominant proteins of the bacterial cell their promoters must be very strong and efficient. For example, the promoter of the S-layer gene from *Lactobacillus acidophilus* is twice as effective as that of the gene encoding lactate dehydrogenase, which is considered to be one of the strongest promoters in many bacteria.

Important for the understanding of S-layer gene regulation was the observation that single bacterial strains can express different genes. Currently, the best investigated organism is *Campylobacter fetus* which interferes with reproductive function in ungulates. In this system all studies have demonstrated that only a single promoter exists and that antigenic variation is due to recombination events. *Campylobacter fetus* rearranges a single promoter strictly by a single DNA inversion event and at frequencies independent of the size of the DNA fragment. This allows expression of different S-layer gene cassettes. The variation enables the organism to circumvent the host's immune response.

Environmental factors can also induce changes in S-layer synthesis. This phenomenon has been studied in detail in *Bacillus stearothermophilus* strains. When the wild-type strain was grown in continuous culture under oxygen limitation the corresponding S-layer gene was stably expressed. After relieving oxygen limitation, expression of a second S-layer gene was induced, resulting in an S-layer protein with decreased molecular mass of the monomeric unit. Both genes showed only low homology (<50%) and they possess quite different N termini. These regions recognize different secondary cell wall polymers of the bacterium as binding sites for S layers and indicate a highly coordinated change of cell envelope components due to different physiological conditions.

Concomitant with the genetic studies, knowledge was gathered about the secretion of S-layer proteins. General protein secretion pathways are known in many bacteria. With the exception of the S layers from *Campylobacter* and *Caulobacter* strains, all others are produced with a signal peptide, suggesting the classical route of secretion. For the S layers of *Aeromonas salmonicida* and *Caulobacter crescentus*, specific secretion pathways, such as an ABC transporter system, have been described.

The remarkable diversity in glycan structures raised interesting questions about the biosynthesis of prokaryotic glycoproteins. Recently, a model was proposed for how the different N-linked glycans are synthesized in *Halobacterium halobium*. It includes transfer of dolichol-linked saccharides to consensus sequences for N-glycosylation on the S-layer polypeptide. Lipid-activated oligosaccharides with short-chain ($C_{55}$–$C_{60}$) dolichol species rather than undecaprenol for S-layer glycosylation were observed not only in *H. halobium* but also in *Haloferax volcanii* and *M. fervidus*. In comparison to archaeal S-layer glycoproteins, less detailed information is available regarding the biosynthesis of glycosylated S layers of bacteria. In *Paenibacillus* (formerly *Bacillus*) *alvei,* dolichol ($C_{55}$) carrier lipids are involved in glycan biosynthesis, whereas for *Thermoanaerobacterium* (formerly *Clostridium*) *thermosaccharolyticum* only nucleotide-activated sugars have been characterized. Of particular interest is the observation that in all investigated prokaryotic systems, in addition to nucleotide-activated monosaccharides, nucleotide-activated oligosaccharides also play an important role in S-layer glycan synthesis.

## V. FUNCTIONAL ASPECTS AND APPLICATION POTENTIAL

Since prokaryotic organisms possessing S layers are ubiquitous in the biosphere, it can be expected that the porous network of monomolecularly arranged (glyco)proteins has evolved as the result of quite diverse interactions of the bacteria with specific environmental and ecological conditions.

Although relatively few data are available on specific functions of S layers, there is strong evidence that the crystalline arrays have the potential to function as (i) a cell shape-determining framework; (ii) protective coats, molecular sieves, and molecule or ion traps; and (iii) promoters of cell adhesion and surface recognition (Table I).

### A. Cell Shape Determination

Because of their structural simplicity and from a morphogenetic point of view, it was suggested that S layers, like lipid membranes, could have fulfilled barrier and supporting functions as required for self-reproducing systems (progenotes) during the early period of biological evolution.

Analysis of the distribution of lattice faults of hex-

**TABLE I**
**Functions of S Layers**

- Determination of cell shape and cell division (in archaea that possess S layers as the exclusive wall component)
- Protective coats
    Prevents predation by *Bdellovibrio bacteriovorus* (in gram-negative bacteria)
    Phage resistance by S-layer variation
    Prevention or promotion of phagocytosis
- Adhesion site for exoenzymes
- Surface recognition and cell adhesion to substrates
    S layers function as physicochemical and morphological well-defined matrices
    Masking the net negative charge of the peptidoglycan-containing layer in Bacillaceae
- Isoporous molecular sieves
    Molecular sieves in the ultrafiltration range
    Delineating in gram-positive bacteria a compartment (periplasm)
    Preventing nonspecific adsorption of macromolecules
- Virulence factor in pathogenic organisms
    Important role in invasion and survival within the host
    Specific binding of host molecules
    Protective coat against complement killing
    Ability to associate with macrophages and to resist the effect of proteases
    Production of S layers which do not immunologically cross-react (S-layer variation)
- Fine grain mineralization

agonal S layers of archaea which possess an S layer as their sole cell wall constituent (Fig. 1a) provided strong evidence that complementary pairs of pentagons and heptagons play an important role in the site for the incorporation of new subunits, in the formation and maintenance of the lobed cell structures, and in the cell fission process. The latter appears to be determined by the ratio between the increase in protoplast volume and the increase in actual S-layer surface area during cell growth.

### B. S Layers Related to Pathogenicity

Particular attention has been paid to S layers present on pathogenic organisms. Crystalline arrays present on members of the genera *Aeromonas* and *Campy-*

*lobacter* comprise one of the best studied S-layer systems. In *Aeromonas salmonicida,* which causes furunculosis in salmons, generally an S layer is required for virulence. The S layer physically protects the infecting cells against proteolysis and complement and is essential for macrophage infiltration and resistance. In *Campylobacter fetus* subspecies *fetus,* the agent that causes abortion in sheep and cattle and various systemic infections or acute diarrheal illness in humans, S layers appear to make the cells resistant to phagocytosis and bactericidal activity of serum.

Crystalline surface layers identified on other pathogens of humans and animals, including species of *Bacteroides, Brucella, Chlamydia, Cardiobacterium, Rickettsia, Wolinella, Treponema, Clostridium,* and *Bacillus,* may be of similar functional relevance as virulence factors.

### C. S Layers as Molecular Sieves and Promoters for Cell Adhesion and Surface Recognition

Data obtained by high-resolution electron microscopy indicate that S layers are highly porous structures with pores of defined size and morphology (Fig. 3). Permeability studies on S layers of mesophilic and thermophilic Bacillaceae provided information on their molecular sieving properties. For example, S layers of *B. stearothermophilus* revealed sharp exclusion limits for molecules larger than 30–40 kDa, indicating a limiting pore diameter in the crystalline protein meshwork of approximately 4.0 nm. With some mesophilic Bacillaceae, pore sizes as small as approximately 2.5 nm have been determined. These permeability studies also showed that the pores in the S-layer membranes have a low tendency for fouling, a feature regarded as essential for an unhindered exchange of nutrients and metabolites up to a defined molecular size.

S layers acting as molecular sieves have the potential to function not just as barriers preventing molecules from entering the cell (e.g., lytic enzymes, complements, antibodies, and biocides). They can also generate a functional equivalent to the periplasmic space of gram-negative bacterial envelopes in preventing the release of molecules (e.g., enzymes and toxins) from the cell. On the other hand, S layers of

Bacillaceae were found to function as adhesion site for cell-associated exoenzymes.

Cells of *Aquaspirillum serpens* and other gram-negative species were shown to be resistant to predation by *Bdellovibrio bacteriovorus* when they were covered by an S layer. However, S layers of different organisms (e.g., Bacillaceae) were demonstrated to act as specific sites for phage adsorption. Analysis of phage-resistant mutants of *Bacillus sphaericus* showed that although the crystalline arrays were present on all mutants, the molecular weight of the S-layer subunits had changed.

With regard to cell adhesion and cell recognition properties of S layers, an important aspect is the frequently observed anisotropic distribution of charged groups on both faces of the (glyco)protein lattice. Most Bacillaceae possessing S layers reveal a charge-neutral outer surface, which physically masks the net negatively charged peptidoglycan sacculus. In comparison with S-layer-deficient strains, S-layer-carrying Bacillaceae have also shown a greater ability to adsorb to positively charged or hydrophobic surfaces.

### D. Application Potential

Based on the data obtained in fundamental studies on S layers, a considerable potential in biotechnological and nonbiological applications is evident. Applications for S layers have been found in the production of isoporous ultrafiltration membranes, as supports for a defined covalent attachment of functional molecules (e.g., enzymes, antibodies, antigens, protein A, biotin, and avidin) as required for affinity and enzyme membranes, in the development of biosensors, or in solid-phase immunoassays. S-layer membranes have also been used as support for Langmuir lipid films or liposomes, mimicking the molecular architecture of gram-negative archaea (Fig. 1A). S-layer fragments or self-assembly products are well suited for a geometrically well-defined covalent attachment of haptens and immunogenic or immunostimulating substances. These haptenated S-layer structures act as strong immunopotentiators. Finally, cloning and characterization of genes encoding S-layer proteins, opened new areas of applied S-layer research. Incorporation of functional domains without hindering self-assembly of S-layer subunits into regular arrays will lead to new types of recombinant vaccines, affinity matrices, diagnostics, and biocompatible surfaces. Recently it was demonstrated that S layers can be employed in nanostructure technologies and as a matrix for controlled biomineralization.

## See Also the Following Articles

ABC TRANSPORT • CELL WALLS, BACTERIAL • PROTEIN SECRETION

## Bibliography

Beveridge, T. J. (1994). Bacterial S-layers. *Curr. Opin. Struct. Biol.* **4**, 204–212.

Beveridge, T. J., and Graham, L. L. (1991). Surface layers of bacteria. *Microbiol. Rev.* **55**, 684–705.

Boot, H. J., and Pouwels, P. H. (1996). Expression, secretion and antigenic variation of bacterial S-layer proteins. *Mol. Microbiol.* **21**, 1117–1123.

Dworkin, J., and Blaser, M. J. (1997). Molecular mechanisms of *Canpylobacter* fetus surface layer protein expression. *Mol. Microbiol.*, **26**, 433–440.

König, H., and Messner, P. (Eds.) (1997). International Workshop on Structure, Biochemistry, Molecular Biology, and Applications of Microbial S-Layers [Special issue]. *FEMS Microbiol. Rev.* **20**, 1–178.

Messner, P. (1997). Bacterial glycoproteins. *Glycoconjugate J.* **14**, 3–11.

Messner, P., and Schäffer, C. (2000). Surface layer (S-layer) glycoproteins of Bacteria and Archaea. *In* "Glycomicrobiology" (R. J. Doyle, Ed.). Kluwer Academic/Plenum Publishers, New York, in press.

Messner, P., Christian, R., Neuninger, C., and Schulz, G. (1995). Similarity of "core" structures in two different glycans of tyrosine-linked eubacterial S-layer glycoproteins. *J. Bacteriol.* **177**, 2188–2193.

Pum, D., and Sleytr, U. B. (1999). The application of bacterial S-layers in molecular nanotechnology, *TIBTECH* **17**, 8–12.

Sidhu, M. S., and Olsen, I. (1997). S-layers of *Bacillus* species. *Microbiology* **143**, 1039–1052.

Sleytr, U. B. (1997). I. Basic and applied S-layer research: an overview. *FEMS Microbiol. Rev.* **20**, 5–12.

Sleytr, U. B., and Beveridge, T. J. (1999). Bacterial S-layers. *Trends Microbiol.* **7**, 253–260.

Sleytr, U. B., and Sára, M. (1997). Bacterial and archaeal S-layer proteins: Structure–function relationships and their biotechnological applications. *TIBTECH* **15**, 20–26.

Sleytr, U. B., Messner, P., Pum, D., and Sára M. (1993). Crystalline bacterial cell surface layers. *Mol. Microbiol.* **10**, 911–916.

Sleytr, U. B., Messner, P., Pum, D., and Sára, M. (Eds.) (1996). "Crystalline Bacterial Cell Surface Layer Proteins." Landes/Academic Press, Austin, TX.

Sleytr, U. B., Messner, P., Pum, D., and Sára, M. (1999). Crystalline bacterial cell surface layers (S-layers): from supramolecular cell structure to biomimetics and nanotechnology. *Angew. Chem. Int. Ed.* **38**, 1034–1054.

Sleytr, U. B., Sára, M., and Pum, D. (2000). Crystalline bacterial cell surface layers (S-layers): a versatile self-assembly system. *In* "Supramolecular Polymerization" (A. Ciferri, Ed.). Marcel Dekker, New York, in press.

Sumper, M., and Wieland, F. T. (1995). Bacterial glycoproteins. *In* "Glycoproteins" (J. Montreuil, J. F. G. Vliegenthart, and H. Schachter, Eds.), pp. 455–473. Elsevier, Amsterdam.

# Cyanobacteria

## Ferran Garcia-Pichel

*Arizona State University*

I. Biodiversity: Taxonomy and Phylogeny
II. Cytology and Morphogenesis
III. Physiology and Metabolism
IV. Molecular Genetics
V. Ecology and Adaptations
VI. Fossil Record and Evolutionary History
VII. Commercial Use and Applications

## GLOSSARY

**benthos** Collection of organisms living on or within the sediments of water bodies.

**oxygenic photosynthesis** Type of metabolism based on the coordinated action of two photosystems by means of which radiant energy is converted to chemical energy in the form of ATP, and reduction equivalents are obtained in the form of NADPH from the (photo)oxidation of water to free molecular oxygen.

**phycobilisomes** Macromolecular aggregates serving as antenna systems for the capture of light in photosynthesis, typical of cyanobacteria. They are composed of multimers of different phycobiliproteins and of linker polypeptides. Phycobiliproteins are polypeptides containing covalently bound open tetrapyrrols chromophores: the phycobilins.

**plankton** Collection of organisms living suspended in open waters. According to their function, oxygenic phototrophic organisms in the plankton are termed phytoplankton. By an unorthodox convention, planktonic organisms smaller than 2 $\mu$m in size are called picoplankton.

**sheath** Structurally well-defined, usually laminated, extracellular polysaccharide investment. The term is usually, but not exclusively, applied to those of filamentous cyanobacteria.

**trichome** Row of vegetative cells in filamentous cyanobacteria, excluding the extracellular polysaccharide structures (sheaths). The term is complemented by "filament," which includes both the trichome and the sheaths.

**CYANOBACTERIA (= OXYPHOTOBACTERIA)** constitute a phylogenetically coherent group of evolutionarily ancient, morphologically diverse, and ecologically important phototrophic bacteria. The cyanobacteria are defined by the ability to carry out oxygenic photosynthesis (water-oxidizing, oxygen-evolving, plant-like photosynthesis). They all synthesize chlorophyll a as photosynthetic pigment, and most types synthesize phycobiliproteins as light-harvesting pigments. All cyanobacteria are able to grow using $CO_2$ as the sole source of carbon, which they fix using primarily the reductive pentose phosphate pathway. Their chemoorganotrophic potential is restricted to the mobilization of reserve polymers (mainly starch) during dark periods, although some strains are known to grow chemoorganotrophically in the dark at the expense of external sugars. Cyanobacteria have left fossil remains as old as 2000–3500 million years, and they are thought to be ultimately responsible for the oxygenation of the earth's atmosphere. Today, cyanobacteria make a significant contribution to the global primary production of the oceans and become locally dominant primary producers in many extreme environments, such as hot and cold deserts, hot springs, and hypersaline environments. Blooms of cyanobacteria are important features for the ecology of many eutrophic fresh and brackish bodies of water. The aerobic nitrogen-fixing capacity of some cyanobacteria makes them important players in the biogeochemical nitrogen cycle of tropical oceans and economically important in some agricultural practices. Because of their sometimes large size, their type of metabolism, and their ecological role, the cyanobacteria were long considered algae; even today it is not uncommon to refer to them as blue-green algae, especially in ecological studies.

Cyanobacteria have been labelled "the largest and most diverse group of prokaryotes." Indeed, the diversity of cyanobacteria in terms of morphology, ecology, and physiological adaptations is large. However, at the same time, their central metabolism is remarkably conserved throughout all known forms. With the possible exception of their capacity for facultative anoxygenic photosynthesis, cyanobacteria in nature are all oxygenic photoautotrophs. It can be said with little hesitation that, after the evolutionary advent of oxygenic photosynthesis, the evolutionary history of cyanobacteria has been one geared towards optimizing and extending this metabolic capacity to an increasingly large number of habitats. Also, according to the extent of their present-day ecological distribution, they have been quite successful at it. This article provides an overview of the characteristics of their central metabolism and a necessarily limited impression of their diversity. However, generalizations might, in the face of such diversity, easily become either superfluous or, worse, misleading. Whenever generalizations are made, the reader is reminded to bear this in mind. Whenever generalizations are not made, I have tried to provide an impression of the range of adaptations by selecting some that can be explained on the basis of experimental studies. However, many questions regarding the biology of cyanobacteria remain unsolved.

## I. BIODIVERSITY: TAXONOMY AND PHYLOGENY

### A. Taxonomy

For the newcomer, the taxonomy of cyanobacteria can easily become a nightmare; for the initiated, it is a persistent headache. Due to their ecological role, which in many cases is indistinguishable from that of eukaryotic microalgae, the cyanobacteria had been studied originally by botanists. The epithets blue-green algae, Cyanophyceae, Cyanophyta, Myxophyceae, and Schizophyceae all apply to the cyanobacteria. Their original taxonomy was built, according to botanical tradition, using overwhelmingly morphological criteria based on observations from materials collected in nature. Actually, two parallel botanical

taxonomic treatments exist. The "Geitlerian" system, recognizing approximately 1300 species grouped in 145 genera and three orders, has been the most widely accepted. The Drouet system represents an attempt to arbitrarily simplify the previous one: It recognized only 62 species in 24 genera. Although this system was never judged appropriate by most taxonomists, it was welcome by many biochemists and physiologists because of its ease of use. Many names of typical laboratory strains such as *Anacystis nidulans*—perhaps the *Escherichia coli* of cyanobacteria—stems from Drouet's system. From the 1970s onwards, the prokaryotic nature of cyanobacteria began to be fully recognized and a taxonomic system based on the International Code of Nomenclature of Bacteria was initiated. This system relies on the study of cultured axenic strains, and it draws heavily on morphological and cytological information but integrates some genetic and physiological traits as well. The maximal taxonomic resolution so far achieved in this system is at the generic level. The current state of the bacteriological taxonomic treatment of the cyanobacteria is described in the last edition of the *Bergey's Manual of Determinative Bacteriology*. Agreement exists on both camps that eventually the systems should converge, but to date parallel systems coexist with their own advantages and shortcomings. One is left with the choice of either using a system that allows identification of species but is largely unreliable or using a more reliable system in which species are yet to be defined. The diagnostic key to the subsections of the cyanobacteria, as given in the *Bergey's Manual,* is reproduced in Table I. Genera recognized within each subsection can be found in Fig. 1, in which they have been gathered according to some simple, mostly visual keys. This unavoidably abridged overview is not intended as a substitute for more thorough generic descriptions. In this article, for the sake of consistency, taxa not recognized in *Bergey's Manual* will appear in quotation marks, without intended detriment to their validity.

In addition, *Bergey's Manual* recognizes a separate group of organisms with equal rank to the cyanobacteria—the Prochlorophytes (with two genera: *Prochloron* and *Prochlorothrix*). The recently recognized genus *Prochlorococcus* could be included here. They

**TABLE I**
**Diagnostic Key to the Subsections of the Cyanobacteria According to the**
***Bergey's Manual of Determinative Bacteriology***

| Subsection | Definitory criteria |
|---|---|
| **Subsection I** (order Chroococcales) | Unicellular and nonfilamentous; cells occur singly or in aggregates; cell division by binary fission in one to three planes, symmetric or assymetric, or by budding |
| **Subsection II** (order Pleurocapsales) | Unicellular and nonfilamentous; cells occur singly or in aggregates; reproduction by multiple fission without growth yielding beaocytes (cells smaller than the parent cell) or by binary and multiple fission |
| **Subsection III** (order Oscillatoriales) | Filamentous; binary fission in one plane yielding uniseriate trichomes without true branching; no heterocysts or akinetics formed |
| **Subsection IV** (order Nostocales) | Filamentous; division occurring only in one plane to yield uniseriate trichomes without true branching; heterocysts formed when combined nitrogen is low |
| **Subsection V** (order Stigonematales) | Filamentous; division periodically or commonly in more than one plane yielding multiseriate trichomes, truly branched trichomes, or both |

were differentiated from cyanobacteria on the basis of pigment composition: lack of phycobiliproteins and the presence of chlorophyll *b*. Some of these original distinctions are questionable, and molecular phylogeny has shown that the separation of "prochlorophytes" from cyanobacteria is very arbitrary. The inclusion of "prochlorophytes" within the cyanobacteria proper (as defined previously) is a matter of time, and they consequently are not treated separately here.

## B. Phylogeny

The most widely accepted reconstructions of cyanobacterial phylogeny are those based on comparisons of the 16S ribosomal RNA gene sequences, although sequence comparisons of other genes and proteins have also been used. The number of sequences publicly available has increased considerably in the past few year, and continues to increase. Currently, several characteristics of cyanobacterial evolution can be inferred, and some taxonomic controversies have been settled: however, several apparent paradoxes have been unveiled. Extreme caution should be exercised in the interpretation of phylogenetic trees of cyanobacteria because the nomenclatural chaos has already pervaded the molecular databases. In Fig. 2, a phylogenetic tree for the cyanobacterial radiation is presented. According to this analysis, the cyanobacteria are a diverse phylum of organisms within the

Bacterial radiation, well separated from their closest relatives. The trees support clearly the endosymbiotic theory for the origin of plant chloroplasts because they place plastids (from all eukaryotic algae and higher plants investigated) in a very diverse but monophyletic deep-branching cluster. Members of the "prochlorophytes" are not closely related to each other and do not seem to constitute the origins of plastids, as had been proposed on the basis of pigment analogies. However, the gross structure in the evolutionary history of extant cyanobacteria cannot be resolved; most of the cyanobacterial diversity probed seems to be due to an explosive radiation taking place early during their evolution. In any event, according to phylogenetic reconstructions, it seems clear that the current taxonomic treatment of the cyanobacteria diverges considerably from a natural system that reflects their evolutionary relationships. For example, the orders Chroococcales and Oscillatoriales, and perhaps also the Pleurocapsales, do not find support in the trees. The heterocystous cyanobaceria (orders Nostocales and Stigonematales) form a monophyletic group with relatively low sequence divergence. Several other statistically well-supported groups of strains can be distinguished that may or may not correspond to currently defined taxa. The botanical genus "*Microcystis*" (see Section V.B) of unicellular colonial freshwater plankton species is very well supported by phylogenetic reconstruction, as is the genus *Trichodesmium* (see Section V.A)

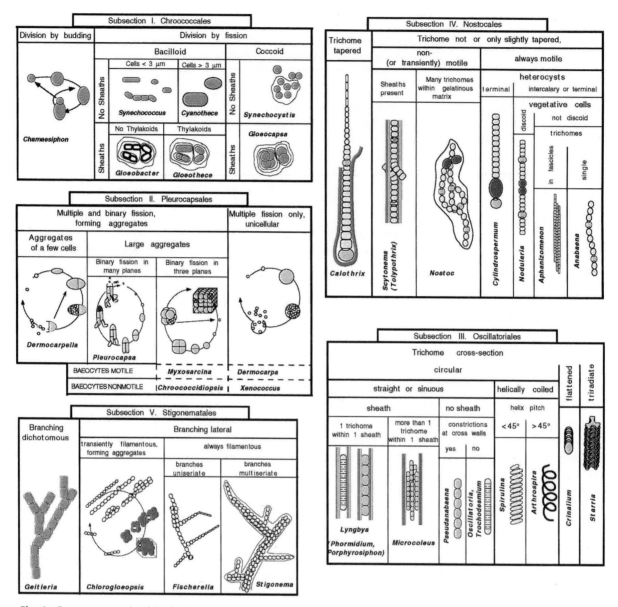

**Fig. 1.** Genera recognized in the *Bergey's Manual of Determinative Bacteriology* within each of the five subsections of the cyanobacteria. Genera have been arranged according to the most important (abridged) definitory criteria, and drawings are provided depicting their abstracted morphological appearance and/or their life cycles.

of filamentous, non-heterocystous nitrogen-fixing species typical from oligotrophic tropic marine plankton. A grouping not corresponding to any official genus, the Halothece cluster, is composed of unicellular strains that are extremely tolerant to high salt and stem from hypersaline environments. A second grouping, bringing together very small unicellular open-ocean cyanobacteria (picoplankton: see

Section V.A), includes members of the genera *Synechococcus* and *Prochlorococcus*. The picture that seems to emerge from these studies is that ecology and physiology are extremely important parameters to understanding the phylogenetic relationships of cyanobacteria and to achieving an evolutionarily coherent taxonomic system. Reaching this goal will necessitate continued efforts in the future.

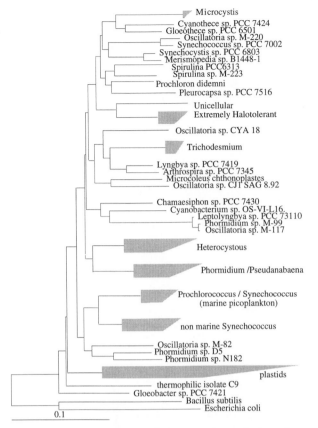

**Fig. 2.** Phylogenetic tree of the cyanobacteria based on (complete) 16S ribosomal RNA sequences. Scale at the bottom represents genetic distance. Vertical distances bear no meaning. Clusters of (more than two) sequences that were well supported statistically have been collapsed into polygonal boxes of fixed width. The distance contained within each cluster is represented by the difference in horizontal length of opposing sides.

## II. CYTOLOGY AND MORPHOGENESIS

### A. Cytology and Ultrastructure

Cyanobacterial cells range in size (width) between 0.5 $\mu$m (e.g., *Prochlorococcus*) and 50–100 $\mu$m or more (e.g., "*Chroococcus*" and some *Oscillatoria*); the modal size of described species is significantly larger than that of most other Bacteria and Archaea (approximately 4 $\mu$m). In unicellular and colonial cyanobacteria, cells may be spherical, bacilloid, or fusiform, and some strains present considerable pleiomorphism. Cells of filamentous cyanobacteria may range from discoid to barrel shaped, and the tri-

chomes often attain lengths on the order of millimeters. The filamentous genus *Starria* has triradiate cells. Several types of cells may be present in morphologically complex cyanobacteria. The cells of most cyanobacteria are surrounded by a more or less defined exopolysaccharide investment. In some species this may form a distinct, structured capsule or sheath, and the steric constrictions to cell growth imposed by the presence of mechanically strong capsules or sheaths may even dictate cellular shape (Fig. 3j). Several ultrastructural features are typical for cyanobacteria (Fig. 4). The cell envelope is of a gram-negative type but may attain a considerable thickness in the peptidoglycan layer (from several to 200 nm). Pores of different sizes, orderly arranged or not, perforate the cyanobacterial cell wall. Pore pits may allow close contact of the cytoplasmatic membrane with the lipopolysaccharide outer membrane. The photosynthetic machinery of cyanobacteria resides on intracellular membranes (thylakoids). Each thylakoid consists of a double unit membrane enclosing an intrathylakoidal space. Thylakoids may be arranged parallel to the cell membrane, radially, or in small disorderly stacks, depending on species. They may be single or stacked, usually depending on illumination conditions. The phycobilisomes, used by most cyanobacteria as light-harvesting structures, can be distinguished in electron microscopic preparations as rows of particles ca. 50 nm in diameter on the cytoplasmatic side of the thylakoids. These are obviously absent from chlorophyll *b*-containing, phycobiliprotein-lacking species ("Prochlorophytes"). A central electron-clear region in the cell, the nucleoplasm or centroplasm, hosts the cellular DNA. This nucleoplasm may be considerably extended in large-celled species. Several intracellular non-membrane-bound granules can be distinguished on transmission electron microscope preparations or even under the light microscope which typically correspond to polymeric reserve materials, such as glycogen (polyglucose, usually present in the intrathylakoidal space), poly-phosphate, poly-$\beta$-hydroxyalkanoates, and lipid droplets found in the cytoplasm proper, which are also common in other bacteria. Cyanophycin [multi-L-arginyl-poly (L-aspartic acid)] is a cytoplasmatic, exclusively cyanobacterial nitrogen reserve polymer. Carboxysomes (or polyhedral bodies) are com-

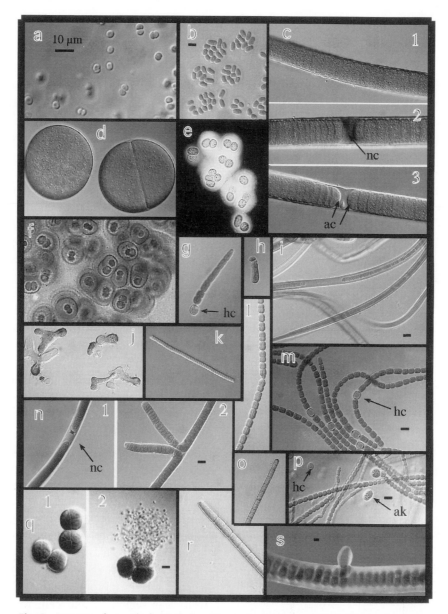

**Fig. 3.** Aspects of morphological diversity and morphogenetic processes in cyano-bacteria. Scale bar in a applies to all photographs unless they contain their own scale bar. Scale bars = 10 $\mu$m (a) Coccoid cells of *Synechocystis* sp. strain PCC 6803, one of the most widely studied cyanobacteria. (b) Loosely aggregated colonies of a unicellular extremely halotolerant cyanobacterium belonging to the Halothece cluster. (c) Trichome division in a *Lyngbya*-like ("Porphyrosiphon") filamentous strain. The sequence displays the formation of necridial cells (nc), its degradation, and the formation of two rounded apical cells (ac) different from the discoid intercalary cells. (d) "Chroococcus turgidus," the largest unicellular cyanobacterium known with the right cell undergoing fission. (e) Negative stain (india ink) of a colony of *Gloeothece* sp., rendering the diffuse extracellular polysaccharide invest-ments visible. (f) Field sample of *Gloeocapsa* "*sanguinea,*" with red-stained, well-structured extracellular polysaccharide sheaths. (g) A young filament of *Calothrix* displaying a terminal heterocyst (hc) and a tapering trichome. (h) Assymmetric division (budding) in unicellular cyanobacteria of the genus *Chamaesiphon*.

monly seen as membrane-bound intracellular inclusions, and they consist of accumulations of the enzyme ribulose 1,5-bisphosphate carboxylase/oxygenase (RubisCO), which is responsible for the initial carboxylation step in the Calvin cycle (see Section III.A.3). Gas vesicles are air-filled, cylindrical proteinaceous structures present in many planktonic species and in the dispersal stages of benthic forms; they provide buoyancy to the organisms. Many gas vesicles may gather in some region of the cytoplasm, forming gas vacuoles (or aerotopes) which are visible under the light microscope as highly refractile inclusions. A large variety of ultrastructural inclusions of restricted occurrence are also known from particular species or strains.

## B. Growth and Cell Division

Cyanobacteria show widely divergent rates of growth. Some strains cultured under optimal conditions display doubling times of as little as several hours. In nature, one or more doublings per day is common in blooming planktonic populations, and cell division may be strongly governed by daily periodicity. Most of the advances in biochemistry and molecular biology of cyanobacteria attained in the past few decades stem from the study of a few fast-growing strains. However, doubling times in most other strains in culture are in the order of several days. Under extreme conditions in the natural environment, net growth is sometimes best measured in units of percentage increase in biomass per year. Many cyanobacteria owe their ecological dominance and success not so much to their fast growth as to their ability to grow slowly and steadily in the face of environmental adversity, and slow growth rates may be an integral, genetically fixed part of the biology of many cyanobacteria.

Cyanobacterial cells divide basically by fission, but the patterns of cell division are varied. These patterns form the base of a morphological diversity unparalleled among prokaryotic organisms and contribute significantly to the currently used taxonomic treatment of the group (Fig. 1). It is surprising that, because morphological complexity is such a unique cyanobacterial trademark in the bacterial world, our knowledge of the regulation of cell division patterns and morphogenetic implications at the biochemical and molecular level is virtually nonexistent. The extracellular slime layers or sheaths may contribute considerably to morphogenesis in some cyanobacteria by simply holding cells together after division in disorderly colonies (as in "*Microcystis*"), by holding filaments together into bundles (as in *Microcoleus*), or by allowing a localized extrusion of trichomes that results in "false branching" (as in *Scytonema*; Fig. 3n).

### 1. Unicellular and Colonial Types

Cell division in the morphologically simplest types occurs by inward growth of all tegumentary structures (cytoplasmatic membrane, cell wall, outer membrane, and slime sheath), usually at an equatorial position. Asymmetrical division in one pole of unicells may results in small-sized daughter cells (budding; Figs. 3h and 3j), as in *Chamaesiphon*. A genetic capacity to alternate between two or three

(i) Ensheathed filaments of the desiccation-resistant *Lyngbya* "aestuarii," typical of upper intertidal marine littoral, with some sheaths colored by the suncreen pigment scytonemin. (j) Pleiomorphy in a unicellular cyanobacterium, "Cyanophanon," with the morphology being a result of steric constrictions to growth by their tough sheath. (k) Helically coiled filament of *Spirulina*. (l) Filaments of a *Pseudanabaena*-like "Konvophoron," with deep constrictions at cross-walls and displaying trichome division by direct differentiation of mamillated (nipple-bearing) apical cells without mediation of necridia. (m) Filamentous *Anabaena* with intercalary heterocysts (hc). (n) Heterocystous *Scytonema* showing the formation of false branches from recently divided trichomes (see vestigial necridium, nc) break free from the sheath and continue to grow (not glide). (o) Trichome of *Phormidium* with cylindrical cells. (p) Cell differentiation in *Nostoc* showing vegetative barrel-shaped cells, heterocysts (hc), and akinetes (ak). (q) Formation and extrusion of baeocytes in unicellular colonial cyanobacteria after repeated rounds of division without growth. (r) Single trichome of *Microcoleus* "chthonoplastes" with slight constrictions at the cross-walls and bullet-shaped apical cell. (s) Biseriate filament of *Stigonema* and a true branch (b and q reproduced with permission from Garcia-Pichel *et al.,* 1998).

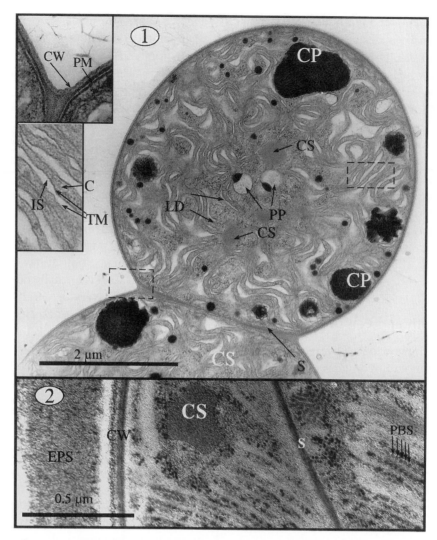

**Fig. 4.** Aspects of cyanobacterial ultrastructure as seen by transmission electron microscopy. **(1)** End cell in a *Nostoc* trichome, with characteristic cyanophycin granules (CP), carboxysomes (CS), polyphosphate granules (volutine, PP), lipidic droplets (LD), and septum or cross-wall (S). The inserts show close-ups of the cell wall layers (CW) and plasma membrane (PM) in a region around the septum and of a thylakoid-rich region with thylakoid membranes (TM), intrathylakoidal space (IS), and cytoplasm (C). **(2)**. Outer regions in an *Oscillatoria* filament (in cross-view) with (from left to right) exopolysaccharide (EPS) layer, cell wall (CW), a carboxysome (or polyhedral body; CS), rows of phycobilisomes (PBS) sitting on the cytoplasmatic side of the thylakoid membranes, and a septum (S) (originals from M. Hernández-Mariné, with permission).

orthogonal division planes yields spatially ordered colonial forms, as in "*Merismopedia*" (planar colonies—two alternating division planes) or in *Myxosarcina* (cubical colonies—three alternating division planes). Multiple divisions occurring in the absence of cell growth result in the formation of a multiplicity of minute daughter cells (baeocytes) that eventually break free from the cell wall remains of the parental cell, as in all "pleurocapsalean" cyanobacteria (Fig. 3q).

## 2. Filamentous Types

Repetitive division in a single plane without complete cell separation yields simple filamentous forms. The filamentous nature of some cyanobacteria may simply be due to this fact and may not imply a functional integration of the cells into a truly multicellular organism. The apparently easy transition between unicells and filaments in culture by simple mutation is not rare in some strains. In morphologically complex filamentous forms, the outer tegumentary layers may be continuous along the trichome, and the formation of cross-walls or septa (s. septum) may involve the invagination of plasma membrane and cell wall only. In filamentous oscillatorian cyanobacteria, one or more tegumentary invaginations (future cross-walls) may be initiated before cell division is completed. A widespread change of division plane in the cells along the trichome results in bi- or multiseriate trichomes (two or more rows of cells), and a change in plane of division occurring in a single cell and maintained for several rounds of fission results in true branching, as in *Stigonema.* (Fig. 3g). In morphologically complex filamentous forms, cell division may be meristematic, occurring only in certain portions of the trichome (e.g., *Calothrix* and allied forms).

## C. Multicellularity and Cell Differentiation

The dimension of the morphological complexity that has evolved within the cyanobacterial radiation is exemplified by the achievement of multicellularity. Some groups of filamentous cyanobacteria (the heterocystous group and some oscillatorians) are not merely linear arrays of unicells but truly multicellular organisms, possessing all the attributes required for such a distinction: supracellular structural elements, integrated behavioral responses to environmental stimuli, and distribution of labor through cell differentiation into distinct cellular types. The most important examples of cellular differentiation in cyanobacteria are reviewed here. Additionally, in many cases cyanobacteria form colonies or structurally organized macroscopic bodies (thalli in botanical terminology) that are quite large in size. Spherical colonies of *Nostoc "pruniforme"* exceeding 15 cm in diameter

are known from the benthos of oligotrophic cold springs, but somewhat smaller ordered arrangements of organisms are common in other *Nostoc* species as well as in *Calothrix* and allied genera (e.g., "Rivularia"). This metadifferentiation is seldom achieved in culture.

### 1. Hormogonia

Hormogonia (s. hormogonium) are short (approximately 5–25 cells) chains of cells formed and released from the parental trichome. They serve a function in the dispersal of the organism. Hormogonial cells may or may not be different in size and shape from vegetative cells. Detachment may involve the differentiation of a necridic cell separating the vegetative trichome from the hormogonium. Dispersal is aided by the expression of phenotypic traits, which may vary according to strains, such as gliding motility, development of gas vesicles, or changes in surface hydrophobicity. Hormogonia eventually settle and dedifferentiate into a typical vegetative organism. Hormogonium formation may be triggered by environmental factors such as phosphate repletion or changes in light quality.

### 2. Heterocysts

Heterocysts (Figs. 3g, 3m, and 3p) are morphologically distinct cells that develop in response to a lack of combined nitrogen sources in the environment. The ability to develop heterocysts occurs without exception within a monophyletic group of filamentous cyanobacteria (heterocystous), corresponding to the orders Nostocales and Stigonematales in the bacterial taxonomy. They are usually larger than vegetative cells, develop thick tegumentary layers and intracellular hyaline buttons at the points of attachment to the vegetative cells, and usually display a pale coloration and reduced autofluorescence. As such, heterocysts are easy to recognize under the microscope. They may differentiate from end cells (terminal heterocysts, as in *Calothrix*) or from cells within the trichome (regularly spaced intercalary heterocysts, as in *Anabaena*). Heterocysts are highly specialized in the fixation of gaseous dinitrogen under aerobic conditions. They represent a successful solution to the non-trivial problem of avoiding nitrogenase inactivation by free oxygen in oxygen-evolving organisms. Heterocyst biology has been relatively well studied at the biochemical and molecular level. In heterocystous cyanobacteria, heterocysts are the only cells which express *nif* (nitrogen fixation) genes and synthesize nitrogenase. Apparently, heterocysts do not evolve oxygen themselves (photosystem II activity is absent or restricted) but a functional photosystem provides ATP. The source of reductant for nitrogen fixation is provided (as organic carbon) by the adjacent vegetative cells, which in turn obtain fixed nitrogen from the heterocyst in the form of amino acids (mostly glutamine). The heterocysts protect their nitrogenase from oxygen inactivation by maintaining reduced internal partial pressures of oxygen, a situation that is attained by means of increased rates of cellular respiration and, apparently, by restricting diffusive entry of oxygen from the environment as a result of their thick envelope. The developmental regulation of heterocysts is beginning to be understood at the genetic level. The autoregulated gene *hetR*, which is activated by the deficiency in combined nitrogen, seems to play a crucial role in initiation of heterocyst development.

### 3. Akinetes

These non-motile cells (Fig. 3p) are characterized by their enlarged size with respect to vegetative cells, their thick cell wall and additional tegumentary layers, and their high content of nitrogen reserves in the form of cyanophycin granules. They are formed exclusively by heterocystous filamentous cyanobacteria but not by all, and they may differentiate en masse or at special locations within the filaments (usually close or next to a heterocyst). Akinetes are resistant to desiccation, low temperature (including freeze–thaw cycling), and digestion in animal guts, and they are considered to be resting stages. They are fundamentally different from typical bacterial spores in that they are not heat-resistant. In natural planktonic populations, massive akinete formation occurs at the end of the growth season. In the laboratory, the effects of light (energy) limitation and of phosphate limitation on growth have been implicated as the main factors eliciting akinete differentiation. The process of differentiation may be mediated by specific hormone-like compounds produced by vegetative cells. Germination of akinetes into vegetative

cells occurs when the environmental conditions (light intensity and phosphate availability) become favorable for the growth of a vegetative filament. Genetic evidence suggest that the early regulatory process of akinete development is common to that of heterocysts.

### 4. Terminal Hairs

These are multicellular differentiations occurring at the tips of trichomes in some members of the genus *Calothrix* and allied cyanobacteria (botanical family *Rivulariaceae*). In response to nutrient limitation (e.g., phosphate), the terminal parts of the trichome differentiate irreversibly into thin and long rows of narrow, almost colorless, vacuolated cells (hence the term hair). The hair is a site of preferential expression of cell surface-bound phosphatase activity.

### 5. Necridic Cells (Necridia)

Necridic cells occur in truly multicellular cyanobacteria (Figs. 3c and 3n). Necridic cells undergo a suicidal process (apoptosis), which begins with the loss of turgor and leakage of some cellular contents and continues with shrinkage and the separation of the cross-walls (septa) from the adjoining cells. Eventually, the necridic cells will either rupture and disintegrate or remain as small, isolated vestigial cells. Cells adjacent to the necridium will usually develop morphologies typical for terminal (apical) cells. The formation of necridia may lead to the separation of one trichome into two (proliferation) or in the detachment of hormogonia from the vegetative filament. Most of the information about necridia is observational, and no studies have been performed to investigate the regulation of this morphogenetic mechanism.

## III. PHYSIOLOGY AND METABOLISM

Cyanobacteria are photoautotrophic organisms par excellence and their metabolism is typically geared towards anabolic reactions. The basis of their metabolism is the conversion of radiant energy into chemically usable energy and the reduction of $CO_2$

into organic matter. The electron donor for the reduction of $CO_2$ is water, which is oxidized to molecular oxygen. The name of this type of metabolism is derived by the release of oxygen: oxygenic photosynthesis. It is exclusively carried out by organisms in the cyanobacterial radiation (cyanobacteria proper and the plastids of algae and plants).

## A. Photosynthesis

In the light reactions of photosynthesis, radiant energy is captured and used to generate energy in the form of ATP and unlike in other bacterial phototrophs, reduction equivalents in the form of NADPH. The light reactions of oxygenic photosynthesis are based on the coordinated action of (i) light-harvesting systems; (ii) two chlorophyll *a*-containing, membrane-bound, multisubunit enzymes known as photosystems; and (iii) a series of both soluble and membrane-bound electron-carrier proteins linking both photosystems (Fig. 5).

### 1. Light Harvesting

Light harvesting in most cyanobacteria (and in red algal plastids) is accomplished by highly ordered and structurally versatile supramolecular complexes known as phycobilisomes, which are primarily composed of phycobiliproteins. Phycobiliproteins are water-soluble proteinaceous pigments containing covalently bound, open-chain tetrapyrroles (phycobilines) as cromophores. Universal cyanobacterial phycobilines are the blue-colored allophycocyanin (absorbing maximally at a wavelength of 650 nm) and phycocyanin (maximum at 620 nm). Phycoerythrocyanin (maximum at 575 nm) and the red-colored phycoerythrin(s) (maximum at approximately 500 nm) are also common. Multimeric disc-shaped phycobiliprotein complexes are stacked into either central cores or radially protruding rods (Fig. 5) to form a functional phycobilisome. The radiant energy absorbed by the phycobiliproteins along the rods is channeled vectorially (as excitation energy) towards the core region and from the core onto the reaction center of photosystem II or (partially) to

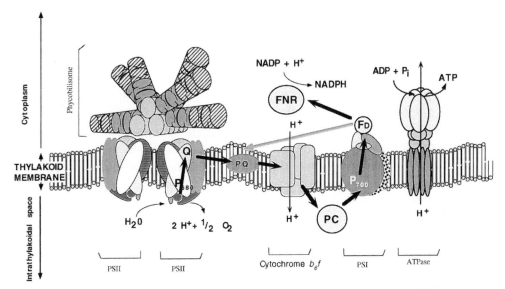

*Fig. 5* Idealized organization of the photosynthetic components in cyanobacterial thylakoids and their associated activities. Multimeric complexes are indicated by brackets. Q, bound quinone; PQ, plastoquinone; PC, plastocyanin; FD, ferredoxin; FNR, ferredoxin:NADP oxidoreductase. Thick black arrows indicate the direction of electron flow from water to NADPH the gray arrow depicts the shortcut under cyclic phosphorylation conditions. Thin arrows depict either transformation of chemical reactants or the traffic of protons across the membrane. (Modified with permission from Bryant, 1996.)

that of photosystem I. Phycobiliproteins are arranged orderly within the phycobilisome: The shorter the wavelength of maximum absorbance, the more peripheral their location. This allows for the centripetal channelling of excitation energy down a thermodynamically allowed sequence. In such a light-harvesting system, 300–800 phycobilin chromophores capture additional energy for the ca. 50 Chl *a* molecules associated with photosystem II. In some strains the phycobilin composition of phycobilisomes can be regulated to optimize the capture of photons according to the color of the available light, a phenomenon known as complementary chromatic adaptation.

## 2. Light Reactions of Photosynthesis

Photosystem II (PSII), which contains a reaction center (known as P680) of very high basal reduction potential (+1 V), catalyzes the transfer of electrons from water to a bound quinone, with the production of oxygen. The electrons then enter an electron transport chain involving successive redox reactions of a membrane-bound protein (plastoquinone), a membrane-bound protein complex (cytochrome $b_6f$), and one of two intrathylakoidal soluble proteins (cytochrome $c_{533}$ or plastocyanin). Because the electrons are stripped from water in a vectorial fashion (charge separation), an electrochemical gradient of protons is created across the thylakoid membrane in the process of electron transport. This is used by the thylakoidal F-type ATPase complex to generate ATP, the cell's energy currency. When excited, PSI, with a reaction center (known as P700) of intermediate reduction potential, catalyzes the reoxidation of reduced plastocyanin (or cytochrome $c_{533}$) with the concomitant reduction of ferredoxin (a soluble iron–sulfur protein) against a steep thermodynamic gradient. Reduced ferredoxin is used by ferredoxin : NADP+ oxidoreductase (an enzyme physically tethered to phycobilisomes, if present) to generate the NADPH necessary for the dark reactions. In short, the light-driven formation of ATP and NADPH has been achieved. Additionally, electron flow around PSI alone may also occur (cyclic electron transport). In this case, electrons flow from reduced ferredoxin directly to plastoquinone, through the cytochrome $b_6f$ complex and plastocyanin, back to PSI and, with light, to oxidized ferredoxin, closing the cycle. The net effect of this cycle is the generation of energy but no reductant.

## 3. Dark Reactions of Photosynthesis: Carbon Fixation and Uptake

The reduction of $CO_2$ to organic matter (carbon fixation) occurs in all cyanobacteria mainly through the reductive pentose phosphate (Calvin) cycle, in which the net formation of a triose from 3 $CO_2$ is powered by ATP and NADPH formed in the light reactions and supplies important intermediates for anabolic reactions (triose, pentose, and hexose phosphate). Additional $CO_2$ may be fixed by phosphoenolpyruvate carboxylase, yielding $C_4$ acids, and by carbamylphosphate synthetase/carbamylphosphate-ornithine carbamyl transferase, yielding citrulline and glutamate from glutamine, ornithine, and $CO_2$. The Calvin cycle is related to the catabolic (oxidative) pentose phosphate pathway, differing in two key enzymes that allow it to function anabolically. These are PRK (phosphoribulosekinase) and RubisCO, a very interesting enzyme and the most abundant protein on Earth. RubisCO is characterized by a low affinity for $CO_2$ and by possessing internal monooxygenase activity. This results in a competitive inhibition of carboxylation by free oxygen, a fact of obvious importance for oxygen-producing phototrophs. Under conditions of low $CO_2$ and high $O_2$ partial pressure, RubisCO catalyzes the oxidation of ribulosebisphosphate to phosphoglycerate and phosphoglycolate. After dephosphorylation, glycollate is excreted by the cells in what seems to be a wasteful loss of carbon. Probably in order to prevent conditions leading to such losses, cyanobacteria possess a carbon concentrating mechanism, by which inorganic carbon, either as bicarbonate or as $CO_2$, is actively and at the expense of energy transported into the cell so that the intracellular concentrations can be 1000-fold higher than those outside the cells. A carbonic anhydrase-like enzyme keeps intracellular carbon in the form of bicarbonate to prevent leakage of $CO_2$. A carbonic anhydrase located within the carboxysomes (or polyhedral bodies, the site of RubisCO accumulation; Fig. 4) generates $CO_2$. With this system, a high $CO_2$ partial pressure is maintained locally in close proximity to the carboxylation sites of RubisCO, and the carboxylating activity of the enzyme is promoted.

## B. Dark Metabolism

Energy generation in the dark occurs through aerobic respiration at the expense of glycogen accumulated during the light phase. Monomeric sugars are degraded using the oxidative pentose phosphate cycle. A complete tricarboxylic acid cycle has never been shown for—and $\alpha$-aketoglutarate dehydrogenase has never been detected in—any cyanobacterium. NADPH formed in sugar catabolism is fed to the membrane-bound electron transport chain at the level of plastoquinone. Terminal oxidases are cytochrome oxidases of the aa$_3$ type. The respiratory electron transport chain of cyanobacteria is housed in both the plasma and the thylakoidal membrane and it shares many functional components with photosynthetic electron transport. Approximately half of all cyanobacterial strains tested are obligate phototrophs, which are unable to use exogenous carbon sources aerobically. Some are photoheterotrophs, which are able to use some sugars as a carbon source, and some are facultative heterotrophs, which are able to grow, albeit slowly, at the expense of externally supplied sugars (usually only one) in the dark. All strains retain pigmentation and all components necessary for photosynthesis under dark growth conditions. The lack of sugar transport systems has been heralded as one of the main reasons for the inability of many strains to use exogenous sugars while being able to respire endogenous glucose.

Cyanobacteria may also be subject to periods of anoxia, particularly in the dark (e.g., benthic forms thriving in sulfidogenic environments and biofilm or colony formers under diffusion limitation of O$_2$ supply). The only known electron acceptors besides oxygen for cyanobacterial chemoorganotrophy are organic compounds and elemental sulfur. Fermentation seems to be a relatively widespread ability in benthic and bloom-forming cyanobacteria, but it is not universal. As in aerobic heterotrophy, fermentation occurs at the expense of endogenous sugars (usually glycogen but also sugar osmolytes such as trehalose or glucosyl-glycerol) accumulated in the light period. Some strains ferment, or even grow

on, exogenous substrates anaerobically. In all cases investigated, fermentative enzymes are expressed constitutively. Homolactic, heterolactic, homoacetate, and mixed acid fermentation have all been described. There is evidence that the Embden–Meyerhof–Parnas glycolitic pathway, unoperative for aerobic respiration, is used in the fermentative degradation of sugars by cyanobacteria. With regard to sulfur compounds, an *Oscillatoria* strain oxidizes endogenous carbohydrates largely to CO$_2$ in the presence of elemental sulfur with the concomitant production of sulfide. In other cyanobacteria, sulfur may be used as a sink for electrons, otherwise released as H$_2$, with or without concomitant modification of the fermentative products. A thermophilic *Synechococcus* reduces sulfate and thiosulfate to sulfide anaerobically in the dark. In none of these examples, however, has it been demonstrated that the reduction of sulfur compounds per se is coupled to electron transport or energy generation.

## C. Secondary Metabolism

Cyanobacteria have been reported to synthesize a variety of natural products that are not components of universal biochemical pathways, but rather components of restricted distribution among taxa (secondary metabolites). These are thought to serve particular functions relevant for the ecology of the strains or groups in question. Several important cyanobacterial metabolites are peptidic in nature but synthesized in a non-ribosomal setting by specific peptide synthetases. In a few cases, the biological role played by these secondary metabolites has been deduced, but in most cases their function remains unresolved. Compounds such as cyanobacterin (Fig. 6, **3**), a herbicide produced by strains of the genus *Scytonema,* have a strong inhibitory activity on PS II of algae and cyanobacteria other than the producing strain, thus preventing competition. Scytonemin, a widespread UV-absorbing indole alkaloid, is synthesized, excreted, and accumulated in large quantities in extracellular sheaths in response to UV radiation exposure. It serves a sunscreen role (Figs. 3i and 3j, Fig. 6, **8**). A similar sunscreen role has been proposed for a large variety of colorless mycosporine-like compounds (Fig. 6, **6** and **7**). Specific triterpenoids of

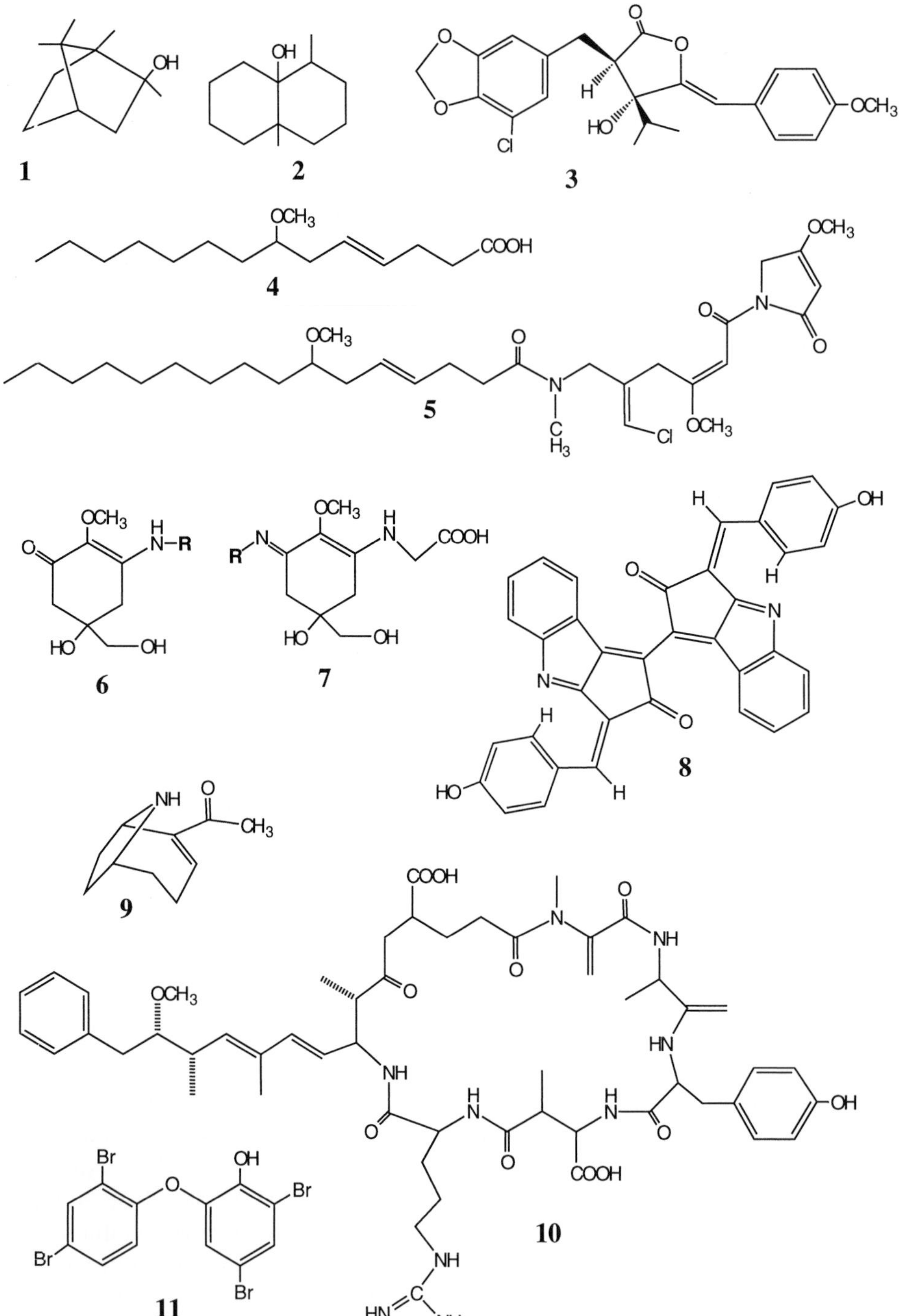

*Fig. 6.* Diversity of cyanobacterial secondary metabolites. **1**, 2-Methylisoborneol **2**, geosmin; **3**, cyanobacterin; **4**, 7-methoxy-4-tetradecenoic acid; **5**, malyngamide A; **6** and **7**, mono- and bisubstituted mycosporines, respectively, where R-(amino) acidic moiety; **8**, scytonemin; **9**, anatoxin a; **10**, microcystin YR; **11**, a brominated phenyldiphenol.

the hopane series found in thermophilic strains may stabilize the cell membranes under high temperatures. Some cyanobacterial natural products display antibiotic activity, such as the antibacterial brominated biphenyls from *Oscillatoria "chalybea"* (Fig. 6, **11**) or the methoxytetradecenoic acid of *Lyngbya "majuscula"* (Fig. 6, **4**). However, for most cyanobacterial secondary metabolites identified, their biological function remains elusive. Such is the case for the volatile compounds 2-methylisoborneol and geosmin (Fig. 6, **1** and **2**, respectively), which are of common occurrence and responsible for the earthy smell and off-flavors in lakes harboring cyanobacterial blooms. A defined biological role for the notoriously famous cyanobacterial toxins (Fig. 6, **9** and **10**; see Section V.B) is lacking. Among the bioactive compounds of unknown natural function, some have antineoplastic, antiviral, antiinflammatory, antimitotic, ichtiotoxic, and dermatitic activity. Efforts to study the largely untapped cyanobacterial inventory of secondary metabolites and their biology are likely to increase substantially in the near future due to their relevance to pharmaceutical research and public health.

## D. Nutrition

Apart from liquid water, light, and inorganic nutrients, cyanobacteria have few, if any, additional requirements for growth. A requirement for vitamin $B_{12}$ has been demonstrated in some strains. However, processes devoted to the provision of nutrients may account for a significant part of the energy and reduction equivalents obtained in the light reactions of photosynthesis. Cyanobacteria possess specific uptake systems for nutrient assimilation. Orthophosphate can be taken up and stored intracellularly as polyphosphate, and the uptake may be aided by the action of surface-bound phosphatases, which release phosphate bound to organic molecules. The availability of phosphorous may often be the growth-limiting factor in natural fresh-water populations. The production of siderophores (iron-chelating organic compounds) seems to be important in the assimilation of iron because $Fe^{3+}$ ions, required for many of the enzymes involved in redox reactions, are very insoluble in water. The availability of iron may be growth limiting in oceanic planktonic species. In addition to uptake mechanisms, sulfur and nitrogen assimilation require additional reduction steps and are discussed separately in the following sections.

### 1. Nitrogen Assimilation

Among inorganic nutrients, nitrogen is of paramount importance since it accounts for approximately 10% of the dry weight of cyanobacterial cells. Nitrate ($NO_3^-$) and ammonium ($NH_4^+$) are virtually universal sources of nitrogen for cyanobacteria, but urea or other organic nitrogenous compounds can be used by some strains. In addition, many strains can fix gaseous dinitrogen ($N_2$). Plasma membrane-bound transport systems exist for both nitrate and ammonium, whereas $N_2$ enters the cells by diffusion. Intracellular nitrate must be reduced to ammonium. This is accomplished by the stepwise reduction to nitrite (catalyzed by nitrate reductase) and ammonium (catalyzed by nitrite reductase). The reduction equivalents for both processes stem from reduced ferredoxin. Ammonium (either taken up or endogenously generated) is assimilated by the glutamine synthetase/glutamate synthase enzyme system. The net action of this system is the formation of glutamate from $\alpha$-ketoglutarate and ammonium, with the expenditure of ATP and the oxidation of ferredoxin. Glutamate can donate its amino moiety to various precursors of central metabolism by the action of specific transaminases. Many, but not all, cyanobacteria are able to fix dinitrogen; this is of great ecological significance because $N_2$ is a source of nitrogen ubiquitous in the environment. The process is carried out by the enzyme nitrogenase and is a costly one, involving consumption of both ATP and reduction equivalents (supplied by ferredoxin). In addition, nitrogenase will also inevitably reduce protons to $H_2$ in what represents a wasteful decrease in efficiency for the process. Another drawback of $N_2$ fixation is that nitrogenase is inherently very sensitive to irreversible inactivation by oxygen. Several strategies have evolved in cyanobacteria to circumvent this problem. Some strains will only carry out nitrogen fixation under anoxic conditions, but some will also do it in the presence of oxygen. Several strains have been shown to restrict temporally $N_2$ fixation to the dark period, thus decreasing exposure of nitrogenase to photosynthetic oxygen. Strains belonging to the Nostocales and Stigonematales have evolved a specialized cell type (the heterocysts; see Section II.C.2) in which nitrogen fixation is spatially separated from photosynthesis and protected from oxygen inactivation. Heterocystous strains display the highest specific rates of nitrogen fixation among all cyanobacteria. However, some non-heterocystous cyanobacteria, such as *Trichodesmium*, are able to fix substantial, biogeochemically significant amounts of $N_2$ in the light; their mode of adaptation is unknown. The various mechanisms for nitrogen assimilation are tightly regulated so that the presence of less costly sources (ammonium) immediately inhibits nitrate (and nitrite) uptake, or $N_2$-fixation activity, and represses the expression of the enzymes involved in the reduction of alternative $N_2$ sources. In the same way, the presence of abundant nitrate represses the expression of nitrogenase genes and results in the halting of new heterocyst differentiation.

## 2. Sulfur Assimilation

Sulfate is seemingly the universal source of sulfur for cyanobacterial cells, and it is only rarely growth limiting in the environment. Other sources of sulfur may be taken up alternatively, such as sulfate esters, sulfonate, hydrogen sulfide, and organic thiols. Sulfate is taken up by a sulfate permease in an energy-depending process, reduced to sulfide, and incorporated into cysteine. The cyanobacterial assimilatory sulfate reduction pathway is similar to those of other bacteria, involving activation of sulfate by binding to ADP and reduction of the sulfonucleotide to free sulfite using thioredoxin as a reducing agent. Sulfite is further reduced to sulfide by sulfite reductase using NADPH as an electron donor, and free sulfide is incorporated into cysteine by specific synthases. An oxidized sulfur source may also be a requirement for growth since, unlike other bacteria, cyanobacteria possess important structural components containing oxidized sulfur moieties: the sulfolipids of the photosynthetic membranes and, in some strains, the sulfate esters constituent of the extracellular polysaccharide sheaths.

## E. Regulation

The regulation of cellular activities in cyanobacteria is similar in nature to that found in other prokaryotes, but photobiological aspects of regulation play a particularly important role. The presence and nature of the cyanobacterial photoreceptor systems (a cell's light meter) are only beginning to be determined. Although specific photoreceptor molecules (some that are structurally similar to plant phytochromes) do exist, in many cases it is the effect of light conditions on the overall redox state of the cell that determines the cellular responses. Small redox-sensitive proteins such as thioredoxin may act as general modulators of enzyme activity in carbon and nitrogen metabolism. Short-term (photo)responses can also be based on protein phosphorylation mechanisms, as seems to be the case for the process leading to redistribution of captured energy between photosystems I and II (so-called state transitions) or for the direct regulation of phosphoenolpyruvate carboxylase activities. By means of its multiple targeting, phosphorylation of a serine residue of $P_{11}$, a small regulatory protein, is thought to provide coordinated regulation of carbon and nitrogen metabolism.

There is abundant evidence for light-responsive regulation of gene expression, leading to long-term responses, either to light intensity or to spectral composition. This is particularly true for genes encoding components of the photosynthetic apparatus, such as phycobiliproteins and PSII polypeptides. Some strains grown under light–dark cycles are capable of incorporating specific metabolic tasks into the swing of the cycle, relegating, for example, protein synthesis or nitrogen fixation to the dark periods. At least some of these daily patterns are maintained by an internal clock since the periodicity remains even in the absence of environmental stimuli. Although the nature of the cyanobacterial internal clock is not known, the expression of various central genes has been shown to be under its control. Cyanobacteria are the only prokaryotes for which the presence of internally generated daily rhythmicity has been demonstrated.

## F. Motility and Taxes

Cyanobacteria do not have flagella, but many unicellular and filamentous cyanobacteria display gliding motility. In some strains of oceanic marine *Synechoccocus,* slow-swimming motility has also been described. Gliding is a movement across a solid or semisolid material in the absence of flagella or other conspicuous propulsion mechanisms and without apparent change in cellular (or trichome) shape. Gliding is typically accompanied by the secretion of slime; in filamentous forms rotation of the trichomes along their main axes often occurs while gliding. The structural involvement of a $Ca^+$ binding glycoprotein, oscillin, in cyanobacterial gliding has been determined; it forms supracellular helical fibrils in the outermost surface of the trichomes. However, the actual mechanism of cyanobacterial motility remains unknown. Gliding motility may be displayed only transiently (i.e., in hormogonia or in baeocytes but not in vegetative cells). Photosensory and chemosensory systems allowing the organisms to respond to temporal or spatial environmental gradients are tightly coupled to motility, resulting in the so-called tactic behavior. Positive tactic responses to chemical species (chemotaxis) such as bicarbonate and nitrate have been shown in cyanobacteria (i.e., they move up chemical gradients of concentration of those substances). All motile cyanobacteria display phototactic behavior so that the populations are able to seek optimally illuminated areas. Like other bacteria, cyanobacteria usually respond by stopping and changing the direction of movement (reversing) upon crossing a sharp boundary in light intensity (photophobic response); however, some filamentous oscillatorians and heterocystous forms are also capable of perceiving the angular direction of the light and responding by steering towards or away from the direction of the incoming light. This capacity (known as true phototaxis) has no parallel in any other prokaryotic microorganisms.

## IV. MOLECULAR GENETICS

### A. Genomes

The genome is typically prokaryotic in nature and located in the centroplasm. The genomes of free-living cyanobacteria vary widely in G + C base composition from 32 to 71%, a range comparable to that spanned by all Bacteria. They also vary in size, approximate correlating with morphological complexity, from 2 to $14 \times 10^6$ base pairs (by rule of thumb, approximately 1000–7000 genes). The smallest cyanobacterial genomes are thus similar in size to those of most bacteria, whereas the largest ones are in the range of eukaryotic fungal genomes. Symbiotic cyanelles and plastids have retained only $0.13 \times 10^6$ base pairs in their genomes. The DNA of cyanobacteria is subject to very extensive modification, which in some cases is so thorough that a role for methylation beyond protection from restriction enzyme cleavage has been postulated. The presence of widespread, highly iterated short palindromic sequences is a trait shared by many, but not all, cyanobacterial genomes. Genomic rearrangements involving deletion, operon fusion, and translocation events are known to occur during heterocyst differentiation. Plasmids or extrachromosomal replicons are commonly encountered (some as large as $1.5 \times 10^5$ base pairs), but they are usually cryptic and do not appear to be responsible for antibiotic resistance phenotypes, as in other bacteria. Some are known to bear genes encoding for isozymes involved in assimilatory sulfate reduction.

### B. Gene Transfer

There is evidence from phylogenetic comparisons that horizontal genetic exchange among related cyanobacteria has played a significant role in their evolution. Nevertheless, the mechanisms leading to genetic exchange are difficult to pinpoint. Despite the abundance and spread of cyanobacterial plasmids, natural conjugation among cyanobacteria has not been reported. The same is true for viral transduction, despite the wealth of cyanophages (cyanobacteria-specific phages) described in the laboratory and from natural populations. Some strains are naturally highly competent for taking up foreign DNA, but unaided transformation seems to be restricted to some unicellular strains of the genera *Synechococcus* and *Synechocystis.*

### C. Gene Expression

Control of gene expression at the level of transcription seems to play a significant role in the adaptation to changing environmental conditions. Cyanobacteria possess a transcriptional apparatus of unique characteristics among Bacteria, but the biological significance of this is only beginning to be addressed. The cyanobacterial DNA-dependent RNA polymerase is structurally different from that of the common Bacterial type, possessing an additional subunit in its core, and several sigma factors (polypeptides whose association with the core of the polymerase is needed for effective initiation of transcription) have been identified. It has been shown that a "principal" sigma factor is commonly present under normal growth conditions, whereas alternative factors are temporarily expressed upon, for example, a change to nitrogen-limiting conditions. It is thought that particular sigma factors may be responsible for the preferential transcription of particular sets of genes involved in the adaptation. Because the (limited number of studied) cyanobacterial promoters lack some of the distal consensus sequences of other Bacteria, it has been hypothesized that regulation of transcription may often be activated by accessory factors other than sigma factors.

## D. Molecular Genetic Studies

The development of systems for the molecular study of cyanobacteria in the past 20 years has contributed greatly to our knowledge of cyanobacterial biology. Techniques for random and directed mutagenesis, as well as for transformative and conjugal gene transfer, have been developed and optimized. Reporter systems have been successfully employed to monitor the temporal dynamics of gene expression. Genomes have been mapped and, in one strain (*Synechocystis* strain PCC 6803), fully sequenced. Studies in molecular biology have contributed centrally to the clarification of the structure of the cyanobacterial photosynthetic apparatus, to the process of dinitrogen fixation, to heterocyst differentiation mechanisms, to the responses to light and nutrients, to the study of cyanobacterial circadian clocks, and to many other aspects of cyanobacterial biology. Regulatory genes have been identified that modulate the expression of other genes, for example, transcription regulators involved in phycobiliprotein gene expression resulting in complementary chromatic adaptation.

General regulatory mechanisms, through which the responses of different parts of metabolism are coordinated, are beginning to emerge. Molecular biological techniques have already had a large impact in evolutionary and phylogenetic studies and are beginning to be applied in ecological studies. It is expected that molecular biological techniques will continue to provide much information in the future. Nevertheless, a note of caution is warranted: Because the systems currently available for genetic manipulation are restricted to a few strains, the information available covers only a portion of cyanobacterial diversity—probably strongly biased towards strains that display fast growth rates and are amenable to problem-free laboratory cultivation. Any generalizations may be premature or of restricted applicability.

## V. ECOLOGY AND ADAPTATIONS

The range of environmental conditions under which cyanobacteria can develop is impressively wide, and equally wide is the variety of ecological adaptations that they display. One can find cyanobacteria as an important part of the primary producer community in almost any habitat in which light penetrates. Thermophilic cyanobacteria can grow up to temperatures of 73°C in hot springs, which is the upper temperature limit for any phototrophic organism, and develop stable populations in polar soils, rocks, and ponds in which temperatures rarely exceed a few degrees Celsius. Some forms thrive in rain or snow-melt puddles of extremely low inorganic solute concentrations, and some halotolerant types grow in NaCl saturated brines. Cyanobacteria are found in caves, deep in lakes, and in coastal areas, where light is extremely dim, but some terrestrial forms develop permanent populations in mountainous tropical areas, which are exposed to the highest levels of solar radiation found on Earth. Many terrestrial cyanobacteria are desiccation resistant, and they withstand freeze–thaw cycles. Benthic marine cyanobacteria flourish under supersaturated oxygen, often exceeding 1 atm in partial pressure during daytime, but they are exposed to anoxia at night. It is common that more than one of these extreme conditions coincide in one particular habitat. One of the most conspicuous limitations to the development of cyanobacteria seems to be acidity: Although many cyanobacteria are known from alkali lakes, no bona fide reports of growth below pH 4.5 exist. The ecological success of cyanobacteria in many of these extreme habitats is often a result of their metabolic resilience in the face of environmental insults rather than a consequence of sustained growth. A few environmentally relevant cyanobacterial habitats are discussed in the following sections.

## A. Marine Plankton

With the possible exception of polar areas, morphologically simple, coccoid cyanobacteria of small size (0.5–2 $\mu$m) inhabit in large numbers the upper zone of the oceans where light penetrates. These populations are referred to as picoplankton and consist of two phenotypically distinct but phylogenetically related groups (Fig. 2): the open-ocean marine *Synechococcus* and *Prochlorococcus*. Population sizes typically range between $10^4$ and $10^5$ cells/ml for both types. One can easily calculate that the global biomass of picoplankton must be on the order of 1 billion metric tons. The shear size of the global populations of this group of cyanobacteria indicates their ecological importance. It has been calculated that as little as 11% and as much as 50% of the primary production of non-polar open-ocean regions is due to their activity. This group has developed interesting adaptations to the light field of clear oligotrophic waters: Their light-harvesting complexes have differentiated to match the predominantly blue light available. *Synechococcus* cells synthesize a special kind of bilin chromophore, phycourobilin, absorbing maximally at 490–500 nm, thus increasing the ability of cells to use blue light. Evolutionary pressure of a similar nature has probably resulted in the virtual loss of phycobiliprotein-based light harvesting in *Prochlorococcus* and the evolution of antenna mechanisms based on (divinyl) chlorophylls (*a* and *b*), which are optimally suited to capture blue light. The life strategy of picoplankton populations is based on fast growth, with cells often displaying several doublings per day. Grazing pressure and viral infection seem to be the major factors controlling population sizes. The comparatively small size of picoplank-

ton genomes, the absence of nitrogen-fixing capacity and of some reserve polymers such as phycocyanin, and the lack of mechanisms to withstand small concentrations of toxic metals such as copper may be the result of reductionist evolutionary pressures favoring fast growth. Their small size (large surface to volume ratio) may provide selective advantage in nutrient-poor environments. Phenotypic and genetic variation exists within the picoplanktonic cyanobacteria, resulting in strains that diverge in light and temperature optima for growth: high- and low-light-loving strains of *Prochlorococcus* have been described as have mesophilic and moderately psychrophilic strains of *Synechococcus*.

The intensely red (phycoerythrin-containing) oscillatorian cyanobacteria of the genus *Trichodesmium*, which typically occur as bundles of filaments in the wild, constitute the second most important group of marine planktonic cyanobacteria. They are inhabitants of oligotrophic (nutrient-poor) tropical open-ocean regions worldwide, in which they may form blooms that can be detected as surface accumulations with the naked eye. They are responsible for much of the global oceanic nitrogen fixation, and this nitrogen-fixing capacity is a key factor of their ecological success. The particular adaptations that allow non-heterocystous *Trichodesmium* filaments to fix nitrogen in the light, however, are not well understood. They also contain large amounts of gas vesicles which provide positive buoyancy to the filaments so that they remain in the upper wind-mixed layer of the ocean. *Trichodesmium* gas vesicles are among the sturdiest in prokaryote, apparently so that they can withstand the large hydrostatic pressures experienced upon mixing of the water column.

## B. Freshwater Plankton

A large variety of cyanobacteria are found as components of the phytoplankton of fresh waters, but they are particularly prominent or dominant under conditions of nutrient eutrophication. In eutrophic lakes and man-made reservoirs (and in enclosed brackish water basins such as the Baltic), the formation of cyanobacterial blooms results in serious water quality problems regarding not only the degradation of the recreation potential due to greening of the waters, musty odors, and off-flavors that are associated with bloom development but also the likelihood of fish killings due to anoxic events after bloom decay and the production and release of cyanobacterial toxins. These are known to have caused animal and, in extreme cases, human deaths. The problems associated with cyanobacterial blooms reached beyond local environmental agencies and are being considered in rulings of the World Health Organization. Gasvacuolated species in the heterocystous genera *Anabaena, Nodularia, "Gloeothrichia,"* and *Aphanizomenon,* as well as in the non-heterocystous genera *Oscillatoria* and particularly *"Microcystis,"* are notoriously responsible for bloom formation and for reported cases of intoxication.

## C. Terrestrial Environments

Desiccation-resistant terrestrial cyanobacteria are of widespread occurrence. They may be found growing on bare surfaces (rocks, trees, buildings, and soils) or several millimeters within more or less soft diaphanous substrates (soils, sandstone, and limestone). Some species actively bore into the rock substrate. The availability of liquid water, in the form of rain or dew, determines the potential growth of cyanobacteria in the terrestrial environment. Growth of terrestrial cyanobacteria can be fast and luxurious in tropical humid climates, but in most other regions it is usually only intermittent. Their life strategy is usually one of slow growth and enhanced resilience. Adaptations to this environment are directed to withstand both desiccation (e.g., by abundant exopolysaccharide production) and exposure to solar radiation under inactive conditions (by the synthesis of sunscreen pigments). However, the exclusion of higher plant vegetation by climatic rigors determines the relative importance of cyanobacteria in terrestrial habitats. Thus, extensive endolithic cyanobacterial communities, usually dominated by members of the genus *Chroococcidiopsis,* have been described from tropical, desert, and polar environments. These communities play a significant role in rock erosion processes, and their actions have become a concern for the preservation of stone monuments. Edaphic cyanobacteria are also distributed worldwide, especially in basic soils; sheathed oscillatorian forms (*Microcoleus* and *"Schizothrix"*) along with heterocystous ones

(*Nostoc,* and *Scytonema*), are major ecological players in arid and semiarid regions (hot or cold). The socalled cyanobacterial desert crusts contribute significantly to the physical stability of arid soils.

## D. Sulfidogenic Environments

Hydrogen sulfide interferes with PSII and acts as a potent inhibitor of oxygenic photosynthesis. Many marine and fresh-water habitats, such as hot-springs, marine littoral sediments, and the deep water of lakes, may contain significant amounts of free sulfide. Cyanobacteria develop the most conspicuous populations of oxygenic phototrophs in such environments when sufficient light is available. Specific adaptations to these habitats include the ability to express sulfide-resistant forms of PSII so that oxygenic photosynthesis can proceed even in the presence of sulfide (e.g., in the marine benthic *Microcoleus "chthonoplastes"* and in some hot spring and fresh-water oscillatorians) and also an ability to perform anoxygenic photosynthesis using hydrogen sulfide as a source of electrons instead of water (e.g., in *Oscillatoria "limnetica"* and members of the Halothece cluster from hypersaline waters, *Oscillatoria "amphigranulata"* from hot springs, or *Pseudanabaena* sp. from hard-water lakes). Many strains display both adaptations simultaneously. The ability to use sulfide as an electron donor has been traced to the inducible expression of an enzyme, sulfide:quinone oxidoreductase, which when reduced by sulfide is able to reduce plastoquinone, thus allowing non-cycling functioning of PSI (Fig. 5) with the formation of both ATP and NADPH. Although some strains in culture show continued growth using anoxygenic photosynthesis alone, they cannot compete successfully for sulfide with phototrophic sulfur bacteria in the environment. It is thought that cyanobacteria use anoxygenic photosynthesis as a means for sulfide detoxification. Indeed, many use anoxygenic photosynthesis only temporarily, until local concentrations of sulfide are sufficiently low and (sulfide-resistant) oxygenic photosynthesis can begin.

## E. Symbioses

Although they show an apparent lack of a taste for matters sexual, cyanobacteria have displayed a considerable evolutionary promiscuity, entering into intimate symbiotic associations with various unrelated organisms. The list of cyanobacterial symbioses is large. So large, in fact, that at the turn of the century cyanobacterial symbioses (syncyanoses) earned a nomenclature of their own, from which only the term "cyanelle," applied to the blue-green photosynthetic organelles of some protistants, is still in use. There is also a large variation in the degree of independence maintained by the cyanobacterial partners. In some cases the distinction of two organisms may no longer be possible because cyanobacteria have lost their distinct appearance and a large portion of their genomes to their hosts. This is obviously the case in higher plant and eukaryotic algal plastids, in which massive loss of genes to the nucleus has occurred. Cyanelles have retained the peptidoglycan and phycobilins, but their identity losses are substantial as well. These cases are no longer considered symbioses. At the other end of the spectrum, loose but mutualistic relationships between cyanobacteria and other bacteria or fungi (so-called consortia) have been described, but these are not considered here. Well-known cyanobacterial symbioses can be functionally divided into those formed by heterocystous cyanobacteria, in which the main contribution of the cyanobacteria partner is the supply of fixed nitrogen, and those formed by non-heterocystous types, in which their contribution is often the supply of fixed carbon. According to the degree of intimacy attained, they can be classified into intracellular (in which cyanobacterial cells are found within cells of other organism) and extracellular (in which cyanobacterial cells are located within the tissues but outside the cells of other organisms). The most common extracellular symbioses of non-heterocystous cyanobacteria (involving the unicellular genera *Chroococcidiopsis*, *Gloeocapsa*, "*Chroococcus*," and *Gloeothece*) are in the form of cyanolichens. Both *Prochloron* and large-celled *Synechocystis* are known from extracellular symbioses with ascidians in tropical or subtropical marine waters. Extracellular symbioses of Pseudanabaena-like "*Konvophoron*" occur in Mediterranean sponges. Filamentous *Phormidium* has been reported in symbioses with some green algae. Intracellular symbioses of non-heterocystous cyanobacteria are known from tropical sponges

("*Aphanocapsa*", *Oscillatoria*, *Synechocystis*, and *Prochloron*), from green algae (*Phormidium*), and from dinoflagellates (unidentified). Heterocystous cyanobacteria in the genus *Nostoc* are known to form extracellular symbioses with liverworts and higher plants (Cycads and duckweed). *Anabaena* enters into symbiosis with water ferns of the genus *Azolla*. Cyanolichens are known to contain members of the genera *Nostoc*, *Calothrix*, *Scytonema*, *Stigonema*, and *Fischerella* as photobionts. Intracellular symbioses of heterocystous cyanobacteria occur in oceanic diatoms of the genera *Hemiaulus* and *Rhizosolenia* (cyanobacterial genus *Richelia*) and in *Trifolium* (clover) with *Nostoc*. *Nostoc* also enters into intracellular symbioses with the terrestrial non-lichenic fungus *Geosiphon pyriforme*. With the notable exception of lichenic photobionts, many symbiotic cyanobacteria have resisted cultivation despite continued efforts.

## VI. FOSSIL RECORD AND EVOLUTIONARY HISTORY

The fossil record of cyanobacteria contains the oldest entries that can be confidently assigned to any extant group of organisms. Excellently preserved microfossils 1000 million years old bear virtually indisputable cyanobacterial morphologies. Fossil cyanobacteria showing considerable morphological diversification have been described dating back at least 2500 million years. Additionally, filamentous bacteria of putative cyanobacterial identity are known from as far back as 3500 million years. In fact, it has been suggested that cyanobacteria have evolved only very slowly in the intervening time since present and past morphologies are very similar. In view of the biochemical and physiological diversity of adaptations that particular cyanobacteria display, some doubts may be cast on such a perception. The fossil record of the Archaean and Proterozoic Eons (before 500 million years ago) offers strong evidence not only for the presence of cyanobacteria but also for a type of environment they must have inhabited: the sedimentary environment of shallow coastal waters. This is recorded in the abundant organosedimentary laminated macrofossils known as stromatolites, which became geographically restricted in the Phanerozoic. Stromatolites are analogous to present-day cyanobacterial mats, benthic compact assemblages built by cyanobacteria in extreme environments. Stromatolites have provided evidence for the sustained importance of photoresponses in the ecology of cyanobacteria in the form of "heliotropic" accretions. Precambrian fossil microborings on marine carbonaceous substrates reveal the sustained role of cyanobacteria in small-scale geomorphological processes. Fossil evidence for the presence of eukaryotic algae is also quite old, perhaps as much as 2000 million years, which is in agreement with the early offshoot of the plastidic line of evolution suggested by phylogenetic reconstructions. The oldest fossil evidence for terrestrial cyanobacteria, in the form of *Gloeocapsa*-like cells symbiont in lichens, is comparatively young (400 million years). Thus, cyanobacteria have inhabited Earth for a long time and survived through geological periods of environmental conditions very different than those reigning today. In the early days of cyanobacterial evolution, high fluxes of short-wavelength UV radiation penetrated the oxygen- and ozone-free, carbon dioxide-rich atmosphere. Oceans were shallow and rich in reduced iron and poor in sulfate and nitrate. In fact, it is thought that oxygenic photosynthesis was the ultimate cause, regulated by geochemical events of carbon burial, for the change in most of these parameters, including the late Proterozoic oxygenation of the atmosphere.

Comparative biochemistry of photosystems suggests homologies between PSII and the photosystems of purple sulfur bacteria and *Chloroflexaceae* as well as between PSI and the photosystems of green sulfur bacteria. The hypothesis has been presented that genetic fusions between different oxygenic phototrophs may have led to the evolution of a two photosystem photosynthetic apparatus in the predecessor of cyanobacteria, perhaps using iron as an electron donor. The evolutionary lowering of the basal potential of the type II photosystem allowing the retrieval of electrons from water would have supposed the tapping of a ubiquitous and unlimited source of electrons for $CO_2$ reduction, providing the first cyanobacterium with a wide range of new potential niches and possibly enabling an early explosive radiation of particular adaptations.

## VII. COMMERCIAL USE AND APPLICATIONS

The use of cyanobacteria for industrial purposes has long been sought but in most cases has not reached the commercial stage. Procedures and modified strains have been devised, for example, for the industrial production of amino acids, ammonia, or hydrogen and for the control of mosquito larvae using cyanobacteria genetically engineered to produce *Bacillus* toxins. The main commercial uses of cyanobacteria is the production of bulk biomass for human consumption, a practice that has a long history in traditional cultures. Natural blooms of *Arthrospira* (previously assigned to *Spirulina*) were collected, sun-dried, and cut into cakes for human consumption in pre-Hispanic Mexico; this "tecuitlatl" of the Aztecs was highly regarded and commercialized at the time. A very similar procedure is used today to manufacture "Dihé" cakes by the Kanembu tribeswomen from the shores of Lake Chad. Indeed, dried *Arthrospira* contains 60–70% protein. Today, it is also produced commercially in outdoor man-made facilities and commercialized under the trade name "Spirulina" for the health-food market as a protein-rich, low-calorie, cholesterol-free, vitamin-loaded food supplement. Due to the cult that has developed regarding this form of food supplement, blooms of other species ("*Aphanizomenon*," traditionally not consumed and strains of which are known to contain toxins) also being commercially sold. *Nostoc commune*, a terrestrial cyanobacterium, is considered a delicacy and has been collected and marketed for centuries in China. Given the central role that natural populations of cyanobacteria play in maintaining the long-term fertility of paddy soils for rice cultivation, inoculating rice fields with mixed cyanobacterial preparates is currently a standard agricultural practice in some Asian countries. The symbiotic association *Anabaena/Azolla* (see Section V.E) is intensively cultivated in the Far East for its use as green manure and as fodder for poultry and swine; written instructions for this practice date to 500 BC. In addition, on a much smaller scale cyanobacteria are used as sources for fine biochemicals. $\beta$-Carotene and phycocyanin are commercialized as food colorants. Chlorophyll a, radiolabeled nucleotides and amino acids, and some restriction endonucleases of cyanobacterial origin are sold for research purposes.

## See Also the Following Articles

<small>CELL DIVISION, PROKARYOTES • HORIZONTAL TRANSFER OF GENES BETWEEN MICROORGANISMS • NUTRITION OF MICROORGANISMS • ORIGIN OF LIFE • SECONDARY METABOLITES</small>

## Bibliography

Bryant, D. A. (Ed.) (1996). "The Molecular Biology of Cyanobacteria." Kluwer, Dordrecht.

Castenholz, R. W., and Waterbury, J. B. (1989). Cyanobacteria. In "Bergey's Manual of Systematic Bacteriology" (Staley, J. T., Bryant, M. P., Pfennig, N., and Holt, J. G., Eds.), Vol. 3, pp. 1710–1800). Williams & Wilkins, Baltimore.

Cohen, Y., and Gurewitz, M. (1992). The cyanobacteria—Ecology, physiology and molecular genetics. In "The Prokaryotes" (Balows, A., Trüper, H. G., Dworkin, M., Harder, W., and Schleifer, K. H., Eds.), 2nd ed., Vol. 2, pp. 2079–2104. Springer-Verlag, New York.

Fay, P., and van Baalen, C. (Eds.) (1987). "The Cyanobacteria." Elsevier, Amsterdam.

Garcia-Pichel, F., Nübel, V., and Muyzer, G. (1998). *Arch. Microbiol.* **169**, 473.

Mann, N. H., and Carr, N. G. (Eds.) (1992). "Photosynthetic Prokaryotes." Plenum, New York.

Packer, L., and Glazer, A. N. (Eds.) (1988). Cyanobacteria. *Methods Enzymol.* **167**.

Potts, M., and Whitton, B. A. (Eds.) (1999). "The Ecology of Cyanobacteria. Their Diversity in Time and Space." Kluwer, Dordrecht.

Schenk, H. E. A. (1992). Cyanobacterial symbioses. In "The Prokaryotes (Balows, A., Trüper, H. G., Dworkin, M., Harder, W., and Schleifer, K.-H., Eds.), 2nd ed., Vol. 4, pp. 3820–3854. Springer-Verlag, New York.